Fruit, Berry and Nut Inventory
Third Edition

An Inventory of Nursery Catalogs
Listing All Fruit, Berry and Nut Varieties
Available by Mail Order in the United States

Edited by Kent Whealy
Varietal Descriptions Compiled and Updated by Joanne Thuente
List of Mail-Order Nurseries Updated by Arllys Adelmann
Programming and Typesetting by John W. Francis
Front Cover Art Copyright © by Judith Ann Griffith

Fruit, Berry and Nut Inventory: Third Edition
was made possible by generous support from the
C. S. Fund

Seed Savers Exchange®
3076 North Winn Road
Decorah, Iowa 52101

(Office)   319-382-5990
(Fax)   319-382-5872
(Web site) SeedSavers.org

ISBN 1-882424-57-3 (Softcover)
ISBN 1-882424-56-5 (Hardcover)
Library of Congress Control Number: 00-136265

Printed on Recycled Paper with Soy Ink
in the
United States of America

Contents

Fruits

Berries

Nuts

Tropicals

Miscellaneous

Fruit, Berry and Nut Inventory: Third Edition
is dedicated to the memory of
Professor Elwyn Meader
for his quiet kindness and wisdom
and the enduring richness he developed
for the world's orchardists and gardeners.

Seed Savers Exchange® (SSE) is a nonprofit, tax-exempt organization of vegetable gardeners and fruit hobbyists working to save heirloom vegetable and fruit varieties from extinction. Revenue from the various editions of the *Fruit, Berry and Nut Inventory* has been used to develop and maintain the genetic preservation projects at Heritage Farm®, SSE's headquarters near Decorah, Iowa. Heritage Farm's projects (on display to the public from Memorial Day until the end of September) include: a dozen organic Preservation Gardens where up to 2,000 endangered vegetables are grown for seed each summer (out of a total collection of 18,000 rare varieties); Historic Orchard containing 700 varieties of 19th century apples and 200 hardy grapes; and herds of extremely rare Ancient White Park cattle. To receive a free 68-page copy of the current Seed Savers Catalog (heirloom seeds, books and gifts), including a two-page section describing the organization's projects and how to become a member, write or call: Seed Savers Exchange, 3076 North Winn Road, Decorah, Iowa 52101 (phone 319-382-5990, fax 319-382-5872), or visit Seed Savers' web site: www.SeedSavers.org.

Introduction

Fruit, Berry and Nut Inventory: Third Edition is a comprehensive inventory of fruits, berries, nuts and edible tropicals available by mail order in the United States. Today's orchardists are blessed with access to an immense pomological cornucopia. This amazingly rich heritage is the result of centuries of plant collecting (both in North America and abroad), extensive foreign importations, and constant breeding by amateurs, professionals and agricultural institutions. The continued existence of these unique resources, however, presently depends more on current economic pressures than on the actual merits of the cultivars. Many unique varieties and irreplaceable collections are lost each year when nurseries change owners, and when elderly collectors and breeders retire or pass away. Other ongoing and accelerating losses are the result of increasing emphasis on commercial varieties suited for large-scale production, refrigerated controlled storage, and nationwide (and even international) food distribution systems.

Fruit, Berry and Nut Inventory has proven to be of great value in widely varied applications. Fruit hobbyists are using it to locate alternative sources whenever access to favorite varieties is lost. Every commercially available cultivar can now be scanned to locate those specifically suited to regional climates, or resistant to local diseases and pests. Northern and high-altitude growers can search out hardy, short-season plant material. Agricultural experiment stations and clonal repositories can use this unique inventory to substantially improve their collections. Fruit breeders, plant collectors, landscape architects and botanical gardens can find new sources for unique varieties, especially foreign material that recently has become available. Extension agents, garden writers and magazine staffs can refer to it when answering questions concerning where to locate specific varieties. And public libraries are making this comprehensive sourcebook available to horticultural readers in the 25 million U.S. households that grow part of their own food.

The primary goal of the Seed Savers Exchange (SSE), a nonprofit tax-exempt organization, is to provide increased access to genetic resources for use by gardeners and orchardists who are growing healthy food for their families. In addition to expanding the awareness of the true scope of the genetic diversity that is available to today's growers, the complete access provided by this inventory also makes possible the effective conservation of these genetic resources. SSE hopes that concerned individuals and conservation organizations will use this study to quickly incorporate rare varieties into permanent collections while sources still exist.

Any inventory is out-of-date even before it is published and becomes less effective with each passing year. The previous *Second Edition* of the *Fruit, Berry and Nut Inventory* was published back in 1993, using 1992 catalogs, so it was certainly time for an updated edition to be compiled and printed. The Database Manager here in SSE's offices has spent the greater portion of two years (March through October) compiling this incredible inventory that includes 277 mail-order catalogs, 6,471 varietal descriptions, and a coded list of every U.S. nursery that offers each one. To our knowledge, these are the only comprehensive inventories of U.S. nurseries ever accomplished. Because this *Third Edition* took two years to complete, mail-order nursery catalogs from both 1999 and 2000 were used. Considerable effort was made to acquire every appropriate catalog, but our strict printing deadline prevented several recently received catalogs of tropical and semi-tropical edibles from being included in this edition. Other U.S. mail-order catalogs that are unknown to us most certainly exist, especially small obscure nurseries that may be rich in unique varieties. SSE's staff would appreciate being informed of additional mail-order sources that are offering fruits, berries, nuts and tropical edibles. SSE intends to publish an updated edition of the *Fruit, Berry and Nut Inventory* about every five years, so that the access it provides will remain current and effective.

Those of us who compiled, edited and formatted this inventory became increasingly fascinated as it approached completion. When viewed in its entirety, the combined collections of all U.S. mail-order nurseries is almost beyond belief. For example, this *Third Edition* provides access to 1,513 different apples, up substantially from the 1,180 varieties in the *Second Edition*. The diversity of other "Fruits" is equally impressive: 93 apricots, 101 sweet cherries, 82 figs, 41 jujubes, 125 nectarines, 38 pawpaws, 464 peaches, 204 pears, 48 American persimmons, 39 Oriental persimmons and 224 plums. The section of "Berries" is just as rich: 56 blackberries, 109 blueberries, 86 currants, 48 gooseberries, 444 grapes, 109 kiwis, 41 mulberries, 106 raspberries, 31 serviceberries and 136 strawberries. The listings of "Nuts" are also quite extensive: 71 chestnuts, 63 filberts (hazelnuts), 127 pecans, 84 black walnuts and 63 Persian walnuts. Although greatly improved, the "Tropicals" section could still be better: 33 annonas, 94 bananas, 33 guavas, 25 lemons, 32 mangos, 41 oranges, 32 passionflowers, 21 pomegranates and 35 tangerines. For the first time, this edition includes flowering trees: 160 flowering apples (crab apples primarily used for fruit are still in the Apple section), 17 flowering peaches, 28 flowering pears and 8 flowering plums. As always, "Miscellaneous" includes a remarkable and almost unimaginable collection from every corner of the world.

This unparalleled bounty is a living legacy with roots extending back into antiquity. Some of the most notable historic examples include White Doyenne that originated in France, entered the U.S. in 1559 from Italy, and was described much earlier as the Roman pear Sementinum. A small, beautiful, aromatic, highly flavored, Christmas dessert apple named Lady was grown in the gardens of Louis XIII at Orleans in 1628, and is also known to date back to Roman times. Calville Blanc d'Hiver, grown by Le Letier (the *procureur* for Louis XIII), entered the U.S. in 1598 and became a favorite apple of Thomas Jefferson. Rousselet de Reims was a favorite pear of Louis XIV and was in the King's gardens at Versailles in 1688. Gravenstein, an apple whose superb flavor generated an entire industry earlier this century in California, originated in Italy in the early 1600s, arrived in Denmark in 1669 and was introduced into the U.S. from Germany in 1790.

Many well-known apples and some of our best pears originated in the U.S. centuries ago. Rhode Island Greening, a favorite American cooking apple since Colonial times, was widely known in Rhode Island by 1650. Grimes Golden originated with Thomas Grimes in the mountains of Brook County, West Virginia and was sold to traders from New Orleans in 1804. Wolf River, which produces enormous fruits often weighing more than a pound, was found growing on the banks of the Wolf River near Fremont, Wisconsin in 1875. Seckel, so sweet that it is often called the Sugar Pear, was discovered south of Philadelphia about 1790; small fruited and not very attractive, it is a connoisseur's delight.

All of us owe an enormous debt to a small group of fruit and nut breeders, mentioned repeatedly throughout various editions of the *Fruit, Berry and Nut Inventory*, whose work unfortunately often remains relatively unknown. Each of our lives is richer because of the life's work of outstanding breeders such as Luther Burbank, George Darrow, Robert Dunston, Albert Etter, Jack Gellatly, Felix Gillet, Nels Hansen, Jesse Hepler, Elwyn Meader, T. V. Munson, H. P. Olmo, Elmer Swenson, Roger Way, Albert Yeager, Floyd Zaiger and many others. Although some of these breeders worked strictly on a particular specialty, many are generalists whose wide, varying interests resulted in valuable contributions to a vast assortment of different fruits, berries, nuts and vegetables. Their breeding skills and intimate awareness of the minute differences in populations of plants are sometimes legendary.

Portions of the collections of some of these breeders, plus material from public and nonprofit collections, are available to individual growers. Greenmantle Nursery (California) specializes in old homestead fruits and varieties developed by Albert Ettter in the 1920s and later. Lake Sylvia Vineyard Nursery (Minnesota) offers unreleased selections of hardy northern grapes from the ongoing breeding program of Elmer Swenson, thus providing northern growers with access to outstanding hardy grapes not available elsewhere. Bay Laurel Nursery (California) is offering 336 total varieties, including an extensive selection of stone fruits developed by Floyd Zaiger. Foundation Plant Materials Service (University of California, Davis) offers certified stock of 167 grapes, 32 grape rootstocks and 21 strawberries. Nebraska Nut Growers Association (University of Nebraska, Lincoln) is a nonprofit organization offering seeds and scionwood of nut species adaptable to Nebraska, including 43 pecans and 45 walnuts. And the Worcester County Horticultural Society (Massachusetts) is making available scionwood of 119 heirloom apples.

Many of the nurseries featured in this edition are family-owned businesses, some with histories that reach back more than a century. Some of the oldest include Gardens of the Blue Ridge (North Carolina) that has been in business since 1892. Ledden Brothers (New Jersey) was founded in 1864 and purchased by Oral Ledden in 1904. Logee's Greenhouses (Connecticut) has been owned and operated by the same family since being founded in 1892. McKay Nursery Company (Wisconsin) was established in 1897 and specializes in varieties for rigorous northern Midwest climates. And the Park Seed Co. (South Carolina), flower seed specialists since 1868, is known today to most gardeners as a vegetable and flower seed company, but also offers an fine collection of berries.

Some nurseries and individuals are making available amazingly extensive collections of a particular species. Calhoun's Nursery (North Carolina) specializes in heirloom Southern apples and carries 311 varieties. Double A Vineyards (New York) is offering 78 varieties of grapes. Finch Blueberry Nursery (North Carolina) offers 45 different blueberries. Foster Concord Nurseries (New York) is offering 60 grapes. Going Bananas (Florida) lists 67 bananas. The collection of Hollydale Nursery (Tennessee) includes 132 peaches. Ison's Nursery and Vineyards (Georgia) specializes in Muscadine grapes and carries 48 kinds. Roger and Shirley Meyer (California) are making available 34 jujubes and 56 kiwis. Puget Sound Kiwi Co. (Washington) offers 44 different kiwis. Lon Rombough (Oregon), SSE member and grape breeder, is offering 131 grapes. Sonoma Grapevines (California), which specializes in grafted vinifera wine and table grapes, offers 140 varieties of grapes and 22 grape rootstocks. And the Whitman Farm Nursery (Oregon) specializes in *Ribes*, offering 108 total varieties including 51 currants and 30 gooseberries.

Mail-order nurseries have been included in this inventory, even if their catalogs contain only one appropriate variety. On the other hand, some of the companies in this *Third Edition* are making available truly vast collections that are often extremely varied. Edible Forest Nursery (Wisconsin) offers 335 total varieties, and specializes in super-hardy fruit varieties for Zones 3 and 4, grafted walnuts and hickories for Zone 3, Canadian prairie apples and hardy Asian pears. Noland River Nut Tree Nursery (Kentucky) offers more than 200 varieties of disease-resistant grafted nut trees (13 butternuts, 10 chestnuts, 60 hickories, 36 pecans and 42 walnuts), plus 9 pawpaws and 24 persimmons. One Green World (Oregon) offers 241 unique and unusual fruits and ornamentals, including an interesting collection of fruits and berries from the former Soviet Union. Oregon Exotics (Oregon), offering

370 varieties, is a rare fruit nursery that specializes in mulberries, persimmons, and rare and unusual fruits from around the world. Pacific Tree Farms (California) specializes in new and unusual trees and plants, offering 350 varieties. Raintree Nursery (Washington) offers 341 varieties of fruits, berries, nuts and bamboo for edible landscapes, most tested in the Pacific Northwest for over 20 years. Sonoma Antique Apple Nursery (California), which offers 312 varieties, specializes in organically grown heirloom and unusual fruits including 145 apples, 19 peaches, 45 pears and 17 plums. Southmeadow Fruit Gardens (Michigan) offers 436 total varieties, including 241 apples, 16 cherries, 17 peaches, 47 pears, 20 plums, 19 currants, 15 gooseberries and 28 grapes. And, finally, Dave Wilson Nursery (California), which specializes in bareroot fruit and nut trees, offers 487 total varieties.

Just as this manuscript was about to be sent to the printer, we learned that Bear Creek Nursery has gone out of business. Because of our strict deadline, Bear Creek Nursery's listings had to be left in this edition, but the company has been marked as "Out of Business" in the list of Sources and Codes. Bear Creek Nursery was a large family-run operation that always carried a vast, excellent collection. In 1992, Bear Creek was offering 254 fruits, 64 berries, 47 nuts and 13 miscellaneous varieties. Their 2000 catalog offered 451 total varieties, including many that were available on an extensive selection of cold-hardy, drought-resistant rootstocks for northern growers. (For more than a decade, all of the grafting for the Historic Orchard here at Heritage Farm has been done on rootstock purchased from Bear Creek Nursery.) Out of 451 varieties in their last catalog, 357 are being offered by other companies, but the other 94 were unique and will not be available elsewhere. Losing a company of this size is a real blow to the mail-order nursery industry and to growers everywhere. We can only hope that a buyer will step forward that is capable of carrying on the fine work of Bear Creek Nursery.

Canadian nurseries have not been included in any of the editions due to quarantine restrictions on foreign plant material entering the U.S. SSE urges concerned individuals in Canada and other countries to use the *Fruit, Berry and Nut Inventory* as a model for similar local efforts, and we will gladly provide assistance in helping to set up the necessary databases. SSE would like to be informed of any similar inventories of commercially available fruits or vegetables in other countries, so that possible exchanges of rare plant material might occur. Anyone interested in obtaining woody plant material from a foreign country should contact the USDA's Plant Protection and Quarantine Permit Unit in Hyattsville, Maryland (toll free 877-770-5990 or 301-436-8645). Their staff will issue the proper permits for importation, inspection and release. Also, senior staff at the nine USDA clonal repositories are sometimes willing to help serious collectors import material, especially cultivars that might be of interest for their repository's collection.

USDA's clonal repositories were put into place during the last couple of decades to serve as collections of breeding material for use by fruit, berry and nut breeders currently and in the future. Before these relatively new clonal collections were developed, most of the State Agricultural Experiment Stations at land-grant universities had active fruit and vegetable breeding programs. Unique plant material was collected from around the world and used to develop varieties especially suited for growers in that particular state. These invaluable collections are gradually being abandoned due to federal and state budget cuts, breeders retiring and not being replaced, and the rapid decline of traditional breeding programs at state universities. Most of the public sector plant breeding being done today focuses almost entirely on commercial traits and large-scale production.

Student enrollments in plant breeding courses at agricultural colleges have steadily decreased for several decades. Many of our remaining traditional plant breeders, both pomologists and horticulturists, are quite concerned because few students are currently choosing plant breeding in the public sector as their life's work. Valuable young talent is being siphoned off into high-paying careers in private industry or more glamorous positions in biotechnology. We probably will never again witness the superb breeding programs that characterized the first half of this century, which were always so heavily dependent on free exchange and collaborative efforts. Many of our truly great breeders are approaching retirement or are already semi-retired. When they are gone, the resulting void may never be filled. Who will carry on their invaluable work? Will the torch that has always been passed from one breeder to the next simply fade away?

The fruits, berries, nuts and tropical edibles available to American growers today are the result of centuries-old traditions of plant collection and amateur development, further refined by some of the finest breeding programs the world has ever seen. Backyard gardeners, fruit hobbyists and specialty growers are truly blessed with access to an incredibly rich heritage of food crops. That irreplaceable legacy, however, is definitely in rapid decline. Amateur growers and preservation projects must do everything in their power to maintain what remains, because extinction is forever. SSE hopes the *Fruit, Berry and Nut Inventory* will play a valuable, timely role in helping to conserve the vanishing heritage of our orchards and vineyards.

Kent Whealy
Executive Director
Seed Savers Exchange
(December 2000)

How To Use This Book

This inventory is divided into five sections: Fruit, Berry, Nut, Tropical and Miscellaneous. Each section is further divided into various plant types. For example, the "Fruit" section contains Apples, Apricots, etc. Within each plant type, varieties are arranged alphabetically by name. Each variety has a separate description that includes: variety name, synonyms, plant description, source history and source codes. These elements of a varietal description are explained briefly below.

Variety Name – also referred to as the plant's common name. In some cases, names have been reversed to allow for better groupings. For example, under Apples you will find these descriptions: <u>McIntosh, Double Red</u>; <u>McIntosh, Rogers Red</u>; and <u>McIntosh, Summerland</u>.

Synonyms – other names sometimes used for that variety. If they occur, synonyms are enclosed in parentheses following the variety name. A synonym is listed even if mentioned by only one company out of several dozen. Almost no combining has been done on the basis of synonyms, because it is impossible to know if they are accurate.

Plant Description – a composite pieced together from sometimes dozens of catalog descriptions. The information is listed in the following order: Taxonomy and Parentage; Fruit Characteristics (fruit, skin, flesh, flavor, quality, keeping ability); Plant Characteristics (tree, leaf, flower, fertility, productivity, disease resistance, soil and regional preferences); Requirements (ripening, chilling, hardiness); History (origin, developer, introduction date, patent number). These composites of catalog descriptions may lack accuracy and completeness, representing only what the nurseries selling these varieties say about them, not a scientific description. *Fruit, Berry and Nut Inventory* is not a nomenclature or botanical reference, and shouldn't be used as such. Unless otherwise indicated in the "Sources" section, all listings are assumed to be rooted plants. You can assume that named varieties are clonally propagated, whereas species listings (such as Fox Grape for *Vitus labrusca*) could be either clones or seedlings. Nurseries offering scionwood and budwood for grafting are also identified in "Sources." Hardiness zones, where indicated, are USDA zones ranging from Zone 2 in northernmost U.S. to Zone 10 in southern Florida. All listings were checked against documents from the U.S. Plant Variety Protection Office, and descriptions indicate varieties with patents issued or pending.

Source History – the number of companies offering that variety in each inventory (1988, 1992 and 2000). These statistics show the flow of gains and losses in availability, providing a clear picture of which varieties are in danger of being lost.

Source Codes – three-letter codes for each of the 277 mail-order nurseries in this inventory. Each code is the first three letters of the company's name (example: **Arb** stands for **Arb**orvillage Farm). When two or more names start with the same three letters, a number replaces the third letter (example: **Ad2**). Retail sources have only an initial capital letter (as in the examples above). *Wholesale only sources* have codes that are all capital letters (example: **BAL**). To order a variety from this inventory, look up one of its *retail codes* in the Sources section, send the correct amount for that company's catalog or price list, and place your order. If you look up a wholesale code, you will see that the company's sales are "Wholesale only!" Don't try to send for its catalog. However, sometimes wholesale varieties can be obtained by having a local company that deals in nursery stock order for you.

Sources and Codes

All of the "sources" (mail-order nursery catalogs) inventoried for the *Fruit, Berry and Nut Inventory: Third Edition* are listed in this section, alphabetically by code. The code for each source is the first three letters of the source's name. Whenever two (or more) sources start with the same three letters, then the third letter has been replaced with a number. Sources that only sell wholesale have codes that are all capital letters. Individual growers should not contact these wholesale sources, which typically sell only in volume to established commercial accounts. Companies whose sales are both retail and wholesale have been given codes that are lower case letters, because individuals can buy from them. This way backyard growers can tell at a glance which nurseries will sell to them.

Please turn to page 23, where you will find some clear examples that illustrate all of the types of codes described above. **Eno** stands for Enoch's Berry Farm which sells retail to individuals. A few listings later, **FAI** is Fairacre Farm and Nursery which sells "Wholesale only!" (its code is all capital letters). Also, on that same page, note that Farmer Seed and Nursery comes before Fairacre Farm and Nursery because the listings are alphabetical by code, not by the source's name. So, when looking for the name of a specific nursery, be certain to look through all possible matches (all of the codes whose first two letters match the first two letters of the nursery's name).

Each source's name and address is followed by: phone number, fax, e-mail, web site, type of catalog (or price list), specialties, rootstocks used, total number of varieties offered, and the numbers of the various plant types offered. As an additional service, whenever noted in the catalogs (or from direct correspondence), the rootstocks that the nurseries use to propagate grafted trees have been listed. Buyers who want their trees grafted onto a particular rootstock should assume that sources for which no rootstocks are noted do not specify how their trees are propagated, and could look for an alternate source that does use the desired rootstock.

Abu **Abundant Life Seed Foundation**, PO Box 772, Port Townsend, WA 98368. Phone: 360-385-5660. Fax: 360-385-7455. E-mail: abundant@ olypen.com. Web site: csf.colorado.edu/perma. $2 for catalog, $30 suggested donation for membership which includes seed catalog and book list plus periodic newsletters and 10% discount on purchases. Specializes in rare and heirloom vegetables; herbs, flowers and Pacific Northwest natives are also included. All seeds are open-pollinated and never chemically treated and most are organic. Pacific Northwest seeds and plants are emphasized. Retail and bulk prices are listed in the same catalog. Offered 27 total varieties in 2000, including 1 cherry, 1 blackberry, 1 blueberry, 1 currant, 2 elderberries, 1 gooseberry, 2 huckleberries, 1 raspberry, 1 serviceberry, 1 pine nut and 15 miscellaneous varieties.

Ad2 **Adams Co. Nursery, Inc.**, PO Box 108, 26 Nursery Lane, Aspers, PA 17304. Phone: 717-677-8105. Fax: 717-677-4124. E-mail: acn@cvn.net. Web site: www.acnursery.com. Free catalog. Specializes in fruit trees and horticultural supplies. Retail and wholesale prices are listed in the same catalog. Apple rootstock: EMLA 7, EMLA 9, EMLA 26, EMLA 106, EMLA 111, EMLA 9 interstem on EMLA 111, and Bud-9. Cherry rootstock: Mahaleb and Mazzard. Offered 190 total varieties in 2000, including 67 apples, 7 apricots, 16 cherries, 10 nectarines, 59 peaches, 13 pears and 18 plums.

AG2 **Agri Sun Nursery**, 6910 E. Clarkson Ave., Selma, CA 93662. Wholesale only! Specializes in bare root fruit trees. Apples on all rootstocks. Pear rootstock: Domestic Seedling, OH x F selections. Almond, apricot, nectarine, peach and plum rootstock: Nemaguard, Lovell, Marianna 26/24, Myrobalan 29C, St. Julian A and Stark Red Leaf. Cherry rootstock: Mahaleb, Mazzard and Colt. Offered 154 total varieties in 2000, including 45 apples, 5 apricots, 1 cherry, 21 nectarines and 62 peaches and 20 plums.

Ag4 **Ag Resource**, 35268 State Highway 34, Detroit Lakes, MN 56501. Phone: 800-288-6650. Fax: 218-847-9351. E-mail: dgbari@tekstar.com. Retail only. Offered 39 total varieties in 2000, including 5 blueberries, 2 cranberries, 2 currants, 8 raspberries, 20 strawberries, 2 miscellaneous varieties.

Al2 **Allen Plant Co.**, PO Box 310, Fruitland, MD 21826-0310. Phone: 410-742-7123. Free catalog. Retail only. Specializes in strawberry plants. Offered 27 total varieties in 2000, including 2 blackberries, 8 blueberries, 3 raspberries and 14 strawberries.

Al8 **Aloha Tropicals**, 1247 Browning Ct., Vista, CA 92083. $4 for catalog, refundable with first order. Specializes in tropical plants – ginger, banana, heliconia, plumeria, tropical fruiting and flowering trees, shrubs and vines. Retail and wholesale prices are listed in the same catalog. Offered 31 total varieties in 2000, including 1 annona, 22 bananas, 1 guava, 1 papaya, 3 passionflowers, 1 pepino and 2 miscellaneous varieties.

ALD **Aldrich Berry Farm and Nursery**, 190 Aldrich Road, Mossyrock, WA 98564. Phone: 360-983-3138. Fax: 360-983-8588. Free catalog. Wholesale only! A horticultural farm since 1944. Offered 7 total varieties in 2000, including 1 blackberry, 1 elderberry, 1 strawberry, 1 pine nut and 3 miscellaneous varieties.

AMM **A. G. Ammon Nursery, Inc.**, PO Box 488, Chatsworth, NJ 08019. Phone: 609-726-1370. Fax: 609-726-1270. Wholesale only! Sells highbush blueberry plants only. Offered 18 blueberries in 2000.

An4 **J. D. Andersen Nursery**, 2790 Marvinga Lane, Fallbrook, CA 92028. $2 for catalog. Specializes in palms, cycads and tropical fruit trees. Retail only. Offered 79 total varieties in 2000, including 3 cherries, 1 jujube, 1 macadamia, 2 annonas, 1 avocado, 48 bananas, 1 miscellaneous citrus, 3 guavas, 1 loquat, 1 mango, 3 sapotes and 14 miscellaneous varieties.

Arb **Arborvillage Farm**, PO Box 227, Holt, MO 64048. $1 for catalog. Specializes in ornamental trees and shrubs. Mainly retail, with very limited wholesale activity. Offered 110 total varieties in 2000, including 66 apples, 2 cherries, 1 pawpaw, 11 pears, 1 pear rootstock, 4 persimmons, 1 stone rootstock, 3 elderberries, 1 mulberry, 4 serviceberries, 1 chestnut, 2 filberts, 3 hickories, 1 pecan, 3 walnuts and 6 miscellaneous varieties.

Ba3 **Barber Nursery**, 14282 Rogers Road, Willis, TX 77378. Phone: 409-856-8074. Free price list. Retail and wholesale prices are given on the same price list. Specializes in native and uncommon tree and shrub seedlings. Offered 12 total varieties in 2000, including 1 cherry, 2 dates, 1 pawpaw, 1 persimmon, 1 quince, 1 blueberry, 1 hickory, 1 miscellaneous nut, 1 citrus rootstock and 2 miscellaneous varieties.

Ba8 **Baker Creek Heirloom Seeds**, 2278 Baker Creek Road, Mansfield, MO 65704. Phone: 417-924-8917. Web site: www.rareseeds.com. Free catalog. Sells only non-hybrid seeds. Specializes in heirloom seeds including many rare types and Oriental and European varieties. Mainly retail, but catalog includes a page of wholesale offerings. Offered 12 total varieties in 2000, including 2 blackberries, 4 blueberries and 6 grapes.

BA9   **Balance Restoration Nursery**, 27995 Chambers Mill Road, Lorane, OR 97451. Wholesale only! Specializes in native wetland and riparian plants. Offered 8 total varieties in 2000, including 1 cherry, 1 currant, 2 elderberries, 1 huckleberry, 1 serviceberry and 2 miscellaneous varieties.

BA10   **Barwacz Farm**, 05146 59th St., Grand Junction, MI 49056. Wholesale only! Offered 22 total varieties in 2000, including 17 blueberries and 5 miscellaneous varieties.

BA14   **Bachman's Nursery Wholesale Center**, 6877 235th St. W., Farmington, MN 55024. Wholesale only! Offered 74 total varieties in 2000, including 23 apples, 2 apricots, 5 cherries, 2 pears, 3 plums, 2 blackberries, 6 blueberries, 4 cranberries, 2 currants, 2 gooseberries, 5 grapes, 1 mulberry, 6 raspberries, 2 serviceberries, 1 filbert, 1 pine nut, 1 walnut, 1 rhubarb and 5 miscellaneous varieties.

BAL   **Ball Horticultural Company**, 622 Town Road, West Chicago, IL 60185-2698. Wholesale only! Offered 2 strawberries in 2000.

Ban   **The Banana Tree**, 715 Northampton St., Easton, PA 18042. Phone: 610-253-9589. Web site: www.banana-tree.com. Order from online catalog at www.banana-tree.com. Since 1955 shipping thousands of seeds and bulbs worldwide. Specializes in tropicals which are grown on their farms: Heliconia, Neem, Tea, Champaca, Coffee, Cinnamon, Mangrove, Teak, Ephedra, Papaya, Monkey Puzzle, Sacred Water Lily, Baobob and numerous others. Retail and wholesale prices are listed in the same catalog. Offered 79 total varieties in 2000, including 1 jujube, 1 pawpaw, 3 persimmons, 3 kiwis, 1 macadamia, 4 miscellaneous nuts, 5 annonas, 3 bananas, 1 miscellaneous citrus, 1 citrus rootstock, 3 guavas, 1 loquat, 6 papayas, 5 passionflowers, 1 pomegranate and 40 miscellaneous varieties.

Bar   **Vernon Barnes and Son**, PO Box 250F3, McMinnville, TN 37110. Free catalog. Separate retail and wholesale catalogs, each containing varieties not in the other. Serving the public since 1950. Offered 104 total varieties in 2000, including 20 apples, 2 apricots, 5 cherries, 2 figs, 4 nectarines, 10 peaches, 7 pears, 1 persimmon, 7 plums, 7 blackberries, 5 blueberries, 1 gooseberry, 5 grapes, 1 mulberry, 5 raspberries, 11 strawberries, 1 butternut, 1 chestnut, 1 filbert, 1 hickory, 2 pecans, 2 walnuts, 1 miscellaneous nut and 2 miscellaneous varieties.

Bas   **Bass Pecan Company**, 925 East Main St., Lumberton, MS 39455. Phone: 601-796-2461. Fax: 601-796-3630. Free price list. Separate but identical retail and wholesale price lists. Offered 41 total varieties in 2000, including 3 apples, 2 figs, 1 nectarine, 7 peaches, 5 pears, 3 persimmons, 4 plums, 3 blueberries and 13 pecans.

Bay   **Bay Laurel Nursery**, 2500 El Camino Real, Atascadero, CA 93422. Phone: 805-466-3406. Fax: 805-466-6455. E-mail: info@BayLaurel Nursery.com. Web site: www.BayLaurelNursery.com. Free catalog. Specializes in deciduous fruit and nut trees including many low-chill, miniature/genetic dwarf varieties and an extensive selection of varieties developed by Zaiger Genetics. Also offers grapevines, berries, flowering trees, shrubs and roses. Offered 336 total varieties in 2000, including 6 apple rootstocks, 45 apples, 14 apricots, 11 cherries, 9 figs, 2 jujubes, 20 nectarines, 53 peaches, 28 pears, 5 pear rootstocks, 6 persimmons, 28 plums, 4 quinces, 10 stone fruit crosses, 10 stone rootstocks, 7 blackberries, 7 blueberries, 24 grapes, 5 kiwis, 5 raspberries, 7 almonds, 2 chestnuts, 5 filberts, 8 pecans, 8 walnuts, 4 pomegranates, 1 rhubarb, 2 miscellaneous varieties.

Be4   **Berlin Seeds**, 3649 State Route 39, Millersburg, OH 44654. Free catalog. Retail only. Offered 21 total varieties in 2000, including 4 blueberries, 16 strawberries and 1 rhubarb.

Bea   **Bear Creek Nursery**, PO Box 310, Northport, WA 99157. Family OUT OF BUSINESS (December 2000) operation offering cold-hardy and drought-resistant stocks for northern growers. Fruits offered as scionwood, custom benchgrafts or one-year whips. Apple rootstock: Antanovka, Budagovski 9, EMLA 7, EMLA 9, EMLA 26, EMLA 27. Apricot rootstock: Manchurian, Myrobalan and Siberian C. Cherry rootstock: Colt, Mahalab and Mazzard. Nectarine rootstock: Lovell and Siberian C. Peach rootstock: Himalayan, Lovell and Siberian C. Pear rootstock: Harbin, OH x F and Standard. Plum rootstock: American Plum, Asian Plum, Manchurian and Myrobalan. Offered 451 total varieties in 2000, including 12 apple rootstocks, 273 apples, 6 apricots, 15 cherries, 3 nectarines, 5 peaches, 16 pears, 2 pear rootstocks, 1 persimmon, 13 plums, 3 stone fruit crosses, 7 stone rootstocks, 3 blackberries, 4 blueberries, 1 cranberry, 9 currants, 3 elderberries, 4 gooseberries, 6 grapes, 1 kiwi, 2 mulberries, 4 raspberries, 2 serviceberries, 2 butternuts, 11 chestnuts, 16 filberts, 1 heartnut, 2 hickories, 1 pecan, 6 walnuts, 3 miscellaneous nuts, 1 rhubarb and 13 miscellaneous varieties.

Big   **Bigelow Nurseries**, Box 718, Northboro, MA 01532. Free catalog. Separate but identical retail and wholesale catalogs. In business since 1915. Specializes in nursery stock. Offered 50 total varieties in 2000, including 28 apples, 3 cherries, 4 pears, 2 plums, 1 quince, 2 blueberries, 3 cranberries, 1 elderberry, 2 serviceberries and 4 miscellaneous varieties.

Bl4   **Bluebird Orchard and Nursery**, 4711 Three Mile Road NE, Grand Rapids, MI 49525. Phone: 616-361-0919. E-mail: stickbioga@yahoo.com. Free price list. Specializes in old and selected new apple varieties. Offering scionwood only. Offered 168 apples in 2000.

BO4   **Boyd Nursery Company**, PO Box 71, State Highway #55, McMinnville, TN 37110. Wholesale only! Offered 23 total varieties in 2000, including 1 apricot, 2 cherries, 1 pawpaw, 2 pears, 1 persimmon, 1 elderberry, 6 grapes, 1 serviceberry, 1 chestnut, 1 filbert, 1 hickory, 1 pecan and 4 miscellaneous varieties.

Bo5   **Boyer Nurseries and Orchards Inc.**, 405 Boyer Nursery Rd., Biglerville, PA 17307. Phone: 717-677-8558. Fax: 717-677-4026. E-mail: boyer nurseries@boyernurseries.com. Web site: www.boyernurseries.com. Free price list. Separate retail and wholesale price lists, each containing varieties not in the other. Specializes in flowering crabs and fruit and shade trees. Offered 220 total varieties in 2000, including 1 apple rootstock, 69 apples, 7 apricots, 19 cherries, 3 nectarines, 28 peaches, 18 pears, 13 plums, 2 quinces, 4 blackberries, 5 blueberries, 2 currants, 1 elderberry, 2 gooseberries, 14 grapes, 7 raspberries, 1 serviceberry, 15 strawberries, 1 almond, 1 chestnut, 1 pecan, 1 miscellaneous nut, 2 rhubarbs and 3 miscellaneous varieties.

B010 **Bobtown Nursery**, 16212 Country Club Road, Melfa, VA 23410. Wholesale only! Specializes in native and wetland material. Offered 75 total varieties in 2000, including 11 apples, 1 apricot, 6 cherries, 1 fig, 1 pawpaw, 3 peaches, 7 pears, 3 persimmons, 6 plums, 1 quince, 2 blueberries, 1 elderberry, 1 huckleberry, 3 kiwis, 1 mulberry, 4 serviceberries, 1 chestnut, 2 filberts, 3 hickories, 1 pecan, 1 walnut, 1 miscellaneous nut, 1 loquat, 1 passionflower and 12 miscellaneous varieties.

Bos **Boston Mountain Nurseries**, 20189 N. Hwy. 71, Mountainburg, AR 72946. Phone: 501-369-2007. Fax: 501-369-2007. E-mail: BMNGPense @aol.com. Send a self-addressed stamped envelope for price list. Offers a wholesale list to licensed nurseries and a separate, more informative list to growers, with wholesale and retail prices. Family owned and operated. Specializes in berry plants and grapevines. Offered 68 total varieties in 2000, including 14 blackberries, 6 blueberries, 3 currants, 1 elderberry, 3 gooseberries, 20 grapes, 13 raspberries, 7 strawberries and 1 miscellaneous variety.

Bou **Bountiful Gardens**, 18001 Shafer Ranch Rd., Willits, CA 95490. Phone: 707-459-6410. Fax: 707-459-6410. E-mail: bountiful@sonic.net. Web site: www.bountifulgardens.org. Free catalog in U.S. Retail and wholesale varieties are listed in the same catalog. Sole U.S. distributor for Chase Seeds of England. Offers untreated heirlooms. Offered 3 total varieties in 2000, including 1 peach, 1 strawberry and 1 rhubarb.

BR2 **Briggs Nursery, Inc.**, 4407 Henderson Blvd., Olympia, WA 98501. Wholesale only! Specializes in perennials and rhododendrons. Offered 28 total varieties in 2000, including 19 blueberries, 1 huckleberry, 1 serviceberry and 7 miscellaneous varieties.

BR6 **Brooks Tree Farm**, 9785 Portland Road NE, Salem, OR 97305. Wholesale only! Offered 2 miscellaneous varieties in 2000.

BR10 **Brandt's Fruit Trees**, PO Box 10, Parker, WA 98939. Wholesale only! Apple rootstock: Bud 9, M 7A, M 9, M 26, MM 106 and MM 111. Pear rootstock: OH x F 40, OH x F 87, OH x F 97 and OH x F 217 and OH x F 513. Cherry rootstock: Mazzard. Offered 23 total varieties in 2000, including 9 apples, 6 cherries and 8 pears.

Bu1 **Burgess Seed and Plant Co.**, 905 Four Seasons Road, Bloomington, IL 61701. $1 for catalog. Unique and popular seeds and plants since 1913. Offered 74 total varieties in 2000, including 6 apples, 2 apricots, 4 cherries, 1 fig, 1 nectarine, 1 pawpaw, 3 peaches, 2 pears, 2 plums, 3 blackberries, 4 blueberries, 1 currant, 2 elderberries, 1 gooseberry, 15 grapes, 1 kiwi, 8 raspberries, 7 strawberries, 1 almond, 1 butternut, 1 chestnut, 1 filbert, 1 pecan, 2 walnuts, 1 banana, 1 rhubarb and 1 miscellaneous variety.

Bu2 **W. Atlee Burpee and Co.**, 300 Park Ave., Warminster, PA 18991. Phone: 215-674-4900. Fax: 215-674-4170. Web site: www.burpee.com. Call 800-888-1447 to place an order. Free catalog. Separate wholesale and retail catalogs; retail catalog contains additional varieties. Extensive selection including many original introductions. Offered 23 total varieties in 2000, in cluding 2 blackberries, 4 blueberries, 3 grapes, 1 kiwi, 5 raspberries, 6 strawberries and 2 rhubarbs.

Bu7   **Burnt Ridge Nursery**, 432 Burnt Ridge Rd., Onalaska, WA 98570. Phone: 360-985-2873. Fax: 360-985-0882. E-mail: burntridge@myhome .net. Web site: landru.myhome.net/burntridge/. Send one first-class stamp for catalog. Retail and wholesale prices are listed in the same catalog. Specializes in unusual and ornamental trees, shrubs and vines that produce edible fruits or nuts and are hardy and disease resistant. Apple rootstock: Mark and EMLA 26. Asian Pear rootstock: OH x F 333. Cherry rootstock: GM 61. Pear rootstock: OH x F 333. Plum rootstock: St. Julian. Offered 239 total varieties in 2000, including 23 apples, 1 apricot, 8 cherries, 4 figs, 1 jujube, 1 nectarine, 7 pawpaws, 3 peaches, 15 pears, 6 persimmons, 7 plums, 1 quince, 16 blueberries, 1 cranberry, 9 currants, 4 elderberries, 4 gooseberries, 11 grapes, 3 huckleberries, 7 kiwis, 6 mulberries, 2 raspberries, 2 serviceberries, 2 strawberries, 1 almond, 1 butternut, 14 chestnuts, 11 filberts, 3 heartnuts, 4 hickories, 5 pecans, 2 pine nuts, 21 walnuts, 7 miscellaneous nuts, 1 loquat and 25 miscellaneous varieties.

BU12   **Burpee Peninsula Farm**, PO Box 8, Selbyville, DE 19975. Wholesale only! Formerly Peninsula Nurseries. Offered 48 total varieties in 2000, including 1 cherry, 2 figs, 1 pawpaw, 1 plum, 1 quince, 3 blackberries, 4 blueberries, 2 elderberries, 1 gooseberry, 10 grapes, 2 kiwis, 5 raspberries, 1 serviceberry, 11 strawberries, 2 rhubarbs and 1 miscellaneous variety.

BZN   **B and Z Nursery, Inc.**, 1850 S. Newcomb, Porterville, CA 93257. Phone: 559-781-7438. Fax: 559-781-6493. Wholesale only! Offered 47 total varieties in 2000, including 5 miscellaneous citrus, 5 citrus rootstocks, 6 grapefruits, 5 lemons, 1 lime, 17 oranges and 8 tangerines.

Ca7   **Carter Seeds**, 475 Mar Vista Dr., Vista, CA 92083. Phone: 740-724-5931. Fax: 740-724-8832. Free catalog. Retail and wholesale prices are listed in the same catalog. Specializes in seeds for trees, shrubs, ornamentals, tropicals, palms, grass and wildflowers. Offered 57 total varieties in 2000, including 4 cherries, 1 date, 1 jujube, 1 pear rootstock, 3 persimmons, 2 stone rootstocks, 1 cranberry, 1 kiwi, 1 mulberry, 1 hickory, 1 macadamia, 6 pine nuts, 2 walnuts, 4 miscellaneous nuts, 1 banana, 2 guavas, 2 loquats, 1 mango, 1 passionflower, 1 pineapple guava, 1 pomegranate, 1 sapote and 18 miscellaneous varieties.

Ca8   **Cascade Forestry Nursery**, 22033 Fillmore Road, Cascade, IA 52033. Phone: 319-852-3042. Fax: 319-852-5004. E-mail: Cascade@netins.net. Web site: www.cascadeforestry.com. Free catalog. Specializes in growing northern-hardy pecan, walnut, butternut, American chestnut, shellbark and shagbark hickories, hazelnuts and other hardwoods and evergreen transplants. Also provides tree planting, maintenance, consulting, timber appraisals and timber sales. Offered 18 total varieties in 2000, including 2 cherries, 1 persimmon, 1 plum, 1 cranberry, 1 serviceberry, 1 butternut, 1 chestnut, 1 filbert, 4 hickories, 1 pecan, 1 walnut, 1 miscellaneous nut and 2 miscellaneous varieties.

Ca12   **Callahan Seeds**, 6045 Foley Lane, PO Box 5531, Central Point, OR 97502. Phone: 541-855-1164. Send a self-addressed, stamped envelope for price list. Retail and wholesale prices are given in the same price list. Has offered seeds of western North American trees and shrubs since 1977. Offered 45 total varieties in 2000, including 4 cherries, 1 peach, 2 persimmons, 1 plum, 2 elderberries, 1 huckleberry, 1 chestnut, 1 filbert, 15 pine nuts, 4 walnuts, 2 miscellaneous nuts and 11 miscellaneous varieties.

CA14 **Carino Nurseries**, PO Box 538, Indiana, PA 15701. Wholesale only! Specializes in bare root seedlings and transplants, deciduous shrubs and nut trees. Offered 5 total varieties in 2000, including 1 butternut, 1 chestnut, 1 hickory, 1 walnut and 1 miscellaneous variety.

Ca15 **Calhoun's Nursery**, 295 Blacktwig Road, Pittsboro, NC 27312. Free catalog. Specializes in heirloom southern apple varieties. Apple rootstock: EMLA 111 and M 7A. Offered 311 apples in 2000.

Cam **Camellia Forest Nursery**, 9701 Carrie Road, Chapel Hill, NC 27516-7955. Send $2 in stamps for catalog. Retail prices are listed. Specializes in cold-hardy camellias, conifers and rare ornamental trees and shrubs, but carries a few uncommon fruit varieties. Offered 1 miscellaneous nut and 1 miscellaneous variety in 2000.

Car **Carroll Gardens, Inc.,** 444 E. Main St., Westminister, MD 21157. Phone: 410-848-5422. Fax: 410-857-4112. E-mail: order@carrollgarden.com. Web site: carrollgarden.com. $2 for two-year catalog, deductible from any order of $25 or more from that catalog. Retail catalog has a price sheet included for wholesale orders. Offered 18 total varieties in 2000, including 1 pawpaw, 7 blueberries, 5 serviceberries, 1 filbert, 2 citrus rootstocks and 2 miscellaneous varieties.

Ced **Cedar Valley Nursery**, 3833 McElfresh Rd. SW, Centralia, WA 98531. Phone: 360-736-7490. Fax: 360-736-6600. E-mail: boyd@myhome.net. Free catalog. Retail and wholesale prices are listed in the same catalog. Specializes in tissue culture propagation of blackberry and raspberry varieties grown commercially. Inquire for custom propagation of other species. Offered 30 total varieties in 2000, including 21 blackberries and 9 raspberries.

Ch9 **Christian Homesteading Movement**, Turner Road, Oxford, NY 13830. Offers scionwood of 500 varieties of fruits and nuts. Send a long self-addressed stamped envelope and $2 for price list. Retail and wholesale prices are given in the same price list. Specializes in disease and insect resistant cultivars for organic growers. Offered 477 total varieties in 2000, including 425 apples, 11 cherries, 12 pears, 25 plums, 2 stone fruit crosses, 1 stone rootstock and 1 mulberry.

Cid **Cider Hill Nursery**, Lee and Mary Elliott, 1852 Woodson-Winchester Road, Winchester, IL 62694. Send a self-addressed, stamped envelope for catalog. Retail only. Specializes in English, French and American cider apple trees and Perry pears. Offered 96 total varieties in 2000, including 81 apples and 15 pears.

Cla **Classical Fruits**, 8831 AL Highway 157, Moulton, AL 35650. Phone: 256-974-8813. Free catalog. Retail and wholesale prices are listed in the same catalog. Family owned and operated. Apple rootstock: M 7A, M 27 and MM 106. Offered 166 total varieties in 2000, including 90 apples, 4 cherries, 2 figs, 6 nectarines, 13 peaches, 13 pears, 1 persimmon, 14 plums, 1 stone fruit cross, 4 blackberries, 4 blueberries, 9 grapes, 3 raspberries, 1 strawberry and 1 chestnut.

CLI **Clifty View Nursery**, Rt. 1, Box 509, Bonners Ferry, ID 83805. Wholesale only! Offered 25 total varieties in 2000, including 5 apples, 8 cherries,

1 gooseberry, 1 serviceberry, 2 miscellaneous nuts and 8 miscellaneous varieties.

Clo **Cloud Mountain Farm and Nursery**, 6906 Goodwin Rd., Everson, WA 98247. Phone: 360-966-5859. Fax: 360-966-0921. $1 donation for catalog. Retail only. Carries varieties carefully selected to do well and ripen consistently in the Pacific maritime region, specializing in woody plants including fruits. A nursery kept small in order to ensure individual attention to customers. Apple rootstock: M 27, M 26 and M 106. Cherry rootstock: Gisela 5. Asian Pear rootstock: OH x F 333. Peach rootstock: Semi-Dwarf Citation. Pear rootstock: OH x F 333 and Provence Quince. Plum rootstock: Semi-Dwarf Citation. Offered 147 total varieties in 2000, including 21 apples, 2 apricots, 9 cherries, 2 figs, 1 nectarine, 4 pawpaws, 1 peach, 11 pears, 2 persimmons, 7 plums, 2 quinces, 1 stone fruit cross, 4 blackberries, 15 blueberries, 1 cranberry, 9 currants, 3 elderberries, 3 gooseberries, 11 grapes, 1 huckleberry, 9 kiwis, 2 mulberries, 5 raspberries, 6 strawberries, 2 filberts, 3 walnuts, 1 rhubarb and 9 miscellaneous varieties.

Co2 **C and O Nursery Co.**, PO Box 116, Wenatchee, WA 98807. Phone: 509-662-7164. Fax: 509-662-4519. E-mail: tree@c-onursery.com. Web site: www.c-onursery.com. Free catalog. Family owned and operated nursery founded in 1906. Specializes in fruit trees. Apple rootstock: EMLA 7, EMLA 9, EMLA 26, EMLA 106, EMLA 111, M-9. Apricot rootstock: Colt. Cherry rootstock: Colt, Gisela (R) 5, Mahaleb and Mazzard. Peach rootstock: Halford. Pear rootstock: OH x F 97. Offered 144 total varieties in 2000, including 54 apples, 10 apricots, 19 cherries, 5 nectarines, 33 peaches, 12 pears and 11 plums.

CO3 **Congdon and Weller Wholesale Nursery, Inc.**, Mile Block Road, PO Box 1507, North Collins, NY 14111-1507. Wholesale only! Offered 41 total varieties in 2000, including 1 cherry, 2 blackberries, 3 blueberries, 5 cranberries, 3 currants, 3 elderberries, 2 gooseberries, 6 grapes, 10 raspberries, 1 serviceberry and 5 miscellaneous varieties.

CO5 **L. E. Cooke Co.**, 26333 Road 140, Visalia, CA 93292. Wholesale only! Offered 340 total varieties in 2000, including 50 apples, 12 apricots, 16 cherries, 11 figs, 3 jujubes, 11 nectarines, 53 peaches, 34 pears, 8 persimmons, 23 plums, 4 quinces, 2 stone fruit crosses, 17 blackberries, 9 blueberries, 1 currant, 1 gooseberry, 26 grapes, 5 mulberries, 10 raspberries, 4 strawberries, 6 almonds, 12 pecans, 13 walnuts, 4 pomegranates, 1 rhubarb and 4 miscellaneous varieties.

Co6 **Cooley's Strawberry Nursery**, PO Box 472, Augusta, AR 72006. Phone: 870-347-2026. Free catalog. Retail and wholesale prices listed in the same catalog. Sells strawberry plants only. Offered 12 strawberries in 2000.

Co12 **Country Carriage Nurseries and Seed, Inc.**, PO Box 548, 84351 First Street, Hartford, MI 49057-0548. Phone: 616-621-2491. Formerly known as Country Heritage Nursery. Retail and wholesale prices are listed in the same catalog. Offered 92 total varieties in 2000, including 14 blackberries, 11 blueberries, 3 currants, 2 elderberries, 3 gooseberries, 8 grapes, 1 kiwi, 1 mulberry, 21 raspberries, 21 strawberries, 2 rhubarbs and 5 miscellaneous varieties.

Co15 **Cold Stream Farm**, 2030 Free Soil Road, Free Soil, MI 49411-9752. Phone: 616-464-5809. E-mail: csf@jackpine.com. Retail and wholesale prices are listed in the same catalog. Specializes in wildlife habitat. All stock is bare root; no seed sold. Offered 26 total varieties in 2000, including 6 apples, 2 cherries, 1 plum, 1 cranberry, 1 elderberry, 1 mulberry, 1 serviceberry, 1 chestnut, 1 filbert, 2 walnuts, 2 miscellaneous nuts and 7 miscellaneous varieties.

Co24 **Colvos Creek Nursery**, PO Box 1512, Vashon Island, WA 98070. Retail, with a wholesale price schedule available upon request. Specializes in unusual trees, shrubs and perennials. Offered 50 total varieties in 2000, including 3 apples, 2 cherries, 1 pawpaw, 1 blueberry, 1 cranberry, 1 currant, 3 elderberries, 1 grape, 3 huckleberries, 1 raspberry, 1 serviceberry, 9 pine nuts, 4 miscellaneous nuts, 1 citrus rootstock, 1 loquat, 1 passionflower, 1 pineapple guava, 1 pomegranate and 14 miscellaneous varieties.

COL **Columbia Basin Nursery**, PO Box 458, Quincy, WA 98848. Phone: 509-787-4411. Fax: 509-787-3944. Wholesale only! Offered 76 total varieties in 2000, including 26 apples, 5 apricots, 15 cherries, 4 nectarines, 11 peaches, 8 pears and 7 plums.

Coo **The Cook's Garden**, PO Box 535, Londonderry, VT 05148. Phone: 800-457-9703. Fax: 800-457-9705. E-mail: catalog@cooksgarden.com. Web site: www.cooksgarden.com. Retail only. Free catalog, which lists heirloom culinary vegetable seeds from around the world. Also many herbs, cut flowers and annual vines plus some seed saving books and supplies. Offered 1 strawberry and 1 rhubarb in 2000.

CR6 **Cross Nurseries, Inc.**, 19774 Kenwood Trail, Lakeville, MN 55044. Wholesale only! Specializes in trees, shrubs, evergreens and perennials. Offered 42 total varieties in 2000, including 10 apples, 4 cherries, 1 plum, 5 cranberries, 1 currant, 2 elderberries, 6 grapes, 2 raspberries, 2 serviceberries, 1 filbert, 1 rhubarb and 7 miscellaneous varieties.

Cu4 **Cummins Nursery**, 18 Glass Factory Bay Road, Geneva, NY 14456. Web site: www.dabney.com/cumminsnursery. Retail and wholesale prices are listed in the same catalog. Apple rootstock: M 7, M 9, M 26, MM 106, MM 111, G 11, G 16, G 65 and Standard. Apricot rootstock: Manchurian and GF 8-1. Cherry rootstock: Mahaleb. Pear rootstock: OH x F and *P. betulifolia*. Offered 280 total varieties in 2000, including 14 apple rootstocks, 163 apples, 5 apricots, 20 cherries, 22 peaches, 25 pears, 21 plums, 5 raspberries and 5 strawberries.

Cum **Cumberland Valley Nurseries**, PO Box 471, McMinnville, TN 37110. Phone: 931-668-4153. Fax: 931-668-7251. Free catalog. Retail and wholesale prices are listed in the same catalog. Specializes in fruit trees. In business since 1902. Apple rootstock: M 7A, M 26, MM 106, MM 111 and Standard. Cherry rootstock: Mahaleb. Peach, plum, nectarine and apricot rootstock: Halford and Nemaguard. Asian and standard pear rootstock: *P. calleryana*. Offered 136 total varieties in 2000, including 15 apples, 3 cherries, 12 nectarines, 83 peaches, 10 pears and 13 plums.

Dab **Dabney Herbs**, PO Box 22061, Louisville, KY 40252. Phone: 502-893-5198. Fax: 502-893-5198. E-mail: dabneyherb@win.net. Web site: dabney herbs.com. $2 for catalog. Separate retail and wholesale catalogs, each containing additional varieties not in the other. Specializes in old-fashioned herb seeds and also offers seeds for ginseng, goldenseal, echinacea and other traditional medicinal plants, depending on availability. Offered 3 total varieties in 2000, including 1 elderberry, 1 strawberry and 1 miscellaneous variety.

DAl **Daisy Farms**, 91098 60th St., Decatur, MI 49045. Wholesale only! Offered 34 total varieties in 2000, including 5 raspberries, 27 strawberries and 2 rhubarbs.

De2 **DeGrandchamp's Blueberry Farm**, 15575 77th St., South Haven, MI 49090. Phone: 616-637-3915. Fax: 616-637-2531. E-mail: dechamp @cybersol.com. Web site: degrandchamps.com. Free catalog. Retail and wholesale prices are listed in the same catalog. Specializes in northern highbush blueberries and cranberries. Offered 41 total varieties in 2000, including 24 blueberries, 10 cranberries and 7 miscellaneous varieties.

Do7 **Double A Vineyards, Inc.**, 10277 Christy Road, Fredonia, NY 14063. Retail and wholesale prices are listed in the same catalog. Family-owned operation specializing in quality grapevines. Offered 79 total varieties in 2000, including 1 apple and 78 grapes.

DYK **Dyke's Berry Farm**, R.R. 4 Box 178, Vincent, OH 45784. Wholesale only! Offered 6 blueberries in 2000.

Ea3 **Earth's Rising Trees**, PO Box 334, Monroe, OR 97456. Free catalog. Retail only. All trees are organically grown and, except for the figs, Oregon Tilth Certified. Offered 80 total varieties in 2000, including 32 apples, 4 cherries, 8 figs, 4 peaches, 17 pears, 4 pear rootstocks, 7 plums and 4 stone rootstocks.

Ech **ECHO Seed Sales**, 17391 Durrance Road, North Fort Myers, FL 33917. Phone: 941-543-3246. Fax: 941-543-5317. E-mail: echo@echonet.org. Web site: www.echonet.org. $1 for catalog. Retail only. Nonprofit organization specializing in tropical or subtropical fruits and vegetables. Seed sale profits are used to cover some of the cost for free packets of seeds sent to small farmers in the Third World. Offered 1 papaya and 1 passionflower in 2000.

Ed2 **Edible Landscaping**, Michael McConkey, PO Box 77, Afton, VA 22920. Phone: 804-361-9134. Fax: 804-361-1916. E-mail: el@cstone.net. Web site: www.eat-it.com. Free 48-page color catalog. Retail only. Specializes in fruit varieties that require less care. Offered 190 total varieties in 2000, including 7 apples, 1 apricot, 9 cherries, 13 figs, 1 jujube, 4 pawpaws, 9 peaches, 6 pears, 8 persimmons, 4 plums, 1 quince, 3 blackberries, 9 blueberries, 2 cranberries, 6 currants, 5 elderberries, 5 gooseberries, 7 grapes, 9 kiwis, 8 mulberries, 3 raspberries, 3 serviceberries, 9 strawberries, 1 almond, 3 chestnuts, 4 filberts, 1 heartnut, 5 pecans, 3 pine nuts, 1 banana, 3 miscellaneous citrus, 2 citrus rootstocks, 3 lemons, 2 limes, 1 loquat, 1 orange, 1 passionflower, 2 pomegranates, 1 tangerine, 1 hop, 1 rhubarb and 22 miscellaneous varieties.

Ed5 **Edible Forest Nursery**, PO Box 260195, Madison, WI 53726-0195. Phone: 608-256-2659. Toll-free number to request free catalog is 877-745-8267. Retail only. Specializes in super-hardy fruit varieties for Zones 3 and 4, Canadian prairie apples, grafted walnuts and hickories for Zone 3 (on very specialized rootstocks) and hardy Asian pears. Most rootstocks raised from seed. Stock is grown without pesticides or herbicides. Apple rootstock: Standard, primarily Antonovka. Offered 335 total varieties in 2000, including 198 apples, 4 apricots, 11 cherries, 42 pears, 1 pear rootstock, 1 persimmon, 22 plums, 4 stone fruit crosses, 4 blueberries, 3 currants, 20 grapes, 6 kiwis, 3 raspberries, 1 serviceberry, 1 almond, 1 chestnut, 4 hickories, 1 pine nut, 3 walnuts and 5 miscellaneous varieties.

Emp   **Empire Chestnut Company**, 3276 Empire Road SW, Carrollton, OH 44615. Phone: 330-627-3181. Fax: 330-627-3181. E-mail: empire@eohio .net. Specializes in high quality chestnut nursery stock for orchard, wildlife and landscaping. Offered 19 chestnuts in 2000.

Eno   **Enoch's Berry Farm**, Rt. 2, Box 227, Fouke, AR 71837. Phone: 870-653-2512. E-mail: plants@berryfarm.com. Web site: www.berryfarm.com. Toll-free phone is 877-772-2806. Free price list. Retail and wholesale prices are given in the same price list. Sells naturally grown blackberry root cuttings and plants. Offered 3 blackberries in 2000.

Er2   **Erik's Edible Orchard**, 162 Creekside Drive, Sequim, WA 98382. Small family owned and operated orchard. Apple rootstock: Geneva 30, M 9, EMLA 26 and Mark. Offered 59 total varieties in 2000, including 52 apples, 1 fig, 4 pears and 2 plums.

Fa1   **Farmer Seed and Nursery Co.**, Division of Plantron, Inc., 818 NW 4th St., Faribault, MN 55021. Free catalog. Retail only. Offered 95 total varieties in 2000, including 22 apples, 2 apricots, 6 cherries, 1 fig, 3 pears, 6 plums, 3 stone fruit crosses, 6 blueberries, 1 cranberry, 2 currants, 2 elderberries, 1 gooseberry, 10 grapes, 1 kiwi, 9 raspberries, 2 serviceberries, 11 strawberries, 1 filbert, 1 banana, 1 tangerine, 1 rhubarb and 3 miscellaneous varieties.

FAl   **Fairacre Farm and Nursery**, 155608 West King Tull Road, Prosser, WA 99350. Phone: 509-786-2974. Fax: 509-786-7499. Wholesale only! Formerly Lewis and White. Offered 22 grapes in 2000.

FAL   **Fall Creek Farm and Nursery Inc.**, 39318 Jasper-Lowell Rd., Lowell, OR 97452. Phone: 541-937-2973. Fax: 541-937-3373. E-mail: dmom bell@fallcreeknursery.com. Web site: www.fallcreeknursery.com. Wholesale only! Specializes in blueberries and related *Vacciniums*. Offered 35 total varieties in 2000, including 31 blueberries, 4 miscellaneous varieties.

FE7   **Femrite Nursery Company**, 13193 Arndt Road NE, Aurora, OR 97002. Web site: www.femrite.com. Wholesale only! Offered 45 total varieties in 2000, including 26 apples, 2 cherries, 8 pears, 4 plums, 1 stone rootstock, 1 serviceberry, 1 miscellaneous nut and 2 miscellaneous varieties.

Fed   **Fedco Trees**, PO Box 520, Waterville, ME 04903-0520. Phone: 207-873-7333. Fax: 207-872-8317. E-mail: ftrees@mint.net. Web site: fedcoseeds .com. Free catalog, but send a self-addressed, stamped envelope if possible. Specializes in hardy, primarily food-producing trees and shrubs, largely Maine-grown. Mail orders and pick-ups, but no phone orders. Offered 222 total varieties in 2000, including 3 apple rootstocks, 100 apples, 4 apricots, 6 cherries, 1 nectarine, 4 peaches, 21 pears, 20 plums, 2 stone rootstocks, 9 blueberries, 5 cranberries, 2 elderberries, 17 grapes, 7 raspberries, 2 serviceberries, 6 strawberries, 1 butternut, 2 filberts, 1 pine nut, 1 walnut, 3 hops, 2 rhubarbs and 3 miscellaneous varieties.

Fi1   **Henry Field's Seed and Nursery Co.**, 415 North Burnett St., Shenandoah, IA 51602. Phone: 800-235-0845. Web site: www.henryfields.com. Free catalog. Founded in 1893. Offered 172 total varieties in 2000, including 21 apples, 6 apricots, 14 cherries, 2 figs, 3 nectarines, 1 pawpaw, 10 peaches, 10 pears, 2 persimmons, 7 plums, 2 stone fruit crosses, 5 blackberries, 6 blueberries, 2 cranberries, 2 currants, 1 elderberry, 2 gooseberries, 11 grapes, 3 kiwis, 1 mulberry, 15 raspberries, 1 serviceberry, 15 strawberries, 1 almond, 1 butternut, 2 chestnuts, 1 filbert, 2 hickories, 6 pecans, 3 walnuts, 1 banana, 1 guava, 1 lemon, 1 lime, 1 orange, 1 tangerine, 1 hop, 4 rhubarbs and 3 miscellaneous varieties.

Fi4   **Finch Blueberry Nursery**, PO Box 699, Bailey, NC 27807. Phone: 252-235-4664. Fax: 252-235-2411. Call 800-245-4662 to place an order. Free price list. Specializes in all types of blueberry varieties. Retail and wholesale prices are given in the same price list. Offered 45 blueberries in 2000.

Fo2   **Forestfarm Nursery**, 990 Tetherow Rd., Williams, OR 97544. Phone: 503-846-7269. $3 for catalog. Retail catalog, with price list available for wholesale orders. Company's concept is to offer many kinds of "starter plants" at affordable prices. Offered 257 total varieties in 2000, including 40 apples, 16 cherries, 1 pawpaw, 3 peaches, 6 pears, 1 persimmon, 9 plums, 2 quinces, 2 blackberries, 21 blueberries, 5 cranberries, 8 currants, 9 elderberries, 4 gooseberries, 2 grapes, 3 huckleberries, 2 kiwis, 7 mulberries, 6 raspberries, 8 serviceberries, 2 strawberries, 2 chestnuts, 4 filberts, 2 hickories, 1 pecan, 14 pine nuts, 1 walnut, 6 miscellaneous nuts, 1 miscellaneous citrus, 2 citrus rootstocks, 1 loquat, 1 passionflower, 1 pineapple guava, 2 pomegranates and 62 miscellaneous varieties.

Fo3   **Foster Concord Nurseries, Inc.**, 10175 Mileblock Road, North Collins, NY 14111-9770. Phone: 800-223-2211. Fax: 800-448-1267. E-mail: concordnurseries@aol.com. Formerly Foster Grapevines. Free catalog. Retail and wholesale prices are listed in the same catalog. Minimum order of $70. In business since 1924. Specializes in grapevines. Offered 60 grapes in 2000.

Fo4   **Four Seasons Nursery**, Division of Plantron, Inc., 1706 Morrissey Dr., Bloomington, IL 61704. Free catalog. Offered 64 total varieties in 2000, including 7 apples, 2 apricots, 3 cherries, 1 pawpaw, 3 peaches, 2 pears, 2 plums, 3 blackberries, 3 blueberries, 2 elderberries, 11 grapes, 1 kiwi, 6 raspberries, 4 strawberries, 1 almond, 1 butternut, 1 chestnut, 2 filberts, 1 pecan, 2 walnuts, 1 banana, 1 rhubarb and 4 miscellaneous varieties.

Fo8   **Foundation Plant Materials Service**, University of California, 1 Shields Avenue, Davis, CA 95616-8600. Phone: 530-752-3590. Fax: 530-752-2132. E-mail: fpms@ucdavis.edu. Web site: fpms.ucdavis.edu. Free price list. Retail and wholesale prices are given in the same price list. Offers certified cherry, peach and plum rootstock seed, also non-certified *Betulaefolia* pear rootstock seed. Offered 228 total varieties in 2000, including 1 pear rootstock, 6 stone rootstocks, 167 grapes, 32 grape rootstocks, 21 strawberries and 1 miscellaneous nut.

FO10   **Forest Nursery Company, Inc.**, 2362 Beersheba Highway, McMinnville, TN 37110. Wholesale only! Offered 48 total varieties in 2000, including 9 apples, 2 apricots, 4 cherries, 1 pawpaw, 6 peaches, 4 pears, 1 persimmon, 7 plums, 1 cranberry, 1 elderberry, 4 grapes, 1 mulberry, 1 chestnut, 1 filbert, 1 pecan, 1 walnut, 1 miscellaneous nut and 2 miscellaneous varieties.

Fr4   **Freshops**, 36180 Kings Valley Hwy., Philomath, OR 97370. Phone: 541-929-2736. Fax: 541-929-2702. E-mail: sales@freshops.com. Web site: www.freshops.com. Separate but identical retail and wholesale catalogs. Specializes in hop rhizomes, flowers and oils. Offered 11 hops in 2000.

Fra   **The Fragrant Path**, PO Box 328, Fort Calhoun, NE 68023. $2 for catalog. Specializes in seeds for fragrant, rare and old-fashioned plants. Offered 16 total varieties in 2000, including 1 apple, 1 apricot, 1 cherry, 1 jujube, 1 persimmon, 1 kiwi, 1 guava, 1 passionflower, 1 pomegranate and 7 miscellaneous varieties.

Fro   **Frosty Hollow Ecological Restoration**, PO Box 53, Langley, WA 98260. Phone: 360-579-2332. Fax: 360-579-2332. E-mail: wean@whidbey.net. Send a self-addressed, stamped envelope for price list. Retail and wholesale prices are listed in the same price list. Specializes in Pacific Northwest native species, usually wild collected seed. Consultants in ecological restoration. No nursery stock sold – seeds only. Offered 16 total varieties in 2000, including 1 cranberry, 1 currant, 2 elderberries, 2 huckleberries, 1 raspberry, 1 serviceberry, 1 filbert and 7 miscellaneous varieties.

Ga6   **Gardeners' Choice**, 81961 County Road 687, PO Box 8000, Hartford, MI 49057. $2 for catalog. Retail and quantity prices are listed in the same catalog. Offered 18 total varieties in 2000, including 1 apricot, 1 cherry, 1 fig, 1 peach, 1 plum, 1 blackberry, 1 blueberry, 1 grape, 1 kiwi, 3 raspberries, 3 strawberries, 1 walnut and 1 banana and 1 rhubarb.

Ga8   **Gardens of the Blue Ridge**, PO Box 10, Pineola, NC 28662. Phone: 828-733-2417. Fax: 828-733-8894. E-mail: gardensblueridge@boone.net. Web site: gardenosoftheblueridge.com. $3 for catalog. Specializes in wildflowers and native ferns, trees, shrubs and bog plants. In business since 1892. Offered 8 total varieties in 2000, including 1 pawpaw, 1 blueberry, 1 elderberry, 1 raspberry, 1 serviceberry, 1 strawberry and 2 miscellaneous varieties.

Ga11   **Garden of Delights**, 14560 SW 14th St., Davie, FL 33325-4217. Phone: 954-370-9004. Fax: 954-236-4588. E-mail: godelights@aol.com. Web site: gardenofdelights.com. $2 for catalog. Specializes in palms, rare tropical and subtropical fruit trees and horticultural curiosities. Offered 121 total varieties in 2000, including 1 fig, 2 jujubes, 1 persimmon, 1 mulberry, 1 raspberry, 1 macadamia, 2 miscellaneous nuts, 9 annonas, 3 avocados, 1 banana, 5 miscellaneous citrus, 1 citrus rootstock, 3 grapefruits, 4 guavas, 3 lemons, 3 limes, 2 loquats, 3 mangoes, 4 oranges, 2 papayas, 2 passionflowers, 1 pineapple guava, 1 pomegranate, 7 sapotes, 2 tangerines and 56 miscellaneous varieties.

Ga20   **Garcia River Nursery**, PO Box 235, 38705 Eureka Hill Road, Point Arena, CA 95468. Free catalog. Separate but identical retail and wholesale catalogs. Specializes in propagating antique fruit varieties. Offered 50 total varieties in 2000, including 44 apples, 1 peach and 5 pears.

Gl3   **Gill Nursery**, 100 County Road 1595, Baileyton, AL 35019. Phone: 256-796-5618. Fax: 256-796-8029. E-mail: gillnsry@bellsouth.net. Wholesale only! Specializes in bare root fruit, shade and ornamental trees, also has a container operation. Offered 81 total varieties in 2000, including 27 apples, 4 cherries, 3 nectarines, 22 peaches, 10 pears, 11 plums and 4 grapes.

Gir   **Girard Nurseries**, PO Box 428, Geneva, OH 44041. Phone: 440-466-2881. Fax: 440-466-3999. E-mail: girardnurseries@suite244.net. Web site: www.girardnurseries.com. Free catalog. Separate retail and wholesale catalogs; retail catalog contains additional varieties. Specializes in rare and unusual plants, conifers and flowers (azaleas and rhododendrons); no seeds. Offered 19 total varieties in 2000, including 5 apples, 1 cherry, 3 plums, 6 blueberries, 1 filbert, 1 pine nut and 2 miscellaneous varieties.

Gl3 **Glasshouse Works,** Church Street, PO Box 97, Stewart, OH 45778-0097. Phone: 740-662-2142. $2 for catalog. Retail only. Specializes in ornamentals, rare, exotic and hard-to-find plants, especially variegates. Offered 6 total varieties in 2000, including 2 bananas, 3 passionflowers and 1 pomegranate.

Go7 **Going Bananas,** Don and Katie Chafin, 24401 SW 197 Avenue, Homestead, FL 33031. Phone: 305-247-0397. Fax: 305-247-7877. E-mail: going bananas@bellsouth.net. Web site: going-bananas.com. Wholesale and retail catalogs available. Specializes in bananas. Offered 67 bananas in 2000.

Gor **John Gordon Nursery,** 1385 Campbell Blvd., Amherst, NY 14228-1404. Phone: 716-691-9371. Fax: 801-881-8842. E-mail: nuttreegordon@hotmail .com. Web site: geocities.com/nuttreegordon. Free price list. Specializes in hardy nut varieties, pawpaws and native persimmons that ripen earlier than Early Golden. Offered 70 total varieties in 2000, including 5 pawpaws, 10 persimmons, 2 mulberries, 4 chestnuts, 12 filberts, 4 heartnuts, 17 hickories, 3 pecans and 13 walnuts.

Gos **Gossler Farms Nursery,** 1200 Weaver Rd., Springfield, OR 97478. Phone: 541-746-3922. Fax: 541-744-7924. $2 for catalog. Retail catalog contains additional varieties not included in its wholesale price list, which is available only to nurseries and landscapers. Specializes in companion plants. Offered 6 total varieties in 2000, including 2 blueberries, 1 cranberry, 1 kiwi and 2 miscellaneous varieties.

Gr4 **Greenmantle Nursery,** 3010 Ettersburg Rd., Garberville, CA 95542. Phone: 707-986-7504. $4 for catalog. Small, family operated nursery specializing in old homestead fruits, varieties created by Albert Etter and chestnut seedlings. Apple rootstock: seedling and MM 111. Cherry rootstock: Colt and Mazzard F-12-1. Pear rootstock: domestic seedling. Asian pear rootstock: *P. betulifolia.* Plum rootstock: Myrobalan seedling. Custom grafting is also offered. Offered 194 total varieties in 2000, including 140 apples, 18 cherries, 2 figs, 3 peaches, 16 pears, 6 plums, 1 quince, 4 chestnuts and 4 miscellaneous varieties.

Gr8 **Somer's Greenhaven Farm Nursery,** 3426 Grenlund Rd., Rt. 1, Perrinton, MI 48871. Free price list. Retail only. Specializes in winter-hardy Carpathian (English) walnut seed nuts from their orchard. Offered 1 walnut in 2000.

Gr16 **Greer Gardens,** 1280 Goodpasture Island Road, Eugene, OR 97401-1794. Phone: 541-686-8266. $3 for three years of catalogs, two per year. Retail only. Specializes in rare and unusual trees, shrubs and perennials including rhododendrons and magnolias. Offered 106 total varieties in 2000, including 17 apples, 1 apricot, 1 cherry, 3 figs, 3 pawpaws, 1 peach, 11 pears, 4 persimmons, 4 plums, 3 stone fruit crosses, 1 blackberry, 11 blueberries, 2 cranberries, 4 currants, 4 elderberries, 1 gooseberry, 1 huckleberry, 10 kiwis, 1 mulberry, 1 filbert, 2 walnuts, 1 passionflower, 1 pineapple guava, 1 pomegranate, 1 rhubarb and 16 miscellaneous varieties.

GR18 **Grinnell Nursery,** 14495 Morrice Road, Perry, MI 48872. Phone: 517-625-7176. Fax: 517-625-0442. E-mail: grinnellnursery@tps.com. Wholesale only! Specializes in grafted hazelnut and English walnut varieties. Offered 13 total varieties in 2000, including 7 filberts and 6 walnuts.

GR26 **Green Acres Nursery, Inc.**, 4990 McIntyre St., Golden, CO 80403. Formerly listed as Arapahoe Acres Nursery, Inc. Wholesale only! Offered 122 total varieties in 2000, including 29 apples, 10 cherries, 2 peaches, 9 pears, 2 pear rootstocks, 5 plums, 1 quince, 2 blackberries, 6 cranberries, 4 currants, 3 elderberries, 3 gooseberries, 6 grapes, 1 kiwi, 1 mulberry, 4 raspberries, 7 serviceberries, 4 strawberries, 2 filberts, 2 walnuts, 1 miscellaneous nut, 1 hop and 17 miscellaneous varieties.

Gra **Russell Graham**, Purveyor of Plants, 4030 Eale Crest Rd. NW, Salem, OR 97304. $2 for catalog. Separate retail and wholesale catalogs; retail catalog contains additional varieties. Specializes in hardy herbaceous perennials. Offered 2 miscellaneous varieties in 2000.

Gur **Gurney's Seed and Nursery Co.**, 110 Capital Street, Yankton, SD 57079. Free catalog. Retail only. Specializes in garden seed and nursery items. Offered 154 total varieties in 2000, including 21 apples, 6 apricots, 13 cherries, 1 fig, 1 nectarine, 1 pawpaw, 6 peaches, 8 pears, 2 persimmons, 5 plums, 3 stone fruit crosses, 7 blackberries, 5 blueberries, 2 cranberries, 2 currants, 1 elderberry, 2 gooseberries, 8 grapes, 3 kiwis, 1 mulberry, 11 raspberries, 1 serviceberry, 17 strawberries, 1 almond, 1 butternut, 2 chestnuts, 2 filberts, 2 hickories, 5 pecans, 1 walnut, 1 banana, 1 guava, 1 lemon, 1 lime, 1 orange, 1 pineapple guava, 1 pomegranate, 1 tangerine, 1 hop and 4 rhubarbs.

Ha12 **Hartmann's Plantation, Inc.**, PO Box 100, Lacota, MI 49063. Phone: 616-253-4281. Fax: 616-253-4457. E-mail: info@hartmannsplantcompany .com. Web site: www.hartmannsplantcompany.com. Free catalog. Separate wholesale and retail catalogs. In business since 1944. Specializes in blueberry plants, hardy kiwi, raspberry, blackberry, pawpaw and miniature roses. Offered 142 total varieties in 2000, including 2 cherries, 1 fig, 1 pawpaw, 5 blackberries, 52 blueberries, 12 cranberries, 7 currants, 2 elderberries, 4 gooseberries, 1 grape, 2 huckleberries, 17 kiwis, 15 raspberries, 1 serviceberry, 5 strawberries, 2 miscellaneous citrus, 2 passionflowers, 1 rhubarb and 10 miscellaneous varieties.

Hi2 **Highlander Nursery**, PO Box 177, Pettigrew, AR 72752. Phone: 501-677-2300. E-mail: lmccoy@alltel.net. Free price list. Separate retail and wholesale price lists; retail price list contains additional varieties. Specializes in Northern and Southern highbush blueberry varieties. Offered 15 blueberries in 2000.

Hl7 **Hillis Nursery Co., Inc.**, 92 Gardner Road, McMinnville, TN 37110. Wholesale only! Offered 30 total varieties in 2000, including 1 cherry, 1 pawpaw, 7 pears, 1 persimmon, 1 stone rootstock, 1 cranberry, 1 elderberry, 1 chestnut, 1 filbert, 5 hickories, 2 pecans, 1 walnut, 1 miscellaneous nut and 6 miscellaneous varieties.

Hi9 **Hilltop Nurseries, Inc.**, PO Box 578, Hartford, MI 49057. Phone: 616-621-3135. Fax: 616-621-2062. Formerly listed as Newark Nurseries, Inc. Retail and wholesale prices are listed in the same catalog. Specializes in fruit trees. Apple rootstock: Bud 9, EMLA 7, EMLA 9, EMLA 26, EMLA 106, EMLA 111, Geneva 30 and Mark. Apricot rootstock: Manchurian. Cherry rootstock: M x M, M x M 2, M x M 60, Mahaleb and Mazzard. Peach rootstock: Bailey Seedling and Lovell. Pear rootstock: OH x F, OH x F 18, OH x F 97, OH x F 282 and OH x F 333. Plum rootstock: Marianna 2624 and Myrobolan. Offered 245 total varieties in 2000, including 95 apples, 8 apricots, 35 cherries, 12 nectarines, 61 peaches, 15 pears and 19 plums.

HI10 **Hines Nurseries**, 12621 Jeffrey Road, Irvine, CA 92620-2101. Wholesale only! Offered 48 total varieties in 2000, including 3 cherries, 2 blackberries, 2 blueberries, 1 currant, 8 grapes, 12 raspberries, 3 strawberries, 1 miscellaneous nut, 2 lemons, 1 lime, 2 oranges, 3 passionflowers, 1 pineapple guava, 2 pomegranates and 5 miscellaneous varieties.

Hid **Hidden Springs Nursery**, 170 Hidden Springs Lane, Cookeville, TN 38501. Phone: 931-268-2592. $1 for two-year catalog subscription. Small family-owned business specializing in organically grown, disease-resistant fruit trees including pawpaws, persimmons, mulberries, cherries, nitrogen-fixing fruit shrubs and more. Offered 154 total varieties in 2000, including 51 apples, 3 cherries, 4 figs, 13 pawpaws, 8 pears, 6 persimmons, 6 quinces, 1 blackberry, 2 blueberries, 1 cranberry, 4 currants, 2 elderberries, 2 gooseberries, 7 grapes, 2 kiwis, 2 mulberries, 1 raspberry, 1 serviceberry, 1 almond, 1 chestnut, 1 pine nut, 1 miscellaneous citrus, 1 citrus rootstock, 1 lemon, 1 lime, 2 pomegranates and 29 miscellaneous varieties.

Ho5 **Hollydale Nursery**, PO Box 69, Pelham, TN 37366. Phone: 931-467-3600. Fax: 931-467-3062. Free price list. Retail and wholesale prices are listed in the same catalog. Specializes in fruit and ornamental trees. Offered 195 total varieties in 2000, including 25 apples, 12 nectarines, 132 peaches, 11 pears and 15 plums.

Ho8 **Horizon Herbs**, PO Box 69, Williams, OR 97544. Phone: 541-846-6704. Fax: 541-846-6233. E-mail: herbseed@chatlink.com. Web site: chatlink .com/~herbseed. $3 for *Strictly Medicinal* catalog and growing guide. Retail and wholesale prices are listed in the same catalog. Specializes in rare and unusual medicinal plants of North America, Europe, India and China. Offers over 700 species of certified organically grown or sustainably wild-harvested seed of medicinal plants, also nursery-propagated live rootstock of goldenseal, wild yam, black cohosh, Fo Ti, etc. Offered 3 total varieties in 2000, including 1 elderberry, 1 passionflower, 1 miscellaneous variety.

Hud **J. L. Hudson**, **Seedsman**, Star Route 2 Box 337, LaHonda, CA 94020. $1 for catalog. Specializes in seeds of rare and unusual plants, Zapotec varieties and seeds of useful wild and cultivated plants. Established in 1911, successors to Harry Saier. Stresses open-pollinated, non-hybrid seeds and preservation of biological and cultural diversity, since 1973. Offered 42 total varieties in 2000, including 1 jujube, 1 cranberry, 1 elderberry, 1 grape, 1 kiwi, 1 strawberry, 7 pine nuts, 1 annona, 1 guava, 7 passionflowers, 1 pineapple guava, 2 pomegranates and 17 miscellaneous varieties.

IM2 **Imperial Nurseries**, 4877 Vulcan Avenue, Columbus, OH 43228-9482. Wholesale only! Offered 31 total varieties in 2000, including 19 apples, 1 cherry, 4 pears, 2 serviceberries, 1 filbert and 4 miscellaneous varieties.

In5 **Indiana Berry and Plant Co.**, 5218 West 500 South, Huntingburg, IN 47542. Phone: 812-683-3055. Fax: 812-683-2004. E-mail: inberry@ psci.net. Web site: www.inberry.com. Free catalog. Separate but identical retail and wholesale catalogs. Specializes in strawberry, raspberry and blackberry plants. In business since 1929. Offered 106 total varieties in 2000, including 1 pawpaw, 11 blackberries, 12 blueberries, 1 cranberry, 11 currants, 1 elderberry, 4 gooseberries, 11 grapes, 1 kiwi, 21 raspberries, 1 serviceberry, 28 strawberries, 2 rhubarbs and 1 miscellaneous variety.

IN7   **Ingleside Plantation Nurseries,** 5870 Leedstown Road, Oak Grove, VA 22443. Wholesale only! Offered 9 total varieties in 2000, including 2 pears, 1 plum, 1 cranberry, 2 serviceberries, 1 miscellaneous nut and 2 miscellaneous varieties.

Ins   **Insti Trees Nursery,** PO Box 1370, Rhinelander, WI 54501. Free catalog. Retail only. Specializes in genetically improved trees and fast-growing hybrid poplars. Offered 3 total varieties in 2000, including 1 butternut, 1 chestnut and 1 walnut.

Int   **Inter-State Nurseries,** Division of Plantron, Inc., 1800 Hamilton Road, Bloomington, IL 61704. $2 for catalog. Retail only. Specializes in roses. Offered 25 total varieties in 2000, including 1 apricot, 2 cherries, 1 fig, 1 pawpaw, 3 blueberries, 2 kiwis, 1 serviceberry, 6 strawberries, 1 butternut, 1 chestnut, 1 filbert, 1 pecan, 1 walnut, 1 banana, 1 rhubarb and 1 miscellaneous variety.

Iso   **Ison's Nursery and Vineyards,** P.O. Box 190, Brooks, GA 30205. Phone: 800-733-0324. Fax: 770-599-1727. Local phone number is 770-599-6970. Free catalog. Separate but identical wholesale and retail catalogs. Specializes in Muscadine grapes and other fine fruits and berries. Offered 147 total varieties in 2000, including 16 apples, 5 cherries, 4 figs, 4 nectarines, 12 peaches, 10 pears, 4 persimmons, 9 plums, 9 blackberries, 5 blueberries, 48 grapes, 5 raspberries, 4 strawberries, 1 chestnut, 7 pecans, 2 walnuts, 1 pomegranate, 1 miscellaneous variety.

Je2   **Jersey Asparagus Farms, Inc.,** 105 Porchtown Road, Pittsgrove, NJ 08318. Free catalog. Separate but identical retail and wholesale catalogs. Specializes in Jersey male hybrid asparagus and strawberry plants. Offered 12 total varieties in 2000, including 3 blueberries and 9 strawberries.

Jer   **Jersey Persimmon Farm,** 58 Van Duyne Ave., Wayne, NJ 07470-4705. Phone: 973-694-1220. Free price list. Retail only. Specializes in American persimmon trees with extremely cold-hardy roots. Offered 1 persimmon in 2000.

Jo1   **Johnny's Selected Seeds,** 1 Foss Hill Road, Albion, ME 04910-9731. Phone: 207-437-4301. Fax: 800-437-4290. Web site: www.johnnyseeds .com. Free catalog. Retail only. Vegetable, flower, herb and farm seed for northern climates including Alpine Strawberry. Many heirlooms and new introductions. Extensive trial grounds throughout North America. Satisfaction 100% guaranteed. Offered 1 strawberry in 2000.

Jo3   **Johnson Nursery,** 5273 Hwy. 52E, Ellijay, GA 30540. Phone: 706-276-3187. Free catalog. Retail and wholesale prices are listed in the same catalog. Specializes in fruit trees. Offered 100 total varieties in 2000, including 37 apples, 1 apricot, 4 cherries, 3 figs, 1 nectarine, 8 peaches, 14 pears, 6 plums, 3 blackberries, 6 blueberries, 11 grapes, 4 raspberries and 2 strawberries.

JO4   **Johnston Nurseries,** RD 1, Box 100, Creekside, PA 15732. Wholesale only! Offered 4 total varieties in 2000, including 1 cherry, 1 mulberry, 1 walnut and 1 miscellaneous variety.

JOY   **Joyce Farms,** 21725 SW Chapman Road, Sherwood, OR 97140. Phone: 503-625-6834. Fax: 503-625-2144. Wholesale only! Offered 62 total varieties in 2000, including 22 apples, 4 apricots, 9 cherries, 2 nectarines, 6 peaches, 8 pears, 7 plums, 2 almonds, 1 chestnut and 1 walnut.

Ju2   **Just Fruits Nursery**, 30 St. Francis St., Crawfordville, FL 32327. Phone: 850-926-5644. E-mail: justfruits@hotmail.com. $3 for catalog. Retail and wholesale prices are listed in the same catalog. Specializes in fruits for southern climates, plus many exotic fruits. Offered 176 total varieties in 2000, including 5 apples, 14 figs, 3 jujubes, 4 nectarines, 1 pawpaw, 8 peaches, 11 pears, 14 persimmons, 7 plums, 2 quinces, 1 stone fruit cross, 4 blackberries, 21 blueberries, 16 grapes, 2 kiwis, 4 mulberries, 1 raspberry, 3 strawberries, 1 chestnut, 1 pecan, 1 avocado, 8 bananas, 9 miscellaneous citrus, 1 citrus rootstock, 3 grapefruits, 3 lemons, 2 loquats, 4 oranges, 2 pineapple guavas, 3 pomegranates, 5 tangerines and 12 miscellaneous varieties.

Jun   **J. W. Jung Seed Co.**, 335 S. High St., Randolph, WI 53957-0001. Phone: 800-247-5864. Fax: 800-692-5864. E-mail: info@jungseed.com. Web site: www.jungseed.com. Free retail catalog; wholesale price information available by request. Quality seeds since 1907. Family owned and operated. Specializes in seeds and nursery stock suitable for northern climates. Offered 113 total varieties in 2000, including 33 apples, 1 apricot, 10 cherries, 1 pawpaw, 2 peaches, 5 pears, 1 persimmon, 4 plums, 2 blackberries, 5 blueberries, 2 cranberries, 3 currants, 2 elderberries, 1 gooseberry, 7 grapes, 1 kiwi, 10 raspberries, 13 strawberries, 1 hickory, 1 walnut, 1 passionflower, 2 rhubarbs and 5 miscellaneous varieties.

Ka3   **Kartuz Greenhouses**, 1408 Sunset Drive, Vista, CA 92083-6531. Phone: 760-941-3613. $2 for catalog. Retail only. Specializes in tropical and subtropical plants. Offered 21 total varieties in 2000, including 1 papaya, 15 passionflowers, 2 pepinos and 3 miscellaneous varieties.

KAN   **Kankakee Nursery Company**, PO Box 288, Aroma Park, IL 60910. Wholesale only! Offered 48 total varieties in 2000, including 24 apples, 3 cherries, 4 pears, 1 pear rootstock, 1 plum, 5 cranberries, 1 currant, 2 serviceberries, 1 miscellaneous nut and 6 miscellaneous varieties.

KEE   **Forrest Keeling Nursery**, 88 Forrest Keeling Lane, Elsberry, MO 63343. Phone: 573-898-5571. Wholesale only! Offered 48 total varieties in 2000, including 6 apples, 3 cherries, 1 pawpaw, 3 pears, 2 persimmons, 1 plum, 2 cranberries, 2 serviceberries, 2 filberts, 1 heartnut, 3 hickories, 2 pecans, 11 walnuts, 1 miscellaneous nut and 8 miscellaneous varieties.

KI3   **King Nursery**, 6849 Rt. 34, Oswego, IL 60543. Wholesale only! Offered 54 total varieties in 2000, including 39 apples, 1 cherry, 4 pears, 1 pear rootstock, 1 plum, 1 elderberry, 3 serviceberries, 1 filbert, 1 miscellaneous nut and 2 miscellaneous varieties.

Kiw   **Kiwi's "R" Us**, 5 Tippets Road, Nesquehoning, PA 18240. Retail only. Specializes in hardy kiwis. Offered 26 kiwis in 2000.

Ko2   **Koppes Plants**, PO Box 441, Watsonville, CA 95076. Phone: 831-724-6009. Fax: 831-724-5123. Formerly inventoried as Coash/Koppes Plants. Free price list. Retail and wholesale. In business since 1949 and ships bare root strawberry plants all over the world. Offered 6 strawberries in 2000.

KR3   **Krieger's Wholesale Nursery**, PO Box 116, Bridgman, MI 49106. Wholesale only! Specializes in quality small fruit plants. Offered 22 total varieties in 2000, including 4 blueberries, 3 currants, 1 gooseberry, 7 grapes and 7 raspberries.

Kro   **William Krohne Plant Farms**, 65295 CR 342, Hartford, MI 49047. Phone: 616-424-5423. Free brochure. Retail and wholesale prices are listed in the same brochure. Specializes in strawberry plants. Offered 19 strawberries in 2000.

La3   **Lawson's Nursery**, 2730 Yellow Creek Road, Ball Ground, GA 30107. Phone: 770-893-2141. Free catalog. Retail and wholesale prices are listed in the same catalog. Specializes in old-fashioned and unusual fruits, berries and nut trees; maintains an excellent collection of old-time apples. Apple rootstock: EMLA 7, EMLA 27, EMLA 106, EMLA 111 and Mark. Peach rootstock: dwarf. Pear rootstock: Provence Quince. Offered 119 total varieties in 2000, including 74 apples, 4 cherries, 2 figs, 7 peaches, 9 pears, 2 plums, 2 quinces, 6 blackberries, 3 blueberries, 1 gooseberry, 3 grapes, 2 raspberries, 1 butternut, 1 filbert, 1 walnut and 1 rhubarb.

LA4   **Lawyer Nursery, Inc.**, 950 Hwy. 200 West, Plains, MT 59859. Phone: 406-826-3881. Fax: 406-826-5700. E-mail: seeds@lawyernsy.com. Web site: trees@lawyernsy.com. Wholesale only! No retail sales. Supplies tree and shrub seed to commercial nurseries, seed dealers and other horticultural and commercial firms. Offered 137 total varieties in 2000, including 21 apple rootstocks, 35 apples, 1 apricot, 8 cherries, 1 pear, 6 pear rootstocks, 1 plum, 16 stone rootstocks, 2 cranberries, 2 currants, 4 elderberries, 1 mulberry, 4 serviceberries, 1 butternut, 2 chestnuts, 4 filberts, 1 pine nut, 8 walnuts, 1 miscellaneous nut and 18 miscellaneous varieties.

La5   **Lake Sylvia Vineyard Nursery**, 13835 51st Ave., South Haven, MN 55382. Retail and quantity prices are given in the same price list. Specializes in unreleased selections of hardy northern grape varieties from the breeding program of Elmer Swenson. Offered 30 grapes in 2000.

Lar   **Larner Seeds**, PO Box 407, 235 Fern Rd., Bolinas, CA 94924. Phone: 415-868-9407. Fax: 415-868-2592. Web site: www.larnerseeds.com. Retail and wholesale prices are listed in the same catalog. Specializes in California native plant seed. Offers rare and unusual wildflowers, many edible natives and a workshop series. Offered 5 total varieties in 2000, including 1 currant, 1 grape, 1 huckleberry and 2 miscellaneous varieties.

Las   **Las Pilitas Nursery**, 3232 Las Pilitas Road, Santa Margarita, CA 93453. Phone: 805-438-5992. Web site: www.laspilitas.com. $8 for catalog, or free through their Web site; free price list also. Specializes in California native plants including wild fruits and berries. Retail and wholesale prices are listed in the same catalog. Offered 30 total varieties in 2000, including 3 cherries, 1 peach, 8 currants, 2 elderberries, 2 gooseberries, 1 grape, 1 huckleberry, 2 strawberries, 1 pine nut, 2 walnuts and 7 miscellaneous varieties.

Le2   **Lewis Nursery and Farms Inc.**, 3500 NC Highway 133, Rocky Point, NC 28457. Phone: 800-453-5346. Fax: 910-675-2394. Local phone number is 910-675-9409. Free catalog. Retail and wholesale prices are listed in the same catalog. In business since 1951. Specializes in strawberry plants. Offered 19 strawberries in 2000.

Led   **Ledden Brothers**, 195 Center and Atlantic, Sewell, NJ 08080. Phone: 856-468-1002. Fax: 856-464-0947. E-mail: seeds@ledden.com. Web site: www.leddens.com. Free catalog. Separate but identical retail and wholesale catalogs. Founded in 1864, purchased by Orol Ledden in 1904. "The highest quality seeds obtainable." Offered 21 total varieties in 2000, including 1 blackberry, 3 blueberries, 1 currant, 1 elderberry, 1 gooseberry, 6 grapes, 2 raspberries, 4 strawberries and 2 rhubarbs.

Lee   **Lee's Nursery**, PO Box 489-SSE, McMinnville, TN 37111-0489. Phone: 931-668-4870. Free catalog. Separate retail and wholesale catalogs; retail catalog contains additional varieties. Offered 76 total varieties in 2000, including 9 apples, 2 apricots, 6 cherries, 3 figs, 2 nectarines, 1 pawpaw, 7 peaches, 3 pears, 1 persimmon, 4 plums, 1 blackberry, 8 blueberries, 5 grapes, 1 mulberry, 2 raspberries, 5 strawberries, 1 butternut, 1 chestnut, 2 filberts, 1 hickory, 5 pecans, 2 walnuts, 1 miscellaneous nut, 1 passionflower and 2 miscellaneous varieties.

Leu   **Henry Leuthardt Nurseries, Inc.**, Montauk Hwy., Box 666, East Moriches, Long Island, NY 11940-0666. Phone: 631-878-1387. Fax: 631-874-0707. Free price list; $2 for *How to Select, Plant and Care for Dwarf Fruit Trees and Espalier Trained Fruit Trees, Hybrid Grape Vines, Berry Plants* (deductible from orders of $100 or more). A small family-run business since 1921. Specializes in espalier plant material. Offered 97 total varieties in 2000, including 33 apples, 2 apricots, 7 cherries, 2 nectarines, 6 peaches, 16 pears, 9 plums, 5 blueberries, 1 currant, 1 gooseberry, 10 grapes and 5 raspberries.

Li5   **Linwood Nurseries**, 3613 W. Linwood Ave., Turlock, CA 95380. Phone: 209-634-1836. Fax: 209-634-1836. Retail and wholesale prices are given in the same price list. Specializes in pecan trees; pecan growers since 1915. Offered 11 pecans in 2000.

Ll7   **Little Valley Wholesale Nursery**, 13022 East 136th Ave., Brighton, CO 80601. Wholesale only! Specializes in trees, shrubs and perennials. Offered 66 total varieties in 2000, including 16 apples, 10 cherries, 1 pear, 2 plums, 3 cranberries, 4 currants, 4 elderberries, 2 gooseberries, 3 raspberries, 3 serviceberries, 1 filbert, 1 pine nut, 1 miscellaneous nut, 1 hop and 14 miscellaneous varieties.

Lit   **Little Valley Farm**, 5693 Snead Creek Road, Spring Green, WI 53588. Send a first-class stamp for catalog. Specializes in native plants of eastern and central North America. Selling shrubs only in 2001; no seeds. Offered 7 total varieties in 2000, including 1 cranberry, 1 elderberry, 1 serviceberry, 1 filbert and 3 miscellaneous varieties.

Lo5   **Logee's Greenhouses, Ltd.**, 141 North St., Danielson, CT 06239-1939. Phone: 860-774-8038. Fax: 860-774-9932. E-mail: logeeinfo@logees.com. Web site: www.logees.com. $3 for catalog, deductible with first order. Owned and operated by the same family since its founding in 1892. Offered 13 total varieties in 2000, including 4 miscellaneous citrus, 1 lemon, 2 limes, 1 orange, 4 passionflowers and 1 pomegranate.

LO6   **Louisiana Forest Seed Co.**, 303 Forestry Road, Lecompte, LA 71346. Wholesale only! Offered 28 total varieties in 2000, including 1 cherry, 1 jujube, 1 pawpaw, 1 pear rootstock, 1 persimmon, 2 plums, 1 elderberry, 2 mulberries, 1 chestnut, 6 hickories, 1 walnut, 2 miscellaneous nuts, 1 citrus rootstock and 7 miscellaneous varieties.

Lo7   **Lowder Farm and Nursery**, 15251 NW Hwy. 129, P.O. Box 1623, Trenton, FL 32693. Web site: http://members.aol.com/llowder779/index .html. Specializes in oriental persimmons and hybrid daylilies. Retail only. Offered 7 persimmons in 2000.

LOV   **Lovelace Seeds, Inc.,** 1187 Browns Mill Road, Elsberry, MO 63343. Phone: 573-898-2103. Fax: 573-898-2855. E-mail: lovelace@inweb.net. Web site: www.inweb.net/~lovelace. Wholesale only! Offered 34 total varieties in 2000, including 3 cherries, 1 pawpaw, 1 persimmon, 1 plum, 2 cranberries, 2 mulberries, 3 serviceberries, 1 butternut, 1 chestnut, 2 filberts, 2 hickories, 1 pecan, 2 walnuts, 1 miscellaneous nut and 11 miscellaneous varieties.

Mc3   **McKay Nursery Company,** 254 Jefferson St., PO Box 185, Waterloo, WI 53594. Phone: 800-236-4242. Fax: 920-478-3615. Local phone number is 920-478-2121. $5 for catalog. Separate retail and wholesale catalogs; wholesale catalog contains additional varieties. Established in 1897. Specializes in the best varieties for its rigorous northern Midwest climate. Offered 112 total varieties in 2000, including 49 apples, 7 cherries, 2 peaches, 4 pears, 8 plums, 1 quince, 3 cranberries, 2 currants, 2 elderberries, 1 gooseberry, 7 grapes, 1 mulberry, 4 raspberries, 4 serviceberries, 1 butternut, 3 filberts, 1 walnut, 1 miscellaneous nut, 1 rhubarb and 10 miscellaneous varieties.

Me2   **Roger and Shirley Meyer,** 16531 Mt. Shelley Circle, Fountain Valley, CA 92708. Phone 714-839-0796 evenings only until 11 p.m. Pacific time. E-mail: exoticfruit@95net.com. Send a self-addressed, stamped long envelope for catalog. Retail and wholesale prices are listed in the same catalog. Specializes in jujube, hardy kiwi, kiwifruit for warm winter areas and other exotics. Offered 135 total varieties in 2000, including 34 jujubes, 1 pawpaw, 2 pears, 4 persimmons, 56 kiwis, 1 macadamia, 3 annonas, 1 avocado, 1 banana, 2 miscellaneous citrus, 3 guavas, 1 mango, 1 papaya, 1 passionflower, 1 pepino, 5 sapotes and 18 miscellaneous varieties.

ME3   **Meyer Nursery and Orchards,** 3795 Gibson Road NW, Salem, OR 97304. Wholesale only! Specializes in deciduous shade, flowering and fruit trees. Offered 160 total varieties in 2000, including 39 apples, 2 apricots, 12 cherries, 2 nectarines, 10 peaches, 20 pears, 20 plums, 1 quince, 7 gooseberries, 41 grapes, 1 serviceberry, 2 almonds, 1 filbert, 1 walnut and 1 miscellaneous variety.

MEA   **Meadow Lake Nursery Co.,** PO Box 1302, McMinnville, OR 97128. Phone: 800-852-5322. Fax: 503-435-1312. Web site: www.meadowlake .com. Wholesale only! Offered 80 total varieties in 2000, including 24 apple rootstocks, 1 apricot, 5 cherries, 9 pear rootstocks, 1 plum, 1 quince, 13 stone rootstocks, 6 cranberries, 1 currant, 4 serviceberries, 1 chestnut, 1 walnut, 1 miscellaneous nut and 12 miscellaneous varieties.

Mel   **Mellinger's, Inc.,** 2310 W. South Range Road, North Lima, OH 44452. Phone: 330-549-9861. Fax: 330-549-3716. E-mail: mellgarden@aol.com. Web site: www.mellingers.com. Free catalog within the U.S., containing 4,000 items for country living including seeds (vegetable, tree, herb), bulbs, perennials, trees, shrubs and lawn/garden supplies. Retail and wholesale prices are listed in the same catalog. Offered 188 total varieties in 2000, including 4 apple rootstocks, 18 apples, 3 apricots, 14 cherries, 1 fig, 3 nectarines, 1 pawpaw, 11 peaches, 10 pears, 2 persimmons, 8 plums, 5 quinces, 1 stone rootstock, 3 blackberries, 6 blueberries, 2 cranberries, 1 currant, 4 elderberries, 2 gooseberries, 12 grapes, 4 kiwis, 1 mulberry, 7 raspberries, 9 strawberries, 1 almond, 1 butternut, 2 chestnuts, 6 filberts, 2 hickories, 1 pecan, 2 pine nuts, 3 walnuts, 1 banana, 1 miscellaneous citrus,

1 grapefruit, 1 guava, 1 lemon, 1 lime, 1 orange, 1 pineapple guava, 1 pomegranate, 2 tangerines, 1 hop, 2 rhubarbs, 24 miscellaneous varieties.

Mey **Meyer Seed Co.**, 600 S. Caroline St., Baltimore, MD 21231. Free catalog. Retail and wholesale prices are listed in the same catalog. Quality seeds since 1911. Offered 9 strawberries in 2000.

Mi1 **Miller Nurseries**, 5060 W. Lake Rd., Canandaigua, NY 14424. Phone: 800-836-9630. Fax: 716-396-2154. Free catalog. Specializes in fruiting plants. Offered 229 total varieties in 2000, including 72 apples, 4 apricots, 13 cherries, 2 figs, 3 nectarines, 14 peaches, 11 pears, 2 persimmons, 9 plums, 1 quince, 2 blackberries, 12 blueberries, 2 cranberries, 4 currants, 2 elderberries, 1 gooseberry, 36 grapes, 1 kiwi, 1 mulberry, 10 raspberries, 13 strawberries, 1 butternut, 2 chestnuts, 4 filberts, 1 heartnut, 4 walnuts, 1 hop and 1 rhubarb.

MI5 **Mid-Western Nurseries**, PO Box 768, Tahlequah, OK 74465. Wholesale only! Offered 179 total varieties in 2000, including 45 apples, 5 apricots, 17 cherries, 3 figs, 14 nectarines, 17 peaches, 16 pears, 17 plums, 1 stone rootstock, 2 blackberries, 3 blueberries, 2 cranberries, 1 gooseberry, 5 grapes, 1 mulberry, 2 raspberries, 2 serviceberries, 2 strawberries, 5 almonds, 8 pecans, 1 walnut, 3 miscellaneous nuts, 1 pomegranate, 1 rhubarb and 5 miscellaneous varieties.

MI10 **Mill Creek Nursery Co.**, 6416 Short Mountain Road, Smithville, TN 37166. Wholesale only! Specializes in container-grown trees. Offered 43 total varieties in 2000, including 11 apples, 3 cherries, 1 fig, 7 peaches, 7 pears, 5 plums, 3 grapes, 5 pecans, 1 miscellaneous variety.

MIS **Mistletoe Sales**, 780 N. Glen Annie Rd., Goleta, CA 93117. Phone: 805-968-4818. Fax: 805-968-2242. E-mail: mistle@silcom.com. Wholesale only! Offers tree, shrub, palm, flower and foliage seed. Offered 37 total varieties in 2000, including 4 cherries, 1 pear rootstock, 2 elderberries, 1 kiwi, 1 mulberry, 1 serviceberry, 1 macadamia, 4 pine nuts, 1 miscellaneous nut, 2 guavas, 2 loquats, 1 passionflower, 1 pineapple guava, 1 pomegranate and 14 miscellaneous varieties.

Mo8 **Walter K. Morss and Son**, RFD 2, Boxford, MA 01921. Phone: 978-352-2633. Free catalog. Separate but identical retail and wholesale catalogs. Specializes in raspberries and strawberries. Offered 52 total varieties in 2000, including 11 blueberries, 1 grape, 18 raspberries, 21 strawberries and 1 rhubarb.

M010 **Monrovia**, 13455 SE Lafayette Highway, Dayton, OR 97114. Wholesale only! Specializes in containerized landscape shrubs. Offered 85 total varieties in 2000, including 10 apples, 4 figs, 3 pears, 1 plum, 2 blackberries, 2 cranberries, 1 currant, 9 grapes, 3 kiwis, 4 raspberries, 2 miscellaneous nuts, 2 bananas, 6 miscellaneous citrus, 3 grapefruits, 7 lemons, 2 limes, 8 oranges, 1 pineapple guava, 2 pomegranates, 5 tangerines and 8 miscellaneous varieties.

Mo19 **Mount Vernon Research and Extension Unit**, Washington State University, 16650 State Route 536, Mount Vernon, WA 98273. Web site: http://mtvernon.wsu.edu. Free price list. Retail only. Sells only scionwood. Research station whose main purpose in putting out a scionwood list is for home orchardists wanting non-patented varieties that may not be readily found commercially. Offered 73 total varieties in 2000, including 45 apples, 3 apricots, 6 cherries, 11 pears and 8 plums.

Mu2   **Musser Forests, Inc.**, P.O. Box 340, Rt. 119 North, Indiana, PA 15701. Phone: 800-643-8319. Fax: 724-465-9893. E-mail: info@musserforests .com. Web site: musserforests.com. Free catalog. Separate retail and wholesale catalogs; retail catalog contains additional varieties. "The largest nursery of its kind in North America." Specializes in evergreen and hardwood seedlings and transplants, ornamental shrubs, nut trees, groundcovers, native and wetland plants. Offered 19 total varieties in 2000, including 2 apples, 2 cherries, 1 cranberry, 1 elderberry, 1 serviceberry, 2 chestnuts, 1 pecan, 1 walnut, 1 miscellaneous nut and 7 miscellaneous varieties.

Na4   **National Arbor Day Foundation**, 100 Arbor Ave., Nebraska City, NE 68410. Free catalog. Retail only. Annual foundation membership is $15 which includes a bi-monthly full-color publication, *The Tree Book*, and discounts on specially selected items. Offered 39 total varieties in 2000, including 7 apples, 2 apricots, 4 cherries, 7 peaches, 4 pears, 5 plums, 1 almond, 1 butternut, 1 chestnut, 1 filbert, 1 hickory, 1 pecan, 2 walnuts, 1 miscellaneous nut and 1 miscellaneous variety.

NA5   **Native Seed Foundation**, Star Route, Moyie Springs, ID 83845. Phone: 208-267-7938. Fax: 208-267-3265. Wholesale only! $1 for catalog. Offered 16 total varieties in 2000, including 2 cherries, 1 currant, 2 elderberries, 1 huckleberry, 1 serviceberry and 9 miscellaneous varieties.

Na13   **Native Habitat Ethnobotanicals**, PO Box 644023, Vero Beach, FL 32964-4023. Web site: www.nativehabitat.com. $1 for catalog. Retail catalog but can also "contract grow." Specializes in "the rarest of the rare" tropical fruits, spices, palms, medicinals, entheogens, Angel Trumpets, etc. Offered 44 total varieties in 2000, including 1 jujube, 1 miscellaneous nut, 1 annona, 1 avocado, 7 bananas, 1 loquat, 1 papaya, 2 passionflowers, 4 sapotes and 25 miscellaneous varieties.

Ne4   **Neon Palm Nursery**, 3525 Stony Point Road, Santa Rosa, CA 95407. Phone: 707-585-8100. $2 for catalog. Retail only. Specializes in hardy subtropical plants, particularly palms. Offered 6 total varieties in 2000, including 1 miscellaneous nut, 1 avocado, 1 loquat and 3 miscellaneous varieties.

Neb   **Nebraska Nut Growers Assn.**, University of Nebraska, 122 Mussehl Hall, Lincoln, NE 68583-0716. Free list of scionwood and seeds available. Retail and wholesale. Nonprofit organization offering seeds and scionwood of nut species adaptable to Nebraska. Offered 98 total varieties in 2000, including 3 persimmons, 1 mulberry, 6 hickories, 43 pecans and 45 walnuts.

Ni1   **Nichols Garden Nursery**, 1190 N. Pacific Hwy., Albany, OR 97321. Phone: 541-928-9280. Fax: 800-231-5306. E-mail: nichols@gardennursery .com. Web site: www.nicholsgardennursery.com. Free catalog. Retail and wholesale prices are listed in the same catalog. Offered 6 total varieties in 2000, including 1 strawberry and 5 hops.

NO3   **Norcal Nursery, Inc.**, PO Box 1012, Red Bluff, CA 96080. Phone: 530-527-6200. Fax: 530-527-2921. Wholesale only! Free price list. Specializes in strawberry rooted cuttings. Offered 46 strawberries in 2000.

Nol   **Nolin River Nut Tree Nursery**, 797 Port Wooden Rd., Upton, KY 42784. Phone: 270-369-8551. E-mail: john.brittain@gte.net. Web site: nolin nursery.com. Free catalog. Offers over 200 varieties of disease-resistant grafted nut trees, persimmons and pawpaws. Offered 201 total varieties in 2000, including 9 pawpaws, 24 persimmons, 13 butternuts, 10 chestnuts, 7 heartnuts, 60 hickories, 36 pecans and 42 walnuts.

Nou **Nourse Farms, Inc.,** 41 River Road, S. Deerfield, MA 01373. Phone: 413-665-2658. Fax: 413-665-7888. E-mail: info@noursefarms.com. Web site: noursefarms.com. Free catalog. Retail and wholesale prices are listed in the same catalog. Specializes in disease-free strawberry, raspberry and blackberry plants and high quality asparagus. In business since 1932. Offered 63 total varieties in 2000, including 3 blackberries, 7 blueberries, 4 currants, 2 gooseberries, 21 raspberries, 24 strawberries and 2 rhubarbs.

Nrs **NRSP5/IR-2 Virus-Test Fruit Tree Collection,** IAREC, WSU, 24106 N. Bunn Road, Prosser, WA 99350. Phone: 509-786-9251. Fax: 509-786-9370. E-mail: bhowell@tricity.wsu.edu. Web site: www.nrsp5.wsu.edu. NRSP5/IR2 stands for National Research Support Project 5/Inter-Regional Project 2. "NRSP5" was recently added to the name; some may know the organization as IR-2. Offers budwood and seeds only. All cultivars are virus-free. See Web site for present list of varieties. Offered 675 total varieties in 2000, including 25 apple rootstocks, 211 apples, 30 apricots, 63 cherries, 27 nectarines, 126 peaches, 77 pears, 15 pear rootstocks, 72 plums, 4 stone fruit crosses, 21 stone rootstocks and 4 almonds.

Oik **Oikos Tree Crops,** PO Box 19425, Kalamazoo, MI 49019. Phone: 616-624-6233. Fax: 616-624-4019. E-mail: oak24@aol.com. Free catalog. Retail and wholesale prices are listed in the same catalog. Specializes in tree and shrub seedlings, particularly nuts, oaks and native fruits. Offered 87 total varieties in 2000, including 1 apple, 5 cherries, 2 pawpaws, 1 peach, 2 pears, 1 pear rootstock, 4 persimmons, 3 plums, 2 quinces, 1 stone rootstock, 3 cranberries, 2 currants, 1 elderberry, 1 kiwi, 3 raspberries, 3 serviceberries, 1 strawberry, 2 chestnuts, 8 filberts, 1 heartnut, 8 hickories, 2 pecans, 1 pine nut, 8 walnuts and 21 miscellaneous varieties.

On3 **One Green World,** 28696 S. Cramer Road, Canby, OR 97038. Phone: 503-651-3005. Web site: www.onegreenworld.com. Free catalog. Formerly Northwoods Retail Nursery, which continues to handle the wholesale orders as "Northwoods Wholesale Nursery" at the same address and phone number. One Green World handles the retail orders. Specializes in unique and unusual fruits and ornamentals. Offered 241 total varieties in 2000, including 3 apple rootstocks, 20 apples, 7 cherries, 6 figs, 2 jujubes, 1 nectarine, 10 pawpaws, 3 peaches, 16 pears, 2 pear rootstocks, 10 persimmons, 4 plums, 10 quinces, 2 stone rootstocks, 6 blackberries, 8 blueberries, 2 cranberries, 13 currants, 1 elderberry, 7 gooseberries, 9 grapes, 1 huckleberry, 22 kiwis, 3 mulberries, 3 raspberries, 2 strawberries, 2 chestnuts, 4 filberts, 3 walnuts, 1 miscellaneous nut, 1 passionflower, 2 pineapple guavas, 1 pomegranate and 54 miscellaneous varieties.

On4 **Ong Nursery,** 2528 Crandall Dr., San Diego, CA 92111. Separate but identical retail and wholesale catalogs. Specializes in fruit trees from Asia. Offered 108 total varieties in 2000, including 5 apples, 1 fig, 1 jujube, 3 nectarines, 8 peaches, 3 pears, 4 persimmons, 3 plums, 6 annonas, 5 miscellaneous citrus, 1 grapefruit, 2 guavas, 1 lime, 1 loquat, 14 mangoes, 2 oranges, 4 papayas, 1 passionflower, 2 pomegranates, 1 sapote, 6 tangerines and 34 miscellaneous varieties.

OR1 **Oregon Blueberry Farms and Nursery**, 8474 Hazelgreen Road, Silverton, OR 97381. Wholesale only! Offered 11 blueberries in 2000.

Or2 **Oregon Exotics**, Rare Fruit Nursery, 1065 Messinger Road, Grants Pass, OR 97527. Phone: 541-846-7578. Fax: 541-846-9488. Web site: exotic fruit.com. $4 for catalog. Separate retail and wholesale catalogs; retail catalog contains additional varieties. Specializes in mulberries, persimmons, rare and unusual fruits and nuts from around the world. Offered 370 total varieties in 2000, including 2 apricots, 5 cherries, 33 figs, 5 jujubes, 9 pawpaws, 11 pears, 28 persimmons, 9 quinces, 4 blackberries, 6 blueberries, 1 cranberry, 16 currants, 5 elderberries, 7 gooseberries, 5 grapes, 1 huckleberry, 7 kiwis, 10 mulberries, 3 raspberries, 4 serviceberries, 1 butternut, 2 chestnuts, 4 filberts, 1 heartnut, 2 hickories, 4 pine nuts, 3 walnuts, 7 miscellaneous nuts, 1 annona, 5 avocados, 1 banana, 23 miscellaneous citrus, 1 citrus rootstock, 2 grapefruits, 9 guavas, 1 lemon, 5 loquats, 4 oranges, 2 papayas, 7 passionflowers, 3 pepinos, 4 pineapple guavas, 3 pomegranates, 3 sapotes, 5 tangerines and 96 miscellaneous varieties.

Or9 **Orchard Lane Growers**, 5014 Orchard Lane, Gloucester, VA 23061. $2 for catalog. A family business specializing in antique/heirloom and contemporary apple varieties. Apple rootstock: EMLA 111. Offered 240 total varieties in 2000, including 1 apple rootstock, 238 apples and 1 pear.

ORA **Orange County Nursery, Inc.**, PO Box 0, Norwalk, CA 90651-5017. Wholesale only! Offered 221 total varieties in 2000, including 26 apples, 13 apricots, 8 cherries, 9 figs, 2 jujubes, 14 nectarines, 45 peaches, 27 pears, 13 persimmons, 21 plums, 5 quinces, 3 stone fruit crosses, 15 grapes, 3 mulberries, 5 almonds, 1 pine nut, 1 walnut, 1 miscellaneous nut, 1 loquat, 1 pineapple guava, 3 pomegranates and 4 miscellaneous varieties.

Our **Our Kids Tropicals Nursery and Landscape**, 17229 Phil C. Peters Road, Winter Garden, FL 34787. $2 for catalog. Specializes in tropical fruit trees, flowering and culinary gingers, bamboo and other exotics. Retail and wholesale catalogs are separate but contain almost identical offerings. Offered 25 total varieties in 2000, including 2 miscellaneous nuts, 1 annona, 9 bananas, 2 guavas, 2 lemons, 2 limes, 1 papaya, 1 sapote and 5 miscellaneous varieties.

Pa2 **Pacific Tree Farms**, 4301 Lynwood Dr., Chula Vista, CA 91910. Phone: 619-422-2400. Fax: 619-422-6759. $2 for catalog. Retail and wholesale prices are listed in the same catalog. Specializes in new and unusual trees and plants. Offered 350 total varieties in 2000, including 12 apples, 4 apricots, 2 cherries, 6 figs, 1 jujube, 4 nectarines, 1 pawpaw, 13 peaches, 7 pears, 5 persimmons, 12 plums, 1 quince, 6 stone fruit crosses, 3 blackberries, 4 blueberries, 11 grapes, 9 kiwis, 3 mulberries, 1 raspberry, 2 strawberries, 2 almonds, 2 chestnuts, 3 macadamias, 3 pecans, 7 pine nuts, 4 walnuts, 3 miscellaneous nuts, 15 annonas, 10 avocados, 21 bananas, 28 miscellaneous citrus, 2 citrus rootstocks, 4 grapefruits, 10 guavas, 5 lemons, 4 limes, 5 loquats, 16 mangoes, 15 oranges, 3 papayas, 1 passionflower, 5 pineapple guavas, 3 pomegranates, 7 sapotes, 12 tangerines and 53 miscellaneous varieties.

Pa6 **Pampered Plant Nursery**, Douglas Armstrong, PO Box 3, Bourbonnais, IL 60914-0003. Phone 815-937-9387 evenings and weekends. E-mail: douglasarmstrong@hotmail.com. Free price list. Specializes in seedling and grafted pawpaws, grafted black walnut trees including acclaimed figured-grain and fast-growing varieties, grafted northern, mid-range and southern pecan varieties, and custom and site grafting. Offered 75 total varieties in 2000, including 5 jujubes, 17 pawpaws, 1 5 butternuts, 4 heartnuts, 8 hickories, 1 macadamia, 14 pecans, 15 walnuts, 2 miscellaneous nuts and 3 miscellaneous varieties.

Par   **Park Seed Co.**, 1 Parkton Avenue, Greenwood, SC 29647-0001. Phone: 800-845-3369. Fax: 864-941-4206. E-mail: info@parkseed.com. Web site: www.parkseed.com. Free catalog. Separate retail and wholesale catalogs; retail catalog contains additional varieties. Flower seed specialists since 1868. Also offers a full line of vegetables and a number of small fruit varieties. Offered 20 total varieties in 2000, including 3 figs, 1 pawpaw, 2 blackberries, 1 blueberry, 1 cranberry, 2 grapes, 2 kiwis, 2 raspberries, 2 strawberries, 1 passionflower, 2 pomegranates and 1 miscellaneous variety.

Pe2   **Peaceful Valley Farm Supply**, PO Box 2209, Grass Valley, CA 95945. Phone: 888-784-1722. Fax: 530-272-4794. E-mail: contact@groworganic .com. Web site: www.groworganic.com. Free 132-page catalog with 2,000 items including fertilizers, vegetable and cover crop seeds, weed and pest controls, beneficial insects, irrigation and (in Fall) bulbs, garlic, onions, potatoes and fruit trees. Tools and supplies for organic gardeners and farmers since 1976. Offered 86 total varieties in 2000, including 10 apples, 5 apricots, 7 cherries, 4 figs, 3 nectarines, 7 peaches, 8 pears, 1 persimmon, 6 plums, 1 stone fruit cross, 3 blueberries, 1 currant, 7 grapes, 4 raspberries, 8 strawberries, 1 almond, 2 chestnuts, 3 pecans, 3 walnuts, 1 pomegranate and 1 rhubarb.

Pe3   **Pense Nursery Inc.**, 16518 Marie Lane, Mountainburg, AR 72946. Phone: 501-369-2494. Fax: 501-369-2494. Web site: www.alcasoft.com/pense. Free catalog. Separate but identical retail and wholesale catalogs. Specializes in small fruit plants, berries and grapes. Offered 75 total varieties in 2000, including 17 blackberries, 5 blueberries, 3 currants, 4 elderberries, 1 gooseberry, 26 grapes, 13 raspberries, 4 strawberries and 2 miscellaneous varieties.

Pi2   **Pikes Peak Nurseries**, 8289 Route 422 Highway E., Penn Run, PA 15765. Phone: 724-433-7747. Fax: 724-433-0775. Free catalog. Retail and wholesale prices are listed in the same catalog. In business since 1921; specializes in evergreen and deciduous seedlings and transplants. Offered 47 total varieties in 2000, including 13 apples, 6 cherries, 4 peaches, 3 pears, 4 plums, 4 blueberries, 1 elderberry, 4 grapes, 1 butternut, 1 chestnut, 1 walnut, 1 miscellaneous nut and 4 miscellaneous varieties.

Pl3   **Pine Island Nursery**, 16300 SW 184th, Miami, FL 33187. Phone: 305-233-5501. Fax: 305-233-5610. E-mail: pin@dellnet.com. Wholesale only! Specializes in mango, lychee, longan, anonna, sapote and avocado. Offered 31 total varieties in 2000, including 3 annonas, 1 avocado, 4 miscellaneous citrus, 2 grapefruits, 2 limes, 2 mangoes, 2 oranges, 1 sapote, 1 tangerine and 13 miscellaneous varieties.

Pi4   **Pierce and Sons Nurseries, Inc.**, 24175 Dayton Avenue, Newberg, OR 97132. Phone: 503-538-2363. Fax: 503-538-1010. Free price list. Separate retail and wholesale price lists. Specializes in filberts. Offered 14 total varieties in 2000, including 6 chestnuts and 8 filberts.

Pin   **Pinetree Garden Seeds**, Box 300, New Gloucester, ME 04260. Phone: 207-926-3400. Fax: 888-527-3337. E-mail: pinetree@superseeds.com.

Web site: www.superseeds.com. Free catalog. Specializes in flavorful varieties for home gardeners and offers some unique material. "Smaller packets and lower prices." Over 300 gardening books plus tools and bulbs. Mail order only. Offered 7 total varieties in 2000, including 1 raspberry, 4 strawberries and 2 rhubarbs.

PL2   **Plant It Hawaii, Inc.,** PO Box 388, Kurtistown, HI 96760. Phone: 808-966-6633. Fax: 808-966-6900. E-mail: hami@plantithawaii.net. Web site: www.plantithawaii.com. Wholesale only! Specializes in tropical and exotic fruit and fruit trees. Offering avocados, citrus, exotics, longans, lychees and rambutan. Founded in 1979. Offered 87 total varieties in 2000, including 2 figs, 1 mulberry, 1 miscellaneous nut, 1 annona, 7 avocados, 4 bananas, 9 miscellaneous citrus, 1 citrus rootstock, 1 grapefruit, 3 guavas, 2 lemons, 1 lime, 2 loquats, 10 mangoes, 5 oranges, 1 passionflower, 5 sapotes, 5 tangerines and 26 miscellaneous varieties.

Pl5   **Plants of the Wild,** PO Box 866, Tekoa, WA 99033. Free catalog. Retail and wholesale prices are listed in the same catalog. Specializes in plants native to the Northwest. Offered 24 total varieties in 2000, including 2 cherries, 1 plum, 2 currants, 3 elderberries, 1 huckleberry, 1 raspberry, 1 serviceberry, 1 strawberry and 12 miscellaneous varieties.

Pla   **Plants of the Southwest,** Agua Fria, Rt. 6, Box 11A, Santa Fe, NM 87501-9806. Phone: 505-438-8888. Fax: 505-438-8800. E-mail: contact @plantsofthesouthwest.com. Web site: plantsofthesouthwest.com. $3.50 for 100-page color catalog. Retail catalog; call for wholesale prices. Specializes in Southwestern native plants including berry- and nut-producing trees and shrubs. Catalog also includes native grasses, wildflowers, ancient and drought-tolerant vegetables including little-known Native American crops. Offered 9 total varieties in 2000, including 2 cherries, 1 plum, 1 currant, 1 serviceberry and 4 miscellaneous varieties.

Po7   **Ben Poirier,** PO Box 222, Fallbrook, CA 92028. Send a self-addressed stamped envelope for price list. Retail only, except plants are sold locally on a wholesale basis. Specializes in fruiting subtropical and tropical plants for the landscape and collectors including many *Myrtaceae* and *Sapotaceae*. Offered 69 total varieties in 2000, including 1 cherry, 1 pawpaw, 1 blackberry, 2 mulberries, 2 raspberries, 1 miscellaneous nut, 10 annonas, 3 miscellaneous citrus, 1 citrus rootstock, 4 guavas, 1 loquat, 3 sapotes and 39 miscellaneous varieties.

Pu2   **Puget Sound Kiwi Co.,** 1220 NE 90th St., Seattle, WA 98115. Send a self-addressed stamped envelope for catalog. Retail and wholesale prices are listed in the same catalog. Specializes in kiwi fruit and its relatives. Offered 44 kiwis in 2000.

RA4   **Rainbow Star Nursery,** Paul and Donna Miller, 2324 SW 36th Terrace, Gainesville, FL 32607. Wholesale only! Specializes in fruit grown in the Gulf Coast states areas and Florida: apples, pears, plums, nectarines, peaches and persimmons (mainly Asian). Offered 68 total varieties in 2000, including 1 apple rootstock, 4 apples, 6 figs, 6 nectarines, 19 peaches, 8 pears, 1 pear rootstock, 19 persimmons, 3 plums and 1 stone rootstock.

Rai   **Raintree Nursery,** 391 Butts Road, Morton, WA 98356. Phone: 360-496-6400. Fax: 800-770-8358. E-mail: info@raintreenursery.com. Web site: www.raintreenursery.com. Free 88-page catalog and backyard growers guidebook. Fruits, berries, nuts and bamboo for the edible landscape, most tested in the Pacific Northwest for over 20 years. Apple rootstock: EMLA 7, EMLA 26, EMLA 27, Mark, MM 106, P-22 and Standard. Cherry rootstock: Giessen 148-2 and GM 61. Peach rootstock: Seedling. Pear and Asian Pear rootstock: OH x F and OH x F 333. Plum rootstock: St. Julian A. Offered 341 total varieties in 2000, including 6 apple rootstocks, 44 apples, 2 apricots, 19 cherries, 7 figs, 2 jujubes, 2 nectarines, 5 pawpaws, 8 peaches, 24 pears, 1 pear rootstock, 9 persimmons, 19 plums, 7 quinces, 6 stone fruit crosses, 3 stone rootstocks, 9 blackberries, 17 blueberries, 3 cranberries, 13 currants, 5 elderberries, 8 gooseberries, 14 grapes, 4 huckleberries, 6 kiwis, 6 mulberries, 7 raspberries, 3 serviceberries, 12 strawberries, 3 almonds, 1 butternut, 5 chestnuts, 5 filberts, 5 walnuts, 2 miscellaneous nuts, 2 miscellaneous citrus, 1 lemon, 1 lime, 2 oranges, 1 papaya, 2 passionflowers, 1 pineapple guava, 2 pomegranates, 1 tangerine and 36 miscellaneous varieties.

RAM   **L. J. Rambo's Wholesale Nursery**, 10495 Baldwin Rd., Bridgman, MI 49106. Phone: 616-465-6771. Fax: 616-465-4026. E-mail: rambonurs @aol.com. Wholesale only! Offered 41 total varieties in 2000, including 6 blackberries, 4 blueberries, 2 currants, 2 gooseberries, 9 grapes, 10 raspberries, 5 strawberries, 2 rhubarbs and 1 miscellaneous variety.

Rid   **Rider Nursery**, Rt. 2, Box 78, Farmington, IA 52626. Phone: 319-878-3313. Retail and wholesale prices are listed in the same catalog. Specializes in small fruits. Offered 37 total varieties in 2000, including 5 apples, 3 blackberries, 3 blueberries, 5 grapes, 5 raspberries, 15 strawberries and 1 rhubarb.

Ro3   **Rocky Meadow Orchard and Nursery**, 360 Rocky Meadow NW, New Salisbury, IN 47161. Phone: 812-347-2213. Fax: 812-347-2488. Retail and wholesale prices are listed in the same catalog. Specializes in fruit varieties which possess superior or unique flavor characteristics. Rootstocks also for sale. Offered 88 total varieties in 2000, including 8 apple rootstocks, 50 apples, 1 peach, 17 pears, 4 pear rootstocks, 7 plums and 1 stone rootstock.

Ro13   **Royal Palm Enterprises**, PO Box 645, Kurtistown, HI 96760. Free catalog. Retail and wholesale prices are listed in the same catalog. Specializes in hardy tropicals and exotic fruit trees. Offered 32 total varieties in 2000, including 1 macadamia, 1 miscellaneous nut, 2 annonas, 5 guavas, 1 loquat, 3 papayas, 4 passionflowers, 2 sapotes, 13 miscellaneous varieties.

Roh   **P. L. Rohrer and Bro. Inc.**, PO Box 250, Smoketown, PA 17576. Phone: 717-299-2571. Fax: 800-468-4944. Free catalog. Retail only. Quality farm and garden seeds since 1918. Seeds and bulbs for over 950 varieties of vegetables, flowers, herbs, cover crops and lawn grasses. Many organic and heirloom seeds. Offered 15 total varieties in 2000, including 3 blueberries, 3 grapes, 2 raspberries, 6 strawberries and 1 rhubarb.

Rom   **Lon Rombough**, PO Box 365, Aurora, OR 97002-0365. Web site: www.hevanet.com/lonrom. Send a self-addressed, stamped envelope for catalog. Retail and wholesale prices are listed in the same catalog. Specializes in grape varieties. Offered 131 grapes in 2000.

Sav   **Savage Nursery Center**, 6255 Beersheba Highway, McMinnville, TN 37110. Free catalog. Retail only. Established in 1942. Offered 75 total varieties in 2000, including 9 apples, 2 apricots, 7 cherries, 3 figs, 1 nectarine, 1 pawpaw, 8 peaches, 4 pears, 1 persimmon, 4 plums, 1 quince, 8 blueberries, 5 grapes, 1 mulberry, 2 raspberries, 5 strawberries, 1 butternut, 1 chestnut, 2 filberts, 1 hickory, 4 pecans, 2 walnuts, 1 miscellaneous nut and 1 miscellaneous variety.

Sc2 **F. W. Schumacher Co., Inc.**, PO Box 1023, Sandwich, MA 02563-1023. Phone: 508-888-0659. Fax: 508-833-0322. Web site: treeshrubseeds.com. Free catalog. Retail and wholesale prices are listed in the same catalog. Specializes in tree and shrub seed for nurserymen and foresters. Offered 104 total varieties in 2000, including 1 apple rootstock, 4 apples, 2 apricots, 11 cherries, 2 dates, 1 jujube, 1 pawpaw, 3 pears, 4 pear rootstocks, 4 persimmons, 3 plums, 6 stone rootstocks, 2 cranberries, 3 elderberries, 2 kiwis, 4 mulberries, 3 serviceberries, 1 butternut, 1 chestnut, 3 filberts, 2 hickories, 1 pecan, 7 pine nuts, 6 walnuts, 3 miscellaneous nuts, 1 citrus rootstock, 3 passionflowers, 1 pineapple guava, 1 rhubarb and 18 miscellaneous varieties.

Sc6 **Schlabach's Nursery**, 3901 County Road 135, Millersburg, OH 44654. Free catalog. Separate but identical retail and wholesale catalogs. Specializes in heirloom and antique varieties and local favorites, all suitable for home orchards. Apple rootstock: EMLA 7, EMLA 9, EMLA 26 and EMLA 27. Cherry, peach, pear and prune-plum rootstock: Standard. Offered 143 total varieties in 2000, including 96 apples, 1 apricot, 9 cherries, 1 nectarine, 10 peaches, 8 pears, 3 plums and 15 grapes.

Sh2 **Shepherd's Garden Seeds**, 30 Irene St., Torrington, CT 06790-6658. Phone: 860-482-3638. Fax: 860-482-0532. Web site: www.shepherdseeds .com. Free catalog. Offered 20 total varieties in 2000, including 1 blackberry, 5 blueberries, 2 currants, 1 gooseberry, 3 grapes, 1 kiwi, 3 raspberries and 4 strawberries.

Sh3 **Sherwood's Greenhouses**, PO Box 6, Sibley, LA 71073. Phone: 318-377-3653. Send a self-addressed, stamped envelope for price list. Retail only. Small nursery with unusual fruit and plants including mayhaw, citrus, pawpaw and many varieties of Japanese maple. Specializes in container-grown varieties. Offered 99 total varieties in 2000, including 3 cherries, 22 figs, 1 jujube, 12 pawpaws, 2 blackberries, 3 grapes, 3 kiwis, 1 mulberry, 1 raspberry, 3 chestnuts, 15 miscellaneous citrus, 4 citrus rootstocks, 2 grapefruits, 3 lemons, 1 lime, 1 orange, 5 pomegranates, 6 tangerines and 11 miscellaneous varieties.

SH8 **Sherman Nursery Co.**, PO Box 579, 1300 Grove St., Charles City, IA 50616. Wholesale only! Offered 243 total varieties in 2000, including 87 apples, 4 apricots, 17 cherries, 3 peaches, 17 pears, 11 plums, 2 quinces, 1 stone fruit cross, 4 blackberries, 7 blueberries, 8 cranberries, 4 currants, 4 elderberries, 1 gooseberry, 19 grapes, 2 mulberries, 11 raspberries, 7 serviceberries, 17 strawberries, 2 filberts, 1 walnut, 2 miscellaneous nuts, 2 rhubarbs and 10 miscellaneous varieties.

Sh10 **Shooting Star Nursery**, 444 Bates Road, Frankfort, KY 40601. $2 for catalog, refundable with first order. Specializes in plants native to the eastern U.S.: wildflowers, trees, shrubs, wetland plants and wildflower seeds. Retail only. Offered 11 total varieties in 2000, including 1 pawpaw, 1 persimmon, 1 plum, 1 elderberry, 1 serviceberry, 1 chestnut, 1 miscellaneous nut and 4 miscellaneous varieties.

Sh14 **Sheffield's Seed Company, Inc.**, 273 Auburn Road, Route 34, Locke, NY 13092. Free catalog. Retail and wholesale prices are listed in the same

catalog. Specializes in woody plants and herbaceous seeds. Offered 67 total varieties in 2000, including 5 apples, 1 cherry, 1 jujube, 1 pawpaw, 6
pear rootstocks, 1 persimmon, 1 plum, 1 quince, 4 stone rootstocks, 1
blueberry, 2 cranberries, 1 currant, 5 kiwis, 2 mulberries, 4 serviceberries,
4 hickories, 5 walnuts, 3 miscellaneous nuts, 1 annona, 1 guava, 1 passionflower, 1 pomegranate and 15 miscellaneous varieties.

Sha   **Shady Oaks Nursery**, 1101 South State Street, PO Box 708, Waseca, MN
56093-0708. Phone: 800-504-8006. Fax: 507-835-8772. E-mail: shady
oaks@shadyoaks.com. Web site: www.shadyoaks.com. Free catalog. Specializes in plants for shady places including over 700 varieties of perennial
plants. Offered 7 total varieties in 2000, including 2 kiwis, 2 hops and 3
miscellaneous varieties.

Shu   **R. H. Shumway, Seedsman**, PO Box 1, Graniteville, SC 29829. Phone:
803-663-9771. Fax: 888-437-2733. Free catalog. Separate retail and
wholesale catalogs, each containing varieties not in the other. Specializes
in heirloom, heritage and open-pollinated seeds. Offered 27 total varieties
in 2000, including 3 blackberries, 2 blueberries, 3 currants, 1 gooseberry, 3
grapes, 1 kiwi, 5 raspberries, 8 strawberries and 1 rhubarb.

Si3   **Sierra Gold Nurseries**, 5320 Garden Hwy., Yuba City, CA 95991. Phone:
800-243-4653. Fax: 530-674-1007. E-mail: sierragold@sierragoldtrees
.com. Web site: www.sierragoldtrees.com. Local phone number is 530-
674-1145. Retail and wholesale prices are listed in the same catalog. Specializes in fruit and nut trees. Offered 117 total varieties in 2000, including
16 apples, 4 apricots, 11 cherries, 3 nectarines, 46 peaches, 3 pears, 1 pear
rootstock, 3 plums, 4 stone rootstocks, 14 almonds and 12 walnuts.

SIM   **Simpson Nurseries**, PO Box 160, Monticello, FL 32345. Wholesale only!
Offered 161 total varieties in 2000, including 22 apples, 2 apricots, 6 cherries, 4 figs, 5 nectarines, 25 peaches, 16 pears, 3 persimmons, 11 plums, 2
blackberries, 4 blueberries, 18 grapes, 3 raspberries, 1 chestnut, 1 hickory,
34 pecans, 2 walnuts, 1 miscellaneous nut and 1 pomegranate.

Sis   **Siskiyou Rare Plant Nursery**, 2825 Cummings Rd., Medford, OR 97501.
Phone: 541-772-6846. $3 for catalog (four issues). Retail only. Specializes
in hard-to-find hardy perennials, shrubs, smaller conifers and alpine and
rock garden plants. Offered 7 total varieties in 2000, including 3 blueberries, 2 strawberries and 2 miscellaneous varieties.

Sm6   **Smith Berry Gardens**, 9402 Snow Hill Road, Ooltewah, TN 37363. Retail and wholesale prices are listed in the same catalog. Specializes in certified virus-free strawberry plants. Offered 24 strawberries in 2000.

So5   **Southmeadow Fruit Gardens**, 10603 Cleveland Avenue, PO Box 211,
Baroda, MI 49101. Phone: 616-422-2411. Fax: 616-422-1464. Free price
list; $9 for illustrated catalog. Specializes in choice and unusual fruit tree
varieties for the connoisseur and home gardener. Apple rootstock: Antonovka, M 7, M 9, MM 106 and MM 111. Cherry rootstock: Standard.
Nectarine rootstock: *P. besseyi* and St. Julian A. Peach rootstock: seedling.
Pear rootstock: Angers Quince and Standard. Asian Pear rootstock: *Pyrus
calleryana*. Offered 436 total varieties in 2000, including 5 apple rootstocks, 241 apples, 8 apricots, 16 cherries, 3 nectarines, 17 peaches, 47
pears, 1 pear rootstock, 20 plums, 1 quince, 3 stone rootstocks, 1 cranberry,
19 currants, 15 gooseberries, 28 grapes, 1 serviceberry and 10 miscellaneous varieties.

So6 **Sonoma Grapevines, Inc.**, 3600 Fulton Road, PO Box 293, Fulton, CA 95439-0293. Phone: 707-542-5510. Fax: 707-542-4801. Web site: www. sonomagrapevines.com. Send a self-addressed, stamped envelope for price list. Separate but identical wholesale and retail price lists. Specializes in grafted vinifera wine and table grapes. Offered 162 total varieties in 2000, including 140 grapes and 22 grape rootstocks.

So12 **Sourcepoint Organic Seeds**, 1349 2900 Road, Hotchkiss, CO 81419-9475. Phone: 970-872-4941. $3 for catalog. Retail only. Offers only organically grown or wild-crafted seeds. Offered 20 total varieties in 2000, including 1 apricot, 1 jujube, 1 currant, 1 elderberry, 1 mulberry, 1 raspberry, 1 serviceberry, 1 pine nut, 2 walnuts and 10 miscellaneous varieties.

Son **Sonoma Antique Apple Nursery**, 4395 Westside Rd., Healdsburg, CA 95448. Phone: 707-433-6420. Web site: applenursery.com. Free catalog. Wholesale prices for 10 trees of a variety. Separate but identical retail and wholesale catalogs. Specializes in unusual varieties of apples, pears, plums and figs grown organically on size-controlling rootstocks; other fruits, nuts and berries available on conventionally grown rootstocks. Apple rootstock: Budagovski 9, MM 106, MM 111 and seedling. Pear rootstock: OH x F 513, OH x F 333, Pyrodwarf, Quince and seedling. Stone fruits rootstock: Citation, Colt, GM 61, Lovell, Mahaleb, Mariana, Mazzard, Myrobalon and Nemaguard. Offered 312 total varieties in 2000, including 145 apples, 5 apricots, 8 cherries, 10 figs, 6 nectarines, 3 pawpaws, 19 peaches, 45 pears, 6 persimmons, 17 plums, 3 quinces, 6 stone fruit crosses, 3 blackberries, 7 blueberries, 1 currant, 1 gooseberry, 12 grapes, 5 kiwis, 2 raspberries, 2 almonds, 2 pecans, 2 walnuts and 2 pomegranates.

SPO **Ken M. Spooner Farms**, 9710 SR 162 E, Puyallup, WA 98374. Phone: 253-845-5519. Fax: 253-845-5717. Wholesale only! Offered 24 total varieties in 2000, including 15 raspberries and 9 strawberries.

Spr **Spring Hill Nurseries**, 6523 N. Galena Road, Peoria, IL 61632. Phone: 309-689-3849. Web site: MySeasons.com. Free spring and fall catalogs upon request. Retail only. Established in 1849. Specializes in perennials, roses and flowering trees and shrubs. Offered 8 total varieties in 2000, including 1 blueberry, 2 raspberries, 2 strawberries, 1 filbert, 1 lemon and 1 orange.

St4 **Stark Brothers Nursery**, Hwy. 54, PO Box 10, Louisiana, MO 63353. Phone: 573-754-4734. Fax: 573-754-5290. E-mail: wholesale@starkbros .com. Web site: www.wholesale-starkbroswholesale.com. Phone number for catalog requests and orders only: 800-325-4180. Free catalog. Separate retail and wholesale catalogs, each containing varieties not in the other. Specializes in deciduous fruit trees, nut trees, small fruits and related nursery stock. Offered 252 total varieties in 2000, including 66 apples, 7 apricots, 14 cherries, 2 figs, 11 nectarines, 1 pawpaw, 49 peaches, 19 pears, 2 persimmons, 12 plums, 2 stone fruit crosses, 9 blackberries, 5 blueberries, 2 currants, 2 elderberries, 2 gooseberries, 11 grapes, 2 kiwis, 9 raspberries, 7 strawberries, 1 almond, 1 chestnut, 2 filberts, 1 hickory, 6 pecans, 6 walnuts and 1 rhubarb.

St6 **Stanek's Garden Center**, 2929 27th Ave. E., Spokane, WA 99223. Phone: 509-535-2939. Free catalog. Specializes in roses and fruits, with a large selection of landscape shrubs and trees. Offered 8 total varieties in

2000, including 1 apple, 2 blackberries, 1 cranberry, 1 currant, 1 grape and 2 strawberries.

St12 **Starhill Forest Arboretum**, Guy and Edie Sternberg, Rt. 1 Box 272, Petersburg, IL 62675-9736. Web site: www.gardenweb.com/directory/sfa. Send a self-addressed, stamped envelope or $1 for price list. Retail price list, but quantity discounts can be arranged for some of the varieties. Order deadline is August 15. Specializes in oak species and hybrids and other selected woody ornamentals. Offered 4 total varieties in 2000, including 1 butternut, 1 hickory, 1 walnut and 1 miscellaneous nut.

Stl **St. Lawrence Nurseries**, 325 State Highway 345, Potsdam, NY 13676. Phone: 315-265-6739. Web site: www.sln.potsdam.ny.us. Free catalog. Small family-run business specializing in organically grown super-hardy (to -40 degrees F.) Zone 3 fruit and nut trees, berry plants and edible landscaping plants. Apple rootstock: Antanovka. Pear rootstock: OH x F. Plum rootstock: St. Julian A and *P. americana*. Offered 257 total varieties in 2000, including 1 apple rootstock, 137 apples, 1 apricot, 13 cherries, 19 pears, 11 plums, 1 stone rootstock, 9 blueberries, 3 cranberries, 5 currants, 4 elderberries, 1 gooseberry, 11 grapes, 1 mulberry, 4 raspberries, 9 serviceberries, 1 butternut, 1 filbert, 1 hickory, 10 walnuts, 3 rhubarbs and 11 miscellaneous varieties.

Sto **Stokes Seeds, Inc.**, Box 548, Buffalo, NY 14240-0548. Phone: 716-695-6980. Fax: 800-834-3334. E-mail: stokes@stokeseeds.com. Web site: www.stokeseeds.com. Free catalog. Retail and wholesale prices are listed in the same catalog. Specializes in short-season vegetables. Offered 1 strawberry in 2000.

STR **Stribling's Nurseries**, PO Box 793, Merced, CA 95341. Wholesale only! Specializes in fruit and shade trees. Offered 156 total varieties in 2000, including 26 apples, 7 apricots, 10 cherries, 3 figs, 14 nectarines, 30 peaches, 13 pears, 2 persimmons, 18 plums, 2 stone fruit crosses, 2 blackberries, 8 grapes, 3 raspberries, 6 almonds, 3 pecans, 6 walnuts, 2 pomegranates and 1 miscellaneous variety.

Tex **Texas Pecan Nursery, Inc.**, PO Box 306, Chandler, TX 75758. Phone: 800-205-3008. Fax: 903-849-3660. Local number is 903-849-6203. Separate but identical retail and wholesale catalogs. Specializes in grafted pecan trees. Offered 120 total varieties in 2000, including 11 apples, 4 apricots, 4 cherries, 3 figs, 4 nectarines, 27 peaches, 12 pears, 5 persimmons, 6 plums, 15 grapes, 27 pecans and 2 walnuts.

Th3 **Thomas Jefferson Center for Historic Plants**, Monticello, PO Box 316, Charlottesville, VA 22902. Phone: 804-984-9821. Fax: 804-977-6140. Web site: www.monticello.org/shop. $2 for annual journal and catalog. Retail only. Specializes in vegetables and flowers that were grown by Thomas Jefferson. Offered 1 strawberry in 2000.

Tho **Thompson and Morgan, Inc.**, PO Box 1308, Jackson, NJ 08527-0308. Phone: 800-274-7333. Free full-color catalog. Retail only. Offers rare and exotic varieties, many unobtainable elsewhere. Offered 8 total varieties in 2000, including 1 strawberry and 7 passionflowers.

To7 **Tollgate Gardens**, 20803 Junction Road, Bellevue, MI 49021. Phone: 616-781-5887. Fax: 616-781-6535. E-mail: toll3gate1@juno.com. Formerly listed as Corwin Davis. Send a self-addressed, stamped envelope for price list. Retail only. Specializes in pawpaw seedlings. Offered 18 total varieties in 2000, including 15 pawpaws, 1 chestnut and 2 filberts.

TOW **Tower View Nursery**, 70912 CR-388, South Haven, MI 49090. Phone: 616-637-1279. Fax: 616-637-6257. Wholesale only! Specializes in blueberry, rhododendron, azalea and lingonberry. Offered 26 total varieties in 2000, including 25 blueberries and 1 miscellaneous variety.

TR8 **TRECO-Oregon Rootstock and Tree Co.**, 10906 Monitor-McKee Road NE, PO Box 98, Woodburn, OR 97071. Wholesale only! Specializes in apple rootstocks and trees. Offered 64 total varieties in 2000, including 20 apple rootstocks, 40 apples, 3 pear rootstocks and 1 stone rootstock.

Tr10 **Tropical Fruit Trees**, 7341 121 St. Ter. North, Largo, FL 33773. Send self-addressed, stamped envelope for catalog. Retail and wholesale prices are listed in the same catalog. Specializes in tropical fruit trees. Offered 41 total varieties in 2000, including 5 figs, 1 pawpaw, 1 macadamia, 4 annonas, 3 miscellaneous citrus, 2 guavas, 2 lemons, 2 limes, 1 mango, 1 papaya, 4 passionflowers, 4 sapotes, 2 tangerines, 9 miscellaneous varieties.

TR19 **Triangle Nursery Inc.**, 8526 Beersheba Hwy., McMinnville, TN 37110. Wholesale only! Offered 24 total varieties in 2000, including 11 apples, 1 cherry, 4 pears, 3 plums, 1 cranberry, 1 serviceberry and 3 miscellaneous varieties.

Tri **Tripple Brook Farm**, 37 Middle Rd., Southampton, MA 01073. Free catalog. Retail only. Specializes in native plants, ground covers, unusual fruits, ornamental grasses and hardy bamboo. Offered 70 total varieties in 2000, including 1 cherry, 5 figs, 1 pawpaw, 1 persimmon, 2 plums, 1 blueberry, 2 cranberries, 1 elderberry, 21 kiwis, 8 mulberries, 1 raspberry, 3 strawberries, 2 citrus rootstocks, 1 passionflower, 1 pomegranate and 19 miscellaneous varieties.

TU5 **Turner's Bend Nursery**, 3133 Turner's Bend Road, McMinnville, TN 37110. Wholesale only! Offered 71 total varieties in 2000, including 12 apples, 7 cherries, 2 nectarines, 1 pawpaw, 14 peaches, 7 pears, 1 pear rootstock, 1 persimmon, 8 plums, 1 quince, 5 grapes, 1 mulberry, 1 serviceberry, 1 chestnut, 1 filbert, 1 hickory, 1 pecan, 1 walnut, 1 miscellaneous nut and 4 miscellaneous varieties.

Ty2 **TyTy-South Orchards**, 208 W. Henderson St., Ocilla, GA 31774-1927. Offered 178 total varieties in 2000, including 15 apples, 11 figs, 2 jujubes, 2 nectarines, 1 pawpaw, 17 peaches, 11 pears, 3 persimmons, 12 plums, 4 quinces, 1 stone fruit cross, 7 blackberries, 5 blueberries, 23 grapes, 4 mulberries, 5 raspberries, 5 strawberries, 1 almond, 1 butternut, 3 chestnuts, 1 filbert, 2 hickories, 13 pecans, 3 walnuts, 1 miscellaneous nut, 7 bananas, 3 miscellaneous citrus, 3 lemons, 1 lime, 1 loquat, 1 orange, 3 pomegranates, 1 tangerine and 5 miscellaneous varieties.

Und **Underwood Gardens**, 1414 Zimmerman Road, Woodstock, IL 60098. Fax: 888-382-7041. E-mail: info@underwoodgardens.com. Web site: www.underwoodgardens.com. $3 for catalog. Retail sales, with bulk seed available depending on harvest. Specializes in hard-to-find, untreated, open-pollinated and heirloom seeds, many of which are grown organically. Offered 12 apples in 2000.

Uni **University of Hawaii Seed Program**, Dept. of Horticulture, 3190 Maile Way, Rm. 112, Honolulu, HI 96822. Phone: 808-956-7890. Fax: 808-956-

3894. Free price list. Retail only. Specializes in vegetables developed by University of Hawaii horticulturists that do well in tropical climates. Offered 3 papayas in 2000.

Va2 **Van Well Nursery**, PO Box 1339, Wenatchee, WA 98801. Phone: 509-886-8189. Fax: 509-886-0294. E-mail: vanwell@vanwell.net. Web site: www.vanwell.net. $1 for catalog. Separate but identical retail and wholesale catalogs. Specializes in fruit trees. A family business run by five Van Well brothers. Apple rootstock: B 9, B 118, C 16, C 30, M 7, M 9, MM 106, MM 111 and seedling. Pear rootstock: OH x F 87, OH x F 97 and seedling. Offered 175 total varieties in 2000, including 62 apples, 12 apricots, 22 cherries, 6 nectarines, 34 peaches, 13 pears, 4 pear rootstocks, 12 plums, 2 stone rootstocks, 3 almonds, 3 filberts and 2 walnuts.

Va5 **Valley Nursery**, PO Box 4845, Helena, MT 59604. Phone: 406-458-5919. Fax: 406-458-5919. $1 for catalog, or send self-addressed, stamped envelope. Separate retail and wholesale catalogs, each containing varieties not in the other. Specializes in winter-hardy trees and shrubs for cold climates. Offered 71 total varieties in 2000, including 24 apples, 2 apricots, 7 cherries, 5 pears, 2 plums, 2 stone rootstocks, 1 blackberry, 3 cranberries, 3 currants, 2 elderberries, 1 grape, 5 raspberries, 1 serviceberry, 1 strawberry, 1 butternut, 2 filberts, 1 pine nut, 2 walnuts and 6 miscellaneous varieties.

Ver **Vermont Bean Seed Co.**, Garden Lane, Fair Haven, VT 05743-0250. Phone: 803-663-0217. Fax: 888-500-7333. Free catalog. Retail and wholesale prices are listed in the same catalog. Known for having the world's largest selection of beans, plus gourmet specialties and rare and unusual flowers. All seeds are untreated. Offered 6 strawberries in 2000.

VIR **Virginia Berry Farm**, Box 4, Ruther Glen, VA 22546. Wholesale only! Specializes in wholesale production of container-grown fruit and berry plants, ground covers and vines. Offered 53 total varieties in 2000, including 1 cherry, 3 figs, 4 blackberries, 18 blueberries, 3 cranberries, 2 currants, 1 gooseberry, 8 grapes, 1 huckleberry, 8 raspberries, 2 strawberries and 2 miscellaneous varieties.

Wa3 **Wayside Gardens**, 1 Garden Lane, Hodges, SC 29695-0001. Phone: 800-845-1124. Fax: 803-841-4239. Web site: www.waysidegardens.com. Free catalog. Specializes in trees, shrubs and perennials including many rare and exclusive varieties. Retail only. Offered 17 total varieties in 2000, including 1 cherry, 2 figs, 1 pawpaw, 1 blackberry, 2 cranberries, 1 kiwi, 1 raspberry, 1 strawberry, 1 filbert and 6 miscellaneous varieties.

WA7 **Walters Gardens, Inc.**, 96th Avenue and Business I-196, PO Box 137, Zeeland, MI 49464-0137. Wholesale only! Specializes in perennials. Offered 8 strawberries in 2000.

WA8 **Warren County Nursery Inc.**, 6492 Beersheba Hwy., McMinnville, TN 37110. Phone: 931-668-8941. Fax: 931-668-2245. E-mail: WCNursery @blomand.net. Web site: www.TNNursery.com/WCN. Wholesale only! Offered 94 total varieties in 2000, including 11 apples, 2 apricots, 5 cherries, 3 figs, 1 nectarine, 1 pawpaw, 10 peaches, 7 pears, 1 persimmon, 6 plums, 1 blackberry, 4 blueberries, 2 cranberries, 1 elderberry, 8 grapes, 2 mulberries, 1 raspberry, 1 serviceberry, 2 strawberries, 1 butternut, 1 chestnut, 1 filbert, 3 hickories, 5 pecans, 1 walnut, 1 miscellaneous nut, 1 rhubarb and 11 miscellaneous varieties.

Wa12 **Wavering Place Gardens**, Rt. 2 Box 269, Eastover, SC 29044. Separate but identical retail and wholesale catalogs. Specializes in plants native to the Southeast. Offered 1 persimmon and 1 cranberry in 2000.

Wa13 **Wavecrest Nursery**, 2509 Lakeshore Dr., Fennville, MI 49408. $1 for catalog. Separate retail and wholesale catalogs, each containing varieties not in the other. Specializes in ornamentals (over 1,500 varieties). Offered 7 total varieties in 2000, including 1 cherry, 1 pawpaw, 2 elderberries and 3 miscellaneous varieties.

Wa16 **Wallace-Woodstock, Inc.**, W6291 State Road 95, Neillsville, WI 54456. Also doing business as Woodstock Nursery. Free catalog. Retail and wholesale prices are listed in the same catalog. Specializes in evergreen and deciduous seedlings and transplants. Offered 119 total varieties in 2000, including 38 apples, 3 apricots, 10 cherries, 4 peaches, 4 pears, 6 plums, 7 blueberries, 2 cranberries, 2 currants, 1 elderberry, 2 gooseberries, 8 grapes, 1 mulberry, 6 raspberries, 4 strawberries, 1 butternut, 3 chestnuts, 3 filberts, 1 heartnut, 1 pecan, 5 walnuts, 2 miscellaneous nuts and 5 miscellaneous varieties.

WAF **Wafler Nursery**, 10662 Slaght Road, Wolcott, NY 14590. Phone: 315-594-2399. Fax: 315-594-8827. E-mail: wafler@zlink. Web site: wafler nursery.com. Wholesale only! Specializes in dwarf and semidwarf apple trees. Offered 43 total varieties in 2000, including 39 apples and 4 cherries.

Wbn **WBN Berry Patch**, PO Box 21116, Keizer, OR 97307. Web site: www.weeksberry.com. Offered 84 total varieties in 2000, including 13 blackberries, 21 blueberries, 1 cranberry, 5 currants, 2 elderberries, 2 gooseberries, 4 grapes, 1 huckleberry, 14 raspberries, 18 strawberries, 1 rhubarb and 2 miscellaneous varieties.

We4 **Weeks Berry Nursery**, 6494 Windsor Island Rd. N., Keizer, OR 97303. Free catalog. Separate retail and wholesale catalogs, each containing varieties not in the other. Specializes in small fruits. Offered 134 total varieties in 2000, including 17 blackberries, 29 blueberries, 1 cranberry, 7 currants, 2 elderberries, 4 gooseberries, 29 grapes, 1 huckleberry, 5 kiwis, 16 raspberries, 20 strawberries, 1 hop and 2 miscellaneous varieties.

We8 **Weston Nurseries, Inc.**, East Main St., Rt. 135, PO Box 186, Hopkinton, MA 01748. Phone: 800-322-2002. Fax: 508-435-3274. Local phone number is 508-435-3414. Free catalog. In business since 1923. Retail only. Offered 75 total varieties in 2000, including 19 apples, 4 cherries, 7 pears, 2 plums, 4 quinces, 15 blueberries, 1 cranberry, 1 currant, 2 elderberries, 1 kiwi, 5 serviceberries, 1 strawberry, 2 filberts, 2 pine nuts and 9 miscellaneous varieties.

We15 **Westside Exotic Plants**, PO Box 143, Westley, CA 95387. Send a self-addressed, stamped envelope for catalog. Retail only. Offered 1 miscellaneous variety in 2000.

We18 **WE-DU Nurseries**, Rt. 5 Box 724, Marion, NC 28752-9338. Web site: www.we-du.com. $2 for catalog. Retail only. Specializes in nursery-propagated natives and collector rarities of bulbs, herbaceous perennials and woody ornamentals. Offered 13 total varieties in 2000, including 1 pawpaw, 2 blueberries, 3 cranberries, 1 elderberry, 2 serviceberries, 2 filberts and 2 miscellaneous varieties.

Wel   **Bob Wells Nursery**, PO Box 606, Lindale, TX 75771. Phone: 903-882-3550. Fax: 903-882-8030. Free catalog. Separate but identical retail and wholesale catalogs. Specializes in new and old varieties of berry plants and fruit trees, shade and ornamental trees, grapes, roses and flowering shrubs. Offered 176 total varieties in 2000, including 15 apples, 6 apricots, 5 cherries, 5 figs, 3 nectarines, 28 peaches, 14 pears, 5 persimmons, 8 plums, 13 blackberries, 5 blueberries, 23 grapes, 4 raspberries, 11 strawberries, 3 almonds, 1 hickory, 23 pecans, 2 walnuts and 2 miscellaneous varieties.

Wga   **WGA Grape Nursery**, 11926 Rosetree Place S., Seminole, FL 33772. Phone: 727-393-7436. Fax: 727-391-0899. E-mail: WGANursery@aol.com. Web site: members.aol.com/WGANursery. Send a self-addressed, stamped envelope for price list. Separate but identical wholesale and retail price lists. Specializes in Florida bunch grape varieties. Only cuttings, including grafted cuttings, are mailed. Offered 10 total varieties in 2000, including 8 grapes and 2 grape rootstocks.

Wh3   **Whitman Farms Nursery**, 3995 Gibson Road NW, Salem, OR 97304-9527. Phone: 503-585-8728. Fax: 503-363-5020. E-mail: lucile@whitmanfarms.com. Web site: www.whitmanfarms.com. $1 for catalog (refunded with purchase). Separate retail and wholesale catalogs, each containing additional varieties not in the other. Specializes in unusual fruits and ornamental trees, e.g. *Ribes*, *Morus* and *Acer*. Offered 108 total varieties in 2000, including 2 apples, 1 pawpaw, 51 currants, 2 elderberries, 30 gooseberries, 4 kiwis, 5 mulberries, 6 chestnuts, 4 filberts, 2 walnuts and 1 miscellaneous variety.

Wh4   **White Oak Nursery**, 494 White Oak Road, Strasburg, PA 17579. Free catalog. Retail and wholesale prices are listed in the same catalog. Specializes in antique apple varieties. Apple rootstock: Bud 9, EMLA 7 and EMLA 106. Offered 120 total varieties in 2000, including 53 apples, 2 apricots, 10 cherries, 2 nectarines, 12 peaches, 9 pears, 4 plums, 2 blackberries, 6 blueberries, 8 grapes, 2 kiwis, 3 raspberries, 5 strawberries and 1 walnut and 1 rhubarb.

Wl4   **Dave Wilson Nursery Inc.**, 19701 Lake Road, Hickman, CA 95323. Web site: www.davewilson.com. Wholesale only! Specializes in bare-root fruit and nut trees, grape vines, shade and flowering trees. Almond rootstock: Nemaguard and Lovell. Apple: M 7, M 27, M 111, Bud 9 and seedling. Apricot and plum rootstock: Citation, Myro 29C, Marianna and Nemaguard. Cherry rootstock: Colt, Gm61/1, Mahaleb and Mazzard. Peach and nectarine rootstock: Citation, Lovell and Nemaguard. Pear rootstock: OH x F 97, OH x F 333 and Winter Nelis. Asian Pear rootstock: OH x F 97, OH x F 333, *P. calleryana* and *P. betulaefolia*. Walnut rootstock: Paradox and NCB. Offered 487 total varieties in 2000, including 75 apples, 27 apricots, 21 cherries, 10 figs, 2 jujubes, 38 nectarines, 4 pawpaws, 110 peaches, 34 pears, 2 pear rootstocks, 7 persimmons, 39 plums, 3 quinces, 10 stone fruit crosses, 7 stone rootstocks, 8 blueberries, 25 grapes, 6 kiwis, 1 mulberry, 19 almonds, 3 chestnuts, 6 filberts, 9 pecans, 17 walnuts, 2 miscellaneous nuts and 2 pomegranates.

Wi6   **Willits and Newcomb, Inc.**, PO Box 428, Arvin, CA 93203. Phone: 661-327-9345. Fax: 661-366-6419. E-mail: jackiem@wncitrus.com. Web site: wncitrus.com. Retail and wholesale prices are listed in the same catalog. Specializes in citrus propagating materials. Established over 30 years ago.

Named varieties are budwood for people who want to do their own grafting; rootstock material is seeds, not seedlings. Offered 88 total varieties in 2000, including 16 miscellaneous citrus, 45 citrus rootstocks, 1 grapefruit, 4 lemons, 12 oranges and 10 tangerines.

WI12   **Willow Drive Nursery**, 3539 Road 5 NW, Ephrata, WA 98823. Wholesale only! Specializes in fruit tree and rootstock sales. Apple rootstock: M 7, M 9, M 26, M 106, M 111, Mark and seedling. Apricot, plum and nectarine rootstock: apricot seedling and Lovell. Cherry rootstock: Mahaleb and Mazzard. Pear rootstock: OH x F and seedling. Offered 125 total varieties in 2000, including 11 apple rootstocks, 49 apples, 12 apricots, 14 cherries, 4 peaches, 10 pears, 5 pear rootstocks, 13 plums and 7 stone rootstocks.

Wi21   **Herman J. Wiemer Vineyard, Inc.**, Route 14, Box 38, Dundee, NY 14837-0038. Free catalog. Retail and wholesale prices are listed in the same catalog. Carries grafted vinifera grapevines only. Offered 15 total varieties in 2000, including 10 grapes and 5 grape rootstocks.

Win   **Windy Hills Farm**, 1565 E. Wilson Rd., Scottville, MI 49454. Free price list. Retail and wholesale prices are given in the same price list. Specializes in native Michigan hardwood, nut and wildlife habitat species. Offered 7 total varieties in 2000, including 1 cranberry, 1 elderberry, 1 butternut, 1 heartnut, 1 walnut and 2 miscellaneous nuts.

Wo2   **Woodlanders, Inc.**, 1128 Colleton Ave., Aiken, SC 29801. Phone: 803-648-7522. Fax: 803-648-7522. E-mail: woodland@triplet.net. Web site: www.wolanders.net. Specializes in rare and hard-to-find trees, shrubs, vines and perennials from around the world that are suited to the American Southeast and similar climates. Woodlanders offers nursery stock grown from seed or cuttings taken in the wild, from its stock plants, or from cultivated specimens elsewhere (it is against their policy to sell collected plants). Offered 49 total varieties in 2000, including 1 apple, 2 cherries, 1 jujube, 2 pawpaws, 1 persimmon, 2 plums, 4 blueberries, 3 serviceberries, 4 chestnuts, 1 filbert, 6 hickories, 1 miscellaneous nut, 2 miscellaneous citrus, 1 citrus rootstock, 1 loquat, 4 passionflowers, 1 pineapple guava, 5 pomegranates, 1 tangerine and 6 miscellaneous varieties.

Wo7   **Worcester County Horticultural Society**, Tower Hill Botanic Garden, 11 French Drive, PO Box 598, Boylston, MA 01505-0598. Free price list. Retail only. Specializes in scionwood of heirloom apples. Offered 119 apples in 2000.

Wom   **Womack Nursery Co.**, Rt. 1, Box 80, De Leon, TX 76444. Phone: 254-893-6497. Fax: 254-893-3400. Free catalog. Separate but identical wholesale and retail catalogs. Family business started in 1937. Specializes in fruit and pecan trees, blackberries and grapevines; plants are adapted to southern plantings. Apple rootstock: MM 111. Peach rootstock: Nemaguard. Offered 136 total varieties in 2000, including 14 apples, 5 apricots, 4 figs, 2 nectarines, 31 peaches, 10 pears, 5 persimmons, 6 plums, 1 stone fruit cross, 7 blackberries, 20 grapes, 1 grape rootstock, 2 mulberries, 1 raspberry, 1 strawberry, 1 almond, 20 pecans, 1 miscellaneous nut, 1 pomegranate and 3 miscellaneous varieties.

Wor   **Worley Nursery**, 98 Braggtown Rd., York Springs, PA 17372. Phone: 717-528-4519. Free catalog. Separate but identical retail and wholesale catalogs. Specializes in fruit trees including many old-time apple varieties.

Offered 153 total varieties in 2000, including 70 apples, 1 apricot, 11 cherries, 4 nectarines, 22 peaches, 7 pears, 8 plums, 6 blueberries, 9 grapes, 5 raspberries, 7 strawberries, 1 chestnut and 1 walnut and 1 rhubarb.

ZEL **Zelenka Nursery, Inc.,** 16127 Winans St., Grand Haven, MI 49417. Wholesale only! Specializes in nursery stock for garden centers and retailers. Offered 33 total varieties in 2000, including 6 apples, 1 cherry, 2 peaches, 1 pear, 1 plum, 1 quince, 1 stone rootstock, 4 blackberries, 1 blueberry, 3 cranberries, 1 currant, 1 gooseberry, 3 grapes, 4 raspberries, 1 serviceberry and 2 miscellaneous varieties.

Apple

Malus pumila

Abbondanza - *Source History: 1 in 2000.* **Sources: Ed5.**

Accordian - Southern variety. *Source History: 1 in 2000.* **Sources: Ca15.**

Adanac - Open-pollinated seedling of Battleford. Fruit is yellow and striped with a red wash. Good cooking apple. Ripens early. Will keep 2-3 months. Hardy to -50 degrees F. *Source History: 1 in 1988; 1 in 1992; 1 in 2000.* **Sources: Stl.**

Adina, Stark (Frankad Cultivar) - Large, round to conical fruits with red to purplish red skin and an occasional overlaying stripe. Firm, very juicy, creamy white flesh. Sweet flavor with a distinctive hint of cinnamon. Tree is vigorous and early bearing. Requires only 100-350 hours of chilling. Hardy in Zones 6-9. U.S. Plant Patent No. 6361. *Source History: 3 in 1988; 4 in 1992; 2 in 2000.* **Sources: ORA, Pa2.**

Airlie Red Flesh - Medium size conical fruit. Dark red flesh has a crisp texture and delicious sweet-tart flavor. Good keeper. Ripens early October. Hardy to Zone 4. Discovered near the town of Airlie in western Oregon. *Source History: 4 in 2000.* **Sources: Gr16, On3, Or9, Wh3.**

Akane (Prime Red Akane, Prime Red, Tokyo Rose, Tohoku No. 3) - Jonathan x Worcester Pearmain. Round, bright red fruit with hard, crisp, juicy, white flesh. Tart, sprightly flavor resembling Jonathan. Outstanding red dessert apple; good for drying. Hangs well on tree; better keeper than most early fall varieties. Tree is precocious, medium productive and winter hardy. Leaves have yellow tinge. Mid to late season bloom. Thin well to get good size. Does well in warmer districts. Ripens late August to mid-September depending on location. Requires 800 hours of chilling. Zones 5-9. Introduced in 1970 by the Tohoku Agricultural Experiment Station in Japan. *Source History: 20 in 1988; 26 in 1992; 19 in 2000.* **Sources: Bea, Bl4, Bu7, Ch9, Clo, Cu4, Ea3, Er2, Gr4, ME3, Mo19, Nrs, Or9, Rai, So5, Son, TR8, WI12, WI4.**

Akero - Swedish dessert apple. Roundish, cone-shaped fruit is tile red over yellow. Crisp, juicy flesh with raspberry tang. Summer apple with excellent keeping qualities. Ripens July or August depending on location. *Source History: 2 in 1988; 4 in 1992; 3 in 2000.* **Sources: Ch9, Ed5, So5.**

Alaska - Large, well formed, almost white fruit. Very crisp, tender, refreshing flesh. Fine eating quality. Hangs well on the tree. Ripens in October. Name was chosen to conjure up the image of cool white majesty. Original name was probably Bedfordshire Jr., indicating its origin as a seedling of the old Bedfordshire Foundling. Albert Etter creation. Formerly patented. *Source History: 4 in 1988; 4 in 1992; 1 in 2000.* **Sources: Gr4.**

Albemarle Pippin - *Source History: 1 in 2000.* **Sources: Ca15.**

Alexander (Emperor Alexander, Alexander the First, Beauty of Queen, English King, Aporta, Albertin, Grand Alexander) - Old Russian variety. Parent of Wolf River. Very large, uniform, conical fruit. Greenish yellow skin is streaked and splashed with red and orange. Coarse, tender, juicy, yellowish white flesh. Brisk, mildly subacid flavor. Cooking and culinary use; not a good keeper. One of a very few that will reproduce a close likeness when propagated from seed. Trees are noteably vigorous growers; come into bearing quickly. Very large blossoms. Ripens continuously over 4-6 weeks. Fruit often persists on the tree in reasonable condition through the fall. Hardy to -50 degrees F. Known before 1817. *Source His-*

tory: 3 in 1988; 5 in 1992; 6 in 2000. **Sources: Bea, Gr4, Or9, Son, Stl, Wo7.**

Alexis - *Source History: 1 in 2000.* **Sources: Bea.**

Alkmene (Red Alkmene) - Cox cross from Belgium. Bright red fruit with crisp, juicy flesh. Distinctive flavor. Very good quality eating and multi-purpose apple. Fruit hangs well on the tree but not a keeper. Compact, almost spur-type tree. Ripens in mid-September. *Source History: 2 in 1992; 5 in 2000.* **Sources: Clo, Ed5, Er2, Mo19, Rai.**

Allington Pippin - Medium size, conic fruit with red blush or striping over green-yellow background. Cream colored, firm flesh holds its shape when cooked. Flavor starts out sharp and mellows to intense pineapple-like flavor. Originated in the United Kingdom in 1894. *Source History: 2 in 2000.* **Sources: Or9, Son.**

Almata - Beautiful Arcade x Fluke 38 Crab. Small to medium size, solid pale red fruit covered with greyish bloom. Striking watermelon-red flesh throughout. Tart flavor. Makes excellent cranberry red applesauce. Also good for pickling. Susceptible to fire blight and scab infection. Ripens in July or August depending on location. Hardy to -50 degrees F. with occasional winter injury. Russian and Canadian parentage. Bred in 1942 by Dr. Nels Hansen at the South Dakota Agricultural Experiment Station. *Source History: 3 in 1988; 7 in 1992; 7 in 2000.* **Sources: Bea, Bl4, Ch9, Er2, Or9, So5, Stl.**

Alton - Early McIntosh x NY 845. Skin color is red wash over yellow background. White, fine grained flesh bleeding to pink when fully ripe. Flavorful. Good for eating or cooking. Not a keeper. Early season. Hardy to -50 degrees F. *Source History: 1 in 2000.* **Sources: Stl.**

Amanishiki - *Source History: 2 in 1992; 1 in 2000.* **Sources: Nrs.**

Ambrosia - Discovered as a whole tree sport in British Columbia, Canada in 1980. Red blush covers 70-90% of the fruit. Clean smooth skin with no russeting. Crisp, juicy flesh. Sub-acid flavor. Creamy texture. U.S. Plant Patent No. 10,789. *Source History: 1 in 2000.* **Sources: WI12.**

American Beauty (Beauty of America, Sterling Beauty) - Yellow skin overlaid with red with small brown dots. Tender, dense, yellow flesh. Annual bearer. Noted by Elliott in 1854. Originated in Sterling, Massachusetts. *Source History: 4 in 1992; 4 in 2000.* **Sources: Ch9, GI3, Nrs, Wo7.**

American Pippin (Grindstone) - Introduced in the U.S. around 1817. *Source History: 1 in 1992; 2 in 2000.* **Sources: Or9, Wo7.**

Amish Black - Large fruit with smooth heavy skin. Dark red skin color is almost black. Quality resembles Winesap but does not store as well. Fairly vigorous tree bears annual crops. Ripens early October. *Source History: 2 in 1988; 1 in 1992; 6 in 2000.* **Sources: Bea, Ca15, Ch9, Cla, Or9, Sc6.**

Amsib - *Source History: 1 in 2000.* **Sources: Ch9.**

Amur Red - Possibly the seedling of the 1912 Amur variety. Tight clusters of dark crimson, 1.5" fruits. Excellent for canning and jelly. Upright tree is a consistent yielder. Ripens mid-September. Hardy to Zone 2. Originated in Manitoba, Canada in 1940. *Source History: 1 in 2000.* **Sources: Bea.**

Amy - Southern variety. *Source History: 1 in 2000.* **Sources: Ca15.**

Anana's Reinette - Golden skin with russet freckles. Crisp, juicy flavor with intense, sweet, sharp pineapple flavor late in the season. Good for fresh eating, cooking and juice. Zones 6-9. Originated in the Netherlands in 1821. *Source History: 1 in 2000.* **Sources: Son.**

Anders - Trademarked variety. *Source History: 1 in 2000.* **Sources: CO5.**

<u>Andy Reed</u> - Southern variety. *Source History: 1 in 2000.* **Sources: Ca15.**

<u>Anna</u> - Best for home and commercial orchards in the deep South. Developed in Israel from Golden Delicious. Green fruits overlaid with one-third red blush. Good flavor and crispness. Can be used fresh or for cooking. Large, strong tree bears when extremely young. Requires pollination by Golden Dorsett or Ein Shemer, and a full spray program. Early ripening and excellent for warm winter climates and some of the hottest areas. Can be grown in Florida and low desert areas of the Southwest. Ripens in mid-June or July depending on location. Requires only 100-300 hours of winter chilling. Hardy in Zones 5-9. *Source History: 18 in 1988; 35 in 1992; 27 in 2000.* **Sources: Bar, Bay, CO5, Cum, Er2, FO10, Ga20, GI3, Ho5, Iso, Jo3, Ju2, MI5, Nrs, On4, ORA, Pa2, RA4, SIM, Son, STR, Tex, Ty2, WA8, Wel, WI4, Wom.**

<u>Annie Elizabeth</u> - *Source History: 1 in 2000.* **Sources: Ch9.**

<u>Anoka</u> - Mercer x Duchess. Big yellow apples striped and heavily overlaid with red. Mild, subacid flavor. Good for culinary use. May be used for pies or sauce weeks before ripening. Very productive tree grows 15-20' tall. Known as "The Old Man's Apple" because it often bears fruit the first or second year after planting. For proper pollination and best yields, plant near other varieties. Moderately resistant to fire blight. Hardy summer apple. Ripens in September. *Source History: 5 in 1988; 7 in 1992; 5 in 2000.* **Sources: Ch9, Fi1, Nrs, Sc6, Stl.**

<u>Api Etoile</u> (Star Lady) - Unusual oblate flattened shaped fruit looks like a rounded star from the end. Flavor is aromatic with a pleasing acid and sweet fruity taste. Ripens late. Zones 5-9. Originated in Switzerland. Possibly dates back to the 1600s. *Source History: 2 in 2000.* **Sources: Or9, Son.**

<u>Apple Babe</u> - Medium size, attractive russet-free fruit with waxy finish. Crisp, sweet, juicy, flavorful flesh. Genetic dwarf tree grows 6-10' tall. Bears heavily when pollinated with Garden Delicious. Excellent quality even in hot inland climates. Requires 700 hours of chilling. Hardy in Zones 4-8. Developed by Floyd Zaiger. Plant patent applied for. *Source History: 3 in 1988; 5 in 1992; 2 in 2000.* **Sources: Bay, WI4.**

<u>Apricot</u> - Large, round, orange-red fruit. Light orange flesh has a subtle apricot aftertaste. Good for fresh eating and baking. Ripens in late September. *Source History: 3 in 2000.* **Sources: Ch9, On3, Or9.**

<u>Arkansas Black</u> - Extremely beautiful, medium size, smooth, round, dark purplish red fruits turn nearly black at maturity. Waxy skin. Crisp, juicy, very firm, yellow flesh. Distinctive aromatic flavor lends itself well to cider blending. Very good quality. Used for fresh eating or cooking. Excellent keeper; mellows in storage. Large, vigorous tree. Resistant to cedar-apple rust; somewhat resistant to codling moth. Infertile pollen; pollinate with Yates or Yellow Delicious. Ripens in late October or November depending on location. Hardy in Zones 5-8. Originated in Benton County, Arkansas around 1870. Probably a seedling of Winesap. *Source History: 18 in 1988; 27 in 1992; 35 in 2000.* **Sources: Bar, Bea, Bl4, Bo5, Ca15, Ch9, Cla, CO5, Cu4, Cum, Ea3, Ed2, Er2, Fo2, Ga20, Gr4, Hid, Ho5, Iso, Jo3, La3, MI5, Or9, Ro3, Sc6, So5, Son, STR, TU5, Ty2, Ur2, WA8, Wh4, Wo7, Wor.**

<u>Arkansas Black, Boyd</u> - *Source History: 1 in 2000.* **Sources: Hid.**

<u>Arkansas Black, Compspur</u> (Compspur Arkblack) - J-spur sport of the Colonial Arkansas Black. Fruit exposed to full sun develops a waxy sheen from ruby black to jet black. Firm, golden flesh. Sprightly flavor. Good for baked apples, spiced apple slices, sauces and pies. Keeps until spring. Ripens around October 25.

Source History: 1 in 1988; 1 in 1992; 1 in 2000. **Sources: Mi1.**

Arkansas Black, Spur - Very compact spur mutation of this old variety. Medium size, purplish red fruit. Firm, coarse, crisp, greenish white flesh. Good dessert and cooking apple. Keeps all winter. Partly self-fruitful. Popular as fresh market variety in southeast United States. Ripens in October or November depending on location. Requires 800 hours of chilling. *Source History: 4 in 1988; 4 in 1992; 4 in 2000.* **Sources: Bay, Hid, Pe2, WI4.**

Arkansas Black, Starkspur (Lonacre Cultivar) - Dark red, 3" fruits ripen to almost black. Tart flesh. Excellent sauce apple. Keeps eight months in refrigeration. Ripens in late October. Hardy in Zones 5-8. Trademarked. *Source History: 1 in 1988; 1 in 1992; 1 in 2000.* **Sources: St4.**

Arkansas Sweet - *Source History: 1 in 2000.* **Sources: Ca15.**

ArkCharm - Excellent eating apple with sweet, juicy flesh. Keeps for only 3-5 weeks. Upright, vigorous tree. Ripens in late August. Released in France. Introduced by the University of Arkansas. *Source History: 1 in 2000.* **Sources: Ro3.**

Arlet - Very high quality fruit. Disease resistant. Hardy. Zone 4, possibly 3. *Source History: 1 in 1992; 3 in 2000.* **Sources: Ch9, Ed5, Or9.**

Aroma (Priddy) - *Source History: 2 in 1992; 4 in 2000.* **Sources: Ch9, Ed5, Er2, Mo19.**

Aromatic Pippin - *Source History: 1 in 2000.* **Sources: Ed5.**

Ashmead's Kernel (Ashmead) - Medium size, greenish yellow fruit with brown flush, usually covered with a heavy russet. Flattish round shape, sometimes slightly conical. Crisp, yellowish juicy flesh. Unique, nut-like flavor. Tart when tree-ripe; peak flavor quality in early November. Rated first in quality a few years ago in blindfold taste tests conducted by the Royal Horticultural Society. Makes excellent tasting cider. Will keep 3-4 months. Large precocious tree. Resists powdery mildew. Ripens in late October. Hardy to -40 degrees F. Raised by Dr. Ashmead, an eminent physician in Gloucester, England in the 18th century. Introduced in the early 1700s. *Source History: 14 in 1988; 16 in 1992; 20 in 2000.* **Sources: Bea, Bl4, Ch9, Cla, Clo, Cu4, Ea3, Ed5, Er2, Fed, Ga20, Gr4, On3, Or9, Sc6, So5, Son, Stl, Wh4, WI4.**

Assumption - *Source History: 1 in 1992; 1 in 2000.* **Sources: Ch9.**

Astrachan Crab - Red Astrachan parentage. Small, flavorful fruit. Red-yellow skin color. Ripens early. Hardy to -50 degrees F. with occasional winter injury. St. Lawrence Nurseries introduction. *Source History: 1 in 1992; 1 in 2000.* **Sources: Stl.**

Astrachan, Honeydew White - Appearance resembles White Astrachan with the pale ivory skin with faint pink stripes and the dusky bloom covering the skin. Large fruit often over 1 lb. Excellent eating quality. Vigorous, healthy tree. *Source History: 1 in 2000.* **Sources: Gr4.**

Astrachan, Red (Abe Lincoln, Red Ashmore, American Red, Hamper's American, Waterloo) - Small to medium, round to slightly flattened fruit; very pale creamy yellow skin, striped and splashed with bright red, covered with heavy bloom. White flesh is tinged or striped with red when fully ripe; good eating although tart. Harvest for kitchen use when slightly green. Excellent for sauce and pies. Tends to become mealy when overripe. Very short storage. Medium-large, vigorous tree; bears when young. Whitish blue blossoms. Productive but biennial bearer. Ripens unevenly for a 3-5 week period from July to early September. 700 hours of chilling. Hardy to -45 degrees F. Grows well in hotter areas. Russian apple imported into England from Sweden in 1816. Introduced to U.S. in 1835. *Source History: 15 in 1988; 19 in 1992; 18 in 2000.* **Sources: Bea, Bl4, Ca15, Ch9, Cu4, Ed5, Fed, Ga20, Gr4, Hid, Leu, Mi1, Or9, Sc6, So5, Son, Stl, Wo7, Wor.**

<u>Astrachan, White</u> (Muscovite Transparent, Transparent) - Medium size fruit with whitish green skin. Fine, tender, crisp, sweet, subacid, very white, perfumed flesh. Fair keeper. Large tree. Requires cross-pollination. Very early. Requires 600 hours or less of chilling. Introduced from Russia in 1748. *Source History: 3 in 1988; 4 in 1992; 2 in 2000.* **Sources: Gr4, Son.**

<u>Atlas</u> - Winter St. Lawrence x Duchess. Good cooking and eating apple. Stores well. Strong, productive tree. Ripens midseason. Hardy to -50 degrees F. with occasional winter injury. *Source History: 2 in 1992; 2 in 2000.* **Sources: Ch9, Stl.**

<u>August Sweet</u> - Pippin type with flat-round shape. Light yellow skin. Sweet flesh. Makes excellent cider and apple butter. Ripens mid-August. *Source History: 1 in 2000.* **Sources: Sc6.**

<u>Aunt Cora's Field Apple</u> - Southern variety. *Source History: 1 in 2000.* **Sources: Ca15.**

<u>Aunt Cora's Yard Apple</u> - Southern variety. *Source History: 1 in 2000.* **Sources: Ca15.**

<u>Aunt Rachel</u> - Southern variety. *Source History: 1 in 2000.* **Sources: Ca15.**

<u>Aunt Sally</u> - Southern variety. *Source History: 1 in 2000.* **Sources: Ca15.**

<u>Autumn Arctic</u> - Arctic x Northern Spy. Red and yellow striped fruit. Good tasting. Productive, scab resistant. Ripens midseason. Hardy to -50 degrees F. *Source History: 1 in 1988; 2 in 1992; 2 in 2000.* **Sources: Ch9, Stl.**

<u>Autumn Gold</u> - Skin shows red blush over yellow-green ground color. Fine grained flesh with firm texture and crisp subacid flavor. Spreading tree shows medium vigor. Regular bearer. Matures early to mid October. U.S. Plant Patent No. 9907. *Source History: 2 in 2000.* **Sources: COL, WI12.**

<u>Autumn Sweet</u> - *Source History: 1 in 1992; 1 in 2000.* **Sources: Bl4.**

<u>Avenarius</u> - Green-yellow skin with rosy blush. Small fruit. White, sweet, juicy flesh. Vigorous grower. Ripens early. Extremely hardy, to -50 degrees F or colder. *Source History: 1 in 2000.* **Sources: Stl.**

<u>Avista</u> - *Source History: 1 in 2000.* **Sources: Ed5.**

<u>Babe</u> - Delicious, medium size fruit with waxy finish. Genetic dwarf tree grows 6-10' tall. *Source History: 1 in 2000.* **Sources: MI5.**

<u>Bailey Sweet</u> (Bailey's Golden Sweet, Patterson's Sweet, Edgerly Sweet, Howard's Sweet) - Smooth, bright yellow skin is flushed with deep red and striped with darker red. Somewhat coarse, yellowish flesh is juicy and tender with sweet flavor. Short storage life. Ripens in September. Sometimes called Sweet Winesap, which is a distinct variety. Originated in Perry, Wyoming County, New York in the 1840s. *Source History: 3 in 1992; 2 in 2000.* **Sources: Bl4, Ch9.**

<u>Baker Sweet</u> (Late Golden Sweet, Long Stem Sweet, Winter Golden Sweet) - Medium to large, uniform, golden yellow fruit with patches of russet. Rich, firm, very sweet, juicy, yellow flesh. Useful for home, local market and cider. Not a keeper. Moderately vigorous and hardy tree. Ripens in late fall or early winter depending on location. Originated in New England in the 1880s. *Source History: 1 in 1988; 2 in 1992; 1 in 2000.* **Sources: Bea.**

<u>Bald Mountain</u> - Southern variety. *Source History: 1 in 2000.* **Sources: Ca15.**

Baldwin (Woodpecker, Butters, Pecker, Felch, Steele's Red Winter) - Large winter apple. Tough, smooth, bright red skin with white stars. Crisp, solid, juicy, somewhat aromatic, yellowish flesh. Good for fresh eating and all culinary purposes. Adds body, spiciness and aroma to cider. Excellent keeper. Vigorous, long-lived tree can get quite large. Tends to bear in alternate years, but can be regulated by timely pruning and thinning. Triploid, so pollen is sterile. Ripens late September to November depending on location. Hardy to Zone 4. Seedling that originated in Lowell, Massachusetts about 1740. Named after Col. Loammi Baldwin of Woburn. Most widely planted apple of New England by 1852; most widely planted in U.S. until late 1920s. *Source History: 11 in 1988; 15 in 1992; 18 in 2000.* **Sources: Bea, Bl4, Ch9, Cid, Cla, Cu4, Ed5, Fed, Ga20, Gr4, Mi1, Nrs, Or9, So5, Son, Wh4, Wo7, Wor.**

Baldwin, Red Fleshed - *Source History: 1 in 2000.* **Sources: Or9.**

Ball's Choice - *Source History: 1 in 2000.* **Sources: Or9.**

Bancroft - McIntosh x Forest. Red fruit. Quality fair when ripe; improves with storage. Exceptionally good keeper. Tree bears at a young age. Ripens late. Hardy to -50 degrees F. *Source History: 1 in 1988; 2 in 1992; 3 in 2000.* **Sources: Ch9, Ed5, Stl.**

Banks - *Source History: 1 in 2000.* **Sources: Or9.**

Banon's Seedling - *Source History: 1 in 2000.* **Sources: Or9.**

Barre - *Source History: 1 in 1992; 1 in 2000.* **Sources: Ch9.**

Barry - *Source History: 1 in 2000.* **Sources: Ch9.**

Baumann Reinette - *Source History: 1 in 2000.* **Sources: Ch9.**

Beacon (Minn 243, Early Delicious, Fenton, Miller Red) - Malinda x Wealthy. Medium to large fruit with tough, yellow skin that is splashed and striped orange-red. Juicy, mildly subacid flesh. Excellent early eating apple; good for cooking. Does not store well. Vigorous, productive, heavy bearing tree. Ripens over a long period during the summer. Hardy to -50 degrees F. with occasional winter injury. Developed in Minnesota. Introduced in 1936. *Source History: 8 in 1988; 16 in 1992; 11 in 2000.* **Sources: Bea, Bl4, Ch9, Ed5, Fa1, Fed, GR26, Mc3, SH8, Stl, Wa16.**

Beauties of Wellington - Chance seedling discovered in Charlotte, Maine by James Johnson Wellington who gave scionwood to Rule Furlong in the 1940s who in turn gave the wood to his son, Damon Furlong to graft. Named by Mr. Furlong. Light golden yellow skin color is overlaid 80-90% with areas of solid red, deeper red stripes and areas of small red spots, which is overlaid with a mass of small white dots. Fine grained, slightly off-white flesh with a hint of pink when ripe. Excellent flavor. *Source History: 1 in 2000.* **Sources: Fed.**

Beautiful Arcade - Old Russian apple. Yellow fruit splashed with red. Good quality. Annual bearer. Good for fresh use and short storage. Used as a pollinator and rootstock. Ripens in September. Hardy in Zones 2 and 3. Arrived in the U.S. via Canada in the mid-1800s. *Source History: 1 in 1988; 3 in 1992; 2 in 2000.* **Sources: Bea, Ch9.**

Bedan (De Jaune Bedan) - Cider variety. *Source History: 1 in 2000.* **Sources: Cu4.**

Bedford - Cluster seedling. Canadian prairie apple. Fruit is yellow with dull red. Small size, especially if not thinned. Fire blight resistant. Hardy to Zone 3. Introduced in 1916. *Source History: 1 in 2000.* **Sources: Ed5.**

Beecher - Southern variety. *Source History: 1 in 2000.* **Sources: Ca15.**

Belle de Boskoop (Boskoop) - Bud sport of Reinette de Montfort. Large, greenish yellow fruit with dark red blush. Rough skin. Crisp, tangy, highly aromatic flesh. Outstanding for dessert, cooking and baking. Sweetens in storage. Excellent keeper. Needs a pollinator. Ripens in November or December depending on location. Hardy to Zone 4. Named after a small community in southern Holland where it originated in 1856. Favorite in England. *Source History: 5 in 1988; 9 in 1992; 15 in 2000.* **Sources: Bea, Bl4, Ch9, Ed5, Er2, Fed, Gr4, Mo19, Nrs, Or9, Rai, Sc6, So5, Son, WI4.**

Belle Fille - *Source History: 1 in 2000.* **Sources: Cid.**

Bellflower - Old-time winter dessert apple with a subtle flavor. Long, lanky, often lopsided shape. Pale lemon-yellow skin with a subtle red blush and conspicuous russet dots. Creamy flesh is firm, tender and aromatic. Large spreading tree. Requires a pollinator. 400 chilling hours. *Source History: 1 in 2000.* **Sources: Ga20.**

Belmont (Gate, Gait, Belmont Late, Kelley White, Mamma Bean, Waxen Apple, White Apple) - Large, globular, clear bright yellow fruit with waxy skin. Yellowish flesh is crisp, firm but tender; excellent mild flavor. Subject to diseases and preharvest drop. Ripens in late September or early October. Old 19th century Pennsylvania dessert and cooking apple once highly popular in Belmont County, Ohio. Sometimes called Gate, because it was found beside the garden gate of a Mrs. Bean. *Source History: 1 in 1988; 2 in 1992; 1 in 2000.* **Sources: So5.**

Ben Davis (Baltimore Pippin, Kentucky Pippin, New York Pippin, Virginia Pippin, Hutchinson Pippin, Joe Allen, Red Pippin, Victoria Pippin, Red Streak, Funkhouse) - Large, handsome, red and red-striped fruit. Hard, coarse white flesh. Bruise resistant. Exceptional keeper, lasting until June or July. Good pollinator; one of the parents of Cortland. Some disease resistance. Ripens late. Once called "mortgage lifter" for the income it generated by shipping barge loads on the Mississippi River to New Orleans for export. For many years following the Civil War, the leading winter eating apple in the south central states. Hardy in Zone 3. Originated in Arkansas in 1880. *Source History: 5 in 1988; 8 in 1992; 10 in 2000.* **Sources: Bl4, Ca15, Ch9, Cid, Cu4, Hid, Or9, Sc6, So5, Wo7.**

Ben Davis, Black (Gano) - Medium to large fruit. Firm, somewhat coarse, moderately crisp, juicy flesh. Mildly subacid flavor; good quality. Ripens very late. Hardy to Zone 6. Originated about 1880 on the farm of a Mr. Black of Washington County, Arkansas. *Source History: 1 in 1988; 4 in 1992; 5 in 2000.* **Sources: Bea, Ca15, Cla, La3, Ur2.**

Ben Davis, Striped - Southern variety. *Source History: 1 in 2000.* **Sources: Ca15.**

Benanders Hard Red - *Source History: 1 in 2000.* **Sources: Bea.**

Benham - Cooking apple used for pies and frying. Not a good keeper. Some disease resistance. Ripens in the fall. Developed in Kentucky. *Source History: 3 in 1988; 4 in 1992; 6 in 2000.* **Sources: Bea, Bl4, Ca15, Ch9, Gr4, Ur2.**

Beni No Mai - *Source History: 1 in 2000.* **Sources: Or9.**

Benoni - Orangish yellow with red fruit striped with carmine. Highly flavored. Fine for dessert. Biennial bearer. Originated in Dedham, Massachusets about 1832. *Source History: 3 in 1988; 6 in 1992; 6 in 2000.* **Sources: Bl4, Ch9, Gr4, Sc6, So5, Wo7.**

Bentley (Bentley's Sweet) - Yellow skin is blushed and striped with dull red; inconspicuous dark brown dots cover the surface. Creamy, fine grained, crisp, juicy, yellow flesh. Long keeper. Susceptible to bitter rot. Ripens in October. First noted in 1845. *Source History: 1 in 1992; 1 in 2000.* **Sources: Ca15.**

Berne Rose (Berner Rosen) - Swiss apple similar to Baldwin, but bears heavily every year. Irregularly shaped, flat fruit with red-yellow skin color and green-yellow dots. Very good keeper. Ripens in October. *Source History: 1 in 1988; 2 in 1992; 1 in 2000.* **Sources: Or9.**

Bessemianka-Micurina - *Source History: 1 in 2000.* **Sources: Ch9.**

Bethel - Blue Pearmain type. Red striped fruit. Crisp, firm, yellow flesh. Excellent keeper. Ripens late. Hardy to -50 degrees F. Originated in Bethel, Vermont. *Source History: 1 in 1992; 1 in 2000.* **Sources: Stl.**

Betsy Deaton - Southern variety. *Source History: 1 in 2000.* **Sources: Ca15.**

Bevan's Favorite (Early Bevans, Striped June) - Yellow skin with bright red stripes. Crisp, firm flesh. Subacid flavor. Vigorous, heavy bearer. Ripens in July. Originated in Salem, New Jersey before 1849. Last appeared in nursery catalogs in 1893. *Source History: 1 in 1992; 1 in 2000.* **Sources: Ca15.**

Beverly Hills - Medium to large fruit. Pale, greenish yellow skin with an orangish red flush and streaked, dark red, russet dots. Slightly tart flavor. Very good for fresh eating or cooking. Self-fruitful. Adapted to warm climates. Ripens in August. Requires 300-500 hours of chilling. *Source History: 6 in 1988; 10 in 1992; 6 in 2000.* **Sources: CO5, Nrs, ORA, Si3, STR, WI4.**

Bidy - *Source History: 1 in 2000.* **Sources: Bea.**

Bietigheimer (Red Bietigheimer) - Very large fruit of uniform size. Skin is pale yellow to green or white with pink-red. Crisp white flesh is firm, juicy and subacid. Very coarse but crisp. Good for cooking. Bears early and annually but production is usually light; subject to preharvest drop. Ripens in the fall. Originated in Germany. *Source History: 2 in 1988; 3 in 1992; 4 in 2000.* **Sources: Ca15, Ed5, Gr4, Or9.**

Big Cheese - *Source History: 1 in 2000.* **Sources: Or9.**

Big Hill - Southern variety. *Source History: 1 in 2000.* **Sources: Ca15.**

Big Red - *Source History: 1 in 2000.* **Sources: Ch9.**

Big Stem - Southern variety. *Source History: 1 in 2000.* **Sources: Ca15.**

Bill's Red Flesh - *Source History: 1 in 2000.* **Sources: Ch9.**

Billy Bound - *Source History: 1 in 1992; 1 in 2000.* **Sources: Ch9.**

Black Annie - Southern variety. *Source History: 1 in 2000.* **Sources: Ca15.**

Black Baltimore - Southern variety. *Source History: 1 in 2000.* **Sources: Ca15.**

Black Gilliflower (Sheepnose, Black Sheepnose, Red Gilliflower, Black Spitzenburg) - Large, oblong, conical ribbed fruit. Dark red deepening almost to black. Greenish white flesh. Rich, mild, sweet flavor. Distinctive aroma. Prized for baking, desserts and drying. Vigorous, healthy and fruitful tree. Hangs long on the tree, but must not be allowed to become overripe as flesh soon becomes dry. Ripens in September or October depending on location. Zones 6-9. Thought to have originated in Connecticut in the late 1700s. *Source History: 9 in 1988; 13 in 1992; 13 in 2000.* **Sources: Bea, Bl4, Ch9, Cu4, Ea3, Gr4, Leu, Mi1, Or9, So5, Son, Und, Wo7.**

Black Oxford - Rare heirloom. Unknown parentage. Medium size, round fruit is deep-purple with a black bloom. Excellent eating and cooking qualities; makes great cider; dries well. Shy biennial bearer. Resistant to insects and disease. Ripens in November. Hardy in Zones 3-4. Originated in Oxford County, Maine in the

1860s. *Source History: 3 in 1992; 5 in 2000.* **Sources: Ch9, Cu4, Fed, Or9, Wo7.**

Black Twig (Mammoth Black Twig, Paragon) - Large to medium size fruit. Green to yellow skin flushed with red. Very firm, fine grained, yellow flesh. Excellent tart eating apple. Good for cooking. Tannic juice adds kick to cider. Distinct from Arkansas Black, but shares its good keeping characteristics. Fine eating apple. Good for cooking and cider. One of the best keeping southern apples. Said to be resistant to major apple diseases. Zones 6-9. Originated as a seedling on the farm of Major Rankin Toole near Fayetteville, Tennessee. Mr. Twitty, a nurseryman from the same area, distributed the variety which became one of the most popular varieties in early 20th-century central Virginia orchards. Introduced in 1833. *Source History: 7 in 1988; 10 in 1992; 13 in 2000.* **Sources: Bea, Bl4, Bo5, Ca15, Cid, Cla, Cu4, Ga20, Jo3, Or9, So5, Son, Ur2.**

Blairmont - Fruit 3" in diameter. Dark red over pale yellow skin. Ripens 112 days after full bloom. Blossoms have good frost tolerance. Trees have not been attacked by powdery mildew. Moderately resistant to black rot and bitter rot. Ripens early. Released by Jim Thompson, USDA, Byron, Georgia in 1982. Especially well adapted to the Southeast where high temperatures often prohibit growing of high quality apples. "In both appearance and quality, Blairmont is rated very good to excellent. - HortScience." *Source History: 2 in 1988; 5 in 1992; 1 in 2000.* **Sources: Nrs.**

Blaxstayman - *Source History: 1 in 1992; 1 in 2000.* **Sources: Nrs.**

Blaze - Collins x Fanny. Mild, red Jonathan-type apple that ripens three weeks earlier. Introduced by the Illinois Agricultural Experiment Station. *Source History: 1 in 1988; 2 in 1992; 1 in 2000.* **Sources: So5.**

Blenheim (Blenheim Orange, Beauty of Hants, Rosy Blenheim, Kempster's Pippin, Blenheim Pippin, Woodstock Pippin) - There are a number of cultivars, but the one with the broad eye is considered the original. Large, yellow and red fruit with creamy, white, coarse flesh. Sharply subacid, aromatic flavor resembles Roxbury Russet. Vigorous, spreading tree; tip bearer. Some mildew resistance; immune to fire blight; susceptible to scab. Found at Old Woodstock about 1740 near Blenheim, Oxfordshire, England. Available in London nurseries in 1818 under the name Kempster's Pippin. Apparently discovered by Kempster. *Source History: 2 in 1988; 5 in 1992; 5 in 2000.* **Sources: Bea, Ch9, Gr4, Or9, So5.**

Blushing Golden (Griffith Cultivar, Stark Blushing Golden) - Fruit has orange-red blush and is russet free. Waxy skin is bruise resistant and will not shrivel, even in storage. Strong, early producer. Remarkably disease resistant. Ripens mid-October. Hardy in Zones 5-8. Trademarked. *Source History: 1 in 1988; 3 in 1992; 3 in 2000.* **Sources: AG2, Ch9, St4.**

Bonnie Best - Unknown parentage; possible cross of Wolf River and Secor. Medium to large fruits with attractive pale red striping. Crunchy, tender, juicy flesh is slightly tart. Resists fire blight. Ripens in early October. Zones 4-7. Discovered in Cooksville, Wisconsin. *Source History: 1 in 1992; 3 in 2000.* **Sources: Ch9, Jun, WI12.**

Bottle Greening - Medium to large fruit. Grass-green to yellow skin. Flesh is very tender, juicy, aromatic and subacid. Good dessert apple. Tree is hardy and productive. Ripens in late October. Originated in New York in early 1800s. Named because a large hollow in the tree was a popular hiding place for workmen's liquor bottles. *Source History: 1 in 1988; 2 in 1992; 1 in 2000.* **Sources: Bea.**

Bough - *Source History: 1 in 2000.* **Sources: Or9.**

Boughen's Delight - *Source History: 1 in 2000.* **Sources: Bea.**

Bower's Nonpareil - Southern variety. *Source History: 1 in 2000.* **Sources: Ca15.**

Braeburn - Unknown parentage; speculated to be an open-pollinated seedling of Lady Hamilton. Medium to large fruit of very high quality. Orangish red blush over yellow background. Crisp, tangy flavor. Triploid. Very early bearing. Low vigor. Susceptible to scab, mildew and fire blight; bitter pit and sunburn can be problems. Requires thinning. Ripens in late October-November. Requires 700 hours of chilling. Hardy in Zones 6-7. Originated in New Zealand. Introduced in 1952. *Source History: 4 in 1988; 31 in 1992; 37 in 2000.* **Sources: Ad2, AG2, Bay, Bea, Bl4, Bo5, Ch9, Cla, CO5, Cu4, Cum, Ea3, Fi1, Ga20, Hi9, Jo3, La3, ME3, Mel, Mi1, Mo19, Nrs, On3, Or9, ORA, Pa2, Pe2, Rai, Sc6, Si3, Son, St4, STR, Ty2, Va2, WI4, Wom.**

Braeburn, Hillwell Strain (Hidala Red Braeburn) - Medium to large fruit with predominantly red skin color. Medium sweet flavor. Good for fresh use, cooking and canning. Moderately vigorous tree shows good precocity with proper thinning. Keeps up to six months in common storage. Ripens about 10 days earlier than standard Braeburn and about two weeks before Granny Smith varieties. U.S. Plant Patent No. 7526. *Source History: 1 in 1992; 2 in 2000.* **Sources: Co2, TR8.**

Braeburn, Joburn (Aurora) - Natural striped mutation of the standard Braeburn with heavy red stripes on red over a cream ground color. Requires chemical thinning to prevent overcropping. Tree vigor is weak to moderate with a spreading habit. Originated in New Zealand. Plant patent applied for. *Source History: 2 in 2000.* **Sources: COL, WI12.**

Braeburn, Lochbuie - Blush sport of Braeburn. Medium-large fruit with 80-85% solid red color. Outstanding eating quality. Excellent keeper. Originated in New Zealand. Trademarked. *Source History: 2 in 2000.* **Sources: COL, WI12.**

BraeStar (Brayleet Cultivar) - Trademarked. Plant patent applied for. *Source History: 1 in 2000.* **Sources: St4.**

Bramley's Seedling - Traditional cooking apple of the British Isles. Large flat greenish yellow fruit with broad, broken brown and red stripes. Firm skin. Firm, juicy, sharply acid flesh. Cooks to perfection with rich juice and no hard pieces. Good cider apple; extremely high vitamin C content. Large, vigorous, spreading tree. Heavy, regular bearer. Blooms late; will survive in a frost pocket when some would be killed. Triploid; requires a pollinator. Scab and mildew resistant. Ripens from early October to early November depending on location. Hardy to Zone 5. Originated between 1809 and 1813. *Source History: 9 in 1988; 15 in 1992; 18 in 2000.* **Sources: Bea, Bl4, Ch9, Cid, Cu4, Ea3, Ed5, Er2, Gr4, La3, Leu, Nrs, Or9, Rai, So5, Son, Ur2, WI4.**

Branch - Southern variety. *Source History: 1 in 2000.* **Sources: Ca15.**

Brandy - *Source History: 1 in 2000.* **Sources: Or9.**

Brasher - Southern variety. *Source History: 1 in 2000.* **Sources: Ca15.**

Breakswell - Cider apple. *Source History: 1 in 1992; 2 in 2000.* **Sources: Cid, Nrs.**

Breaky (Calville Rouge Seedling, Breakey) - Medium size yellow-green fruit striped with bright red. Excellent for fresh eating, sauce or pies. Ripens in mid-August. Very hardy to Zone 2. Developed in Canada in 1935. *Source History: 1 in 1988; 4 in 1992; 3 in 2000.* **Sources: Bea, Ed5, Va5.**

Brewster's Twig - *Source History: 1 in 2000.* **Sources: Bea.**

Brightness - *Source History: 1 in 2000.* **Sources: Bea.**

Britemac - Melba x Kildare. Red-striped fruit. Juicy, crisp, white flesh. Eating quality as good or better than McIntosh. Ripens midseason. Hardy to -50 degrees F. with occasional winter injury. *Source History: 1 in 1988; 1 in 1992; 1 in 2000.* **Sources: Stl.**

Brock (ME 7-492) - Golden Delicious x McIntosh. Large conic fruit is pink-red over a cream background. Small core. Mildly sweet, distinctive flavor. Stores well. Ripens soon after Red Delicious. Hardy to Zone 4. Bred in 1933 by the late Russ Bailey of the University of Maine and named for Henry Brock, an orchardist from Alfred, Maine who first popularized it. Introduced in 1966. *Source History: 3 in 1992; 4 in 2000.* **Sources: Bea, Bl4, Ch9, Fed.**

Brogan - *Source History: 1 in 2000.* **Sources: Hid.**

Brook 27 - *Source History: 1 in 2000.* **Sources: Bea.**

Brookfield - Selection from Royal Gala. Red skin color with bold red stripes. Harvest in two picks. Originated in New Zealand. U.S. Plant Patent No. 10,016. *Source History: 1 in 2000.* **Sources: WI12.**

Brown Russet - Fine sweet cider apple. Good for fresh eating. Scab and mildew resistant. Ripens in late October. *Source History: 1 in 1988; 1 in 1992; 2 in 2000.* **Sources: Er2, Rai.**

Brown Snout - Cider variety. *Source History: 4 in 2000.* **Sources: Cid, Cu4, Mo19, Or9.**

Brown Sweet - *Source History: 1 in 1992; 1 in 2000.* **Sources: Or9.**

Brown's Apple - *Source History: 1 in 2000.* **Sources: Cid.**

Brushy Top - Southern variety. *Source History: 1 in 2000.* **Sources: Ca15.**

Buckingham (Queen, Kentucky Fall Queen, Fall Queen, Equinetely, Ne Plus Ultra, Bachelor, Byer's, Byer's Red, Frankfort Queen, Henshaw, Red Horse, Lexington Queen, Merit, Blackburn) - Large fruit. Tough, thick skin; pale yellow washed and mottled with red stripes and blushed with bright carmine. Ripens August-September. Old-time favorite throughout the South. Probably originated in Louisa County, Virginia. Mentioned by Coxe in 1817. *Source History: 1 in 1988; 4 in 1992; 3 in 2000.* **Sources: Bl4, Ca15, Or9.**

Bud Wolf - Southern variety. *Source History: 1 in 2000.* **Sources: Ca15.**

Buff (Granny Buff) - Large fruit. The shape is flat, rectangular, convex; ribbed at the eye and prominently on the body. Fine-grained, crisp, green-white flesh; sweet flavor. Vigorous tree produces heavily. Originated in North Carolina on the farm of a family named Buff. Was a popular variety with the Cherokee Indians. Recorded in 1854. *Source History: 1 in 1992; 1 in 2000.* **Sources: Ca15.**

Bullock (Fox Apple, Sheep's Snout, Long Tom, Sheepnose) - Golden Russet x Unknown. Small yellow fruit with russeting. Yellow flesh with a mild, rich, spicy flavor. Great for cider. Fruit hangs on the tree even after the leaves have fallen. Tip bearer. Ripens late. Hardy to -50 degrees F. Originated in Burlington County, New Jersey in the late 18th century. *Source History: 1 in 1988; 2 in 1992; 2 in 2000.* **Sources: Ed5, Stl.**

Bulmer's Norman - Cider variety. *Source History: 1 in 1988; 1 in 1992; 3 in 2000.* **Sources: Cid, Cu4, Nrs.**

Buncombe - Southern variety described in 1857. Tall, rectangular to conic shape fruit. Skin color is yellow-white flushed maroon. Tender flesh with sub-acid to slightly sweet flavor. Slightly aromatic. Ripens late. *Source History: 1 in 1992; 2 in 2000.* **Sources: Ca15, Cla.**

Burford's Red Flesh - *Source History: 1 in 2000.* **Sources: Or9.**

Burgundy (NY 161) - Monroe x NY 18491 (Macoun x Antonovka). Large, round, blackish red fruit with solid blush, but without stripes. Skin is smooth and glossy. Crisp, subacid flesh with red coloration. Very good eating quality. Annual bearer. Fruits hang well for three weeks after ripe enough to harvest. Storage life is short, no more than one month. Susceptible to scab and mildew. Ripens in mid-September. Hardy to Zone 3. Introduced in 1974. *Source History: 3 in 1988; 9 in 1992; 8 in 2000.* **Sources: Bl4, Ch9, Cu4, Ed5, Fed, Nrs, So5, Stl.**

Burl (Cager) - Southern variety. *Source History: 1 in 2000.* **Sources: Ca15.**

Burning Green - Southern variety. *Source History: 1 in 2000.* **Sources: Ca15.**

Calder Red - *Source History: 1 in 1992; 1 in 2000.* **Sources: Bl4.**

Callaway Crab - Yellow blushed, medium size fruit. Crisp yellow flesh is mildly tart. Good for fresh eating and jelly. Ripens during September. Originated in Callaway Gardens in Georgia. *Source History: 4 in 1992; 3 in 2000.* **Sources: Iso, Jo3, Nrs.**

Calmoutier - Round fruit with red stripes. Crisp white flesh. Good for fresh eating. Does not store well; good for cooking or sauce. Ripens early September. Originated in northern Holmes County, Ohio where early French immigrants first settled. *Source History: 1 in 2000.* **Sources: Sc6.**

Calville Blanc d'Hiver (White Winter Calville) - Medium to large, flat-round, pale green fruit with light red dots on sunny side. Bottom half sharply segmented; segment lines often extend to the stem. Tender, sweet, spicy, flavorful, yellowish white flesh; banana-like aroma. Excellent for sauce, cooking and dessert. More vitamin C than an orange; 35-40 mg per 100 grams. Excellent keeper; turns yellow in storage. Precocious bearer. Susceptible to cedar-apple rust; resistant to scab. Ripens from late October to December. Hardy to Zone 5. Grown by Le Lectier, procureur for Louis XIII. Still served for dessert in fine Paris restaurants. Favorite of Thomas Jefferson. Dates back to 1598. *Source History: 12 in 1988; 15 in 1992; 17 in 2000.* **Sources: Bea, Bl4, Ch9, Cu4, Ea3, Ed5, Gr4, Mi1, Nrs, On3, Or9, Pe2, So5, Son, Wh4, WI4, Wo7.**

Calville Rouge - *Source History: 2 in 1992; 1 in 2000.* **Sources: Ch9.**

Calville Rouge d'Automne (Autumn Red Calville, Strawberry, Switzerland, Autumn Calville, Violette, Red Blandon) - Large fruit is ribbed at the eye and on the body. Yellow skin is flushed pale to deep red. Tender, coarse flesh is white, tinged with red under the skin. Subacid, aromatic flavor. Not for cold, foggy climates. Ripens in September. Likely came from France. First recorded in 1670. *Source History: 1 in 1992; 2 in 2000.* **Sources: Bea, Son.**

Calvin - Yellow fruit. Fine dessert apple and good for cooking. Brought to Kentucky from Virginia over 100 years ago. Was used in making brandy. Ripens in late July. *Source History: 1 in 1988; 2 in 1992; 2 in 2000.* **Sources: Ca15, La3.**

Cameo (Caudle Cultivar) - Chance seedling. Conic fruit shape resembles Delicious but without the bumps on the bottom. Bright red stripe over cream colored background. Firm, crisp flesh with highly appealing subacid, aromatic flavor. Semi-spur tree shows good vigor, precocity and high productivity. Matures one week before Fuji with similar storage quality. Found by Darrel Caudle near Dryden, Washington in 1987. Trademarked. U.S. Plant Patent No. 9068. *Source History: 3 in 2000.* **Sources: Ad2, Va2, WI12.**

Campbell - Southern variety. *Source History: 1 in 2000.* **Sources: Ca15.**

Campfield - Medium to large fruit is yellow blushed and striped with red. Sweet flesh. Ripens late. Good keeper. Hardy. Zones 4-9. Recommended by Coxe for cider. Originated in New Jersey, 1817. *Source History: 1 in 1992; 3 in 2000.* **Sources: Ch9, Cid, Son.**

Canada Red (Nonsuch, Steele's Winter Red) - Bright red fruit with conspicuous dots. Fine grained, crisp, juicy, white flesh. Delicious, agreeable flavor. Very old New England variety known in 1822 as Nonsuch. Once widely grown in Michigan as Steele's Winter Red. Ripens late. *Source History: 3 in 1988; 7 in 1992; 4 in 2000.* **Sources: Bea, Gr4, So5, Wo7.**

Canada Reinette (Reinette Gris du Canada, Canadian Grise) - Medium to large fruit is somewhat ribbed. Yellow skin with irregular patches of russet. Firm, coarse, crisp, juicy flesh. Distinct aroma. Keeps from November to April. Triploid. Originated in France, 1771. *Source History: 2 in 1988; 4 in 1992; 6 in 2000.* **Sources: Bea, Ed5, Leu, Mo19, Or9, Son.**

Canadian Strawberry - Unknown parentage. Originally planted about 100 years ago in Solon, Maine. The only known trees are still living and producing. Medium to large fruit is round to conic. Skin color is buttery yellow with some green background covered about 50% with stripes and spots of vibrant red-orange. Juicy, slightly tart flesh has a distinct flavor. Ripens early fall. Keeps one month. Hardy to Zone 4. Very rare. *Source History: 1 in 2000.* **Sources: Fed.**

Candy Apple - Southern variety. *Source History: 1 in 2000.* **Sources: Ca15.**

Candy Stripe - *Source History: 1 in 2000.* **Sources: Ch9.**

Carolina Pippin - Southern variety. *Source History: 1 in 2000.* **Sources: Ca15.**

Carpentin (Carnation, Carpentin Reinette) - Reinette-type covered with light cinnamon russet and washed with glossy red on the sunny side. Crisp, very juicy flesh. Old apple of German-French origin grown along the Rhine. Thought to have been lost to cultivation. Once grown in the U.S. under the name Carnation. Introduced in 1798. *Source History: 1 in 1988; 2 in 1992; 1 in 2000.* **Sources: So5.**

Carrol County Pound - Very large fruit with striped skin. Ripens late summer. Good for the home orchard. *Source History: 1 in 2000.* **Sources: La3.**

Carroll - Moscow Pear seedling x Melba. Red fruit. Excellent eating apple. Good also for cooking. Strong branching habit. Annual bearer. Ripens early. Hardy to -50 degrees F. with occasional winter injury. *Source History: 3 in 1988; 5 in 1992; 4 in 2000.* **Sources: Ch9, So5, Stl, Va5.**

Carter's Blue - Southern variety. *Source History: 3 in 2000.* **Sources: Ca15, Ch9, Or9.**

Cathead (Kavanagh) - Strictly a cooking and drying apple. Large, long-lived tree. Ripens in September. Hardy to Zone 4. Brought from Ireland by renowned shipbuilder James Kavanagh as a seed or small tree when he moved to Maine. Described in 1688. *Source History: 1 in 1992; 1 in 2000.* **Sources: Fed.**

Cauley - Unknown parentage. Extremely large fruit can weigh one pound each. Skin shows faint red stripes. Crisp, juicy, yellow flesh. High yields. Originated in Grenada, Mississippi. Introduced in 1942. *Source History: 2 in 2000.* **Sources: Ca15, Cla.**

Centennial Crab (MN 1472) - Wealthy x Dolgo crab. Fruiting crab apple. Oval, bright scarlet over yellow fruit. Crisp, juicy, white flesh. Sweet, almost nutty flavor. Good for canning, jelly or fresh eating. Small, compact, natural dwarf tree with horizontal branches. Heavy crops of red flower buds, snowy white blossoms and 1.5-2" fruits. Highly scab resistant. Midseason bloom makes it an excellent pollinator for all other apple varieties. Ripens in mid-August. Zones 2-3. Introduced by the University of Minnesota in 1957. *Source History: 2 in 1988; 14 in 1992; 10 in 2000.* **Sources: Ch9, Cu4, Ed2, Ed5, Fed, Mo19, Rai, SH8, So5, Va5.**

Century 21 - *Source History: 1 in 2000.* **Sources: Bea.**

Cestra Belter Kitaika - *Source History: 1 in 2000.* **Sources: Bea.**

Chamberlain - *Source History: 1 in 1992; 1 in 2000.* **Sources: Ch9.**

Chambers, Hardy - *Source History: 1 in 2000.* **Sources: Er2.**

Champlain (Nyack, Sourbough, Summer Pippin, Calkin's Pippin, Geneva Pearmain, Haverstraw Pippin, Large Golden Pippin, Paper, Paper Skin, Tart Bough, Underdunk, Vermont, Walworth) - Round-conic fruit with pale yellow skin. Fine, tender, juicy flesh. Excellent sprightly flavor. Ripens in August. Old American apple of unknown origin rediscovered by Conrad Gemmer of New Jersey. Introduced in 1850. *Source History: 2 in 1988; 3 in 1992; 1 in 2000.* **Sources: So5.**

Chandler - Originated in Connecticut, 1835. *Source History: 1 in 1988; 1 in 1992; 1 in 2000.* **Sources: Wo7.**

Charette (The Donut Apple) - Possibly brought to Fort Kent, Aroostock County, Maine as a seed, graft or seedling by French Missionaries in the 18th century. Huge, oblate fruit. Blossom end is sunken in toward the stem, so that when sliced perpendicular to the core, the slices resemble a donut. Almost always seedless. Excellent for fresh eating and drying. Ripens late September. *Source History: 1 in 2000.* **Sources: Fed.**

Charlamoff - *Source History: 1 in 2000.* **Sources: Ed5.**

Chataignier - Uniform, attractive, above average apple. Fair to good flavor. Blooms and ripens late. Good for cider blends. *Source History: 1 in 1992; 2 in 2000.* **Sources: Ch9, Hid.**

Cheddar Cross - Allington Pippin x Star of Devon. Green fruit is covered with russet. Creamy white flesh. Subacid to slightly sweet flavor. Dense tree growth; spurs freely. Scab resistant. Ripens in September. Originated in England. Introduced in 1949. *Source History: 1 in 1988; 2 in 1992; 2 in 2000.* **Sources: Ch9, Cu4.**

Chehalis - Large greenish yellow apple, usually with pink blush on exposed side. Resembles Golden Delicious in looks and flavor but larger, crisper and more elongated. Crisp, cream colored flesh. Medium-fine texture. Good baking apple. Moderately vigorous tree is self-pollinating. Highly scab resistant; somewhat mildew resistant. Excellent for organic growers who like a big, sweet, yellow apple. Ripens late September to mid-October. Zones 5-9. Developed north of Chehalis, Washington, near Oakville. *Source History: 5 in 1988; 9 in 1992; 12 in 2000.* **Sources: Bl4, Bu7, Ch9, Clo, Cu4, Ea3, Er2, JOY, ME3, Nrs, Rai, WI4.**

Chenango Strawberry (Buckley, Chenango, Frank, Jackson, Sherwood's Favorite, Smyrna) - Medium to large, long, conical fruit. Shiny, almost translucent skin is smooth, tough, yellowish or greenish white and striped with crimson. Firm, tender, juicy white flesh; mildly subacid and very aromatic. Pick just when the skin begins to develop a milky appearance, or the overripe flesh becomes dry and tasteless. Dessert quality; excellent for all uses. Hardy, long-lived tree; early, regular bearer. Susceptible to fire blight. Ripens over several weeks during August and September. Hardy throughout most of Maine; withstands -40 degrees F. Originated either in Lebanon, New York or brought into Chenango County from Connecticut. Known since 1850. *Source History: 12 in 1988; 16 in 1992; 16 in 2000.* **Sources:**

Bea, Bl4, Ch9, Er2, Gr4, La3, Mi1, Or9, Sc6, So5, Son, Stl, Und, Ur2, Wo7, Wor.

Cherry Cox - Sport of Cox's Orange Pippin from Denmark. Identical to Cox's Orange Pippin except for the dark red skin color. Often shows dark red stripes and splashes on the solid red fruit. Keeps in storage one month longer. Ripens in September. Introduced in 1950. *Source History: 2 in 1988; 5 in 1992; 4 in 2000.* **Sources: Er2, Or9, Rai, So5.**

Cherryville Black - Medium size fruit. Crisp, flavorful, juicy flesh. Ripens in July. Hangs well on the tree. Grown by a family in Cherryville, North Carolina for over 100 years. *Source History: 1 in 2000.* **Sources: Ca15.**

Chesapeake - Open-pollinated seedling of Red Rome. Fruit shape is similar to Red Rome with highly colored skin. Stores without scalding. Medium size tree is vigorous, hardy and productive. Ripens slightly ahead of Rome in September. Discovered in 1958 in Kentucky. Introduced in 1967. *Source History: 2 in 1992; 1 in 2000.* **Sources: Ch9.**

Chesney - Southern variety. *Source History: 1 in 1988; 1 in 1992; 1 in 2000.* **Sources: Ca15.**

Chesney Excellent - *Source History: 1 in 2000.* **Sources: Hid.**

Chestnut Crab (MN 240) - Malinda x Siberian crab apple. Large cooking and dessert crab apple. Attractive, reddish bronze fruit with some russeting. Crisp, juicy, sweet flesh with a pleasing nut-like flavor. Excellent fresh. Vigorous tree is upright but a little weeping. Large white blossoms with good shape and aroma; medium pollen producer. Fruit hangs well and ripens over a long period. Annual bearer. Cedar-apple rust resistant. Hardy to -50 degrees F. with occasional winter injury. Developed at the Minnesota Agricultural Experiment Station, 1946. *Source History: 7 in 1988; 14 in 1992; 9 in 2000.* **Sources: Bea, Ch9, Cu4, Ed5, Fa1, Fed, SH8, Stl, Va5.**

Chieftain - Jonathan x Delicious. Medium size, round, bright red fruit. Firm, juicy white flesh; subacid with flavor milder than Jonathan but more sprightly than Delicious. Dual purpose, high quality. Keeps well in cold storage without developing Jonathan spot. Tree is medium vigorous, hardy and productive. Ripens in early October. Hardy enough to withstand hot summers and cold winters in Iowa. Developed by the Iowa Agricultural Experiment Station. *Source History: 2 in 1988; 5 in 1992; 4 in 2000.* **Sources: Bl4, Ch9, Co2, Nrs.**

Chimney - Southern variety. *Source History: 1 in 2000.* **Sources: Ca15.**

Chinese Golden Early - Unknown parentage. Fruits grow 1.5" with lemon-yellow skin color. Keeps up to 3 weeks. Ripens 1 week before Yellow Transparent; early August. Hardy to Zones 1-2. *Source History: 1 in 1992; 2 in 2000.* **Sources: Bea, Nrs.**

Chipman - Columbia x Melba. Canadian prairie dessert apple with the same shape and flavor as Delicious. Ripens late October; stands frost better than others. Hardy to Zone 3, possibly Zone 2. Named after George C. Chipman, 1944. *Source History: 2 in 2000.* **Sources: Bea, Ed5.**

Chisel Jersey - Bittersweet fruit is green with red flush. Used to make cider of full body, good flavor and aroma. Tree is vigorous; heavy though somewhat biennial bearer. Branch spreaders should be used to avoid narrow crotch angles. Blooms late. *Source History: 1 in 1988; 1 in 1992; 2 in 2000.* **Sources: Cid, Nrs.**

Cinnamon Spice - Medium to small, predominantly wine-red fruit blushed with some yellow. Very rich, sharp cinnamon flavor which lasts in the mouth for some time. Tree shows medium vigor. Upright shoots. Discovered by Living Tree Centre in an ancient planting in the Bolinas-Olema Valley. Ripens in late October. Hardy to Zone 5. *Source History: 1 in 1988; 2 in 1992; 6 in 2000.* **Sources: Bea, Ch9, Ed5, Ga20, Or9, Son.**

Clark's Orange - Southern variety. *Source History: 1 in 2000.* **Sources: Ca15.**

Clingtight - *Source History: 1 in 2000.* **Sources: Ed5.**

CLR11T95 - Conic-shaped yellow fruit with light blush. Crisp, juicy, slightly astringent flesh. Cedar-apple rust resistant. Ripens late September. Trial variety from Purdue University. *Source History: 1 in 2000.* **Sources: Cla.**

CLR13T45 - Green-yellow to yellow skin color with light pink blush. Crisp, breaking, juicy flesh. Coarse to medium texture. Severe fire blight resistance. Light mildew. No cedar-apple rust. Open tree habit. Ripens late October. Trial variety from Purdue University. *Source History: 1 in 2000.* **Sources: Cla.**

CLR20T14 - Round fruit with green to cream ground color, washed 75-100% with medium to dark red. Cream colored flesh is mildly acid, spicy and full flavored. Light to medium mildew susceptibility. Small yields. Ripens early September. Trial variety from Purdue University. *Source History: 1 in 2000.* **Sources: Cla.**

CLR20T22 - Conic to long conic fruit. Yellow background covered with medium to dark red. Crisp, breaking flesh. Mildly to weakly acid. Light to moderate mildew susceptibility. Possibly susceptible to fire blight. Good keeper. Hangs well on the spur-type tree. Ripens mid-September. Trial variety from Purdue University. *Source History: 1 in 2000.* **Sources: Cla.**

CLR22T30 - Short-conic to conic fruit. Green to cream ground color is slightly splashed and striped with light to medium red. Crisp, breaking, medium textured flesh. Sprightly acid, slightly spicy flavor. No cedar-apple rust. No mildew. Light to moderate light fire blight. Ripens mid-August. Trial variety from Purdue University. *Source History: 1 in 2000.* **Sources: Cla.**

CMR2T13 - Large, round to conic, 3" fruit. Moderately striped skin. Juicy, crisp flesh with mildly acid to sweet flavor. Spreading growth habit. No cedar-apple rust or fire blight or mildew. Ripens mid to late August. Trial variety from Purdue University. *Source History: 1 in 2000.* **Sources: Cla.**

Co-op 3 - *Source History: 1 in 2000.* **Sources: Ch9.**

Co-op 27 - Fruit is round to oblate-round; 2.5-3" diameter. Pale yellow ground color is splashed and occasionally mottled with dark red. Fine grained, cream colored flesh is firm and slightly tough at harvest and mellows to firm and moderately crisp in storage. Spicy, sub-acid, full, rich flavor. Good quality. Fruit hangs on the tree well. Moderate to heavy annual cropping. Matures one week after Delicious. Moderately vigorous, full spur type tree with strong branches. Field immune to apple scab and cedar-apple rust; moderately resistant to powdery mildew; highly resistant to fire blight. Trial variety from Purdue University. *Source History: 1 in 2000.* **Sources: Cla.**

Co-op 29 - Winter storage apple. Round to short-conic fruit; 2.75-3" diameter. Pale yellow skin with pink to orange blush. Moderate stem-end russet, occasionally conspicuous. Russeted lenticels. Cream colored flesh is medium to coarse grained; very firm and crisp. Moderate to sprightly sub-acid flavor mellows in storage to spicy, full rich flavor. Retains good quality for five months in refrigerated storage. Fruit hangs well on the tree until overripe. Moderate to heavy cropping. Slightly upright tree with slight tendency to bear fruit in clusters. Tends toward biennial bearing. Matures 2-3 weeks after Delicious. Field immune to apple scab; moderately resists powdery mildew; highly resistant to cedar-apple rust and fire blight. Trial variety from Purdue University. *Source History: 2 in 2000.* **Sources: Cla, Ro3.**

Co-op 31 - Performs best under hot, dry conditions; excellent performance noted in 1988 and 1990 droughts. Large round, green-yellow to yellow fruit finishes to dull to moderate or bright finish. Sometimes splashed and striped, mottled with green in some seasons; 80-99% dark purple-red. 2.25-3" diameter. Very crisp, breaking flesh. Mildly sub-acid, spicy, full rich flavor. Very good quality. Retains flesh texture and quality for six months under refrigeration. Some tendency to drop when ripe. Moderate to heavy cropping; single harvest. Biennial tendency after heavy cropping. Flavor peaks after one month in storage. Moderately vigorous, spreading tree with round top. Field immune to apple scab; moderately resistant to powdery mildew; moderately susceptible to cedar apple rust; good resistance to fire blight; susceptible to rot in storage. Trial variety from Purdue University. *Source History: 2 in 2000.* **Sources: Cla, Ro3.**

Co-op 33 - Round fruit is 75-90% medium to dark red to purple-red over light green ground color at harvest; deep yellow ground color and somewhat orange cast after maturity. Extremely crisp, breaking, yellow flesh is somewhat melting. Medium to fine grained and juicy. Moderately to mildly acid, rich, spicy, full flavor. Flavor declines after two months in storage. Moderate to heavy cropping. Ripens mid-September. Field immune to apple scab; susceptible to rust and mildew; moderately susceptible to fire blight. Trial variety from Purdue University. *Source History: 2 in 2000.* **Sources: Cla, Ro3.**

Co-op 34 - Quality and flavor is similar to Jonathan. Skin is washed 60-80% light to medium red over pale green-yellow ground color at harvest; matures to pale or light yellow. Slightly tough, moderately thick skin. White to cream flesh; slightly crisp; medium grained. Sprightly flavor reduced to moderately acid in storage. Retains texture and quality for three months in refrigerated storage. Annual cropper. Ripens early to mid-October. Field immune to apple scab; highly resistant to rust and fire blight; moderate resistance to mildew. Trial variety from Purdue University. *Source History: 1 in 2000.* **Sources: Cla.**

Co-op 35 - Seedling of Golden Delicious. Oblate-conic to short conic fruit. Green-yellow skin color with moderate orange blush on the sun-exposed surface which matures to yellow. Smooth glossy finish with little russet and inconspicuous lenticels. Moderately thick, slightly tough skin. Cream colored, firm, crisp, breaking flesh. Mildly acid flavor is pleasant and somewhat bland. Retains quality and texture 4-5 months under refrigeration. Moderate bearing with some biennial tendencies. Harvest early to mid-October. Field immune to apple scab; susceptible to rust; high resistance to mildew; moderately resistant to fire blight. Trial vareity from Purdue University. *Source History: 1 in 2000.* **Sources: Cla.**

Co-op 36 - Golden Delicious seedling. Fruit is short conic to conic. Thin, tender skin is pale green-yellow with slight pink blush on sun-exposed surface; matures to pale yellow. Flesh is cream colored, crisp and breaking yet melting, medium grained and juicy. Moderate to mildly acid flavor is rich, fruity and full. Retains texture and quality for 3-4 months under refrigeration. Tends to overcrop if not thinned. Moderately vigorous, slightly upright tree with limited branching; semi-spur type growth habit. Fruit tends to be borne in clusters on relatively short spurs inside the canopy of the tree. Moderate to heavy producer. Ripens October 15-20. Field immune to apple scab; moderately resistant to rust; highly resistant to mildew and fire blight. Trial variety from Purdue University. *Source History: 1 in 2000.* **Sources: Cla.**

<u>Co-op 37</u> - Seedling of Golden Delicious. Short-conic to conic-shaped fruit. Green-yellow skin at harvest with slight orange blush. Matures to yellow. Little russeting; inconspicuous lenticels. Medium to fine grained, pale yellow to cream colored, firm flesh. Juicy and flavorful. Semi-spur type tree. Ripens mid-October. Field immune to scab, susceptible to rust, highly mildew resistant and fireblight resistant. Trial variety from Purdue University. *Source History: 1 in 2000.* **Sources: Cla.**

<u>Co-op 43</u> (Juliet) - Skin shows bright red splashes over cream background. Tart-sweet flavor. Excellent keeper. Moderately vigorous, slightly upright tree. Ripens in early October. Originated in France. *Source History: 1 in 2000.* **Sources: Ro3.**

<u>Coat Jersey</u> - Cider variety. *Source History: 1 in 1988; 1 in 2000.* **Sources: Cid.**

<u>Coconut Crunch</u> - *Source History: 2 in 1992; 1 in 2000.* **Sources: Ch9.**

<u>Coe's Golden Drop</u> (Bishop's Thumb, Coe's Golden, Golden Drop) - Small, flat, conical fruit; yellow blushed with bright crimson. Crisp, yellow flesh; very juicy, brisk, sugary and vinous. Scab resistant. Ripens in late August. Zones 6-9. Originated in England around 1842. *Source History: 2 in 1988; 3 in 1992; 3 in 2000.* **Sources: Ga20, Or9, Son.**

<u>Coffey Seedling</u> - Southern variety. *Source History: 1 in 2000.* **Sources: Ca15.**

<u>Cole's Quince</u> (Quince, Pear Apple, Seneca Favorite, Seneca Spice, Quince of Cole) - Large, ribbed, yellow fruit with a red flush on the sun exposed side. Firm, juicy flesh. Mild, rich, high quince flavor and aroma. Does not store well. Ripens in August. Old Maine apple so named because its shape and color resembles that of a quince. Very rare. Introduced in 1849. *Source History: 3 in 1988; 7 in 1992; 4 in 2000.* **Sources: Bea, Fed, So5, Wo7.**

<u>Coley</u> - *Source History: 1 in 2000.* **Sources: Or9.**

<u>Collett</u> - *Source History: 1 in 1988; 2 in 1992; 2 in 2000.* **Sources: So5, Va5.**

<u>Collins June</u> - Southern variety. *Source History: 1 in 2000.* **Sources: Ca15.**

<u>Colorado Delicious</u> - *Source History: 1 in 2000.* **Sources: Ed5.**

<u>Colvis Spice</u> - *Source History: 1 in 1988; 1 in 1992; 3 in 2000.* **Sources: Ca15, Or9, So5.**

<u>Concord</u> - Fall red apple. *Source History: 1 in 2000.* **Sources: Pi2.**

<u>Connell Red</u> - Red sport of Fireside. McIntosh x Longfield. Large, round, solid red fruit. Sweet, mild, perfumed flesh retains its parent's distinctive flavor; better color. Smaller percentage of small apples. Excellent for eating fresh or cooking. Remarkable keeper, holding its juice and crisp texture into April. Tree is a heavy annual bearer. Ripens in October. Hardy to Zone 3. Discovered in Dunn County, Wisconsin. Introduced in 1957. *Source History: 8 in 1988; 14 in 1992; 9 in 2000.* **Sources: Bea, Ch9, Ed5, Fa1, Hi9, Jun, Mc3, SH8, Stl.**

<u>Cooper's Market</u> - *Source History: 1 in 1992; 2 in 2000.* **Sources: Ch9, Ed5.**

<u>Coos River Beauty</u> - Large, round, red-green to all red fruit. Mild, tender skin. White flesh. Distinctive flavor. Good for fresh eating, applesauce and pie. Average keeper. Heavy bearer. Seems to be disease resistant. Propagated and named by Lorance Eckworth's grandfather who had a nursery on the Coos River in Oregon. *Source History: 2 in 1988; 2 in 1992; 1 in 2000.* **Sources: Gr4.**

<u>Coppertone</u> - *Source History: 1 in 1988; 1 in 1992; 1 in 2000.* **Sources: So5.**

<u>Cornish Gilliflower</u> (Julyflower, Cornish Julyflower) - Old Cornish variety

from England. Fruit is an ugly duckling, usually a dull green with some dull brownish red and webbed with thin rough russet. Only in a rare year do a few develop clear dark red. Round-conic shape, tapering at the base to a 5-pointed nose. Firm yellow flesh has rich, clove-like aroma. Tip bearer on long, thin shoots. Ripens in October. Zones 6-9. Said to have been discovered in a cottage garden in Truro, Cornwall at the end of the 18th century. Considerably older by other accounts. *Source History: 5 in 1988; 6 in 1992; 7 in 2000.* **Sources: Bea, Ch9, Cu4, Gr4, Or9, So5, Son.**

<u>Coromandel Red</u> (Corodel) - Nearly solid-red skin color. Mildly subacid, crisp, juicy flesh. Good storage. Heavy cropper. Annual bearer. Originated in New Zealand. *Source History: 1 in 1992; 1 in 2000.* **Sources: Cu4.**

<u>Cortland</u> - McIntosh x Ben Davis. Widely grown, all-purpose, late McIntosh type; one of the standards. Larger fruit with dark red skin underlaid with stripes. Crisp, pure white flesh resists browning when cut. Tart, tangy flavor. Dessert quality. Excellent for eating, cooking and cider. Vigorous, long-lived tree is annually productive and starts bearing early. Excellent pollinator. Ripens 2-3 weeks before McIntosh; does not drop as readily. Ripens from mid-September to early October depending on location. Hardy to -40 degrees F. in Zones 3-8. Developed at the New York State Agricultural Experiment Station in 1915. *Source History: 34 in 1988; 35 in 1992; 39 in 2000.* **Sources: Ad2, AG2, Amb, Bar, Bea, Bl4, Bo5, Ch9, Co2, Cu4, Fed, Gur, Hi9, JOY, Jun, La3, Leu, Mc3, ME3, Mel, Mi1, MI5, Nrs, Or9, Pi2, Sc6, SH8, So5, Son, St4, TR8, Va2, Wa16, WA8, WAF, Wh4, WI4, Wor, ZEL.**

<u>Cortland, Early</u> - Cortland x Lodi. Large, uniform, 3.5" round fruit; 60% splashed with red striping over light green background. Creamy, semi-firm, white flesh. Slightly more tart than Cortland. Tree is hardy and productive. Growth habits are similar to Cortland; fruit hangs well. Good for both commercial and home orchards. Ripens in early September. Developed at the New York State Agricultural Experiment Station in Geneva by Dr. Roger Way. Introduced in 1982. *Source History: 4 in 1988; 7 in 1992; 5 in 2000.* **Sources: Bea, Ch9, La3, Mi1, Nrs.**

<u>Cortland, Red</u> - *Source History: 1 in 1992; 1 in 2000.* **Sources: Ch9.**

<u>Court Pendu Plat</u> (Wise Apple) - Known by this name in England America; by the name Court Pendu Rouge in France. Very flat fruit with a barely perceptible stem, causing it to lay tight against the branch like a peach. Bright yellow or orange flushed with rose over a fawn russet skin. Antique appearance like Italian marble. Firm, yellow flesh; rich flavor. Hardy, upright tree. Scab resistant. Self-fertile. Ripens in November or December depending on location. Zones 5-9. Known by some as the Wise Apple because it flowers very late, escaping spring frosts. Ancient apple known in the 16th century. *Source History: 3 in 1988; 7 in 1992; 8 in 2000.* **Sources: Bea, Ch9, Gr4, Hid, Or9, So5, Son, Und.**

<u>Court Royal</u> - *Source History: 1 in 2000.* **Sources: Cid.**

<u>Cox's Krummer</u> - *Source History: 1 in 2000.* **Sources: Er2.**

<u>Cox's Orange Pippin</u> (Cox Orange) - Regarded by the British as the finest flavored dessert apple. Medium size, conical fruit with rather dull finish; red stripes over thin, tough, smooth orange skin. Firm, tender, juicy, aromatic, yellow flesh. Distinctive flavor; mellow aftertaste and unsurpassed aroma. Excellent processing apple for desserts, pies, cooking and cider. Keeps from October to January. Tree produces many branches which require thinning; early bearer. Blooms late, missing most frosts. Scab susceptible. Ripens from mid-September to mid-October. Re-

quires 600-800 hours of chilling. Hardy in Zones 4-8. Used as a parent in many breeding programs. Seedling of Ribston Pippin from England in 1830. *Source History: 17 in 1988; 26 in 1992; 30 in 2000.* **Sources: Bay, Bea, Bl4, Ch9, Cid, CO5, Cu4, Ea3, Ed5, Fed, Ga20, GR26, Gr4, LA4, Leu, ME3, Mi1, Nrs, On3, Or9, Pe2, Ro3, Sc6, So5, Son, Ur2, Wh4, WI4, Wo7, Wor.**

Coyle - *Source History: 1 in 1992; 1 in 2000.* **Sources: Ch9.**

CQR10T17 - Short-conic to conic fruit. Yellow ground color splashed 50-100% with red, showing a slight orange cast. Very crisp, breaking, slightly hard, cream colored flesh. Mildly acid, spicy and full flavored. Light cropper. Light mildew. No cedar-apple rust. Slightly open calyx. Some watercore. Ripens mid-September. Trial variety from Purdue University. *Source History: 1 in 2000.* **Sources: Cla.**

Craft - Possibly Layman's Large Summer. Green skin color. Blooms midseason. *Source History: 1 in 2000.* **Sources: Hid.**

Cranberry Pippin - *Source History: 2 in 2000.* **Sources: Ch9, Or9.**

Crandell - Rome Beauty x Jonathan. Medium red fruit. Crisp, juicy flesh. Good for dessert and culinary uses. Developed at the Illinois Agricultural Experiment Station. *Source History: 1 in 1988; 1 in 1992; 1 in 2000.* **Sources: So5.**

Crimson Beauty - Fameuse family. Red striped fruit. Juicy, white flesh. Nice tart flavor. Good for sauce and cooking. Productive, early bearing tree. Ripens very early, about eight or ten days ahead of Lodi. Hardy to -50 degrees F. with occasional winter injury. *Source History: 3 in 1988; 4 in 1992; 3 in 2000.* **Sources: Nrs, Sc6, Stl.**

Crimson Gold - Small to medium size red fruit covered with a dusky bloom. When quartered or sliced and then boiled, the flesh remains solid and takes on a golden yellow color stained red on the edges by the skin, resembling canned cling peaches. Excellent flavor. Ripens late. Originally named Rosy Bloom. *Source History: 1 in 1988; 1 in 1992; 2 in 2000.* **Sources: Gr4, Nrs.**

Crimson King - Cider variety. *Source History: 1 in 2000.* **Sources: Cid.**

Crimson Spire, Stark (Obelisk Cultivar) - Crimson-red skin color. Clean, white flesh with crisp, tangy taste. Harvest in mid-September in Zone 5. Originally from the Stark Colonnade collection. Trademarked. U.S. Plant Patent No. 9060. *Source History: 2 in 2000.* **Sources: MO10, St4.**

Criterion - Cross between Red Delicious, Yellow Delicious and Winter Banana. Red Delicious shape; Yellow Delicious character. Yellowish green skin with a beautiful, distinctive reddish pink blush. Mildly sweet flesh. Good for fresh eating, cooking, freezing, drying or canning. Excellent keeper. Heavy producer; very hardy. Ripens during October. Hardy to Zone 5. Introduced in 1973. U.S. Plant Patent No. 3505. *Source History: 3 in 1988; 6 in 1992; 5 in 2000.* **Sources: Bea, Ch9, Ed5, Mi1, Or9.**

Criterion, Par-Fect Spur (Fechtig Cultivar) - Green to yellow skin blushed with light pink to dark rose. Aromatic, sweet flavor. Extra firmness reduces bruising. Excellent storage life. Matures about two weeks before Criterion. U.S. Plant Patent No. 6043. *Source History: 1 in 1992; 1 in 2000.* **Sources: TR8.**

Croncel - *Source History: 1 in 1992; 1 in 2000.* **Sources: Ch9.**

Crow Egg (Raven Egg) - Pale-yellow or green skin has a faint bronze blush with russet dots. Large core. Tree is spreading and vigorous with long, slender, crooked branches. Ripens in late September and early October. Introduced in 1800. *Source History: 3 in 1992; 4 in 2000.* **Sources: Bea, Ca15, Cu4, Wo7.**

Crow's Egg - Old Southern variety. Dark red, elongated fruit. Grown mostly in western North Carolina and Virginia. Not to be confused with Crow Egg. *Source History: 2 in 2000.* **Sources: Ca15, Or9.**

Crown Jewell - *Source History: 2 in 1992; 2 in 2000.* **Sources: Ch9, Ed5.**

CRR1T73 - Round to oblate-round fruit. Green-yellow ground color; 85% medium to dark purple-red overlay. Mildly acid, spicy and full flavored flesh. Very good quality. Light mildew, moderate frogeye leafspot. Ripens mid-September. Trial variety from Purdue University. *Source History: 1 in 2000.* **Sources: Cla.**

CTR10T38 - Short conic, bright yellow fruit. Light blush; light stem end russet; inconspicuous lenticels. Fine textured, crisp flesh. Mildly acid and spicy. Very good quality. Moderate cedar rust. Ripens mid to late October. Trial variety from Purdue University. *Source History: 1 in 2000.* **Sources: Cla.**

Cullasaga - Southern variety. *Source History: 1 in 2000.* **Sources: Ca15.**

Cumberland, Hardy - *Source History: 1 in 2000.* **Sources: Cla, Hid.**

D'Arcy Spice (D'Arcy, Baddow Pippin, Essex Spice, Spice, Spice Apple, Spring Ribston, Winter Ribston) - The rough textured, yellow-green skin is flushed a dull red with russet patches and dots. Greenish white flesh is fine grained and crisp. Sweet, rich, vinous flavor. Scab resistant. Stores well. Slow growing tree. Tendency to biennial bearing. Blossoms have some resistance to frost damage. Ripens in October. Zones 5-9. Originated in England. Dates back to 1785. Introduced in 1848. *Source History: 1 in 1988; 1 in 1992; 1 in 2000.* **Sources: Son.**

D-14-97 - Conic, red, 3" fruit. Bright white flesh is crisp, juicy and mild. Hangs well on the tree. Excellent appearance and flavor. Heavy cropper. Ripens late August. Trial variety from Purdue University. *Source History: 1 in 2000.* **Sources: Cla.**

Dabinett - Medium to large, round fruit with dull red flush over green. Bittersweet flesh. Small spreading tree. Blooms late. Cider apple. Ripens in late October. *Source History: 2 in 1988; 2 in 1992; 3 in 2000.* **Sources: Cid, Or9, So5.**

Dakota - Wealthy x Whitney. Large, dark red fruit. Good for fresh eating. Keeps for one month. Hardy. Ripens early September. Zone 3. Mandan Field Station introduction. *Source History: 2 in 1992; 2 in 2000.* **Sources: Ed5, Va5.**

Dakota Gold - Unknown parentage, possibly Golden Delicious. Large yellow fruit. Good dessert, sauce and pie apple. Hardy, vigorous tree bears annually. Resists fire blight. Keeps one week. Ripens late August. Developed at North Dakota State University. *Source History: 2 in 2000.* **Sources: Ed5, Stl.**

Daughter of Susie - *Source History: 1 in 2000.* **Sources: Hid.**

Dauphin (Rosybloom) - Canadian prairie apple. Small fruit. Yellow skin with red streaks. Mild flavor. Produces early. Hardy to Zone 3, possibly Zone 2. Introduced in 1928. *Source History: 1 in 2000.* **Sources: Ed5.**

Davenport Russet - *Source History: 1 in 1988; 1 in 1992; 1 in 2000.* **Sources: So5.**

Davey - Seedling of McIntosh discovered in 1928 by S. Lothrop Davenport, Director of Worcestershire County Horticultural Society's orchard of old American apple varieties. Highly colored red fruit. High quality; distinctive flavor. Baldwin texture and keeping qualities. Keeps all winter. Resistant to scab. Awarded first-class certificate in 1945 by Massachusetts Horticultural Society. *Source History: 3 in 1988; 7 in 1992; 5 in 2000.* **Sources: Ch9, Ed5, So5, Stl, Wo7.**

Davidson Sweeting - Southern variety. *Source History: 1 in 2000.* **Sources: Ca15.**

Davies - *Source History: 1 in 1992; 1 in 2000.* **Sources: Bl4.**

Davis - Large fruit. Keeps well. Ripens in October. Originated in Mississippi. *Source History: 2 in 2000.* **Sources: Ca15, Hid.**

Dayton - Medium to large fruit with 90% glossy red over yellow. Pale yellow flesh. Refrigerated storage life at one month. Scab resistant. Moderately resistant to powdery mildew and fire blight. Ripens in September. U.S. Plant Patent No. 5584. *Source History: 12 in 1992; 5 in 2000.* **Sources: Bu7, Ch9, Cla, Cu4, Rai.**

Deacon Jones - Originated in Pennsylvania. Introduced in 1892. *Source History: 1 in 1992; 3 in 2000.* **Sources: Ch9, Cu4, Wo7.**

Deaderick (Ozark Pippin) - Southern variety. *Source History: 1 in 2000.* **Sources: Ca15.**

Dean Watt's Scion - Seedling favorite of the former Pennsylvania State Professor of Pomology. *Source History: 1 in 1988; 2 in 1992; 1 in 2000.* **Sources: Ch9.**

Dearborn's Unknown - Possible cross of Rescue x Chinese Golden Early x Summered by Dr. Curtis Dearborn of Alaska. Red-orange blush over a light yellow background. Firm, juicy, slightly yellow flesh. Good for fresh eating. Stands heat and keeps well. Ripens early August. Hardy to Zone 4. *Source History: 1 in 2000.* **Sources: Bea.**

Delicates - *Source History: 1 in 2000.* **Sources: Ch9.**

Delicious, Hyatt Original - *Source History: 1 in 2000.* **Sources: Cu4.**

Delicious, Original - Faint pink stripes on greenish yellow background. More elongated and flavorful than Red Delicious. Used as a parent line in breeding dozens of modern variants. *Source History: 2 in 1988; 2 in 1992; 1 in 2000.* **Sources: Ch9.**

Delicious, Schlect Spur - Very early coloring sport. Blush color begins in June; reaches full color by mid-August. Crisp, juicy, white flesh. C and O Nursery exclusive variety. *Source History: 1 in 1992; 1 in 2000.* **Sources: Co2.**

Delicious, Standard (Starking Standard Delicious) - Parent of Red Delicious. Green skin with red stripes; familiar elongated shape and five points at the bottom. Very crisp flesh; superior flavor. Good storage. Medium size tree. Ripens late. Zones 6-10. *Source History: 1 in 1988; 2 in 1992; 2 in 2000.* **Sources: Nrs, Son.**

Delicious, Sweet - Large, greenish yellow fruit flushed reddish orange with red streaks. Firm, fine creamy white flesh. Sweet, aromatic flavor. Excellent keeper. Medium-large tree. Ripens late. Zones 5-10. Originated in New York in 1911. *Source History: 1 in 1988; 2 in 1992; 3 in 2000.* **Sources: Bl4, Sc6, Son.**

Delightabite - *Source History: 1 in 2000.* **Sources: Ch9.**

Detroit Red (Detroit, Crimson Pippin) - Classic, deep red apple. Soft, snow white flesh. Curious ridges about the calyx. North Georgia favorite for sauce. Bears young and annually. Some disease resistance. Ripens in late July. Described in 1845. *Source History: 4 in 1988; 6 in 1992; 5 in 2000.* **Sources: Bl4, Gr4, Jo3, La3, Or9.**

Devonshire Quarrendon (Red Quarrendon, Sack Apple) - Very old English variety. Medium size, dark-red fruit, except under a leaf shadow where it is sharply defined green. White flesh sometimes stained with red. Refreshing vinous flavor. Must be picked at exactly the right time as it ripens in the heat. Ripens in August. *Source History: 2 in 1988; 2 in 1992; 1 in 2000.* **Sources: So5.**

Discovery - Medium size, brilliant red-striped fruit. Crisp flesh; excellent flavor. Early season eating and market apple. Good for fresh eating or sauce. Not a keeper; fruit tends to crack. Hardy compact tree is a natural semi-dwarf. Shy tip bearer; bears fruit second or third year. Some resistance to scab. Pollinate with

Gravenstein, Lodi or Summer Red. Ripens from early to mid-August depending on location. Hardy in Zone 4. Originated in England around 1900 as Thurston August; renamed Discovery in 1962. *Source History: 6 in 1988; 8 in 1992; 6 in 2000.* **Sources: Bea, Ch9, Ed5, Er2, ME3, Rai.**

Dixie Red Delite - Large, red fruit good for fresh eating. Dependable bearer. Southern variety. *Source History: 1 in 1992; 1 in 2000.* **Sources: Ca15.**

Doctor - Very old Germantown, Pennsylvania apple named in honor of a physician. Yellow fruit marked with carmine splashes; crisp, mild, aromatic flesh. Believed to have been lost from cultivation but recently rediscovered by Conrad D. Gemmer of New Jersey. Ripens in October. *Source History: 1 in 1988; 1 in 1992; 1 in 2000.* **Sources: So5.**

Dodd's Banana - *Source History: 1 in 1992; 1 in 2000.* **Sources: Ch9.**

Dolgo Crab - Siberian crab. Juicy, 1.5" olive-shaped, crimson fruits. Name means "long" in Russian, referring to fruit shape. Highly flavored; rich in pectin. Makes ruby red jelly; ideal for canning, preserving whole. Fair keeper. Sturdy, vigorous, upright, spreading, open tree; can grow 40' tall by 30' wide. Dense, reddish green foliage; willowy branches. Dependable, abundant crops. Large, white flowers. Resistant to cedar-apple rust, mildew, scab, sun scald and fire blight. Ripens in late August or September. Requires 400 hours of chilling. Hardy in Zone 2. Imported from Russia by Professor Hansen of South Dakota. Introduced in 1897. *Source History: 26 in 1988; 48 in 1992; 38 in 2000.* **Sources: Arb, Bea, Bo5, Bu7, Ch9, CLI, CO5, Cu4, Ea3, Fa1, Fed, Fil, GI3, GR26, Gr4, Hi9, Ho5, Iso, Jo3, LA4, LI7, Mc3, MI5, Nrs, On3, ORA, Rai, SH8, So5, Son, Stl, Ty2, Va5, Wa16, WA8, We8, Wel, WI4.**

Domaine - Cider variety. *Source History: 1 in 2000.* **Sources: Cu4.**

Domine - Southern variety. Introduced in 1831. *Source History: 1 in 1992; 2 in 2000.* **Sources: Ca15, Wo7.**

Dorsett Golden - Developed in the Bahamas from Golden Delicious. Medium size, golden yellow apple for warm winter areas. Crisp, firm, sweet flesh; often seedless. Good for fresh eating, cooking, canning and freezing. Stores up to three months without getting mealy. Upright, vigorous, early bearing tree. Self-fruitful. Excellent yellow apple for southern and coastal areas; productive throughout southern California and the Phoenix, Arizona area. Reported to produce fruit in tropical areas. Ripens from June to July depending on location. Chilling requirement very low, less than 100 hours. Zones 5-9. *Source History: 18 in 1988; 31 in 1992; 22 in 2000.* **Sources: Bar, Bay, CO5, Cum, GI3, Ho5, Iso, Jo3, Ju2, On4, ORA, Pa2, RA4, SIM, Son, STR, Tex, Ty2, WA8, Wel, WI4, Wom.**

Douglas Wormless - Stone x Duchess. Red-yellow fruit. Good keeper. Ripens in mid-season. Resistant to tent caterpillar and scab. Hardy to -50 degrees F. with occasional winter injury. *Source History: 1 in 1988; 1 in 1992; 1 in 2000.* **Sources: Stl.**

Doux Normandie - *Source History: 1 in 2000.* **Sources: Cid.**

Downingland - Golden Delicious x Cox Rome Beauty. Medium size fruit with yellow skin, nearly covered with deep red to crimson. Develops color when left on the tree. Good keeper. Very susceptible to fire blight. Ripens in September. Developed in Ohio. Introduced in 1934. *Source History: 1 in 1988; 1 in 1992; 1 in 2000.* **Sources: Bea.**

Dr. Bush's Sweet Apple - Southern variety. *Source History: 1 in 2000.* **Sources: Ca15.**

Dr. Matthews - Red and red-striped fruit. Fine crisp, juicy, creamy white flesh. Mild but sprightly, aromatic flavor. Excellent keeper. Ripens in September. Indiana apple of unknown origin. Introduced in 1899. *Source History: 2 in 1988; 4 in 1992; 4 in 2000.* **Sources: Bea, Ca15, Er2, So5.**

Duchess of Oldenburg (Borovinka, New Brunswick, Queen Mary, Smith's Beauty of Newark) - Grandparent of Northern Spy and McIntosh. Commonly called Duchess. Known in Europe as Borovitski or Charlamowsky. Medium size, flat, rectangular fruit. Thick, glossy, greenish to pale yellow skin almost covered with crimson stripes and splashes. Almost too tart to eat fresh; makes excellent pies and sauces. Becomes mealy if overripe. Poor keeper. Medium size, spreading, extremely hardy, long-lived, heat resistant tree. Annual producer; bears when young. Resistant to apple scab, cedar-apple rust and fire blight. Tolerates moist or heavy soils. Ripens during August. Zones 3-7. Originated in Russia; brought from England in 1835. *Source History: 13 in 1988; 14 in 1992; 17 in 2000.* **Sources: Bea, Bl4, Ch9, Cu4, Fed, Gr4, Hi9, Jun, Mc3, Mi1, Or9, So5, Son, Stl, Und, WI12, Wor.**

Duchess, Red (Red Duchess of Oldenburg) - Displays better coloring than the old Duchess of Oldenburg; retains the same hardiness. Striped with cherry red color. Tart, tangy, juicy flesh. Good for fresh eating, pies or applesauce. Only keeps well for two weeks. Ripens during August. Hardy in Zone 3. Popular for both home and commercial orchards. *Source History: 3 in 1988; 9 in 1992; 3 in 2000.* **Sources: Ed5, Fa1, SH8.**

Dudley (Dudley Winter, North Star, Dudley's Winter) - Open-pollinated seedling of Duchess of Oldenburg. Medium-large, uniform fruit. Bright greenish yellow skin splashed and striped with red. Yellow-tinged flesh; firm, crisp, very juicy. Briskly subacid flavor becoming mild in storage. Excellent for sauce and baking. Reasonable keeper. Moderately vigorous tree; very hardy and productive. Hardy to -50 degrees F. Developed in Maine. Introduced in 1891. *Source History: 3 in 1988; 4 in 1992; 3 in 2000.* **Sources: Bea, Ed5, Fed.**

Dufflin - Cider variety. *Source History: 1 in 2000.* **Sources: Cu4.**

Duke of Devonshire - *Source History: 1 in 2000.* **Sources: Bea.**

Dula Beauty - Southern variety. *Source History: 1 in 2000.* **Sources: Ca15.**

Dumelow (Dumelow's Seedling, Wellington (English)) - Large cooking apple with coarse, highly acidic flesh. Thinning is necessary to increase fruit size. Ripens in September. Originated in England around 1800. *Source History: 2 in 1992; 1 in 2000.* **Sources: Wo7.**

Dunkerton's Late Sweet - *Source History: 1 in 2000.* **Sources: Cid.**

Dunning - Cox's Orange Pippin x McIntosh. Red fruit. Sweet nonacid flavor. Good quality. Ripens in early August. Developed at the New York State Agricultural Experiment Station. Introduced in 1938. *Source History: 2 in 1988; 3 in 1992; 2 in 2000.* **Sources: Bea, Ch9.**

Dyer (Golden Spice, Pomme Royal, Bard Apple, Beard Burden, Bullripe, Coe's Spice, Pomme Water, Smithfield Spice, White Spice, Woodstock) - Medium size fruit is greenish yellow with a shade of red, covered with veins of russet. Spicy flavor. Ripens in late summer. Originated in France in the 1600s. *Source History: 2 in 1988; 3 in 1992; 3 in 2000.* **Sources: Ed5, Or9, Wo7.**

Dymock Red - Cider variety. *Source History: 1 in 2000.* **Sources: Cid.**

Earliest (Stark's Earliest) - Ripens from July to August. *Source History: 1 in 1988; 3 in 1992; 1 in 2000.* **Sources: Ch9.**

Earligold - Uniform, medium to large, round-conical fruit. Smooth, whitish green skin. High fruit solids and high acid levels. Good eating and cooking apple. Early, annual producer. Self-pollinating and a good pollinator for other varieties. Less susceptible to fire blight than Lodi or Transparent. Longer storage life with full retention of quality. Trademarked. U.S. Plant Patent No. 4820. *Source History: 1 in 1988; 2 in 1992; 3 in 2000.* **Sources: Ch9, Co2, Ed5.**

Early Blaze (Earliblaze) - Old-timer. Ripens from July to August depending on location. *Source History: 2 in 1988; 3 in 1992; 1 in 2000.* **Sources: Ch9.**

Early Blaze, Starkspur (Mooney Cultivar) - Smooth striped, cherry-red fruit. Strong tree doubles as a consistent pollinator and heavy bearer of juicy 3" apples. Plant with Stark Summer Treat or Starkrimson Red Delicious. Ripens in mid-August. Hardy in Zones 5-8.Trademarked. *Source History: 1 in 1988; 1 in 1992; 2 in 2000.* **Sources: Bea, St4.**

Early Dawn - Low chill apple. Medium size, yellow fruit blushed with red. Aromatic, sweet-tart flavor. Flesh slow to discolor when sliced. Vigorous, beautiful tree. Ripens in August. Requires 250 hours of chilling. Developed by L. D. Claypool in Ontario, California. U.S. Plant Patent No. 4956. *Source History: 2 in 1988; 2 in 1992; 1 in 2000.* **Sources: Pa2.**

Early Harvest (Canada, Early French Reinette, Early July Pippin, Early June, July Pippin, Prince's Early Harvest, Sinclair's Yellow, Tart Bough, Prince's Harvest, Bracken, Glass Apple) - High-yielding golden cooking apple. Round, medium size fruit. Pale yellow skin with slight blush of brownish orange and white dots. Crisp, tender, creamy white flesh. Subacid flavor. Good quality fruit. Bruises readily. Fine for pies; especially good for sauce. Becomes agreeable for dessert when fully ripe. Erect, high yielding tree grows fast and bears young. Ripens from July to September depending on location. Hardy to -50 degrees F. Originated in America. Existed in 1800 according to the National Apple Register of the United Kingdom. *Source History: 16 in 1988; 16 in 1992; 18 in 2000.* **Sources: Bar, Bea, Bl4, Ca15, Ch9, Cu4, Ed5, Er2, Gr4, La3, Na4, Or9, Sc6, So5, Stl, Ur2, Wo7, Wor.**

Early Joe - Small, round, red-striped fruit. Crisp, juicy flesh. Rich pear-like flavor. Requires optimum conditions to produce good fruit. Susceptible to scab. Ripens from July to August depending on location. Came from the same seedling orchard which produced Northern Spy and Melon; planted in the Chapin orchard in East Bloomfield, New York. Introduced in 1800. *Source History: 3 in 1988; 6 in 1992; 5 in 2000.* **Sources: Bea, Bl4, Ca15, So5, Wo7.**

Early Red - *Source History: 1 in 1988; 1 in 1992; 1 in 2000.* **Sources: So5.**

Early Red Delight - Southern variety. *Source History: 1 in 2000.* **Sources: Ca15.**

Early Redbird - Southern variety. *Source History: 1 in 2000.* **Sources: Ca15.**

Early Ripe - Old-time southern variety. *Source History: 1 in 1988; 1 in 1992; 1 in 2000.* **Sources: Ca15.**

Early Sauce - *Source History: 1 in 2000.* **Sources: Bea.**

Early Strawberry - Small, solid, rich, dark red fruit. Crisp, yellowish flesh sometimes streaked with red. Sprightly, aromatic flavor. Ripens from July to August depending on location. Originated in New York before 1838. Introduced in 1800. *Source History: 3 in 1988; 4 in 1992; 5 in 2000.* **Sources: Ca15, Ch9, Gr4, So5, Wo7.**

Eastman Sweet - Attractive, red, striped fruit. Rich, sweet, yellowish flesh. Long-lived tree bears heavily. Ripens late. Hardy to -50 degrees F. Old native variety; origin unknown. *Source History: 1 in 1988; 2 in 1992; 2 in 2000.* **Sources: Ch9, Stl.**

Edore - *Source History: 1 in 1992; 2 in 2000.* **Sources: Ch9, Ed5.**

Edward VII (King Edward, King Edward VII) - Golden Noble x Blenheim Orange. Large, smooth, waxy, shiny green or yellow fruit with brownish red blush. Extremely firm, tart, juicy, yellow flesh. Blooms late. Ripens in October. Some resistance to scab. Zones 4-9. Named in 1902 after the new English monarch and since grown in English gardens. Imported from England. Introduced in 1908. *Source History: 2 in 1988; 5 in 1992; 5 in 2000.* **Sources: Bea, Ch9, Or9, Rai, So5.**

Edwards' Winter - Southern variety. *Source History: 1 in 2000.* **Sources: Ca15.**

Egremont Russet - Prized as the most delicious of the English russets. Small, round, golden brown russet fruit often with black spots or markings. Greenish yellow, richly flavored flesh resembles Gravenstein. Very high quality. Like all russets, it is a good keeper. Upright growing tree is a heavy spur bearer and regular cropper. Fruit size decreases as the tree ages and the quality will vary from year to year. Ripens in October. Hardy to -40 degrees F. Originated in England, but history unknown. Introduced in 1880. *Source History: 3 in 1988; 8 in 1992; 9 in 2000.* **Sources: Bea, Bl4, Ch9, Cu4, Ed5, Rai, So5, Son, Stl.**

Egyptian - *Source History: 1 in 2000.* **Sources: Or9.**

Ein Shemer - Large, low chilling, Golden Delicious type from Israel. Yellow fruit with slight tinge of blush. Refreshing, crisp, sweet-tart flavor; more tart than Golden Delicious. Strong, early bearing, prolific scab resistant tree. Somewhat self-pollinating, but yields are improved when pollinated with Dorsett Golden. Good pollinator for Anna. Ripens from early to late June depending on location. Requires from 100-400 hours of chilling. Good for hotter areas of the South; Zones 8-9. *Source History: 12 in 1988; 23 in 1992; 15 in 2000.* **Sources: Bay, CO5, Cum, FO10, GI3, Ho5, MI5, Nrs, ORA, Pa2, SIM, Tex, Ty2, Wel, WI4.**

Elah - Skin color is bright yellow splashed with a heavy pink blush. Fine grained, crisp flesh. Sweet flavor. Disease resistant variety. Ripens from mid-June to late July. Pollinate with Maayan or Michal. *Source History: 1 in 1992; 1 in 2000.* **Sources: Ju2.**

Ellis Bitter - Cider variety. *Source History: 2 in 2000.* **Sources: Cid, Cu4.**

Ellison's Orange (Ellison's Orange Pippin, Ellison) - Cox Orange x Calville Blanc d'Ete. Medium size, oblong, golden yellow dessert fruit with crimson stripes and a slight flush. Tender, juicy, yellow flesh. Sweet, aromatic flavor. Tendency to biennial bearing. Subject to canker; resistant to scab. Ripens midseason. First recorded in England in 1904. Introduced in 1911. *Source History: 3 in 1988; 4 in 1992; 2 in 2000.* **Sources: Bl4, So5.**

Elstar - Golden Delicious x Ingrid Marie. Medium to large, round, yellow fruit with 80% light red stripe. Firm, cream colored flesh. Very good for fresh eating and cooking. Flavor increases with about four weeks of storage. Appearance and eating quality similar to Jonagold; better keeper than Jonagold. Ripens late September to mid-October. Zones 5-9. Developed in Holland in 1955. Introduced to the U.S. in 1972. Very popular in Europe. U.S. Plant Patent No. 6450. *Source History: 3 in 1988; 6 in 1992; 6 in 2000.* **Sources: Ch9, Clo, Er2, Rai, Son, WI4.**

Emerald Spire, Stark (Tuscan Cultivar) - Columnar tree form. White flowers tinged with pink. Green skin color blushed with gold. Ripens mid-September.

Originally from the Stark Colonnade collection. Trademarked. U.S. Plant Patent No. 6225. *Source History: 2 in 2000.* **Sources: MO10, St4.**

Emerging Blaze - Southern variety. *Source History: 1 in 2000.* **Sources: Ca15.**

Emperor Alexander - Ripens in September. *Source History: 2 in 1988; 2 in 1992; 1 in 2000.* **Sources: So5.**

Empire - McIntosh x Red Delicious. McIntosh type with better color and flavor, longer shelf life and refrigerated keeping ability. Medium size, round, firmer, darker, waxy fruit. Creamy white, crisp, juicy, moderately subacid flesh. High quality dessert apple; also good for cider. Vigorous, upright, early bearing tree; strong, wide crotch angles. Tendency toward spur-type habit. Sets heavy bloom; produces annually. Needs some thinning. Fruit hangs on tree longer than McIntosh. Somewhat self-fruitful. Ripens two weeks after McIntosh. Requires 800 hours of chilling. Hardy in Zones 4-7 and to -30 degrees F. Developed at the Geneva Station in 1945. Introduced in 1966. *Source History: 26 in 1988; 35 in 1992; 30 in 2000.* **Sources: AG2, Amb, Bay, Bea, Bl4, Ch9, Co2, Cu4, Ea3, Ga20, GR26, Hi9, Iso, Jo3, Jun, Leu, Mi1, Mo19, Nrs, Sc6, SH8, So5, Son, St4, TR8, Wa16, WAF, Wh4, WI4, Wor.**

Empire, Crown (Crist Cultivar) - Red blush sport shows full red color two weeks ahead of Empire. Intense flavor. Trees show somewhat less vigor than Empire but are a better annual bearer. Discovered at Crist Brothers Orchard, Walden, New York, 1990. Plant patent applied for. *Source History: 1 in 2000.* **Sources: Ad2.**

Empire, Royal (Teeple Red Empire Cultivar) - Whole limb sport of Empire. Similar to Empire in all respects except for earlier coloring. Vigorous, upright tree has good crotch angles. Ripens during October. Developed in New York. U.S. Plant Patent No. 7820. Introduced in 1990. *Source History: 2 in 1992; 9 in 2000.* **Sources: Ad2, AG2, Bo5, Co2, Cu4, St4, Va2, WAF, WI12.**

Empire, Thome (TF-808 Cultivar) - Sport of Empire that colors to a deep burgundy three weeks earlier than standard Empire; other characteristics the same. Non-spur tree. Discovered at Thome Farms, Comstock Park, Michigan. Trademarked. U.S. Plant Patent No. 8010. *Source History: 3 in 1992; 2 in 2000.* **Sources: AG2, Hi9.**

Empress (New York 651) - Jonamac x Vista Bella cross. Medium size fruit is 90% red. Excellent eating quality. Tree habit is round but not vigorous. Resembles Empire but ripens a month sooner. Released by New York State Fruit Testing Association. Plant patent applied for. Introduced in 1988. *Source History: 6 in 1992; 2 in 2000.* **Sources: Ch9, Mo19.**

English Beauty (American Nonpareil, Cling Tight, Cheat, Domine, English Rambo, English Winter Red Streak, Hogan, Well Apple, Wells, Williamson) - Fruit resembles Summer Rambo in appearance, but has more color and is a long keeping winter apple. Medium to large fruit has yellow-green skin mottled and striped with red. Flesh is coarse, tender and juicy. Vigorous tree sets heavy crops biennially. Ripens in October. First noted in 1831. *Source History: 1 in 1988; 2 in 1992; 1 in 2000.* **Sources: So5.**

English Redstreak - Southern variety. *Source History: 1 in 2000.* **Sources: Ca15.**

Enigma - *Source History: 1 in 2000.* **Sources: Er2.**

Enos - Southern variety. *Source History: 1 in 2000.* **Sources: Ca15.**

Enterprise (Co-op 30) - Medium-large, deep red fruit with good keeping qualities. Late bloom. Annual bearer. High quality storage apple. Immune to apple
scab, highly resistant to fireblight and cedar apple rust and moderately resistant to
powdery mildew. Ripens mid-October; two weeks after Red Delicious. Zones 4-9.
Developed by Purdue University. U.S. Plant Patent No. 9193. *Source History: 13
in 2000.* **Sources: Ad2, AG2, Bo5, Bu7, Cla, Clo, Cu4, Ed2, Hi9, Rai, Ro3, St4,
TR8.**

Erickson (Ericson) - *Source History: 1 in 1988; 1 in 1992; 2 in 2000.* **Sources:
Fed, So5.**

Erwin Baur - Lightly striped red over yellow fruit. Especially hard and crisp
flesh. High flavor of Cox's Orange Pippin. Ripens late September to early October.
Open-pollinated seedling of Oldenburg discovered in Muncheberg, Germany near
Berlin. Named after the founder of the Institute of Plant Breeding in that town.
Introduced in 1928. *Source History: 2 in 1988; 5 in 1992; 6 in 2000.* **Sources:
Bl4, Ch9, Cu4, Ed5, So5, Und.**

Esopus Spitzenburg (Esopus) - Thomas Jefferson's favorite; dessert apple for
connoisseurs. Medium to large, round-conical, orangish fruit with tough skin, russet dots and inconspicuous stripes. Crisp, fine grained, spicy, juicy, yellowish flesh.
Rich, aromatic flavor. Ripens unevenly; hangs well into November. Average to
good when tree ripe; radically improves in storage. Best at Christmas; keeps until
May. Distinctive slender growth habit; long, willowy hanging limbs. Tends to bear
biennially. Pollinator required. Susceptible to fire blight, scab and canker. Ripens
during October. Requires 800 hours of chilling. Hardy in Zones 4-8. Originated in
Esopus, New York. Introduced in 1790. *Source History: 21 in 1988; 28 in 1992;
33 in 2000.* **Sources: Bay, Bea, Bl4, Bu7, Ca15, Ch9, Cid, Cla, Cu4, Ea3, Fed,
Ga20, Gr4, Hid, Jo3, JOY, La3, Leu, ME3, Mi1, Nrs, On3, Or9, Pe2, Ro3, Sc6,
So5, Son, Ur2, Wh4, WI4, Wo7, Wor.**

Etter's Gold - Wagener x Transcendent Crab. Medium to large, greenish yellow
fruit ripening to a clear golden color. Excellent eating quality. Good for cooking.
Flesh remains crisp and juicy even after months in storage. Reliable annual producer with spur-type growth habit. Outstanding productivity. Requires cross-
pollination. Ripens midseason. Requires 600 or less hours of chilling. Known to
produce good fruit near the coast. One of the first seedling varieties developed by
Albert Etter in Humboldt County, California; perhaps his best. Originally named
Allgold. *Source History: 3 in 1988; 4 in 1992; 2 in 2000.* **Sources: Ch9, Gr4.**

Eureka - *Source History: 1 in 2000.* **Sources: Ed5.**

Evereste Crab - Tart, round, 1" fruit is used to make jelly, pickled apples or as a
cider blend. Remains on the tree until mid-winter. Disease resistant. Trademarked.
Source History: 1 in 2000. **Sources: Rai.**

Fall Harvey - Originated in Massachusetts. Introduced in 1836. *Source History:
1 in 1992; 1 in 2000.* **Sources: Wo7.**

Fall Orange - Southern variety. *Source History: 1 in 2000.* **Sources: Ca15.**

Fall Pippin (Philadelphia Pippin, American Fall, Autumn Pippin, Cobbet's Fall,
Episcopal, Golden Pippin, Prince's Large Pippin, Sudlow's Fall Pippin, Summer
Pippin, York Pippin) - Large yellow fall apple. Tender flesh; good flavor. Good
keeper. Some disease resistance; subject to scab. Ripens over a long period around
early to mid-September. First recorded in 1806. *Source History: 6 in 1988; 6 in
1992; 8 in 2000.* **Sources: Bea, Ca15, Ch9, Gr4, La3, Mi1, Wo7, Wor.**

Fall Queen - Good cooking apple. Dwarf tree; vigorous grower. *Source History:
1 in 1992; 1 in 2000.* **Sources: Ed5.**

Fall Russet - Small, unattractive, yellowish green or golden russet fruit, often irregularly webbed with grey and dark green. Exceedingly high flavor; a combination of sweetness and tartness which later mellows into pear-like richness. Excellent for drying. Tree fruits heavily in clusters. Located in an old family orchard in Franklin, Michigan. True identity remains uncertain; some believe it to be the Autumn Pomme Gris. Introduced in 1875. *Source History: 3 in 1988; 4 in 1992; 2 in 2000.* **Sources: Gr4, So5.**

Fall Wine (Hawer, House, Hower, Musk Spice, Ohio Wine, Sharpe's Spice, Sweet Wine, Uncle Sam's Best, Wine, Wine of Cole) - Clear yellow overlaid with red blush. Sweet, tender, juicy, yellow flesh. Ripens in mid-September. Very old American variety of New England origin which was long lost to cultivation. Recently rediscovered by Mr. Fred Ashworth of Heuvelton, New York. *Source History: 1 in 1988; 2 in 1992; 1 in 2000.* **Sources: Or9.**

Fallawater (Tulpehocken, Winter Blush, Talpahawkins, Formwalder, Mountain Pippin, Green Mountain Pippin, Pim's Beauty of the West, Pine's Beauty of the West, Pound, Kelly, Brubacker, Molly Whopper) - Very large, green fruit; some over 6" in diameter. Good for eating, applesauce and cooking. Good, regular bearer; triploid. Subject to cedar apple rust. Ripens early October. Hardy in Zone 4. Originated in Bucks County, Pennsylvania. A great favorite there in the 19th century. *Source History: 2 in 1988; 9 in 1992; 12 in 2000.* **Sources: Bea, Bl4, Bo5, Ca15, Ch9, Cu4, Fed, Or9, Sc6, So5, Ur2, Wo7.**

Fallawater, Flat - Southern variety. *Source History: 1 in 2000.* **Sources: Ca15.**

Fameuse (Snow, Snow Apple, Snow Chimney, Chimney Apple, Red American, Royal Snow, Pomme de Neige, Chimney Point) - Possible parent of McIntosh. Small to medium fruit with beautiful red over cream skin. Name comes from its pure white flesh, occasionally stained crimson near the skin. Tender, spicy, aromatic, distinctive flavor. Excellent for cider, fresh eating and cooking. Fair to good storage. Very hardy, heavy bearing tree. Main fault is biennial production. Requires pollination. Dislikes heavy soils; can develop scab during a wet summer. Excellent for home orchards. Ripens during September. Requires 600 hours of chilling. Hardy from Zones 4-8. Originated from French seed planted in Canada in the late 1600s. Introduced to the U.S. in 1739. Thought to be the parent of McIntosh. *Source History: 16 in 1988; 20 in 1992; 19 in 2000.* **Sources: Bea, Bl4, Cid, Ea3, Fed, Fo2, Gr4, Hi9, Jun, Leu, Mi1, Nrs, Sc6, So5, Son, Stl, Ur2, Wo7, Wor.**

Fameuse, Winter (Fameuse West) - Sport of Fameuse with better keeping quality. Medium size, round, deep bright red, thin skin. White flesh is sometimes stained red. Excellent eating, sauce and cider apple. Scab susceptible. Zones 3-4. Rare. Originated in Farmington, Maine. *Source History: 1 in 2000.* **Sources: Fed.**

Fanny - Southern variety. *Source History: 1 in 2000.* **Sources: Ca15.**

Farmer's Sweet - *Source History: 1 in 2000.* **Sources: Ch9.**

Father Abraham (Abraham's Apple, Florentiner, Abram, Father Abram) - Medium size fruit with prominent ribbing at the eye and some from the base to the apex. Green-yellow skin is almost totally flushed and streaked brown-red. Greasy. Yellow-white flesh is tinged red under the skin. Sweet subacid flavor. Regular bearer; stores well. September ripening. *Source History: 2 in 1992; 3 in 2000.* **Sources: Ca15, Or9, Ro3.**

Faust's Winter - Southern variety. *Source History: 1 in 2000.* **Sources: Ca15.**

Fearn's Pippin - Brilliant scarlet skin color. Crisp, juicy flesh with an acid and sweet flavor resembling lemons, mellowing to a slight raspberry flavor. Ripens early autumn. Medium sized, upright tree. Zones 6-9. Originated in England, 1780. *Source History: 1 in 2000.* **Sources: Son.**

Fenouillet Gris - *Source History: 1 in 1992; 1 in 2000.* **Sources: Ch9.**

Ferguson Late - Southern variety. *Source History: 1 in 2000.* **Sources: Ca15.**

Fiesta - Cox's Orange Pippen x Idared. Fruit color is 75% red over green background. Blooms mid to late season. Tangy, aromatic sweet flavor. Stores up to 6 weeks. Disease resistant. Ripens late September. Easier to grow than many Cox types. U.S. Plant Patent No. 7956. *Source History: 1 in 1992; 3 in 2000.* **Sources: Clo, Er2, Rai.**

Fig Apple - *Source History: 1 in 2000.* **Sources: Ed5.**

Fillbarrel - *Source History: 2 in 2000.* **Sources: Cid, Cu4.**

Fireside - McIntosh x Longfield. Delicious type that is hardy for Minnesota. Better flavor and texture than Delicious, although not so highly colored. Large, conical fruit. Green skin with broad scarlet stripes and sometimes a mottled orange flush. Crisp, sweet, juicy greenish white flesh, not flat and mealy. Sweet, subacid flavor. Good keeper. Resistant to cedar-apple rust; somewhat susceptible to scab and fire blight. Ripens in October. Hardy to -50 degrees F. with occasional winter injury. Released by the University of Minnesota in 1943. *Source History: 11 in 1988; 15 in 1992; 14 in 2000.* **Sources: Bea, Ch9, Ed5, Fa1, Gur, Hi9, LA4, Mc3, Nrs, SH8, So5, Stl, Wa16, ZEL.**

Firmgold (Gibson Strain) - Yellow skin color. Fine textured, sweet flesh. Fruit hangs well on the tree. Biennial cropper if not thinned properly. Good rust resistance. Recommended on dwarf rootstock only. Trademarked. U.S. Plant Patent No. 4166. *Source History: 3 in 1992; 3 in 2000.* **Sources: Ad2, Ch9, Va2.**

Fitchburg Mac - Bud mutation of McIntosh that colors earlier than other McIntosh strains to a full bright red blush. Shows slightly less tree vigor than the standard strain. Originated in Fitchburg, Massachusetts. *Source History: 1 in 2000.* **Sources: Hi9.**

Flat Fall Cheese - Southern variety. *Source History: 3 in 2000.* **Sources: Ca15, Nrs, Or9.**

Florence Crab - Large yellow fruit. Good for jelly or pickling. Ripens in July. *Source History: 1 in 1992; 1 in 2000.* **Sources: Wom.**

Florina - Large, red striped fruit. Aromatic spicy flavor. Vigorous tree. Immune to scab. Ripens mid to late October. Keeps into January. *Source History: 4 in 2000.* **Sources: Clo, Cu4, Ed5, Ro3.**

Flower of Kent - *Source History: 2 in 2000.* **Sources: Ed5, Or9.**

Foot Around - Southern variety. *Source History: 1 in 2000.* **Sources: Ca15.**

Fortune (New York 429) - Red Spy x Empire. Large, attractive fruit; yellow flesh. Tree has dense foliage; very vigorous. Blooms between Red and Golden Delicious. Very good fresh eating quality. Ripens midseason. Developed at the New York Station. Trademarked. Plant patent applied for. Introduced in 1995. *Source History: 1 in 1988; 1 in 1992; 7 in 2000.* **Sources: Ad2, Cu4, Ed5, Hi9, St4, WAF, WI12.**

Fortune, Laxton's - Cox Orange seedling x Wealthy. Medium size, dull red fruit with some russeting and striping. Sweet, creamy white flesh. Aromatic, lively flavor. Good keeper. Holds flavor well in storage. Blooms midseason. Some scab resistance but somewhat susceptible to canker. Ripens in early September. Originated in England. Introduced in 1931. *Source History: 3 in 1988; 2 in 1992; 1 in*

2000. **Sources: So5.**

Fox - *Source History: 1 in 2000.* **Sources: Bea.**

Fox Whelp - English cider variety. Small, round, red fruit covered with some russet. Blooms and ripens late. Zones 6-9. First recorded in 1854. *Source History: 5 in 1988; 8 in 1992; 10 in 2000.* **Sources: Bl4, Ch9, Cid, Ed5, Gr4, La3, Mo19, Or9, So5, Son.**

Franklin - Delicious x McIntosh. Well-colored fruit. Tender, crisp flesh; mild flavor. Resembles the shape of Delicious, but far superior in eating quality. Ripens in late September. Introduced by the Ohio Agricultural Experiment Station. *Source History: 2 in 1988; 2 in 1992; 3 in 2000.* **Sources: Sc6, So5, Wor.**

Frazier Yellow - *Source History: 1 in 1992; 1 in 2000.* **Sources: Ed5.**

Freedom (Macoun x Antonovka) x NY 49821-46. Sister tree to Liberty. Medium to large, round, bright red fruit with almost invisible yellow background. Crisp, juicy, medium-coarse flesh. Subacid, spright flavor. Good quality apple for fresh eating, cider and cooking. Stores until January. Vigorous, spreading tree with leathery leaves. Good pollinator for Liberty. Resistant to fire blight, mildew, cedar-apple rust, scab and other diseases. Should require no sprays. Ripens from late September to early October depending on location. Hardy to -45 degrees F. Developed and patented by Cornell Research Foundation. Introduced in 1983. U.S. Plant Patent No. 52723. *Source History: 10 in 1988; 19 in 1992; 19 in 2000.* **Sources: Ad2, Bea, Bo5, Bu7, Ch9, Clo, Cu4, Ea3, Ed5, Er2, Fa1, Fi1, Gur, Hi9, Jo3, Mi1, SH8, Stl, Ur2.**

Freiherr von Berlepsch (Red Berlepsch) - Classic gourmet quality apple of Germany. *Source History: 1 in 2000.* **Sources: Cu4.**

Frettingham - White flowers. Tree blooms late. Good pollinator for Golden Delicious. *Source History: 1 in 1988; 1 in 1992; 1 in 2000.* **Sources: Amb.**

Freyberg - Cox's Orange Pippin x Golden Delicious. Small, Reinette-type fruit; yellow-green with some russeting. Juicy, aromatic, creamy white flesh with firm, fine texture; hint of liquorice flavor. Lightly acidulous and sugary. Ripens in early October. Zones 6-9. Developed in New Zealand. *Source History: 5 in 1988; 10 in 1992; 8 in 2000.* **Sources: Bl4, Ch9, Gr4, Or9, Rai, Ro3, So5, Son.**

Frostproof - *Source History: 1 in 1992; 1 in 2000.* **Sources: Ed5.**

Frumos de Voinesti - *Source History: 1 in 1992; 1 in 2000.* **Sources: Nrs.**

Fugate - *Source History: 1 in 1992; 1 in 2000.* **Sources: Or9.**

Fuji (Tohoku #7) - Ralls Janet x Delicious. High quality apple with fairly poor appearance. Tall, rectangular, medium size fruit. Yellowish green skin with an orangish red flush and darker stripes; darker blush on sun side. Crisp, juicy, slightly subacid, white flesh with outstanding texture. May require up to 200 days to mature and to achieve its characteristic sweet taste. Good keeper. Vigorous, productive, somewhat bushy tree; needs annual detailed pruning. Requires cross-pollination. Heat resistant. Ripens from September to October depending on location. Requires 100-400 hours of chilling. Zones 6-10. Developed in Japan. Introduced in 1962. *Source History: 17 in 1988; 43 in 1992; 39 in 2000.* **Sources: Ad2, AG2, Bay, Bl4, Bu7, Ch9, Cla, CO5, Cu4, Cum, Ea3, Fi1, Ga20, Gr16, Gr4, Iso, Jo3, JOY, La3, LA4, Mel, Mi1, Mo19, On3, On4, Or9, ORA, Pa2, Pe2, Sc6, SH8, SIM, So5, Son, STR, Tex, Wel, Wom, Wor.**

Fuji, Akiful No. 1 - *Source History: 1 in 1992; 1 in 2000.* **Sources: CO5.**

Fuji, Jubilee - Medium size fruit with reddish blush over a green to yellow ground color. Creamy white flesh with flavor typical of Fuji. Early ripening. Plant patent applied for. *Source History: 1 in 2000.* **Sources: Co2.**

Fuji, Myra - U.S. Plant Patent No. 9645. *Source History: 1 in 2000.* **Sources: St4.**

Fuji, Spike (Fuji Lynd-Spur) - Whole-tree mutation that is easier to manage than non-spur type trees. Sweet, crisp fruit resembles Fuji. Ripens mid-October. Discovered by Mitch Lynd of Ohio. U.S. Plant Patent No. 9508. *Source History: 1 in 2000.* **Sources: Ro3.**

Fuji, Sun - Standard Fuji sport. Skin color shows pink-red over yellow-green background. Sweet, fruity, crisp flesh with sub-acid flavor. Ripens late October. Extremely firm flesh makes it an outstanding keeper. Discovered in Brentwood, California. Trademarked. *Source History: 8 in 2000.* **Sources: Ad2, Co2, COL, Cu4, Hi9, Va2, WAF, WI12.**

Fuji, Yataka (Early Fuji) - Discovered as a limbsport of Fuji in Japan. Matures about 3-4 weeks earlier than standard Fuji. Recommended for areas that cannot mature standard Fuji. Trademarked. U.S. Plant Patent No. 7001. *Source History: 1 in 1992; 2 in 2000.* **Sources: Ad2, Bea.**

Fukunishiki - Ralls Janet x Delicious. Light red over green background with broken red stripes on the side exposed to the sun. Crisp, juicy, mild-flavored flesh. Requires long warm season to ripen to perfection when it is one of the finest late winter and early spring apples for dessert. Ripens in early November. Developed at the Aomori Apple Experiment Station in Japan. *Source History: 1 in 1988; 3 in 1992; 2 in 2000.* **Sources: Ch9, So5.**

Fushuai - *Source History: 2 in 1992; 1 in 2000.* **Sources: Nrs.**

Fyan - *Source History: 1 in 1992; 1 in 2000.* **Sources: Ch9.**

Gable - Southern variety. *Source History: 1 in 2000.* **Sources: Ca15.**

Gala (Kidd's D-8 Cultivar, Stark Gala) - Golden Delicious x Cox's Orange. Heavy red striping on golden skin gives it a red-orange color. Crisp, dense, aromatic flesh. Fine flavor for a Golden; subacid or semisweet. Excellent quality. Keeps very well. Approved by commercial growers and fruit tasters. Large, vigorous tree. Some self-fertile characteristics, but probably should be pollinated with Red or Golden Delicious. Ripens during September. Requires 600 or less hours of chilling. Hardy throughout Maine except in far north and west; Zone 4. Developed in New Zealand in 1934. Introduced in 1965. Gala is a registered trademark of Stark Brothers Nursery. U.S. Plant Patent No. 3637. *Source History: 5 in 1988; 21 in 1992; 35 in 2000.* **Sources: Ad2, Bay, Bea, Bl4, Bo5, Ch9, Cla, CO5, Cu4, Cum, Ea3, Er2, Ga20, Gr16, Iso, Jo3, Jun, LA4, Leu, Mi1, Or9, ORA, Pe2, Sc6, SH8, SIM, Son, STR, Tex, Ty2, Wel, Wh4, WI4, Wom, Wor.**

Gala, Big Red - New Gala strain with 30-40% larger fruit. Originated in Indiana. Licensed through ProTree Nursery. U.S. Plant Patent No. 10,458. *Source History: 2 in 2000.* **Sources: Ro3, WAF.**

Gala, Brookfield - Derived from Royal Gala. Boldly striped fruit colors early. Harvested in two pickings. Originated in Hawkes Bay, New Zealand, 1985. U.S. Plant Patent No. 10,016. *Source History: 1 in 2000.* **Sources: WI12.**

Gala, Buckeye (PV 1001) - Sport of Imperial Gala with the same fruit flavor, texture, size and handling qualities. Color develops well through summer heat. Vigorous, upright tree with semi-spur habit. Annual bearer. U.S. Plant Patent No. 10,840. *Source History: 4 in 2000.* **Sources: COL, Hi9, WAF, WI12.**

Gala, Crimson (Waliser Cultivar) - Striped strain of Tenroy Gala with similar size and flavor. Matures 3-5 days later. Tree has upright growth habit that produces strong wide-angle crotches. Precocious annual bearer. Recommended for Southern growing districts where color is difficult to achieve. Trademarked. U.S. Plant Patent No. 8673. *Source History: 5 in 2000.* **Sources: Ad2, BR10, COL, Cu4, WI4.**

Gala, Fulford (Fulford Strain, Regal Gala) - Larger sized Gala; bright orange-red with red blush rather than stripe. Ripens earlier than other Gala strains. Originated in Hastings, New Zealand. Trademarked. U.S. Plant Patent No. 7589. *Source History: 4 in 1992; 2 in 2000.* **Sources: Ad2, Hi9.**

Gala, Galaxy - Differs from Royal Gala in that the color is more complete. Develops a bright cherry-red layer under the more intense red stripes. U.S. Plant Patent No. 6955. *Source History: 2 in 2000.* **Sources: Co2, Si3.**

Gala, Gale (Malaga Cultivar) - The most highly colored strain of Gala available with deeper red stripes and fuller red color. Conical, medium size fruit. Can be harvested in one or two pickings. Discovered by Wally Gale in Malaga, Washington. U.S. Plant Patent No. 10,114. *Source History: 1 in 2000.* **Sources: Va2.**

Gala, Hilltop (Mitchell Cultivar) - Popular Gala variety. Starts coloring early and finishes to a yellow-orange background striped with bright red. Firm flesh with crisp texture and sweet, juicy, mildly aromatic taste. Trademarked. *Source History: 1 in 2000.* **Sources: Hi9.**

Gala, Imperial (Mitchell Cultivar) - Medium size, oval to round reddish orange fruit. Extremely firm, very juicy, sweet, mildly aromatic, yellow flesh. Vigorous tree with long, pliant branching. U.S. Plant Patent No. 4121. *Source History: 2 in 1988; 2 in 1992; 3 in 2000.* **Sources: Ad2, WAF, WI12.**

Gala, Improved (Mitchell Cultivar) - Medium size fruit with bright red striping over yellowish ground color. Outstanding flavor. Multiple picks. *Source History: 1 in 2000.* **Sources: Co2.**

Gala, Lydia's Red - Blush-type Gala colors to a smooth orange-red finish one week ahead of Imperial or Fulford Gala. Typical Gala tree characteristics. Trademarked. *Source History: 1 in 2000.* **Sources: Hi9.**

Gala, Pacific - Discovered as a whole tree mutation of Royal Gala. Fruit colors well throughout the tree. Colors early and uniformly and retains a strong stripe. Holds well on the tree for several days after ripening. Sweet flavor is retained in storage. Trademarked. U.S. Plant Patent No. 9681. *Source History: 3 in 2000.* **Sources: Co2, COL, TR8.**

Gala, Red No. 42 (Cooper Cultivar, TRECO Red Gala #42) - Large fruit with stripes similar to other Galas. Exceptional juice content. Firm, sweet, flesh with a crisp flavor. Retains high quality even after long storage. U.S. Plant Patent No. 7396. *Source History: 1 in 1992; 1 in 2000.* **Sources: TR8.**

Gala, Royal (Tenroy Cultivar, Stark Royal Gala) - In most areas, Royal Gala matures to a brighter overall red color rather than the orangish red blush of Gala. Medium size, conical to round fruit. Bold red stripes over yellow background. Firm, juicy, fine textured, yellow-white flesh. Sweet, slightly tart flavor. Hangs well on tree. Compact growth habit; prolific bearer. Needs heavy thinning to maintain fruit size and prevent biennial bearing. Blooms midseason with Melrose. Ripens from early September to early October depending on location. Hardy in Zones 5-8. Developed in New Zealand. Trademarked. U.S. Plant Patent No. 4121. *Source History: 4 in 1988; 8 in 1992; 7 in 2000.* **Sources: AG2, Bo5, Co2, ME3, Pa2, St4, Va2.**

Gala, Scarlet - Medium size, oval to round fruit. Firm, juicy, yellow flesh. Sweet flavor. Requires thinning. Shows more blight resistance than other Gala varieties.

Originated in Kentucky. U.S. Plant Patent No. 6172. *Source History: 1 in 1988; 3 in 1992; 4 in 2000.* **Sources: Ch9, Co2, Mel, Ro3.**

Gala, Stark Galaxy - Highly colored Gala strain with dark red skin. Ripens in July. U.S. Plant Patent No. 6955. *Source History: 2 in 2000.* **Sources: AG2, St4.**

Gala, Twin Bee - Highly colored limb sport of Tenroy Gala. Red stripes cover 90-100% of the red-orange background color. Crisp, juicy, firm flesh with sweet flavor. Discovered in Michigan. Trademarked. Plant patent applied for. *Source History: 1 in 2000.* **Sources: Hi9.**

Gala, UltraRed (Obrogala Cultivar) - Discovered as a whole tree mutation of Royal Gala in Washington. Royal Gala quality. Exceptional color. Excellent flavor. U.S. Plant Patent No. 8621. *Source History: 2 in 1992; 3 in 2000.* **Sources: AG2, Si3, St4.**

Galasupreme (Davis Cultivar) - Chance seedling that came up from a Red Delicious root in a Wenatchee, Washington orchard. Not a Gala sport but resembles it in color and flavor. Ripens late-midseason. Sweet, tangy flesh resembles Gala. U.S. Plant Patent No. 10,010. *Source History: 1 in 2000.* **Sources: Va2.**

Gallen - Extremely early yellow Finnish apple. *Source History: 1 in 1988; 2 in 1992; 1 in 2000.* **Sources: Ch9.**

Gano (Mesa Red, Jacks Red, Ozark, Payton, Reagan, Red Ben Davis, Black Ben Davis) - Old-timer. Light yellow skin is flushed and striped a light red that turns to a purple-red on ripening. Firm, coarse, whitish flesh is tinged with yellow. Crisp, juicy, subacid flavor. Stores well. Ripens in late September. Hardy to Zone 5. Some consider Gano the same as Black Ben Davis. Popular in the Blue Ridge Mountains of Virginia in the late 19th and early 20th centuries. *Source History: 1 in 1988; 2 in 1992; 2 in 2000.* **Sources: Bea, Ca15.**

Garden Delicious (Garden Delicious Genetic Dwarf) - Medium size greenish yellow fruit with a light pink blush; in colder areas the fruit turns deep red. Sweet, crisp flesh. Excellent dessert quality; good cooking apple. Keeps well. Genetic dwarf tree grows 5' tall x 4' wide. Rather slow growing; bears heavily and early. Pinkish white blossoms in spring. Self-pollinating, but for best pollination plant another apple nearby. Ripens in September, about two weeks after Golden Delicious. Requires from 600-700 hours of chilling. Hardy in Zones 4-8. Developed by Floyd Zaiger. U.S. Plant Patent No. 3808. *Source History: 7 in 1988; 8 in 1992; 6 in 2000.* **Sources: Bay, CO5, MI5, ORA, ORA, WI4.**

Garden Royal - Small to medium size fruit, generally round in shape. Thin, green-yellow skin is nearly flushed red with stripes and splashes of carmine. Russet dots cover the surface. Juicy, yellow flesh almost melts with tenderness. Tends to biennial bearing but begins to bear early. Vigorous tree produces heavily. If the weather is warm and dry after picking, the fruit usually shrivels. Ripens in August. Zone 4. Once was extremely popular because of its exquisite flavor. Originated in Massachusetts. Recorded in 1847. *Source History: 1 in 1992; 1 in 2000.* **Sources: Fed.**

Garden Sweet - *Source History: 1 in 2000.* **Sources: Fed.**

Garland - *Source History: 1 in 1992; 1 in 2000.* **Sources: Ch9.**

Geeveston Fanny - *Source History: 1 in 2000.* **Sources: Cu4.**

Genesis II - *Source History: 1 in 2000.* **Sources: Or9.**

Geneva - Medium size, red fleshed, very tart fruit. Cider variety. Dark maroon-red foliage. Ripens late August to early September. *Source History: 3 in 1992; 3 in 2000.* **Sources: Er2, Nrs, Ro3.**

Geneva Black - *Source History: 1 in 1992; 1 in 2000.* **Sources: Nrs.**

Geneva Crab - Cider apple. Attractive tree with red veined leaves in spring. Red-pink blossoms. Edible dark red fruit remains on the tree until frost. Very hardy. *Source History: 3 in 2000.* **Sources: Cid, Or9, Sc6.**

Geneva Early - Quinte x July Red. Large, slightly flattened, round fruit with 60-80% red blush. Tender and soft aromatic flesh with very short shelf life. Useful for local sale; not a shipping variety. Good eating quality, but requires two to three pickings. Ripens in mid-July. Winter hardy. Developed at the New York State Agricultural Experiment Station in Geneva. Introduced in 1982. *Source History: 6 in 1988; 6 in 1992; 5 in 2000.* **Sources: Ch9, Er2, Mi1, Nrs, So5.**

George Cave - *Source History: 1 in 2000.* **Sources: Or9.**

George Webster - Large yellow-red fruit. Good culinary apple. Late-winter keeper. Ripens late in the season. Hardy to -40 degrees F. Origin unknown. *Source History: 1 in 1988; 1 in 1992; 1 in 2000.* **Sources: Stl.**

Gerne's Red Acre - Possible sport of Spitzenburg; discovered on the Spitzenburg branch of a 3-in-1 tree. Glossy, deep red skin color. Firm yellow flesh. Good flavor. Excellent keeper. Heat resistant. Zones 5-10. Introduced in 1985. *Source History: 1 in 2000.* **Sources: Son.**

Gideon - *Source History: 1 in 1992; 1 in 2000.* **Sources: Ed5.**

Gideon Sweet - *Source History: 1 in 2000.* **Sources: Ed5.**

Gilbert Gold - Possibly a russet sport of Golden Delicious with more flavor. Crisp, juicy flesh. Fruit hangs well on the tree. Same uses as Golden Delicious. Zones 5-9. *Source History: 1 in 2000.* **Sources: Son.**

Gilpin (Carthouse, Romanite, Barker's Liner, Roman Knight, Little Red Romanite, Dollars and Cents) - Famous old Virginia cider apple. Yellow skin is blushed and striped with red. Tender, sweet, coarse, crisp, yellowish flesh. Blooms late. Ripens in October. Originated in Virginia, 1817. *Source History: 1 in 1988; 5 in 1992; 6 in 2000.* **Sources: Bea, Ca15, Cid, Or9, So5, Wo7.**

Ginger Gold (Mountain Cove Cultivar) - Golden Delicious type. Can be picked green but will turn an attractive yellow with a blush if allowed to hang on the tree. Uniform fruit size. Keeps up to 6 months in storage. Ripens six weeks before Gibson Golden. Vigorous tree habit but no limb spreading is necessary. Zones 5-9a. Found as a chance seedling in the orchards of Clyde and Ginger Harvey of Lovingston, Virginia. U.S. Plant Patent No. 7063. *Source History: 3 in 1992; 5 in 2000.* **Sources: Ad2, Ch9, Jo3, Va2, Wh4.**

Glass Apple - Southern variety. *Source History: 1 in 2000.* **Sources: Ca15.**

Glenton - *Source History: 1 in 1992; 1 in 2000.* **Sources: Ch9.**

Gloria Mundi (American Gloria Mundi, American Mammoth, Baltimore, Baltimore Pippin, Belle Dubois, Belle Josephine, Copp's Mammoth, Glazenwood, Kinderhook Pippin, Melon, Monstrous Pippin, Mountain Flora, Ox Apple, Pound, Vandyne) - Very large greenish apple. Once grown as a show apple for county fairs because of its huge size. Large, hardy, spreading tree; shy bearer. Ripens in mid-September. Uncertain origin. Recorded in 1804. *Source History: 1 in 1988; 4 in 1992; 5 in 2000.* **Sources: Bea, Ca15, Ch9, Gr4, Or9.**

Gloster (Gloster 69) - Weisser Winterglockenapfel x Richard Delicious. Conic shape, fully red fruit with calyx-end shoulder bumps. Larger, mostly 3" diameter; tarter flavor than Delicious. Extremely productive tree. Ripens late in the season. Originated in Germany. Introduced in 1969. *Source History: 1 in 1988; 5 in 1992; 3 in 2000.* **Sources: Bea, Bl4, Ch9.**

Glover Goldie - Unknown parentage; possibly Tolman Sweet. Large, yellow fruit resembles Golden Delicious in both flavor and quality. Ripens midseason. Hardy to -50 degrees F. with occasional winter injury. St. Lawrence Nurseries introduction. *Source History: 1 in 1992; 1 in 2000.* **Sources: Stl.**

Goldblush, Spur - Spur-type sport of Blushing Golden discovered in Cobden, Illinois. Red blushed fruit with outstanding flavor. Russet resistant. Matures 7 days later than regular Golden Delicious. Retains its shape, flavor and texture when cooked. Flesh remains firm for over 7 months in cold storage. Trademarked. U.S. Plant Patent No. 7878. *Source History: 2 in 2000.* **Sources: Co2, Cu4.**

Golden Delicious - Chance seedling of Grimes Golden. Generally large, conic, golden yellow fruit. Firm, crisp, juicy, flavorful flesh. Mild, sweet, distinctive flavor. High quality; all purpose. Shrivels in storage. Medium tall, moderately vigorous, round-headed tree with wide angle crotches. Bears very young and annually if thinned. Requires gentle picking; bruise marks are very prominent. Sometimes serious russeting. Self-fertile. Ideal pollinator; three different sets of blooms in midseason. Ripens from mid-September to late October depending on location. Requires 600-700 hours of chilling. Hardy in Zones 5-9. Introduced in 1900. *Source History: 31 in 1988; 31 in 1992; 31 in 2000.* **Sources: Bas, Bay, Bea, Bl4, BO10, Bo5, Ch9, Co2, Fi1, Ga20, Gr4, Hi9, Ho5, Jo3, Jun, La3, Mel, Nrs, Or9, Pe2, Ro3, Si3, SIM, So5, Son, Ty2, Ur2, Va2, Wa16, WI4, Wom.**

Golden Delicious, Empress Spur - Compact growing sport of Golden Delicious. All spur Golden varieties require heavier rates of fertilizer to maintain desired growth rate. Can result in slightly green fruit and slower maturity. *Source History: 1 in 1988; 2 in 1992; 1 in 2000.* **Sources: Ch9.**

Golden Delicious, Gibson Strain - Most russet resistant Golden Delicious clone commercially available. Smoother finish than regular Golden Delicious. Good size, firmness and flavor. Good keeper. Vigorous, productive tree. Easy to train. A strain that is used for both processing and fresh market. *Source History: 3 in 1988; 7 in 1992; 10 in 2000.* **Sources: Ad2, Co2, COL, Cu4, Si3, St4, TR8, Va2, WAF, Wh4.**

Golden Delicious, Golden Glory - Limb sport of Golden Delicious Smoothee discovered in Ohio. Excellent for fresh market or processing. Semi-spur type tree. Trademarked. U.S. Plant Patent No. 7857. *Source History: 1 in 2000.* **Sources: Hi9.**

Golden Delicious, Goldspur (Sundale Strain) - Naturally semi-dwarf. Heaviest cropper of all Golden Delicious strains. Large fruit similar to regular Golden Delicious; same color, distinctive flavor and crisp flesh. Extremely heavy producer. Must be thinned to maintain annual production. Tendency to russet in the early producing years. U.S. Plant Patent No. 2334. *Source History: 3 in 1988; 2 in 1992; 2 in 2000.* **Sources: Co2, Va2.**

Golden Delicious, Razor Russet - Russeted Golden Delicious with very pretty golden color. Slightly spicy flavor. Southern variety. *Source History: 3 in 2000.* **Sources: Ca15, Cu4, Sc6, Wh4.**

Golden Delicious, Smoothee - Fruit averages larger than regular Goldens. Glossy skin is smoother to the touch, without the usual abrasiveness of conventional Goldens. Far superior in russet resistance to the other Golden strains. Trademarked. *Source History: 1 in 1988; 4 in 1992; 5 in 2000.* **Sources: Amb, Ch9, Ed5, Hi9, WI12.**

Golden Delicious, Spur - Heaviest cropper of all Golden Delicious. Produces heavily on compact tree. Tends to be slightly more susceptible to russeting than regular Golden. Ripens in late October. Zone 4. *Source History: 4 in 1988; 5 in 1992; 3 in 2000.* **Sources: Jo3, LA4, STR.**

Golden Delicious, Stark (Mullins Cultivar) - Golden fruit. Sweet, juicy flesh. Mild, sweet, crisp texture. Ripens in early October. Hardy in Zones 5-8. Trademarked. *Source History: 1 in 1988; 2 in 1992; 2 in 2000.* **Sources: AG2, St4.**

Golden Delicious, Starkspur (Gilbert Cultivar) - Non-browning flesh with very good flavor. Self-pollinating and best of pollinators for other varieties. Expect five bushels each year from a dwarf tree; 10 from a semi-dwarf. Ripens in early October. Hardy in Zones 5-8 and the cooler areas of Zone 9. *Source History: 1 in 1988; 1 in 1992; 1 in 2000.* **Sources: St4.**

Golden Delicious, UltraGold (Goldensheen #2 Cultivar, Stark UltraGold) - Originated as a mutation of Belgolden (Goldensheen) in the test orchards of Stark Brothers. Large golden apple with slightly more conical shape than Golden Delicious. Smooth, russet-resistant, glossy skin. Better storage life and less susceptibility to shriveling. Vigorous tree with spreading growth habit with strong crotch angles. U.S. Plant Patent No. 4731. *Source History: 2 in 1992; 2 in 2000.* **Sources: AG2, St4.**

Golden Delicious, Yelo Spur - Very similar to Golden Delicious. Grows on a spur type tree. *Source History: 1 in 2000.* **Sources: Bay.**

Golden Glory - *Source History: 1 in 2000.* **Sources: WI12.**

Golden Harvey (Bradley's Golden Pippin, Brandy, Brandy Apple, Guernsey Pippin, Round Russet Harvey, Harvey Apple) - Russeted yellow skin with a red cheek; sometimes covered with a rough russet. Spicy sweet flavor. Good cider apple. Hardy tree is slow to begin bearing. Ripens in September. Originated in the 17th century, likely in England. *Source History: 1 in 1992; 2 in 2000.* **Sources: Ca15, Or9.**

Golden Melon - *Source History: 1 in 2000.* **Sources: Cu4.**

Golden Noble (Glow of the West, John Peel, Lady Richardson, Golden Stranger, Carlisle Codlin) - Large, round, clear bright yellow fruit, sometimes with a few red spots. Of great culinary value, the creamy white flesh cooks into a rich-flavored frothy puree. Recently discovered to exceed most other edible apples in vitamin C. Upright, spreading tree with moderate vigor. Partial tip bearer. Zones 6-9. Originated in England. Introduced to the U.S. in 1820. *Source History: 2 in 1988; 3 in 1992; 4 in 2000.* **Sources: Bea, Cu4, So5, Son.**

Golden Nugget - Small to medium, broadly conical, long stemmed fruit; yellow streaked and splashed with orange, sometimes spotted with russet. Extra sweet, crisp, juicy flesh. Sugary sweet, rich, mellow flavor. Fine for eating fresh; excellent for pies, sauce and apple butter. Poor keeper. Semi-dwarf, spur-type tree grows 12-15' tall; vigorous, disease resistant, hardy and long-lived. Big dependable yields. Produces at an early age. Ripens during September. A 1932 cross of Golden Russet and Cox's Orange Pippin made for a pollination investigation; later selected by Dr. Bishop of Kentsville, Nova Scotia Station in 1949. Introduced in 1964. *Source History: 5 in 1988; 4 in 1992; 7 in 2000.* **Sources: Bea, Cid, Cla, Ed5, Or9, So5, TU5.**

Golden Pippin (Butter Pippin, Mammoth, Pound Royal, York Pippin) - Old American apple of beautiful shape. Greenish turning to deep gold. Tender, juicy, melting, yellowish flesh. Valuable for cooking and dessert. Ripens in September. Unknown parentage. Originated in America about 1800. *Source History: 2 in 1988; 4 in 1992; 4 in 2000.* **Sources: Ch9, Or9, So5, Wo7.**

Golden Reinette - Southern variety. *Source History: 1 in 2000.* **Sources:**

Ca15.

Golden Russet (English Golden Russet) - Seedling of English Russet. The champagne of old-time cider apples. Medium size fruit. Gray-green to golden bronze with a coppery orange cheek; heavily splotched with light brown russet. Crisp, highly flavored, fine textured, yellow flesh. Very sugary juice. Used for cider, dried apples, fresh eating and cooking. Excellent keeper; under proper moisture conditions will keep from December until April. Vigorous, medium to large tree; often a tip bearer. Requires cross-pollination. Scab resistant; suffers little from pests. Ripens late in October. Hardy to Zones 4-5. Originated in New York. Described by Downing in 1845. *Source History: 19 in 1988; 24 in 1992; 26 in 2000.* **Sources: Bar, Bea, Bl4, Bu7, Ch9, Cid, Clo, Cu4, Er2, Fed, Ga20, Gr4, Hi9, La3, Leu, Mi1, Nrs, Or9, Sc6, So5, Son, Stl, Wh4, WI4, Wo7, Wor.**

Golden Russet, American - Southern variety. *Source History: 1 in 2000.* **Sources: Ca15.**

Golden Russet, Wheeler's - Very large, flattened, russet fruit. Lively, acidulous, spicy flavor. Fine quality Golden Russet strain found in the orchards of Mr. Sidney Wheeler of Belchertown, Massachusetts. *Source History: 1 in 1988; 1 in 1992; 1 in 2000.* **Sources: So5.**

Golden Sentinel - Very large attractive fruit with solid golden skin color. Sweet juicy, flavorful flesh. Productive. Disease resistant. Ripens from early to mid-September. Trademarked. Plant patent applied for. *Source History: 3 in 2000.* **Sources: Mi1, On3, Rai.**

Golden Spice - *Source History: 1 in 1992; 3 in 2000.* **Sources: Ch9, Hid, Or9.**

Golden Square - *Source History: 1 in 2000.* **Sources: Ch9.**

Golden Supreme (Carnefix Cultivar) - Appearance is similar to Golden Delicious with smooth, yellow, russet resistant skin. Creamy white, firm, juicy flesh with good flavor. Vigorous, non-spur type tree has tendency to biennial bearing which can be controlled by good bloom management. Requires pollinator. Ripens 10-12 days before Golden Delicious. Originated in Idaho, 1960. Trademarked. U.S. Plant Patent No. 7209. *Source History: 4 in 1992; 7 in 2000.* **Sources: Ch9, Co2, COL, Hi9, Si3, St4, WI12.**

Golden Sweet - Medium to large, pale yellow fruit. Very sweet, rich flavor. Good for cider and home use. Excellent for sauce. Rather vigorous, long-lived tree. Early bearer; tends to heavy biennial bearing. Some disease resistance. Ripens over a long period during August and September. Developed in Connecticut. Introduced in 1832. *Source History: 5 in 1988; 5 in 1992; 5 in 2000.* **Sources: Bl4, Ca15, Ch9, Cid, So5.**

Goldgelb - *Source History: 1 in 2000.* **Sources: Ch9.**

Goldrush (Co-op 38) - Golden Delicious x Co-op 17. Sweet, crisp, flavorful fruit that keeps for up to ten months. Resists oxidation when cut. Slightly upright tree with semi-spur habit. Scab and mildew resistant; moderate resistance to fireblight. Not recommended for northern areas. Ripens mid-October. Zones 4-9. Developed at Purdue University. Trademarked. U.S. Plant Patent No. 9392. *Source History: 15 in 2000.* **Sources: Ad2, AG2, Bo5, Bu7, Cla, Cu4, Fed, Fi1, Gur, Hi9, Ro3, Sc6, St4, TR8, WI12.**

Goodhue - *Source History: 1 in 2000.* **Sources: Ed5.**

Goodland - Open-pollinated seedling of Patten Greening. Roundish, red and yellow fruit. Crisp, juicy, tender white flesh. Makes delicious aromatic sauce; also an excellent eating apple. Productive, annual bearer. Ripens late August to early

September. Hardy to -50 degrees F. with occasional winter injury. Developed in Manitoba, Canada. Introduced in 1948. *Source History: 2 in 1988; 9 in 1992; 6 in 2000.* **Sources: Bea, Ed5, Er2, SH8, Stl, Va5.**

Gordon - Round, medium to large fruit. Green skin, blushed or striped with red. Firm, crisp, juicy, nearly white flesh. Sweet-tart flavor with good aroma. Excellent for cooking and eating. Good storage ability. Requires cross-pollination. Consistent high quality crops. Ripens from August to October depending on location. Requires 250-400 hours of chilling. Thrives in warm sunbelt climate areas as well as in colder climates. Popular variety for southern California. U.S. Plant Patent No. 4144. *Source History: 9 in 1988; 10 in 1992; 6 in 2000.* **Sources: Bay, CO5, ORA, Pa2, Pe2, WI4.**

Gragg - Southern variety. *Source History: 1 in 2000.* **Sources: Ca15.**

Graham Spy - *Source History: 1 in 1992; 1 in 2000.* **Sources: Ch9.**

Grandaddy - Southern variety. *Source History: 1 in 2000.* **Sources: Ca15.**

GrandGala, Stark (Caitlin cultivar) - Trademarked. Plant patent applied for. *Source History: 1 in 2000.* **Sources: St4.**

Graniwinkle (Granny Winkle) - Old New Jersey cider apple described by Coxe in *Cultivation of Fruit Trees* in 1817. Green-yellow fruit is flushed with red. Very small core. Once used for livestock feed. Was mixed with Harrison to make superior quality cider. Fine for desserts as well. Disease resistant. Ripens late in the season. *Source History: 1 in 1988; 2 in 1992; 3 in 2000.* **Sources: Cid, La3, Or9.**

Granny Smith - Large, waxy, grass-green fruit; firm and bruise resistant. Hardy, crisp, juicy, white flesh. Moderately sweet, snappy flavor. Superb eating and cooking qualities. Keeps good texture during baking; never gets mushy. Keeps 180 days in cold storage. Good shelf life. Very vigorous; annual and early bearing. Strong grower and tip bearer; very heavy producer. Self-fertile. Unusually long season; harvest 170-190 days after full bloom. Holds well in heat. Requires 500-600 hours of chilling. Hardy in Zones 5-8. Originated in 1868 from some discarded apples which Mrs. Thomas Smith of Eastwood Ryde, Paramatta Rive, New South Wales, Australia brought from Tasmania. *Source History: 53 in 1988; 72 in 1992; 64 in 2000.* **Sources: Ad2, AG2, Bar, Bay, Bea, Bl4, Bo5, BR10, Bu1, Bu7, Ch9, Cla, Co2, CO5, COL, Cu4, Cum, Fa1, Fi1, Fo2, Fo4, Ga20, GI3, Gr4, Gur, Hi9, Hid, Ho5, Iso, Jo3, JOY, LA4, Lee, Leu, Mc3, ME3, Mel, Mi1, MI10, MI5, Nrs, Or9, ORA, Pi2, Po2, Rid, Sav, SH8, Si3, So5, Son, St4, STR, TR8, TU5, Ty2, Va2, Wa16, WAF, Wel, Wh4, WI12, WI4, Wor.**

Granny Smith, Compspur - Pure green skin may develop a red cheek in cooler climates. Crisp white flesh. Keeps its good flavor in storage. Ripens from late October to early November. *Source History: 1 in 1988; 1 in 1992; 1 in 2000.* **Sources: Mi1.**

Granny Smith, Early Grannee (Cooper Cultivar, Stark Earlee Grannee) - Tart, snappy flavor. Sport of Granny Smith that requires only 165 frost-free days to mature. Hardy in Zones 6-9. U.S. Plant Patent No. 5761. *Source History: 1 in 1988; 2 in 1992; 2 in 2000.* **Sources: Ch9, TR8.**

Grapefruit - *Source History: 1 in 2000.* **Sources: Ed5.**

Gravenstein - Large, round to slightly flattened, orangish yellow fruit with red stripes. Thin skin. Crisp, juicy, fine grained, yellowish white flesh. Known for fine flavor. Unexcelled for cooking. Makes wonderful pies, desserts, sauces and cider. Keeps until early November. Large, vigorous tree. Pick frequently, because of uneven ripening and tendency to drop. Tendency to biennial bearing can be somewhat controlled by heavy pruning. Triploid; requires a pollinator. Ripens during August. Requires 600-700 hours of chilling. Zones 2-9. Originated in Italy in the early 1600s. Arrived in Denmark in 1669. Introduced into the U.S. from Germany in 1790. *Source History: 26 in 1988; 30 in 1992; 31 in 2000.* **Sources: Bay, Bea, Bu7, Ca15, Ch9, Cla, Clo, Co2, CO5, Cu4, Ea3, Ed5, Fed, Ga20, Gr4, JOY, Leu, ME3, Mi1, MI5, Mo19, Nrs, Or9, ORA, Sc6, SH8, Son, STR, WI4, Wo7, Wor.**

Gravenstein, Bank's
(Banks, Banks Red Gravenstein, Red Gravenstein, Crimson Gravenstein) - Bud sport of Gravenstein with less ribbing; more regular in shape; usually smaller and a bright red color. Otherwise comparable to the Gravenstein. Originated in 1880; propagated by C. E. Banks of Berwick, Nova Scotia, Canada. *Source History: 1 in 1992; 1 in 2000.* **Sources: Ca15.**

Gravenstein, Fall
- *Source History: 1 in 2000.* **Sources: Bea.**

Gravenstein, Mead Selection
- Large, ribbed fruit; fine grained, juicy flesh. Classic dessert and cooking apple of Denmark. Old-timer. *Source History: 2 in 1988; 3 in 1992; 1 in 2000.* **Sources: Nrs.**

Gravenstein, Red
- Improved red strain of the old favorite cooking apple; darker red stripes. Firmer, snappy, white flesh with distinctive flavor. Excellent quality. Vigorous, productive tree. Triploid. Ripens from late August to September depending on location. Zone 2. Originated in Germany in 1873. *Source History: 9 in 1988; 14 in 1992; 17 in 2000.* **Sources: Bay, Bea, Bl4, Er2, Ga20, Hi9, JOY, ME3, Mo19, Or9, Rai, So5, Son, Va2, Wh4, WI12, WI4.**

Gravenstein, Rosebrook
- Sport of Gravenstein which is more heavily red striped. No difference in flavor. Lively red stripes on yellow background. All purpose. Late blooming. Pollinate with Winter Banana or White Winter Pearmain. Subject to winter injury in severe climates. Zones 6-10. *Source History: 2 in 1988; 3 in 1992; 1 in 2000.* **Sources: Son.**

Greasy Pippin
- *Source History: 1 in 2000.* **Sources: Cu4.**

Green Buckingham
- Southern variety. *Source History: 1 in 2000.* **Sources: Ca15.**

Green Cheese
- Southern variety. *Source History: 2 in 2000.* **Sources: Ca15, Or9.**

Green Lane
- *Source History: 1 in 1992; 1 in 2000.* **Sources: Bl4.**

Green Newtown Pippin
- Introduced in 1759. *Source History: 1 in 1992; 3 in 2000.* **Sources: Ca15, Ch9, Wo7.**

Green River
- Southern variety. *Source History: 1 in 2000.* **Sources: Ca15.**

Green Sweet
- Skin color is yellow with occasional red-orange blush. Delicious, sprightly flavor is sweet and unusual. Medium size, open, upright tree. Scab resistant. Keeps until late spring. Hardy to Zone 4. Uncertain origin; possibly from northern Massachusettss in the early 1800s. *Source History: 2 in 2000.* **Sources: Ch9, Fed.**

Greenskin
- Southern variety. *Source History: 1 in 2000.* **Sources: Ca15.**

Greensleeves
- Golden Delicious x James Grieve. Early Granny Smith type. Yellow skin color. Compact spur habit. Bears fruit 2-3 years after grafting. Developed in England in the 1970s. *Source History: 2 in 1992; 2 in 2000.* **Sources: Ch9, Rai.**

Grimes Golden
(Grimes, Grimes Golden Pippin) - Medium to large, bright, golden yellow fruit. Crisp, fine grained, yellow flesh. Rich, distinctive, aromatic, spicy flavor. Superior dessert quality. Excellent, juicy, cider apple; good for all

kitchen uses except baking. Keeps until January. Productive tree; medium vigor. Bears young and annually. Self-pollinating. Plant with graft 8-12" above ground to avoid collar rot. Moderately resistant to fire blight and cedar-apple rust. Ripens midseason. Hardy in Zones 5-8. Possible parent of Yellow Delicious. Originated with Thomas Grimes in the mountains of Brook County, West Virginia. Sold to New Orleans traders in 1804. *Source History: 24 in 1988; 31 in 1992; 35 in 2000.* **Sources: Ad2, Bea, Bl4, Bo5, Ca15, Ch9, Cid, Cla, Cu4, Ed5, Er2, Fi1, GI3, Gr4, Ho5, Jo3, La3, Lee, Leu, Mi1, Or9, Ro3, Sav, Sc6, SIM, So5, Son, St4, Stl, Ty2, Ur2, Va2, Wh4, Wo7, Wor.**

Grindstone (American Pippin, Stone, Green Everlasting, Flat Vandevere) - Medium size, green-yellow fruit is splotched and striped with red. Excellent cider apple. *Source History: 1 in 1988; 3 in 1992; 4 in 2000.* **Sources: Bea, Ch9, Cid, Cu4.**

Grove - *Source History: 1 in 1992; 1 in 2000.* **Sources: Ch9.**

Guyandotte - Southern variety. *Source History: 1 in 2000.* **Sources: Ca15.**

Haas - Old-timer. Medium size fruit. Good storage quality. Ripens in October. Hardy to Zone 5. *Source History: 1 in 1988; 1 in 1992; 2 in 2000.* **Sources: Bea, Bl4, Hid.**

Hackworth (Red Hackworth) - Yellow skin with red stripes and numerous dots. Ripens July and August. Old Alabama favorite. *Source History: 2 in 1992; 2 in 2000.* **Sources: Ca15, La3.**

Hadlock Reinette - McIntosh x Golden Russet. Bronze fruit. Juicy, flavorful, firm, fine textured flesh. Good for eating or cider. Similar to Golden Russet. Late ripening. Hardy to -40 degrees F. *Source History: 1 in 1988; 2 in 1992; 2 in 2000.* **Sources: Ch9, Stl.**

Hall Keeper - *Source History: 1 in 2000.* **Sources: Cu4.**

Hammond's - Rough, green-yellow skin shows rusty color on the sun side. Good flavor. Remains on the tree into January and February. Good variety for attracting wildlife. Originated in South Carolina. *Source History: 1 in 2000.* **Sources: La3.**

Haralred (HarralRed) - Red selection of Haralson. Earlier, redder and sweeter, without the common russeting problem many Haralsons have. Juicy, tart, firm flesh. Good keeper. Fire blight resistant. Excellent variety for northern U.S. and Canada. Hardy to Zone 3. Discovered by Louis Lautz, orchardist at La Crescent, Minnesota. U.S. Plant Patent No. 4824. *Source History: 3 in 1988; 10 in 1992; 9 in 2000.* **Sources: BA14, Ed5, Fa1, LA4, MI5, SH8, Stl, TR8, Wa16.**

Haralson - Malinda x Ben Davis. Medium size, red-striped to deep red fruit. Crisp, juicy, firm, medium tender, white flesh. Mild, pleasantly tart flavor. Good for fresh eating and cider. Even better for baking; holds its shape and texture. Stores well for 4-6 months. Vigorous, productive tree; tends to be biennial. Noted for early production; often bears the second year after planting. Moderate resistance to fire blight and cedar-apple rust. Known for its hardiness, productivity and quality. Ripens from September to October depending on location. Hardy to -50 degrees F; Zone 2. Developed at the University of Minnesota. Introduced in 1923. *Source History: 13 in 1988; 21 in 1992; 17 in 2000.* **Sources: Bea, Ch9, Cu4, Ed5, Fa1, Fi1, Gur, Jun, LA4, Mc3, ME3, MI5, Nrs, SH8, So5, Stl, WI4.**

Haralson, Red - Fruit colors with solid red blush. Good fruit size. Firm flesh. Crisp, juicy, aromatic flavor. Tree characteristics are the same as Haralson. Bears good crops at an early age. Regional variety suited to growing in Minnesota, Wisconsin or other cold climates. *Source History: 2 in 1988; 3 in 1992; 3 in 2000.* **Sources: Ch9, Hi9, WI12.**

Harcourt - Ripens early August. Hardy to Zone 3. *Source History: 1 in 2000.* **Sources: Bea.**

Harris - Southern variety. *Source History: 1 in 2000.* **Sources: Ca15.**

Harrison - Cider variety. *Source History: 2 in 2000.* **Sources: Cid, Or9.**

Harry Masters Jersey - Cider variety. Heavy crops of small red fruit. Ripens mid-October. *Source History: 2 in 2000.* **Sources: Cid, Rai.**

Harvest Queen - *Source History: 1 in 2000.* **Sources: Ed5.**

Harvey - *Source History: 1 in 2000.* **Sources: Or9.**

Hatsuaki - Japanese apple. Russeted, red skin. Excellent sweet flavor. Ripens late September. Heavy producer. *Source History: 1 in 1992; 3 in 2000.* **Sources: Mo19, Nrs, Rai.**

Hauer Pippin - Seedling of Cox's Orange Pippin with the same fine flavor. Still grown commercially. Russeted, green, thick skin. Good keeper. Well suited for shipping. Very good eating. Ripens from November to December. Stays on the tree through December. Zones 6-10. Developed in the 1890s by Peter Hauer of Pleasant Valley, Santa Cruz County, California. *Source History: 1 in 1988; 4 in 1992; 3 in 2000.* **Sources: Cla, Hid, Son.**

Hawaii - Golden Delicious x Gravenstein. Gourmet dessert apple with a flavor and aroma like pineapple. Large, yellow fruit with light pinkish orange striping which gives overall orange appearance. Exceptionally sweet flavor is largely influenced by Gravenstein. Growth habit is moderate, spreading and easily trained. Tends to bear heavily one year and lightly the next; proper pruning is necessary to discourage this. Resists cedar apple rust; susceptible to scab and somewhat to bitter pit. Ripens in September. Hardy to Zone 5. Originated in California. Introduced in 1945. *Source History: 3 in 1988; 7 in 1992; 8 in 2000.* **Sources: Bea, Bl4, Ch9, Ga20, Nrs, Or9, Sc6, So5.**

Hawkeye - The progenitor to Delicious. Later named "Delicious" and used for breeding purposes for over a hundred years to achieve apples that ripen earlier, show more red color and are more elongated than Hawkeye. This strain retains the original great flavor. Zone 4. Originated in Iowa in the 1880s. *Source History: 2 in 2000.* **Sources: Cu4, Ed5.**

Hawkins Gold - *Source History: 1 in 1992; 1 in 2000.* **Sources: Nrs.**

Hawley (Dowse) - Large gold and green fruit with sometimes a brownish or dark-red blush in the sun. Tender, fine grained, yellow flesh. Rich, juicy, mild flavor. Slow to begin bearing, then bears moderate crops regularly. Ripens from September to October. Originated in New Canaan, New York from seed brought from Connecticut. Introduced in 1750. *Source History: 1 in 1988; 5 in 1992; 3 in 2000.* **Sources: Bea, Bl4, Wo7.**

Haynes (Haynes Seedling) - *Source History: 1 in 1992; 1 in 2000.* **Sources: Hid.**

Hazen - Duchess x Starking Delicious. Large, round, dark red fruit. Greenish yellow, medium firm, juicy flesh; mildly subacid flavor. Pleasant for eating; good dessert and cooking apple. Naturally semi-dwarf tree grows about 7-10' tall with a 15' spread. Annual bearer. Fire blight resistant. Ripens from early to mid-September. Hardy to Zone 3. Released by North Dakota State University. Introduced in 1979. *Source History: 5 in 1988; 13 in 1992; 8 in 2000.* **Sources: Bea, Ch9, Fa1, Fed, Mc3, Nrs, SH8, Stl.**

Henneuse Pearl - *Source History: 1 in 2000.* **Sources: Or9.**

Henry Clay - Southern variety. Yellow and red fruit is similar to Yellow Transparent. Greenish white, soft flesh. Slight acidic flavor. Becomes greasy in storage. Ripens midseason. Hardy to -50 degrees F. with occasional winter injury. Stark offered this variety in the 1900s. *Source History: 2 in 1988; 3 in 1992; 3 in 2000.* **Sources: Ca15, Or9, Stl.**

HER 3T166 - Round-conic, yellow fruit with light blush. Pale yellow flesh. Slightly aromatic with mild sub-acid flavor. Crisp and juicy. Spur-type tree. Ripens around September 21. Trial variety from Purdue University. *Source History: 1 in 2000.* **Sources: Cla.**

HER 4T112 - Round, green-yellow fruit with 75% red overlay. Crisp, juicy, slightly spicy flavor. Ripens late September. Trial variety from Purdue University. *Source History: 1 in 2000.* **Sources: Cla.**

HER19T124 - Slightly oblate fruit. Yellow background color covered with 80% medium red. Crisp flesh. Ripens mid-October. Trial variety from Purdue University. *Source History: 1 in 2000.* **Sources: Cla.**

Herefordshire Redstreak (English Red Streak, Red Streak) - Small, oblong fruit with red and yellow streaks. Yellow flesh is rich, firm and semisweet. Dryness of the flesh helps it store well. Makes a fine strong flavored cider. Fruits hang well on the tree after ripening. Ripens mid-September. Hardy to Zone 5. Originated in England. Introduced in 1803. *Source History: 3 in 2000.* **Sources: Bea, Cid, Ed5.**

Herfordshire - *Source History: 1 in 2000.* **Sources: Or9.**

Herman Isfield - Canadian prairie apple. Crisp, juicy flesh makes excellent sauce. Introduced in 1948. *Source History: 1 in 2000.* **Sources: Ed5.**

Hewes (Virginia Crab) - Old variety. Small fruit, 1.5" diameter. Translucent, yellow flesh with strong, musky flavor. Productive tree; good pollinator. Ripens early September. *Source History: 1 in 1992; 1 in 2000.* **Sources: Ro3.**

Hewes Virginia Crab - Makes a highly flavored dry cider. Dull red skin is dotted with white specks. Translucent yellow flesh has a strong musky flavor. Productive tree is a good pollinator. Zones 5-9. *Source History: 1 in 2000.* **Sources: Son.**

Heyer 2 - *Source History: 1 in 2000.* **Sources: Bea.**

Heyer 12 - Russian parentage. Straw-colored fruit. Excellent for cooking and preserving. Fruit must be picked before full maturity to be stored. Highly productive. Ripens early; mid-August. Very hardy up into Canada; Zone 2. Originated in Saskatchewan. Introduced in 1940. *Source History: 1 in 1988; 6 in 1992; 3 in 2000.* **Sources: Bea, SH8, Stl.**

Heyer 20 - Medium to medium-large yellow-green fruit. Crisp, juicy flesh. Sweet flavor. Drought resistant. Ripens in late August. Hardy to Zone 2. Developed in Saskatchewan in 1936. *Source History: 1 in 1988; 2 in 1992; 1 in 2000.* **Sources: Bea.**

HFR24T178 - Attractive, oblate-round fruit. Yellow background color; 90% medium dark red. Slightly conspicuous lenticels. Pale yellow flesh is slightly astringent. Spreading tree. Cedar rust susceptible. Ripens early September. Trial variety from Purdue University. *Source History: 1 in 2000.* **Sources: Cla.**

Hibernal - Huge, yellow, striped fruit. Somewhat astringent; good when dried. Tree is useful for top-working as it imparts some hardiness to tender varieties. Ripens midseason. Hardy to -50 degrees F. Old Russian variety. *Source History: 3 in 1988; 3 in 1992; 1 in 2000.* **Sources: Stl.**

Hickman - Southern variety. *Source History: 1 in 2000.* **Sources: Ca15.**

Hidden Rose - Red fleshed fruit. *Source History: 4 in 2000.* **Sources: Ch9, Or9, Ro3, So5.**

Hightop Sweet (Early Sweet, Spence's Early, Yellow Sweet June, Summer Sweet, Summer Sweet of Ohio, Sweet June of Illinois) - Old variety of obscure origin, but a favorite in the early days of the Plymouth Colonies. Medium size fruit with sweet, yellow flesh. Especially suitable for drying. Short storage life. Vigorous tree bears heavily. Ripens from July to August depending on location. Introduced in 1822. *Source History: 3 in 1988; 5 in 1992; 4 in 2000.* **Sources: Bea, Ch9, So5, Wo7.**

Hillieri - Outstanding pollen source for commercial varieties in tests in England. Small, single flowers are cream with tinge of pink. Fruit under 1". Tree is extremely heavy bloomer. Blooms between Red and Golden Delicious. *Source History: 1 in 1988; 1 in 1992; 1 in 2000.* **Sources: Bl4.**

Himakami - *Source History: 2 in 1992; 1 in 2000.* **Sources: Nrs.**

Hog Sweet - Old mountain apple of north Georgia. Thought to be extinct at one time. Yellow skin with red stripes. Very sweet flavor. Midseason bloom. Very productive. Makes a fine cider when mixed with tart apples. *Source History: 1 in 1988; 1 in 1992; 2 in 2000.* **Sources: Hid, La3.**

Hoke - Medium size fruit with red flesh. *Source History: 1 in 2000.* **Sources: Hid.**

Hokuto - Fuji x Mutsu. Large round fruit. Yellow skin with red stripes. Pale yellow flesh has a high sugar content. Excellent flavor. Ripens in late September, two weeks before Fuji. Originated in Japan. *Source History: 3 in 2000.* **Sources: Cla, Nrs, Ro3.**

Holiday - Cross of Jonathan x Macoun (McIntosh x Jersey Black). Has inherited rich flavor of Jonathan and white, juicy flesh of Macoun. Shiny bright red over yellow skin with prominent bloom and dots. Ripens late in the season. Introduced by the Ohio Agricultural Experiment Station in 1964. *Source History: 1 in 1988; 5 in 1992; 5 in 2000.* **Sources: Bea, Bl4, Ch9, Sc6, So5.**

Holland - Large, red fruit. Tree makes good growth; bears well. Ripens in mid-July. Good market apple. *Source History: 3 in 1988; 6 in 1992; 4 in 2000.* **Sources: CO5, Tex, Wel, Wom.**

Hollow Log - Southern variety. *Source History: 1 in 2000.* **Sources: Ca15.**

Holly - Jonathan x Macoun. Yellow skin with red splotches. High quality flesh with crisp texture of Jonathan and fine flavor of Macoun. Developed in Wooster, Ohio. *Source History: 2 in 1992; 4 in 2000.* **Sources: Ca15, Ch9, Nrs, Sc6.**

Holstein (Holstein Pippin) - Open-pollinated seedling of Cox's Orange Pippin from Hamburg, Germany dating back to 1918. Larger, deep yellow fruit with varying reddish orange blush; sometimes lightly russeted. Creamy yellow, firm, juicy flesh. Delicious, aromatic flavor of its parent Cox's Orange. Superior quality. Good keeper. Tree has nice spreading habit; vigorous grower. Triploid, so will not pollinate other varieties. Very scab resistant. Ripens late September to mid-October. Zone 4. *Source History: 7 in 1988; 6 in 1992; 9 in 2000.* **Sources: Bea, Bl4, Ch9, Cu4, Ed5, Er2, Gr4, So5, Son.**

Home Sweet - Used fresh and for preserves. *Source History: 1 in 2000.* **Sources: Hid.**

Homestead - Large yellow fruit is blushed with red. Excellent cooking apple. Scab resistant. Hardy. Ripens early Sept. Originated as a seedling in western New York State. *Source History: 1 in 2000.* **Sources: Sc6.**

Honey Ball - *Source History: 1 in 2000.* **Sources: Cu4.**

Honey Cider (Honey Sweet) - Originally used as a blending apple to sweeten apple cider. Flat-shaped, light green fruit with some russet. Crisp, juicy, sweet, translucent flesh. Good for fresh eating; great dessert apple. Round, upright, open, spreading, handsome tree; needs little pruning. Bears young. Good disease tolerance. Ripens in early August. Hardy in Zones 5-7. Rediscovered at an abandoned homesite in Shenandoah Valley of Virginia by Dr. Elwood Fisher. *Source History: 4 in 1988; 7 in 1992; 5 in 2000.* **Sources: Bl4, Ca15, Gr4, Or9, Wh4.**

Honey Sweet - Old-timer. *Source History: 1 in 1992; 1 in 2000.* **Sources: Ed5.**

Honeycrisp (Minn. 1711R Cultivar) - Macoun x Honeygold. Fruit is mottled red over yellow ground color. Very crisp flesh. Excellent eating and keeping qualities. Annual bearer. Rated superior to McIntosh and Delicious for fresh eating. Keeps up to five months in common storage. Ripens late September to late October. Hardy to Zone 3. Released by the University of Minnesota, 1991. Trademarked. U.S. Plant Patent No. 7197. *Source History: 12 in 1992; 25 in 2000.* **Sources: Ad2, AG2, BA14, Bea, Ch9, Clo, Co2, COL, Cu4, Ed5, Er2, Fa1, Fed, Hi9, Jun, Rai, Ro3, SH8, Si3, St4, Stl, TR8, Va2, WAF, WI12.**

Honeygold (MN 1595) - Golden Delicious x Haralson. Hardy substitute for Golden Delicious developed especially for cold, northern areas. Golden Delicious flavor; Haralson hardiness. Medium to large, golden to yellowish green fruit with very smooth finish and reddish bronze blush. Flavor is sweeter and more bland than Golden Delicious. High quality. Superior storage qualities. Moderately vigorous tree. Susceptible to fire blight; shows moderate resistance to scab. Ripens during October. Hardy to -50 degrees F. with occasional winter injury. Thrives where Golden Delicious is not hardy. Developed in Minnesota, 1970. *Source History: 8 in 1988; 15 in 1992; 16 in 2000.* **Sources: Bea, Bl4, Ch9, Ed5, Er2, Fa1, Fed, Gur, Hi9, Jun, LA4, LI7, Nrs, SH8, Stl, Wa16.**

Hoople's Antique Gold - Bud mutation from standard Golden Delicious tree. Russet fruit with antique gold coloration. Extraordinary flavor. Same season as Golden Delicious. Zones 6-10. Discovered in the orchards of Mr. Harry Hoople of Hoople Fruit Farm in Otway, Ohio. *Source History: 1 in 1988; 1 in 1992; 3 in 2000.* **Sources: Ch9, So5, Son.**

Hoover (Black Coal) - Large yellow fruit overlaid with red stripes. Firm, tender, yellow flesh with brisk acid flavor. Mid to very late season. Raised in 1850 in South Carolina. *Source History: 1 in 1988; 2 in 1992; 4 in 2000.* **Sources: Ca15, Gr4, La3, Or9.**

Hopa Crab - Red-orange fruit makes fine jelly. Upright tree to 20'. Hardy in Zone 4. *Source History: 29 in 1992; 15 in 2000.* **Sources: Big, CO5, GI3, Gur, Ho5, LA4, LI7, MI10, Nrs, ORA, SH8, SIM, STR, Wel, WI4.**

Horse Apple - Greenish yellow fruit with a pink blush. Very tart until fully ripened. Distinctive flavor. Very good for jelly, drying and cooking. Slower to bear than most. Ripens in late July. Zones 5-8. Probably originated in North Carolina in the 1700s. *Source History: 2 in 1988; 4 in 1992; 6 in 2000.* **Sources: Cla, Iso, Jo3, La3, Or9, Ur2.**

Horse Apple, Red - Southern variety. *Source History: 1 in 2000.* **Sources: Ca15.**

Hubbardston Nonesuch (Hubbardston, Hubbardston Nonsuch, American Blush, American Nonpariel, Farmer's Profit, Hubbardston's Pippin, Old Town Pippin, Orleans, Van Fleet, John May) - Large, rugged fruit. Mostly red skin with golden highlights. Hard, crisp, yet fine grained flesh. Sprightly and rich in flavor; becomes mild and sweet when fully ripe. Regularly produces large crop of evenly sized fruit. Ripens during October. Zones 6-10. One of the greatest Massachusetts apples of the 19th century. Introduced in 1832. *Source History: 5 in 1988; 11 in 1992; 13 in 2000.* **Sources: Bea, Bl4, Ca15, Ch9, Cu4, Ed5, Gr4, Hid, Or9, Sc6, So5, Son, Wo7.**

<u>Hudson's Golden Gem</u> - Large, high quality russet. Conical, elongated fruit. Smooth, uniformly dull yellow russet skin; very long stem. Sugary, juicy, crisp flesh. Flavor is somewhat nutty. Excellent dessert apple. Keeps in storage for three months. Heavily russeted fruit sometimes cracks when ripe. Hangs on the tree well into winter. Large, vigorous, spreading, productive tree bears annually. Notable disease resistance, especially to scab. Requires cross-pollination. Ripens in late October. Requires 600 hours of chilling. Hardy in Zones 3. Discovered as fence row seedling at Hudson Nursery in Tangent, Oregon, 1931. *Source History: 12 in 1988; 13 in 1992; 16 in 2000.* **Sources: Bea, Bl4, Ch9, Ea3, Ed5, Er2, Fed, Gr4, On3, Or9, Rai, Sc6, So5, Son, Wh4, WI4.**

<u>Huffman Red</u> - Southern variety. *Source History: 1 in 2000.* **Sources: Ca15.**

<u>Humboldt Crab</u> - Crab hybrid selected by Albert Etter for its ornamental quality. Yellowish cream fruit has shiny transparent skin that reveals pinkish tint of the outer flesh. Masses of 2-3" fragrant blossoms tinted pink. Original name was Jumbo Transcendent which indicates its crab apple lineage as well as its size; small apple or a very large crab. Apples hang on the tree like Christmas ornaments a long time after ripening in September. *Source History: 1 in 1988; 1 in 1992; 1 in 2000.* **Sources: Gr4.**

<u>Hunge</u> - Large red fruit is covered with a russet netting. Excellent for cooking or drying and fresh eating. Mild flavor. Juicy texture. Ripens in late August. Listed in many North Carolina nursery catalogs until about 1905. *Source History: 1 in 2000.* **Sources: Ca15.**

<u>Hunt Russet</u> (Russet Pearmain) - Old-timer. Rare. Sometimes has bronze red cheek in full sun; generally yellow lightly overlaid with russet. Acidulous, pear-like flavor. Known to keep in root cellars over a year. Hardy in Zone 3. Reported to have originated on the Hunt farm in Concord, Massachusets in the 1750s. *Source History: 2 in 1988; 6 in 1992; 5 in 2000.* **Sources: Bl4, Ch9, Or9, So5, Wo7.**

<u>Huntsman</u> (Huntsman Favorite) - Large, oblate-shaped fruit with smooth, green-yellow skin, blushed with orange-red. Firm flesh is tinged with yellow; not very crisp but juicy and tender. Vigorous tree does not begin to bear early but produces heavily when it does. Scab and bitter rot susceptible in some regions where sunburn is a problem. Ripens in late September. Originated on the farm of John Huntsman in Fayette, Missouri about 1850. *Source History: 2 in 1992; 2 in 2000.* **Sources: Or9, Wo7.**

<u>Hyde King</u> - Originated in the Midwest; at one time showed commercial potential. Quite rare. Large fruit with golden yellow skin blushed with red. Uncommonly hard, crisp, juicy flesh. Flavor is a well-balanced blend of sugar and acid. Excellent kitchen apple. Ripens in mid-October. Will hang on the tree in good condition into December. *Source History: 2 in 1988; 5 in 1992; 3 in 2000.* **Sources: Ch9, Gr4, So5.**

<u>Hyslop Crab</u> - Yellow flesh is juicy upon ripening but quickly becomes dry and mealy. Good for jelly, pickling and cider blending. Recorded in 1869. *Source History: 2 in 1992; 5 in 2000.* **Sources: Bo5, Cid, Nrs, Or9, Wor.**

<u>Idamac</u> - Complex cross of Red Delicious x Red Rome. Oblong-conical fruit.

The beautiful skin color is mottled red over a green ground color that fades to a salmon color and is covered by large white lenticels. Crisp, juicy, sweet flesh is mildly subacid with a distinctive flavor. Edible one month before ripening in mid-September. Hardy in Zone 4. *Source History: 1 in 2000.* **Sources: Bea.**

Idared - Wagener x Jonathan. Large, solid, strikingly bright red fruit. Smooth, waxy, medium thick skin. Crisp, fine grained, aromatic, white flesh. Mildly acid flavor. Excellent dessert apple; good for baking, sauce and pies. Fine processing qualities. Tart at harvest time; quality develops in storage. Small to medium size tree bears heavy crops annually. Blooms early; ripens late. Pollinate with Summer-red, Spartan or Lodi. Susceptible to fire blight. Some resistance to scab. Ripens from mid to late October. Hardy in Zone 4. Developed at the Idaho Agricultural Experiment Station for commercial processing. Introduced in 1942. *Source History: 22 in 1988; 27 in 1992; 22 in 2000.* **Sources: Ad2, Amb, Bea, Bl4, Bo5, Ch9, Clo, Co2, Gr4, Hi9, LA4, Mel, Mi1, Nrs, Sc6, So5, Son, TR8, Va2, WAF, Wh4, Wor.**

Idared, Marquis - More red color than standard Idared strain. Firm, white flesh is crisp and mildly acid. Tart at harvest time; quality develops in storage. Good processing apple. Late keeper. Medium size tree bears young. Annual bearer. Fire blight susceptible. Trademarked. *Source History: 1 in 2000.* **Sources: Hi9.**

Idared, Spur - Fruit shows slightly more red than regular Idared. Smaller tree size due to heavier bearing characteristics. Fire blight susceptible. *Source History: 1 in 2000.* **Sources: Wh4.**

Indian Summer - *Source History: 1 in 2000.* **Sources: WI12.**

Ingram - Seedling of Ralls. Thick, tough, clear yellow skin is mottled, dotted and streaked with pink to crimson. Bears very heavy crops biennially; thinning is necessary to prevent limb breakage. Blooms late; subject to fire blight. Stores well. Ripens in October. Found on the farm of Martin Ingram near Springfield, Missouri about 1850. *Source History: 2 in 1992; 3 in 2000.* **Sources: Ca15, Ch9, Cid.**

Ingrid Marie - Danish seedling of Cox's Orange Pippin. Very dark red fruit with large, white dots. Crisp, refreshing, sprightly, white flesh. Good cropper. Ripens in late September. Widely grown in Denmark. Introduced in 1920. *Source History: 1 in 1988; 4 in 1992; 2 in 2000.* **Sources: Ch9, So5.**

Iowa Beauty - Yellow and red skin color. Flesh is very juicy with a sweet tang. The core becomes pink sugar when overripe. Ripens early. Hardy to -50 degrees F. Patten introduction. *Source History: 2 in 1992; 2 in 2000.* **Sources: Ed5, Stl.**

Irazu - *Source History: 1 in 2000.* **Sources: RA4.**

Irish Peach (Early Crofton, Early Apple) - Ancient Irish apple; Irish seedling x Yellow Transparent. Small, green fruit with faint red stripes. Pleasantly rich flavor; fine aroma. Crisp, juicy, good for baking. Becomes greasy in storage. Upright growth. Inclined to be a shy bearer when young. Tip bearer. Ripens during mid-summer. Hardy to -50 degrees F. with occasional winter injury. Originated in Eire, Ireland around 1820. *Source History: 4 in 1988; 8 in 1992; 8 in 2000.* **Sources: Bl4, Ch9, Ed5, Gr4, Or9, So5, Son, Stl.**

Iron Black - *Source History: 1 in 2000.* **Sources: Or9.**

Isam - Southern variety. *Source History: 1 in 2000.* **Sources: Ca15.**

Isayev's Desertnyi - *Source History: 1 in 2000.* **Sources: Ch9.**

Jacob Sweeting - Southern variety. *Source History: 1 in 2000.* **Sources: Ca15.**

Jager Reinette - Southern variety. *Source History: 1 in 2000.* **Sources: Ca15.**

Jake's Seedling - Southern variety. *Source History: 1 in 2000.* **Sources: Ca15.**

James Grieve - Speculated to be a seedling of either Potts Seedling or Cox's Orange Pippin. Medium to large, conical fruit. Almost solid crimson over yellow. Very juicy yellowish flesh. Excellent flavor. Poor keeper. Excellent cropper. Ripens in early September. Originated around 1890 from a seed planted by James Grieve of Edinburgh, Scotland. *Source History: 2 in 1988; 6 in 1992; 3 in 2000.* **Sources: Bea, Ch9, So5.**

Jarrett - Southern variety. *Source History: 1 in 2000.* **Sources: Ca15.**

Jean - *Source History: 1 in 2000.* **Sources: Ch9.**

Jefferis (Everbearing, Grantham) - Thin skinned, light red fruit with darker red stripes. Juicy, crisp yet tender and melting yellow flesh. Rich pear-like flavor. Bruises easily. Hardy tree bears heavy crop every year. Scab and mildew resistant. Ripens mid-September. Hardy to Zone 4. Originated on the farm of Isaac Jefferis of Chester County, Pennsylvania in 1830. Was awarded premium for best seedling apple exhibited by the Pennsylvania Horticultural Society in 1848. *Source History: 6 in 1988; 9 in 1992; 11 in 2000.* **Sources: Bea, Ca15, Ch9, Cu4, Ed5, Gr4, La3, Or9, So5, Son, Wo7.**

Jenner Sweet - Fameuse x crab. Yellow with red stripes. Good flavored, sweet apple. Similar to Fameuse. Hardy to -50 degrees F. with occasional winter injury. *Source History: 1 in 1988; 1 in 1992; 1 in 2000.* **Sources: Stl.**

Jersey Black - Southern variety. *Source History: 1 in 2000.* **Sources: Ca15.**

Jerseymac - NJ24 x July Red. Early McIntosh strain; ripens 2-4 weeks earlier and colors better. Medium to large fruit with 80% red skin over light straw background. Firm, crisp, juicy, aromatic flesh. Medium firm texture, but fruits show bruises easily. Medium sweetness. Useful for sauce, pies, eating fresh. Reasonably good keeper for a summer apple. Upright, spreading tree; vigorous, productive, annual bearer. Resistant to cedar-apple rust. Ships well; very marketable, making a mark in the commercial market. Ripens from early July to early August depending on location. Hardy to Zone 5. Developed in New Jersey. Introduced in 1971. *Source History: 14 in 1988; 15 in 1992; 9 in 2000.* **Sources: Bea, Bl4, Ch9, Hi9, Nrs, So5, TR8, Va2, Wom.**

Jerseyred - Hard, green-red processing type. Vigorous and productive. Grown extensively in New Jersey. *Source History: 2 in 2000.* **Sources: Ad2, Ch9.**

Jesse Hall - Old Southern Appalachian variety. Smooth textured fruit. Some disease resistance. *Source History: 2 in 1988; 1 in 1992; 1 in 2000.* **Sources: Bea.**

Jewett Red (Jewett's Fine Red, Nodhead) - Old New Hampshire and Maine apple. Deep crimson fruit covered with dark red stripes, heavy blue bloom and yellow specks. Very short stem. Ripens in late October; reaches perfection by late December; keeps until January. Zone 4. Originated in Hollis, New Hampshire in the early 1800s. *Source History: 3 in 1988; 5 in 1992; 5 in 2000.* **Sources: Bea, Ch9, Cu4, Fed, Wo7.**

Joe Little - Southern variety. *Source History: 1 in 2000.* **Sources: Ca15.**

John Apple - Southern variety. *Source History: 1 in 2000.* **Sources: Ca15.**

John Downie - Flavorful, conic-shaped, red-orange fruit. Eaten fresh or for jelly. Disease resistant tree. Heavy producer. Originated in England. *Source History: 1 in 2000.* **Sources: Rai.**

Johnson's Fine Winter Keeper - *Source History: 1 in 2000.* **Sources: Or9.**

Jon-A-Red, Stark (Rasa Cultivar) - Improved strain of the famous Jonathan apple. Glossy bright red skin. Snappy crisp flesh. Vigorous grower; dependable cropping. Self-pollinating. Ripens in mid-September. Hardy in Zones 5-8.

Trademarked. *Source History: 1 in 1988; 1 in 1992; 2 in 2000.* **Sources: AG2, St4.**

Jonadel - Jonathan x Delicious. Solid red skin color sometimes flushed with orange-red and streaked carmine with scattered russet dots. Sweet, subacid flavor. Larger, milder and more blight resistant than Jonathan. Subject to premature drop. Bears annually. Stores well. Developed at the Iowa Agricultural Experiment Station. Introduced in 1958. *Source History: 1 in 1988; 6 in 1992; 3 in 2000.* **Sources: Bl4, Ch9, Nrs.**

Jonafree (Co-op 22) - Improved Jonathan type with good dessert quality. Fruit is 75% medium red with smooth russet-free skin. Firm, crisp, juicy, pale yellow flesh. Tree is field immune to scab, resistant to fire blight and cedar-apple rust. Somewhat susceptible to mildew. Fruit hangs well to maturity. Ripe fruit does not develop Jonathan Spot; much less tendency to internal breakdown. Zones 5-8. U.S. Plant Patent No. 4633. *Source History: 1 in 1988; 10 in 1992; 10 in 2000.* **Sources: Bea, Bu7, Ch9, Gur, Hi9, Jun, Mi1, St4, TR8, Va2.**

Jonagold - Golden Delicious x Jonathan. Large fruit striped red over bright yellow. Firm, cracking, juicy, slightly tart flesh. Superb, rich, full flavor. Finest dessert and eating quality; good cooking properties. Will store in common refrigeration for three months. Handsome, sturdy, vigorous, spreading tree; annually productive. Triploid; requires a pollinator. Susceptible to scab and mildew. Ripens from mid-September to late October depending on location. Requires from 700-800 hours of chilling. Hardy in Zones 5-8. Currently the most planted variety in Europe. Developed at the Geneva Station in New York. Introduced in 1968. *Source History: 28 in 1988; 38 in 1992; 35 in 2000.* **Sources: AG2, Bay, Bea, Bl4, Bo5, Bu7, Ch9, Cla, Clo, Co2, CO5, Cum, Ea3, Er2, Gur, Hi9, JOY, La3, LA4, Leu, ME3, Mi1, Mo19, Nrs, Rai, Ro3, Sc6, SH8, So5, Son, St4, Ur2, Wh4, WI4, Wor.**

Jonagold, Crimson (Romagold Cultivar) - Large fruit with excellent color. Flavorful. Long storage life. Triploid; requires pollination. U.S. Plant Patent No. 9541. *Source History: 2 in 2000.* **Sources: BR10, Cu4.**

Jonagold, De Coster - Red cultivar of Jonagold is one of the leading strains planted in Europe. Fruit has an attractive red blush over a yellow background. Vigorous, productive trees with spreading habit. Triploid. Zones 5-8. Developed by Henry De Coster, prominent horticulturist from Belgium. U.S. Plant Patent No. 8049. *Source History: 1 in 1992; 3 in 2000.* **Sources: Ad2, Jo3, Va2.**

Jonagold, Jomured - *Source History: 1 in 2000.* **Sources: Mo19.**

Jonagold, Nicolai's Jored King (Pi-A 11, 24) - Consistently produces 80-90% red blushed fruit. Cream colored juicy flesh with crisp texture and sweet-sour taste. Tree habit resembles that of standard Jonagold. Trademarked. Plant patent applied for. *Source History: 1 in 1992; 1 in 2000.* **Sources: TR8.**

Jonagold, Red (New Jonagold) - Japanese strain. Red blush over yellow ground. Juicy, semisweet taste. Usually large. All purpose. Keeps well. Triploid; cannot pollinate other varieties. Cross incompatible with Golden Delicious. Fruit must be exposed to sunlight for coloration. Best apples will not have over 75% red color. Matures during end of Red Delicious harvest. Should be grown in moderate vigor to prevent winter injury. *Source History: 2 in 1988; 6 in 1992; 4 in 2000.* **Sources: Amb, Ch9, Jo3, WAF.**

Jonagold, Rubinstar - Excellent quality, early coloring Jonagold strain. Compact tree. U.S. Plant Patent No. 7590. *Source History: 1 in 1992; 3 in 2000.* **Sources: Co2, COL, WAF.**

Jonagored Supra - Medium to large round fruit. Red-blushed skin with very fine red stripes. Cream colored, firm, crisp, juicy flesh. Fine taste. Trademarked. U.S. Plant Patent No. 10,401. *Source History: 1 in 2000.* **Sources: Hi9.**

Jonagram - Jonathan x Ingram. Medium to large, round fruit with thin, tough, smooth, pale bright yellow skin overlaid with red. Firm, white flesh is fine grained, juicy, crisp and tender. Subacid flavor. Ripens about the same time as Jonathan. Developed at the Missouri Agricultural Experiment Station. Introduced in 1956. *Source History: 1 in 1988; 3 in 1992; 1 in 2000.* **Sources: Ch9.**

Jonagrimes (Stark Jongrimes, Hoosier Seedling) - Unknown parentage, despite the name. Oblong, truncate-shaped fruit. Skin is orange-red striped over greenish yellow ground color; covered with small inconspicuous dots. Tart flavor. Shy bearer. Highly mildew susceptible. Severe preharvest drop makes it unsuitable for the commercial orchardist. Ripens in late August. Originated in Indiana in the 1920s. *Source History: 2 in 1988; 5 in 1992; 2 in 2000.* **Sources: Bl4, Ch9.**

Jonalicious - Ripens late in the season. *Source History: 2 in 1988; 3 in 1992; 1 in 2000.* **Sources: Ch9.**

Jonalicious, Stark (Daniels Cultivar) - Bright red skin with yellow undertones. Keeps for months in cold cellar or refrigerator. Pollinate with Stark Jon-A-Red or Starkspur Golden Delicious. Ripens in mid-September. Hardy in Zones 5-8. *Source History: 1 in 1988; 2 in 1992; 2 in 2000.* **Sources: AG2, St4.**

Jonamac - Jonathan x McIntosh. McIntosh-type dessert apple with improved color. Medium size, firm fruit with 90% dark red color over greenish background. Firm, crisp, high quality flesh. Flavor similar to McIntosh. Superior to McIntosh in eating quality. Medium size, productive, medium vigor tree. Fruit hangs well on tree. Ripens in late September. Hardy to -50 degrees F. with occasional winter injury. Developed by the New York State Agricultural Experiment Station. Introduced in 1972. *Source History: 10 in 1988; 15 in 1992; 15 in 2000.* **Sources: Ad2, Amb, Bea, Ch9, Co2, Cu4, Hi9, Mo19, Nrs, Sc6, So5, Stl, Va2, WAF, Wh4.**

Jonared - Jonathan cross. Very productive. *Source History: 2 in 1992; 3 in 2000.* **Sources: Ch9, Nrs, Wel.**

Jonathan (Philip Rick, Red Jonathan, Ulster Seedling) - Medium to large, almost round fruit. Highly colored in sunny climates; striped red in cool climates. Thin, tough skin. Fine, juicy flesh. Sprightly, subacid flavor. Good for cooking and eating fresh. Keeps until late winter. Tree is a naturally small, moderate grower that bears young, annually and heavily. Self-fruitful, but crops are improved with cross-pollination. Bred for scab resistance. Ripens from mid-September to mid-October depending on location. Requires 700-800 hours of chilling. Hardy in Zones 4-8. First description published in 1826 by J. Buel of Albany, New York, according to Beach. *Source History: 41 in 1988; 59 in 1992; 44 in 2000.* **Sources: Bar, Bay, Bea, Bl4, Cid, Cla, CO5, Cu4, Fi1, FO10, Ga20, GI3, GR26, Ho5, JOY, LA4, Lee, Leu, Mc3, Mel, Mi1, MI10, MI5, Na4, Nrs, ORA, Pi2, Po2, Rid, Sav, Sc6, SH8, So5, Son, STR, Tex, TU5, Ur2, Wa16, Wel, Wh4, WI4, Wo7, Wor.**

Jonathan, Chambers Strain - Bright red fruit. Distinctive, fruity flavor. Ripening date varies with climate and exposure. *Source History: 1 in 1988; 1 in 1992; 1 in 2000.* **Sources: Gr4.**

Jonathan, Dark Red - Medium size fruit. Bright red skin. Tender, crisp, very juicy, yellow flesh. Sweet-tart flavor. Excellent cooking apple; also good for eating fresh. Bears heavily in just a few years. Good keeper. Ripens in mid-October. *Source History: 3 in 1988; 3 in 1992; 2 in 2000.* **Sources: Bu1, Fo4.**

Jonathan, Double Red - Medium to large fruit. Improved color; solid bright red. Bears young; produces heavy crops every year. Excellent pollinator for other varieties. Ripens during early winter. Popular in both commercial and home orchard plantings. Original budwood for this strain was selected from the Experimental Farm at Kearneysville, West Virginia. Good strain for the middle of the Jonathan season. *Source History: 4 in 1988; 4 in 1992; 2 in 2000.* **Sources: Hi9, SIM.**

Jonathan, Improved Red (Snyder Strain) - Red sport of Jonathan that develops red color earlier than other Jonathan strains. Reliable cropper. Excellent pollinator. Shows good blending quality for apple cider; preferred for candied apples. *Source History: 1 in 1992; 1 in 2000.* **Sources: Ad2.**

Jonathan, King Red - Red sport of Jonathan. Similar except that it colors earlier and more highly, and is more mildew resistant. Firm fruit. Often used to make candied apples. Characteristically sets fruit during late spring frosts. Often used to pollinate Red Delicious. *Source History: 1 in 1988; 2 in 1992; 1 in 2000.* **Sources: Nrs.**

Jonathan, Ruby Red - Early coloring Jonathan sport. Develops full color by August 1 in north central Washington. Crisp, juicy flesh with a slightly tart flavor. *Source History: 1 in 2000.* **Sources: Va2.**

Jonathan, Sport Nured - Discovered as a bud sport of Blackjon in the C and O Nursery Orchards. True Jonathan flavor, quality and productiveness plus very early coloring. *Source History: 1 in 1988; 1 in 1992; 1 in 2000.* **Sources: Co2.**

Jonathan, UltraRed Stark (Higred Cultivar) - U.S. Plant Patent No. 6406. *Source History: 1 in 1992; 2 in 2000.* **Sources: AG2, St4.**

Jonathan, Welday - *Source History: 1 in 1992; 1 in 2000.* **Sources: Ch9.**

Jones' Favorite - Southern variety. *Source History: 1 in 2000.* **Sources: Ca15.**

Jonica (Schneica Cultivar) - Sport of Jonagold discovered in Germany. Fruit color similar to Jonagold, but with a deeper blush and faded red color. Stores well. Ripens midseason. Zones 5-8. U.S. Plant Patent No. 7146. *Source History: 1 in 1992; 2 in 2000.* **Sources: Mel, Va2.**

Jonwin - Albert Etter variety claimed to be a cross of Jonathan and Baldwin. General appearance of a well-colored Jonathan, but is much larger. Has the crisper texture of Baldwin combined with Jonathan's distinctive aromatic flavor and is brighter red than either. At one time it was rated as a promising new commercial variety by the Oregon State Experiment Station, but never caught on with the industry. Ripens during September. *Source History: 1 in 1988; 3 in 1992; 2 in 2000.* **Sources: Ch9, Gr4.**

Jordan Russet - Juicy, hard, red russet. Excellent keeper. Makes delicious cider. Ripens late in the season. Hardy to -50 degrees F. Origin unknown. *Source History: 1 in 1988; 1 in 1992; 1 in 2000.* **Sources: Stl.**

Joy's Delight - *Source History: 1 in 2000.* **Sources: Ed5.**

Joyce - McIntosh x Livland Raspberry. Yellow fruit washed with crimson. Juicy, aromatic, white flesh. Somewhat similar to McIntosh. Hardy to -50 degrees F. with occasional winter injury. *Source History: 1 in 1988; 1 in 1992; 1 in 2000.* **Sources: Stl.**

Jubilee - McIntosh x Grimes Golden. Medium size, shiny, solid bright red fruit. Crisp, juicy, cream colored flesh; agreeably flavored. Drops from the tree when ripe. Keeps very well. Ripens during October. Developed at Dominion Experiment Station in Summerland, British Columbia. Introduced in 1926. *Source His-*

tory: 1 in 1988; 1 in 1992; 2 in 2000. **Sources: Ed5, So5.**

July Golden (Booth's July Gold) - *Source History: 1 in 1988; 2 in 1992; 2 in 2000.* **Sources: Ch9, CO5.**

July Red - Medium size, red fruit. Firm, tasty flesh. Ripens in late July. Developed in New Jersey as the result of a long and complex breeding program. Introduced in 1962. *Source History: 2 in 1988; 5 in 1992; 5 in 2000.* **Sources: Bea, Bl4, Ch9, Nrs, TU5.**

July Tart - Conical shape. Green skin color. High quality tart flesh. Outstanding cooking and sauce apple. Productive tree tends toward biennial bearing. Ripens in August. *Source History: 1 in 1988; 2 in 1992; 3 in 2000.* **Sources: Ch9, Gr4, Sc6.**

July-August Go-No-Further - Southern variety. *Source History: 1 in 2000.* **Sources: Ca15.**

June Sweeting - Southern variety. *Source History: 1 in 2000.* **Sources: Ca15.**

Kandil Sinap (Jubilee) - Tall, narrow, cylindrical-shaped apple. Creamy yellow porcelain-like skin washed with brilliant red blush. Crisp, juicy, fine grained flesh. Excellent flavor. Tree grows in a pronounced narrow pyramidal dwarfish form. Heavy, regular bearer. Ripens in early October. Zones 6-9. Originated in Turkey in the early 1800s. *Source History: 2 in 1988; 7 in 1992; 7 in 2000.* **Sources: Bl4, Ch9, Gr4, Or9, Sc6, So5, Son.**

Kane (Cane) - Southern variety. *Source History: 1 in 2000.* **Sources: Ca15.**

Kaneb Sweet - Tolman Sweet x Yellow Transparent. Small to medium size fruit with tender yellow skin. Juicy sweet flesh. Excellent for fresh eating and sauce. Keeps 2-3 months in storage. Early ripening. Hardy to -50 degrees with occasional winter injury. *Source History: 1 in 2000.* **Sources: Stl.**

Karminj de Sonnaville (Karmine) - Cox's Orange Pippin x Jonathan. Fruit is brick red over a yellow-green ground color. Flavorful. Excellent winter keeper. Growth habit is spreading and vigorous. May be flower tender. Triploid; requires a pollinator. Ripens in September. Zones 6-9. Originated in Europe around 1949. *Source History: 1 in 1988; 6 in 1992; 7 in 2000.* **Sources: Bl4, Ch9, Clo, Mo19, Rai, So5, Son.**

Katharine - Wagener x Reinette Ananas. Resembles Wagener in form and color, only with more refined appearance. Firm, juicy flesh. Fine flavor. Excellent cooking quality. Keeps its high quality for a long time in storage. Ripens late. *Source History: 1 in 1988; 1 in 1992; 1 in 2000.* **Sources: Gr4.**

Kathryn's Favorite - Yellow skin with red wash and stripes. Rich, sweet, spicy flesh. Excellent for fresh eating. Good keeper. Midseason ripening. Hardy to -50 degrees F. with occasional winter injury. *Source History: 1 in 2000.* **Sources: Stl.**

Katja - James Grieve x Worcester Pearmain. Medium size red fruit. Juicy, yellow-white flesh with good flavor. Moderately vigorous, upright, spreading tree. Mildew scab tolerant. Good keeper. Ripens during September. Originated in Sweden. Introduced in 1966. *Source History: 3 in 1992; 3 in 2000.* **Sources: Bea, Ch9, Ed5.**

Keener Seedling - Southern variety. *Source History: 1 in 2000.* **Sources: Ca15.**

Keepsake - Malinda x Northern Spy. Unattractive, irregularly-shaped, 2.25-2.75" diameter, 90% red fruit. Fine grained, hard, very crisp, juicy, light yellow flesh. Strongly aromatic flavor. Very hard when picked. Mellows with age; attains peak fresh eating quality in January or February. Developed for its keeping qualities.

Keeps in storage through April. Moderately vigorous, spreading tree. Resistant to fire blight and cedar-apple rust. Ripens from Mid-October to mid-November depending on location. Hardy throughout Minnesota, but may not mature in northernmost counties. Withstands temperatures of -40 degrees F. Developed at the University of Minnesota. Introduced in 1979. *Source History: 8 in 1988; 13 in 1992; 11 in 2000.* **Sources: Bar, Bea, Ch9, Cu4, Ed5, Fed, Gr4, Hi9, Nrs, SH8, Stl.**

Kendall - *Source History: 1 in 1992; 2 in 2000.* **Sources: Bl4, Cu4.**

Kent - Cox's Orange Pippin x Jonathan. Medium size, conical fruit. Light red with smooth russet radiations from stem end. Crisp, white flesh. Sweeter, milder flavor than either parent. Ripens later than Cox's Orange Pippin; keeps longer. Developed at East Malling Research Station in England in the 1960s. *Source History: 1 in 1988; 3 in 1992; 2 in 2000.* **Sources: Ch9, So5.**

Kerr - Dolgo x Haralson. Red fruit. Good fresh after a mellowing period. Stores well. Very productive. Ripens midseason. Hardy to -50 degrees F. One of the very best apple x crab apple crosses. *Source History: 1 in 1988; 2 in 1992; 5 in 2000.* **Sources: Ch9, Ed5, LA4, Stl, Va5.**

Kerry Pippin (Kerry, Kerry Irish Pippin, Aromatic Pippin, Edmonston's Aromatic Pippin, Odelson's, Red Streak Pippin) - Old Irish apple. Small, shiny yellow fruit sometimes striped in the sun. Crisp, crunchy, hard flesh. Fine flavor. Singular characteristic is the frequent pushing over of the stem by the filling in of the flesh over the cavity. Fair storage quality. Ripens during late August. Hardy to Zone 5. Introduced in 1802. *Source History: 2 in 1988; 4 in 1992; 6 in 2000.* **Sources: Bea, Ch9, Chi, Or9, So5, Son.**

Keswick Codlin (Codlin, Keswick, Everbearing, White Codlin, Pinder's Apple) - Large, oblong, conical and not uniform fruit. Greenish yellow, sometimes with faint blush. Fine tart flavor. Ripens in early August. Zones 6-9. Ancient lineage; the classic early tart and sauce apple of England. First recorded in 1793. *Source History: 3 in 1988; 4 in 1992; 4 in 2000.* **Sources: Ed5, Gr4, So5, Son.**

Keystone Red - *Source History: 1 in 1992; 1 in 2000.* **Sources: Ch9.**

Kidd's Orange Red - Cox's Orange Pippin x Red Delicious. Shape and size of Delicious; quality and coloring are much closer to Cox's Orange Pippin. Medium to large, red blushed fruit. Thick skin with russet in some seasons. Juicy, crisp, quite firm, cream colored flesh. Pleasant aroma. Excellent flavor. High quality. Long stem holds well to the tree. Very spreading growth habit. Quite vigorous and productive. Ripens midseason. Zones 6-9. Developed in New Zealand in 1924. Was on a list of 20 favorite dessert apples compiled by Dr. Roger Way, Professor of Pomology at Geneva, New York where the largest apple collection in the U.S. is being kept. *Source History: 7 in 1988; 8 in 1992; 9 in 2000.* **Sources: Bea, Bl4, Ch9, Ea3, Ga20, Or9, So5, Son, Wor.**

Kimrome - Large green apple with red blush. Can weigh up to 2 lbs. each. Sprightly, semi-tart flavor. Excellent for fresh eating, cooking, freezing or drying. Good storage quality. Ripens mid-September. Should be trialed in all zones. Found in an old orchard in Ellijay, Georgia. *Source History: 2 in 2000.* **Sources: Ca15, Jo3.**

King - Large dessert apple. Red striping over yellow ground color. Crisp, sweet, white flesh. Good cooking; fair eating. Stores well. Pollinate with Golden Delicious, Lodi, McIntosh or Melrose. Ripens from late September to mid-October depending on location. Hardy in Zones 5-9. Highly recommended for the West Coast. *Source History: 11 in 1988; 9 in 1992; 9 in 2000.* **Sources: Bea, Bu7,**

Ea3, Er2, Hid, JOY, ME3, Nrs, WI12.

King David - Medium size, pale green fruit overlaid with deep dark red. Firm, crisp, spicy, juicy, yellow flesh. Thought to be a Jonathan x Arkansas Black cross. Very rich and flavorful. Resembles Winesap in appearance and taste. Versatile apple for cider, pies, sauce and eating. Fruits never seem to drop, all the while increasing in brilliance of color. For best eating, should be picked when the red color becomes complete. Good storage ability. Large tree. Very early to bear. Cross-pollinate. Resistant to fire blight. Ripens in late October. Hardy to Zone 5. Found in a fence row near Durham in Washington County, Arkansas in 1893. Introduced by Stark Brothers in 1902. *Source History: 13 in 1988; 15 in 1992; 19 in 2000.* **Sources: Bea, Bl4, Ca15, Ch9, Cid, Cu4, Ed5, Ga20, Gr4, Hid, Jo3, La3, Or9, Ro3, So5, Son, Ur2, Wom, Wor.**

King Luscious - Large fruit with irregular shape. Red over green skin color. Not attractive but has superior flavor and quality. Hardy tree bears consistently. Ripens in Oct. Chance seedling discovered in North Carolina in 1935. *Source History: 2 in 1992; 3 in 2000.* **Sources: Ca15, Ch9, Sc6.**

King of Pippins - Fine grained, creamy white flesh has a sprightly, vinous flavor. Some detect an almond-like or nutty flavor. One of the best pollinators for Cox's Orange Pippin. Believed to have originated in England under this name, having originally been called Golden Winter Pearmain. *Source History: 2 in 1992; 1 in 2000.* **Sources: Or9.**

King Solomon - Possibly a seedling or sibling of Arkansas Black. Dark purplish red fruit with bluish bloom and russet pattern around the stem. Color resembles Arkansas Black. Distinctive flavor resembles pineapple. Excellent dessert and cooking apple. Remains firm through cooking. Ripens during November and hangs on the tree a long time. *Source History: 1 in 1988; 1 in 1992; 1 in 2000.* **Sources: Gr4.**

Kingston Black (Kingston) - Famous English cider apple. One of only three English varieties used as a single-variety cider. Classed as a bitter sharp; 14.75% sugar content. Makes a distinctively flavored cider without blending. Medium size, round fruit. Crimson to purplish over yellowish orange background. Strongly astringent aftertaste. Vigorous, rounded tree. Somewhat hard to grow. Ripens from mid-September to mid-October depending on location. Hardy to Zone 5. Originated in England. Introduced in 1820. *Source History: 7 in 1988; 9 in 1992; 14 in 2000.* **Sources: Bea, Bl4, Ch9, Cid, Cla, Clo, Cu4, Ed5, Ga20, Gr4, La3, Or9, So5, Son.**

Kinnard's Choice (Kinnaird, Red Winter Cluster) - Winesap seedling that originated in Tennessee in the mid-1800s. Moderately thick, tough, smooth, yellow skin mottled and blushed with red. In the sun it becomes a lively deep red with shading of purplish red. Crisp, moderately fine to a little coarse, white flesh tinged with yellow. Fine for eating and cider. Ripens in September. Old-time favorite once grown widely throughout northern Georgia. Noted by Downing in 1872. *Source History: 1 in 1988; 3 in 1992; 3 in 2000.* **Sources: Ca15, Hid, La3.**

Kinsei - Golden Delicious x Ralls. Japanese variety. Large blushed yellow apple. Sugar content has been measured as high as 18%. Excellent keeper. Matures after Golden Delicious. *Source History: 2 in 1992; 3 in 2000.* **Sources: Ch9, Cla, Nrs.**

Knight - Medium size fruit with green-yellow skin covered with red. Good keeper. Originated in South Carolina. *Source History: 2 in 2000.* **Sources: Ca15, Hid.**

Knobbed Russet (Knobby Russet, Old Maid's Winter, Winter Apple, Winter Russet) - Green and yellow fruit, sometimes scarlet streaked in the sun. Uneven surface is overlaid with rough grey and black russet, welts and knobs; worthy of its name. Crisp, rich, sugary, highly flavored flesh of the highest quality. Ripens late. Originated in Sussex, England. Rescued from oblivion when the National Fruit Trials collection was put together after World War II. Introduced in 1819. *Source History: 3 in 1988; 4 in 1992; 4 in 2000.* **Sources: Ch9, Ed5, Gr4, So5.**

Kogetsu - *Source History: 2 in 1992; 1 in 2000.* **Sources: Nrs.**

Kotoku - *Source History: 1 in 1992; 1 in 2000.* **Sources: Nrs.**

Lacy - Medium size fruit is blushed on the sunny side. Flesh is sweet, crisp and juicy. Ripens in July and August. Fruit seldom rots on the tree. Grown for over one hundred years only in Union County, North Carolina. Listed by a southern nursery in 1858. *Source History: 1 in 2000.* **Sources: Ca15.**

Lady (Christmas Apple, Lady Apple, Pomme d' Api) - Traditionally a Christmas dessert apple. Small, smooth, creamy yellow fruit with glossy red cheek. Crisp, juicy, pure white flesh. Highly aromatic. Much of its fragrance and high flavor is in its skin; should not be peeled. Highest quality. Excellent cider variety. Keeps from December to May. Small, upright, refined tree that produces heavily; not quick to bear. Tends to bear biennially. Produces fruits in bunches. Requires cross-pollination. Susceptible to apple scab. Ripens late November or early December. Hardy to Zone 5. Grown in the gardens of Louis XIII at Orleans in 1628. Dates back to Roman times. *Source History: 10 in 1988; 16 in 1992; 19 in 2000.* **Sources: Ad2, Bea, Bl4, Bo5, Cid, Cla, Cu4, Ed5, Ga20, Gr4, Leu, Mi1, Or9, Sc6, So5, Son, WAF, Wo7, Wor.**

Lady Sudeley - *Source History: 1 in 2000.* **Sources: Ch9.**

Lady Sweet (Lady Sweeting, Roa Yon, Pommeroy, Roa Jon, Ladies Sweeting) - Green-yellow skin overlaid with bright red with carmine splashes. Sweet flavor. Tree is a moderate grower, regular heavy bearer and begins to fruit early. Thinning is necessary. Subject to scab. Ripens in October. Introduced in the 1840s. *Source History: 3 in 1988; 5 in 1992; 2 in 2000.* **Sources: La3, So5.**

Lady Williams - Red fruit. Outstanding quality. Remains crisp in storage. Vigorous tree; precocious bearer. Needs cross-pollination. Ripens in October. Does best only in Zones 7-8. Imported from Australia in 1968. *Source History: 1 in 1988; 4 in 1992; 4 in 2000.* **Sources: Ca15, Ch9, Cla, Hid.**

Lakeland - Medium size fruit. Mildly flavored, creamy yellow flesh. Good for eating fresh, baking, pies, sauce and freezing. Good storage. Ripens late September. Hardy to Zone 3. *Source History: 1 in 1992; 1 in 2000.* **Sources: Bea.**

Laking - *Source History: 1 in 1992; 1 in 2000.* **Sources: Ch9.**

Late Harrison - *Source History: 1 in 2000.* **Sources: Ch9.**

Late Strawberry (Autumn Strawberry, Fall Strawberry, Strawberry) - Small to medium, yellow-striped fruit splashed with light and dark red. Fine, crisp, tender, juicy, yellowish white flesh. Very good, slightly aromatic, subacid flavor. Ripens in September. Old New York apple that originated at Aurora in Cayuga County. First described in 1848. *Source History: 3 in 1988; 3 in 1992; 2 in 2000.* **Sources: So5, Wo7.**

Laurared - *Source History: 1 in 1992; 1 in 2000.* **Sources: Ch9.**

Law Rome, Starkspur (Peace Valley Cultivar) - *Source History: 1 in 2000.* **Sources: AG2.**

Lawver (Black Spy, Delaware Winter, Lawyer, Louver) - Named for the Illinois pomologist, A. M. Lawver. Popular variety in France in the late 19th century. Medium to large fruit with yellow skin nearly covered with bright red, shading a darker purple-red. Dense, green-yellow, crisp, tender flesh. Subacid flavor. Some susceptibility to scab. Ripens in late September and early October. Originated in Kansas. *Source History: 1 in 1992; 1 in 2000.* **Sources: Ca15.**

Laxton's Fortune - Cox's Orange Pippin x Wealthy. Yellow fruit striped with red. Small, compact tree. Crops well from an early age but inclined to biennial bearing. Scab resistant. Ripens during September. Developed in 1904 by Laxton's, the notable English nurserymen. *Source History: 1 in 1988; 2 in 1992; 1 in 2000.* **Sources: Bea.**

Laxton's Superb - Wyken Pippin x Cox's Orange Pippin. Medium to large, round fruit with green-yellow skin mottled with dull purple-red. White flesh is tinged with green. Firm, tender, juicy flesh with flavor of Cox. Hardy in the north. Ripens in the fall. Originated in England around 1897. *Source History: 1 in 1988; 2 in 1992; 2 in 2000.* **Sources: Bea, Or9.**

Leafland Greening - Greenish yellow fruit. Green cooking apple especially nice for pies and cobblers. Ripens midseason. Hardy to -40 degrees F. Origin unknown. *Source History: 1 in 1988; 1 in 1992; 1 in 2000.* **Sources: Stl.**

Leather Coat - *Source History: 1 in 2000.* **Sources: Or9.**

Lehigh Greening (French Pippin) - *Source History: 1 in 1992; 1 in 2000.* **Sources: Ch9.**

Leonard's Transparent - Early yellow cooking apple; an improved Yellow Transparent. *Source History: 1 in 2000.* **Sources: Hid.**

Leslie - Chance seedling of Golden Delicious, which it resembles. Large, good looking apple with bright yellow skin splashed with red. Crisp, sweet, juicy flesh. Distinctive pleasing aroma. Vigorous, heavily productive tree; early and regular bearer. *Source History: 1 in 1988; 2 in 1992; 1 in 2000.* **Sources: Gr4.**

Liberty - Most disease resistant apple ever developed. Macoun x Purdue 54-12. Medium to large, bright, shiny, McIntosh-type fruit with 90% red blush. Crisp, juicy, light yellow flesh. Sprightly flavor. Good for eating fresh, cooking, canning or desserts. Stores until February. Flavor intensifies in storage. Hardy, spreading, vigorous, heavily spurred, productive tree; annual bearer. Sets heavy fruit loads, resulting in small fruit; requires thinning. Resistant to scab, fire blight, mildew and cedar-apple rust. No spraying needed. Ripens early October. Requires 800 hours of chilling. Hardy in Zones 4-8. Released from the New York Station in 1978. *Source History: 21 in 1988; 46 in 1992; 46 in 2000.* **Sources: Ad2, AG2, Amb, Bay, Bea, Bl4, Bu7, Ch9, Cla, Clo, Cu4, Ea3, Ed2, Ed5, Er2, Fed, Fi1, Ga20, GR26, Gr4, Gur, Hi9, Jo3, Jun, La3, Leu, ME3, Mel, Mi1, Nrs, On3, Or9, Rai, Ro3, Sc6, SH8, Son, St4, Stl, TR8, Ur2, Va2, Wh4, WI12, WI4, Wor.**

Limbertwig - Medium size, rather rough fruit. Greenish yellow skin covered with dull red blush. Hard, aromatic yellowish flesh. Good for fresh eating, pies and jelly; extra good for cider. Late winter keeper. Ripens late. Old northern Georgia strain that was once a well-known Southern apple. *Source History: 4 in 1988; 6 in 1992; 4 in 2000.* **Sources: Bl4, Gr4, La3, So5.**

Limbertwig, American - *Source History: 1 in 2000.* **Sources: Ca15.**

Limbertwig, Black - Dark red fruit. Creamy flesh with good, spicy flavor. Sweetens in storage. Suitable for cider and apple butter. Long keeper. Resistant to fire blight and cedar-apple rust. Ripens in October. *Source History: 1 in 1988; 3 in 1992; 4 in 2000.* **Sources: Ca15, Hid, Or9, Ur2.**

Limbertwig, Black Newman - Old variety. *Source History: 1 in 2000.* **Sources: Hid.**

Limbertwig, Brushy Mountain - Old Southern apple. Round fruit is lemon-yellow and dull red in color. Firm, crisp, yellow flesh; juicy, distinctive flavor. Long keeper. Tree grows in a weeping form. Commercially grown in the Brushy Mountains of North Carolina. Ripens in October. Appears to have higher than average frost tolerance. *Source History: 1 in 1988; 2 in 1992; 3 in 2000.* **Sources: Ca15, Cla, Hid.**

Limbertwig, Kentucky - Southern variety. *Source History: 1 in 2000.* **Sources: Ca15.**

Limbertwig, Levering - Southern variety. *Source History: 1 in 2000.* **Sources: Ca15.**

Limbertwig, Myer's Royal (Myers Strain Limbertwig) - Somewhat larger fruit with more color than regular Limbertwig. Hard yellow flesh. Highly aromatic. Very fine flavor. Good for fresh eating, pies and jelly. Late keeper. *Source History: 1 in 1988; 2 in 1992; 2 in 2000.* **Sources: Cla, Ur2.**

Limbertwig, Old Fashioned - Southern variety. *Source History: 2 in 1992; 2 in 2000.* **Sources: Ca15, Ur2.**

Limbertwig, Ramsey's Smoky Mountain - Beautiful red fruit. Fine flavor. Tree has long drooping branches. Good keeper. *Source History: 1 in 1988; 2 in 1992; 1 in 2000.* **Sources: La3.**

Limbertwig, Red - Southern variety. *Source History: 1 in 1988; 1 in 1992; 4 in 2000.* **Sources: Bea, Ca15, Or9, Ur2.**

Limbertwig, Red Royal - Red fruit with green-yellow stripes and white dots. Aromatic, firm, crisp, juicy flesh. Stores well. Ripens in late September, early October. *Source History: 1 in 1988; 2 in 1992; 3 in 2000.* **Sources: Ca15, Ed5, Or9.**

Limbertwig, Royal (Carolina Baldwin) - Of the many Limbertwig varieties, Royal Limbertwig is better adapted to the warmer areas of the South. Large fruit is almost covered with dull red overlaid with indistinct red stripes. Tender, juicy, fine-grained flesh with subacid flavor. Makes an excellent apple butter. Fine eating apple. Good keeper. Ripens early October. Widely sold by Southern nurseries beginning around 1860. *Source History: 1 in 1988; 1 in 2000.* **Sources: Ca15.**

Limbertwig, Ruby - Southern variety. *Source History: 1 in 2000.* **Sources: Ca15.**

Limbertwig, Summer Strain - Bright yellow fruit with a tart flavor. Fine for jelly and culinary uses. Sturdier branch growth than other Limbertwigs; doesn't droop as much. Ripens during August. *Source History: 1 in 1988; 2 in 2000.* **Sources: Ca15, La3.**

Limbertwig, Sweet - *Source History: 1 in 1992; 1 in 2000.* **Sources: Or9.**

Limbertwig, Swiss - Southern variety. *Source History: 2 in 1992; 3 in 2000.* **Sources: Bl4, Ca15, Ch9.**

Linda Mac - McIntosh strain. Colors nearly 100% blush red by harvest. Spur-type tree. *Source History: 3 in 2000.* **Sources: Do7, Fo2, WAF.**

Little Benny - Southern variety. *Source History: 1 in 2000.* **Sources: Ca15.**

Lobo - Open-pollinated seedling of McIntosh. Large, red fruit. Good quality which sells well at roadside stands. Tree bears at a young age. Tends to biennial bearing. Ripens early to midseason. Hardy to -40 degrees F. An old-timer. Developed in Ottawa, Canada. Introduced in 1927. *Source History: 3 in 1988; 3 in 1992; 3 in 2000.* **Sources: Bea, Ch9, Cu4.**

Lodi (Improved Yellow Transparent, Large Transparent) - Montgomery x Yellow

Transparent. Extra early, large, green cooking apple. Larger, firmer and keeps longer than Yellow Transparent; does not get mealy as fast. Clear, yellow skin. Crisp, juicy, mildly subacid, white flesh. Sweet-tart flavor. Harvest for pies and sauce when full size. Fine white applesauce; great for early pies. For fresh eating, pick when partly yellow. Dependable, productive tree. Less alternate bearing if properly thinned. Resistant to apple scab. Requires cross-pollination. Ripens during July. Hardy in Zones 3-8 and to -45 degrees F. Produced by the New York Fruit Testing Association in 1911. *Source History: 44 in 1988; 52 in 1992; 41 in 2000.* **Sources: Ad2, Bar, Bea, Bl4, Bo5, Bu1, Bu7, Ch9, Ea3, Ed5, Fi1, Fo4, GI3, Hi9, Jun, LA4, Lee, Mc3, ME3, Mel, Mi1, MI5, Na4, Nrs, Pi2, Po2, Rid, Sav, Sc6, SH8, SIM, So5, Stl, TU5, Ty2, Ur2, Va2, Wa16, WI12, WI4, Wor.**

Lodi, Compspur - Good for freezing, sauces and pies. Compact tree yields up to twice the crops of its parent. Ripens from early to late July. *Source History: 1 in 1988; 1 in 1992; 1 in 2000.* **Sources: Mi1.**

Lodi, Stark - Improved L-1 cultivar of Yellow Transparent. Smooth-skinned fruit. Crisp white flesh. Vigorous tree. Pollinate with Starkspur Earli-Blaze or Prima. Ripens in early July. Hardy in Zones 4-8. Trademarked. *Source History: 1 in 1988; 1 in 1992; 2 in 2000.* **Sources: AG2, St4.**

Long Stem (Longstem) - Southern variety. *Source History: 1 in 1992; 1 in 2000.* **Sources: Ca15.**

Longfield - Southern variety. *Source History: 2 in 2000.* **Sources: Ca15, Ed5.**

Lonnie's Summer Giant - Southern variety. *Source History: 1 in 2000.* **Sources: Ca15.**

Lord Lambourne - James Grieve x Worcester Pearmain. High quality dessert apple. Somewhat self-fruitful. Ripens in September. Developed in England in 1907. *Source History: 1 in 1988; 2 in 1992; 1 in 2000.* **Sources: Nrs.**

Lord's Seedling (Lord) - Sent in 1892 to the New York Experiment Station by James S. Lord, who found the variety as a seedling in his Baldwin orchard on the old home farm at Linden, New York. Fruit tends to be large and uniform. Short storage capabilities. Heavy and regular bearer. Ripens in late August. Has withstood -46 degree F. temperature in Fairbanks, Alaska with no winter injury. *Source History: 4 in 1988; 7 in 1992; 5 in 2000.* **Sources: Bea, Ch9, Gr4, Or9, So5.**

Lowell (Greasy Pippin) - Yellow fruit with some russeting. Juicy, slightly coarse flesh. Good for eating and cooking. Tree is long-lived and a reliable cropper. Fruit ripens over period of several weeks. Hardy to -50 degrees F. with occasional winter injury. *Source History: 1 in 1988; 3 in 1992; 1 in 2000.* **Sources: Bl4.**

Lowland Raspberry (Livland Raspberry) - Medium to large, round fruit. Attractive, red stripe on a cream background. Tender, white flesh. Mild, pleasantly sweet flavor. Mature trees are not very large; tend toward biennial production. Good scab and fire blight resistance. Ripens during August. Hardy to -50 degrees F. Old Russian variety from the 1860s. *Source History: 5 in 1988; 9 in 1992; 11 in 2000.* **Sources: Bea, Bl4, Ca15, Ea3, Ed5, Fed, Gr4, Hid, Or9, Stl, Ur2.**

Lowry (Dixie, Mosby's Best, Red Winter) - Old-timer. Dark red on greenish yellow background; striped and flushed with red. Skin is covered with irregularly shaped dots. Firm flesh at peak of ripening; quickly becomes mealy off the tree. Ripens in September. Found in central Virginia with slight variations that can be attributed to environmental rather than varietal differences. Originated on the farm of John Lowry of Afton, Virginia about 1850. First sold by nurseries in Virginia in 1913. *Source History: 1 in 1988; 2 in 1992; 1 in 2000.* **Sources: Ca15.**

Lubsk Queen (Lubsk Reinette) - Medium to large fruit. Glistening white porcelain-like skin with splashes and blushes of brightest pink and rosy red. Firm, juicy, tart snow white flesh. Brisk, sprightly flavor. Dessert apple; also good for pie and sauce. Good keeper for an early apple. Ripens in early September. One of some 350 Russian apples brought into the U.S. by Professor J. L. Budd of Iowa State Agricultural College and Charles Gibb of Quebec between 1879 and 1885 in an attempt to find cold-hardy varieties. *Source History: 6 in 1988; 7 in 1992; 5 in 2000.* **Sources: Bea, Ch9, Ed5, Gr4, So5.**

Lucky Rose (Lucky Stemilt Cultivar) - Excellent eating apple with a sweet-tart flavor. Skin is blushed with red by the sun. Requires summer pruning to allow good light penetration. Flesh does not brown when cut. Firm flesh is more bruise resistant than regular Golden Delicious. Good keeper. Strong tree has good angle crotches. Plant patent applied for. Trademarked. *Source History: 2 in 2000.* **Sources: Co2, Va2.**

Lugar Red - Southern variety. *Source History: 1 in 2000.* **Sources: Ca15.**

Lurared (Stark LuraRed, Ellis Cultivar) - *Source History: 2 in 1992; 1 in 2000.* **Sources: Bea.**

Lyman's Large Summer (Lyman Large, Large Yellow Summer) - Large, smooth, green, sometimes yellow fruit. Crisp, juicy, breaking flesh. Refreshing, rich, clean, sweet-tart flavor. Good for table use or cooking. Moderately hardy tree. A tip bearer. Ripens in early August. Hardy to Zone 4. James Dougall of Amherstberg, Ontario exhibited this fruit on August 24, 1847 in Detroit at the first exhibition of the Horticultural Society of Michigan. Thought to have been lost entirely. Accidentally rediscovered in 1941 when a tree thought to be Cole's Quince, a famous Maine apple rated highly by pomologists a century ago, was recognized to be Lyman's Large Summer. *Source History: 4 in 1988; 7 in 1992; 6 in 2000.* **Sources: Bea, Ch9, Or9, So5, Son, Ur2.**

Lyscom - Originated in Massachusetts around 1817. *Source History: 1 in 1992; 2 in 2000.* **Sources: Ch9, Wo7.**

Maayan - Dark, dull red, yellow fleshed fruit. Tangy flavor. Tends to over produce without proper thinning. Pollinate with Elah or Michal. Ripens in July. *Source History: 1 in 1992; 1 in 2000.* **Sources: Ju2.**

Macoun - McIntosh x Jersey Black. Size and shape like McIntosh; more striped with deeper red coloring. Dark purplish red blush over green background. Firm, aromatic, white flesh. High quality, all-purpose, dessert apple. Fruit drops readily; bruises easily. Good for local markets; not for shipping. Medium size, vigorous, hardy, spur-type, productive tree. Upright habit; needs training to develop a spreading top. Must thin to maintain fruit size and annual bearing. Very resistant to fire blight. Blooms late. Ripens several weeks after McIntosh. Requires 600 hours of chilling. Hardy to Zone 4. Developed at the Geneva Station. Introduced in 1923. *Source History: 19 in 1988; 27 in 1992; 28 in 2000.* **Sources: Ad2, AG2, Amb, Bea, Bl4, BO10, Bo5, Ch9, Co2, Cu4, Ed5, Gr4, Hi9, Leu, Mi1, Nrs, Sc6, SH8, So5, Son, St4, Stl, TR8, Und, Wa16, WAF, Wh4, WI12, Wor.**

Maglemer - *Source History: 1 in 1988; 1 in 1992; 1 in 2000.* **Sources: So5.**

Magnun Bonum - Old Southern variety. Medium size yellow fruit is nearly covered with red. Ripens in September. Widely adapted to Southern growing conditions. Old references say it was first grown by Squire Kinney of Davidson County, North Carolina in 1828. Southern nurseries sold this variety until about 1930. Old trees are very rare. *Source History: 1 in 1988; 2 in 1992; 3 in 2000.* **Sources: Bl4, Ca15, Or9.**

Magog Red Streak - Cider variety. *Source History: 1 in 2000.* **Sources: Cid.**

Mahogany - *Source History: 1 in 1988; 1 in 1992; 1 in 2000.* **Sources: So5.**

Mai - *Source History: 1 in 2000.* **Sources: Ed5.**

Maiden Blush (Lady Blush, Maiden's Blush) - One of the oldest American apples. Flat, perfectly round fruit. Thin, tough, smooth, waxy, yellow skin with crimson blush. Crisp, tender, white flesh with maybe a slight yellow tinge. Fine for cooking, eating fresh, drying or making cider. Vigorous grower; bears early and annually. Subject to scab. Long harvest period. Ripens from mid-August to mid-September depending on location. Hardy to -50 degrees F. with occasional winter injury. Original tree traces back to New Jersey. Described in 1817 by Coxe as very popular in the Philadelphia market. *Source History: 8 in 1988; 13 in 1992; 16 in 2000.* **Sources: Bea, Bl4, Ca15, Ch9, Cu4, Ed5, Gr4, La3, Or9, Sc6, So5, Son, Stl, Ur2, Wh4, Wo7.**

Maigold - Swiss variety. Crisp, juicy flesh; mildly subacid, sweet flavor. Bruise resistant; early bearing. Blooms same time as Golden Delicious. Keeps well in storage. Ripens late. Zones 6-10. Originated in Switzerland, 1944. *Source History: 1 in 1988; 2 in 1992; 4 in 2000.* **Sources: Bl4, Ch9, Ed5, Son.**

Major - *Source History: 1 in 2000.* **Sources: Ch9.**

Mala Carla - Southern variety. *Source History: 1 in 2000.* **Sources: Ca15.**

Malinda - Yellow fruit with pretty red blush. Excellent eating with sweet aftertaste. Zone 3. Antique variety of distinction. Originated in Vermont. Introduced in 1860. *Source History: 1 in 1988; 4 in 1992; 4 in 2000.* **Sources: Bea, Ch9, Ed5, Wo7.**

Mammoth Pippin - *Source History: 1 in 2000.* **Sources: Ed5.**

Mammy - Southern variety. *Source History: 1 in 2000.* **Sources: Ca15.**

Manalta - *Source History: 1 in 2000.* **Sources: Bea.**

Mandan - Duchess x Starking Delicious. Red fruit. Firm, yellowish flesh; juicy and good eating. Keeps well for two months in storage. Tree has considerable resistance to fire blight. Ripens midseason. Hardy to -50 degrees F. with occasional winter injury. *Source History: 1 in 1988; 2 in 1992; 3 in 2000.* **Sources: Ed5, Stl, Va5.**

Manitoba - Duchess x Tolman Sweet. Yellow with scarlet blush fruit. Fine grained, melting, white flesh with spicy flavor. Very good cooking quality. Tree is a vigorous grower. Ripens late. Hardy to -50 degrees F. with occasional winter injury. *Source History: 1 in 1988; 1 in 1992; 1 in 2000.* **Sources: Stl.**

Manitoba Spy - *Source History: 1 in 1988; 1 in 1992; 2 in 2000.* **Sources: Ch9, So5.**

Mann - *Source History: 1 in 2000.* **Sources: Ch9.**

Mantet - Tetofsky x McIntosh. Medium to large, summer apple. Amber fruit washed with red. Juicy, tender, aromatic, white flesh. Sweet and juicy with pleasing flavor. High quality. Excellent for fresh eating. Upright, productive tree grows vigorously. In some seasons, such as early and excessive heat, breakdown is a problem. Ripens in mid-July. Hardy to -50 degrees F. with occasional winter injury. Developed in Manitoba, Canada. Introduced in 1929. *Source History: 6 in 1988; 15 in 1992; 10 in 2000.* **Sources: Bea, Bl4, Ch9, CLI, Ed5, Fa1, Nrs, Sc6, SH8, Stl, Wa16.**

Manx Codlin - *Source History: 1 in 1988; 1 in 1992; 1 in 2000.* **Sources: Gr4.**

Margil (Neverfail, Small Ribston, Reinette Musquee) - Medium to small, slightly conical fruit. Orangish red skin with dark red stripes; always russeted on one side. Firm, sugary, yellow flesh. Delicious, aromatic flavor; one of the best flavored.

Small, slender, light cropping tree. Ripens in late September. Possibly of French origin. Introduced in 1750. *Source History: 3 in 1988; 5 in 1992; 3 in 2000.* **Sources: Cu4, Or9, So5.**

Marin Oufroy - Cider variety. *Source History: 1 in 2000.* **Sources: Cu4.**

Mark's Sweet - *Source History: 1 in 2000.* **Sources: Bea.**

Marlin Stephens - Large, juicy, red and yellow fruit. Good for dessert or culinary use. Ripens midseason. Hardy to -50 degrees F. with occasional winter injury. Origin unknown; introduced in Montana. *Source History: 2 in 1988; 1 in 1992; 3 in 2000.* **Sources: Bea, Ed5, Stl.**

Mary Reid - Southern variety. *Source History: 1 in 2000.* **Sources: Ca15.**

Mattamuskeet (Mattamusket) - Old apple listed in a North Carolina catalog in 1853 and sold by most Southern nurseries until about 1910. Excellent keeping quality which is rare for a Southern variety. Possibly originated as a wild seedling near Lake Mattamuskeet, a huge shallow lake in eastern North Carolina. Fruit is medium size with yellow skin covered with light to dark purple-red. Crisp, moderately juicy flesh has a wine-like flavor. Ripens in October. *Source History: 1 in 2000.* **Sources: Ca15, Ch9.**

Matthews - *Source History: 1 in 2000.* **Sources: Or9.**

May - Southern variety. *Source History: 1 in 2000.* **Sources: Ca15.**

McGhee's Seedling - Large, green fruit occasionally with a light red blush on the sunny side. Up to 4" diameter. Ripens during November. Hangs on the tree until mid-April with no loss of flavor either raw or cooked. Very vigorous. Discovered by William Loren McGhee just south of the Oregon border. *Source History: 1 in 1988; 2 in 1992; 1 in 2000.* **Sources: Ch9.**

McIntosh (Red McIntosh) - Fameuse x Detroit Red. Medium to large, bright or dark red fruit; variable size. Very tender, thin skin. Subacid, sweet, crisp, white flesh. Small core. Tart, spicy flavor; delicious aroma. Makes an aromatic cider. Excellent for fresh eating; good for cooking. Keeps into January if chilled storage. Large, vigorous, productive, 25-30' tree bears young, annually and abundantly. Sets heavily; larger apples if thinned. Self-fertile. Resists cedar-apple rust, drought and cold weather. Leading variety in the Northeast. Ripens during September. Requires 900 hours of chilling. Hardy in Zones 4-8. Hardy to -45 degrees F. First discovered by John McIntosh on his farm near the St. Lawrence River in 1811. Introduced in 1870. *Source History: 37 in 1988; 56 in 1992; 46 in 2000.* **Sources: BA14, Bar, Bay, Bea, Bl4, BO10, Bu1, CLI, Fa1, Fed, Fi1, FO10, Fo4, Ga20, GI3, GR26, Gr4, Gur, Ho5, JOY, Lee, Leu, LI7, Mc3, Mel, Mi1, MI10, MI5, Nrs, Pi2, Sav, Sc6, SH8, SIM, So5, Son, St6, Stl, STR, TU5, Va2, Wa16, Wh4, WI4, Wo7, Wor.**

McIntosh Red - Thought to have been propagated from the original McIntosh tree in Dundela, Ontario, Canada, 1811. The original McIntosh apples were solid red and predate the striped strains. The modern red Macs of the last 60 years are mutations of the striped strains. Found in western Maine. *Source History: 1 in 2000.* **Sources: Fed.**

McIntosh, Acey Mac - Fruit resembles McIntosh in appearance, taste, shape, flesh color and texture with larger size and firmer texture. Less preharvest drop. Non-spur type tree. Originated in western New York. Trademarked. *Source History: 1 in 1988; 1 in 1992; 2 in 2000.* **Sources: COL, WAF.**

McIntosh, Boyer - *Source History: 1 in 2000.* **Sources: Bo5.**

McIntosh, Compact (Compact Mac, Compact Red McIntosh) - Medium size, bright red fruit. Tart, white, high acid flesh. Excellent quality. Three-quarters size tree. Hardy and strong; early bearer. Where apples touch one another a lack of color will result. Originated at Kelowna, British Columbia. *Source History: 2 in 1988; 2 in 1992; 1 in 2000.* **Sources: Va2.**

McIntosh, Compspur - Tangy, aromatic flesh. Even more compact and heavier bearing than regular semidwarf McIntosh. Yields almost twice the crops of its parent. Ripens in September. *Source History: 1 in 1988; 1 in 1992; 1 in 2000.* **Sources: Mi1.**

McIntosh, Double Red - Medium size, nearly round, bright cherry red apple with all the fine qualities of the famous old McIntosh. Subacid, sweet, aromatic, very juicy, tender, white flesh. Makes an aromatic cider. Tree is a vigorous grower with good cold hardiness. Requires 1,000 hours of chilling. Can be grown farther south than the old McIntosh. Will give fancy apples to the grower who could not obtain enough color with the regular McIntosh. *Source History: 3 in 1988; 4 in 1992; 3 in 2000.* **Sources: CO5, ME3, Nrs.**

McIntosh, Early - McIntosh x Yellow Transparent. Juicy, fine flavored fruits. Similar to McIntosh; ripens earlier. Vigorous, productive grower. Ripens from early to late August depending on location. *Source History: 5 in 1988; 5 in 1992; 6 in 2000.* **Sources: Bl4, Er2, Leu, Mi1, Pi2, Stl.**

McIntosh, Hermann - *Source History: 1 in 1992; 1 in 2000.* **Sources: Amb.**

McIntosh, Imperial Red - *Source History: 1 in 1988; 1 in 1992; 1 in 2000.* **Sources: Nrs.**

McIntosh, Improved (Worcester Strain) - Large, juicy, aromatic fruit. Vigorous tree. Colors ten days ahead of other strains. *Source History: 1 in 1992; 1 in 2000.* **Sources: Co2.**

McIntosh, Klein #2 - *Source History: 1 in 2000.* **Sources: Bo5.**

McIntosh, MacFree - Somewhat disease resistant McIntosh sport. Medium, oblate fruit with 80% red stripe on green background. Slightly tender, juicy, fine flesh. Good McIntosh flavor, but gets mealy in hot summers. Should be stored before eating to allow it to mellow up. Will keep in refrigerated storage until March. Tree is vigorous, spreading and moderately productive. Immune to apple scab. Resistant to powdery mildew, cedar-apple rust and fire blight. Ripens from September to October. Very cold hardy. Does best in Zones 4-5. Developed in Canada. Introduced in 1974. *Source History: 6 in 1988; 5 in 1992; 5 in 2000.* **Sources: Bea, Ch9, Mi1, Rai, Stl.**

McIntosh, MacSpur (Spur Mac, Spur McIntosh, Spur Red McIntosh) - Spur-type McIntosh sport with heavier yields. Very firm, typical McIntosh fruit with stronger color. Crisp, tender flesh. Sprightly flavor. All purpose. Stores extremely well into the spring. Tree is compact, solid, rugged and upright growing with strong stocky branches. As spur bearing surface develops, light distribution is maintained throughout the tree resulting in uniform, highly colored fruit. Requires much less pruning to maintain good fruiting. Matures a week later than McIntosh. Concentrated harvest. Zone 4. Trademarked. U.S. Plant Patent No. 2982. *Source History: 9 in 1988; 5 in 1992; 4 in 2000.* **Sources: Amb, Hi9, LA4, Stl.**

McIntosh, Marshall (Worcester Strain) - New selection discovered in Massachusetts. Identical to its parent McIntosh except for its intense red color. Ripens 7-10 days ahead of Spur McIntosh. Trademarked. Patent applied for. *Source History: 2 in 1988; 4 in 1992; 4 in 2000.* **Sources: Ad2, Amb, TR8, WAF.**

McIntosh, Mor-Spur - Fruit has bright, cherry red blush. True McIntosh with strong, stocky branches heavily spurred. Tree develops a few large, strong framework branches with very limited side shoot development. Shows a tendency to more dwarf stature than other strains of spur McIntosh. Early, heavy producer. U.S. Plant Patent No. 3390. *Source History: 1 in 1988; 1 in 1992; 2 in 2000.* **Sources: Co2, Ed5.**

McIntosh, Pioneer Mac (Greiner Strain, EG-506) - Excellent fruit quality. Resistance to late season drop on mature trees. Although considered a non-spur, the tree shows semi-spur flower bud formation. Tree is less vigorous than Marshall McIntosh. Ripens with Rogers McIntosh and up to 10 days later. U.S. Plant Patent No. 7002. *Source History: 1 in 1992; 1 in 2000.* **Sources: Ad2.**

McIntosh, Redmax - Fruit has a deep, rich red blush over slight, barely noticeable understripe. Everything about the fruit's flavor, size and shape is typically McIntosh, except it colors much sooner and more completely. Tree is vigorous and productive. Zones 4-7. Trademarked. U.S. Plant Patent No. 7167. *Source History: 1 in 1988; 3 in 1992; 3 in 2000.* **Sources: Hi9, Jun, WI12.**

McIntosh, Roger's Mac (Buhr Strain) - Selection of Roger's Mac by Wafler Nurseries with improved red color and firmness. Excellent for roadside market. *Source History: 1 in 2000.* **Sources: WAF.**

McIntosh, Rogers Red (Rogers Red Spur, Rogers Red Strain) - Most widely grown older red strain. Colors to solid blush without stripes. Crisp, juicy, white flesh. Hardy, productive, long-lived tree. Annual bearer. Ripens in late September. Proven by many years of production in commercial orchards. *Source History: 4 in 1988; 5 in 1992; 4 in 2000.* **Sources: Ad2, Ch9, Hi9, Nrs.**

McIntosh, Starkspur (Gatzke Cultivar) - *Source History: 1 in 1992; 1 in 2000.* **Sources: St4.**

McIntosh, Summer Mac (Arend's Strain) - Solid red skin over creamy white flesh. Holds well in short term storage. Maintains quality up to two weeks in the market. Annual bearer. Very precocious; requires good thinning practices. Grown in the Northeast as a late summer McIntosh type. Ripens three weeks before McIntosh. Originated in Canada. Introduced in 1929. *Source History: 1 in 1988; 1 in 1992; 2 in 2000.* **Sources: Ad2, WAF.**

McIntosh, Summerland (Nured McIntosh) - One of the most attractively colored red sports of McIntosh. Blushed color pattern with very little striping. Attains its color early. Crisp, juicy, distinctive flavor. Widely adapted. Especially desirable for higher elevations. Early blooming. Excellent pollinator. Ripens mid-season. Introduced in 1929. *Source History: 3 in 1988; 4 in 1992; 1 in 2000.* **Sources: Nrs.**

McIntosh, Sweet - Lawver x McIntosh. Large, red-yellow fruit. In spite of its name, does not resemble McIntosh. Sweet, aromatic fruit. Keeps 150 days at 30 degrees F. Ripens late. Hardy to -50 degrees F. with occasional winter injury. *Source History: 1 in 1988; 1 in 1992; 1 in 2000.* **Sources: Stl.**

McIntosh, Ultramac (Dewar Cultivar, Starkspur Ultramac) - Firm, crispy, tart fruit. Ripens in early September. Resists bitter winters; hardy in Zones 4-6. Trademarked. *Source History: 1 in 1988; 1 in 1992; 1 in 2000.* **Sources: St4.**

McIntosh, Wijcik Super Compact - Summerland Red McIntosh sport with true McIntosh flavor. *Source History: 1 in 2000.* **Sources: Cu4.**

McIntosh, Worcester Red - Red color develops early throughout the tree for easy picking. Classic McIntosh flavor. *Source History: 1 in 1992; 1 in 2000.* **Sources: Cu4.**

McLean - Medium sized, pale-yellow fruit with a light red blush. Mildly acid

flesh of good quality. Tree is considered hardy. Fall ripening. Developed in Canada. Introduced in 1960. *Source History: 1 in 1988; 1 in 1992; 1 in 2000.* **Sources: Ca15.**

McLellan - Light, smooth, straw-colored fruit covered with stripes and marblings of lively red. Always has a good crop. Good keeper. Ripens in the late fall. Very old Woodstock, Connecticut seedling. Introduced in 1780. *Source History: 1 in 1988; 3 in 1992; 3 in 2000.* **Sources: Or9, So5, Wo7.**

McLemore - Delicious seedling from a planting by the late J. V. McLemore of Muskogee, Oklahoma. Good dessert apple. Stores well. Ripens mid-July. *Source History: 1 in 1992; 2 in 2000.* **Sources: Ca15, Wom.**

McMahon (White McMahon) - Possibly a seedling of Alexander. Excellent flavor with a nice subtle spicy aftertaste. Marginal in Zone 3. Originated in Richland County, Wisconsin. Introduced in 1850. *Source History: 1 in 1988; 1 in 1992; 1 in 2000.* **Sources: Ed5.**

Mean's Seedling - Southern variety. *Source History: 1 in 2000.* **Sources: Ca15.**

Medaille d'Or - Cider apple. Golden yellow skin covered with brown russet marbling. Tender, yellowish flesh. Very sweet juice with a strong but not unpleasant, astringent aftertaste. Fruit is borne in clusters. Originated in France. *Source History: 1 in 1988; 2 in 1992; 2 in 2000.* **Sources: Cid, So5.**

Melba - McIntosh x Livland Raspberry. Attractive, high quality, yellow washed with crimson fruit. Red, crisp, tender, juicy flesh. Tree is productive and bears at a young age. Ripens in mid-August. Hardy to -50 degrees F. with occasional winter injury. Developed at the Canadian Department of Agricultural Research Station, Ottawa, Canada in 1924. Silver medal winner by the American Pomological Society in 1927. *Source History: 4 in 1988; 7 in 1992; 5 in 2000.* **Sources: Ch9, Fed, La3, Leu, Stl.**

Melba, Red (Melred) - Canadian sport of Melba which in turn is a McIntosh seedling. Highly aromatic with white flesh. Ripens in late summer. Hardy to Zone 2. Originated in Ottawa, Canada. Introduced in 1909. *Source History: 2 in 1988; 5 in 1992; 3 in 2000.* **Sources: Bea, Er2, Nrs.**

Melon (Melon Norton, Norton Watermelon) - Round-conic shaped fruit with slight ribbing. Smooth, green-yellow skin is overlaid with bright red and carmine stripes. Slightly subacid flavor. Looses flavor and quality quickly in storage. Subject to scab. Requires annual pruning. Ripens late September, early October. Originated in New York. Introduced in 1845. *Source History: 1 in 1988; 4 in 1992; 3 in 2000.* **Sources: Bl4, So5, Wo7.**

Melrose - Official Ohio State apple. Red Delicious x Jonathan. Large, flattened fruit. Yellowish green skin flushed and streaked dark red with russet spots. Firm, coarse, juicy, creamy white flesh. Slightly acid flavor. Very good cooking and dessert quality. Best for eating after Christmas when it develops its fruity aroma. Stores at 31 degrees F. until April. Tree is a vigorous, productive, annual bearer. Growth habit is spreading and moderate. Midseason bloom. Good pollinator. Ripens from mid to late October. Good apple for roadside market and local sales. Zones 5-9. Planted extensively in Ohio. Introduced in 1944. *Source History: 24 in 1988; 29 in 1992; 26 in 2000.* **Sources: Ad2, Amb, Bay, Bea, Bl4, Ch9, Clo, Ea3, Ed5, Er2, Gr4, Hi9, JOY, La3, ME3, Mel, Mo19, Nrs, Rai, Sc6, So5, Son, TR8, Va2, WI4, Wor.**

Melrouge - Redder sport of Melrose with more intense flavor. *Source History: 1 in 1988.* **Sources: Hi9.**

Merritt - Southern variety. *Source History: 1 in 2000.* **Sources: Ca15.**

Merton Beauty - *Source History: 1 in 1992; 3 in 2000.* **Sources: Bea, Ch9, Er2.**

Merton Russet - *Source History: 1 in 2000.* **Sources: Or9.**

Michael Henry Pippin - Southern variety. *Source History: 1 in 2000.* **Sources: Ca15.**

Michal - Light gold-yellow skin streaked with red and orange. Hard, crispy flesh with snappy flavor. Makes delicious pie. Ripens early to late July. Pollinate with Maayan or Elah. *Source History: 1 in 1992; 1 in 2000.* **Sources: Ju2.**

Michelin - Medium size, round, yellow fruit. Cider apple; bittersweet. Upright grower; heavy cropping. Blooms midseason. Can be mildew susceptible. Ripens early mid-October to November. *Source History: 1 in 1988; 2 in 2000.* **Sources: Cid, Rai.**

Michinoko - *Source History: 2 in 1992; 1 in 2000.* **Sources: Nrs.**

Midnight Spur - Sport limb of Oregon Spur found in Milton-Freewater, Oregon. Blush red skin color starts in late May. Flesh is whiter than other reds harvested in mid to late August. Precocious tree. Trademarked. *Source History: 2 in 2000.* **Sources: Co2, Si3.**

Milam - *Source History: 2 in 1992; 1 in 2000.* **Sources: Bl4, Ca15, Gr4, Or9.**

Milan - *Source History: 1 in 2000.* **Sources: Bea.**

Milden - Once common in northern New England orchards. Large, oblate to conic, pale yellow fruit is mottled and splashed with bright red. Coarse, juicy, crisp whitish flesh is tinted with yellow. Tart flavor. Good for eating fresh and cooking. Ripens late; keeps until mid-winter. Can be picked after a hard freeze. Zones 3-4. *Source History: 1 in 2000.* **Sources: Fed.**

Milo Gibson - Red and yellow fruit. A fine-tasting apple with unique licorice flavor. Ripens midseason. Hardy to -50 degrees F. with occasional winter injury. Unknown origin. *Source History: 1 in 1988; 2 in 1992; 2 in 2000.* **Sources: Ch9, Stl.**

Milton (Milton Early McIntosh) - McIntosh x Yellow Transparent. Pinkish red fruit. Similar to McIntosh in flavor and texture, but more aromatic. Great for sauce. Tree is annual bearer and tolerant to rust. Ripens from July to August depending on location. Developed at the New York State Agricultural Experiment Station at Geneva. Introduced in 1923. *Source History: 4 in 1988; 7 in 1992; 4 in 2000.* **Sources: Bl4, Ch9, Sc6, Stl, Wor.**

Milwaukee - Yellow, red-striped fruit. Flavorful; somewhat tart. Good for cooking and cider. Excellent keeper. Annual bearer and produces at a young age. Ripens late. Hardy to -50 degrees F. Originated in Russia. *Source History: 1 in 1988; 2 in 1992; 2 in 2000.* **Sources: Ed5, Stl.**

Minjon (MN 700) - Minnesota Jonathan that thrives in northern Minnesota. Brilliant, all red fruit. Rather sharp flavor which mellows with age. Good for cooking and eating. Productive, hardy, annual bearer. Bears heavy loads; hangs tightly to the tree until picked. Ripens in late fall. Zone 3. Developed at the University of Minnesota in 1942. *Source History: 3 in 1988; 4 in 1992; 4 in 2000.* **Sources: Ch9, Ed5, Fed, Nrs.**

Minnesota 447 - *Source History: 1 in 2000.* **Sources: Bea.**

Minnesota 1734 - Bronze russet fruit. Hard, yellow flesh. Rich flavor. Makes excellent tasting cider. Annual producer of heavy crops. Ripens late. Hardy to -50 degrees F. *Source History: 2 in 1988; 2 in 1992; 3 in 2000.* **Sources: Bea, Ch9,**

Stl.

Mio - Worcester Pearmain x Oranie. Medium to small, solid bright red fruit; crisp, juicy, refreshing white flesh. One of the most beautiful of all apples. Originated in Sweden. Introduced in 1932. *Source History: 1 in 1988; 1 in 1992; 1 in 2000.* **Sources: So5.**

Mississippi Pippin - Southern variety. *Source History: 1 in 2000.* **Sources: Ca15.**

Mitchell - Southern variety. *Source History: 1 in 2000.* **Sources: Ca15.**

Mollies Delicious - Summer apple not to be confused with Red Delicious strains. Attractive, large fruit with unique, slightly conic shape. Light yellow background about half covered with a red blush. Snappy, high quality flesh. Good, very distinctive flavor. Quality holds for 10 weeks in common refrigeration. Vigorous, productive tree. Fruit tends to set in clusters; requires 2-3 pickings. Excellent pollinator. Some disease resistance. Well adapted to the Southeast and southern states. Mostly for local sales. Ripens in early August. Requires 400-500 hours of chilling. Best in Zones 5-8. Introduced in 1966 by the New Jersey Agricultural Experiment Station. *Source History: 10 in 1988; 23 in 1992; 22 in 2000.* **Sources: Bas, Bea, Ch9, Cla, CO5, Cum, Ed5, Er2, Hi9, Ho5, Iso, La3, Nrs, Or9, Ro3, Sc6, St4, Tex, Va2, Ur2, Wom, Wor.**

Monark - Large to very large, round fruit is red to red striped. Firm flesh with superb tartness. Vigorous, spreading tree. Annual bearer. Ripens in early July. Stores for 3-4 months. Developed at the University of Arkansas. Plant patent applied for. *Source History: 3 in 2000.* **Sources: Ch9, Cla, Ro3.**

Monroe - Jonathan x Rome Beauty. Resembles old Baldwin in shape and texture, but superior in flavor and beauty. Hard, crisp, juicy flesh. Good dessert quality. Excellent for pies, sauce and baking. Developed at the New York State Agricultural Experiment Station. Introduced in 1949. *Source History: 1 in 1988; 3 in 1992; 1 in 2000.* **Sources: Ch9.**

Montreal Beauty Crab - Wild crab seedling. White blossoms. Oblong fruit up to 1" diameter. Yellow-green splashed red skin color. Used for jams and jellies. Ripens midseason. Hardy to -50 degrees F. with occasional winter injury. *Source History: 2 in 2000.* **Sources: Ed5, Stl.**

Moonlight - *Source History: 1 in 1992; 1 in 2000.* **Sources: Ch9.**

Moore's Sweet - *Source History: 1 in 2000.* **Sources: Ch9.**

Morden 359 - Wealthy x Melba. Large, juicy, red fruit. Useful for pies and sauce. Very hardy. Keeps until January. Developed at the Dominion Experimental Farm in Manitoba for growers in Zones 2-3. *Source History: 2 in 1988; 2 in 1992; 2 in 2000.* **Sources: Bea, Ed5.**

Morden 363 - Haralson x Melba. Large fruit, less colored than Morden 359. Mildly acid. Very hardy. Developed in Manitoba. *Source History: 1 in 1988; 3 in 1992; 3 in 2000.* **Sources: Bea, Ed5, Va5.**

Morden Ruby - *Source History: 1 in 2000.* **Sources: Ed5.**

Morden Russet - Seedling of Anisim. Canadian prairie apple. Small yellow russeted fruit. Good for dessert and juice. Vigorous, productive tree. Good keeper. Ripens mid-October. Rated as "least susceptible" to fire blight. Developed at the Morden Research Station. Zone 3. *Source History: 1 in 2000.* **Sources: Ed5.**

Morgan - Southern variety. *Source History: 1 in 2000.* **Sources: Ca15.**

Morgan Spur - Trademarked. *Source History: 1 in 2000.* **Sources: WI12.**

Morgenduft (Hoary Morning) - Flat-shaped fruit is sometimes ribbed on the bottom. Pale yellow skin is covered with dull red stripes. Heavy bloom. Red tinged, yellow flesh. Slightly acid flavor. Zones 6-9. Originated in England, 1819. *Source History: 1 in 2000.* **Sources: Son.**

Morning Star - *Source History: 1 in 1992; 1 in 2000.* **Sources: Ch9.**

Morren's Jonagored (Red Jonagold) - Limb mutation of Jonagold. Flesh is more juicy and crisper than Jonagold; may be less susceptible to sunburn. Develops color early. Originated in the orchard of Joseph Morren, a Belgian orchardist. U.S. Plant Patent No. 5937. *Source History: 3 in 1992; 6 in 2000.* **Sources: AG2, Hi9, Si3, St4, TR8, WI12.**

Moses Wood - Unknown parentage. Medium size, round to conic-shaped fruit with distinct ribbing and lobes around the calyx end. Light yellow skin with pink blush and red striping. Pleasantly subacid, fine grained, tender, juicy flesh. Good dessert and cooking apple. Vigorous upright tree. Zone 4. Originated at the farm of Moses Wood, Winthrop, Maine, 1847. *Source History: 1 in 2000.* **Sources: Fed.**

Mother (Gardener's Apple, Queen Anne) - American dessert apple. Medium to large, round oval fruit. Smooth, solid bright red skin. Juicy, aromatic, creamy yellow flesh. Distinctive balsamic, sweet-acid flavor. Poor storage ability. Crops well from an early age. Midseason bloom. Requires cross-pollination. Zones 4-9. Has almost disappeared in America; still grown widely in England. Developed in Massachusetts. Introduced in 1840. *Source History: 8 in 1988; 13 in 1992; 12 in 2000.* **Sources: Bea, Bl4, Ca15, Ch9, Cu4, Gr4, Or9, So5, Son, Ur2, Wo7, Wor.**

Mountain Boomer - Southern variety. *Source History: 2 in 1988; 3 in 1992; 4 in 2000.* **Sources: Bea, Ca15, Ch9, Gr4.**

Moyer's Spice - Medium size red fruit. Aromatic, white flesh. Subacid to sweet taste. Hardy and vigorous. Fall ripening. *Source History: 1 in 1988; 2 in 1992; 2 in 2000.* **Sources: Bar, Hid.**

Mrs. Bryan - Southern variety. *Source History: 1 in 2000.* **Sources: Ca15.**

Munson Sweet - Good baking apple. Yellow-green skin with orange undertones; covered with green dots that become russeted in the sun. Bears heavy crops annually. Ripens in July. Described in 1867. *Source History: 1 in 1992; 1 in 2000.* **Sources: Ca15.**

Murray - McIntosh cross from Agriculture Canada. Good all-purpose apple. Scab resistant. Ripens one week before McIntosh. *Source History: 1 in 2000.* **Sources: Cu4.**

Muscat de Bernay - Bittersweet-type cider apple from Normandy, France. Hardy in Zones 6-9. *Source History: 1 in 1992; 2 in 2000.* **Sources: Cid, Son.**

Muscat de Deippe - Cider apple. *Source History: 2 in 2000.* **Sources: Cid, Mo19.**

Muskmelon Sweet - Southern variety. *Source History: 1 in 2000.* **Sources: Ca15.**

Muster - Small, round, flat fruit. Striking, orangish red or pink skin with prominent brown or grey spots. Coarse but crisp, pure white flesh. Very sweet flavor. Ripens in early September. Origin and history are unknown. An old-timer. *Source History: 2 in 1988; 3 in 1992; 1 in 2000.* **Sources: So5.**

Mutsu (Crispin) - Golden Delicious x Indo. Yellow Delicious type. Large, round, yellow fruit. Crunchier flesh; more juice and tartness. Distinctive, delicate, spicy flavor; faintly anise-like. Good dessert and processing apple. Applesauce award winner. Extra good for cider. Keeps until March; does not shrivel in storage like Golden Delicious. Large, spreading, vigorous tree; reliable, annual, early producer. Triploid. Unlike Golden Delicious, will not overset or russet. Resists powdery mildew. Susceptible to scab and blister spot. Ripens during October. Requires 500-600 hours of chilling. Hardy in Zones 4-8. Developed in Japan in 1948. *Source History: 38 in 1988; 53 in 1992; 45 in 2000.* **Sources: Ad2, AG2, Amb, Bar, Bay, Bea, Bl4, Bo5, Ch9, Cla, Co2, CO5, Cu4, Cum, Ea3, Er2, Ga20, Gr4, Hi9, Ho5, Jo3, JOY, La3, Leu, ME3, Mel, Mi1, Mo19, Nrs, Or9, ORA, Pe2, Sc6, So5, Son, St4, TR8, Va2, WA8, WAF, Wh4, WI12, WI4, Wom, Wor.**

Native Crab - Selected strain of the wild crab apple found throughout northern Georgia. Very fragrant blooms. Green fruit turning yellow; up to 2" diameter. Makes fine jelly. Ripens late fall. *Source History: 1 in 1988; 1 in 1992; 1 in 2000.* **Sources: Ch9.**

Nebuta - *Source History: 2 in 1992; 1 in 2000.* **Sources: Nrs.**

Nehou - English cider apple. Small to medium fruit; soft and easily bruised. Bittersweet juice. Harvesting period 10 days. Ripens during September. Zones 6-9. *Source History: 2 in 1988; 1 in 1992; 3 in 2000.* **Sources: Cid, Cid, Son.**

New Summer Scarlet - Medium to large, red fruit. Firm, crisp, juicy flesh. Fine flavor. Keeps well for an early apple. Ripens mid-August. Tree discovered in a meadow in the summer of 1955. *Source History: 1 in 1988; 1 in 1992; 1 in 2000.* **Sources: Mi1.**

Newell's Winter (Newell, Newell's Orange) - Flat-round, sometimes irregular shape. Good size, solid yellow-green fruit entirely covered with minute green or black dots. Firm, crisp, juicy, rich, white flesh. Regular cropper. Ripens late. Originated in Sauk County, Wisconsin; planted by Orange Newell from seeds of Perry Russet brought from New York. Introduced in 1850. *Source History: 1 in 1988; 1 in 1992; 2 in 2000.* **Sources: So5, Und.**

Newfane - *Source History: 1 in 1992; 1 in 2000.* **Sources: Bl4.**

Newt Grindle - Originally grown from seed many years ago. *Source History: 1 in 2000.* **Sources: Fed.**

Newton Wonder - Said to be a cross of Dumelow's Seedling and Blenheim Orange. Large fruit often grows to 3.5" in diameter. Greenish yellow skin is flushed with brown-red which brightens to scarlet as the fruit ripens. October ripening. Originated in England about 1887. *Source History: 2 in 1988; 2 in 1992; 1 in 2000.* **Sources: Ed5.**

Newtosh - McIntosh x Yellow Newtown Pippin. Red-striped fruit. Skin similar to McIntosh; flesh like Yellow Newtown. Late ripening. Hardy to -30 degrees F. *Source History: 1 in 1988; 2 in 2000.* **Sources: Ch9, Stl.**

Newtown Pippin (Albemarle Pippin, Yellow Newtown, Yellow Newtown Pippin) - Does not owe its success to good looks. Medium size, squat, yellowish green fruit, usually russeted around the stem. Ripens yellow, unless over fertilized. Rich, aromatic, crisp, coarse, creamy yellow flesh; refreshing piney tartness. High quality; dessert and processing. Excellent for cider. Great keeper; develops full sugar and rich flavor in March. Large, vigorous, early bearing, self-fruitful tree. Tends to bear biennially. Susceptible to scab, notably on clay soil. Heat resistant. Requires good soil and full sun. Ripens during October. 700 hours of chilling. Zones 5-8. Originated in Newtown, Long Island in the early 1700s. *Source History: 25 in 1988; 29 in 1992; 27 in 2000.* **Sources: Bay, Bea, Bl4, Cid, Cla, Co2, CO5, Cu4, Fo2, Ga20, Gr4, Hid, JOY, ME3, Mi1, Or9, Ro3, Sc6, Si3, So5, Son, TR8, Ur2, Va2, Wh4, WI4, Wor.**

Newtown Spitzenburg - Greenish yellow skin flushed orangish red with dark red stripes and russet dots. Firm, coarse, creamy yellow flesh. Sweet, subacid flavor. Ripens very late. First recorded in 1817. *Source History: 1 in 1988; 3 in 1992; 2 in 2000.* **Sources: Ch9, Wo7.**

Niagara - Carlton x McIntosh. Red fruit is similar to McIntosh; high dessert quality. Ripens early to midseason. Hardy to -50 degrees F. with occasional winter injury. *Source History: 1 in 1988; 2 in 1992; 2 in 2000.* **Sources: Ch9, Stl.**

Nickajack (Padgett Strain) - Greenish yellow skin flushed with orange-red streaks. Crisp, yellow flesh. Subacid to sweet flavor. Ripens late. Possibly dates from late 1700 or 1800; recorded in 1853. *Source History: 2 in 1992; 4 in 2000.* **Sources: Ca15, Ed5, La3, Or9.**

Nittany - York Imperial type. Fruit of the clonotype tree has been essentially free of corking, a serious disorder of York Imperial and its sports. Can be held in refrigerated storage for at least six months. Flesh oxidizes very slowly and imparts a desirable yellow color to processed products. Its use as a fresh market apple is limited primarily by lack of skin color. Developed and introduced by Pennsylvania State University. *Source History: 2 in 1988; 3 in 1992; 7 in 2000.* **Sources: Ad2, Bl4, Bo5, Ch9, Cu4, Nrs, Or9.**

Noel - *Source History: 1 in 1992; 1 in 2000.* **Sources: Ch9.**

Noel de Champs - Cider variety. *Source History: 1 in 2000.* **Sources: Cu4.**

Nonpareil - *Source History: 1 in 2000.* **Sources: Or9.**

Noran - Columbia Crab x Redant. Medium size fruit. Green with red blush. Crisp, tart, cream colored flesh. Excellent for cooking. Begins bearing at an early age. Ripens midseason. Extremely hardy; to -50 degrees F. or colder. Canadian introduction, 1975. *Source History: 2 in 2000.* **Sources: Bea, Stl.**

Norda - Rosilda x Trail. Yellow skin with red streaking. Cream colored flesh is crisp and juicy. Good for fresh eating or culinary use. Bears young. Good keeper. Ripens late midseason. *Source History: 1 in 2000.* **Sources: Stl.**

Norenberg Redfall - *Source History: 1 in 2000.* **Sources: Ed5.**

Noret - Rescue x Mantet. Small, 2" fruit is yellow-green overlaid with dark red. Moderately firm flesh is slightly tart. Excellent cooking and dessert apple. Stores up to 6 weeks. Ripens early September. Hardy to Zone 1. Canadian introduction, 1975. *Source History: 1 in 2000.* **Sources: Bea.**

Norfolk Beefing (Norfolk Beaufin) - Southern variety. Large, rectangular fruit with a ribbed base. Green-yellow skin is flushed a dull red with light white dots. Coarse green-yellow flesh. Subacid flavor. Used for cider and cooking. Ripens in October. Likely originated in Norfolk, England. Recorded in 1809. *Source History: 2 in 2000.* **Sources: Ca15, Or9.**

Norkent - *Source History: 1 in 2000.* **Sources: Er2.**

Norland - Rescue x Melba. Medium size, oblong fruit. Dark red stripes on pink background. Green-cream flesh. Good for cooking and fresh eating. Good quality fruit; stores well. Keeps about 16 weeks in cold storage. Ripens mid-August. Winter hardy into Zone 2; down to -40 degrees F. Naturally dwarf tree does better where summers are cooler. Introduced by Morden Research Station, Canada, 1980. *Source History: 5 in 1988; 13 in 1992; 10 in 2000.* **Sources: Bea, Ch9, Ed5, Fed, Mc3, Nrs, SH8, So5, Stl, Wa16.**

Norson - Haralson x Rescue. Green-yellow skin with dark red overlay. High quality, 2.2" fruit stores well for over 4 months. Consistent yields. Ripens early September. Hardy to Zone 1. Canadian introduction, 1958. *Source History: 1 in 2000.* **Sources: Bea.**

North Carolina Greening - Southern variety. *Source History: 1 in 2000.*
Sources: Ca15.

North Carolina Keeper - Southern variety. *Source History: 1 in 2000.*
Sources: Ca15.

Northern Lights (NY 17-207) - Haralson x McIntosh. Glossy, bright red blushed fruit with slightly tart McIntosh flavor. High quality dessert apple. Very cold hardy; useful for home orchards in severely cold areas. Developed by the New York and North Dakota research stations. Introduced in 1990. *Source History: 2 in 1992; 7 in 2000.* **Sources: Ch9, Cu4, Ed5, Mc3, SH8, Stl, Wa16.**

Northern Spy (Red Spy, Red Northern Spy) - Large, round, often flattened, greenish yellow fruit flushed and striped pinkish red with a delicate bloom and occasional russet patches. Fine grained, rather firm, very tender, crisp, juicy yellowish flesh. Tart, aromatic, subacid flavor. Excellent, all-purpose apple, except for drying and cider. Keeps into March; May, if temperature regulated. Remarkably fresh after long storage. Very large, vigorous, productive, upright tree; tends to bear biennially. Blooms late. Takes about 12 years to bear. Requires pollination. Ripens in late October. 800 hours of chilling. Hardy to Zone 4. Seedling discovered about 1800 by Herman Chapin in East Bloomfield, New York. *Source History: 27 in 1988; 37 in 1992; 39 in 2000.* **Sources: Ad2, Bay, Bea, Bl4, Bo5, Ca15, Ch9, Cid, Co2, Cu4, Ea3, Fed, Fo2, Ga20, Gr4, Hi9, JOY, LA4, Leu, ME3, Mel, Mi1, MI5, Nrs, Or9, Pi2, Sc6, So5, Son, St4, Ur2, Va2, Wa16, WAF, Wh4, WI12, WI4, Wo7, Wor.**

Northern Sweet - Originated in Vermont. Introduced in 1800. *Source History: 2 in 1992; 3 in 2000.* **Sources: Bl4, Or9, Wo7.**

Northfield Beauty - When Albert Etter began his homesteading program back around the turn of the century, he obtained scionwood through the University of California for 600 different varieties. He grafted these to established trees. Winner of this trial was Northfield Beauty, an obscure apple from the hills of Vermont. Medium to large, predominantly red fruit. Ripens late August. Hangs well on the tree. Maintains its quality longer both on the tree and in storage. Heavy producer. Immune to apple scab. Hardy to Zone 4. This tree was found in the remains of Etter's orchard near Ettersburg, California and rescued from oblivion. *Source History: 1 in 1988; 1 in 1992; 4 in 2000.* **Sources: Bea, Ch9, Ed5, Gr4.**

Northpole (Northpole Columnar Apple) - Large, bright red, McIntosh-type fruit with tasty, crisp, juicy flesh. Compact growth habit is straight up with virtually no branching. Works well for container culture or in confined spaces. Pollinate with Golden Sentinel. Trademarked variety. *Source History: 6 in 2000.* **Sources: Bay, Gr16, Mi1, On3, Rai, WI4.**

Northwestern Greening - Golden Russet x Alexander. Popular old winter variety. Large to very large, handsome fruit; up to 5" across. Waxy, smooth, pale green skin with a hint of yellow; turns to yellow when mature. Juicy, mild subacid flavor. Excellent cooking apple, especially for pies. Known for its keeping qualities; keeps well into the winter. Often used as a late-season pollinator. Ripens during October. Hardy to -50 degrees F. Originated in Wisconsin. Introduced in 1872. *Source History: 10 in 1988; 19 in 1992; 15 in 2000.* **Sources: Ad2, Bl4, Bo5, Co2, Cu4, Ed5, Hi9, Jun, Mc3, Nrs, Or9, SH8, Stl, Wh4, Wor.**

Notley P. - Southern variety. *Source History: 1 in 2000.* **Sources: Ca15.**

Nova Easygro - Spartan x PRI 565. Scab-resistant variety introduced by the Canadian Department of Agriculture. Large, flattened fruit with 80% red stripe over greenish yellow background. Firm, crisp, slightly juicy flesh. Fair, somewhat sweet flavor. Flesh is slightly tough at picking time, but mellows up in storage. Similar to Cortland. Moderately productive, moderately vigorous tree. Blooms one day after McIntosh. Excellent scab and cedar-apple rust resistance; moderate mildew and fire blight resistance. Ripens early October. Hardy to -50 degrees F. with occasional winter injury. Developed in Nova Scotia. Introduced in 1971. *Source History: 6 in 1988; 8 in 1992; 9 in 2000.* **Sources: Bea, Ch9, Cu4, Ed5, Er2, Mo19, Ro3, Sc6, Stl.**

Novamac - Flattened fruit with 70% red stripe on green background. Crisp, tender, juicy, fine textured flesh. Slight McIntosh flavor. Good quality. Ripens during September. Introduced in 1978. *Source History: 1 in 1988; 5 in 1992; 2 in 2000.* **Sources: Ch9, Ed5.**

Novaspy - Disease resistant version of Northern Spy. Flavor has a hint of vanilla. Ripens in early October. Originated in Nova Scotia, Canada. *Source History: 2 in 2000.* **Sources: Cu4, Ro3.**

November Peach - *Source History: 1 in 1992; 2 in 2000.* **Sources: Ch9, Ed5.**

NuRed, Lucky Jon - Discovered as a whole tree mutation of NuRed Jonathan in 1986. Dark red blush covers 80-95% of fruit surface. Trademarked. *Source History: 1 in 2000.* **Sources: Hi9.**

Nutmeg (Nutmeg Pippin) - Small, conical dessert apple. Green skin ripens to yellow with a orange-brown flush and brown russet netting. Fine grained, creamy white flesh has a nutty flavor. Ripens in September. Originated in England about 1800. *Source History: 1 in 1988; 1 in 1992; 2 in 2000.* **Sources: Ed5, Or9.**

Nutting Bumpus - Seedling of Duchess of Oldenburg from Perham, Maine in the 19th century. Introduced by orchardist James Nutting who was dedicated to developing apples that would thrive in northern Maine. Large, round-conic fruit with light yellow ground color with a faint washing and penciling of dull red on the sunny side. Yellow-white flesh is juicy, fine grained and mildly sub-acid. Better for fresh eating than its parent. Hardy to Zone 3. *Source History: 1 in 2000.* **Sources: Fed.**

NY 617 - *Source History: 1 in 2000.* **Sources: Cla.**

NY 674 - Skin shows orange-red stripes over yellow background. Non-browning flesh. Productive. Ripens near McIntosh season. *Source History: 1 in 2000.* **Sources: WAF.**

Ohio Nonpareil - Large green and yellow fruit. Firm, crisp, juicy, white flesh. Agreeable, mildly subacid flavor. Good, early, cooking and marketing apple. Ripens during September. Hardy. Discovered in Massilon, Ohio before 1850. *Source History: 4 in 1988; 4 in 1992; 2 in 2000.* **Sources: Or9, Sc6, So5.**

Okabena - *Source History: 1 in 1992; 1 in 2000.* **Sources: Ed5.**

Old Cider - *Source History: 1 in 2000.* **Sources: Ed5.**

Old Faithful - Southern variety. Russeted fruit. Good keeper. *Source History: 1 in 2000.* **Sources: Hid.**

Old Fashioned Lewis - *Source History: 1 in 2000.* **Sources: Hid.**

Old Nonpareil - Small, broad-round, regular shaped fruit. Yellowish green with slight pale orange flush, spotted and streaked with brown russet. Fine, tender yet crisp greenish flesh. Superb flavor. Ripens late October. Ancient English apple, possibly dating back to Queen Elizabeth's time. First described in the 17th century by French writers. *Source History: 2 in 1988; 4 in 1992; 3 in 2000.* **Sources: Ch9, Gr4, So5.**

Old Smokehouse - Fruit has true pearmain shape with a 50% dull red blush.

Fine white flesh. Less disease problems than Smokehouse. Tends toward biennial bearing. *Source History: 1 in 2000.* **Sources: Wh4.**

Old Town Crab - *Source History: 1 in 2000.* **Sources: Or9.**

Oldenburg - Originated in Russia in the late 1700s. *Source History: 1 in 1992; 1 in 2000.* **Sources: Wo7.**

Oliver (Oliver's Red, All-Over-Red, Senator) - Medium to large fruit with smooth, waxy, golden yellow skin covered with crimson and streaked darker red. Large russet dots. Rich, spritely flavor. Some susceptibility to fire blight and crown gall. Ripens in late September. Very rare. Introduced in 1831. *Source History: 3 in 1992; 2 in 2000.* **Sources: Ca15, Wo7.**

Ontario - *Source History: 1 in 1988; 1 in 1992; 2 in 2000.* **Sources: Cu4, Gr4.**

Opalescent - Large fruit with smooth skin entirely covered with dark red, occasionally shading to purplish with splashes of carmine. Firm, juicy, mildly subacid, yellow flesh. Ripens in late fall. Once widely grown commercially in New England because of its great attractiveness. Found as a sprout by George Hudson of Barry County, Michigan. He sent out specimens under the name Hudson's Pride of Michigan, but was changed to Opalescent by Dayton Star Nurseries which first propagated it. Introduced in 1880. *Source History: 7 in 1988; 9 in 1992; 7 in 2000.* **Sources: Bl4, Cu4, Gr4, Mi1, Or9, So5, Wo7.**

Ophir - Southern variety. *Source History: 1 in 2000.* **Sources: Ca15.**

Orange - *Source History: 1 in 2000.* **Sources: Ch9.**

Orange Sweet (Northern Sweet, Early Golden Sweet, Trenton Early, Golden Sweeting) - Small, somewhat conical fruit. Orangish yellow when ripe. Sweet but not insipid. Uncommonly good aroma and taste for its season. Moderately vigorous and long-lived. Ripens late July. Introduced in New York in 1849. *Source History: 1 in 1988; 3 in 1992; 1 in 2000.* **Sources: Fed.**

Orenco - Medium to large fruit. Solidly bright red with inconspicuous light colored dots. Tender, crisp, juicy, white flesh. Sweet, mild but piquant flavor. Shy bearer. Scab resistant. Ripens mid-September. Hardy to Zone 2. Introduced in 1920 by Oregon Nursery Co. of Orenco, Oregon. *Source History: 5 in 1988; 6 in 1992; 3 in 2000.* **Sources: Ch9, Gr4, So5.**

Orin - A selection from the same crosses that produced the Crispin-Mutsu apple; Golden Delicious x Indo. Yellow skin is blushed red-orange and dotted with conspicuous white lenticels. Moderately vigorous, spreading tree is an annual tipbearer. Ripens in October. Developed in Japan. *Source History: 4 in 1992; 6 in 2000.* **Sources: Ch9, Cla, COL, Cu4, Mo19, Nrs.**

Oriole - Yellow Transparent x Livland Raspberry. Large, yellow fruit striped with red. Excellent quality for eating fresh and cooking. Vigorous, hardy, extremely productive tree; heavy, annual cropper. Ripens in July or August depending on location. Hardy to -50 degrees F. with occasional winter injury. Developed in Minnesota. Introduced in 1949. *Source History: 5 in 1988; 7 in 1992; 5 in 2000.* **Sources: Bea, Ch9, Ed5, Nrs, Stl.**

Orleans - Red Delicious x Deacon Jones. Large, sweet, red-purple fruit with heavy bloom. Shape of Red Delicious but larger in size. Keeps 4-6 weeks longer than Red Delicious. Shows good disease resistance in the South. Developed in Geneva, New York, 1924. *Source History: 2 in 1988; 5 in 1992; 2 in 2000.* **Sources: Nrs, Ro3.**

Orleans Reinette - Round, flattened, green-yellow fruit, somewhat netted with slight russet, usually reddish in the sun. Fine, crisp, yellow flesh. rich, nutty flavor.

Ripens in October. Originated in France. Introduced in 1776. *Source History: 2 in 2000.* **Sources: So5, Son.**

Ortley (Greasy Pippin, Woolman's Long Pippin, White Bellflower, White Detroit) - Yellow Bellflower type. Large, long, conical, pale greenish yellow fruit with deep cavity. Thin, tough, smooth, waxy skin. Crisp, juicy, yellowish white flesh. Excellent, sprightly, subacid flavor. Hangs from the tree on a long stem. Medium size, moderately vigorous tree. Ripens in late fall. One of the earliest American apples. Woolman's Long Pippin probably named after famous Quaker preacher and abolitionist, John Woolman. Introduced in 1825. *Source History: 3 in 1988; 6 in 1992; 6 in 2000.* **Sources: Bea, Bl4, Ch9, Or9, So5, Wo7.**

Oxheart Pippin - High quality fruit with an intense flavor. More tart than sweet. Crunchy white flesh with vanilla-like aroma. Ripens early November. Zone 5. Seedling from Weston's Antique Apple Orchard in the 1930s. *Source History: 2 in 2000.* **Sources: Ed5, Fed.**

Ozark Beauty - Southern variety. *Source History: 1 in 2000.* **Sources: Ca15.**

Ozark Gold - Ben Davis parentage. Very similar to Golden Delicious with less russeting and ripens three or more weeks earlier. Wide angle branches. Very hardy and disease resistant. Bears young. Originated in Missouri. Introduced in 1970. *Source History: 2 in 1988; 10 in 1992; 9 in 2000.* **Sources: AG2, Ch9, Cla, Jo3, La3, Sc6, So5, Son, St4.**

Paduckah - Excellent for eating fresh or cooking. Holds up well for a summer apple. Very hardy, disease resistant tree. *Source History: 1 in 1988; 1 in 1992; 2 in 2000.* **Sources: Hid, La3.**

Palmer Green (Palmer Greening) - *Source History: 1 in 1988; 2 in 1992; 2 in 2000.* **Sources: Ch9, So5.**

Palouse - Tomkins King seedling from Washington State. Large, bright yellow fruit blushed and striped with red and carmine. Firm, yellowish flesh is crisp, juicy, subacid and very aromatic. Quite productive tree. Ripens late July. Introduced in 1879. *Source History: 3 in 1988; 4 in 1992; 4 in 2000.* **Sources: Bea, Ch9, So5, Wo7.**

PAR12T101 - Round green-yellow fruit is 75% red blushed and striped; 50-99% red-orange color. Slightly conspicuous lenticels. Cream-white, semi-firm flesh with fine texture. Harvest late July. Trial variety from Purdue University. *Source History: 1 in 2000.* **Sources: Cla.**

PAR26T4 - Conic, yellow fruit. Fine, firm, crisp yellow flesh. Sub-acid flavor. Fair quality. Ripens around September 22. Trial variety from Purdue University. *Source History: 1 in 2000.* **Sources: Cla.**

Paragon - Originated in Tennessee. Introduced in 1830. *Source History: 1 in 1992; 1 in 2000.* **Sources: Wo7.**

Parchland - *Source History: 1 in 1988; 1 in 1992; 1 in 2000.* **Sources: So5.**

Parentene - Thought to be a Transparent x Gravenstein cross. Large blocky, light green fruit with bright red on the sunny side. Zesty flavor. Ripens early. *Source History: 2 in 1988; 2 in 1992; 1 in 2000.* **Sources: Bea.**

Park - *Source History: 1 in 2000.* **Sources: Ed5.**

Parkland (PF26) - Rescue x Melba. Similar to Norland, but keeps better. Medium size, greenish yellow fruit with red stripes. Suitable for fresh eating or preserves. Stores well. Ripens in late August. Very hardy; Zone 2. Developed in the Canadian plains for cold, short season areas. Introduced by the Lacombe Alberta Research Station, 1979. *Source History: 1 in 1988; 7 in 1992; 4 in 2000.* **Sources:**

Bea, Fed, Mc3, Sc6, Stl.

Parks Pippin (Gilmer Pippin) - Greenish yellow fruit. Tart until fully ripe. Good keeper. Used for cooking, drying, cider or fresh eating. Ripens late fall. Originated in northern Georgia in the mid-1800s. *Source History: 2 in 1992; 1 in 2000.* **Sources: La3.**

Parmar (Yellow Flat) - Dark yellow skin with irregular russet patches. Dark yellow dense flesh. Dessert apple suitable for applesauce and apple butter. Ripens in early August. *Source History: 1 in 1992; 1 in 2000.* **Sources: Or9.**

Parson Pat - *Source History: 1 in 2000.* **Sources: Ch9.**

Pasha - *Source History: 1 in 2000.* **Sources: Ch9.**

Patterson - Columbia x Melba. Canadian prairie apple. Medium to large size fruit is green-yellow with occasional red streaking. Good for fresh eating, juice and drying. Good keeper. Requires thinning. Zone 3. Introduced in 1960. *Source History: 1 in 1992; 2 in 2000.* **Sources: Ed5, Va5.**

Patton - Medium long conical fruit. Green-red to dark red skin color. Sprightly tart flavor mellows with storage. Good for fresh eating and sauces. Stores well. Ripens over a 3 to 4 week period. *Source History: 1 in 1988; 2 in 1992; 2 in 2000.* **Sources: Bea, Ca15.**

Paulared - Beautiful, solid-red blush fruit. Light to creamy, firm, crisp, juicy, mildly tart flesh. All-purpose quality. Excellent for pies and sauce. Fruit hangs well, colors evenly throughout the tree, can be harvested in one or two pickings. Ripens early. Requires thinning in order to maintain size and annual crops. Trademarked. Zones 4-7. U.S. Plant Patent No. 2800. *Source History: 5 in 1988; 6 in 1992; 9 in 2000.* **Sources: Amb, Bo5, Ch9, Hi9, Jun, Sc6, So5, Stl, WI12.**

Pawpaw (Paw-Paw Sweet) - Medium size, good quality dessert apple. Keeps well. Originated in Michigan in 1858. *Source History: 2 in 1992; 3 in 2000.* **Sources: Ch9, Or9, Wo7.**

Peace Garden - Malinda x Duchess. Red, striped fruit. Juicy flesh. Excellent keeper. Hangs well on the tree. Ripens late. Hardy to -50 degrees F. with occasional winter injury. *Source History: 1 in 1988; 2 in 1992; 3 in 2000.* **Sources: Ch9, Ed5, Stl.**

Pear Apple (Pear Apple Cross) - *Source History: 1 in 1992; 1 in 2000.* **Sources: Ch9.**

Pearleaf - *Source History: 1 in 2000.* **Sources: WI12.**

Pearmain, Adam's (Norfolk Pippin) - An old English variety that was brought to the attention of the London Horticultural Society in 1826 by a gentleman named Adams. Originated in Herefordshire where it was called Hanging Pearmain. Has the true pearmain shape, yellow streaked fruit with red on the sunny side, covered with delicate brown russet. Flesh is rich and sugary. Excellent dessert apple. Small tree bears regularly, early and profusely on slender shoots and is most amenable to pruning. Introduced in 1826. *Source History: 5 in 1988; 5 in 1992; 4 in 2000.* **Sources: Ch9, Gr4, Or9, So5.**

Pearmain, Blue - Unknown parentage. Said to be the parent of Rolfe. Large, dark purplish red fruit with large dots and covered with dull bluish bloom. True Pearmain flavor; mild, aromatic and sweet. Will keep all winter. Ripens in early October. Hardy to -50 degrees F. with occasional winter injury. Originated in England in the 1700s. Grown throughout much of Maine for over 200 years. Introduced in 1833. *Source History: 5 in 1988; 9 in 1992; 9 in 2000.* **Sources: Bea, Bl4, Ed5, Fed, Gr4, Or9, So5, Stl, Wo7.**

Pearmain, Cannon (Alpian, Anderson) - Green-yellow skin flushed with brick red, striped with carmine and usually covered with red dots. All-purpose apple that stores exceptionally well; resists bruising. Biennial bearer. Ripens in October. Grown commercially in central Virginia in the early 20th century. *Source History: 1 in 1992; 2 in 2000.* **Sources: Ca15, Or9.**

Pearmain, Cherry - *Source History: 1 in 2000.* **Sources: Cu4.**

Pearmain, Christmas (Bunyard's Christmas Pearmain) - Small dessert apple. Green-yellow skin with over one-half flushed a dull orange-red and striped red. Conspicuous lenticels appear as russet spots. Long conical shape with broad flat-tened ends. Firm, creamy yellow flesh. Flavor is aromatic with a hint of astringency. Small, compact tree. Scab resistant. Ripens in October. *Source History: 1 in 1992; 1 in 2000.* **Sources: Or9.**

Pearmain, Clarke's - Southern variety. *Source History: 1 in 2000.* **Sources: Ca15.**

Pearmain, Claygate - Good size, brown russeted fruit with beautiful splash of crimson in the sun. Crisp, juicy, yellowish flesh. Rich sugary flavor like the Ribston Pippin. Good keeper; excellent bearer. Ripens late. Zones 6-9. Fine old English winter apple found growing in a hedge in the hamlet of Claygate in Surrey before 1820. *Source History: 3 in 1988; 3 in 1992; 5 in 2000.* **Sources: Bea, Ch9, Hid, So5, Son.**

Pearmain, Golden (Clarke Pearmain, Columbian Russet, Gloucester Pearmain) - Medium size, round fruit with a flattened end. Yellow skin with red stripes. Crisp flesh. Superior eating apple. Ripens in September. Believed to have originated in North Carolina; was noted in 1755 and described in 1807. *Source History: 2 in 1988; 7 in 1992; 6 in 2000.* **Sources: Bea, Ca15, Ch9, La3, Leu, Or9.**

Pearmain, Lamb Abbey (Lamb Abbey) - Small, red-striped fruit. Crisp, juicy, sugary, yellowish white flesh. Excellent flavor. Fine, sturdy tree; bears early, regularly and heavily. Ripens in mid-September. Rare old English variety raised from a seed of Newtown Pippin imported from America. Introduced in 1804. *Source History: 2 in 1988; 2 in 1992; 3 in 2000.* **Sources: Ch9, So5, Son.**

Pearmain, Pink - Distinctive upside-down shape; broader on the base than at the stem. Develops a red-striped skin when ripe. Flesh color is a deep pink, but varies according to climate. Tart, mildly sweet, distinctive aromatic flavor. Ripens late September. Found growing in an old orchard near Whale Gulch, California. Probably an Etter creation. Trademarked. *Source History: 1 in 1988; 2 in 1992; 1 in 2000.* **Sources: Gr4.**

Pearmain, Summer - Seedling of English Pearmain. Red fruit. Mild, rich, excellent flavor. One of two apples given "best" rating in Beach's *Apples of New York.* Tree is a weak grower and fire blight susceptible. Hardy to -50 degrees F. with occasional winter injury. Introduced in 1817. *Source History: 5 in 1988; 7 in 1992; 4 in 2000.* **Sources: Bl4, Ch9, Stl, Wo7.**

Pearmain, Summer (American) - Green fruit covered with dull red. Excellent flavor. Introduced into the U.S. in 1806. Early in Japan's modern history it was sent to that country and is found in the parentage of many modern Japanese varieties. Introduced in 1806. *Source History: 2 in 1988; 2 in 1992; 2 in 2000.* **Sources: Ca15, So5.**

Pearmain, Suni - *Source History: 1 in 2000.* **Sources: Hid.**

Pearmain, White Winter (Winter Pearmain, Campbellite) - Oldest known English apple; dates back to 1200 A.D. Medium to nearly large, round to oval, light greenish fruit turning pale yellow with numerous dots. Fine-grained, crisp, tender, juicy flesh. Pleasantly rich, aromatic flavor. Fine quality, all-purpose apple. Excellent keeper. Tree is a healthy, vigorous grower; bears regularly and heavily. Splendid vitality; widely adaptable. Self-fruitful; excellent pollinator. Old favorite dessert apple in the Middle West since the early 1800s. Today is grown primarily in warm winter areas where its low chilling requirement renders it one of the few possible apples. Ripens in late October. Requires 400 hours of chilling. Zones 5-10. *Source History: 9 in 1988; 9 in 1992; 13 in 2000.* **Sources: Bay, Ca15, Ea3, Er2, Ga20, Gr4, Nrs, Or9, So5, Son, WI4, Wo7, Wor.**

Pearmain, Worcester - *Source History: 1 in 1988; 1 in 1992; 2 in 2000.* **Sources: Cu4, Gr4.**

Peck's Pleasant (Peck) - Bright yellow skin with red blush on one side. Very aromatic. Ripens in October. Developed in Rhode Island from the last Calville Blanc known to exist. Introduced in 1832. *Source History: 4 in 1988; 7 in 1992; 5 in 2000.* **Sources: Bea, Cu4, So5, Wo7, Wor.**

Pennstayman (Mohr) - *Source History: 1 in 1992; 1 in 2000.* **Sources: Nrs.**

Perry Russet - *Source History: 2 in 1992; 3 in 2000.* **Sources: Ch9, Or9, So5.**

Peters - *Source History: 1 in 2000.* **Sources: Ed5.**

Pettingill - Chance seedling discovered near Long Beach, California. Large fruit. Red overlay on green skin color. Crisp, juicy flesh with a good sugar-acid balance. Good keeper. Large, productive tree. Self-fruitful. Ripens late September to mid-October. Zones 6-11. Requires 100 hours of chilling. Introduced in 1949. *Source History: 2 in 1988; 2 in 1992; 6 in 2000.* **Sources: Bay, CO5, On4, Pa2, Son, WI4.**

Pewaukee - Duchess x Northern Spy. Medium to large fruit. Yellow flushed skin, mottled orang-red or striped red. Fairly firm, rather coarse, tender white flesh. Slightly aromatic, subacid flavor. Ripens late. Keeps well. First recorded in 1870. *Source History: 2 in 1988; 3 in 1992; 4 in 2000.* **Sources: Bl4, So5, Stl, Wo7.**

Pickett - Southern variety. *Source History: 1 in 2000.* **Sources: Ca15.**

Pierce Pasture - Bethel x Alexander. Very large, red striped fruit with coarse, yellow flesh. Excellent flavor. Good for fresh eating, cider and cooking. Keeps well. Ripens late season. Hardy to -50 degrees F. St. Lawrence Nurseries introduction. Old variety. *Source History: 1 in 1992; 1 in 2000.* **Sources: Stl.**

Pig Pen - Southern variety. *Source History: 1 in 2000.* **Sources: Ca15.**

Pilot (Virginia Pilot) - Large yellow fruit is striped red and flecked with specks of russet. Heavy biennial bearer with a light crop in the off year. Stores exceptionally well. Ripens in October. Originated as a seedling at the foot of Pilot Mountain in Virginia in the early 1800s. *Source History: 1 in 1992; 2 in 2000.* **Sources: Ca15, Or9.**

Pink Delight - Large fruit has creamy yellow skin with red stripes. Deep pink flesh is sweet and aromatic. Ripens in mid to late September. *Source History: 1 in 2000.* **Sources: On3.**

Pink Lady (Cripps Pink Cultivar) - A cross between Golden Delicious and Lady Williams from the Western Australian apple breeding program. Oblong, green fruit turns yellow at maturity and is overlaid with pink or light red. Fine-grained, white flesh. Thin skin bruises easily. Fruit will store for six to eight months in common storage, longer in controlled atmosphere. Self-fruitful. Chilling requirement similar to Granny Smith; 400-500 hours. Ripens in late September. Zones 6-9. U.S. Plant Patent No. 7880. *Source History: 2 in 1992; 7 in 2000.* **Sources: Ad2, Bay, BR10, Cu4, Or9, Son, WI4.**

Pink Old Lady - *Source History: 1 in 2000.* **Sources: Or9.**

Pink Pearl - Pink-fleshed variety developed from Surprise, which was first noted in England in 1831. Medium size apple with attractive cream and green skin, sometimes blushed with red cheek in warmer areas. Novel, bright pink flesh. Rich, sweet flavor; fine aroma. Good dessert quality; makes colorful applesauce or pie filling. Good storage ability. Medium to large tree; scab susceptible. Blooms early with a highly ornamental profusion of crimson pink blossoms. Requires cross-pollination. Ripens during September. Requires 600 hours of chilling. Hardy to Zone 4. Developed by California apple breeder, Albert Etter. Introduced in 1944. *Source History: 8 in 1988; 17 in 1992; 18 in 2000.* **Sources: Bay, Bea, Bl4, CO5, Cu4, Ed5, Ga20, Gr16, Gr4, Hid, Jo3, La3, On3, Or9, Sc6, So5, Son, Wh3, WI4.**

Pink Princess - Pink Pearl x Bronze Leaf crab. Medium size fruit. Light green skin changes to yellow with a few faint red stripes. Pink flesh resembles Pink Pearl. Nice fruity flavor is sweeter than Pink Pearl. Zones 6-9. *Source History: 1 in 2000.* **Sources: Son.**

Pink Satin - *Source History: 1 in 1988; 1 in 1992; 1 in 2000.* **Sources: So5.**

Pink Sparkle - Red fleshed fruit. *Source History: 1 in 2000.* **Sources: So5.**

Pink Sugar - *Source History: 1 in 1988; 1 in 1992; 1 in 2000.* **Sources: Bea.**

Pink Surprise - Medium size fruit with glossy red skin. Pink flesh. Fairly tart flavor. Exceptional pie apple. Good cropper. Ripens late October. Likely of Etter origin. *Source History: 1 in 2000.* **Sources: Ga20.**

Pinky - Southern variety. *Source History: 1 in 2000.* **Sources: Ca15.**

Pinova - Clivia (Duchess of Oldenburg x Cox's Orange Pippin) x Golden Delicious cross. High quality, medium size fruit. Very attractive skin with yellow undercolor and fire-color to solid red. Good flavor with excellent sugar-acid balance. Produces regular crops. Benefits from regular pruning and fruit thinning. Introduced by the Fruit Research Institute in Dresden, Germany in 1986. Trademarked. Plant patent applied for. *Source History: 4 in 2000.* **Sources: Co2, COL, TR8, WI12.**

Pippin - *Source History: 1 in 1988; 1 in 1992; 2 in 2000.* **Sources: Bea, STR.**

Pippin Chesneuko - *Source History: 1 in 2000.* **Sources: Ch9.**

Pitmaston Pineapple (Pitmaston Pine) - Broadly conical, golden yellow fruit covered with fine fawn russet. Juicy, sugary flesh; excellent flavor. Ripens mid-September. Belongs to a class of old russeted English dessert apples neglected today because of their small size. Zones 6-9. Originated in England around 1785. *Source History: 2 in 1988; 7 in 1992; 8 in 2000.* **Sources: Bl4, Ch9, Cu4, Fed, Gr4, Or9, So5, Son.**

Polly Eades - Southern variety. *Source History: 3 in 1992; 2 in 2000.* **Sources: Ca15, Ch9.**

Pomme d'Or (Golden Apple) - Unknown parentage. Large, rectangular-shaped, faint yellow fruit. Large open core is partially filled with a sweet nectar. Matures to a rich golden color. Good as a summer cooking apple and for fresh eating. Beautiful and quite rare. Extremely hardy. Located near Fort Kent, Maine in 1998. Possibly originated in Maine or Quebec. *Source History: 1 in 2000.* **Sources: Fed.**

Pomme Gris (French Russet, Gray Apple, Leather Coat of Turic, Pomme Grise) - Small to medium, deep yellow-brown mottled fruit is striped with dark red. Excellent dessert apple. Ripens in September. Very good keeper. Brought to the St.

Lawrence River Valley from Europe by French immigrants. Originated in 1803. *Source History: 4 in 1992; 6 in 2000.* **Sources: Bl4, Ca15, Ch9, Fed, Or9, Wo7.**

Pomme Royale (Dyer) - Greenish yellow fruit usually covered with veins of russet. Fine, highly spicy flavor. Ripens in early September. Believed to be an old French variety brought to Rhode Island by Huguenot settlers who fled France after the revocation of the Edict of Nantes. Introduced in 1685. *Source History: 1 in 1988; 2 in 1992; 1 in 2000.* **Sources: So5.**

Porter (Jennings, Yellow Summer Pearmain) - Uniform tapered conical fruit. Pure yellow skin. Tender flesh. Fine quality for dessert, canning and cooking. Ripens during September. In its earlier editions, the Fanny Farmer Cookbook singled out Porter for mention as the variety for apple pie. Introduced in 1840. *Source History: 3 in 1988; 6 in 1992; 5 in 2000.* **Sources: Bea, Ch9, Gr4, So5, Wo7.**

Porter's Perfection - English cider apple. Striped red on cream. Bittersharp juice; high acid and tannin. Zones 6-9. *Source History: 3 in 1988; 2 in 1992; 3 in 2000.* **Sources: Cid, Nrs, Son.**

Potts - Southern variety. *Source History: 1 in 2000.* **Sources: Ca15.**

Pound Apple (Old Fashioned) - Very large, flattened fruit. Mostly green skin, sometimes with pinkish blush and stripes. Old favorite cooking apple. *Source History: 1 in 1988; 2 in 1992; 1 in 2000.* **Sources: Bo5.**

Pound of Alabama - Southern variety. *Source History: 1 in 2000.* **Sources: Ca15.**

Pound Pippin - Probably the Pound Pippin or Fall Pippin listed in Beach's *Apples of New York*. Beach describes the fruit as large or very large with thin, smooth, greenish yellow skin becoming clear yellow and sometimes faintly blushed. Whitish or yellow tinged flesh; moderately firm, rather fine, tender and very juicy. Somewhat aromatic. Ripens late September. *Source History: 2 in 1988; 2 in 1992; 3 in 2000.* **Sources: Ca15, Hid, Ur2.**

Pound Sweet - Very large, amber to golden fruit when fully ripe. Firm flesh with yellow tinge. Sweet unusual flavor. Fine eating; the very best when baked. Vigorous, long lived tree with open spreading habit. Ripens from late September to early October. Hardy to Zone 4. Sometimes confused with Pumpkin Sweet, another excellent apple. Originated in Connecticut about 1834. *Source History: 6 in 1988; 8 in 1992; 12 in 2000.* **Sources: Bea, Ch9, Cid, Cu4, Ed5, Fed, La3, Mi1, Or9, Sc6, Stl, Wh4, Wor.**

Pound Sweet, Pineapple Sport - *Source History: 1 in 1992; 1 in 2000.* **Sources: Ch9.**

Pound, Longshore Strain - Sometimes referred to as a large Horseapple; possibly a seedling of it. Resembles Horseapple in shape and color but is much larger. Good cooking and drying apple. Ripens midseason. *Source History: 1 in 1992; 1 in 2000.* **Sources: Cla.**

Prairie Fire - Small, persistent, reddish purple fruits. Moderate growth habit with upright branching that forms a rounded head. Exceptionally attractive, deep reddish purple foliage maturing to dark green but retaining the reddish purple in its major veins. Rich dark red blooms. Excellent resistance to scab, rust and fire blight. Hardy in Zone 4. *Source History: 1 in 1988; 5 in 1992; 1 in 2000.* **Sources: Nrs.**

Prairie Spy - Extra long-keeping winter apple. Large fruit with attractive red over yellow skin color. Crisp, juicy flesh with excellent flavor. All purpose. Keeps for three months with flavor developing and improving while in storage. Hardy, vigorous, long-lived, annually productive tree. Bears young and heavily. Blooms ex-

ceptionally late. Shows some resistance to apple scab and cedar-apple rust. Ripens in early October. Hardy to -50 degrees F. with occasional winter injury. Although dropped by commercial orchards, one of the best home varieties. Developed by the University of Minnesota Fruit Breeding Farm. Introduced in 1940. *Source History: 10 in 1988; 13 in 1992; 13 in 2000.* **Sources: BA14, Ch9, Ed5, Fa1, Fi1, GR26, Gur, Jun, Nrs, SH8, Stl, Und, WI12.**

Presbyterian - Southern variety. *Source History: 1 in 2000.* **Sources: Ca15.**

Priam - Disease resistant. *Source History: 1 in 2000.* **Sources: Cu4.**

Priddy's Pride - *Source History: 1 in 2000.* **Sources: Ch9.**

Priestly (Priestley) - Originated in Pennsylvania. Introduced in 1817. *Source History: 1 in 1988; 3 in 1992; 3 in 2000.* **Sources: Ch9, So5, Wo7.**

Prima - Medium to large, round fruit with dark red blush on bright yellow background. Mild subacid, juicy white flesh. Excellent quality. Can be stored through the fall. Hardy, moderately vigorous, open, spreading tree. Bears annually when properly thinned. Fruit and foliage are immune to scab; resistant to fire blight, cedar-apple rust and mildew. Ripens 10 days before McIntosh in late August or late September depending on location. Hardy in Zones 5-8. U.S. Plant Patent No. 3134. *Source History: 4 in 1988; 7 in 1992; 6 in 2000.* **Sources: Bu7, Ch9, Cu4, Fed, Mo19, Or9.**

Primate - Medium to large, smooth, light green fruit. Crisp, juicy, white flesh. Ripens during August. One of the early American dessert summer apples. Originated in Onondaga County, New York. Introduced in 1840. *Source History: 5 in 1988; 7 in 1992; 6 in 2000.* **Sources: Bea, Ch9, Cu4, Gr4, So5, Wo7.**

Prime Gold - Elongated fruit; clear, russet-resistant golden apple. Excellent tree structure, producing wide angle leaders. U.S. Plant Patent No. 2806. *Source History: 1 in 1988; 1 in 1992; 1 in 2000.* **Sources: Va2.**

Priscilla - Starking Delicious seedling. Medium size, slightly conical fruit with 65% bright red blush over yellow background. Crisp, coarse, mildly subacid, white to slightly greenish flesh. Good flavor and quality. Will store for three months. Fruit hangs well. Good pollinator for Prima. Immune to scab; resistant to fire blight, powdery mildew and cedar-apple rust. Picks with Jonathan in mid-September. Hardy in Zones 5-8. U.S. Plant Patent No. 3488. *Source History: 3 in 1988; 5 in 1992; 4 in 2000.* **Sources: Ch9, Fed, Or9, So5.**

Prissy Gum - Southern variety. *Source History: 1 in 2000.* **Sources: Ca15.**

Pristine (Co-op 32 Cultivar) - Glossy yellow skinned fruit with high sugar content. Terminal bearing tree requires multiple pickings. Fruit drops when mature. Ripens early to mid-July, just after Lodi. Disease resistant but susceptible to fire blight. Purdue release. Trademarked. U.S. Plant Patent No. 9881. *Source History: 12 in 2000.* **Sources: Ad2, AG2, Cla, Cu4, Ed2, Hi9, Rai, Ro3, Sc6, St4, TR8, WAF.**

Professor Sprenger - *Source History: 1 in 1992; 1 in 2000.* **Sources: Nrs.**

Progressive - Southern variety. *Source History: 1 in 1992; 2 in 2000.* **Sources: Ca15, Ch9.**

Prussian (Colvert) - *Source History: 1 in 1992; 1 in 2000.* **Sources: Ch9.**

Pumpkin Russet - Originated in New England. Introduced in 1832. *Source History: 1 in 1992; 2 in 2000.* **Sources: Cu4, Wo7.**

Pumpkin Sweet (Rhode Island Sweet) - Very large, yellowish green fruit. Sweet, nonacid flesh. Prized for baking. Ripens during October. Not the same as Pound Sweet. Originated in Connecticut. Introduced in 1834. *Source History: 1 in 1988; 5 in 1992; 8 in 2000.* **Sources: Bl4, Ca15, Ch9, Fed, Or9, So5, Wh4, Wo7.**

Puritan - McIntosh x Red Astrachan. Red fruit. White flesh. Somewhat tart, McIntosh-type flavor. Tree has good structure; tends to bear biennially. Ripens in early August. Hardy to -50 degrees F. with occasional winter injury. Developed at the Massachusetts Agricultural Experiment Station. Introduced in 1953. *Source History: 2 in 1988; 4 in 1992; 3 in 2000.* **Sources: Ed5, Or9, Stl.**

Quality - *Source History: 1 in 1992; 1 in 2000.* **Sources: Nrs.**

Quebec Belle - Open-pollinated seedling of Northern Spy. Red fruit. Resembles Delicious in appearance and Northern Spy in quality. Keeps well. Ripens midseason. Hardy to -40 degrees F. *Source History: 1 in 1988; 1 in 1992; 2 in 2000.* **Sources: Ch9, Stl.**

Queen Cox - The preferred strain of Cox's Orange Pippin in England. Fruit is not as highly colored as Cherry Cox, but is as good an eating quality. Fewer problems with leaf spot and bitter pit than common Cox. Ripens late September to early October. *Source History: 1 in 1992; 3 in 2000.* **Sources: Clo, Er2, Mo19.**

Quinte - Melba x Crimson Beauty. Yellow, heavy, red blush fruit. Cream colored, very tender flesh. Good quality and firmness. Ships well but does not store. Very strong growing tree; requires pruning. Annual bearer of heavy crops. Requires several pickings. Earliest good eating apple. Ripens during July. Hardy to -50 degrees F. with occasional winter injury. Developed in Ottawa, Canada. Introduced in 1964. *Source History: 4 in 1988; 4 in 1992; 5 in 2000.* **Sources: Bea, Ch9, Cu4, Nrs, Sc6, Stl.**

Radiant Runkel - Medium size, bright red fruit. The hard, juicy, sweet flesh makes it great for fresh eating and baking. Keeps for up to 180 days under refrigeration. Productive tree. *Source History: 1 in 2000.* **Sources: Co2.**

Rainbow - *Source History: 1 in 2000.* **Sources: Or9.**

Ralls Janet (Ralls, Ralls Genet, Neverfail, Rock Remain, Rock Rimmon, Winter Genneting, Rawle's Janet, Jeniton) - Small to medium fruit. Yellow or greenish skin flushed, matted and streaked with red and pink-red; also has scars and whitish dots. Firm, fine, crisp, tender, pleasantly aromatic, white flesh. Slightly sweet, subacid flavor. When stored properly, it should maintain its quality through the winter. Especially recommended for late frost areas since it is one of the very last to open its blossoms, hence the synonym Neverfail. Ripens late to very late depending on location. Developed in Virginia in the 1800s. *Source History: 3 in 1988; 8 in 1992; 11 in 2000.* **Sources: Bea, Bl4, Ca15, Ch9, Cid, Cu4, Gr4, Or9, Ro3, Ur2, Wo7.**

Ralph Shay Crab (Ralph Shea) - Showy pink flowers followed by attractive bright red 1.25" fruit. Makes excellent jelly. Vigorous, sturdy tree. Disease resistant. Hardy in Zone 5. *Source History: 1 in 1992; 1 in 2000.* **Sources: Fo2, Gl3, Gr16.**

Rambo (American Seek-No-Further, Bread and Cheese, Delaware, Fall Romanite, Gray Romanite, Terry's Redstreak, Trumpington, Winter Rambo) - Highly flavored winter apple. Ripens in September. Mentioned by Coxe in 1817. *Source History: 1 in 1988; 3 in 1992; 3 in 2000.* **Sources: Or9, St4, Wo7.**

Rambo, Hauser Strain - Pale greenish yellow matted skin with red stripes. Firm, fine, tender, whitish flesh. Subacid flavor. One of the best for jelly, pies and drying. Ripens early July. Dates to the late 1500s. *Source History: 1 in 1988; 1 in 1992; 1 in 2000.* **Sources: La3.**

<u>Rambo, Red Summer</u> (Redsumbo) - Double red Summer Rambo that colors earlier; all the same good qualities as the regular strain. If additional color is necessary for marketing, let it hang for two additional weeks, pick when solid red, put in storage and keep for marketing until mid-winter. Tart, good for cooking. Ripens during August. *Source History: 4 in 1988; 5 in 1992; 4 in 2000.* **Sources: Bea, Bl4, Bo5, Nrs.**

<u>Rambo, Summer</u> (Lorraine, Summer Rambour, Rambour Franc) - Large, brightly striped, red fruit. Breaking, crisp, exceptionally juicy, yellowish green flesh. Fine, rich, agreeably acidulous, aromatic flavor. Good for eating and sauce. Grows rapidly to form rather large tree. Comes into bearing early. Vigorous, hardy and productive. Some disease resistance. Ripens from early August to early September depending on location. Zones 4-9. Originated in 16th century near the village of Amiens in France. Popular in America since colonial times. *Source History: 6 in 1988; 10 in 1992; 15 in 2000.* **Sources: Ad2, Bl4, Ca15, Ch9, Cu4, Gr4, Mil, Nrs, Or9, Sc6, So5, Son, Ur2, Wh4, Wor.**

<u>Ramsdell Sweet</u> (Avery Sweet, English Sweet, Hurlbut Sweet, Red Pumpkin Sweet) - Fairly vigorous tree bears fruit early. Ripens in early October. Developed in Connecticut in the 1850s. *Source History: 2 in 1988; 5 in 1992; 2 in 2000.* **Sources: Bea, Sc6, Wo7.**

<u>Rannels Yellow</u> - *Source History: 1 in 1992; 1 in 2000.* **Sources: Bl4.**

<u>Raritan</u> (Melba x Sonora) x (Melba x Williams x Starr). Small, round fruit is ribbed and somewhat irregularly shaped. Green-yellow skin with splashes of red. Crisp flesh. Juicy, sweet flavor. Scab resistant. Ripens in late August. Developed in New Jersey. Introduced in 1966. *Source History: 2 in 1992; 2 in 2000.* **Sources: Bea, Ch9.**

<u>Rattle Core</u> - Southern variety. *Source History: 1 in 2000.* **Sources: Ca15.**

<u>Rattler</u> - Southern variety. *Source History: 1 in 2000.* **Sources: Ca15.**

<u>Raven</u> - Small to medium cider apple. Ripe fruit in full sun is dark burgundy, almost black. About 50% watercore. Yields a good volume of bright red juice which has excellent flavor and balance and does not turn brown. Makes very good dried fruit and fine wine. Not a good keeper. Ripens during November. *Source History: 1 in 1988; 2 in 1992; 1 in 2000.* **Sources: Ch9.**

<u>Red Baron</u> (MN 1500) - Golden Delicious x Daniels Red Duchess. Medium to large, cherry-red fruit. Crisp, juicy flesh. Pleasantly acidic, tart flavor. Good for pie, sauce and fresh eating. Keeps well until late December. Tolerant to fire blight; resistant to cedar-apple rust. Hardy and consistently productive. Ripens during August or September depending on location. Bred for the North. Hardy to -50 degrees F. with occasional winter injury. Hardy to Zone 4. Developed at the University of Minnesota, 1969. *Source History: 6 in 1988; 14 in 1992; 8 in 2000.* **Sources: Bea, Ch9, Fa1, Fed, LA4, Nrs, Or9, SH8.**

<u>Red Bouquet</u> - Showy pink blossoms. Dark red skinned fruit. Crisp flesh with good flavor makes it ideal for fresh eating. Ripens in September. *Source History: 1 in 2000.* **Sources: Sc6.**

<u>Red Butterscotch</u> - Small to medium size conic apple. Light orange-red stripes on a green background. Firm, sweet flesh. Pleasant flavor with a hint of butterscotch. Good keeper. Ripens late September. Zone 4. Unknown origin. *Source History: 1 in 1988; 1 in 1992; 1 in 2000.* **Sources: Bea.**

<u>Red Canada</u> - Southern variety. *Source History: 2 in 2000.* **Sources: Ca15, Cu4.**

Red Cheese - Southern variety. *Source History: 1 in 2000.* **Sources: Ca15.**

Red Cinnamon - *Source History: 1 in 2000.* **Sources: Or9.**

Red Delicious - Most widely grown red apple in the U.S. Large, waxy, dark red fruit. Round apples become elongated and tapered to the classic Delicious shape in cooler areas. Fine grained, tender, crisp, juicy flesh. Mild flavor; pleasing aroma. Excellent dessert apple; a favorite for fresh eating. Holds crispness and flavor until May if stored well. High yielding, fast growing tree; hardy in growth and bud. Tends to produce full crops every other year unless properly thinned. Needs full sun all day for best fruit production. Resistant to fire blight and cedar-apple rust. Ripens from late September to mid-October. Requires 800 chilling hours. Hardy in Zones 5-8. *Source History: 40 in 1988; 58 in 1992; 36 in 2000.* **Sources: Bar, Bas, BO10, Bu1, CO5, Fi1, FO10, Fo4, GI3, GR26, Gur, Ho5, Iso, JOY, La3, Lee, LI7, Mc3, ME3, MI10, MI5, Na4, ORA, Pi2, Po2, Rid, Sav, Sc6, SH8, So5, STR, Tex, TU5, WA8, Wel, Wom.**

Red Delicious, Ace Spur (Perle Strain) - Limb sport of Oregon Spur. Begins with an early stripe filling out to a solid, dark red blush. Exhibits early color and typical Delicious fruit with high quality flesh. Produces a second layer of red that covers moderate sunburn very well. Heavy producer. Easily pollinated. More vigor than earlier Oregon Spur strains; easier to train. Exhibits 20-30% more growth than Bisbee when young. Ripens mid-October. Developed by Columbia Basin Nursery. Trademarked. U.S. Plant Patent No. 4587. *Source History: 3 in 1988; 2 in 1992; 2 in 2000.* **Sources: Ad2, COL.**

Red Delicious, Best-O-Reds - Old fashioned strain of Red Delicious long considered the best eating of the Reds but has lost favor due to poor coloring. Excellent flavor. *Source History: 1 in 2000.* **Sources: Wh4.**

Red Delicious, Big - Large, solid bright red fruit. Good tasting. Ripens in October. *Source History: 1 in 1988; 1 in 1992; 1 in 2000.* **Sources: Mi1.**

Red Delicious, Bisbee Spur (Bisbee Red Delicious, Starkrimson Red Delicious) - Highly colored, blush type, Red Delicious strain. In cool climates fruit flattens at top and bottom in the classic Delicious shape. Large, red, waxy fruit. Firm, crisp, juicy flesh. Distinctive, sweet, tangy flavor. Keeps well for extended period if stored under cool conditions. Small, compact naturally semidwarfing tree; hardy spurs are abundant along scaffold limbs. Requires spreading to induce early bearing. Should be vigorously thinned for top quality. Pollinate with Golden Delicious, Granny Smith or Liberty. Ripens 6-12 days earlier than other red strains. Requires 700 hours of chilling. Hardy to Zone 4. *Source History: 9 in 1988; 7 in 1992; 7 in 2000.* **Sources: Ad2, Bay, CO5, LA4, Nrs, St4, Wa16, WI4.**

Red Delicious, Campbell Strain - Striped skin fills in to solid deep red color early. Tightly spurred. *Source History: 3 in 2000.* **Sources: Co2, Va2, WAF.**

Red Delicious, Compspur - Compact strain of Big Red Delicious with twice the number of spurs. *Source History: 1 in 1988; 1 in 1992; 1 in 2000.* **Sources: Mi1.**

Red Delicious, Crowder - Early coloring, striped apple. Semi-spur growth habit. Holds well in cold storage. Originated in Washington. Trademarked. *Source History: 1 in 2000.* **Sources: TR8.**

Red Delicious, DixieRed (Hared Cultivar, Starkspur Dixie Red Delicious) - Excellent performer in both the North and the South. U.S. Plant Patent No. 5547. *Source History: 2 in 1992; 2 in 2000.* **Sources: AG2, St4.**

Red Delicious, Double - Extra large, deeper solid bright red fruit. Fine grained, crisp, white flesh. Juicy, tangy, rich flavor. Dessert apple; excellent for fresh eating and cider. Colors early at low elevations. Ripens in mid-October. *Source History: 6 in 1988; 6 in 1992; 3 in 2000.* **Sources: Mel, SIM, Ty2.**

Red Delicious, Early Red One - One of the earliest to color. Heavy production and unsurpassed early color. Although it is a non-spur tree, it tends to throw more fruit spurs than other non-spur varieties. U.S. Plant Patent No. 3556. *Source History: 1 in 1988; 1 in 1992; 1 in 2000.* **Sources: Va2.**

Red Delicious, Harrold Strain - Sweet, crisp, fine flavored fruit. Vigorous, productive tree. Requires 700 hours of chilling. *Source History: 1 in 1988; 3 in 1992; 2 in 2000.* **Sources: Nrs, WI4.**

Red Delicious, Idaho Spur - Fully dark red strain with blushed color patterns; colors early. Tree has spur habit of growth; good yielder. Ripens midseason. One of the best of the 85 Red Delicious sports under test at Geneva. Originally from Idaho. Introduced in 1961. *Source History: 1 in 1988; 2 in 1992; 1 in 2000.* **Sources: Ch9.**

Red Delicious, Imperial - Bright solid blush fruit. Tree has average vigor with tendency to spur. Popular in the northeast and areas where spur types have not performed well. *Source History: 1 in 1988; 2 in 1992; 1 in 2000.* **Sources: Nrs.**

Red Delicious, It - Striped selection of Redchief. Earlier coloring and darker red ground color than Redchief Heinicke. Moderately vigorous, spur type tree with spreading habit. Discovered in Orondo, Washington, 1986. Trademarked. *Source History: 1 in 2000.* **Sources: WI12.**

Red Delicious, Oregon Spur II - Skin color is red with dark striping. Colors earlier than its parent. Superior white flesh. U.S. Plant Patent No. 4819. *Source History: 1 in 1988; 2 in 1992; 2 in 2000.* **Sources: Jo3, Va2.**

Red Delicious, Red Dietrick - *Source History: 1 in 1992; 1 in 2000.* **Sources: CO5.**

Red Delicious, Red Spur - Red Delicious sport. Large fruit size, long type. Early solid red color. True delicious flavor. Exceptional storage qualities. Ripens very early. *Source History: 2 in 1988; 2 in 1992; 1 in 2000.* **Sources: Hid.**

Red Delicious, Red Zenith Spur (Wittkopf Cultivar) - One of the earliest, highly colored, full striped Red Delicious selections grown in the industry today. *Source History: 1 in 2000.* **Sources: BR10.**

Red Delicious, Redstripe - Medium to large size fruit. Dark red with lighter stripes. White flesh is crisp, crunchy and sweet. Heavy cropper. Starts ripening in September and hangs on into November. Excellent for fresh eating, juice, baked and dried. *Source History: 1 in 2000.* **Sources: Ga20.**

Red Delicious, Richared (Richie Red) - Whole tree sport of Red Delicious. Fairly well colored and better tasting than the modern strains of Red Delicious. First improvement from the common Red Delicious. Discovered in Washington State. Hardy to Zone 4. Introduced in 1919. *Source History: 3 in 1988; 2 in 1992; 2 in 2000.* **Sources: Bea, Leu.**

Red Delicious, Roan (Hawkeye Original Red Delicious) - The original Delicious apple that began as a chance seedling of Yellow Bellflower in Iowa. When introduced by Stark Brothers it was a red-striped apple appreciated by some for its very mild flavor and excellent storage properties. As it became more popular, bud sports were selected for stronger coloring. Modern strains of Red Delicious become highly colored weeks before they approach ripeness; often picked prematurely. Not suitable for cooking, but does make a good addition to cider blends. Ripens in late September. Introduced in 1890. *Source History: 1 in 1988; 2 in 1992; 2 in 2000.*

Sources: Ca15, Gr4.

Red Delicious, Royal Red - *Source History: 1 in 1992; 1 in 2000.* **Sources: Nrs.**

Red Delicious, Sali (Moxee Cultivar) - Solid blush fruit colors early. Develops soluble solids ten days before other Red Delicious strains in the same area. Non-spur type tree. Zones 5-9. Originated as a whole tree mutation in Moxee, Washington. Trademarked. U.S. Plant Patent No. 7237. *Source History: 1 in 1992; 2 in 2000.* **Sources: Jo3, Va2.**

Red Delicious, Scarlet Spur (Snipes Cultivar) - New sport of Campbell Cultivar Red Delicious. Large, solid bright red fruit; early color. White flesh. Semi-dwarfing growth. Early, heavy producer. U.S. Plant Patent No. 4839. *Source History: 1 in 1988; 1 in 1992; 2 in 2000.* **Sources: St4, Va2.**

Red Delicious, Skyspur - Large fruit with good red blush. All the fruit colors well due to the spreading growth habit. Plant with Spur Yellow Delicious for best results. Hardy in Zones 5-8. *Source History: 1 in 1988; 1 in 1992; 1 in 2000.* **Sources: Ch9.**

Red Delicious, Spur (Wittkopf Strain) - Discovered as a limb mutation of Oregon Spur. Introduced in the mid-1980s as an early, full coloring striped Red Delicious. Vigorous tree with good precocity. *Source History: 2 in 1988; 4 in 1992; 6 in 2000.* **Sources: Bo5, Co2, Cu4, GI3, STR, Wh4.**

Red Delicious, Stamps - Striped skin. Firm, creamy white flesh. Originated in the Jim Stamps orchard in Chelan, Washington. *Source History: 1 in 2000.* **Sources: Co2.**

Red Delicious, Starkrimson (Bisbee Cultivar) - Most popular of all Red Delicious. Red 4" fruit keeps for many months in storage. Zones 5-8. Trademarked. *Source History: 2 in 2000.* **Sources: AG2, St4.**

Red Delicious, Super - Spur type tree with better yield than Triple Red but less flavorful. Ripens two weeks later. *Source History: 1 in 2000.* **Sources: Wor.**

Red Delicious, Super Chief Spur (Sandage Strain) - Super red sport of Red Delicious. Fruit starts out as a stripe and colors to solid red ten days ahead of its parent. Originated as complete tree sport of Red Chief (Campbell Strain) in the orchards of Ray Sandidge of Entiat, Washington. U.S. Plant Patent No. 6190. *Source History: 2 in 1992; 2 in 2000.* **Sources: Ad2, Va2.**

Red Delicious, Supreme (Paganelli Cultivar, Starkspur Supreme Red Delicious) - U.S. Plant Patent No. 3541. *Source History: 2 in 1992; 2 in 2000.* **Sources: AG2, St4.**

Red Delicious, Topred - Starts coloring with a definite stripe. Solidly colored by the time it is mature. One of the better tasting modern Reds. *Source History: 1 in 1988; 1 in 1992; 1 in 2000.* **Sources: Wh4.**

Red Delicious, Triple - Sport of Red Delicious; identical in size and shape. Richared type that colors red all over about two weeks earlier. Does not mature earlier, but it is especially valuable in the Southern Belt where there is not enough cold weather to get good, early coloring. Beautiful, solid, cherry-red blush with a subdued stripe. *Source History: 2 in 1988; 2 in 1992; 2 in 2000.* **Sources: Nrs, Wor.**

Red Delicious, UltraRed (Flanagan Cultivar) - Trademarked variety. *Source History: 1 in 1992; 1 in 2000.* **Sources: AG2.**

Red Delicious, Vallee Spur (Vallee Cultivar) - Beautiful apple. Fruit reaches full color early. Bears heavily. Trademarked. U.S. Plant Patent No. 6702. *Source*

History: 1 in 1992; 1 in 2000. **Sources: TR8.**

Red Delicious, Vermont Spur - *Source History: 1 in 1992; 1 in 2000.* **Sources: Nrs.**

Red Delicious, Wellspur - Starts coloring early and finishes with a blush. Matures about five days later than Oregon Spur. Keeps well in controlled atmosphere storage. *Source History: 1 in 1988; 1 in 1992; 1 in 2000.* **Sources: Nrs.**

Red Detroit - Southern variety. *Source History: 1 in 2000.* **Sources: Ca15.**

Red Esther (Lawyer Nutmeg) - Red-yellow fruit. Crisp, aromatic flesh with good flavor. Good keeper. Midseason ripening. Hardy in Zone 3. Introduced by Lawyer Nursery. *Source History: 2 in 1992; 1 in 2000.* **Sources: Stl.**

Red Flesh Crab - Deep red fruits are 2" long. Pink flesh makes a clear red jelly. Beautiful, spreading tree with copper colored leaves and red flowers. Blooms late. Biennial bearer. Zones 3-9. *Source History: 1 in 1992; 2 in 2000.* **Sources: Nrs, Rai.**

Red Fuji (Red Fuji Stripe, B.C. Type #2) - Ralls Janet x Delicious. New sport of Fuji, the main late season apple of Japan. Round or oblong fruit. Approximately 80% red color with a distinct stripe. Eating quality similar to a well ripened Delicious. Harder, juicier flesh. Requires a long growing season. Good keeper. Hardy in Zones 6-8. Developed in Japan, 1962. *Source History: 2 in 1988; 23 in 1992; 21 in 2000.* **Sources: AG2, Bay, Bea, Bl4, Bo5, Ch9, CO5, COL, Cu4, ME3, Nrs, On4, ORA, Ro3, Si3, St4, STR, Ty2, Va2, Wh4, WI4.**

Red Fuji (T.A.C. 114) - Began as a single limb sport believed budded from Summerland Redsport #2 Fuji. Exceptional red color with stripes over 80-95% of the skin surface. Matures 4-6 days earlier than standard Fuji. Has the most uniformity at maturity, enabling growers to harvest in one or two pickings. U.S. Plant Patent No. 8032. *Source History: 1 in 1992; 1 in 2000.* **Sources: TR8.**

Red Fuji, Nagafu 2 - *Source History: 3 in 1992; 1 in 2000.* **Sources: Nrs.**

Red Fuji, Nagafu 6 - Sweet, crisp fruit retains freshness up to a year when refrigerated. Begins bearing at a young age. Pollinate with Granny Smith or Stark Royal Gala. Ripens late October. Zones 6-8. *Source History: 3 in 1992; 4 in 2000.* **Sources: AG2, Co2, Nrs, St4.**

Red Fuji, Nagafu 12 - More colorful than other Fuji strains. Skin color is not as brown. The consistent, stable striping pattern is popular in New Zealand. *Source History: 3 in 1992; 2 in 2000.* **Sources: Co2, Nrs.**

Red Giant - Dark red fleshed fruit up to 3" in diameter. Very tart, firm flesh. Vigorous, spreading tree. Ripens early September. *Source History: 1 in 1992; 1 in 2000.* **Sources: Or9.**

Red Gold - Red Delicious x Gold Delicious. Dull red skin with russeted dots. Crisp, off-white flesh. Wonderfully sweet flavor. Excellent when dried. Good cropper. Fruits holds well on the tree. Good keeper. Ripens September to October. *Source History: 1 in 1988; 2 in 1992; 4 in 2000.* **Sources: Bea, Ch9, Ed5, Ga20.**

Red Hall - *Source History: 1 in 2000.* **Sources: Or9.**

Red Hook - McIntosh x Carlton. Large to very large yellow fruit blushed with a lively red. Pinkish flesh. Firm, coarse, juicy, sprightly, subacid flesh. Heavy, annual bearer. Fungus resistant. Excellent early shipper. Ripens mid-late season. Introduced in 1938. *Source History: 3 in 1988; 2 in 1992; 2 in 2000.* **Sources: Or9, Stl.**

Red Horse - Southern variety. *Source History: 2 in 2000.* **Sources: Ca15, Ch9.**

Red June (Carolina Red June, Blush June, Carolina Red, Georgia June, Jones

Early Harvest, June, Knight's Red June, Red Juneating, Susy Clark, Wilson's June) -
Attractive small, deep red over yellow fruit. Crisp, juicy, white flesh stained red.
Brisk, subacid taste. Ready for pies in June, fresh eating in July. Excellent for cider. Poor keeper. Medium size tree; early and heavy bearer. Requires cross-
pollination. Main fault is tendency to overbear one year and skip the next. This
biennial cycle can be somewhat controlled by timely thinning and pruning. Crop
ripens over a period of time in June or July depending on location. Hardy in Zones
5-8. Originated in North Carolina. Described in 1848. *Source History: 15 in
1988; 21 in 1992; 19 in 2000.* **Sources: Bar, Bea, Bl4, Ca15, Ch9, Cla, Ed5, Fi1,
Gr4, La3, Nrs, Or9, Po2, Sc6, SIM, So5, Son, Stl, Ur2, Wo7.**

Red Rebel - Southern variety. *Source History: 1 in 1992; 1 in 2000.* **Sources:
Ca15.**

Red Rome, Cowin Strain - Firm, crisp flesh. Juicy, mild flavor. Good baking
apple. Good keeper. Hardy to Zone 5. *Source History: 1 in 1992; 1 in 2000.*
Sources: LA4.

Red Rome, Spur No. 21 (Tift Cultivar) - Firm, crisp flesh. Mellow flavor.
Ideal for processing and fresh market. Compact tree comes into full production in
five to six years. U.S. Plant Patent No. 7363. *Source History: 1 in 1992; 1 in
2000.* **Sources: TR8.**

Red Russet - *Source History: 1 in 2000.* **Sources: Ch9.**

Red Silver Crab - Red fruit. Good for jelly. Hardy in Zone 4. *Source History:
1 in 1992; 1 in 2000.* **Sources: Nrs.**

Red Sparkle - Medium size, red fruit with sweet, crisp flesh. Retains its crisp,
refreshing quality on the tree into the fall. Zone 3. Canadian prairie apple from the
Morden Research Station. *Source History: 1 in 2000.* **Sources: Ed5.**

Red Spitzenburg - Southern variety. *Source History: 1 in 1992; 1 in 2000.*
Sources: Ca15.

Red Splendor - *Source History: 1 in 1992; 1 in 2000.* **Sources: Nrs.**

Red Spur Delicious, Midnight - Highly colored sport with solid bright red
skin. Colors early. *Source History: 1 in 2000.* **Sources: COL.**

Red Spur Delicious, Radiant - Sport of Ace Spur Red Delicious with brighter
red skin color and whiter flesh than some other early coloring reds. *Source History:
1 in 2000.* **Sources: COL.**

Red Stripe (Saxon) - Stripes become prominent just before ripening in mid-
September. Grown in Wisconsin for over 100 years. Very rare. Zone 4. *Source
History: 1 in 2000.* **Sources: Ed5.**

Red Van Buren - *Source History: 1 in 2000.* **Sources: Bea.**

Red Vein Crab - Large, oblong-conic, 1.75" deep cranberry fruit. Tangy, red
flesh makes lovely red sauce. Self-fertile. Foliage is dark green with a purple tinge.
Zones 6-9. *Source History: 1 in 1992; 1 in 2000.* **Sources: Son.**

Red Warrior - *Source History: 1 in 2000.* **Sources: Ed5.**

Red Willow Twig - Southern variety. *Source History: 1 in 2000.* **Sources:
Ca15.**

Red Winter, Steeles - *Source History: 1 in 1992; 1 in 2000.* **Sources: Bl4.**

Red York - *Source History: 2 in 1992; 2 in 2000.* **Sources: Nrs, TR8.**

Red York, Stark (Ramey Cultivar) - *Source History: 1 in 1992; 2 in 2000.*
Sources: AG2, St4.

Redant - Open-pollinated Antonovka originating in Manitoba, Canada. Skin color is yellow washed with red. Sweet, white flesh with mild flavor which is good for fresh eating and cooking. Keeps well. Ripens mid-late season. Extremely hardy; to -50 degrees F or colder. *Source History: 2 in 2000.* **Sources: Ed5, Stl.**

Redchief - The finest Red Delicious available. Finishes off and reaches full color and maturity early. Strong stripes develop early and blend into a bright red finish at maturity. Zones 5-8. *Source History: 2 in 2000.* **Sources: Cla, Jun.**

Redchief 2000 - Mutation of Redchief Campbell. Develops bright red color early. Compact, spur-type tree. Harvests two weeks sooner. Trademarked. *Source History: 1 in 2000.* **Sources: Hi9.**

Redchief, Campbell Strain (Redchief Red Delicious) - Brilliant, bright red fruit. Crisp white flesh. Top quality in flavor and flesh color. Great for eating fresh. Heavy producing, semidwarf, spur-type tree. Good pollinator for other varieties. Trademarked. U.S. Plant Patent No. 3578. *Source History: 3 in 1988; 4 in 1992; 2 in 2000.* **Sources: Amb, Hi9.**

Redchief, Heinicke Strain - Trademarked. *Source History: 1 in 2000.* **Sources: WI12.**

Redchief, Mercier Strain - Large, rich carmine fruit. White flesh. High quality. More vigor than Redchief; heavy producer. Trademarked. Plant patent applied for. *Source History: 1 in 1988; 1 in 1992; 1 in 2000.* **Sources: Hi9.**

Redcort (Nicklin Cultivar) - Discovered as a limb sport of Cortland at Marlboro, New York in the Hudson Valley. Fruit has a deep, rich 90% bright red finish. Juicy, white flesh with fine crisp texture. Heavy producer that bears terminally as well as from spurs. Vigorous, upright, spreading tree; compatible with dwarfing rootstocks. Ripens early. Trademarked. U.S. Plant Patent No. 5095. *Source History: 1 in 1988; 3 in 1992; 3 in 2000.* **Sources: Amb, Hi9, WI12.**

Redfield - Highly unusual cross between Wolf River and Niedzwetzskayana red crab. Medium to large, waxy pink to red fruit. The deep red flesh is slightly dry, making it a superb baking apple. Produces an exceptional jelly or blood red cider or vinegar. High in pectin. Not a fresh eating apple. Short storage life. Extremely hardy tree is disease and pest free. Heavy annual bearer. Highly ornamental with bronze leaves and red blossoms. Ripens in October. Zones 3-4. Developed at the New York Station, 1938. *Source History: 2 in 1992; 4 in 2000.* **Sources: Bl4, Cu4, Fed, Or9.**

Redfree (Co-op 13) - Medium size, glossy fruit with 90% bright red color. Smooth, waxy, russet-free skin. Light flesh is crisp and juicy; excellent flavor. Tree bears annually. Immune to scab and cedar-apple rust. Moderately resistant to fire blight and mildew. Ripens five days before Paulared; six weeks before Red Delicious. Uneven ripening; may require two pickings. Zones 4-7. Purdue University release, 1981. U.S. Plant Patent No. 4322. *Source History: 1 in 1988; 8 in 1992; 16 in 2000.* **Sources: Ad2, AG2, Ch9, Cla, Cu4, Ed5, Fed, Hi9, Jo3, Jun, Ro3, Sc6, St4, TR8, Va2, WI12.**

Redgold - Medium size fruit; gorgeous rose color overall with russet dots. Tender, yellowish white flesh. Sweet flavor. Especially for those who prefer non-acid apples. Spur-type tree. Ripens in September. Zones 6-10. Originated in Washington. Introduced in 1946. *Source History: 1 in 1988; 1 in 1992; 1 in 2000.* **Sources: Sc6, Son.**

Redsleeves - Medium size red fruit. Good for fresh eating. Ripens midseason. Disease resistant. *Source History: 1 in 2000.* **Sources: Hid.**

Redstone Canyon Gold - High quality yellow apple. Good for eating fresh or cooking. Ripens midseason. Hardy to -50 degrees F. with occasional winter injury.

Originated in Colorado. *Source History: 1 in 2000.* **Sources: Stl.**

Redwell - Open-pollinated seedling of Scott Winter. Large, well colored fruit; red over yellow skin. Cream colored flesh. Mild, excellent flavor. Good for eating fresh, baking and sauce. Keeps until January in storage. Vigorous tree has strong framework and bears annually. Partially dwarfing in habit. Underrated; good home orchard choice. Ripens late. Hardy to -50 degrees F. with occasional winter injury. *Source History: 3 in 1988; 3 in 1992; 4 in 2000.* **Sources: Bea, Ch9, Ed5, Stl.**

Regent - Red Duchess x Red Delicious. Medium size fruit; bright red over yellow. Very pleasing flavor and texture. All purpose. High dessert quality does not diminish in storage. Fruit stores well into late winter. Tree is vigorous, bears young, sets good crops. Resistant to cedar-apple rust. Susceptible to fire blight and scab. Fruit hangs well, rarely dropping before harvest. Ripens mid-October. Hardy to -50 degrees F. with occasional winter injury. Developed at the University of Minnesota in 1941. *Source History: 4 in 1988; 8 in 1992; 6 in 2000.* **Sources: Ed5, Fa1, Fed, Nrs, SH8, Stl.**

Reine des Hatives - *Source History: 1 in 2000.* **Sources: Cid.**

Reine des Pomme - *Source History: 1 in 2000.* **Sources: Ch9.**

Reine des Reinettes (Queen of the Pippins, Reinette Queen) - Although first known in France, this variety may have come from the Netherlands. Fruit has dull yellow skin, flushed and flecked red with dots and patches of russet. The white flesh is tender and dense with a sweet subacid flavor. Ripens in October. Often confused with King of the Pippins. First described in 1802. *Source History: 2 in 1988; 4 in 1992; 2 in 2000.* **Sources: Gr4, So5.**

Reinette Simirenko - Medium to large fruit; sometimes obscurely ribbed. Waxy coating forms when it gets much light. Exposed side tends to turn pale pink. Crisp, tender, juicy, greenish yellow flesh. Sweet, wine-like, tangy flavor. Stem is firmly attached. Keeps well into the spring. Good shipper. Precocious, abundant bearer. Adapted to light or heavy soils. Highly drought resistant. Ripens during December. Developed by 19th century Russian horticulturist Platon F. Simirenko. *Source History: 1 in 1988; 5 in 1992; 3 in 2000.* **Sources: Bl4, Ch9, Fed.**

Reliable Red - *Source History: 1 in 1992; 1 in 2000.* **Sources: Ch9.**

Renown - Seedling of Repla Kislaga. Canadian prairie apple. Yellow skin splashed with red. Mild, sweet flavor. Productive. Ripens late. Zone 3. Introduced in 1936. *Source History: 1 in 2000.* **Sources: Ed5.**

Repla Malenka - *Source History: 1 in 2000.* **Sources: Ed5.**

Republican - Southern variety. *Source History: 1 in 2000.* **Sources: Ca15.**

Rescue Crab - Seedling of Blushed Calville. Sweet flavor. Good quality. Hardy to -50 degrees F. Originated in Canada. *Source History: 3 in 1992; 4 in 2000.* **Sources: Ed5, Er2, Nrs, Stl.**

Reverend Morgan - Seedling of Granny Smith. Pinkish red over green skin. Superb flavor and texture. Excellent dessert quality. Good keeper. Self-fruitful. Disease resistant. Ripens during August. Requires 400-500 hours of chilling. Originated in the Houston, Texas area. Seems to do well in Zone 9 as well as zones farther north. Recommended for trial in most California and Arizona climates. *Source History: 3 in 1988; 5 in 1992; 4 in 2000.* **Sources: Bea, Ch9, Pa2, RA4.**

Rhoda - *Source History: 1 in 2000.* **Sources: Ed5.**

Rhode Island Greening (Rhode Island, Burlington Greening, Russine, Ganges, Greening Green Newtown Pippin, Green Winter Pippin, Jersey Greening) - Favorite American cooking apple known in earliest colonial times. Medium to large, round, symmetrical fruit. Yellowish green skin; occasional orange flush, russet at base or pale dots. Greasy, firm, crisp, juicy, greenish yellow flesh. Peculiar, tart, refreshing, pleasantly acid flavor. Good for fresh eating if tree-ripened. Excellent for cooking and drying. Should be picked when still quite firm. Good keeper. Large, spreading, vigorous, productive, long-lived tree; biennial cropper. Triploid; needs a pollinator. Ripens mid-September to late October depending on location. Hardy to Zone 4. Originated in Rhode Island. Known in 1650. *Source History: 12 in 1988; 15 in 1992; 12 in 2000.* **Sources: Bl4, Ch9, Gr4, Leu, Mi1, Nrs, Or9, Sc6, So5, Son, WAF, Wo7.**

Ribston

(Ribston Pippin, Ribstone Pippin, Essex Pippin, Beautiful Pippin, Formosa, Glory of York, Rockhill's Russet, Travers) - Parent of Cox's Orange Pippin. Classic dessert apple of England. Yellow flushed bright orange fruit with red blush, often sprinkled with russet webbing at base and apex. Hard, crisp, fine grained, extremely sugary flesh. Not attractive but fine, rich flavor and a pleasant aroma. One of the best for eating, cooking and cider. Fair storage ability. Medium size tree. Triploid. Ripens mid-September depending on location. Hardy. Zones 4-9. Originated in Yorkshire, England around 1700. *Source History: 6 in 1988; 12 in 1992; 11 in 2000.* **Sources: Bea, Bl4, Ch9, Cu4, Fed, Gr4, Leu, Or9, So5, Son, Wo7.**

Ribston, Red

- *Source History: 1 in 2000.* **Sources: Bea.**

Richardson

- St. Lawrence x Duchess. Green-yellow fruit. Richly flavored, yellow flesh. Regular producer. Ripens midseason. Hardy to -50 degrees with occasional winter injury. *Source History: 1 in 1992; 1 in 2000.* **Sources: Stl.**

Richelieu

- Medium-large fruit. Ripens 3-5 days before McIntosh. Tolerant to fire blight and powdery mildew; susceptible to rusts. Agriculture Canada introduction. *Source History: 1 in 2000.* **Sources: Cu4.**

Riga Stripe

- *Source History: 1 in 2000.* **Sources: Ed5.**

Robertson Red

- Southern variety. *Source History: 1 in 2000.* **Sources: Ca15.**

Rockingham Red

- Medium size fruit. Good, distinctive flavor, somewhat like a Red June with a touch of crab. Excellent for fresh eating, cider, sauce and pies. One of the best winter keepers, through April if stored in a cool, dry place. Upright growing tree with round crown. Highly resistant to heat, drought, cold, insects, blight and fungi. Periodic bearer. Ripens in October or November depending on location. Developed by John Turner of Reidsville, North Carolina. *Source History: 1 in 1988; 2 in 1992; 2 in 2000.* **Sources: Ca15, Cla.**

Rolfe

- One parent thought to be Blue Pearmain. Fairly soft early fall apple used for fresh eating and cooking. Quite rare. Originated in Guilford, Piscataquis County, Maine about 1820. Popular there until about 1870; now virtually unknown. *Source History: 1 in 2000.* **Sources: Fed.**

Roman Stem

(French Pippin) - Small fruit with rough yellow skin with black spots. Tender, juicy flesh. Mild flavor. Vigorous, productive tree. Excellent early winter apple. Originated in New Jersey. Introduced in 1817. *Source History: 3 in 1992; 4 in 2000.* **Sources: Bea, Ca15, Ed5, Wo7.**

Rome Beauty

(Rome, Starbuck, Gillett's Seedling) - Medium to very large, round fruit with thick, almost solid red skin. Crisp, greenish white flesh of medium texture and firmness. Excellent baking apple; also good for drying, eating fresh and cider. Good keeper on and off the tree. Small to medium size tree, spreading with age. Heavy bearing. Late blooming; good choice where hard freezes in late spring are common. Self-fruitful. Ripens late September through October depending on location. Requires 700-1000 hours of chilling. Zones 6-9. Originated in Ohio.

Introduced in 1848. *Source History: 10 in 1988; 16 in 1992; 11 in 2000.* **Sources: Bea, Ch9, Cla, CO5, Gr4, La3, Nrs, Son, WA8, Wh4, WI4.**

Rome Beauty, Compspur (Compact Red Rome) - Improved Rome Beauty with deep crimson fruit. Superior for baking. Holds up well in storage. Tree has spur-type, compact structure. Ripens late. Originated in East Wenatchee, Washington. *Source History: 2 in 1988; 2 in 1992; 2 in 2000.* **Sources: Mi1, Va2.**

Rome Beauty, Del Red Rome - North Carolina strain. Large fruit. Red skin color does not bleed into the flesh. Good for fresh market or processing. Trademarked. *Source History: 1 in 2000.* **Sources: Va2.**

Rome Beauty, Law Strain (Law Red Rome, Lawspur Rome) - Red sport of Rome Beauty. Has all the qualities of the old Rome, plus extremely high color, producing almost 100% extra fancy grade. Crisp, white flesh sometimes streaked with red. Excellent baking apple. Large, vigorous, hardy tree. Heavy annual producer; hardy and vigorous. Should be thinned to produce larger apples. Excellent apple for fresh market and processing. Superior bruise resistance makes it a very profitable shipping variety. Ripens early. U.S. Plant Patent No. 4096. *Source History: 8 in 1988; 12 in 1992; 7 in 2000.* **Sources: Ad2, AG2, Amb, Co2, Hi9, Jo3, Va2.**

Rome Beauty, Red (Red Rome) - Improved color sport of Rome Beauty. Large, round, uniform size, brilliant red commercial culinary apple. Crisp, juicy, aromatic white flesh. Unique tartness. Good baking apple. Superior keeper. Vigorous, thrifty, productive tree bears young. Late blooming. Self-pollinating. Ripens from late September to mid-October depending on location. Hardy in Zones 5-8. *Source History: 20 in 1988; 23 in 1992; 19 in 2000.* **Sources: Bar, Bo5, Cum, FO10, GI3, Ho5, Iso, JOY, Lee, Mi1, MI5, Na4, Pi2, Sav, So5, STR, TU5, Ty2, Wor.**

Rome Beauty, Red Rome 262 (Rome Beauty-262 Strain) - Solid bright red sport of Rome Beauty colors early. Slightly larger than Law Rome. Does not carry red color into the flesh. Considered a better processing apple than Law Rome. Generally recognized as best of all Red Romes. *Source History: 2 in 1988; 1 in 1992; 1 in 2000.* **Sources: Ad2.**

Rome Beauty, Spur Red (Taylor Strain) - Spur-type Double Red Rome that does not bleed into the flesh. Can be used for fresh market or processing. Compact tree is more willowy than the regular Red Rome. Ripens with Rome Beauty. *Source History: 3 in 1988; 4 in 1992; 3 in 2000.* **Sources: Ad2, Bl4, Bo5.**

Rome Beauty, Spuree - Bright cherry-red blush fruit. Very smooth, glossy skin and very firm flesh. Red color does not bleed into the flesh. Good for fresh market or processing. More productive, compact spur-type tree. Easier to manage because of many lateral fruiting spurs that develop at almost every node. U.S. Plant Patent No. 3198. *Source History: 1 in 1988; 1 in 1992; 1 in 2000.* **Sources: Hi9.**

Rome Beauty, Taylor Strain (Starkspur Red Rome Beauty) - Highly colored, large, smooth fruit. Good baking apple because of tart flavor. Compact tree with heavy production. Resists disease and bruising. Hardy in Zones 5-8. Trademarked. U.S. Plant Patent No. 3121. *Source History: 2 in 1988; 1 in 1992; 3 in 2000.* **Sources: AG2, St4, WAF.**

Rome, Early Spur - Discovered as a bud sport of Lawspur in the Wilfred Berger orchard, Quincy, Washington. Brilliant red fruit. True Rome flavor and quality. Excellent for both fresh market and processing. Handles and stores well; does not bruise easily. Compact tree with spur-type characteristics. Patented. *Source History: 1 in 1992; 1 in 2000.* **Sources: Co2.**

Rosemarine Ukranski - *Source History: 1 in 2000.* **Sources: Ed5.**

Rosemary Russet - *Source History: 1 in 1992; 1 in 2000.* **Sources: So5.**

Ross Nonpareil - Small, round or conical apple covered with thin gold-brown russet, usually with striking scarlet stripes showing through. High sugar and tartness. Ripens early October. Ancient Irish apple which may even have a French origin. Introduced in 1819. *Source History: 2 in 1988; 5 in 1992; 3 in 2000.* **Sources: Bea, Gr4, Or9.**

Rosthern 15 - Bred in northern Saskatchewan as a short season apple. Rarely seen. Of interest to borderline apple growers in cool maritime and short season areas. Ripens in early August. Hardy to Zone 2. *Source History: 1 in 1988; 1 in 1992; 1 in 2000.* **Sources: Bea.**

Rosthern 18 - Medium size red fruit. Excellent yield. Very good for cooking and eating. Ripens in mid-August, earlier than Rosthern 15. Hardy to Zone 2. Developed in Saskatchewan. *Source History: 1 in 1988; 1 in 1992; 1 in 2000.* **Sources: Bea.**

Rosu de Cluj (PI 352656) - *Source History: 1 in 1992; 1 in 2000.* **Sources: Nrs.**

Rosybrook - Trail x Rescue. Canadian prairie apple. Medium size fruit. Pale green skin covered with red. Firm, crisp flesh with a fine texture. Sweet, mild flavor. Good for pies, canning and juice. Ripens in August. Zone 3. Introduced in 1980. *Source History: 1 in 2000.* **Sources: Ed5.**

Roxbury Russet (Roxbury, Shipper's Russet, Belpre Russet, Marietta Russet, Sylvan Russet, Hewe's Russet, Warner Russet, Boston Russet, Putnam Russet) - Excellent old American cider apple. Large fruit. Greenish, sometimes bronze tinged skin almost covered with yellowish brown russet. Firm, slightly coarse, fairly tender, yellowish white flesh. Remarkable for its amount of sugar. Good for eating fresh or cooking; excellent for cider. Notable keeper, until April or May. Medium to large tree; tends to be biennial. Blooms late. Requires cross pollination. Resistant to scab and mildew. Good cropper on rich soils. Ripens mid-October. Hardy to Zone 4. Originated in the Massachusetts town of Roxbury in the early 1600s. Once known as Boston Russet or Putnam Russet. Introduced in 1649. *Source History: 12 in 1988; 15 in 1992; 20 in 2000.* **Sources: Bl4, Ca15, Ch9, Cla, Cu4, Ed5, Fed, Ga20, Gr4, Leu, Mi1, Or9, Ro3, Sc6, So5, Son, Und, Wh4, Wo7, Wor.**

Royal Court (Hartencourt Cultivar) - Discovered as a limb sport of original Cortland by Jacob Hartenhof of Waterville, Nova Scotia. Solid blush fruit. Trademarked. U.S. Plant Patent No. 10,049. *Source History: 2 in 2000.* **Sources: Ad2, WAF.**

Royalty Crab - Red fruit makes good spiced apples. Ornamental tree with deep red leaves and blossoms. Very fire blight resistant. Ripens late. Hardy to -50 degrees F. Originated in Saskatoon, Saskatchewan, Canada. *Source History: 2 in 1992; 8 in 2000.* **Sources: Bay, Big, CR6, LA4, Nrs, So5, Stl, Va5.**

Rubinette (Rafzubin Cultivar) - Golden Delicious x Cox's Orange Pippin. Medium size fruit with bright red striping over golden ground color and slight russeting. Growth characteristics resemble Golden Delicious. Shows some resistance to mildew and apple scab. U.S. Plant Patent No. 6588. *Source History: 2 in 2000.* **Sources: Ro3, Va2.**

Ruby - Gallia Beauty x Starking. Large, hard fleshed, late-keeping red apple. Shape and taste resembles Rome Beauty. Developed at the Ohio Agricultural Experiment Station. *Source History: 1 in 1988; 1 in 1992; 1 in 2000.* **Sources: Ed5,**

Sc6.

Ruby Jon (Jackson Cultivar) - Discovered as a limb sport of Jonnee in Bowling Green, Kentucky. Solid, ruby-red blushed skin color. Earliest and best coloring of the Jonathans. Creamy white flesh is crisp and juicy. Trademarked. U.S. Plant Patent No. 10,115. *Source History: 4 in 2000.* **Sources: AG2, COL, Hi9, St4.**

Rural Russet - *Source History: 1 in 2000.* **Sources: Bea.**

Russell's Russet - Chance seedling of unknown parentage. Excellent early fall apple. Originated in Maine. *Source History: 1 in 2000.* **Sources: Fed.**

Russet King - *Source History: 2 in 2000.* **Sources: Ed5, So5.**

Russett Cow - *Source History: 1 in 1992; 1 in 2000.* **Sources: Ch9.**

Russian Giant Crab - Red fleshed fruit is over 3" across. Very tart flesh. Ripens mid to late season. Vigorous, slightly upright tree is productive. May be scab resistant. *Source History: 1 in 2000.* **Sources: Fo2.**

Rusty Coat - Similar to Golden Russet except that the skin color is a little darker, the russeting on the skin is much heavier and the flesh is drier. Fine flavor. Excellent for drying and applesauce. Very good keeper. Some disease resistance. Fire blight susceptible. Developed in Connecticut. *Source History: 4 in 1988; 4 in 1992; 7 in 2000.* **Sources: Bea, Ca15, Hid, La3, Or9, Ur2, Wh4.**

Rusty Coat, Sweet - Southern variety. *Source History: 1 in 2000.* **Sources: Ca15.**

Salem Cider - *Source History: 1 in 2000.* **Sources: Ch9.**

Sally - Southern variety. *Source History: 1 in 2000.* **Sources: Ca15.**

Sally Gray - Southern variety. *Source History: 1 in 2000.* **Sources: Ca15.**

Salome - Mostly bright red with whitish dots. Crisp, tender, yellow flesh. Sprightly flavor. Very productive. Ripens in late winter. A 19th-century winter apple from Ottawa, Illinois. Introduced in 1853. *Source History: 2 in 1988; 3 in 1992; 4 in 2000.* **Sources: Ca15, Ch9, So5, Wo7.**

Sam Apple - Southern variety. *Source History: 1 in 2000.* **Sources: Ca15.**

Sam Hunt - Southern variety. *Source History: 1 in 2000.* **Sources: Ca15.**

Sam Whitson - Southern variety. *Source History: 1 in 2000.* **Sources: Ca15.**

Sam Young (Irish Russet) - Yellow skinned fruit with orange flush and red blotches, nearly covered with a coarse, brown russet. Crisp, tender, sugary flesh. Heavy bearer. Ripens in September. *Source History: 2 in 1992; 1 in 2000.* **Sources: So5.**

San Jacinto - Southern variety. *Source History: 1 in 2000.* **Sources: Ca15.**

Sandow - Open-pollinated seedling of Northern Spy. Red fruit with high quality, juicy, crisp flesh. Ripens midseason. Hardy to -40 degrees F. *Source History: 3 in 1992; 3 in 2000.* **Sources: Ch9, Er2, Stl.**

Sansa - Gala x Akane. Brilliant red-orange over a golden ground color. High quality dessert apple. Resembles Gala in fruit color and firmness; ripens one week sooner. Good keeping quality. Developed in Japan. U.S. Plant Patent No. 6519. *Source History: 5 in 2000.* **Sources: Ad2, On3, Ro3, Va2, WAF.**

Sawmill - Southern variety. *Source History: 1 in 2000.* **Sources: Ca15.**

Saxton - *Source History: 1 in 2000.* **Sources: Ed5.**

Sayaka - Jonathan x Sekai Ichi. Large to very large fruit with red blush over green-yellow background. Sweet to aromatic flavor. Vigorous, spreading tree. Tip bearer. Ripens midseason. *Source History: 2 in 1992; 4 in 2000.* **Sources: Cla,**

Mo19, Nrs, Ro3.

Scarlet - *Source History: 2 in 1992; 1 in 2000.* **Sources: Nrs.**

Scarlet Beauty - *Source History: 2 in 2000.* **Sources: Ch9, Or9.**

Scarlet Crofton (Red Crofton, Crofton Pippin, Longford Pearmain, Saul Apple, Winter Crofton, Crofton) - Small to medium, flattish fruit. Orange-yellow with brilliant scarlet flush, sometimes solid scarlet, always overlaid with singular network of russet veins and conspicuous dots. Crisp, juicy flesh. Old Irish apple from County Sligo grown since Elizabethan times. Brought to general notice by John Robertson, famous Kilkenny pomologist and nurseryman. Introduced in 1819. *Source History: 1 in 1988; 2 in 1992; 1 in 2000.* **Sources: So5.**

Scarlet O'Hara - Excellent quality fruit with crisp, sweet flesh. Hangs well on the tree. Shows scab resistance but is sensitive to fire blight and moldy core. Productive, spreading tree. Released by Purdue University. Plant patent applied for. *Source History: 1 in 2000.* **Sources: Ro3.**

Scarlet Pimpernel - *Source History: 1 in 1992; 2 in 2000.* **Sources: Bl4, Or9.**

Scarlet Sentinel (Scarlet Sentinel Columnar Apple) - Very large, attractive greenish yellow and red fruit. Crisp, sweet, flavorful white flesh. Attractive tree with very narrow growth habit. Productive. Disease resistant. Trademarked. Plant patent applied for. *Source History: 3 in 2000.* **Sources: Bay, On3, WI4.**

Scarlet Spire, Stark (Trajan Cultivar) - Columnar tree form. Skin color is bright red over green. Good for fresh eating. Ripens in September. Zone 5. Originally from the Stark Connade collection. Trademarked. U.S. Plant Patent No. 6226. *Source History: 2 in 2000.* **Sources: MO10, St4.**

Scarlet Surprise - Beautiful reddish foliage, red fruit and bright red flesh that is sweet and flavorful. Ripens early in September. Zones 4-8. Developed at Oregon State University. Trademarked. *Source History: 3 in 2000.* **Sources: On3, St4, WI4.**

Schell - Southern variety. *Source History: 1 in 2000.* **Sources: Ca15.**

Schockley - *Source History: 1 in 2000.* **Sources: Ch9.**

Schumacher - Southern variety. *Source History: 1 in 2000.* **Sources: Ca15.**

Schweitzer Orange (Swiss Orange) - *Source History: 1 in 1992; 1 in 2000.* **Sources: So5.**

Scott Winter - Vermont seedling with red fruit. Flesh is tinged with yellow, sometimes stained with red. Very juicy; somewhat tart in the early part of the season, becoming milder toward season's end. Tree bears at a young age. Ripens midseason. Hardy to -50 degrees F. with occasional winter injury. *Source History: 1 in 1988; 1 in 1992; 2 in 2000.* **Sources: Ca15, Stl.**

Scotty's Prolific - *Source History: 1 in 2000.* **Sources: Ch9.**

Seaconk Sweeting - Pre-1869 apple from Connecticut. *Source History: 1 in 1992; 2 in 2000.* **Sources: Ch9, Wo7.**

Secor - Salome x Jonathan. Striped red fruit with good texture and flavor. Keeps until spring. Ripens late. Hardy to -40 degrees F. with occasional winter injury. *Source History: 3 in 1992; 2 in 2000.* **Sources: Ch9, Stl.**

Sekai Ichi - Red Delicious x Yellow Delicious. Color of fruit varies from pale pink to darker red with red stripes, sometimes becomes solid red in the sun. Crisp, breaking, juicy flesh. Very sweet, fine mild flavor. If tree is properly thinned, apples reportedly weigh close to 2 lbs. Ripens in September. Hardy to Zone 5. Dr. Robert Stebbins of Oregon State University, reporting on a visit to Japan in 1985, found it to be the highest priced apple in Yokohama at $1.87 each. Developed in Japan. Introduced in 1974. *Source History: 2 in 1988; 4 in 1992; 8 in 2000.* **Sources: Bea, Ch9, Cla, Cu4, Ed5, Or9, ORA, So5.**

Selkirk - *Source History: 1 in 1992; 2 in 2000.* **Sources: Nrs, Va5.**

Senator (All-Over-Red Senator, Oliver) - Flattish round, medium size fruit. Almost solid red over green background with prominent white or russet dots. Tender, crisp, juicy flesh. Most refreshing flavor. Crops very well every year. Ripens in early October. Originated in Arkansas almost a hundred years ago. *Source History: 1 in 1988; 1 in 1992; 2 in 2000.* **Sources: Ch9, So5.**

Senshu - Toko x Fuji. Large fruit is red with yellow speckles. Flavor and size qualities are rated excellent. Flavor resembles Jonagold. Spreading tree reported to be very disease resistant. Ripens early October. Hardy to Zone 5. Developed in Japan. *Source History: 1 in 1988; 4 in 1992; 8 in 2000.* **Sources: Bea, Ch9, Cla, Cu4, Nrs, Sc6, St4, Va2.**

September Ruby - Rescue x Haralson. Canadian prairie apple. Medium to large fruit is bright red with green ribbing. Good for juice. Good keeper. Ripens early. Becoming popular in Alaska as one of the better tasting super hardy apples. Introduced in 1986. *Source History: 1 in 2000.* **Sources: Ed5.**

Shafer - *Source History: 1 in 2000.* **Sources: Bea.**

Shamrock - Spur McIntosh x Spur Golden Delicious. Medium size fruit is very similar in appearance to Granny Smith. Hardy, semispur tree. Ripens about six weeks before Granny Smith for which it was developed as a substitute for areas with a short growing season. Originated in Summerland, British Columbia. *Source History: 3 in 1992; 2 in 2000.* **Sources: Hi9, Va2.**

Sharon - McIntosh x Longfield. Yellow fruit striped with red. Similar to McIntosh, but sweeter and firmer. High quality. Vigorous, productive tree. Ripens midseason. Hardy to -50 degrees F. with occasional winter injury. *Source History: 1 in 1988; 2 in 1992; 2 in 2000.* **Sources: Bl4, Stl.**

Shay - Bright red fruit. Crisp, juicy flesh. Delicious, sweet-tart flavor. Scab and mildew resistant. Ripens late September. Developed at Oregon State University by Dr. Ralph Shay. *Source History: 2 in 1992; 1 in 2000.* **Sources: Rai.**

Sheep Nose (Sheepnose) - Southern variety. *Source History: 2 in 1992; 2 in 2000.* **Sources: Ca15, Wor.**

Shenandoah - Smooth, symmetrical red fruit. Crisp, firm, juicy flesh. Slightly tart flavor. Color and shape resemble Winesap. Good for fresh use and processing. Bears heavily and regularly. Ripens ten days before Red Delicious. *Source History: 1 in 1988; 1 in 1992; 2 in 2000.* **Sources: Ca15, Ch9.**

Shenk - *Source History: 1 in 2000.* **Sources: Or9.**

Sheppard's Sweet - Originated in Connecticut. Introduced in 1850. *Source History: 1 in 1992; 2 in 2000.* **Sources: Ch9, Wo7.**

Sherry - Red striped fruit. Poor quality when picked, but improves to good quality after storing for several months. Annual heavy cropper. Ripens very late. Fruit will hang on the tree all winter. Sherry was the only tree to bear in St. Lawrence County after the test winter of 1980-1981. *Source History: 1 in 1988; 2 in 1992; 1 in 2000.* **Sources: Ch9.**

Shiawassee (Michigan Beauty, Shiwassee Beauty) - Speculated to be a seedling of Fameuse. Yellow skinned, medium size fruit nearly covered with red blush and carmine streaks. Crisp, sweet flesh. Aromatic, subacid flavor. Ripens from September to October. Hardy to Zone 5. Originated in Michigan. Introduced in 1850.

Source History: 3 in 1992; 3 in 2000. **Sources: Bea, Bl4, Wo7.**

Shinko - *Source History:* 1 in 2000. **Sources: Ch9.**

Shinsei - Golden Delicious x Early McIntosh. Medium size, round, greenish yellow fruit. Firm, fine grained, juicy, white flesh. Mild, sweet flavor. Ripens in late September. Zones 6-9. Originated in Japan. Introduced in 1930. *Source History: 3 in 1988; 3 in 1992; 2 in 2000.* **Sources: Ch9, Son.**

Shizuka - Sister to Mutsu. Large to very large fruit. Yellow skin with a red-orange blush. Milder flavor than Mutsu with similar tree vigor. Triploid; requires pollination. Reported to be blister spot resistant. Developed in Japan. *Source History: 2 in 1992; 6 in 2000.* **Sources: Ad2, Hi9, Mo19, Nrs, Ro3, WAF.**

Shockley - Southern variety. *Source History:* 2 in 2000. **Sources: Ca15, Or9.**

Shockley, Cantrell Strain - Yellow skin flushed with brownish red and streaked with pink. Crisp, sweet flesh. Excellent for preserves. Excellent winter keeper. Schockley was known in 1854 in Georgia. The Cantrell strain is somewhat smaller with a longer shape. *Source History:* 1 in 1988; 3 in 1992; 1 in 2000. **Sources: La3.**

Shockley, Grizzle Strain - Yellow skin flushed with brownish red and streaked with pink. Crisp, sweet flesh. Excellent for preserves. Excellent winter keeper. Shockley was known in 1854 in Georgia. Grizzle Strain is larger and more flattened. *Source History:* 1 in 1988; 1 in 1992; 1 in 2000. **Sources: La3.**

Short Core - Southern variety. *Source History:* 1 in 2000. **Sources: Ca15.**

Siberian Crab - Early blooms. Large, crimson, long stemmed fruit. Color and flavor makes it great for pickling and jelly making. Tree has spreading growth habit. Zones 4-9. Originated in France in the 1800s. *Source History:* 2 in 1992; 3 in 2000. **Sources: Ch9, Or9, Son.**

Sierra Beauty - Old California variety. Large, blocky, handsome apple. Greenish yellow skin, striped or blushed with red. Juicy, very crisp, moderately sweet flesh. Rich, tart, sprightly flavor. Excellent for eating fresh or cooking. Good keeper. Self-fruitful. Good seller in farm markets. Ripens in September or October. Requires 700-800 hours of chilling. Zones 6-9. Probably originated in California. Favorite late apple still commercially grown in Anderson Valley in Mendocino County. *Source History:* 6 in 1988; 9 in 1992; 7 in 2000. **Sources: CO5, Ga20, Gr4, Or9, So5, Son, WI4.**

Signe Tillisch - Very waxy, creamy yellow skin with slightly pink or orange flush. Soft, sweet, aromatic, subacid, creamy white flesh. Fine vinous flavor. Excellent for cooking. Ripens early to mid-September. Considered one of the best dessert apples in Sweden. Originated in Denmark. First described in 1889. *Source History:* 2 in 1988; 3 in 1992; 3 in 2000. **Sources: Bea, Ch9, So5.**

Simerinko (Reinette Simirenko) - Possibly the same as the old Wood's Greening. Green fruit. Dessert apple. Annually productive. Ripens late. *Source History:* 1 in 1988; 1 in 1992; 2 in 2000. **Sources: Bea, Or9.**

Simpson - *Source History:* 1 in 2000. **Sources: WI12.**

Sine Qua Non - Southern variety. *Source History:* 1 in 2000. **Sources: Ca15.**

Sinta - Yellow Delicious x Grimes Golden. Medium size fruit. Pale yellow, sometimes almost white with pinkish blush in the sun. Crisp, juicy flesh. Sweet, aromatic flavor superior to that of either parent. Ripens mid-September. Does best in zones lower 4 through upper 7. Developed by Dr. K. O. Lapins at the Summerland, British Columbia Agricultural Research Station. Introduced in 1970. *Source History:* 2 in 1988; 5 in 1992; 3 in 2000. **Sources: Bea, Ch9, So5.**

Sir Prize - Large, greenish yellow fruit. High quality, but very thin tender skin that bruises easily. Strong, vigorous tree. Immune to scab; resistant to mildew and cedar-apple rust. Excellent home garden variety; too tender for commerical markets. U.S. Plant Patent No. 3988. *Source History: 1 in 1988; 4 in 1992; 5 in 2000.* **Sources: Bl4, Ch9, Cla, Cu4, Ed5.**

Skinner's Seedling (Santa Clara King, Skinner) - Seedling of King. Large to very large, flattened conic fruit. Lemon-yellow skin with faint red stripes and white stars surrounded by red auras. Fine grained, juicy, very tender, yellowish white flesh. Sprightly, mildly subacid flavor; distinctive aroma. High quality dessert apple. Good for applesauce, cooking and eating fresh. Poor keeper. Large tree with medium vigor. Productive, but take care not to damage fruit spurs during picking. Midseason blooms. Requires cross-pollination. Ripens in August or September. Zones 6-10. Originated with Judge H. C. Skinner on the bank of Coyote Creek east of San Jose. Introduced in 1887. *Source History: 5 in 1988; 5 in 1992; 2 in 2000.* **Sources: Gr4, Son.**

Skyview - *Source History: 1 in 2000.* **Sources: Ch9.**

Slippery Cider - *Source History: 1 in 1992; 2 in 2000.* **Sources: Ch9, Cid.**

Smith Seedling - Southern variety. *Source History: 1 in 2000.* **Sources: Ca15.**

Smith's Cider (Smith, Poplar Bluff) - Grafts of this variety were brought to Virginia during the Revolutionary War by Hessian soldiers. Variably sized fruit has a clear pale yellow skin with a greenish cast with carmine stripes and splashes. Spreading, vigorous tree has straggling branches. Bears early and fruits heavily. Low chilling requirement. Ripens in October. Originated in Pennsylvania before 1817. *Source History: 2 in 1988; 2 in 1992; 3 in 2000.* **Sources: Ca15, Ch9, Gr4.**

Smokehouse (English Vandervere, Gibbons Smokehouse, Millcreek Vandervere, Millcreek, Red Vandervere, Smoke House) - Open-pollinated seedling of Vandevere. Rather flattish shape. Red-striped yellow fruit. Tender but firm, exceedingly juicy, yellow tinged flesh. Fresh cider flavor. Very good quality cooking, eating and baking apple. Keeps well through March. Vigorous growing tree requires pruning. Young, productive bearer; reliable cropper. Ripens during September. Hardy to -40 degrees F. Fine old Delaware and Pennsylvania apple. Derives its name from the fact that the original tree grew up next to the smokehouse of a Lancaster County farmer. Introduced in 1837. *Source History: 8 in 1988; 15 in 1992; 22 in 2000.* **Sources: Ad2, Bar, Bea, Bl4, Bo5, Ca15, Ch9, Cu4, Fed, Gr4, Hid, Mi1, Nrs, Or9, Sc6, So5, Son, Stl, Ur2, Wh4, Wo7, Wor.**

Smokytwig - Southern variety. *Source History: 1 in 2000.* **Sources: Ca15.**

Snap - *Source History: 1 in 1992; 1 in 2000.* **Sources: Ch9.**

Snow - Small, pale yellow fruit with soft flesh. Used fresh and for cooking. Ripens mid to late season. *Source History: 1 in 1992; 8 in 2000.* **Sources: Ch9, Cu4, Ga20, GR26, Hid, Nrs, Or9, WI4.**

Snow of Iowa - *Source History: 1 in 1988; 1 in 1992; 1 in 2000.* **Sources: Ed5.**

Sofstaholm - *Source History: 1 in 2000.* **Sources: Bea.**

Somerset of Maine (Somerset) - Large oblate fruit striped and splashed with brilliant red. Excellent flavored eating apple. Must not be allowed to get overripe on the tree. Ripens late August. Zone 4. Rare. Originated in Mercer, Maine. First recorded in 1849. Rediscovered by Ira Glackens about a century later. *Source History: 3 in 1988; 4 in 1992; 5 in 2000.* **Sources: Bea, Fed, So5, Und, Wo7.**

Somerset Redstreak - *Source History: 1 in 2000.* **Sources: Cid.**

Sops of Wine (Sops in Wine, Bell's Early, Bennington, Dodge's Early Red, Early Washington, Homing, Hominy, Horning, Pie Apple, Red Shropsavine, Strawberry, Worden's Pie Apple) - Old English culinary and cider apple. Medium to large fruit. Greenish yellow skin overspread with purplish red, mottled and splashed and sometimes striped with dark carmine. Soft, fine grained, juicy, yellowish flesh is often stained with pink or flecked with red. Aromatic, mild, subacid flavor. Highly regarded for cooking, cider and apple wine. Good dessert apple as well. Fair storage ability. Medium to large tree bears early and reliably. Midseason blooms. Requires cross-pollination. Ripens in August or September depending on location. Zones 5-9. Introduced in 1832. *Source History: 8 in 1988; 12 in 1992; 12 in 2000.* **Sources: Bea, Bl4, Cla, Fed, Gr4, Mi1, Or9, Sc6, So5, Son, Wo7, Wor.**

Soulard Crab - *Source History: 1 in 2000.* **Sources: Cid.**

Sour June - Southern variety. *Source History: 1 in 2000.* **Sources: Ca15.**

Southern Sweeting - Southern variety. *Source History: 1 in 2000.* **Sources: Ca15.**

Sparger - Southern variety. *Source History: 1 in 2000.* **Sources: Ca15.**

Spartan - McIntosh x Newtown Pippin. McIntosh type; beautiful, medium size, dark red, almost mahogany, dessert quality apple. Pure white flesh; firmer than McIntosh. Highly aromatic, fine flavor. Superb for eating fresh. Better keeper and shipper than McIntosh. Keeps through January. Annually productive; precocious and consistently heavy bearer. Blooms mid-late. Susceptible to premature drop. Self-pollinating but yields increase if near Lodi. Excellent pollinator for Jonagold. Resistant to scab, mildew and fire blight. Ripens mid-October. Hardy to -45 degrees F. Excellent for the Midwest. Developed at the British Columbia Station. Introduced in 1936. *Source History: 16 in 1988; 27 in 1992; 26 in 2000.* **Sources: Ad2, Bea, Bl4, Bo5, Bu7, Ch9, Clo, Co2, COL, Ea3, Ed5, Er2, Ga20, Hi9, JOY, ME3, Mo19, Nrs, Or9, So5, Stl, TR8, Ur2, Va2, WAF, WI4.**

Spartan x PI 255599 - *Source History: 1 in 2000.* **Sources: Bea.**

Spatebuhenden - *Source History: 1 in 1992; 1 in 2000.* **Sources: Ch9.**

Spencer - McIntosh x Golden Delicious. Large, nearly solid red or red striped over green fruit. Crisp, juicy flesh. Fine flavor. Core smaller than McIntosh. Excellent eating quality. Vigorous, upright, spreading tree. Ripens in late October. Hardy to -50 degrees F. with occasional winter injury. Developed in British Columbia. *Source History: 3 in 1988; 5 in 1992; 7 in 2000.* **Sources: Bea, Ch9, Cu4, Fed, Or9, So5, Stl.**

Spencer Seedless - Southern variety. *Source History: 1 in 2000.* **Sources: Ca15.**

Spigold - Northern Spy x Golden Delicious. Large, golden yellow fruit 75% covered with bright red stripes. Tender skin. Fine grained, firm, crisp, yellow flesh. Dual flavor that resembles sprightly juiciness of Northern Spy, sweetness of Golden Delicious, then an indefinable blend, superior to either parent. Exceptionally high quality. Stores well. Most useful as high quality apple for roadside and local sale. Growth habit is strong, upright; requires early training. Blooms late; biennial bearer. Triploid; has sterile pollen. Ripens during October. Requires 600 hours of chilling. Hardy to Zone 3. Developed at the Geneva Station in New York. Introduced in 1962. *Source History: 13 in 1988; 20 in 1992; 18 in 2000.* **Sources: Amb, Bea, Bl4, Bo5, Ch9, Cid, Cu4, Cu4, Gr4, Mi1, Nrs, Ro3, Sc6, So5, Son, Ur2, WAF, Wh4.**

Spijon - Northern Spy x Jonathan. Good processing apple as well as a fine eating apple. Productive. Geneva introduction. *Source History: 1 in 1992; 2 in 2000.*

Sources: Ch9, Cu4.

Splendour (Starksplendor) - Medium to large fruit. Dull, pinkish red skin with occasional russet. Firm, crisp, yellow flesh. Mild but distinctive, sweet flavor. Lacks tartness but has crisp texture. Exceptionally long storage life. Growth habit is spreading. Ripens in early September. Once featured by Stark Brothers; probably dropped because its appearance was not impressive enough. Zones 6-9. Developed in New Zealand. Introduced in 1967. *Source History: 2 in 1988; 6 in 1992; 8 in 2000.* **Sources: Bea, Bl4, Ch9, Cid, Cu4, Ga20, Gr4, Son.**

Spokane Beauty - Known mainly for its unusual size. Very large fruit to 2 lbs. or more. Variable in shape. Good for drying, cooking or eating fresh. Ripens in the fall. *Source History: 3 in 1988; 6 in 1992; 6 in 2000.* **Sources: Bea, Bl4, Ch9, Er2, Gr4, La3.**

Spytosh - *Source History: 1 in 2000.* **Sources: Ch9.**

St. Anna - *Source History: 1 in 1992; 1 in 2000.* **Sources: Ch9.**

St. Clair - Southern variety. *Source History: 1 in 2000.* **Sources: Ca15.**

St. Edmunds Pippin (St. Edmunds, St. Edmund's Russet) - Most beautiful of all russets. Uniformly flat-round fruit, entirely covered with a flawless, smooth, pure golden or fawn colored russet. Very juicy, crisp, yellowish flesh. Rich, pear-like flavor which reminds one of Seckel. Very juicy; makes an excellent cider. Heavy, annual cropper. Tip bearer. Ripens in early September. Hardy to Zone 4 and sheltered parts of Zone 3. Listed among the six best apples grown in England. Regarded as the best early russet. Originated at Bury St. Edmunds in 1870. *Source History: 8 in 1988; 10 in 1992; 10 in 2000.* **Sources: Bl4, Ch9, Cla, Cu4, Ed5, Gr4, Or9, So5, Son, Stl.**

St. Francis - *Source History: 1 in 1992; 1 in 2000.* **Sources: Ch9.**

St. Johnsbury - Medium size, yellow fruit with some red. Prized by early Vermonters for its sweet, yellow flesh. Keeps well in storage. Bears at a young age. Holds well on the tree. Early-midseason ripening. Appears to be scab resistant. Hardy to -50 degrees F. with occasional winter injury. Old Vermont apple of unknown origin. *Source History: 1 in 1988; 1 in 1992; 1 in 2000.* **Sources: Stl.**

St. Lawrence - Open-pollinated seedling of Fameuse. Yellow, red-striped fruit. Tender, fine grained, white flesh stained with red. Mild, pleasant flavor. Very good for eating fresh. Ripens midseason. Hardy to -50 degrees F. with occasional winter injury. Introduced in 1800. *Source History: 1 in 1988; 2 in 1992; 5 in 2000.* **Sources: Bea, Ed5, Fed, Stl, Wo7.**

St. Lawrence, Red Strain (Roger Luce's Red Strain) - Burgundy red sport of the original St. Lawrence. Pale lime-green overlaid with carmine red and maroon stripes and splashes; covered with blue-white bloom. White flesh is stained with red. High quality dessert apple; does not store well. Vigorous tree; annual bearer. Ripens in September. Hardy to Zones 3-4. Developed by Roger Luce of Newburg, Maine. *Source History: 1 in 1992; 1 in 2000.* **Sources: Fed.**

St. Martin - *Source History: 1 in 2000.* **Sources: Ch9.**

Star Song - Golden Delicious type. Above average fruit hangs well on the tree. Keeps until February. Tends toward biennial bearing. *Source History: 1 in 2000.* **Sources: Ch9.**

Stark (Robinson, Starke Apple, Yeats) - Large fruit with dark purplish red overlaying greenish background that shows through as dots; covered by a dull, waxy bloom. When properly ripened, the coarse flesh is of good, though not high, flavor. Good dessert and cider apple. Biennial bearing. Ripens late October. Prominent apple in most New England orchards in the late 1800s into the turn of the century. This variety should not be confused with the well-known nursery of the same name, which it pre-dates. *Source History: 4 in 1988; 7 in 1992; 4 in 2000.* **Sources: Ch9, Fed, Gr4, Wo7.**

Stark UltraEarli (Senshu Cultivar) - Trademarked variety. *Source History: 1 in 2000.* **Sources: AG2.**

Stark's Earliest - Medium size fruit with pale creamy white, thin skin, flushed with bright scarlet and prominent lenticels. Fruit bruises easily because of the thin skin. Flavor diminishes rapidly after picking. Requires careful thinning to avoid small fruit size. Scab resistant. Ripens in July. Patented and introduced in 1944. *Source History: 1 in 1992; 1 in 2000.* **Sources: Nrs.**

Starkey - Thought to be a seedling of Ribston Pippin. Not to be confused with Stark. Large fruit striped and splashed with bright red over a yellow background. White flesh. Among the best for winter storage. Hardy, regular bearer. Ripens in early October; reaches its best flavor near Christmas. Originated in Vassalboro, Maine on the farm of Moses Starkey around 1820. *Source History: 1 in 1988; 2 in 1992; 2 in 2000.* **Sources: Fed, Or9.**

Starr - An old-timer. Very large yellow-green fruit with smooth skin and faint blush. Yellow flesh is tender, crisp, juicy, sprightly subacid, aromatic. Moderately vigorous tree bears at young age. Ripens late August. Developed in New Jersey. Introduced in 1865. *Source History: 3 in 1988; 3 in 1992; 3 in 2000.* **Sources: Bea, Ca15, So5.**

State Fair (MN 1639) - Mantet (Tetofsky x McIntosh) x Oriole. Round-conic, medium size fruit is brilliantly striped with reddish orange over a yellow background. Creamy flesh is juicy, aromatic, sweet and firmer than most early varieties. Moderately subacid flavor. Excellent for fresh eating. Keeps well for a summer apple. Somewhat susceptible to scab and mildew. Fruit ripens uniformly from early to late August depending on location. Cold hardy to -40 degrees F. Developed at the University of Minnesota, 1979. *Source History: 8 in 1988; 17 in 1992; 13 in 2000.* **Sources: Bea, Ch9, Cu4, Ed5, Fa1, Fed, Hi9, LA4, MI5, Nrs, SH8, Stl, Wa16.**

Staybrite - Sport of Double Red Stayman with richer color. Fruit stays glossy and takes wax better than standard Stayman. Vigorous, productive, non-spur type tree. Triploid. Trademarked. *Source History: 1 in 1992; 1 in 2000.* **Sources: Hi9.**

Stayman - Southern variety. *Source History: 3 in 2000.* **Sources: BO10, Ca15, Or9.**

Stayman Red - The first of the truly tart apples. Hard, aromatic, tart baking apple. *Source History: 1 in 2000.* **Sources: Wor.**

Stayman Winesap (Stayman) - Seedling of Winesap. Medium to large, roundish to cone-shaped fruit. Dull red bloom over greenish base; striped red in less highly colored fruit. Firm, tender, juicy, yellowish flesh. Tart, rich, wine-like flavor. Excellent firm cooking apple with spicy taste. Best for baking and cider. Good keeper. Medium to large, moderately vigorous tree. Early, abundant bearer. Blooms late. Pollen-sterile triploid. Fire blight resistant. Ripens mid to late October. Requires 600-800 hours of chilling. Hardy in Zones 5-8. Originated in Kansas. Introduced in 1895. *Source History: 16 in 1988; 31 in 1992; 24 in 2000.* **Sources: Bea, Bl4, Bo5, Ch9, Cla, Cum, FO10, GI3, Gr4, Ho5, Iso, Jo3, La3, Lee, Mel, MI10, Na4, Sc6, So5, Son, TU5, Ur2, WA8, Wel.**

Stayman Winesap, Double Red (Double Red Stayman) - Greatly improved selection of Stayman. Solid red with a smoother, glossier skin than most strains.

Excellent flavor, quality and late keeping ability. Good shipper. Became very popular because it commanded premium prices on wholesale markets. Very tolerant to cracking. *Source History: 3 in 1988; 4 in 1992; 1 in 2000.* **Sources: SIM.**

Stayman Winesap, Red - Dark red sport of Stayman Winesap. Solid deep red color; larger size and better keeping qualities. Late ripening strain. Fine grained, crisp flesh. Rich, spicy flavor. Vigorous growing tree bears early. Ripens in October. Hardy in Zones 5-8. Originated in Wenatchee, Washington. *Source History: 9 in 1988; 7 in 1992; 7 in 2000.* **Sources: Bar, Mi1, MI5, Nrs, Pi2, Sav, Va2.**

Stayman Winesap, Red 201 Strain (Boyer Strain, Improved Blaxtayman No. 201, No. 201 Western Strain, Nured Stayman) - More extra fancy color than regular Stayman, to which all others are compared. Solid bright red fruit. Colors early; may be harvested ahead of the old Stayman. Same size, eating and cooking qualities. Tougher skin; not as subject to cracking or scald. Better keeper. *Source History: 3 in 1988; 2 in 1992; 4 in 2000.* **Sources: Ad2, Co2, TR8, Wh4.**

Stayman, Snapp (AS510) - Sport of Red Stayman 201; the most highly colored Red Stayman strain. Fruit quality, tree vigor and productivity are identical to Red Stayman 201. Snapp Stayman was discovered in the orchards of Alfred Snapp, Winchester, Virginia. Trademarked. Plant patent applied for. *Source History: 1 in 2000.* **Sources: Ad2.**

Stearns - Seedling of Esopus Spitzenburg. Fruit has red stripes with yellow background. Crisp flesh is melting and tender; almost dissolves on the tongue. Rich, luscious, pure apple flavor. Especially fine for cooking. Ripens early to mid-September. Zones 5-9. Originated in North Syracuse, New York. *Source History: 4 in 1988; 4 in 1992; 3 in 2000.* **Sources: Ch9, So5, Son.**

Stellar - Smooth yellow skin is sometimes blushed with orange. Firm, light yellow flesh is crisp and tart-sweet. Fruit hangs well on the tree which is vigorous, slightly upright and productive. Stores up to four months or more. Ripens about two weeks after Delicious. Developed at the University of Arkansas. Plant patent applied for. *Source History: 3 in 2000.* **Sources: Ch9, Cla, Ro3.**

Stembridge Cluster - *Source History: 1 in 2000.* **Sources: Cid.**

Stembridge Jersey - *Source History: 1 in 2000.* **Sources: Cid.**

Stoke's Red - *Source History: 1 in 2000.* **Sources: Cid.**

Stone - Blue Pearmain x Unknown. Red-striped fruit. Long-lived, healthy tree. Tends to overbear, so fruit may have to be thinned early in the season. Ripens late. Hardy to -50 degrees F. Locally known and esteemed variety. Originated in Vermont. Introduced in 1836. *Source History: 1 in 1988; 5 in 1992; 4 in 2000.* **Sources: Ch9, Ed5, Stl, Wo7.**

Strawberry Parfait (NJ 46) - Red stripes over ivory skin. Flesh is splashed with red. Very good flavor. Not a good keeper. Ripens early. Zones 5-9. *Source History: 1 in 1992; 1 in 2000.* **Sources: Son.**

Strickler - *Source History: 1 in 1992; 1 in 2000.* **Sources: Bl4.**

Striped Harvey - Old Maine apple. *Source History: 1 in 2000.* **Sources: Fed.**

Striped June (Sweet Striped June Apple) - Southern variety. Dark red fruit with striping. *Source History: 3 in 1988; 3 in 1992; 2 in 2000.* **Sources: Ca15, Hid.**

Stronghold - *Source History: 1 in 1992; 2 in 2000.* **Sources: Ch9, Ed5.**

Stump - Southern variety. *Source History: 2 in 2000.* **Sources: Ca15, Ch9.**

Sturmer Pippin - *Source History: 2 in 1992; 1 in 2000.* **Sources: Nrs.**

Sugar Apple - Southern variety. *Source History: 1 in 2000.* **Sources: Ca15.**

Sugar Loaf Pippin - Southern variety. *Source History: 1 in 2000.* **Sources: Ca15.**

Sulser Red - Southern variety. *Source History: 1 in 2000.* **Sources: Ca15.**

Sumac - *Source History: 2 in 1992; 1 in 2000.* **Sources: Nrs.**

Summer Banana - Southern variety. *Source History: 1 in 2000.* **Sources: Ca15.**

Summer Champion - Southern variety. Large red fruit. Tree is an early bearer. *Source History: 2 in 1988; 3 in 1992; 2 in 2000.* **Sources: Ca15, CO5.**

Summer Cider - *Source History: 1 in 1992; 1 in 2000.* **Sources: Bl4.**

Summer Delicious - *Source History: 1 in 1992; 1 in 2000.* **Sources: So5.**

Summer King - Southern variety. *Source History: 1 in 1992; 1 in 2000.* **Sources: Ca15.**

Summer Ladyfinger - Southern variety. *Source History: 1 in 2000.* **Sources: Ca15.**

Summer Orange - Southern variety. *Source History: 2 in 2000.* **Sources: Bea, Ca15.**

Summer Queen (Queen Apple) - Southern variety. Large, striped fruit up to 4" in diameter. Fine, juicy flavor. *Source History: 1 in 1992; 1 in 2000.* **Sources: Ca15.**

Summer Red - *Source History: 1 in 2000.* **Sources: Ed5.**

Summer Rose (French Reinette, Harvest Apple, Lodge's Early, Lippencott's Early, Woolman's Harvest, Woolman's Early, Woolman's Striped Harvest) - Pale green-yellow, striped skin is splashed with red on the sunny side. Fine, white flesh. Agreeably subacid flavor. Ripens in early August. Zones 6-9. Originated in New Jersey. Introduced in 1806. *Source History: 5 in 1988; 7 in 1992; 8 in 2000.* **Sources: Bea, Bl4, Ca15, Gr4, Or9, So5, Son, Wo7.**

Summer Scarlet - Ripens in July or August depending on location. *Source History: 3 in 1988; 3 in 1992; 2 in 2000.* **Sources: Bea, Ch9.**

Summer Song - *Source History: 1 in 2000.* **Sources: Ch9.**

Summer Sweet (King of Sweetings, King Sweet, Sidney Sweet, Sidney Sweeting, Thomas Sweet) - Southern variety sometimes confused with Hightop Sweet. Round-conic, yellow-green fruit with beautiful golden apricot-orange blush and occasional russet splash at the stem end. Yellow, firm flesh. Sweet distinctive flavor. Vigorous, upright, productive tree. Zone 4. Rare. Originated in Sidney, Maine about 1800. *Source History: 1 in 1992; 2 in 2000.* **Sources: Ca15, Fed.**

Summer Treat, Stark (NJ49 Cultivar) - Large, elongated, cherry-red fruit. Crisp flesh. Pollinate with Stark Lodi or Starkspur EarliBlaze. Ripens early August. Hardy in Zones 4-8. U.S. Plant Patent No. 4740. *Source History: 1 in 1988; 3 in 1992; 2 in 2000.* **Sources: AG2, Ch9.**

Summer Yellow - *Source History: 1 in 1988; 1 in 1992; 1 in 2000.* **Sources: So5.**

Summerred - Open-pollinated seedling of Summerland. Medium to large, bright red fruit. Tender flesh. Mellow, sweet flavor. Good eating and cooking apple. Red staining skin makes bright pink applesauce. Self-pollinating. Holds well on the tree, but can crack severely with scab. Ripens in late August. Requires 700 hours of chilling. Fine quality even in hot summer climates. Also an excellent choice for colder areas such as British Columbia and southeast Alaska. Developed in Canada. Introduced in 1964. *Source History: 10 in 1988; 14 in 1992; 7 in 2000.*

Sources: Bay, Bea, Bl4, Ch9, LA4, Nrs, Wa16.

SunCrisp (NJ 55 Cultivar) - Golden Delicious x Cox Orange Pippin. Golden skin with an orange blush. Sweet, mildly subacid taste. Moderately vigorous, upright tree. Shows some susceptibility to blister spot; prone to rust so site selection is critical. Thinning decreases the tendency toward biennial bearing. Matures about one week after Golden Delicious. Trademarked. U.S. Plant Patent No. 8648. *Source History: 5 in 2000.* **Sources: Ad2, AG2, Hi9, Ro3, St4.**

Sundance (Big Green) - Large, greenish fruit with carmine blush. Slightly tart, crisp, white flesh is bruise resistant. Ripens in early October. *Source History: 1 in 1992; 1 in 2000.* **Sources: Jo3.**

Sunday Sweet - Southern variety. *Source History: 1 in 1992; 1 in 2000.* **Sources: Ca15.**

Sundowner (Brand Cripps-2 Cultivar) - Golden Delicious x Lady Williams. Red fruit with crispy, sweet, white flesh. Long shelf life. Vigorous, upright tree tends toward biennial bearing. Matures up to two weeks after Granny Smith. Does well in extreme Southern fruit growing districts. Developed by the Western Australian Department of Agriculture Breeding Program. Trademarked. U.S. Plant Patent No. 9477. *Source History: 1 in 1992; 4 in 2000.* **Sources: Ad2, BR10, Cu4, WI4.**

Sungold - Non-russeting, better keeping, Yellow Delicious type. *Source History: 1 in 1988; 1 in 1992; 1 in 2000.* **Sources: Ch9.**

Sunrise (BC 8C-27-961) - McIntosh x Golden Delicious. Bright red color with pale yellow background. Good eating apple with crisp flesh with unique pear-grape flavor. Ripens midseason, two weeks before Gala. Fresh market. Short storage life. Immune to scab; mildew resistant and moderately resistant to fireblight. Hardy to -40 degrees F. Canadian origin. Trademarked variety. *Source History: 1 in 1988; 1 in 1992; 4 in 2000.* **Sources: Ad2, Cu4, Rai, Stl.**

Suntan - *Source History: 2 in 1992; 3 in 2000.* **Sources: Bea, Ch9, Or9.**

Supreme Staymared, Stark (Tuttle Cultivar) - Trademarked variety. *Source History: 2 in 1992; 3 in 2000.* **Sources: AG2, Bl4, St4.**

Surprise (Red Core) - Small, green, winter apple with creamy white, red stained flesh. Ripens in October. One of the parents of Pink Pearl; developed by plant breeder, Albert Etter. *Source History: 1 in 1988; 4 in 1992; 3 in 2000.* **Sources: Ch9, Or9, So5.**

Surprise Reinette - *Source History: 1 in 2000.* **Sources: Or9.**

Susie - Chance seedling found by the roadside. Yellow skin color. Cream colored flesh is sweet and juicy. Resistant to fire blight, cedar-apple rust and mildew. Ripens in early September in Tennessee. *Source History: 1 in 1992; 1 in 2000.* **Sources: Hid.**

Sutton's Beauty (Beauty, Sutton, Morris Red, Steel's Red) - Believed to be a seedling of Hubbardston. Bright red, symmetrical fruit. Hard, crisp flesh. Flavor intermediate in sweetness between Hubbardston and Baldwin. Ripens during October. Originated in Massachusetts. Introduced in 1849. *Source History: 1 in 1988; 6 in 1992; 5 in 2000.* **Sources: Bea, Ch9, Or9, So5, Wo7.**

Swaar (Hardwick) - Fruit is not fancy. Dull yellow skin mottled with brown specks. Fine grained, hard, crisp flesh. Spicy, aromatic, sweet, rich flavor. Will hang on the tree well into winter. For storage purposes, should be picked while still firm. Undergoes a softening and mellowing process analogous to pears. When stored until slightly soft and rough on the outside, it becomes consistently delicious with a velvety, tender, beautifully balanced, white flesh. One of the finest winter apples. Favorite with home orchards. Ripens in October or November depending on location. Zones 6-9. Originated in Dutch, New York around 1804. Name means "heavy" in Dutch. *Source History: 3 in 1988; 7 in 1992; 11 in 2000.* **Sources: Bl4, Ca15, Ch9, Ed5, Ga20, Gr4, Or9, Sc6, So5, Son, Wo7.**

Swanzie's Sauce Apple - Southern variety. *Source History: 1 in 2000.* **Sources: Ca15.**

Swayzie (Swazie, Swazy) - A variety of the Pomme Grise group. Small to medium, flattened conical fruit is golden yellow sprinkled with russet spots and streaks becoming solid cinnamon russet at the base. Crisp, tender, white flesh. Fine, rich, distinctive russet flavor. Stores well. Shy bearer. Ripens mid-October. Found on a farm near Niagara, Canada. Introduced in 1872. *Source History: 1 in 1988; 2 in 1992; 3 in 2000.* **Sources: Ca15, Or9, So5.**

Sweet Alford - Sweet type cider variety to balance the flavor. Medium to large fruit on a well shaped tree. Zones 6-9. *Source History: 1 in 1992; 3 in 2000.* **Sources: Cid, Nrs, Son.**

Sweet Bough (Bough, August Sweet, Autumn Bough, Early Bough, Large Bough, Sweet Harvest, Washington, Early Sweet Bough, Yellow Bough) - Old American variety. Good size, green fruit with numerous dots. Juicy, tender, crisp, white flesh. Honey-sweet flavor. Disease hardy tree; heavy bearer. Fruit rots readily when damaged. Ripens in late August. Hardy to Zone 4. Generally regarded as the best early sweet apple. Introduced in 1817. *Source History: 6 in 1988; 8 in 1992; 6 in 2000.* **Sources: Ch9, Cu4, Ed5, So5, Wo7, Wor.**

Sweet Caroline - *Source History: 1 in 2000.* **Sources: Ch9.**

Sweet Coppin - Cider variety that also tastes good eaten fresh. Yellow skin color. Consistent cropper. Makes a full bodied cider without blending with other apples. Ripens mid-October. *Source History: 3 in 2000.* **Sources: Ch9, Cid, Rai.**

Sweet Dixon - Southern variety. *Source History: 1 in 2000.* **Sources: Ca15.**

Sweet Gates - *Source History: 1 in 2000.* **Sources: Sc6.**

Sweet King - *Source History: 1 in 1992; 2 in 2000.* **Sources: Ch9, Ed5.**

Sweet Lannie - Southern variety. *Source History: 1 in 2000.* **Sources: Ca15.**

Sweet Russet (Summer Russet) - Medium to small bright yellow russet fruit sprinkled with brown dots, sometimes flushed with red in the sun. Tender, sweet, nonacid flesh. Aromatic, rich flavor. Ripens in late August. *Source History: 1 in 1988; 2 in 1992; 2 in 2000.* **Sources: Ca15, So5.**

Sweet Sal - Seedling of Northern Spy named by Maine orchardist, Morris Towle (1911-1993) from Winthrop, Maine. Produces medium size roundish fruit with dull yellow skin washed with pink dots. Acid-free flesh is perfect for those who do not like or cannot eat tart apples. Edible from August to March but is best in October. Bears late; keeps extremely well. Vigorous, upright tree. Hardy to Zone 4. *Source History: 1 in 2000.* **Sources: Fed.**

Sweet Sixteen (MN 1630) - Malinda x Northern Spy. Red-striped, conic fruit up to 3". Aromatic, moderately acid, firm, crisp, cream-colored flesh with high sugar content. Unique, pleasing, faintly nutty flavored cooking apple. Rates high as a pie and sauce apple; also an excellent dessert apple. Handles and stores well. Early bearing, late blooming tree with moderately spreading, vigorous habit. Dependable, annual bearer. Resistant to scab and fire blight. Extremely cold hardy variety developed at the University of Minnesota in 1978. Can withstand -50 degrees F. with occasional winter injury. PVP. *Source History: 8 in 1988; 21 in*

1992; 19 in 2000. **Sources: Bea, Bl4, Ch9, Cu4, Ed5, Fa1, Fed, Fi1, Gur, Hi9, Jun, LA4, MI5, Nrs, Ro3, SH8, Son, Stl, Wa16.**

Sweet Winesap (Hendrick, Hendrick Sweet, Henry Sweet, Red Sweet Winesap, Rose Sweet, Sweet Pearmain) - Red striped, yellow apple with a long stem. Slow to begin bearing. Subject to fire blight. Originated in Pennsylvania. Introduced in 1867. *Source History: 3 in 1992; 2 in 2000.* **Sources: Ch9, Wo7.**

Swiss Gourmet (Arlet Cultivar) - Golden x Idared. Medium to large fruit is bright red over rich yellow ground color. Crisp, sprightly flavor. Precocious tree bears early. Ripens ten days ahead of Jonathan. Originated in Switzerland. U.S. Plant Patent No. 6689. *Source History: 3 in 1992; 4 in 2000.* **Sources: AG2, Er2, TR8, Va2.**

Switzer - *Source History: 1 in 2000.* **Sources: Ed5.**

Takane (Open Pollinated Redgold) - Medium size round fruit with red-orange blush. Juicy, sweet-tart flesh. Tree is a vigorous, annual bearer. Matures late, but earlier than Fuji. *Source History: 2 in 1992; 2 in 2000.* **Sources: Cla, Nrs.**

Tale Sweet - *Source History: 1 in 2000.* **Sources: Cid.**

Tanyard Seedling - Late bloom time allows this variety to escape late frosts. Yellow fruit is good for pies and cooking. Originated in north Georgia mountains. *Source History: 1 in 2000.* **Sources: La3.**

Tardive Forester - *Source History: 1 in 2000.* **Sources: Cid.**

Tauton Cross - *Source History: 1 in 1992; 1 in 2000.* **Sources: Ch9.**

Taylor's (Taylor's Cider) - Sweet to mild bittersweet type cider apple. Green-yellow skin with red flush. Moderately vigorous tree. Tip bearer. Zones 6-9. Originated in Somerset, England. *Source History: 3 in 2000.* **Sources: Cid, Mo19, Son.**

Tenderskin (Thinskin, Tender Peeling, Tenderine) - Small to medium size fruit with rectangular to conic shape. Yellow skin is blushed and striped pink and covered with a fairly heavy grey bloom. Tender, juicy, yellowish flesh with a pleasing taste even before fully mature on the tree. Suitable for dessert, cooking and cider making. Heavy annual bearer. Some resistance to diseases. Ripens in October. Originated in South Carolina. Introduced in 1884. *Source History: 1 in 1988; 1 in 1992; 1 in 2000.* **Sources: Ca15.**

Terry Winter - Dull red, medium size fruit. Harvested through October and November; good keeper. Originated in Fulton County, Georgia before the Civil War. Grown commercially in north Georgia around 1900. *Source History: 1 in 2000.* **Sources: Ca15.**

Tetofski (Tetofsky, Tetovksy) - Russian crab apple that dates back to 1831. Small greenish yellow fruit occasionally striped with bright red. White, crisp, tender, juicy flesh. Flavorful; can be used for cooking before ripe and eating when ripe. Ripens early. Hardy to -50 degrees F. Brought to the U.S. by the Massachusetts Horticultural Society. *Source History: 3 in 1988; 3 in 1992; 2 in 2000.* **Sources: Bea, Stl.**

Thelma - *Source History: 1 in 2000.* **Sources: Ch9.**

Thewgold - *Source History: 1 in 1992; 1 in 2000.* **Sources: Ch9.**

Thick Banana - *Source History: 1 in 1992; 1 in 2000.* **Sources: Bl4.**

Thompson - Late summer apple of unknown parentage. Some claim this is the same as the Massachusetts apple, Williams. Others say it is the same as John Thompson's other introduction, Somerset of Maine, but it is clear that these are two different varieties. Round-conic shape reminiscent of Red Delicious with solid red overlay with darker red stripes. White flesh with a pink hue just below the skin. Not a keeper. Ripens in August. Zone 4. Rare. *Source History: 1 in 2000.* **Sources: Fed.**

Thompson King - *Source History: 1 in 2000.* **Sources: Ed5.**

Thompson, Early - *Source History: 1 in 2000.* **Sources: Bea.**

Thornberry - Unusual apple found growing in an abandoned orchard near Whitethorn, California. Translucent yellow skin reveals the raspberry-pink flesh inside. Unique berry-like flavor; sprightly and refreshing. Hangs well on the tree. Ripens during October. Thornberry is a registered trademark of Greenmantle Nursery. *Source History: 1 in 1988; 1 in 1992; 1 in 2000.* **Sources: Gr4.**

Tinsley's Quince - *Source History: 1 in 2000.* **Sources: Or9.**

Tioga - Sutton's Beauty x Northern Spy. Large, green fruit ripens to gold. Mild, mellow flavor. Produces large crops. Ripens early November. Zones 5-10. Originated in Minnesota in 1978. *Source History: 2 in 1988; 3 in 1992; 3 in 2000.* **Sources: Ch9, So5, Son.**

Titus Pippin (Hang On, Hangan, Timothy, Titus, Well Apple) - Orange blushed, orange, waxy skin. Large, open core. Vigorous tree is a heavy annual bearer. Short storage life. Ripens in late September. Originated in New York. Introduced in 1841. *Source History: 2 in 1992; 2 in 2000.* **Sources: Ch9, Wo7.**

Tobias - Southern variety. *Source History: 1 in 2000.* **Sources: Ca15.**

Tohoku 2 - *Source History: 1 in 1992; 1 in 2000.* **Sources: Nrs.**

Tohoku 4 - *Source History: 1 in 1992; 1 in 2000.* **Sources: Nrs.**

Tolman Sweet (Tolman, Brown's Golden Sweet, Talman Sweet) - Sweet Greening x Old Russet. Original name was Tolman Sweeting. Round, medium to large fruit. Pale yellow skin, sometimes a little flushed with russet lines and often marked with a slightly rough suture line running from top to bottom. Firm, rather hard, moderately fine, white flesh. Excellent sweet flavor. Highly esteemed for baking, stewing and making cider. Large, hardy, healthy, productive, long-lived tree. Bears early and reliably almost anywhere. Blooms late. Moderately biennial. Ripens during October. Probably the hardiest of all New England apples. Hardy to -50 degrees F. with occasional winter injury. Developed in Massachusetts. Described in 1822. *Source History: 13 in 1988; 18 in 1992; 17 in 2000.* **Sources: Bea, Bl4, Ch9, Ed5, Fed, Gr4, Hi9, La3, Leu, Mi1, Nrs, Sc6, So5, Son, Stl, Und, Wo7.**

Tom Putt (Coalbrook, Devonshire Nine Square, Jeffrey's Seedling, Tom Potter, Izod's Kernel, January Tom Putt, Marrow Bone Ploughman, Thomas Jeffreys) - Culinary apple; also suitable for cider making. Green-yellow fruit with red stripes over half of the skin surface; some red blotches. Becomes greasy in storage. Ripens in September. Originated in England. *Source History: 1 in 1988; 1 in 1992; 2 in 2000.* **Sources: Bea, Cid.**

Tommy - Southern variety. *Source History: 1 in 2000.* **Sources: Ca15.**

Tompkins King (Tompkins County King, Flat Spitzenburg, King, King Apple, King Apple of America, Toma Red, Tommy Red, Tom's Red, Winter King) - Large to very large fruit. Smooth, yellow skin washed with orangish red; sometimes striped. Coarse, tender, yellowish flesh. Rich, subacid, balanced flavor. Excellent for dessert, pies, sauce and cider. Once grown commercially in California's Mattole Valley as a drying apple. Tends to water core which creates translucent, very sweet patches in the flesh; shortens storage life, but many find it enhances flavor. Natural semi-dwarf tree; precocious and vigorous. Tip bearer. Pollen-sterile triploid. Ripens during September. Originated in New Jersey around 1750 and gained its fame in New York State. Introduced in 1804. *Source History: 7 in 1988; 13 in 1992; 17 in 2000.* **Sources: Bea, Bl4, Ch9, Cu4, Er2, Fed, Ga20, Gr4, Mi1, Or9, Rai, Sc6, So5, Son, WI4, Wo7, Wor.**

Tony - Southern variety. *Source History: 1 in 2000.* **Sources: Ca15.**

Trail Crab - Sweet, juicy, unusual flavor. Early ripening. *Source History: 2 in 1992; 1 in 2000.* **Sources: Va5.**

Trailman Crab - Trail x Osman. Extremely hardy crabapple with green overlaid with red. Fruit is about 2" in diameter. Good eating and canning quality. Crisp, juicy flesh. Vigorous, productive tree. Ripens early-midseason. Extremely hardy; to -50 degrees or colder. *Source History: 2 in 2000.* **Sources: Ed5, Stl.**

Transcendent Crab - One of the largest of the Siberian crab apples. Medium to large, round-oval fruit, flattened at the ends. Slightly but regularly ribbed. Golden yellow with rich crimson cheek, sometimes nearly covered with red. Juicy, creamy yellow flesh. Fine flavor. Long, slender stalk. Open, deep cavity. Closed calyx. Good for fresh eating; excellent for jelly. Poor storage ability. Beautiful, heavy bearing, medium size tree. Self-fruitful. Ripens late August to September. Requires 600-800 hours of chilling. Zones 3-10. *Source History: 10 in 1988; 10 in 1992; 8 in 2000.* **Sources: Bay, CO5, Nrs, ORA, SIM, Son, Ty2, Wor.**

Tremlett's Bitter - English cider apple. Firm, medium size fruit. Bittersweet juice. Two week harvesting period in early October. Zones 6-9. *Source History: 3 in 1988; 3 in 1992; 4 in 2000.* **Sources: Cla, Cu4, So5, Son.**

Trent - *Source History: 1 in 2000.* **Sources: Ch9.**

Trinitarian - *Source History: 1 in 1992; 1 in 2000.* **Sources: Ch9.**

Tropical Beauty - Low chill apple. Medium size, round fruit. Excellent quality. Somewhat self-fertile, but plant with Ein Shemer and/or Adina for best results. Requires 350-400 chilling hours. Proven in Australia, Florida and Hawaii. *Source History: 2 in 1988; 2 in 1992; 2 in 2000.* **Sources: ORA, Pa2.**

Tsugaru (Open-Pollinated Golden Delicious, Homei Strain) - Medium size fruit with 75% red blush on yellow background. Crisp, juicy flesh with sweet-tart flavor. Spreading tree. Annual bearer. Does not store well. Ripens in late August. *Source History: 2 in 1992; 7 in 2000.* **Sources: Ch9, Cla, Ed5, Mo19, Nrs, Rai, Ro3.**

Tumanga - Medium size, round to oblate yellow fruit. Half of the fruit is covered with a dusty mauve-red overcoat and a large ring of russet radiates out from the stem. Annual bearer. Semi-vigorous tree. Fruit stores 3-4 months. Some disease resistance. Fall ripening. Originated in Japan before 1950. *Source History: 1 in 1988; 3 in 1992; 3 in 2000.* **Sources: Ch9, Ed5, Fed.**

Twenty Ounce (Aurora, Cayuga Red Streak, Coleman, Eighteen Ounce, Morgan's Favorite, Governor Seward's, Lima, Twenty Ounce Apple, Wine, Wine of Connecticut) - As its name implies, this apple can reach enormous proportions. Attractive fruit with broad, red stripes over greenish background. Skin has the peculiar peened surface found on Granny Smith. Semi-firm white flesh. High quality. Premier cooking apple for more than 100 years. Excellent for dessert. Medium size, vigorous tree often droops; bears young. Ripens unevenly during September or October depending on location. Hardy to Zone 5. Originated in upstate New York. Often mistakenly called Smokehouse. Introduced in 1840. *Source History: 11 in 1988; 10 in 1992; 17 in 2000.* **Sources: Bea, Bl4, Bo5, Ch9, Cu4, Ed5, Gr4, La3, Mi1, Or9, Rai, Sc6, So5, Son, WAF, Wh4, Wo7.**

Twenty Ounce Pippin, Collamer - Darker red sport. Large to huge green fruit with dull red stripes. Coarse grained flesh with an interesting, subacid flavor. Good for fresh use; excellent for cooking and cider. Large, upright, spreading tree is resistant to scab, mildew and insects. Origin uncertain, about 1844. *Source History: 1 in 1988; 4 in 1992; 1 in 2000.* **Sources: Bl4.**

Tydeman's Late Orange - Laxton's Superb x Cox's Orange Pippin. Has the
appearance at picking time of a slightly conical Cox's Orange Pippin, but with much duller color. Skin turns a warm yellow and crimson in storage. Yellow flesh develops a rich flavor similar to Cox's Orange Pippin, but distinctively its own. Does not reach full maturity and finest eating quality until Christmas. Great dessert apple for winter use. Ripens in November or December depending on location. Zones 6-9. Developed at the East Malling Research Station in Kent, England, 1930. Introduced in 1949. *Source History: 4 in 1988; 9 in 1992; 6 in 2000.* **Sources: Bl4, Ch9, Gr4, So5, Son, WI4.**

Tydeman's Red (Tydeman's Early, Tydeman's Early Worcester) - McIntosh x
Worcester Pearmain. Resembles McIntosh in size, shape and color; better firmness. Large, bright red fruit. Firm, high quality, creamy white flesh. Mild, pleasant flavor. Fine eating and cooking apple. Excellent for roadside market. Keeps for about one month. Vigorous, productive tree. Growth habit tends to be leggy; does best with short, heading-type pruning. Annual bearer; tip bearer. Long fruiting season; ideal for backyards. Requires at least three pickings. Scab and mildew resistant. Ripens in late August. Suffers winter injury in northern New England. Developed at the East Malling Research Station in 1964. *Source History: 15 in 1988; 11 in 1992; 7 in 2000.* **Sources: Amb, Bea, Ch9, Nrs, Or9, So5, Stl.**

Ultra Spire, Stark (Telamon Cultivar) - Columnar tree form. Red fruit with a
yellow-green blush. Juicy flesh is tart and tangy. Ripens mid-September. Originally from the Stark Colonnade collection. Trademarked. U.S. Plant Patent No. 6224. *Source History: 2 in 2000.* **Sources: MO10, St4.**

Unity - *Source History: 1 in 2000.* **Sources: Bea.**

Utter - Originated in Wisconsin. Introduced in 1855. *Source History: 1 in 1992; 1 in 2000.* **Sources: Wo7.**

Valentine - Canadian prairie apple. Yellow fruit blushed with red stripes. Introduced in 1965. *Source History: 2 in 2000.* **Sources: Bea, Ed5.**

Valstar - Redder strain of Elstar with the same quality but brighter red color and
more red striping. Excellent, sweet-tart flavor and crispness. Outstanding keeping quality. Originated in France. *Source History: 1 in 2000.* **Sources: Va2.**

Vanderpool Red - Southern variety. *Source History: 1 in 1988; 1 in 1992; 2 in 2000.* **Sources: Ca15, So5.**

Vandevere (Honeydew Grindstone, Pippin Vandevere) - Flattened shape and
very hard, crisp flesh earned it the local name of Grindstone. Has fine, lively flavor to match its texture. Makes good cider. More than just a good keeper. Ripens during October. Originated in Delaware. Introduced in 1806. *Source History: 2 in 1988; 3 in 1992; 6 in 2000.* **Sources: Ca15, Ch9, Cid, Gr4, Or9, Wo7.**

Veedum - *Source History: 1 in 2000.* **Sources: Bea.**

Victoria Sweet - *Source History: 1 in 1992; 1 in 2000.* **Sources: Ch9.**

Viking - Medium size, glossy, smooth fruit with 60% rich red over green. Fine
grained, white flesh. Tart flavor. Best suited for cooler northern apple areas. Can develop internal breakdown in hot weather and warmer producing areas. Ripens 10 days ahead of Paulared. U.S. Plant Patent No. 3420. *Source History: 3 in 1988; 3 in 1992; 1 in 2000.* **Sources: Ch9.**

Vilberie - Cider apple. *Source History: 1 in 2000.* **Sources: Mo19.**

Villemandy - *Source History: 1 in 1992; 1 in 2000.* **Sources: Bl4.**

Vine - *Source History: 1 in 2000.* **Sources: Or9.**

Vine Apple - Southern variety. *Source History: 1 in 2000.* **Sources: Ca15.**

Virginia Beauty - Discovered as a chance seedling on a farm in Carroll County, Virginia in 1826, after which many local growers began grafting it. Very large, deep red fruit. Colored like a Jonathan, but brighter red and globe-shaped. Very crisp. Good keeper. Ripens in mid-October.- *Source History: 4 in 1988; 6 in 1992; 9 in 2000.* **Sources: Bea, Bl4, Ca15, Ch9, Cla, La3, Or9, Ur2, Wh4.**

Virginia Crab (Hugh's Crab) - This variety was often used as an understock before the development of hybrid rootstocks because of its hardiness and compatibility to many varieties. Makes a highly flavored, dry cider. Ripens in September. One of the major cider varieties that Thomas Jefferson planted in his orchard at Monticello. *Source History: 2 in 1992; 4 in 2000.* **Sources: Ca15, Cid, Nrs, Or9.**

Virginia Gold - Golden Delicious x Albemarle Pippin. Smooth, clear, waxy skin. Crisp, juicy, mildly subacid flesh; much firmer than either parent. Flavor less sweet than Golden Delicious; less sprightly than Albemarle Pippin. Quality comparable to Albemarle Pippin. Does not ripen to maximum quality and flavor unless held in cold storage until late January. Excellent for sauce and pies. Heavily productive tree. Tendency toward alternate bearing if allowed to overbear. Ripens very late. Released by the Virginia Agricultural Experiment Station; selected from crosses made nearly 30 years ago. *Source History: 4 in 1988; 10 in 1992; 8 in 2000.* **Sources: Bl4, Ch9, Cu4, Gr4, La3, Nrs, Or9, So5.**

Virginia Greening (Green Mountain Pippin, Rose Greening) - Red blushed fruit with russet dots. Thick, tough skin. Dense, breaking, coarse flesh. Subacid flavor that sweetens as the fruit ripens. Heavy, annual bearer. Stores exceptionally well. Ripens in early October. *Source History: 1 in 1992; 1 in 2000.* **Sources: Or9.**

Vista Bella - Melba x Senora. Medium size, glossy, very dark red fruit. Firm, creamy white flesh. Finely flavored. Good quality dessert apple. Extremely hard for an early summer apple. Watercore is sometimes a problem. Large, very vigorous tree, somewhat upright in growth habit. Light producer in its early years. Requires several pickings. Tends toward biennial bearing. Ripens mid-July to early August depending on location. Hardy to Zone 2. One of the very earliest red apples, but firmer and better eating quality than most summer varieties. Developed in New Jersey. Introduced in 1974. *Source History: 9 in 1988; 8 in 1992; 7 in 2000.* **Sources: Amb, Bea, Bl4, Ch9, Nrs, So5, Stl.**

Von Zuccalmaglio's Reinette (Zuccalmaglio) - Ananas Reinette x Purpurroter Agatapfel. German apple. Rough, sticky skin is flushed with brown red with faint darker red stripes and russet dots and streaks. Dry, fine-grained, yellow-white flesh. Bears early. Shows some disease resistance. Ripens in September. *Source History: 2 in 1988; 3 in 1992; 2 in 2000.* **Sources: Ch9, So5.**

Wagener - Medium to large, irregularly shaped, distinctly five-sided, flattened fruit with slight ribbing. Thin, glossy, smooth skin is striped and mottled pale red over very light yellow. Fine grained, crisp, juicy, tender flesh. Subacid, aromatic, sprightly flavor resembles Northern Spy and improves after frost. Very juicy; excellent cider apple. Cooks down to very fine sauce. Exceptionally long storage life. Small tree bears early; prolific, hardy, moderately biennial. Ripens mid to late October. Hangs long on the tree. Zones 6-9. Possible parent of Northern Spy. Seedling discovered near Penn Yan, New York, 1791. *Source History: 12 in 1988; 14 in 1992; 8 in 2000.* **Sources: Bl4, Ed5, Gr4, Mi1, So5, Son, Wo7, Wor.**

Walker's Pippin - Southern variety. *Source History: 1 in 2000.* **Sources: Ca15.**

Wallace Sweet - Southern variety. *Source History: 1 in 2000.* **Sources: Ca15.**

Waltana - Medium to large fruit of variable shape. Thin red striping over greenish background. Background color becomes yellow and more vivid red as it ripens. Frequently picked a little on the green side and ripened in storage. Crisp, hard, yet juicy texture. Trees are vigorous, healthy and regularly productive. Ripens in October or November depending on location. May not ripen properly in regions with cooler summers or shorter growing seasons. Zones 6-9. An Albert Etter variety named for Albert's brother, Walter, and his wife. Originated in California. Introduced in 1860. *Source History: 3 in 1988; 7 in 1992; 5 in 2000.* **Sources: Bea, Gr4, Or9, So5, Son.**

Walter Tibbs - Southern variety. *Source History: 1 in 2000.* **Sources: Ca15.**

Warsaw - *Source History: 1 in 2000.* **Sources: Or9.**

Washed Russet - *Source History: 1 in 1992; 2 in 2000.* **Sources: Ch9, So5.**

Washington Greening - *Source History: 1 in 1992; 1 in 2000.* **Sources: Wo7.**

Washington Royal - Originated in Massachusetts. Introduced in 1855. *Source History: 1 in 1992; 2 in 2000.* **Sources: Ed5, Wo7.**

Washington Spur - Trademarked. *Source History: 1 in 2000.* **Sources: WI12.**

Washington Strawberry (Washington County Seedling, Washington of Maine, Juniata, Washington) - Medium to large or very large striped red fruit. Firm, yellow flesh is juicy and sprightly subacid. Vigorous tree is hardy, healthy, moderately long lived and an early bearing, reliable cropper. Will keep into early winter. Ripens in early September. Originated in New York. Introduced in 1849. *Source History: 1 in 1988; 4 in 1992; 3 in 2000.* **Sources: Bea, Ch9, Wo7.**

Washington Sweet - Unknown parentage. May be a pseudonym for Bailey's Golden Sweet. Medium to large size, conic fruit. Skin is yellow, mottled with bronze and a slight orange-red blush. Yellow-white flesh is fine grained and dry. Strong, distinctive taste in the same class as Tolman Sweet. Zone 4. Nineteenth century apple from Kennebec County, Sidney, Maine. *Source History: 1 in 2000.* **Sources: Fed.**

Wealthy - Medium size, pale yellow fruit splashed and striped with red. Ripens to all-over scarlet for fresh eating; used weeks earlier for pies, sauces and preserves. Refreshing, crisp, very juicy, white flesh with pink veins. Sprightly, vinous, distinctive flavor with hint of strawberry. Keeps into December. Fine quality. Small, compact tree bears young and heavily; tends to be biennial. Blooms profusely over a long period; excellent pollinator. Resistant to scab, fire blight and cedar-apple rust. Favorite for home orchards in Minnesota and the East. Hardy into Zone 2. Seedling of Cherry Crab planted by Peter Gideon in Excelsior, Minnesota about 1860. *Source History: 19 in 1988; 29 in 1992; 24 in 2000.* **Sources: Bea, Bo5, Ch9, Cid, Cu4, Fa1, Fed, Gr4, Jun, La3, Mc3, ME3, Mi1, MI5, Nrs, Or9, Sc6, SH8, So5, Son, Stl, Va2, WI4, Wo7.**

Wealthy, Double Red - *Source History: 3 in 1992; 2 in 2000.* **Sources: Ch9, Nrs.**

Wealthy, June - *Source History: 1 in 1992; 1 in 2000.* **Sources: Ch9.**

Wealthy, Red - Deep red fruit. Excellent flavor and quality. Open, spreading growth habit allows all fruit to color well. *Source History: 2 in 1988; 1 in 1992; 1 in 2000.* **Sources: WI12.**

Wellington (American) - Cortland x Crimson Beauty. Large, red-striped fruit. Good for eating, local market and sauce. Early, concentrated harvest. Ripens in early August. Hardy to Zone 3. Originated in New York. Introduced in 1955. *Source History: 3 in 1988; 4 in 1992; 2 in 2000.* **Sources: Bl4, Cu4.**

Wellington Bloomless - *Source History: 1 in 1988; 1 in 1992; 1 in 2000.* **Sources: So5.**

Western Beauty - *Source History: 1 in 2000.* **Sources: Or9.**

Westfield Seek-No-Further (Westfield, Seek-No-Further, New England Seek-No-Further, Connecticut Seek-No-Further, Marietta Seek-No-Further, Red Seek-No-Further, Red Winter Pearmain) - Excellent for eating fresh and drying. Flavor intensifies as it dries. Fruit is streaked with red and russet over yellowish background. Crisp, juicy, high quality flesh. Rich, mild, pleasantly aromatic, mildly subacid, distinctive flavor. Beach rates Westfield as very good to best, a rare distinction in his *Apples of New York.* Average keeper. Medium to large tree. Flourishes in well-drained, gravelly or loamy soil. Ripens during October. Hardy to -50 degrees F. with occasional winter injury. Originated in Westfield, Massachusetts. Introduced in 1790. *Source History: 7 in 1988; 13 in 1992; 16 in 2000.* **Sources: Bea, Bl4, Ch9, Cid, Cu4, Ed5, Fed, Gr4, La3, Mi1, Or9, Sc6, So5, Son, Stl, Wo7, Wor.**

Westland - Heyer 12 x Dr. Bill. Large, yellow fruit with light red stripes. Creamy white flesh with red tinge. Fair for eating; excellent for pies and sauces. Keeps about nine weeks in cold storage. Annual bearing compact tree. Ripens in late August. Extremely hardy; Zone 3. Developed in Brooks, Alberta, Canada. *Source History: 4 in 1988; 9 in 1992; 4 in 2000.* **Sources: Bea, Nrs, So5, Stl.**

White Bausel - Southern variety. *Source History: 1 in 2000.* **Sources: Ca15.**

White Jersey - *Source History: 1 in 2000.* **Sources: Cid.**

White Pippin - Introduced in 1848. *Source History: 2 in 1988; 2 in 1992; 4 in 2000.* **Sources: Bea, Ch9, Or9, Wo7.**

White Sweet - Southern variety. *Source History: 1 in 1992; 1 in 2000.* **Sources: Ca15.**

Whiteman - *Source History: 1 in 2000.* **Sources: Ch9.**

Whitney Crab - Round to conic crab apple; often larger than a golf ball. Uniform in size and shape. Light greenish yellow with red blush or stripes. Sweet, juicy, yellowish flesh. Mildly subacid with slight crab apple flavor. Favorite for home canning, preserving, pickling and spicing. Fair keeper. Narrow, upright trees bear heavily, even when young. Pink and white blossoms. Plant two or more trees for top yields. Ripens late July to late August depending on location. Requires 600 hours of chilling. Hardy in Zones 2-9. Originated with A. R. Whitney of Franklin Grove, Illinois. Described by Warder in 1869. *Source History: 15 in 1988; 22 in 1992; 13 in 2000.* **Sources: Bea, Bl4, Cid, Fa1, Fi1, Fo2, Jun, Mi1, Nrs, Sc6, SH8, Son, Va2.**

Whitney Russet King - Southern variety. *Source History: 1 in 2000.* **Sources: Ca15.**

Wickson - Newtown (Albemarle) Pippin x Esopus Spitzenburg. Excellent cider apple. Small yellow and red fruit up to 2" in diameter. Very sweet, up to 25% sugar, but a pronounced acid tang. Highly flavored juice. More crab than apple. Hardy to Zone 3. Albert Etter named this fruit after E. J. Wickson, distinguished California pomologist, who was his friend and mentor. Luther Burbank also named one of his finest plums Wickson in honor of this important fruit authority. Introduced in 1944. *Source History: 2 in 1988; 5 in 1992; 10 in 2000.* **Sources: Bea, Ch9, Cid, Cid, Cla, Ed5, Gr4, So5, Son, Ur2.**

Wild Apple - Cider apple. *Source History: 1 in 2000.* **Sources: Cid.**

Wild Sweet Crab - Yellow-red, 1" fruits used for jelly. Tree grows to 30' tall and wide. Hardy in Zone 4. *Source History: 2 in 1992; 1 in 2000.* **Sources: Fo2.**

William Crump - Cox's Orange Pippin x Worcester Pearmain. Dessert apple once grown on a small commercial scale in England. Greenish yellow skin ripens to deep yellow with red stripes and a light grey russet. Sweet flavor. Tree is a vigorous, upright grower. Ripens in October. Introduced in 1908. *Source History: 2 in 1992; 1 in 2000.* **Sources: So5.**

William's Pride (Co-op 23) - NJ 50 x PRI 1018-101. Yellow fleshed fruit with mildly subacid flavor. Dark maroon-purple skin color with numerous tiny white dots and a thin bloom. Light cream flesh shows red staining just under the chewy thick skin. Flavor is a nice acidic blend of tart and sweet. Vigorous, upright tree requires 2-3 pickings. Thin for annual bearing. Resistant to apple scab and cedar apple rust. Moderate resistance to fire blight and powdery mildew. Zones 4-8. Developed at Purdue University, 1988. U.S. Plant Patent No. 6268. *Source History: 9 in 1992; 14 in 2000.* **Sources: AG2, Bu7, Ch9, Cla, Clo, Cu4, Ed2, Fed, Hi9, Jo3, Rai, Ro3, Son, St4.**

Williams (Williams Red, William's Early Red) - Beautiful bright red fruit. Red tinged firm flesh is moderately crisp and juicy yet mildly subacid. Agreeable mild flavor. Good dessert apple. Reliable annual cropper; pruning encourages larger fruit size. Ripens in late summer. Hardy to Zone 3. Originated in Massachusetts in the 1750s. *Source History: 2 in 1988; 7 in 1992; 4 in 2000.* **Sources: Bea, Bl4, So5, Wo7.**

Williams Favorite - Southern variety. *Source History: 1 in 2000.* **Sources: Ca15.**

Willie Sharp - Large, olive-green fruit with brown or dull red stripes. Juicy, very tart flesh. Long keeping cooking apple; excellent for pie. Ripens late. New Zealand apple about which little is known. *Source History: 1 in 1988; 1 in 1992; 2 in 2000.* **Sources: Or9, So5.**

Willis Williams - *Source History: 1 in 1992; 1 in 2000.* **Sources: Ch9.**

Willow (Willow Twig) - Large fruit. Smooth, yellowish green skin mottled and flushed with red, streaked with darker red and dotted with russet. Crisp, very firm, moderately tender, coarse, yellowish or greenish flesh. Slightly aromatic, subacid flavor. Ripens late. One of the best late winter keepers. First known in Ohio. First reference in 1848. *Source History: 1 in 1988; 1 in 2000.* **Sources: La3.**

Wilson Juicy - Seedling of Fameuse. Fruit is yellow with pink blush. Very juicy, mildly tart flesh with a distinctive flavor. Good keeper. Ripens midseason. Hardy at -50 degrees F. with occasional winter injury. St. Lawrence Nurseries introduction. *Source History: 1 in 1992; 1 in 2000.* **Sources: Stl.**

Wilson Red June - Southern variety. *Source History: 1 in 1992; 1 in 2000.* **Sources: Ca15.**

Winekist - Unknown parentage. Medium size fruit is wine-red with areas and stripes of darker red and very small white dots. Red flesh is extremely tart and coarse. Great addition to cider or sauce. Tree grows to 15'. Zone 4. Rare. Originated in Winthrop, Maine. *Source History: 2 in 2000.* **Sources: Fed, Or9.**

Winesap (Old Fashion Winesap) - Round, medium size, dark red fruit. Noted for its crisp, very juicy yellow flesh and its blend of sugar with high tartness. Gets its name from its spicy, wine-like flavor and aroma. Top quality, multi-purpose apple. Flavor is too sharp for some, preferred for dessert by others. Makes fine cider. Good for cooking; excellent for sauce. Keeps until May. Heavy producer. Will not pollinate other apples. Adapted to a wide range of soils and climates. Ripens from late September to early November depending on location. Requires 800 hours of chilling. Hardy to Zone 5. Originated in the U.S. around 1817. *Source History: 19 in 1988; 27 in 1992; 23 in 2000.* **Sources: Bay, BO10, Ca15, Ch9, Cid, CO5, Cu4, Ea3, Ed5, GI3, Gr4, Gur, JOY, La3, Leu, MI5, Nrs, ORA, Son, STR, Tex, Ur2, WI4.**

Winesap, Compspur - Flavor with a hint of spice. Yields sooner and up to twice as much as regular Winesap. *Source History: 1 in 1988; 1 in 1992; 1 in 2000.* **Sources: Mi1.**

Winesap, Dermen - Large sport. *Source History: 1 in 1992; 1 in 2000.* **Sources: Ch9.**

Winesap, Gilmores Special - Southern variety. *Source History: 1 in 2000.* **Sources: Ca15.**

Winesap, Improved - *Source History: 1 in 1988; 1 in 1992; 1 in 2000.* **Sources: SIM.**

Winesap, Nured - Select strain of Improved Seeando Winesap. Darker, earlier color with a stripe. Good size. Resistant to russeting. *Source History: 1 in 1988; 1 in 1992; 1 in 2000.* **Sources: Co2.**

Winesap, Paragon - *Source History: 1 in 2000.* **Sources: Cid.**

Winesap, Red (Ruble Strain) - Improved all-red Winesap. Hardy, medium size, cooking apple. Aromatic fragrance and rich, spicy flavor. Makes delicious apple juice and cider. With a little care, will store until spring. Self-pollinating. Resistant to russeting and fire blight. Ripens mid-October to early November depending on location. *Source History: 4 in 1988; 6 in 1992; 3 in 2000.* **Sources: Ad2, Jo3, Nrs, Va2.**

Winesap, Starkspur (Thornton Cultivar) - Trees bear young and regularly. Cannot pollinate other varieties. Ripens mid-October. Hardy in Zones 5-8. Has been around since the early 1800s. Trademarked. *Source History: 1 in 1988; 1 in 1992; 1 in 2000.* **Sources: St4.**

Winesap, Sweet - Clear, pale yellow skin nearly covered with bright, light red and carmine stripes. Firm, fine, crisp, tender, white flesh. Fine, sweet flavor. Excellent quality for eating, baking and cooking. Keeps until May in cold storage and until April in common storage. Ripens late. Hardy to -30 degrees F. Described in 1867. *Source History: 2 in 1988; 2 in 2000.* **Sources: Ca15, Stl.**

Winesap, Tex Red - Large fruit with little russet. Color finishes to dark red over the entire fruit. Prolific. Good keeper. Standard old-time variety. *Source History: 1 in 2000.* **Sources: Va2.**

Winesap, Turley - Open pollinated seedling of Stayman Winesap. Round, dull red fruit. Triploid; requires a pollinator. Resembles Stayman Winesap, but is more crack resistant and eating quality is not as good. Used for cooking, drying, cider or fresh. Stores well. Ripens in early October. Originated in Indiana. *Source History: 2 in 1988; 5 in 1992; 6 in 2000.* **Sources: Bl4, Ch9, La3, Nrs, Or9, So5.**

Winesap, Virginia (Old Virginia Winesap) - Medium size, red fruit. Crisp, firm flesh. Good keeper. Adapted to a wide range of soils and climate. In demand for home and commercial plantings. An old-timer. *Source History: 4 in 1988; 4 in*

1992; 2 in 2000. **Sources: Bea, Or9.**

Winter Banana (Flory, Banana) - Strikingly beautiful, large apple. Pale yellow, waxy finish; one side usually blushed with delicate rosy pink; distinct suture line. Moderately firm, slightly coarse, crisp, tangy, juicy flesh. Distinctive, aromatic flavor similar to bananas. Better for eating than cooking; too mild. Favorite for cider. Keeps until March. Medium size, vigorous tree bears young and annually. Medium-heavy crops. Excellent pollinator. Ripens during October and November. Requires 100-400 hours of chilling. Widely grown in mild winter areas on the West Coast. Zones 4-9. Originated on the Flory farm in Cass County, Indiana in 1876. Introduced in 1890. *Source History: 18 in 1988; 21 in 1992; 27 in 2000.* **Sources: Bay, Bea, Bl4, Bo5, Bu7, Ca15, Ch9, CO5, Cu4, Ga20, Gr4, Hid, Jo3, JOY, La3, Mi1, Nrs, On3, Or9, ORA, Sc6, So5, Son, STR, Ur2, WI4, Wo7.**

Winter Banana, Compact - Fruit is clear yellow with faint red striping. Hardy and bears early. One of the best pollinators for Red Delicious. *Source History: 1 in 1988; 1 in 1992; 1 in 2000.* **Sources: Va2.**

Winter Banana, Compspur - Glossy, smooth skin. Fine grained, juicy flesh. Banana-like aroma. Compact, semi-dwarf trees yield heavily. *Source History: 1 in 1988; 1 in 1992; 1 in 2000.* **Sources: Mi1.**

Winter Banana, Spur - Widely used as a pollinator for Granny Smith and Red Delicious. Spur-type strain of this old variety has been quite variable in its degree of spurring. Annual defruiting of tree will optimize return bloom if used as a pollinator. Spur-type growth makes trees compact with little maintenance required. Begins bearing early. Very large leaves. Fairly winter hardy. Original Housden strain was introduced by C and O Nursery. *Source History: 5 in 1988; 9 in 1992; 6 in 2000.* **Sources: Ad2, Co2, Nrs, TR8, Wh4, WI12.**

Winter Cheese - Southern variety. *Source History: 1 in 2000.* **Sources: Ca15.**

Winter Jewel - Crabapple hangs on the tree all winter while the freezing and thawing turns the flesh into a sweet liquid that tastes like maraschino cherry juice. Zone 3. Seedling grown by Frank Foltz, Princeton, Minnesota, 1985. *Source History: 1 in 2000.* **Sources: Ed5.**

Winter Jon - Southern variety. *Source History: 1 in 2000.* **Sources: Ca15.**

Winter Queen - *Source History: 1 in 2000.* **Sources: Bea.**

Winter Red Flesh - Sasha x Redflesh. Red fleshed fruit. Excellent for red applesauce and jelly. Abundant purple flowers; bronze-red leaves. Ripens mid-October. Hardy to -50 degrees F. *Source History: 2 in 1988; 2 in 1992; 3 in 2000.* **Sources: Bea, Ea3, Or9.**

Winter Stein - *Source History: 1 in 2000.* **Sources: Or9.**

Winter Sweet Paradise (Grandmother, Honey Sweet, Paradise Winter, White Robinson, Wine Sweet) - Popular dessert and cooking apple in central Virginia late in the 19th century. Green skin with a brown-red blush. Sweet, subacid flavor. Some resistance to diseases. Ripens in September. First recorded in 1842. *Source History: 1 in 1988; 2 in 1992; 2 in 2000.* **Sources: Bl4, Ca15.**

Winter Terry - Small, red, firm fruit. Fine flavor. Vigorous tree bears heavy crops annually. One of the best for late winter keeping. *Source History: 2 in 1992; 2 in 2000.* **Sources: La3, Or9.**

Winter's Joy - *Source History: 1 in 1992; 1 in 2000.* **Sources: Ch9.**

Winterstein - Gravenstein seedling with less tart flavor and later maturity. Attractive, pink-red fruit with crisp, subacid, flavorful flesh. Zones 6-10. Luther Burbank selection. Introduced in 1901. *Source History: 1 in 1992; 1 in 2000.*

Sources: Son.

Winthrop Greening - Late summer-fall apple that was popular throughout central Maine as late as 1920; now all but unknown. Flat-oblate fruit measures 3.25" across. Light green skin is washed with red-orange and small greenish dots and ribs of russeting, usually with a patch of russet radiating from the stem. Interesting sweet flavor. Crunchy flesh with medium-low acidity. Shy bearer. Hardy to Zone 4. Originated on the Ichabod Howe Farm, Winthrop, Maine before 1800. *Source History: 1 in 1992; 4 in 2000.* **Sources: Ch9, Fed, Or9, Wo7.**

Wismer's Dessert (Wismer) - Beautiful Spitzenburg-red with yellow flesh. Aromatic flavor. Canadian winter apple that originated in Ontario around the turn of the century. Introduced in 1897. *Source History: 2 in 1988; 5 in 1992; 3 in 2000.* **Sources: Bea, Ch9, So5.**

Wodarz - Unknown parentage. Green apple is not very nice looking but is very sweet and stores well. Somewhat tolerant to fire blight. Ripens late. Stores three months. Hardy to -50 degrees F. Zone 3. Joint release of North Dakota and the R. L. Wodarz family. *Source History: 2 in 2000.* **Sources: Ed5, Stl.**

Wolf River - Enormous fruits, often 1 lb. or more. Pale yellow skin almost covered with pale dull red. Soft, tender, slightly mealy, creamy white flesh. Subacid flavor. Primarily used for baking and pies, but in full sun on sandy soil it becomes a fine dessert apple with distinctive flavor. Excellent for drying. Long-lived, very hardy, productive tree. Strong, spreading, sturdy limb growth. Resistant to scab, mildew, fire blight and cedar-apple rust. Ripens from mid-September to early October. Hardy to -50 degrees F. Open-pollinated seedling of Alexander found growing on the banks of the Wolf River near Fremont, Wisconsin in 1875. `Source History: 19 in 1988; 29 in 1992; 31 in 2000.* **Sources: Bar, Bea, Bl4, Ca15, Ch9, Cla, Cu4, Ea3, Ed5, Fed, Gr4, Gur, Hi9, Jun, La3, Mc3, Mi1, Or9, Sc6, SH8, So5, Son, Stl, Und, Ur2, Wa16, Wh4, Wl12, WI4, Wo7, Wor.**

World's Wonder - Southern variety. *Source History: 1 in 2000.* **Sources: Ca15.**

Wright - Introduced in Vermont around 1875. *Source History: 2 in 1992; 2 in 2000.* **Sources: Ch9, Wo7.**

Wrixparent - *Source History: 1 in 1992; 1 in 2000.* **Sources: Ch9.**

Wynooche Early - Thin skinned, red fruit. Great for fresh eating; skin almost disappears when cooked. Will keep until Christmas when refrigerated. Scab resistant. Ripens in early August. Good choice for coastal areas. *Source History: 2 in 1992; 2 in 2000.* **Sources: Ch9, On3.**

Yankee Sweet - Southern variety. *Source History: 1 in 2000.* **Sources: Ca15.**

Yarlington Mill (Yearlington Mill) - English cider apple. Firm, medium size fruit. Sweet to slightly bittersweet juice. Consistent bearer. Ripens in late October. Harvesting period of over three weeks. Zones 6-9. Used with Kingston Black in European countries to make a famous hard cider. *Source History: 4 in 1988; 6 in 1992; 10 in 2000.* **Sources: Bea, Ch9, Cid, Cla, Gr4, La3, Mo19, Nrs, Or9, Son.**

Yates (Jates) - Small fruit with dotted, bright red skin. Firm, juicy, aromatic, red-tinged flesh. Excellent, spicy flavor. Vigorous, heavy bearer. Excellent pollinator. Ripens late and keeps well into the winter. Hardy in Zones 6-9. Originated with Matthew Yates of Fayette County, Georgia about 1844 and was called Red Warrior by many Southerners. *Source History: 8 in 1988; 18 in 1992; 11 in 2000.* **Sources: Bea, Ca15, Cla, GI3, Gr4, Iso, Jo3, La3, Or9, SIM, Ur2.**

Yeager's Sweet - *Source History: 1 in 1988; 1 in 1992; 1 in 2000.* **Sources:**

Bea.

Yellow Bellflower (Lady Washington, Lincoln Pippin, White Bellflower, Warren Pippin, White Detroit) - Fruit size varies; usually large. Easy to identify; elongated, often lopsided shape and bumps around calyx basin. Lemon-yellow with conspicuous white or russet dots; often blushed with pink. Crisp, firm, medium fine grained, medium tender, cream colored flesh. Sweet, slightly subacid flavor. Good for fresh eating, pies and sauce. Fine winter dessert apple, often picked on the tart side and mellowed for several months in storage. Medium to large, healthy, vigorous, spreading tree. Requires cross-pollination. Susceptible to apple scab. Ripens during October. 400 hours of chilling. Hardy to Zone 5. Originated in Burlington County, New Jersey around 1742. *Source History: 11 in 1988; 9 in 1992; 16 in 2000.* **Sources: Bay, Bea, Bl4, Ca15, Ch9, Cid, Cu4, Gr4, Or9, Rai, So5, Son, Wh4, WI4, Wo7, Wor.**

Yellow Cullasaga - *Source History: 1 in 2000.* **Sources: Or9.**

Yellow Delicious - Large, tapered, conical fruit with golden yellow skin, sometimes blushed with rose. Crisp, aromatic, white flesh. Unusually fine, sweet flavor. Best known as an eating apple but also excellent for pies, sauce and preserves. Good keeper. Good for home use and fresh market sales. Very vigorous tree bears quite young and heavily. Ornamental blossom. Self-fruitful but yields are improved when pollinated by Jonathan, Lodi, Melrose or Red Delicious. Excellent pollinator for other apples. Good disease resistance. Ripens from mid-September to mid-October depending on location. Hardy in Zones 5-8. *Source History: 31 in 1988; 51 in 1992; 35 in 2000.* **Sources: Bar, BR10, Bu1, CO5, Cum, FO10, Fo4, GI3, GR26, Gur, Ho5, Iso, JOY, Lee, Leu, Mc3, ME3, MI10, MI5, Na4, Nrs, ORA, Pi2, Po2, Rid, Sav, Sc6, SH8, STR, Tex, TU5, WA8, Wel, Wor, ZEL.**

Yellow Delicious, Eddie April - Large fruited Yellow Delicious spur-type with excellent keeping qualities. Firmer flesh than Yellow Delicious with a strawberry essence. Self-fertile. Zones 4-8. *Source History: 1 in 1988; 1 in 1992; 1 in 2000.* **Sources: Ed2.**

Yellow Delicious, Empress Spur Gold - Large yellow fruit with excellent flavor. Tree requires minimal training. Ripens late September. *Source History: 1 in 2000.* **Sources: Sc6.**

Yellow Flat - Southern variety. *Source History: 1 in 2000.* **Sources: Ca15.**

Yellow Garden - Southern variety. *Source History: 1 in 2000.* **Sources: Ca15.**

Yellow Gold Delicious - Bright, golden yellow fruit. Firm, crisp, very juicy flesh. Excellent quality. Excellent keeper. Bears young and heavily. *Source History: 1 in 1988; 1 in 1992; 1 in 2000.* **Sources: Mi1.**

Yellow Gold Delicious Compspur - Fruit is larger than fist-size. Tender skin without a trace of bitterness. Good for fresh eating, sauces, pies and apple butter. Exceptionally good in storage. Introduced in 1979. *Source History: 1 in 1988; 1 in 1992; 1 in 2000.* **Sources: Mi1.**

Yellow Harvest - Southern variety. *Source History: 1 in 2000.* **Sources: Ca15.**

Yellow Horse (Horse) - Popular in the South up until about 1930. Medium to large fruit with pale yellow skin with brown specks. Tender yellow flesh. Great for fresh eating or for pressing into cider. Was the leading variety for drying as it ripened in the heat of the summer. Hardy in Zones 5-8. Possibly originated in North Carolina about 1800. *Source History: 4 in 1988; 7 in 1992; 3 in 2000.* **Sources: Ca15, Gr4, SIM.**

Yellow June - Medium to large size fruit. Good for pies, sauce and fresh eating.

Ripens from mid to late June in lower Zone 7. *Source History: 1 in 1992; 3 in 2000.* **Sources: Bea, Hid, La3.**

Yellow Mammoth - Southern variety. *Source History: 1 in 2000.* **Sources: Ca15.**

Yellow Newtown - Known since the early 1700s. *Source History: 3 in 1992; 2 in 2000.* **Sources: Nrs, Wo7.**

Yellow Pippin - Large fruit with crisp, firm flesh. Very tart flavor. Excellent for cooking, eating and cider. Self-fertile. Ripens in October. Needs about 700 chilling hours. Productive in most locations except Southern California coastal areas. *Source History: 2 in 1988; 2 in 1992; 1 in 2000.* **Sources: ORA.**

Yellow Sheepnose - Southern variety. *Source History: 2 in 1992; 5 in 2000.* **Sources: Bea, Bl4, Ca15, Ch9, La3.**

Yellow Sweet - *Source History: 1 in 2000.* **Sources: Ed5.**

Yellow Transparent (White Transparent, Grand Sultan) - Medium to large fruit with transparent pale yellow skin. Crisp, very sweet, juicy, white flesh is very light in texture and can be readily solar-dried. When fully ripe it has good, but not high, flavor. Excellent for cooking; some say it makes the best sauce. Wonderful for pies; also good for eating fresh. Where summers are hot, commonly picked while on the green side and used in the kitchen. Tree is an upright, vigorous grower; bears very young. Scab resistant. Tends to bear heavily. Fruit size will be improved by early thinning. Ripens from early July to early August. Hardy to Zone 2-3. In the 1870s, settlers in Minnesota, Michigan and the Dakotas needed cold hardy apple trees so the USDA imported hundreds of Russian apple varieties. Among them was Yellow Transparent, which was chosen not for its winter hardiness but because of its earliness and good quality. *Source History: 27 in 1988; 41 in 1992; 36 in 2000.* **Sources: Ad2, Bea, Bl4, Bo5, Ca15, Ch9, CLI, Cu4, Fed, FO10, Fo4, GI3, Gr4, Gur, JOY, La3, LA4, Leu, Mel, Mi1, Nrs, Or9, Pi2, Sc6, SH8, So5, Son, Stl, TU5, Ur2, Wa16, WA8, Wh4, WI4, Wo7, Wor.**

Yoko - Golden Delicious open-pollinated variety. Yellow skin color with pink blush. Sweet, low acid flesh. Excellent storage. Ripens just after Mutsu. *Source History: 2 in 1992; 4 in 2000.* **Sources: Cla, Cu4, Nrs, Ro3.**

York - Southern variety. *Source History: 1 in 1988; 2 in 1992; 5 in 2000.* **Sources: Ca15, Ch9, Cum, Nrs, WI4.**

York Imperial (York, Johnson's Fine Winter) - Medium to large, rectangular, intermediate to flat fruit. Bright green or yellow skin with light red or pinkish red flush. Firm, crisp, tender, juicy, yellowish flesh. Aromatic, subacid flavor. Excellent for baking, making cider and for drying. One of the best old-time winter keeping apples. Hold until Christmas for best flavor. Ripens in late October. Hardy in Zones 4-7. Favorite in the East. Found about 1830 near York, Pennsylvania. Downing described it as the Imperial of Keepers, hence its name. *Source History: 6 in 1988; 11 in 1992; 12 in 2000.* **Sources: Bea, Bl4, Bo5, Cu4, Ed5, Gr4, La3, Mi1, Or9, Sc6, Ur2, Wo7.**

York Imperial, Red York - Finest of all red York Imperial sports. Solid bright red fruit, otherwise it is the same in every respect as the old original York Imperial that originated in York County, Pennsylvania. Given preference by processors. *Source History: 3 in 1988; 2 in 1992; 2 in 2000.* **Sources: So5, Wor.**

York Imperial, Red Yorking - Sport of regular York Imperial. Colors earlier and produces higher color than its parent. Excellent quality; uniform size. Top rate processing apple. In demand on the fresh fruit market. U.S. Plant Patent No. 125. *Source History: 2 in 1988; 2 in 1992; 2 in 2000.* **Sources: Ad2, Bo5, Nrs, Wh4.**

<u>York, Commander</u> (Ramey Cultivar) - Very intense, deep, rich, solid red fruit. Reaches full color ahead of any other Red York strain. Sharpest York available for fresh market. Has all of the excellent processing qualities needed for the processing market. Trademarked. *Source History: 1 in 1988; 1 in 1992; 1 in 2000.* **Sources: Hi9.**

<u>York, Ramey</u> - Highly colored sport of York. Excellent for processing and fresh market. Vigorous tree is susceptible to fire blight. Discovered by Turner Ramey of Charles Town, West Virginia. *Source History: 2 in 2000.* **Sources: Ad2, Co2.**

<u>York, Spur</u> - Sport of York. Large red fruit colors early. Compact, spur-type tree. Ripens in early October. Trademarked. *Source History: 1 in 2000.* **Sources: Va2.**

<u>Young America Crab</u> - Large fruit of good quality. Makes fine jelly. Vigorous, hardy tree. Heavy yields. Ripens mid-September. *Source History: 1 in 1992; 1 in 2000.* **Sources: Ed5.**

<u>Zabergau Reinette</u> - Huge, gold-brown russet fruit. Crisp, white flesh. Flavor is sometimes described as rich and nutty. Ripens late winter. Hardy in Zones 5-6. Originated in Wurtenburg, Germany, 1885. *Source History: 2 in 1988; 6 in 1992; 8 in 2000.* **Sources: Bl4, Ch9, Cla, Fed, Or9, Sc6, So5, Wh4.**

<u>Zesta</u> (MN 1824 Cultivar) - State Fair x MN 1691 (Connell Red x Goodland). Skin color shows 60-85% red on yellow background. Good sweet-tart flavor. Dessert apple. Above average storage life. One or two pickings. Spreading, somewhat spur-type tree shows moderate vigor. Zone 4. University of Minnesota release, 1997. Trademarked. *Source History: 7 in 2000.* **Sources: COL, Cu4, Ed5, Fed, Hi9, St4, WI12.**

<u>Zoar</u> - Medium size fruit. Red skin. Ripens in September. Found in the village of Zoar, Ohio in the early 1900s. *Source History: 1 in 2000.* **Sources: Sc6.**

Apple / Flowering

Malus spp.

<u>Adams</u> - Round, dense tree. Carmine buds open to large, clear pink blossoms. Medium-small red fruit persists into winter. Disease resistant. Zone 4. *Source History: 13 in 2000.* **Sources: Arb, BA14, Big, Bo5, Hi9, KAN, KI3, Mc3, MI5, Nrs, SH8, We8, Wor.**

<u>Adirondack</u> - Columnar to oval tree. Carmine buds open to large white blossoms. Medium-small red fruit persists into winter. Disease resistant. Zone 4. *Source History: 4 in 2000.* **Sources: Arb, FE7, KI3, Mc3.**

<u>Aldenhamensis</u> - *Source History: 1 in 2000.* **Sources: Nrs.**

<u>Almey</u> - Fiery crimson blossoms in spring followed by small scarlet fruits that remain on the tree into winter. Grows 12-15' tall. Very hardy. *Source History: 7 in 2000.* **Sources: Bay, CO5, Nrs, Sc2, So5, Wel, WI4.**

<u>American Masterpiece</u> - Showy dark maroon foliage. Brilliant red flowers followed by persistent orange fruit. Disease resistant. Hardy to Zone 4. *Source History: 3 in 2000.* **Sources: Arb, BA14, SH8.**

<u>American Spirit</u> - Deep rose-colored blossoms. Bright red persistent fruit. Hardy, compact tree with rounded shape. Height and spread from 15-18'. Disease resistant. Trademarked. *Source History: 1 in 2000.* **Sources: Hi9.**

<u>Anne E. Weeping Crab</u> - Weeping habit. White flowers. Persistent red fruit. Resistant to scab and fire blight. Zones 4-8. *Source History: 1 in 2000.* **Sources:**

KI3.

Atrosanguinea - *Source History: 1 in 2000.* **Sources: Nrs.**

Baccata columnaris - White flowers. Fruit is yellow with red cheek. Narrow tree grows to 15'. Hardy to Zone 2. *Source History: 2 in 2000.* **Sources: Big, LA4, Wa16.**

Barbara Ann - Dark pink, somewhat double flowers. Insignificant fruit. Purple foliage changes to green. Developed at the New York State Testing Station. *Source History: 1 in 1992; 1 in 2000.* **Sources: Son.**

Baskatong - Single, light purple-red flowers followed by 1" purple-red fruit. Purple foliage turns bronze-green. Tree grows to 30' with a spreading habit. Disease resistant. Zones 3-8. *Source History: 2 in 2000.* **Sources: KI3, Nrs.**

Beverly - Round, compact tree. Long lasting, red fruits. Slight susceptibility to fire blight. Zone 3-8. *Source History: 5 in 2000.* **Sources: Fo2, KAN, KI3, Mc3, Nrs.**

Birdland - Fragrant white flowers. Yellow-orange fruit. Attractive to birds. *Source History: 1 in 2000.* **Sources: Arb.**

Blanche Ames - White flowers. Small yellow fruit. Named after the wife of Oakes Ames, Harvard Botany Professor. Introduced through the Arnold Arboretum. *Source History: 1 in 2000.* **Sources: Arb.**

Bob White - White flowers. Yellow, persistent fruit. Height to 20'. Slightly susceptible to fire blight and mildew. Zone 4. *Source History: 3 in 2000.* **Sources: KAN, KI3, Mo19.**

Brandywine - Vase-shaped tree with double, pink, fragrant flowers and purple tinted leaves which turns into deep purple fall color. Green, 1.25" fruit. Shows some susceptibility to cedar-apple rust. Zone 4. Trademarked. *Source History: 12 in 2000.* **Sources: Arb, Big, Bo5, CO5, Fed, GR26, KAN, LI7, Mc3, MI5, SH8, Wa16.**

Brandywine, Scarlet - Improved Brandywine with brighter, more ruffled flowers. Smaller fruit resembles miniature orange pumpkins. Height and spread of 15-20'. Trademarked. *Source History: 1 in 2000.* **Sources: Hi9.**

Calloway - White flowers. Excellent disease resistance. Grows to 25'. One of the best for Southern areas. Zone 4. *Source History: 5 in 2000.* **Sources: Arb, Big, GI3, Ho5, MI5.**

Camelot - Beautiful dwarf tree to 10' tall. Leathery, dark green foliage is overcast with burgundy. Vibrant fuchsia-pink on white blooms. Burgundy fruit in the fall last into the winter. Hardy to Zone 4. Trademarked. *Source History: 5 in 2000.* **Sources: Arb, Gir, GR26, Jun, SH8.**

Candied Apple (Weeping Candied Crabapple) - Red to purple-pink blossoms. Bright red, .5" fruit. Weeping tree grows 10-15'. Moderate disease resistance; slightly scab susceptible. Zone 4. U.S. Plant Patent No. 4038. *Source History: 4 in 2000.* **Sources: Bo5, IM2, KI3, Wa16.**

Candymint - *M. sargentii.* Shrub grows 8-10' high. Deep carmine buds open to pink blooms outlined in red. Purple-green foliage followed by deep purple fruit in the fall. Zone 4. *Source History: 4 in 2000.* **Sources: Arb, Bo5, Fo2, SH8.**

Canterbury - Genetic dwarf tree grows to 10'. Light pink flowers followed by dark green, leathery foliage. Small burgundy colored fruit. Zone 4. Trademarked. *Source History: 1 in 2000.* **Sources: FE7.**

Cardinal - Broad, spreading tree to 15'. Glossy, dark purple leaves. Rose-pink flowers. Dark red, .5" fruit. Hardy to Zone 5. *Source History: 3 in 2000.*

Sources: BO10, Fo2, SH8.

Carmine - Shrub-like tree with a mounded, dense growth habit. Small dark red fruit. Scab resistant. Zones 3-8. *Source History: 2 in 2000.* **Sources: KI3, Nrs.**

Centurion - Vigorous, columnar tree with rose-red blossoms. Reddish leaves turn bronze-green in summer. Cherry-red fruits are attractive for two months. Disease resistant. Height to 20'. Zones 2-9. Trademarked. *Source History: 15 in 2000.* **Sources: Big, Bo5, Fo2, Gr16, GR26, Hi9, IM2, KAN, KI3, LI7, MI5, SH8, Wa16, We8, Wor.**

Cinderella - One of the most dwarf of all crabs. White blossoms. Small gold fruit in late fall and winter. Disease resistant. Height of 8'. Zone 4. *Source History: 3 in 2000.* **Sources: FE7, Gir, Hi9.**

Columbia Crab - *Source History: 1 in 2000.* **Sources: Nrs.**

Coralburst - Deep coral buds open to double rose-pink flowers. Bronze fruit in late summer. Compact dense tree with rounded form. Height to 15'. Shows excellent fire blight resistance. Zone 3. U.S. Plant Patent No. 2983. *Source History: 8 in 2000.* **Sources: BA14, FE7, IM2, KI3, LI7, MO10, SH8, We8.**

Crimson Gold - *Source History: 1 in 2000.* **Sources: WAF.**

David - Small, compact, rounded tree reaches 12'. Light pink buds followed by pink-white flowers. Cherry-red, .5" fruit hangs well on the tree. Disease resistant foliage. Zones 4-9. *Source History: 12 in 2000.* **Sources: Arb, Bo5, Fo2, Gr16,GR26, IM2, KAN, KI3, LI7, Nrs, SH8, Wor.**

Donald Wyman - Tree shape is upright when young and rounded when mature. White flowers. Small persistent red fruit. Height to 20'. Shows excellent disease resistance. Zone 4. *Source History: 15 in 2000.* **Sources: Arb, BA14, Big, BO10, Bo5, CO5, FE7, Fo2, KAN, KI3, Mc3, MI5, Nrs, SH8, Wh2.**

Dorthea - Small tree bears semi-double pink flowers annually. *Source History: 1 in 2000.* **Sources: Arb.**

Doubloons - Rounded, upright tree to 20'. Double white flowers followed by long lasting yellow fruits. Disease resistant. Hardy to Zone 5. *Source History: 3 in 2000.* **Sources: Arb, Fo2, KI3.**

Du Pont - Pink flowers. Insignificant fruit. Used as a pollinator. Developed at the New York State Fruit Testing Station. *Source History: 1 in 2000.* **Sources: Son.**

Echtermeyer - Weeping crab with purple-red flowers fading to pink. Bronze-green foliage. Small purple-red fruit in the fall. Zone 4. *Source History: 5 in 2000.* **Sources: Bay, CO5, ME3, Nrs, WI4.**

Eleyi - Purple-red flowers. *Source History: 5 in 2000.* **Sources: GI3, Ho5, Nrs, SIM, STR.**

Evelyn - Red flowering crab. *Source History: 2 in 2000.* **Sources: MI10, Nrs.**

Fimbriata - *Malus ioensis.* Double pink, 2" fragrant flowers. *Source History: 1 in 2000.* **Sources: Arb.**

Flame - Single pink buds open to white flowers. Bright red fruit. Zone 4. *Source History: 3 in 2000.* **Sources: MI10, Nrs, TR19.**

Foxfire - White blooms. Bright red fruit. Dark green foliage. Disease tolerant. Grows to 15' tall. Zone 4. Trademarked. *Source History: 1 in 2000.* **Sources: FE7.**

Freemanii - Wide spreading tree with purple-bronze foliage. Pink flowers. Originally from the National Arboretum. *Source History: 1 in 2000.* **Sources: Arb.**

Frettingham - White blossoms. Upright tree is easily managed. Blooms late. *Source History: 4 in 2000.* **Sources: COL, Hi9, TR8, WAF.**

Garry - Red flowers. *Source History: 1 in 2000.* **Sources: Va5.**

Gibbs Golden Cage - Old cultivar. Small rounded tree with white flowers and 1" golden fruit which persist until February-March. Zone 4. *Source History: 1 in 2000.* **Sources: Arb.**

Golden Hornet - Single white flowers. Yellow fruit. Good bee activity. Fire blight resistant. Grows to 25'. Zone 4. *Source History: 5 in 2000.* **Sources: Big, Cu4, Hi9, MI5, Nrs.**

Golden Raindrops - Upright form with horizontal branches. Deeply cut, fine textured foliage. White blooms. Small golden yellow fruit. Disease resistant. Hardy to Zone 4. Trademarked. *Source History: 6 in 2000.* **Sources: Arb, BA14, FE7, Fo2, Mc3, SH8.**

Gorgeous - Single white flowers. Orange-red fruit. Nice dense round shape. Zone 4. Introduced by Hayward Wright, Auckland, New Zealand. *Source History: 1 in 2000.* **Sources: Arb.**

Guinevere - Mauve to white blossoms. Persistent red fruit. Compact growing, rounded tree grows 8-10' tall. Dark green foliage has a distinctive deep wine overcast. Zone 4. U.S. Plant Patent No. 7773. *Source History: 7 in 2000.* **Sources: Arb, FE7, GR26, Hi9, Jun, LI7, SH8.**

Gwendolyn - Large single pink blooms followed by heavy 1" red fruit. Zone 4. Introduced by Aire den Boer; named after Gwendolyn Tobin, Des Moines, Iowa. *Source History: 1 in 2000.* **Sources: Arb.**

Harvest Gold - Upright tree to 20'. Showy golden yellow fruit persists on the tree into December. Hardy to Zone 4. Trademarked. *Source History: 6 in 2000.* **Sources: Bo5, FE7, Fo2, GR26, IM2, SH8.**

Henning - White flowers. Orange-red fruit. Upright to spreading tree form. Disease free. *Source History: 1 in 2000.* **Sources: Arb.**

Honan - *Malus honanensis.* Clusters of white flowers. Tiny yellow fruit with rosy blush. Scarlet-red fall foliage. Shrub grows to 20'. Hardy to Zone 5. *Source History: 1 in 2000.* **Sources: LA4.**

Indian Magic - Single red-pink flowers. Small red-orange fruit hangs well into winter. Bronze-green foliage. Enjoyed by birds. Height to 18'. Excellent disease resistance. Zones 3-9. *Source History: 19 in 2000.* **Sources: Big, CR6, Fo2, GI3, Gr16, GR26, Ho5, KI3, LI7, Mc3, ME3, MI5, MO10, Mo19, Nrs, SH8, TR19, We8, ZEL.**

Indian Summer - Round-shaped tree is moderately vigorous and rangy. Height to 18'. Bronze-green foliage. Rose-red flowers. Bright red persistent fruit. Shows excellent disease resistance. Zone 4. *Source History: 18 in 2000.* **Sources: Arb, Bo5, Co2, COL, Cu4, FE7, Fo2, Gr16, GR26, KAN, KI3, Mc3, Nrs, Ro3, SH8, Si3, Wa16, Wor.**

Jacki - White flowers bloom in early spirng. Maroon-red fruit. Upright rounded habit. Slightly susceptible to fire blight. Grows 20-40'. Zones 3-8. *Source History: 1 in 2000.* **Sources: KI3.**

Japanese (Japanese Flowering) - *Malus floribunda.* Considered one of the best crabapples. Tree grows to 20' tall. Broadly rounded irregular habit with dense branching. Deep pink flower buds fade to white. Yellow and red fruit. Good disease resistance. Dependable. Zone 4. *Source History: 5 in 2000.* **Sources: Co24, Fo2, KI3, MI5, Mu2, TR19.**

Jay Darling - *Source History: 1 in 2000.* **Sources: Nrs.**

Jewelberry - Dwarf, round, dense tree matures under 10'. White flowers with pink edges. Bright red, .5" fruit. Disease resistant. Zone 4. *Source History: 8 in 2000.* **Sources: Arb, FE7, Fo2, Mc3, MI5, Mo19, Nrs, SH8.**

Katherine - Large, pink-white, semi-double flowers. *Source History: 1 in 2000.* **Sources: So5.**

Kelsey - Rose-red, semi-double flowers. Rosybloom selection. Hardy to Zone 2. *Source History: 5 in 2000.* **Sources: Arb, GR26, Nrs, SH8, Va5.**

Kibele - Tree grows 8' tall. Red blossoms. *Source History: 2 in 2000.* **Sources: Bo5, Wor.**

Kirk - Profuse white flowers. Red fruit. Tree grows to 15'. Rounded habit. *Source History: 1 in 2000.* **Sources: Arb.**

Klehm's Bechtel (Bechtel) - Large fragrant double pink blooms. Flowers late. Small rounded tree to 20'. Seldom fruits. Zone 4. *Source History: 12 in 2000.* **Sources: Bay, Big, CO5, Fo2, GR26, KAN, ME3, MI5, Nrs, SH8, STR, WI4.**

Klehm's Bechtel Improved - Improved strain of Bechtel Crab with larger leaves and less susceptibility to cedar-apple rust. Large clusters of bell-shaped flowers are double and deep pink. Blooms late. *Source History: 2 in 2000.* **Sources: Arb, Mc3.**

Kola Crab - Elk River x Duchess. Large green fruit. Mainly used as an ornamental. Pink, fragrant blossoms. Hardy to -50 degrees F. *Source History: 1 in 1992; 1 in 2000.* **Sources: Stl.**

Lancelot - Small, oval, upright tree to 10'. Red buds followed by snowy white blooms. Crisp green foliage turns to gold in the fall. Unusual golden fruit persists well into the winter. Hardy to Zone 4. Trademarked. *Source History: 6 in 2000.* **Sources: BA14, FE7, Gir, GR26, Jun, SH8.**

Leprechaun - White flowers. Brilliant red fruit. Mature tree grows under 10' tall. *Source History: 1 in 2000.* **Sources: Arb.**

Leucocarpa - *Malus x robusta.* Pink flowers followed by .6" canary-yellow fruit. Dark green, disease-free foliage. Zone 4. *Source History: 1 in 2000.* **Sources: Arb.**

Liset - Bright rose-red flowers. Tree grows 15-20' tall. Hardy to Zone 4. *Source History: 3 in 2000.* **Sources: Bo5, SH8, STR.**

Lollipop - Produces an abundance of scented white flowers and tiny amber colored fruit. Tight compact head of dense foliage resembles a ball or lollipop. Height and spread of 6'. Trademarked. *Source History: 1 in 2000.* **Sources: Hi9.**

Louisa - Single, pink, weeping flowers. Yellow fruit. Tree has narrow form. Good disease resistance. Hardy to Zone 4. *Source History: 5 in 2000.* **Sources: BA14, Fo2, Gr16, Mc3, SH8.**

Lullaby - Single white flowers and .25" yellow fruit. Totally disease free. Zone 4. *Source History: 1 in 2000.* **Sources: Arb.**

Madonna - Large double white blossoms in early spring. Pleasant gardenia fragrance. Compact, upright tree to 18'. Disease resistant foliage. Hardy to Zone 4. U.S. Plant Patent No. 6672. *Source History: 9 in 2000.* **Sources: Arb, BA14, Big, Bo5, Fo2, GR26, Hi9, SH8, Wa16.**

Magenta - *Source History: 1 in 2000.* **Sources: Co15.**

Makamik - Large purple-red flowers and .75" red fruit. Rosybloom selection named after Lake Makamik in western Quebec, Canada. *Source History: 1 in*

2000. **Sources: Arb.**

<u>Malus baccata var. Jackii</u> - *Source History: 1 in 2000.* **Sources: Mo19.**

<u>Malus florentina</u> - Also classified as *Malosorbus*. White flowers. Red autumn tints. *Source History: 1 in 2000.* **Sources: Arb.**

<u>Malus floribunda</u> - Red buds open pink and fade to white. Seldom fruits. Semi-weeping habit. Disease resistant. Hardy to Zone 4. *Source History: 16 in 2000.* **Sources: Arb, Bay, BO10, Bo5, CO5, FE7, IM2, KAN, ME3, Nrs, Sh14, SH8, SIM, We8, WI4, Wor.**

<u>Malus honanensis</u> - Attractive, little known species related to *M. kansuensis*. Flowers at a young age. Deeply lobed foliage colors brilliant red in the fall. Zone 5. *Source History: 1 in 2000.* **Sources: Arb.**

<u>Malus hupehensis</u> - Profuse fragrant white flowers. Yellow fruit. Unique picturesque branching. *Source History: 1 in 2000.* **Sources: Arb.**

<u>Malus kansuensis</u> - Handsome small tree or large shrub to 15'. Three-lobed leaves. White spring flowers. Small red and yellow fruit. Zone 5. Originated in China. *Source History: 1 in 2000.* **Sources: Fo2.**

<u>Malus prattii</u> - Large tree. Large leaves with orange and purple fall color. *Source History: 1 in 2000.* **Sources: Co24.**

<u>Manchurian Flowering Crab</u> - White flowers boom early to midseason. Small fruit. Upright tree is vigorous. Good pollinator with long bloom period. Heavy bee activity. Mildew susceptible. Zone 4. *Source History: 15 in 2000.* **Sources: Ad2, Bea, BR10, Co2, COL, Hi9, LA4, Nrs, Sh14, Si3, St4, TR8, Va2, WAF, WI12.**

<u>Maria</u> - Small semi-weeping tree with large bright red flowers. Dark maroon fruit. *Source History: 1 in 2000.* **Sources: Arb.**

<u>Mary Potter</u> - Tree grows 10-15' tall. Dark green foliage. Pink buds open to 1" single white flowers. Bears persistent red fruit much enjoyed by birds. One of the showiest crabs. Zones 4-8. *Source History: 5 in 2000.* **Sources: Big, KI3, Mc3, Mo19, Nrs.**

<u>Maypole Flowering Crab, Stark</u> - Deep pink blossoms cover the tree in April. Crimson-red fruit ripens in September. Excellent for apple jelly. Deep burgundy fall foliage. Used as a pollinator for other Stark Colonnade apple trees. Zone 5. U.S. Plant Patent No. 6184. *Source History: 2 in 2000.* **Sources: MO10, St4.**

<u>Midwest</u> - White flowers. Zones 3-8. *Source History: 2 in 2000.* **Sources: Co15, KEE.**

<u>Molten Lava</u> - Crabapple with a weeping form. Red buds; white flowers. Red-orange fruits flow like lava from the pendulous branches. Height to 15'. Attractive to birds. Zones 4-9. Trademarked. *Source History: 10 in 2000.* **Sources: Arb, Bo5, FE7, Fo2, Gir, Gr16, Hi9, KI3, SH8, Wa16.**

<u>Narragansett</u> - Compact, rounded tree. Dark green, leathery foliage. White flowers with pink tinge. Cherry-red, .5" fruit. Disease resistant. Very hardy; Zone 4. U.S. National Arboretum introduction. *Source History: 5 in 2000.* **Sources: Arb, CR6, Gr16, Mc3, We8.**

<u>Oregon Crabapple</u> - *Malus fusca*. Pink-white flowers followed by tiny golden fruit. Red and orange fall color. Wet soil native. Zone 6. *Source History: 1 in 2000.* **Sources: Co24.**

<u>Oriental</u> - *Malus robusta*. *Source History: 1 in 2000.* **Sources: No2.**

<u>Ormiston Roy</u> (Ormison Roy) - White blooms. Yellow fruit blushed with or-

ange. Broadly rounded, spreading habit. Grows to 20'. Slightly susceptible to fire blight. Zone 4. *Source History: 2 in 2000.* **Sources: Arb, KI3.**

Pacific Crab (Swamp Crab Apple) - *Malus fusca.* Does well as a rootstock for apples on sites otherwise too wet. Bears tiny tart fruits for jelly or for the birds. Able to grow in very wet sites. Thorny spur branches. Hardy in Zones 5-8. *Source History: 2 in 2000.* **Sources: Bu7, Fo2.**

Pear Leaf - White flowers. Compact, upright tree. Good bee activity. *Source History: 1 in 2000.* **Sources: Hi9.**

Pink Cascade - *Source History: 1 in 2000.* **Sources: Va5.**

Pink Giant - Large, 2" single pink to lavender flowers. Good disease resistance. *Source History: 1 in 2000.* **Sources: Arb.**

Pink Perfection - Red buds open to double pink flowers. Insignificant fruit. *Source History: 2 in 2000.* **Sources: CO5, Nrs.**

Pink Princess - Naturally dwarf tree to 8-12'. Rose-pink flowers in spring. Purple-bronze foliage. Highly disease resistant. Zone 5. Trademarked. *Source History: 4 in 2000.* **Sources: Arb, FE7, Fo2, KI3.**

Pink Profusion - *Source History: 1 in 2000.* **Sources: Bo5.**

Pink Spires - Upright growth habit. Rose-pink flowers. Small, purple-red fruit. Copper-colored fall foliage. Slow grower. Zones 4-9. *Source History: 11 in 2000.* **Sources: BA14, CR6, Fi1, KAN, LA4, Mc3, Nrs, SH8, Va5, Wa16, We8.**

Pink Star - *Source History: 1 in 2000.* **Sources: Big.**

Pink Weeper - Tree has a weeping habit. Grows to 15'. Pink flowers. Medium size red fruit persists well into winter. Susceptible to scab. Zones 4-8. *Source History: 1 in 2000.* **Sources: KI3.**

Pioneer Scarlet - *Source History: 1 in 2000.* **Sources: Nrs.**

Prairiefire - Upright, spreading tree with maroon leaves. Single, bright pink-red flowers and dark red fruit. Shows excellent disease resistance. Zone 4. University of Illinois, 1982. *Source History: 26 in 2000.* **Sources: BA14, Bay, Big, Bo5, CO5, CR6, FE7, Fed, GI3, Gur, Ho5, IM2, Jun, KAN, KEE, KI3, Mc3, ME3, MI5, MO10, Mo19, SH8, TR19, We8, WI4, Wor.**

Prince Georges - Light rose-pink, fragrant flowers. Small tree blooms annually. Fruitless. *Source History: 1 in 2000.* **Sources: Arb.**

Professor Sprenger - Pink flowers. Orange-red fruit. Grows to 20'. Excellent disease resistance. Developed in the Netherlands. Zones 4-8. *Source History: 4 in 2000.* **Sources: Arb, KI3, Mo19, So5.**

Profusion - Upright, spreading tree with purple foliage that fades to bronze-green. Purple-red flowers with pink centers. Maroon, .5" fruit is persistent. Zone 4-7. *Source History: 19 in 2000.* **Sources: BA14, Bea, Big, Fo2, GI3, Hi9, Ho5, Jun, KAN, KI3, Mc3, MI10, MI5, Nrs, SH8, SIM, So5, Wa16, We8.**

Purple Prince - Single rose-red flowers. Blue-purple, persistent fruit. Small rounded tree to 15'. *Source History: 1 in 2000.* **Sources: Arb.**

Purple Wave - Purplish leaf color. Red flowers. Red fruit. *Source History: 2 in 2000.* **Sources: CO5, Nrs.**

Radiant - Compact, symmetric tree. Deep red flower buds open to bright pink blossoms. Leaf spot resistant. Small, bright red fruit is well liked by birds. Zones 3-9. *Source History: 19 in 2000.* **Sources: BO10, CO5, CR6, Fi1, GR26, Ho5, LA4, LI7, Mc3, MI5, MO10, Nrs, Sc2, SH8, So5, STR, TR19, Va5, WI4.**

Red Barron - Narrow, columnar tree. Red-purple foliage ages to bronze-green in the summer. Light pink blossoms. Small, bright red fruit hangs well into winter. Good disease resistance. Zone 3-8. *Source History: 7 in 2000.* **Sources: Big, Fo2, KI3, LI7, Mc3, Nrs, SH8.**

Red Jade - Chance seedling of *Malus floribunda* that Exzellenz Thiel found growing in the Brooklyn Botanic Garden in 1935. Introduced nearly 20 years later in 1953. Umbrella-shaped weeping crab grows 12' tall. Single white blossoms. Red, .5" persistent fruit. Popular with birds. Zone 4. *Source History: 15 in 2000.* **Sources: Arb, Big, FE7, Fed, Fo2, GR26, IM2, KAN, KI3, ME3, Nrs, Sh14, SH8, TR19, We8.**

Red Jewell - Medium size, rounded tree matures slowly to 15'. Small bright red fruit holds well into winter. Good disease resistance. Extremely hardy; Zone 4. U.S. Plant Patent No. 3267. *Source History: 9 in 2000.* **Sources: Arb, BA14, Bo5, IM2, KAN, KI3, LI7, Mc3, SH8.**

Red Silver - Wine-red buds followed by large, purple-pink flowers. *Source History: 1 in 2000.* **Sources: WI4.**

Red Splendor - Medium size tree with rounded habit. Grows 15-20'. Light pink blooms followed by small, bright red fruit that holds well into winter. Good disease resistance. Extremely hardy. Zone 3. *Source History: 10 in 2000.* **Sources: BA14, Big, Bo5, CR6, Hi9, KAN, KI3, Mc3, SH8, Wa16.**

Redbud - *Malus x zumi.* Pink buds open to white blooms. Bright red fruit clings into the winter for food for the birds. Height to 25'. Zones 4-7. *Source History: 4 in 2000.* **Sources: Arb, Jun, KEE, KI3.**

Riversii - *Malus spectabilus.* Beautiful double pink flowers. Yellow fruit. Somewhat hard to find. *Source History: 1 in 2000.* **Sources: Arb.**

Robinson - Deep rose-mauve flowers. Bronze-green foliage. Small dark red fruit. Disease resistant. Zones 4-8. *Source History: 18 in 2000.* **Sources: Arb, Big, FE7, Fo2, GI3, GR26, Ho5, IM2, KEE, ME3, MI10, MI5, SH8, SIM, St4, TR19, We8, WI4.**

Roselow (Roselow Sargent Crab Apple) - *Malus sargentii.* Seed propagated cultivar. The only true apple shrub. White flowers. Dark red, .25" fruit. Zone 4. USDA-SCS-PMC release. *Source History: 3 in 2000.* **Sources: Co15, Gr16, LA4.**

Royal Fountains - Purple weeping form with rose-red flowers. Red fruit. Deep purple foliage turns bronze-green. Grows to 15'. Zone 4. *Source History: 1 in 2000.* **Sources: Arb.**

Royal Sceptor - Fragrant white and mauve blossoms. Orange-red fruit. Narrow upright tree grows to 18'. Wine-red foliage. Disease resistant. Zone 4. Trademarked. *Source History: 1 in 2000.* **Sources: FE7.**

Royalty - Purple foliage followed by crimson flowers and dark red-purple fruit. Height to 15'. Disease resistant. Zone 3-7. *Source History: 16 in 2000.* **Sources: Bo5, Cu4, FE7, Fo2, Hi9, IM2, Jun, KAN, Mc3, ME3, MI5, Sc2, SH8, Wa16, We8, WI4.**

Rudolph - *Source History: 1 in 2000.* **Sources: Va5.**

Sargent - *Malus sargentii.* Low, dwarf, spreading tree to 6-8'. Bears clusters of white flowers followed by masses of small, dark red fruit which persists well into winter. Grows very low to the ground. Zones 2. *Source History: 25 in 2000.* **Sources: Arb, Bo5, CLI, Co15, FE7, Fo2, Fra, Gr16, GR26, IM2, KAN, KEE, KI3, LI7, Mc3, ME3, MI5, Mu2, Nrs, Sh14, SH8, TR19, We8, Wor, ZEL.**

Scheideckeri - Small tree bears pale rose-pink flowers. Small, inconspicuous fruit. *Source History: 2 in 2000.* **Sources: Arb, Nrs.**

Selkirk - Medium size tree to 20'. Very large deep pink flowers followed by reddish fruit. Glossy red-green foliage fades to bronze-green. Hardy to Zone 2. *Source History: 9 in 2000.* **Sources: Big, CR6, KAN, KI3, LA4, Mc3, SH8, TR19, Wa16.**

Sentinel - *Source History: 1 in 2000.* **Sources: Mo19.**

Siberian - *M. siberica.* Small to medium rounded tree with small fragrant white flowers. Yellow fruits are blushed with red. Cold hardy; Zone 2. *Source History: 5 in 2000.* **Sources: BO10, Co15, Fo2, No2, Sc2.**

Silver Moon - Compact columnar tree bears white flowers. Small red fruits favored by birds. Zones 4-9. *Source History: 2 in 2000.* **Sources: Gr16, Mo19.**

Simpson 10-35 - Prolific small white flowers with slight pink cast. Produces heavy pollen load. Attractive to bees. Blooms late. *Source History: 2 in 2000.* **Sources: Co2, Hi9.**

Sinai Fire - Semi-weeping tree to 15'. White flowers. Profuse orange-red fruit. Disease free. *Source History: 1 in 2000.* **Sources: Arb.**

Sissipuk - Deepest red flowers of all the Rosybloom crabs. Blooms late. Good disease resistance. *Source History: 1 in 2000.* **Sources: Arb.**

Snow Magic - Pyramid-shaped tree bears pink buds that open to white flowers. Deep red fruit. Zone 4. Trademarked. *Source History: 2 in 2000.* **Sources: IM2, MI5.**

Snowcap - *Source History: 1 in 2000.* **Sources: Va5.**

Snowcloud - *Source History: 1 in 2000.* **Sources: Nrs.**

Snowdrift - Long, glossy foliage followed by single, white flowers. Small, orange-red fruit in autumn. Tree has low vigor. Zones 3-8. *Source History: 40 in 2000.* **Sources: Ad2, Arb, BA14, Bea, Big, Bo5, BR10, Bu7, Co2, CO5, COL, CR6, Cu4, FE7, Fo2, Hi9, Ho5, IM2, KAN, KEE, KI3, Mc3, ME3, MI5, MO10, Mo19, Nrs, SH8, Si3, So5, STR, TR19, TR8, Va2, Wa16, WAF, We8, WI12, WI4, Wor.**

Southern - Bears fragrant pink flowers. Zones 5-9. *Source History: 1 in 2000.* **Sources: Wo2.**

Sparkler - Hardy to Zone 4. *Source History: 2 in 2000.* **Sources: Bo5, SH8.**

Spring Glory - Bronze-red foliage followed by a mass of large rose-pink blooms. Deep red, cherry size fruit. Propagated from a tree developed at the Morden Arboretum of Canada. Zones 4-7. *Source History: 1 in 2000.* **Sources: Jun.**

Spring Sensation - *Malus sargentii.* Rose-magenta flower buds followed by pink tinted flowers. Little or no fruit. Heavy dark green foliage. Trademarked. *Source History: 1 in 2000.* **Sources: Arb.**

Spring Snow - Non-fruiting tree with dense, upright habit. White, fragrant, single flowers. Blooms reliably. Zones 3-8. Canadian introduction. U.S. Plant Patent No. 2667. *Source History: 18 in 2000.* **Sources: BA14, Big, CO5, CR6, FE7, GR26, Gur, IM2, Jun, KI3, LI7, Mc3, ME3, MI5, Nrs, SH8, Va5, WI4.**

Strathmore - *Source History: 1 in 2000.* **Sources: Nrs.**

Strawberry Parfait - Single pink flowers followed by yellow fruit with a red blush. Excellent disease resistance. Zone 4. Princeton Nursery introduction. *Source History: 1 in 2000.* **Sources: Arb.**

Sugar - *Source History: 1 in 2000.* **Sources: Nrs.**

Sugar Tyme - Pale pink buds open to white flowers. Very fragrant. Abundant red fruit is present from October through January. Tree is a vigorous upright grower to 18' tall. Disease resistant. Zone 4. U.S. Plant Patent No. 7062. *Source History: 19 in 2000.* **Sources: Arb, BA14, Big, Bo5, FE7, Fo2, Gir, Gr16, Hi9, IM2, KAN, KI3, Mc3, ME3, MI5, SH8, TR19, Wa16, We8.**

Sundog - Pink flowers. Dark red fruit. Columnar growth habit. Canadian introduction. *Source History: 2 in 2000.* **Sources: Arb, Va5.**

Sweet Crab - *Malus coronaria.* Gets its name from the highly fragrant blossoms in mid-May. Bright green fruit remains hard until spring. Dense hardwood tree is slow growing to 25'. Does not show a lot of disease resistance. Hardy to -30 degrees F. The only native crabapple in the east. *Source History: 2 in 2000.* **Sources: Ed5, Oik.**

Tea Crab Apple - *Malus hupehensis.* Fragrant pink flowers bloom in early May. Green-yellow fruit with red blush. Tree grows 15-20'. Hardy to Zone 4. *Source History: 2 in 2000.* **Sources: Big, LA4.**

Thunderchief - Single pink flowers appear before foliage in early spring, followed by deep purple leaves, resembling Royalty Crab. Dark red fruit holds into winter. Fire blight resistant. Grows 15-20'. *Source History: 1 in 2000.* **Sources: Wa16.**

Thunderchild - Sutherland cross. Single pink-red flowers. Dark purple-red, .5" fruit. Dense, compact, upright tree grows 15-20' tall. Striking purple foliage. Resists fire blight. Zone 3. Introduced in 1978. *Source History: 12 in 2000.* **Sources: BA14, Bo5, Fed, Fo2, GI3, GR26, Hi9, MI5, Nrs, SH8, We8, ZEL.**

Tina - *Malus sargentii.* Attractive, dwarf crabapple with a low, dense, spreading tree form. Height of 5'. Carmine buds turn pink and open to white with all three colors present at the same time. Disease resistant. Zone 4. *Source History: 7 in 2000.* **Sources: Arb, BA14, FE7, KI3, Mc3, SH8, We8.**

Van Eseltine - Double, rose-pink flowers. Flattened, yellow .75" fruit with red blush. Susceptible to fireblight but worth the risk. Zone 4. *Source History: 5 in 2000.* **Sources: Arb, Bo5, Cu4, KAN, So5.**

Vanguard - Cascades of pink blossoms. Red foliage. *Source History: 2 in 2000.* **Sources: Cu4, Nrs.**

Velvet Pillar - Deep pink flowers. Medium size fruit. Upright tree with purple foliage. Hardy to Zone 4. U.S. Plant Patent No. 4758. *Source History: 3 in 2000.* **Sources: BA14, IM2, We8.**

White Angel (Inglis) - Dark green foliage. Huge white flowers followed by an abundance of dark red fruit that is enjoyed by birds. *Source History: 4 in 2000.* **Sources: Arb, Mc3, Mo19, So5.**

White Cascade - White flowers look like a cascading waterfall. Pea size yellow fruit. Height to 15'. Disease resistant. U.S. Plant Patent No. 3644. *Source History: 5 in 2000.* **Sources: Arb, Big, IM2, KAN, KI3.**

Winter Gold - White flowers. Disease-free, dark green foliage. One of the best yellow fruiting crabs used extensively in the parenting of many new hybrids. *Source History: 3 in 2000.* **Sources: Arb, Big, Nrs.**

Yellow Jewell - Small yellow, persistent fruit. Compact tree. *Source History: 1 in 2000.* **Sources: Arb.**

Zumarang - White blossoms. Wine-red fruit. Yellow fall color. Relatively disease resistant. Zones 4-8. *Source History: 1 in 2000.* **Sources: KI3.**

Zumi (Red Bud, Zumi Calocarpa) - *Malus x zumi 'Calocarpa'.* Considered one of the best white flowering crabs available. Densely branched, round tree. Small, bright red fruit. Disease resistant. Propagated from open-pollinated seed. Hardy to Zone 5. *Source History: 14 in 2000.* **Sources: Big, Co15, FE7, IM2, KAN, KI3, LA4, Mc3, ME3, MI5, Mo19, Sh14, SH8, Wor.**

Apple Rootstock

Malus spp.

Alnarp 2 - Standard rootstock. Extremely hardy; Zone 2. *Source History: 2 in 1992; 2 in 2000.* **Sources: MEA, Nrs.**

Antanovka - Very hardy Russian rootstock. Comes true to seed and produces a nearly full size standard tree. Vigorous, sturdy and has good branching characteristics. Roots spread deep and wide. Does not sucker. Resistant to drought, crown rot; moderately resistant to collar rot, apple scab, powdery mildew and crown gall. Famous through Eastern Europe for its extreme hardiness and ability to withstand extreme subzero winter temperatures. Hardy to -50 degrees F. When not used as a rootstock, Antonovka produces large, round, yellow apples with white flesh of average quality. *Source History: 14 in 1988; 11 in 1992; 7 in 2000.* **Sources: Bea, Fed, LA4, MEA, Nrs, Sc2, Stl.**

Budagovski 9 (B-9, Bud 9) - Malling 8 x Red Standard. Produces trees that are Malling 9 to EMLA 26 size; 25-30% of standard size. Usually requires support. Induces early fruiting. Very resistant to collar rot. Moderately resistant to powdery mildew and apple scab. Tolerant of common latent viruses. Susceptible to fire blight. Rooting ability comparable to Malling 7. Recommended as an interstem for the colder regions. Produces in 2-3 years; yields are similar to Malling 9. Developed by the late Dr. Budagovski, most successful apple rootstock breeder in Soviet Union, at the College of Horticulture in Michurinsk where temperatures drop to -55 degrees F. *Source History: 2 in 1988; 6 in 1992; 6 in 2000.* **Sources: Bea, Cu4, MEA, Ro3, TR8, WI12.**

Budagovski 118 (B 118, Bud 118) - Moscow Pear x (mixture of Malling 8 and Malling 9 pollen). Produces vigorous trees 75% of standard size at maturity; few lateral branches. Produces large calipered, well-branched maiden trees. Yield efficiency similar to EMLA 111. Resistant to collar rot and apple scab. Slightly susceptible to crown gall and powdery mildew. Well adapted to various soil types. Particularly valuable on dry, sandy soils. Used as an interstem on rich soils or as an understock for spur-type varieties on poor soils. Extremely winter hardy. Recommended for cold climates. *Source History: 1 in 1988; 2 in 1992; 2 in 2000.* **Sources: Rai, TR8.**

Budagovski 490 (B 490, Bud 490) - Budagovski 9 x Budagovski 13-14 (Dr. Budagovski's hardy rootstock). Produces trees that are 65-70% of standard size at maturity. Well anchored; staking not required. Vigor comparable to EMLA 106. Free from suckering. Tendency to develop burrknots. Induces early, very heavy production. Medium resistance to collar rot. Moderately susceptible to fire blight. Very good stooler; also roots well by hardwood cutting. Produces good scion growth. Very winter hardy. Has the potential to be a possible successor to EMLA 106. *Source History: 1 in 1988; 3 in 1992; 2 in 2000.* **Sources: Nrs, TR8.**

Budagovski 491 (B 491, Bud 491) - Produces trees EMLA 27 to Malling 9 size; 20% of standard size at maturity. Well anchored, but requires crop support. Susceptible to collar rot and fire blight. Compatible with Delicious, McIntosh and Mutsu. Can be used as an interstem as well as a dwarfing rootstock. Stoolbeds produce well rooted, straight shanked liners with a high degree of bud survival in

the nursery. Very winter hardy. *Source History: 1 in 1988; 1 in 1992; 1 in 2000.*
Sources: TR8.

Citation PAF - *Source History: 1 in 1988; 1 in 1992; 1 in 2000.* **Sources: MEA.**

Columbia Seedling - Used primarily as rootstocks for fruiting apples and flowering crabapples. Hardy to Zone 3. *Source History: 1 in 1992; 1 in 2000.* **Sources: LA4.**

EMLA 7 - Virus-free replacement for Malling 7, introduced by the East Malling Research Station in England in 1974. Produces a sturdy tree 55-60% of standard size. Less suckering than Malling 7 and Malling 7A. Less precocious and lower yielding than EMLA 9 or EMLA 26. Moderately resistant to collar rot. Good on deep, fertile, loam soils with moderate to heavy texture; poor on light, sandy soils. Recommended for soils with high lead arsenic residues and old orchard sites with replant problems. Little used in Europe; widely used in North America for its exceptional hardiness and anchorage. Introduced in 1974. *Source History: 9 in 1988; 6 in 1992; 9 in 2000.* **Sources: Bea, Fed, LA4, MEA, Rai, Ro3, So5, TR8, WI12.**

EMLA 9 (EM-9) - Virus-free replacement for Malling 9 developed at East Malling Research Station using heat treatment. Produces trees 30-40% of standard size. All 9s rarely sucker, but their roots are brittle; trees on these rootstocks require staking throughout their life. Induces cropping early; larger fruit and earlier ripening. Resistant to collar rot. Not suited to dry, light soils. Withstands heavy soils and wet conditions. Responds well to mulching, but is usually attractive to mice. Useful for high density plantings and as temporary filler in plantings of trees on more vigorous rootstocks. Hardy to Zone 5. *Source History: 5 in 1988; 4 in 1992; 3 in 2000.* **Sources: Bea, LA4, So5.**

EMLA 26 - Virus-free replacement for Malling 26 from East Malling in 1969. Vigor between EMLA 9 and EMLA 106; 40% of standard size. Smaller than EMLA 7 and slightly less vigorous, but produces better quality fruit. Less brittle roots than EMLA 9, but still requires permanent staking on exposed sites. Few but very vigorous suckers. Rootstock union develops large burrknot, so position union a few inches above ground. Susceptible to wooly aphid. Subject to fire blight in the East. Susceptible to collar rot; do not plant on wet or infected soils. Requires well drained, but not droughty soil. Not as hardy as EMLA 7, but easier to manage. Introduced in 1969. *Source History: 8 in 1988; 7 in 1992; 8 in 2000.* **Sources: Bea, LA4, MEA, Rai, Ro3, So5, TR8, WI12.**

EMLA 27 (EM 27) - Virus-free dwarfing rootstock bred from a cross made in the spring of 1929; Malling 13 was the seed parent and EMLA 9 was the pollen parent. Scion varieties grafted onto EMLA 27 grow into small, compact, precocious trees, approximately half the size of trees on EMLA 9 and 15-20% of standard size. Rarely suckers. Heavy crops the second year after planting. Needs little pruning after the first five years. Notable fire blight resistance. Good for pot culture and trellis or espalier systems. Hardy to Zone 5. U.S. Plant Patent No. 3793. *Source History: 2 in 1988; 2 in 1992; 5 in 2000.* **Sources: Bea, MEA, Rai, Ro3, TR8.**

EMLA 106 - Virus-free replacement clone for Malling-Merton 106 introduced by East Malling Research Station in 1969. Produces large calipered, well-branched trees, about 65% of standard size. Well anchored; does not require staking. More sensitive to soil moisture than most; do not plant on poorly drained soils as it is subject to collar rot caused by *Phytophthora cactorum*. Susceptible to mildew, early winter freeze damage and to union necrosis caused by tomato ringspot virus. Recommended density of 200-250 trees per acre. Widely planted in high latitude countries because of heavy crops, freedom from suckering, wooly aphid resistance. Introduced in 1969. *Source History: 6 in 1988; 3 in 1992; 4 in 2000.* **Sources: LA4, MEA, TR8, WI12.**

EMLA 111 - Virus-free replacement for Malling-Merton 111 introduced by East Malling in 1969. Produces trees similar to but more vigorous than EMLA 106; 75% of standard size. Its additional vigor is particularly valuable on dry, light soils; also better adapted to heavier soils than EMLA 106. Well anchored root system. Resistant to wooly aphids. Susceptible to mildew. Very few losses from collar rot. Susceptible to same burrknot problem as EMLA 26. Recommended where vigorous growth is needed to overcome the poorer cropping capacity of dry, sandy soils in low rainfall areas. Excellent for spur-type varieties. Bred to replace EMLA 2. Introduced in 1969. *Source History: 7 in 1988; 4 in 1992; 5 in 2000.* **Sources: LA4, MEA, Or9, TR8, WI12.**

Geneva 11 - Shows same vigor as M-26. *Source History: 1 in 2000.* **Sources: Cu4.**

Geneva 16 - Ottawa 3 x *Malus floribunda* cross hybridized by the Cornell University/Geneva Apple Rootstock Breeding Program in 1981. Produces a tree that is similar to M 9 subclones in vigor and size. Shows hypersensitivity to at least one common latent virus. Tolerant to collar rot, nearly immune to fire blight and immune to scab; susceptible to woolly apple aphids and powdery mildew. *Source History: 5 in 2000.* **Sources: Cu4, LA4, MEA, TR8, WI12.**

Geneva 30 - Cross of Robusta 5 x M 9. Trees are M 7 size and planted in the same density. Support is not required. Resistant to fire blight; shows high tolerance for crown rot. Developed by Cornell University and the Geneva Apple Rootstock Breeding Program. Patent applied for. *Source History: 4 in 2000.* **Sources: Cu4, MEA, Ro3, TR8.**

Geneva 65 - More dwarfing than M-9. *Source History: 1 in 2000.* **Sources: Cu4.**

Geneva 74R5M9-030 - *Source History: 1 in 1992; 1 in 2000.* **Sources: TR8.**

Hibernal - *Source History: 1 in 1992; 1 in 2000.* **Sources: Nrs.**

Interstem: Poland 22 on Antonovka - The Antonovka rootstock provides good anchorage and drought tolerance. P 22 produces a dwarfing, small precocious top. Has all the fine attributes of both these rootstocks. Hardy to Zone 3. *Source History: 1 in 2000.* **Sources: Bea.**

M 9 NAKB T.337 - Parent rootstock is M 9 NAKB. Now the most widely preferred M 9 in Europe. Induces early cropping with large fruit size. May be slightly less vigorous than EMLA 9. Resists collar rot; susceptible to mildew in the nursery. Regular spray program is recommended. *Source History: 2 in 2000.* **Sources: MEA, TR8.**

M 9 NIC 29 - Dwarfing rootstock produces a tree resembling M 9-337 in size and characteristics with more vigor and an expansive root system. Requires support. Developed in Belgium. U.S. Plant Patent No. 10,714. *Source History: 2 in 2000.* **Sources: MEA, WI12.**

M 9 Pajam 2 - Dwarfing rootstock produces a tree resembling M 9-337 in size and characteristics with slightly more vigor and productivity. Shows better compatibility with grafted varieties and slightly better fruit size, improved color and earlier maturity. Winter hardiness compares to other M 9 rootstocks. U.S. Plant Patent No. 7715. *Source History: 1 in 2000.* **Sources: WI12.**

M 9-337 - Dwarfing rootstock produces a tree that is about 30-35% the size of a seedling. Works well for high density plantings. Performance compares to EMLA 9. Requires support due to brittle roots and poor anchorage. *Source History: 1 in 2000.* **Sources: WI12.**

Malling 2 (M 2) - *Source History: 1 in 1992; 1 in 2000.* **Sources: Nrs.**

Malling 4 (M 4) - Semi-dwarfing rootstock that produces a tree which is slightly larger than EMLA 7. Highly recommended for light, sandy soil. Does not do well in heavy, clay soil. Popular in Europe. Increasing popularity in Canada. *Source History: 1 in 1988; 2 in 1992; 1 in 2000.* **Sources: Nrs.**

Malling 7 (M 7) - Malling 7 was selected at East Malling Research Station from a group of traditional French rootstocks known as Doucin. Much of their work on Malling 7 was actually carried out with clone Malling 7A, which is free of the economically important viruses, but known to contain a latent virus. The Malling series was later replaced with the virus-free and wooly aphid resistant EMLA series, a joint breeding project involving the East Malling and Long Ashton Research Stations. Malling 7 is self-standing, produces fruit the third year after grafting and will take heavier soils. *Source History: 4 in 1988; 6 in 1992; 7 in 2000.* **Sources: Bay, Cu4, LA4, Mel, Nrs, On3.**

Malling 7A (M 7A) - Common semidwarf rootstock that produces 11-16' trees; 55-70% of standard size, depending on scion variety. About 20% of the young trees require staking, more if planted in an especially windy area; becomes better anchored with age. Begins bearing in 3-4 years. Susceptible to wooly aphids. Much less susceptible to collar rot than the somewhat larger Malling-Merton 106. Does better than Malling 26 on wet soils. Fairly tolerant of heavy clay soils. Very winter hardy. Anchorage problems with some varieties and heavy suckering are its most serious faults. *Source History: 9 in 1988; 7 in 1992; 1 in 2000.* **Sources: LA4.**

Malling 9 (M 9) - Selected at East Malling from a number of Juane de Metz rootstocks. The original Malling 9, of which a number of variant clones now exist, was followed in 1962 by Malling 9A. Most of the Malling 9 clones and the Malling 9A clone were subsequently shown to be infected with latent virus. Produces a 6-10' tree; about 25% of standard size. Requires permanent staking or support, because of brittle roots. Very productive; bears at an early age. Resistant to collar rot; sensitive to fire blight. Best on rich, loamy soil with consistent, ample moisture. Irrigation is strongly recommended. Responds well to mulch. *Source History: 9 in 1988; 10 in 1992; 6 in 2000.* **Sources: Cu4, LA4, Mel, Nrs, Ro3, TR8.**

Malling 13 - *Source History: 2 in 1992; 1 in 2000.* **Sources: Nrs.**

Malling 25 - *Source History: 1 in 1992; 1 in 2000.* **Sources: Nrs.**

Malling 26 (M 26) - Bred at East Malling Research Station from a cross of Malling 9 and the very vigorous rootstock, Malling 16 (Metziner Ideal). Produces an 8-14' tree; about 45% of standard size. Can occasionally be grown free-standing; usually needs support on light soils and windy sites, especially in early years. Produces fruit in 2-3 years. Does not sucker much. Does better than Malling 7A on sandy soil, although anchorage is not as good. Susceptible to fire blight and wooly aphids. Prefers a fairly light, well drained soil. Will not tolerate poorly drained soils or slow draining soils. Adaptable to close plantings. Medium hardy. *Source History: 11 in 1988; 8 in 1992; 6 in 2000.* **Sources: Cu4, LA4, Mel, Nrs, On3.**

Malling 27 (M 27) - Most dwarfing rootstock; produces a tree only 4-6' tall. Induces early and heavy bearing. Thin or remove fruit for one or two years because once the tree starts bearing it stops growing. Since the tree is so small, branching should begin 12" off the ground. Well suited for container growing. U.S. Plant Patent No. 3793. *Source History: 5 in 1988; 3 in 1992; 2 in 2000.* **Sources: Bay,**

Nrs.

<u>Malling-Merton 104</u> - *Source History: 1 in 1992; 1 in 2000.* **Sources: Nrs.**

<u>Malling-Merton 106</u> (MM 106) - Produced by a joint breeding program of the East Malling Research Station and the John Innes Institute in Merton, England which developed several rootstocks resistant to wooly aphids. Produces a tree about 65% of standard size. Well anchored. Moderately spreading and upright; excellent rootstock for spur varieties. Excellent producer. Does not sucker. Tolerates high temperatures and drought if irrigated. Plant on well drained soil; susceptible to crown rot. Recent problems with tomato ring spot virus. Better adapted to lighter soils than Malling 7A. Hardens off late in the fall, so more susceptible to early freeze damage. *Source History: 12 in 1988; 10 in 1992; 6 in 2000.* **Sources: Bay, Cu4, LA4, Mel, Ro3, So5.**

<u>Malling-Merton 109</u> - *Source History: 1 in 1992; 1 in 2000.* **Sources: Nrs.**

<u>Malling-Merton 111</u> (MM 111) - Another wooly aphid resistant rootstock developed jointly by East Malling Research Station and the John Innes Institute, which also produced Malling-Merton 106. Produces a tree that is 70-80% of standard size. Quite upright with wide crotch angles. Best anchored of all dwarfing rootstocks. Rarely produces root suckers. Very tolerant to drought and high soil temperatures. Best semidwarf rootstock for heavy, poorly drained soils. Quite resistant to collar rot. Tolerates and usually is free of common apple virus. Only real problem is burrknotting (aerial rotting), which produces above-ground nodes where roots tried to form. *Source History: 14 in 1988; 12 in 1992; 7 in 2000.* **Sources: Bay, Bea, Cu4, LA4, Nrs, Ro3, So5.**

Malus baccata (Siberian Crab) - Used for extremely cold climates; not recommended where a less cold hardy rootstock will do. Hardy in Zone 2. *Source History: 1 in 1988; 4 in 1992; 5 in 2000.* **Sources: Bo5, LA4, MEA, No2, Nrs.**

Malus borowinka (Dutchess Apple) - Most compatible and vigorous of the cold hardy rootstocks; hardiness about equal to Antanovka. Does better in heavy moisture conditions. Hardy in Zone 3. *Source History: 2 in 1992; 1 in 2000.* **Sources: LA4.**

Malus columbia (Columbia Apple) - Hardy. Good compatibility. Slight susceptibility to crown rot. Hardy in Zone 3. *Source History: 1 in 1992; 1 in 2000.* **Sources: LA4.**

Malus prunifolia (Plum-Leaved Apple) - Most extensive fibrous root system of any rootstocks. Greater cold hardiness than Antanovka; less than *M. baccata*. Hardy in Zone 3. *Source History: 2 in 1992; 1 in 2000.* **Sources: LA4.**

Malus ranetka - Standard rootstock that produces a tree 24-30' tall. More vigorous than Antanovka and *M. baccata*. More cold hardy than Antanovka; fewer compatibility problems than *baccata*. Chosen by Alaskan growers. Hardy to Zone 2. *Source History: 1 in 1988; 4 in 1992; 2 in 2000.* **Sources: Bea, LA4.**

Malus robusta - *M. baccata* x *M. prunifolia*. Vigorous, hardy rootstock. Very desirable. *Source History: 1 in 1988; 1 in 1992; 1 in 2000.* **Sources: Nrs.**

Mark (Mac 9) - Malling 9 x unknown pollen parent, since seed was from open-pollinated trees. Slightly smaller tree than EMLA 26; about 35-45% of standard size. Strongly anchored, needs no support; may replace the use of interstems. Few or no suckers. Early flowering; heavy fruit set and yields. Precocious and self-spreading, similar to Malling 9. Excellent fruit color due to open structure. Not immune to fire blight, but more resistant than Malling 9. More tolerant of crown rot than Malling 26. Not as hardy as Malling 26; to Zone 4. Bred at Michigan State by Dr. Carlson. Tested in Michigan for 20 years. U.S. Plant Patent No. 4678. *Source*

History: 9 in 1988; 11 in 1992; 5 in 2000. **Sources: Bay, Fed, MEA, Rai, TR8.**

Midget Crab Apple - *Malus baccata x M. spectabilis.* Possibly a genetic dwarf rootstock. Vigorous nursery growth. Hardy to Zone 4. *Source History: 1 in 2000.* **Sources: LA4.**

NAKB M26 - Semi-dwarf. Dutch strain of EMLA 26. Zone 4. *Source History: 1 in 2000.* **Sources: MEA.**

NIC- 8 - Most dwarf of the "NIC" series. Patent applied for. *Source History: 1 in 2000.* **Sources: MEA.**

NIC-19 - Size is reported equal to NAKB 337 and M9. Zone 5. Patent applied for. *Source History: 1 in 2000.* **Sources: MEA.**

Novole - Very vigorous. Vole resistant. *Source History: 1 in 1992; 1 in 2000.* **Sources: Cu4.**

NY 50-4 - *Source History: 1 in 1992; 1 in 2000.* **Sources: Nrs.**

Ottawa 3 - Fully hardy, dwarfing rootstock developed in Canada. Full dwarf that is free standing, drought resistant and cold hardy. A bit experimental, but worth trying for those who have had trouble growing the Malling dwarfs. *Source History: 2 in 1988; 4 in 1992; 2 in 2000.* **Sources: Cu4, MEA.**

Pajam 1 (Lancep) - Reported size slightly smaller than NAKB 337 andM9. Developed in France. U.S. Plant Patent No. 7230. *Source History: 1 in 1992; 1 in 2000.* **Sources: MEA.**

Pajam 2 - Reported size equal to EMLA 9 and NIC 20. Requires staking. Zone 5. Developed in France. U.S. Plant Patent No. 7231. *Source History: 1 in 1992; 2 in 2000.* **Sources: MEA, Rai.**

PK 14 (PI 274840) - *Source History: 1 in 1992; 1 in 2000.* **Sources: Nrs.**

Poland 1 (P-1) - Malling 4 x Antonovka. Produces a tree that is approximately the size of EMLA 26. Fibrous root system similar to Malling 7 and EMLA 111; tree requires staking. Non-suckering with no burrknot tendency. Begins bearing the third year. Resistant to crown gall and mildew. Susceptibility to fire blight and wooly apple aphids is comparable to Malling 9. Requires a rich, well drained soil. Good for high density plantings. Hardiness compares to EMLA 111. Developed by Dr. S. W. Zagaja of the Research Institute of Pomology at Skierniewice, Poland. *Source History: 1 in 1988; 2 in 1992; 1 in 2000.* **Sources: Nrs.**

Poland 2 (P-2) - Malling 9 x Antonovka. Produces a tree 25-35% of standard size. Open growth habit; non-suckering. Good scion growth with numerous lateral branches. Dark green, round leaves with deep serrations. Trees defoliate early in fall and break bud late in spring. Cropping efficiency similar to Malling 9. Precocious; bears the third year. Resistant to collar rot, European canker, perennial canker, silver leaf and crown gall. No burrknot tendency. Slightly susceptible to scab and mildew. Requires rich soil. Extremely winter hardy. Widely used in Poland as an interstem due to its growth habit. Developed by Dr. Zagaja in Poland. *Source History: 2 in 1988; 2 in 1992; 4 in 2000.* **Sources: Bea, Cu4, Nrs, TR8.**

Poland 13 - *Source History: 2 in 1992; 1 in 2000.* **Sources: Nrs.**

Poland 14 (P-14) - Developed from open-pollinated seedlings of Malling 9. Produces a tree 45-50% of standard size. Less vigorous scions are free standing; more vigorous varieties need to be staked. Ideal rootstock for spur-type varieties, producing semidwarf, free standing trees. Thick, round leaves similar to Alnarp 2. Defoliates early in fall and breaks bud late in spring. Non-suckering. Excellent crops similar to EMLA 106. Resistant to apple scab, powdery mildew, collar rot and crown gall. No burrknot tendency. Suitable for medium rich soils. Widely compatible. Winter hardiness compares to EMLA 26. Bred by Dr. Zagaja in Poland. *Source History: 1 in 1988; 2 in 1992; 1 in 2000.* **Sources: Nrs.**

Poland 16 (P-16) - Malling 9 x Antonovka. Produces non-suckering trees comparable in size to Malling 9. Requires staking. Light green, waxy leaves; short leaf petioles similar to Malling 9. Induces early fruiting; begins bearing the second year. Highly resistant to apple scab, powdery mildew and crown gall. As susceptible to fire blight as Malling 9. Suitable for rich, well drained soils. Recommended for use in the central and southern states, but could be grown in northern areas that provide adequate snow cover. Developed by Dr. Zagaja in Poland. *Source History: 1 in 1988; 2 in 1992; 2 in 2000.* **Sources: Nrs, TR8.**

Poland 18 (P-18) - Malling 4 x Antonovka. Produces a free-standing tree similar in size to EMLA 111 or Alnarp 2. Excellent rooting ability similar to EMLA 111. Cropping efficiency comparable to Alnarp 2; slightly lower than EMLA 106. Begins bearing in 3-4 years. Resistant to collar rot, apple scab, powdery mildew and crown gall. No burrknot tendencies. Intermediate susceptibility to fire blight. Susceptible to wooly apple aphids. Good on wet soils because of horizontal rooting habit. Adapted to poor, light, sandy soils as well. Good interstem base due to adaptability to various soils and climates. Hardy to Zone 3. Developed in Poland. *Source History: 2 in 1988; 2 in 1992; 2 in 2000.* **Sources: Bea, TR8.**

Poland 22 (P-22) - Malling 9 x Antonovka. Smaller trees than those on Malling 9; comparable to EMLA 27. Better anchored than Malling 9 and not as brittle. Resembles Malling 9 in growth with numerous lateral branches. Defoliates medium to late. Breaks bud late in the spring. Induces early fruiting. Cropping efficiency like that of Malling 9. Resistant to collar rot, perennial canker, European canker, silver leaf, apple scab, powdery mildew and crown gall. Shows no burrknot tendency. Susceptible to fire blight and wooly apple aphids. Exceptional winter hardiness comparable to Alnarp 2. Developed by Dr. S. W. Zagaja in Poland. *Source History: 2 in 1988; 8 in 1992; 5 in 2000.* **Sources: Bea, MEA, Nrs, On3, TR8.**

Standard Seedling (Domestic Seedling, Seedling Rootstock) - *Malus domestica.* Seedlings that are used as rootstocks which produce vigorous, rugged, standard, full-size trees. Gives excellent anchorage. Few suckers. Adaptable to a wide range of growing conditions. Tolerates wet, dry, poor soil; excellent for old soils. Used primarily today in combinations with spur-type varieties for a smaller tree. Much slower to bear. Hardy in Zone 4. *Source History: 12 in 1988; 9 in 1992; 6 in 2000.* **Sources: Bay, Cu4, LA4, MEA, RA4, WI12.**

Supporter 4 - Cross of M 9 x M 4. Tree vigor is 11-14% higher than M 9 with similar fruit size and production. Tree vigor is similar to M 26. Became more well known after the fall of the Berlin Wall. Tested extensively in Eastern Europe. Bred at the Pillnitz Research Station near Dresden, Germany in 1921. *Source History: 3 in 2000.* **Sources: MEA, TR8, WI12.**

Apricot

Prunus armeniaca

Alfred - Doty x Geneva. Small to medium, round, bright orange fruit, sometimes with a pink blush. Orange, freestone flesh; medium firm, fine grained and juicy. Sweet, rich flavor. Vigorous, hardy tree. Appears to have a measure of resistance to late frost injury. Self-fruitful. Regular, heavy bearer. Ripens from late July to early August. Developed at the New York Agricultural Experiment Station in Geneva. Introduced in 1965. *Source History: 2 in 1988; 3 in 1992; 3 in 2000.*

Sources: Mo19, Nrs, So5.

Ambercot - Medium size, uniform fruit. Firm flesh. Ripens in late May. Considered a good pollinator. *Source History: 1 in 2000.* **Sources: WI4.**

Ansu - Blooms early; good fall color. Small, edible fruit. Zones 4-5. *Source History: 1 in 2000.* **Sources: Fra.**

Autumn Glo - Medium size fruit. Very good flavor and commercial quality. Ripens around August 5. U.S. Plant Patent No. 9864. *Source History: 1 in 2000.* **Sources: WI4.**

Autumn Royal - Sport of Royal. Medium to large, oval, yellow fruit with an orange blush. Firm, juicy flesh. Very high quality equal to that of Blenheim, a California classic. Self-fertile. Blossoms late over a longer period and thus is more apt to escape spring frosts. Susceptible to shot hole fungus, brown rot and peach twig borer. The only late apricot known. Ripens in September. Requires 800 hours of chilling. U.S. Plant Patent No. 2906. *Source History: 5 in 1988; 6 in 1992; 2 in 2000.* **Sources: CO5, Pa2.**

Blenheim (Royal Blenheim, Royal) - Medium to large, pale orange fruit with red dots. Very juicy, orange, freestone flesh. Sweet, aromatic flavor sets the standard for apricots. Famous in California for its canning quality; also good for drying. Early blooming. Self-fertile. Good pollinator. Ripens midseason. Requires 500 hours of chilling. British origin. Blenheim was raised in 1830 by a Miss Shipley, daughter of the gardener to the Duke of Marlborough. *Source History: 16 in 1988; 22 in 1992; 13 in 2000.* **Sources: AG2, Bay, CO5, JOY, ORA, Pe2, Si3, Son, STR, Tex, Va2, WI12, WI4.**

Blenril - *Source History: 1 in 1992; 1 in 2000.* **Sources: Nrs.**

Bryan - Medium size freestone. Very good quality. Heavy bearer. Ripens late May. Requires 700 hours of chilling. Originated as a seedling discovered in Dublin, Texas. *Source History: 1 in 1988; 3 in 1992; 2 in 2000.* **Sources: ORA, Wel.**

Castlebrite - Medium size bright orange fruit with slight red blush. Firm flesh is slightly tart unless fully ripe. Vigorous tree. Early shipping variety; ripens mid to late May. *Source History: 1 in 1988; 4 in 1992; 2 in 2000.* **Sources: AG2, WI4.**

Chinese (Mormon Chinese) - Medium size, yellow to medium orange fruit. Clingstone flesh. Good flavor, texture and quality. Early bearing. Heavy producer. Self-fruitful, but yields are improved with cross pollination. Susceptible to shot hole fungus, brown rot and peach twig borer. Late blooming with frost resistant buds. Recommended for difficult climates prone to late spring frosts. Zone 4. Ripens in July. Requires 700 hours of chilling. *Source History: 10 in 1988; 11 in 1992; 10 in 2000.* **Sources: Bay, Bea, JOY, Nrs, ORA, Pe2, STR, Va2, WI12, WI4.**

Curtis - Medium size, round, rich golden fruit with a bright red blush. Excellent flavor. *Source History: 1 in 1988; 3 in 1992; 3 in 2000.* **Sources: Bo5, Nrs, So5.**

Deatrick - Large, round, golden fruit. Vigorous, productive, upright tree. Blooms late. *Source History: 1 in 1988; 3 in 1992; 4 in 2000.* **Sources: Ad2, Bo5, Wh4, Wor.**

Duecker - Excellent quality fruit. Ripens late May. Originated near Stonewall, Texas. *Source History: 1 in 2000.* **Sources: Wom.**

Earli-Orange, Stark (Roberts Cultivar) - Juicy fruits with rich flavor. Use fresh, canned, frozen or dried. Ripens in late June. Hardy in Zones 5-8. Trademarked. *Source History: 1 in 1988; 1 in 1992; 1 in 2000.* **Sources: St4.**

Earlicot - Firm, flavorful fruit is highly colored. Ripens mid to late May. Requires a pollinator. U.S. Plant Patent No. 7198. *Source History: 1 in 2000.* **Sources: WI4.**

Earligold - *Source History: 1 in 1988; 1 in 1992; 1 in 2000.* **Sources: STR.**

Earliril - *Source History: 1 in 1992; 1 in 2000.* **Sources: Nrs.**

EarliSun - U.S. Plant Patent No. 9173. *Source History: 1 in 2000.* **Sources: AG2.**

Early Golden - Large fruit with smooth, orange-gold skin and highly flavored, orange flesh. Freestone. Fine for eating fresh, baking, canning or drying. Thrifty, prolific tree. Pink or white flowers bloom 7-10 days later than Blenheim in the spring. Attractive leaves. Self-fruitful, but production is improved with a pollinator. Allow fruit to ripen on the tree. Ripens from early July to early August depending on location. Requires 450 hours of chilling. Hardy in Zones 5-8. Especially suited for the South and Southwest. *Source History: 15 in 1988; 15 in 1992; 11 in 2000.* **Sources: Bar, BO10, FO10, Lee, MI5, Na4, Sav, SIM, Tex, WA8, Wel.**

EarlyBlush - Medium size fruit with orange skin with red blush. Good quality. Moderately productive tree. Fruit can soften quickly at the tip. Moderate resistance to bacterial spot. Very susceptible to brown rot. U.S. Plant Patent No. 9255. *Source History: 1 in 2000.* **Sources: Hi9.**

Farmingdale - *Source History: 1 in 1988; 3 in 1992; 1 in 2000.* **Sources: So5.**

Flavor Giant - Large, freestone fruit; good eating and shipping qualities. Self-fertile. Ripens in late May. Requires 350-600 hours of chilling. U. S. Plant Patent No. 5308. *Source History: 4 in 1992; 3 in 2000.* **Sources: Bay, ORA, WI4.**

Flora Gold - All-purpose freestone. Excellent flavor. Reliable producer. Self-fruitful. Ripens early, 4-5 weeks before Blenheim. Requires 500 hours of chilling. Recommended for home orchards. Developed by Floyd Zaiger. *Source History: 2 in 1988; 4 in 1992; 4 in 2000.* **Sources: Bay, MI5, Pa2, WI4.**

Garden Annie - Medium to large, bright yellow fruit. Firm, juicy, clingstone flesh. Genetic dwarf tree. Self-fertile. Ripens in May. Low chill requirement. U.S. Plant Patent No. 3809. *Source History: 3 in 1988; 4 in 1992; 3 in 2000.* **Sources: CO5, ORA, STR.**

Gold Kist - Large fruit with firm, orange, freestone flesh. Superb flavor. Delicious fresh, canned, frozen or dried. Heavy bearing. Requires thinning to obtain large fruit. Self-fruitful. Ripens in early May, 4-5 weeks before Blenheim. Requires 300 hours of chilling. Hardy in Zone 9. Best backyard apricot for warm winter climates. Developed by Floyd Zaiger. U.S. Plant Patent No. 2816. *Source History: 4 in 1988; 5 in 1992; 5 in 2000.* **Sources: Bay, ORA, Pa2, Son, WI4.**

Goldbar - Light yellow-orange fruit with 20% blush. Flowers heavily but sets light crop of very large fruit. Good dessert quality. Vigorous tree. Developed at the Prosser Experiment Station. U.S. Plant Patent No. 7045. *Source History: 6 in 1992; 5 in 2000.* **Sources: Co2, COL, Va2, WI12, WI4.**

Goldbrink - Very large, highly colored fruit. Ripens with Castlebrite. Requires a pollinater. U.S. Plant Patent No. 8433. *Source History: 1 in 2000.* **Sources: WI4.**

Goldcot - Seedling of Perfection. Medium to large, nearly round fruit. Moderately thick, tough, golden yellow skin. Juicy, fine textured, medium orange, freestone flesh. Tangy flavor. Suitable for fresh use, freezing, canning or baby food processing. Exceptionally strong tree. Self-fruitful. Consistently heavy bearer. May require thinning. Buds have above average hardiness. Somewhat resistant to bacterial leaf spot. Ripens from mid-July to early August depending on location.

Hardy in Zones 4-8. Especially good in the Northwest. Developed at Michigan's South Haven Experiment Station for Northern growers. Introduced in 1967. *Source History: 14 in 1988; 14 in 1992; 15 in 2000.* **Sources: Ad2, Fed, Fi1, Gur, Hi9, Jun, ME3, Mel, Sc6, So5, St4, Va2, Wa16, WI12, WI4.**

Golden Amber - Large, light orange fruit. Firm flesh with excellent flavor. Excellent for fresh use, canning and drying. Self-fertile. Blooms and fruits later than Blenheim. Blooming period lasts almost 30 days. Requires less summer heat than Blenheim. Susceptible to shot hole fungus, brown rot and peach twig borer. Resistant to pit burn. Requires 500 hours of chilling. U.S. Plant Patent No. 3067. *Source History: 3 in 1988; 3 in 1992; 3 in 2000.* **Sources: Bay, CO5, ORA.**

Goldenglo, Stark (Zaiglo Cultivar) - Sweet, golden fruit. Tree grows only 4-6' tall. Starts bearing fruit the second summer after transplanting. Ripens in mid-July. Hardy in Zones 5-8. Trademarked. U.S. Plant Patent No. 4553. *Source History: 1 in 1988; 1 in 1992; 1 in 2000.* **Sources: St4.**

Goldrich - Large, oval, waxy, bright orange fruit. Firm, fine textured, deep orange flesh. Ground color must be allowed to develop fully before harvest in order to assure maximum quality and low acidity. Vigorous, productive, hardy tree. Early bloomer. Requires a pollinator. Sensitive to apricot ring pox. Introduced by Washington State University. *Source History: 4 in 1988; 6 in 1992; 3 in 2000.* **Sources: Bo5, Co2, Va2.**

Goldstrike - Similar in size and appearance to Goldbar. Orange flesh with red-purple blush. Fair to good dessert quality; becomes mushy when canned. Vigorous tree. U.S. Plant Patent No. 7035. *Source History: 6 in 1992; 5 in 2000.* **Sources: Co2, COL, Va2, WI12, WI4.**

Haggith - *Source History: 1 in 1988; 2 in 1992; 1 in 2000.* **Sources: Nrs.**

Harcot (HW 401) - Medium to large, oblong, orange fruit with a slight red blush. Firm, smooth, fine-grained, freestone flesh. Very good, sweet flavor. Vigorous, productive, self-fertile tree. Cold hardy. Good resistance to perennial canker, bacterial spot and brown rot. Early ripener; ripens fully on the tree without dropping. Requires 700 hours of chilling. Developed in Canada in 1977. *Source History: 4 in 1988; 11 in 1992; 12 in 2000.* **Sources: Ad2, Bay, Bea, Bo5, CO5, Cu4, Ed5, Hi9, Pe2, So5, Son, WI4.**

Harglow (HW 425) - V51092 x Sun Glo. Medium size, bright orange fruit with no blush. Medium firm, orange, freestone flesh. Good texture and flavor. Compact, late blooming, productive tree. Self-fertile. Resistant to perennial canker and brown rot. Moderately resistant to bacterial spot. Ripens in late July. Requires 800 hours of chilling. Cold hardy. Introduced in 1982. *Source History: 2 in 1988; 3 in 1992; 8 in 2000.* **Sources: Bay, Clo, Hi9, Mo19, Nrs, Rai, WI12, WI4.**

Hargrand (HW 410) - Very large fruit, 2.25-2.5" in diameter. Dull orange skin with a speckled blush. Firm, smooth, orange, freestone flesh. Good texture and flavor. Suitable for fresh market or processing. Productive, cold hardy tree. Tolerant to brown rot, bacterial spot and perennial canker. Ripens in late July. Developed at the Harrow Research Station, Canada. Introduced in 1980. *Source History: 4 in 1988; 4 in 1992; 7 in 2000.* **Sources: Ad2, Bo5, Cu4, Hi9, Nrs, So5, Wh4.**

Harlayne (HW 407) - Medium size, orange fruit with a moderate red blush. Firm, orange, freestone flesh with good texture and flavor. Suitable for fresh use or processing. Productive, cold hardy tree. Resistant to perennial canker, brown rot and bacterial spot. Moderately resistant to bacterial spot and perennial canker. Ripens in late August. Developed at the Harrow Research Station in Canada. Introduced in 1980. *Source History: 2 in 1988; 5 in 1992; 6 in 2000.* **Sources: Ad2,**

Cu4, Fed, Hi9, Nrs, So5.

Harogem (HW 405) - Small to medium, glossy, orange fruit with a bright red blush. Very firm, orange, freestone flesh with good texture and flavor. Excellent for fresh market. Upright tree. Consistently productive. Resistant to perennial canker and brown rot. Moderately susceptible to bacterial spot. Ripens in early August. Cold hardy; Zone 4. Developed at the Harrow Research Station in Canada in 1979. *Source History: 3 in 1988; 5 in 1992; 4 in 2000.* **Sources: Ad2, Bea, Cu4, Hi9.**

Harval (HW 437) - Veecot x HW 435. Freestone fruit colors 30% red blush over bright orange ground. Firm, melting flesh of good quality. Moderately productive tree shows medium vigor and good resistance to canker, bacterial spot, skin cracking and brown rot. Released by the Harrow Station in Canada. Introduced in 1985. *Source History: 2 in 1992; 1 in 2000.* **Sources: Cu4.**

Hasanbey - *Source History: 1 in 2000.* **Sources: Nrs.**

Hopi - Small, sweet, desert fruit. Drought hardy tree. Originated at the Hopi mesas, northeast Arizona. *Source History: 1 in 1992; 1 in 2000.* **Sources: So12.**

Hungarian - Large fruit is excellent for canning and drying. Developed for commercial purposes. Upright tree. *Source History: 1 in 1988; 2 in 1992; 2 in 2000.* **Sources: Wel, Wom.**

Hungarian Rose - Sweet fruit. Use fresh or dry. Ripens in mid-July. Hardy in Zones 6-8. *Source History: 1 in 1988; 1 in 1992; 1 in 2000.* **Sources: St4.**

J. L. Budd - *Source History: 1 in 1992; 1 in 2000.* **Sources: Nrs.**

Japanese Ansu - Round, red fruit. Cultivated in Japan and Korea. *Source History: 1 in 1988; 1 in 1992; 1 in 2000.* **Sources: Sc2.**

Jordanne - Flavorful, large fruit is highly colored. Ripens slightly later than Castlebrite. Pollinator recommended. U.S. Plant Patent No. 8392. *Source History: 1 in 2000.* **Sources: WI4.**

Katy - Medium to large, bright yellow fruit. Semi-freestone. Good flavor. All purpose. Very productive, self-fruitful tree, 8-10' tall. Ripens early June, 4-5 weeks before Blenheim. Requires only 300-400 hours of chilling. Hardy in Zones 7-9. Developed by Floyd Zaiger. U.S. Plant Patent No. 4339. *Source History: 3 in 1988; 6 in 1992; 5 in 2000.* **Sources: Bay, CO5, ORA, St4, WI4.**

Lehrman (Improved Moorpark) - Large, yellow-orange fruit. Excellent for home use. Self-fruitful. Ripens a few days later than Wenatchee Moorpark. *Source History: 1 in 1992; 1 in 2000.* **Sources: Va2.**

Lorna - *Source History: 1 in 2000.* **Sources: Nrs.**

Luizet - *Source History: 1 in 2000.* **Sources: Nrs.**

Manchu - Fine flavored fruit. Hardy, reliable, self-fruitful tree. Good for cold weather regions. Plant on a north facing slope, so blossoms are delayed until after spring frosts. Ripens in mid-July. Developed by Dr. N. E. Hansen at the South Dakota Agricultural Experiment Station. *Source History: 1 in 1988; 2 in 1992; 1 in 2000.* **Sources: Nrs.**

Manchurian Bush Apricot (Manchurian) - *Prunus armeniaca* var. *mandshurica*. Small, plump, golden yellow fruit. Sweet, juicy, freestone flesh. Can be used for fresh eating, preserves and drying. Compact, bush-like tree grows 10-12' tall. Pinkish white, frost resistant blossoms appear in early spring before the glossy, green foliage. Amazingly vigorous. Thrives almost anywhere. Bears young and heavily. Self-fertile, but more fruitful in a group of two or three. Makes a good hedge planting. Dependably hardy when used for rootstock. Requires a minimum annual precipitation of 15". Ripens in mid-July. Hardy in Zones 2-9. Native to Manchuria where it withstands winters of -60 degrees F. and summers of +110 F. *Source History: 15 in 1988; 13 in 1992; 13 in 2000.* **Sources: Bea, BO4, Bu1, Fi1, Fo4, Ga6, Gur, Int, LA4, MEA, Sc2, Stl, WI12.**

Mesa No. 1 - *Source History: 1 in 1992; 1 in 2000.* **Sources: AG2.**

Montrose - *Source History: 1 in 1992; 1 in 2000.* **Sources: CO5.**

Moongold (MN 15) - Superb x *Prunus sibirica* Manchu. Medium size, soft, golden fruit. Firm, yellowish orange, freestone flesh. Sweet, slightly acid, tangy flavor. High quality. Good for fresh eating, canning and preserves. Vigorous, disease-free tree, less than 20' tall. Consistent, reliable bearer. Ripens unevenly with some splitting and premature fruit drop. Needs Sungold as a pollinator. Ripens from mid-July to early August depending on location; slightly earlier than Sungold. Exceptionally winter hardy; grows where others cannot survive. Developed by the University of Minnesota, 1961. *Source History: 9 in 1988; 12 in 1992; 10 in 2000.* **Sources: BA14, Ed5, Fa1, Fed, Fi1, Gur, Mi1, Nrs, SH8, Wa16.**

Moorpark - Very large, 2-2.5" fruit. Smooth, fuzzless, deep yellow skin with an orange red blush. Juicy, sweet, deep orange flesh. Excellent quality. Good for fresh eating, canning and drying. Good shipper. Vigorous dwarf tree grows 8-10' tall. Early, dependable producer. Profusion of showy, pinkish white blossoms in spring. Self-fertile, but fruit set is increased by planting two or more. Long ripening period extends from early July to late August depending on location. Requires 600 hours of chilling. Hardy in Zones 4-8. Originated in 1760 as a seedling of Nancy from Admiral Anson at his estate in Hartford, England. *Source History: 33 in 1988; 49 in 1992; 27 in 2000.* **Sources: Bar, Bay, Bo5, Bu1, CO5, Fi1, FO10, Fo4, Gur, Lee, Mel, Mi1, MI5, Na4, ORA, Po2, Sav, SH8, SIM, So5, Son, STR, Tex, WA8, Wel, WI4, Wom.**

Moorpark, Improved - Self-fruitful. *Source History: 1 in 1988; 1 in 1992; 1 in 2000.* **Sources: Leu.**

Newcastle (Early Newcastle) - Low chill. *Source History: 2 in 1988; 2 in 1992; 1 in 2000.* **Sources: ORA.**

Nugget - *Source History: 1 in 1992; 1 in 2000.* **Sources: WI4.**

Patterson - Large, highly colored fruit with firm flesh. Consistent, heavy producer. Good for canning, freezing, drying and fresh market. Ripens during June. Very popular commercial variety. *Source History: 1 in 1988; 5 in 1992; 3 in 2000.* **Sources: Nrs, Si3, WI4.**

Peggy - Good size, blemish-free, freestone fruit. Ripens in late May. *Source History: 1 in 1988; 1 in 1992; 1 in 2000.* **Sources: Wom.**

Perfection - One of the largest fruited apricots. Oval to oblong. Clear, yellowish orange to deep orange skin and flesh at full maturity. Good quality, texture and flavor. Very hardy, productive tree. Requires a pollinator. Ripens moderately early. One of the finest new commercial varieties. Originated in Washington. Introduced in 1937. *Source History: 10 in 1988; 14 in 1992; 8 in 2000.* **Sources: Co2, COL, JOY, Leu, Nrs, STR, Va2, WI12.**

Poppy - Medium to large size fruit with good flavor. Ripens in May, 5-7 days ahead of Castlebrite. U.S. Plant Patent No. 9593. *Source History: 1 in 2000.* **Sources: WI4.**

Precious - *Source History: 1 in 2000.* **Sources: Nrs.**

Puget Gold - Large, elongated, freestone fruit with very good flavor. Tree can easily be maintained at 15'. Prolific bearer. Blooms in early March. Self-fertile.

Ripens in early August. Zones 6-9. Requires 700 hours of chilling. Officially named and introduced by Washington State University. Formerly called Copeland. *Source History: 1 in 1988; 10 in 1992; 11 in 2000.* **Sources: Bu7, Clo, Co2, CO5, Gr16, ME3, Mo19, Or2, Rai, Son, WI4.**

Reliable - *Source History: 1 in 1992; 1 in 2000.* **Sources: Nrs.**

Rival - Large, oval, symmetrical fruit. Light orange skin develops a pronounced red blush. Firm, fine textured, deep orange flesh. Mild, subacid flavor. Vigorous, productive tree. Slightly susceptible to bacterial spot. Resistant to winter injury. Blooms early and requires an early blooming pollinator. Introduced by Washington State University. *Source History: 5 in 1988; 8 in 1992; 6 in 2000.* **Sources: Bo5, Co2, COL, Nrs, Va2, WI12.**

Robada - *Source History: 2 in 2000.* **Sources: Si3, Si3.**

Royal - Old-time favorite. Medium to large, yellow-orange fruit with excellent flavor. Blooms late. Ripens during June. *Source History: 7 in 1992; 6 in 2000.* **Sources: CO5, MI5, ORA, Pa2, Tex, Wel.**

Royal Rosa - Firm, aromatic, flavorful fruit. Highest quality. Self-fruitful tree bears young and heavily. Extremely vigorous. More disease tolerant than other apricots. Ripens early. Requires 500-600 hours of chilling. Developed by Floyd Zaiger. U.S. Plant Patent No. 3809. *Source History: 1 in 1988; 5 in 1992; 3 in 2000.* **Sources: Bay, ORA, WI4.**

Royalty - *Source History: 1 in 1988; 1 in 1992; 1 in 2000.* **Sources: CO5.**

Scout - Golden fruit with tender, juicy, freestone flesh. Self-fruitful tree, but more productive with a pollinator. Early, reliable bearer. Disease resistant. Ripens in July. Very hardy; Zone 3. Developed in Canada. *Source History: 1 in 1988; 6 in 1992; 5 in 2000.* **Sources: Bea, Ed5, Nrs, SH8, Va5.**

Smith - *Source History: 1 in 2000.* **Sources: Nrs.**

Somerset - Medium-large, shiny black fruit. Firm sweet flesh. Crack tolerant. Moderately vigorous, precocious tree with wide branch angles. Good bacterial canker tolerance. Ripens with Hedelfingen. *Source History: 1 in 2000.* **Sources: Ad2.**

Strathmore - *Source History: 1 in 1992; 1 in 2000.* **Sources: Va5.**

Sundrop - Medium size, round to slightly oval fruit. Bright orange skin with a slight blush. Smooth, medium firm, juicy, orange flesh tends to be clingstone. Sweet, mild flavor. Not self-fruitful. Ripens in late July. One of the most consistent producers at the New York State Fruit Testing Association. Introduced in 1975. *Source History: 2 in 1988; 2 in 1992; 1 in 2000.* **Sources: Nrs.**

SunGem - Medium size, dark orange fruit with bright red blush. Excellent quality. Highly resistant to bacterial spot; may be susceptible to canker and short lived in some areas. Ripens 14 days before Goldcot. U.S. Plant Patent No. 8674. *Source History: 1 in 2000.* **Sources: Hi9.**

Sunglow - Medium size fruit with deep yellow flesh. Acid flavor until fully mature. Fine quality. Attains its color before it ripens, so it can be picked firm. Fine shipper. Productive tree. Superior bud hardiness. *Source History: 2 in 1988; 3 in 1992; 1 in 2000.* **Sources: Co2.**

Sungold (NN 36) - Superb x *L. Manchu.* Orange blushed fruit with mild, sweet flavor. Thin, tender skin. Juicy, clear orange flesh is mild and sweet. Freestone. Good for canning and drying. Medium size, vigorous, slightly upright tree. Ripens midseason. Requires pollination with Moongold. Hardy to Zone 4. Developed at the University of Minnesota, 1940. *Source History: 7 in 1988; 11 in 1992; 11 in*

2000. **Sources: BA14, Bea, Ed5, Fa1, Fed, Fi1, Gur, Mi1, Nrs, SH8, Wa16.**

Super Hardy Chinese (S. H. Chinese) - Medium size fruit with tender, yellow to light orange flesh. Full apricot flavor. Good for fresh eating, freezing or preserves. Heavy bearer. Good pollinator. *Source History: 1 in 1988; 1 in 1992; 1 in 2000.* **Sources: Mi1.**

Sweet Pit - Large, fuzzless, deep orange fruit, 2.25-2.5" in diameter and .5-.75" long. Sweet flesh with a sweet, almond-like kernel. Preferred for jam, drying and roadside market. Self-fruitful tree grows 15-18' tall with a 12-15' spread. Blooms a bit later than most. Ripens in July. Requires a minimum annual precipitation of 15". Hardy in Zones 3-8. Still grown commercially in British Columbia at the northern limits of apricot culture. *Source History: 6 in 1988; 3 in 1992; 3 in 2000.* **Sources: Fi1, Gur, Or2.**

Sweetheart, Stark (Homedale Cultivar) - Firm, juicy, freestone fruit with a sprightly flavor. Good for fresh eating, canning and drying. Use kernels for snacks or in any recipe calling for almonds or nuts. Hardy, productive tree reaches 15-20'. Usually bears fruit in its third year. Ripens in mid-July. Hardy in Zones 5-8. Trademarked. U.S. Plant Patent No. 5651. *Source History: 1 in 1988; 1 in 1992; 1 in 2000.* **Sources: St4.**

Tilton, Stark (Friemann Cultivar) - Medium size, heart-shaped, golden yellow fruit with a dark red blush. Fine flavor. One of the leading commercial varieties for canning and drying. Also used fresh. Vigorous, productive tree. Self-fertile, but yields are improved when pollinated with Perfection or Wenatchee Moorpark. Ripens in mid-July in central California. Requires 600 hours of chilling. Hardy to Zone 5. U.S. Plant Patent No. 3927. *Source History: 17 in 1988; 22 in 1992; 14 in 2000.* **Sources: AG2, Bay, Co2, CO5, Jo3, MI5, Nrs, ORA, Pe2, STR, Va2, Wel, WI12, WI4.**

Tisdale - Consistent producer of medium size fruit. Introduced by R. Tisdale of Belton, Texas. *Source History: 1 in 2000.* **Sources: Wom.**

Tomcot - Large orange fruit with firm, sweet orange flesh. Blooms early. Somewhat self-fertile but should be cross-pollinated for commercial production. Ripens in early July in central Washington. Requires 600 hours of chilling. U.S. Plant Patent No. 7034. *Source History: 6 in 1992; 7 in 2000.* **Sources: Bay, Co2, COL, Mel, Va2, WI12, WI4.**

Traverse - Large fruit with paler yellow skin and flesh than Goldcot. Ripens seven days later than Goldcot. Does not conflict with the Montmorency harvest season. Developed by Michigan State University. *Source History: 1 in 1988; 1 in 1992; 1 in 2000.* **Sources: Nrs.**

Tri Gems - Large, firm fruit. New canning variety. Ripens mid-June. U.S. Plant Patent No. 6755. *Source History: 1 in 2000.* **Sources: WI4.**

Ume - Japanese apricot. Grows to 12'. Fruit is eaten raw, candied, boiled, preserved in sugar, pickled in salt and dried or made into a liqueur. Self-fertile. Zones 5-7. *Source History: 1 in 2000.* **Sources: Ed2.**

Veecot - Medium to large, round, deep orange fruit. Firm, very smooth textured, slightly juicy, freestone flesh. Excellent for canning. Very productive, hardy tree, but not as hardy as Alfred. Ripens in late July. Developed at Vineland, Ontario. Introduced in 1954. *Source History: 2 in 1988; 1 in 1992; 1 in 2000.* **Sources: Nrs.**

Velvaglo - *Source History: 1 in 1992; 1 in 2000.* **Sources: Nrs.**

Vivagold - *Source History: 1 in 1992; 1 in 2000.* **Sources: Nrs.**

Wenatchee Moorpark (Wenatchee) - Large, oval fruit with yellow skin and flesh. Good flavor. Excellent for home use, fresh, dried or canned. Self-fruitful, dwarf tree. Heavy bearer. Inter-fruitful with Perfection and Tilton. Long-time favorite in western Oregon and Washington. Recommended for other western climates where spring rains and frosts limit apricot culture. Requires 700 hours of chilling. Introduced in 1908 by C and O Nursery; one of their first introductions. *Source History: 6 in 1988; 7 in 1992; 8 in 2000.* **Sources: Bay, Co2, JOY, Nrs, Pe2, Va2, WI12, WI4.**

Wilson Delicious (Wilson) - Mutation of Moorpark found in Colorado. Medium to large, firm, golden orange fruit. Distinctive flavor. Excellent quality. Good for fresh use, canning, freezing, drying and desserts. Reliable, heavy bearing tree with extra-heavy foliage. Ripens in early July. Requires 700 hours of chilling. Hardy in Zones 5-8. *Source History: 2 in 1988; 2 in 1992; 1 in 2000.* **Sources: St4.**

Cherry / Sour
Prunus cerasus

Balaton - A sour cherry that is sweeter, larger and more firm than Montmorency. Makes a dark red juice. Extended ripening period. Self-pollinating but bears larger crops with pollination from any other cherry. Zones 5-8. Trademarked. *Source History: 2 in 2000.* **Sources: Hi9, St4.**

Bali - Natural dwarf tree grows 7' tall. Has produced up to 10 gallons of fruit per tree. Large 1" fruit is excellent for pies, sauces, jams and fresh eating. Ripens in late August. Hardy to Zone 3. Discovered near Edmonton, Alberta, Canada. *Source History: 2 in 2000.* **Sources: SH8, Stl.**

Black Beauty - *Source History: 1 in 2000.* **Sources: Ed5.**

CKVL No. 1 - Highly productive. Zones 4-8. *Source History: 1 in 2000.* **Sources: Hid.**

Danube (Erdi Botermo) - New, red-juiced type from the breeding program in Hungary. *Source History: 1 in 2000.* **Sources: Cu4.**

Early Richmond - Medium size, juicy, bright red fruit with thin, light red skin. Strong, healthy, self-pollinating trees grow 15-18' tall. Heavy producer. Leading sour variety that ripens a week or more earlier than other pie cherries. Hardy in Zones 4-8. *Source History: 15 in 1988; 20 in 1992; 18 in 2000.* **Sources: Bar, BO10, Bu1, Fi1, Fo4, Gur, Lee, Mel, MI10, MI5, Na4, Sav, SIM, Tex, TU5, Wel, Wh4, WI4.**

English Morello - Medium size, dark reddish black pie cherry with semifirm, tart flesh and dark-colored juice. Astringent until fully ripe. Trees are naturally semidwarf, upright, spreading, productive and hardy. Ripens in August. Hangs on the tree until the end of August. Originated in England. *Source History: 6 in 1988; 6 in 1992; 8 in 2000.* **Sources: Clo, CO5, Fed, MI5, ORA, Si3, So5, WI4.**

Evans - English Morello type with dark red, 1" fruit. Excellent sour cherry used fresh and for jam, juice, pies and wine. Zone 3. Possibly originated at the Alberta Tree Nursery. Introduced in 1923. *Source History: 1 in 2000.* **Sources: Ed5.**

Galaxy - Stocky, open growth habit results in a tree that shakes well. Requires less pruning and is easier to maintain. Retains all regular Montmorency characteristics of quality, size and processing as well as bloom and maturity dates. Trademarked. *Source History: 1 in 1988; 1 in 1992; 1 in 2000.* **Sources: Hi9.**

Goldrich - Large oval fruit with firm, fine textured, deep orange flesh. Productive, vigorous tree. Hardy. *Source History: 1 in 2000.* **Sources: Ad2.**

Jan and Joy - Montmorency-type fruit. Fall bearing; fruits one year after planting. Used like any pie cherry or left on the tree to dry. Vigorous grower. Highly resistant to powdery mildew, Japanese beetles and cherry worms. Minimal pruning. Hardy to -30 degrees F. Elwyn Meader introduction. *Source History: 2 in 1992; 5 in 2000.* **Sources: Ed2, Ed5, HA12, Stl, VIR.**

Joel - Begins bearing fruit the year after planting. Fruit ripens in late summer; not bothered by birds. Highly resistant to powdery mildew and cherry worms. Pollinate with Joy bush cherry. Hardy to -31 degrees F.; Zones 3-8. Elwyn Meader introduction. *Source History: 3 in 2000.* **Sources: Ed2, HA12, Stl.**

Late Duke - Large, heart-shaped, light red pie cherry with yellow flesh and subacid flavor. Good quality and flavor. Tree has the darker leaves of the tart cherries, but upright growth habit closer to sweet cultivars. Self-fertile according to some sources; requires cross-pollination according to others. Ripens in late July. *Source History: 2 in 1988; 1 in 2000.* **Sources: Rai.**

Late Hungarian - High quality fruit is firmer and sweeter than Montmorency with a larger pit. Vigorous tree may be slightly more susceptible to mid-winter cold temperatures than Montmorency. *Source History: 1 in 2000.* **Sources: Hi9.**

Lee's Select - Black fruit makes an excellent jam. Very productive. *Source History: 1 in 2000.* **Sources: Rai.**

Mesabi - Red fleshed fruits with sugar content midway between pie and sweet cherries. Tree grows 12' tall. Self-fruitful. Hardy at Duluth, Minnesota. *Source History: 2 in 1988; 7 in 1992; 3 in 2000.* **Sources: Nrs, SH8, Wa16.**

Meteor (Meteor Pie) - Montmorency x Russian variety. Large, oblong, bright red fruit resembles Montmorency. Tart, juicy, meaty flesh, colorless juice and a small, free pit. Natural genetic dwarf grows 8-12' tall. Moderately spreading with large, heavy, dark green foliage that shields fruit from sunscald and birds. Leaf spot resistant. Spur-type. Self-fruitful. Bears quite early. Blooms and ripens a week later than Montmorency in late June. Hardy to -50 degrees F. with occasional winter injury. Developed at the Minnesota Fruit Breeding Farm. Introduced in 1952. *Source History: 15 in 1988; 26 in 1992; 22 in 2000.* **Sources: BA14, Ch9, Cu4, Fa1, Fed, Fi1, GR26, Gr4, Gur, Hi9, Jun, LI7, Mc3, Nrs, On3, Pi2, Sc6, SH8, Stl, Va5, Wa16, WI4.**

Montmorency - Sweet cherry x *Prunus tomentosa*. The standard for pie cherries. Medium large, bright red fruits with firm, yellow flesh and clear juice. Rich, tart, tangy flavor. Doesn't get mushy during processing. Spreading, self-fruitful tree grows to 15'. Requires good drainage and aeration. Ripens in late June. Requires approximately 700 hours of chilling. Hardy to -40 degrees F. Originated in France in the 17th century. Introduced to the United States in 1760. *Source History: 58 in 1988; 79 in 1992; 61 in 2000.* **Sources: Bar, Bay, Bea, Bo5, Bu7, Ch9, Cla, Clo, Co2, CO5, COL, Cu4, Cum, Ea3, Ed5, Fi1, FO10, GI3, GR26, Gr4, Gur, Hi9, Iso, Jo3, JOY, Jun, La3, Lee, Leu, LI7, ME3, Mel, Mi1, MI10, MI5, Na4, Nrs, ORA, Pe2, Pi2, Rai, Sav, Sc6, SH8, SIM, So5, Son, St4, Stl, STR, Tex, TU5, Va2, Wa16, WA8, WAF, Wel, Wh4, WI12, WI4, Wor.**

Montmorency, Pennsylvania Certified - Strain of Montmorency propagated from "trees selected for outstanding qualities and grown under the Pennsylvania Fruit Tree Improvement Program." *Source History: 1 in 1988; 1 in 1992; 1 in 2000.* **Sources: Ad2.**

Montmorency, Starkspur (Carnefix Cultivar) - Bright red fruit with pleasant, tangy flavor when ripe. Compact, spur-type tree. Hardy in Zones 5-7. Trade marked. U.S. Plant Patent No. 3304. *Source History: 2 in 1988; 1 in 1992; 1 in 2000.* **Sources: St4.**

New York 13242 - Large red fruit. Clear juice. Self-fertile. *Source History: 1 in 2000.* **Sources: Cu4.**

North Star - Siberian cherry x English Morello. Large fruited Morello-type with thin, light red skin, red flesh, red juice and a small freestone. Will retain quality on the tree up to two weeks after ripening, turning from light red to mahogany. Crack resistant. Natural dwarf tree grows 6-12' tall. Upright, moderately spreading habit. Dense, luxuriant foliage. Vigorous. Self-fruitful. Often bears in its second year. Heavy crops. Ripens from mid-June to early July. Requires 1,000 hours of chilling. Hardy to -40 degrees F. Developed by the Minnesota Agricultural Experiment Station from a seedling found in Yugoslavia. Introduced in 1950. *Source History: 42 in 1988; 53 in 1992; 47 in 2000.* **Sources: BA14, Bay, Bea, BO10, Bo5, Bu1, Ch9, Cla, CO5, Cu4, Cum, Ed2, Ed5, Fa1, Fed, Fi1, FO10, Fo4, GI3, GR26, Gr4, Gur, Hi9, Iso, Jun, Lee, Mc3, ME3, Mel, Mi1, MI5, Or2, Sav, Sc6, SH8, SIM, So5, St4, Stl, STR, TU5, Wa16, WA8, Wel, Wh4, WI12, WI4.**

Sassy (Erdi Botermo) - Large fruit with a firm texture. Excellent flavor is sweeter than Montmorency. Stores well. Can be machine harvested. More susceptible to mid-winter cold and European brown rot than Montmorency. Dry stem scar seals off the fruit when the stem is removed. Trademarked. *Source History: 1 in 2000.* **Sources: Hi9.**

Schatten Morello (Shattenmorelle) - *Source History: 2 in 1992; 1 in 2000.* **Sources: Nrs.**

Sour Chari - Ripens just before CKVL No. 1. Originated in Yugoslavia. *Source History: 1 in 2000.* **Sources: Hid.**

Suda Hardy - Genetic dwarf tree to 10' tall. Red pie cherry of the Morello type. Has darkest juice of all sour cherries. Good flavor. Cans and freezes well. Ripens in early July. Hardy in Zones 4-7. *Source History: 2 in 1988; 1 in 1992; 3 in 2000.* **Sources: Bea, Ch9, Nrs.**

Surefire - Bright red skin and flesh. High sugar content. Blooms late; up to one week later than Montmorency. Crack resistant. Semi-upright, vigorous tree. Trademarked. Plant patent applied for. *Source History: 3 in 2000.* **Sources: Cu4, Hi9, Rai.**

Ujfehertoi Furtos - Dark juice variety highly recommended for fruit size, quality and productivity. Hardiness compares to Montmorency. Ripens late. Zone 4. Hungarian variety that may be the same as the trademarked name "Balaton". *Source History: 1 in 2000.* **Sources: Ed5.**

Wczesna Z Prin - *Source History: 1 in 1992; 1 in 2000.* **Sources: Nrs.**

Cherry / Sweet

Prunus avium

Angela - High quality black sweet cherry from Utah. Large, glossy black fruit with firm, dark red flesh. Good flavor. Vigorous, heavily productive tree. Sometimes oversets, which results in somewhat smaller fruit. Resistant to buckskin and Western-X diseases. Can be pollinated by Lambert. Offers good crack resistance and late blooming. Ripens mid-July. More winter and frost hardy than most. Requires approximately 700 hours of chilling. *Source History: 6 in 1988; 6 in 1992; 5 in 2000.* **Sources: Clo, Gr4, Mo19, Nrs, Rai.**

Attika (Kordia) - Large black fruit with juicy, dark red, firm flesh and long stem.

Blooms late. Ripens about 10 days after Bing. Originated in Czechoslovakia. Trademarked. *Source History: 1 in 1992; 4 in 2000.* **Sources: Co2, COL, Hi9, Va2.**

Bada - Yellow sweet cherry with red blush. Creamy flesh has best flavor when tree ripened. Vigorous, productive, genetic dwarf tree. Can be easily maintained at 12-15'. Heavy, reliable producer. Good pollinator. Recommended by Oregon State University for areas where bacterial canker is a problem. Ripens in mid-June. Hardy in Zones 6-8. *Source History: 3 in 1988; 2 in 1992; 3 in 2000.* **Sources: Ch9, Gr4, Nrs.**

Bear Creek Early - Sweet, firm, dark red fruits. Strong, semidwarf tree on Mazzard rootstock. Excellent for fresh eating and canning. Keeps well. Ripens one week before Bing. Hardy in Zone 5. *Source History: 1 in 1992; 1 in 2000.* **Sources: Bea.**

Bing - The standard for flavor. Large, heart-shaped, freestone fruits with dark red to brownish purple skin. Firm, meaty, purple flesh. Somewhat susceptible to cracking. Fresh market and canning. Good shipper. Large, spreading tree grows 25-30' tall. Medium hardy and a shy bearer. Pollinate with Black Tartarian, Mazzard, Montmorency, Rainier, Sam, Van, Windsor or Stella. Does not pollinate with Emperor Francis, Lambert or Napoleon. Ripens from mid-June to early July depending on location. The leading commercial sweet cherry in the West. Requires 700 hours of chilling. Hardy in Zones 5-8. Introduced in 1850. *Source History: 44 in 1988; 58 in 1992; 43 in 2000.* **Sources: Bar, Bay, Bo5, BR10, Cla, Co2, CO5, COL, Ea3, Fi1, GI3, Gur, Hi9, Iso, JOY, Lee, ME3, Mel, Mi1, MI5, Na4, Nrs, ORA, Pe2, Pi2, Rai, Sav, SH8, Si3, SIM, So5, Son, St4, STR, Tex, TU5, Va2, Wa16, Wel, WI12, WI4, Wor, ZEL.**

Bing, Petrolia Strain - Leading commercial variety. High quality fruit. Ripens in mid-June. *Source History: 1 in 1988; 1 in 1992; 1 in 2000.* **Sources: Gr4.**

Black Gold (NY 13791) - Stella x Gold. Dark red, firm fruit. Blooms late. Self-fertile. Ripens just ahead of Hedelfingen. *Source History: 1 in 2000.* **Sources: Ad2.**

Black Republican - Good quality, medium size fruit. Very dark red, turning black when fully ripe. Distinct flavor. Good keeper and shipper. Excellent pollinator for other sweet cherries. *Source History: 4 in 1988; 7 in 1992; 5 in 2000.* **Sources: Co2, COL, Nrs, Va2, WI12.**

Black Tartarian (Black Tartan, Black Tart, Tartarian) - Medium large, heart-shaped fruits vary from purplish black to red depending on site. Thick, tender, juicy, dark red flesh. Rich, sweet, full bodied flavor. Vigorous tree grows 30' tall. Waxy green foliage. Exceptionally productive once established. Old trees generally show canker, but vigor enables them to go on producing full crops. Best pollinator for dark sweet cherries. Once the most widely grown commercial variety, but a little too juicy to ship well. Excellent for home orchard. Bears early. Ripens from mid-June to early July depending on location. Requires 700 hours of chilling. Hardy in Zones 5-7. *Source History: 41 in 1988; 53 in 1992; 42 in 2000.* **Sources: Bar, Bay, Bo5, Bu1, Cla, Co2, CO5, Cum, Fi1, FO10, GI3, Gr4, Gur, Iso, Jo3, JOY, Lee, Leu, Mel, Mi1, MI10, MI5, Na4, Nrs, ORA, Pe2, Pi2, Sav, SH8, Si3, SIM, So5, STR, Tex, TU5, Wa16, WA8, Wel, Wh4, WI12, WI4, Wor.**

Blackheart (Teickners Schwarze Herzkirsche) - A modern German variety that originated in the Harz mountain region. Medium large, purplish black fruit turning jet-black when fully ripe. Fine, sweet, sometimes slightly almond flavor. Ripens very late. Obtained from the Dresden Nursery. *Source History: 1 in 1988; 2 in*

1992; 1 in 2000. **Sources: Ch9.**

Brooks - Large, firm fruit with good color. Good productivity. Ripens one week before Bing. Introduced by the University of California. U.S. Plant Patent No. 6676. *Source History: 1 in 1988; 4 in 1992; 3 in 2000.* **Sources: AG2, Si3, WI4.**

Burlat, Early (Burlat) - Large, red to purplish red fruit. Medium firm flesh, somewhat softer than Bing. Excellent flavor. Strong growing tree, well branched with moderate, upright growth. Pollinate with Bing, Royal Anne, Black Tartarian and Van. Good resistance to bacterial canker. Early ripening from late May to early June, depending on location. *Source History: 3 in 1988; 4 in 1992; 3 in 2000.* **Sources: Clo, Nrs, Rai, WI4.**

Cavalier - Medium to large fruit with deep, rich color and shiny finish. Dry, firm flesh resists cracking. Upright, spreading tree. Medium vigor. Somewhat slow to come into bearing. Picks easily and has good holding qualities for fresh market. Ripens early. Very hardy. Trademarked. U.S. Plant Patent No. 5096. *Source History: 1 in 1988; 1 in 1992; 2 in 2000.* **Sources: Bo5, Hi9.**

Chelan - Stella x Beaulieu. Medium to large fruit with medium to dark red flesh. Good firmness. Moderate cracking. Ripens 10-12 days before Bing. Developed at Prosser, Washington. Trademarked. U.S. Plant Patent No. 8545. *Source History: 7 in 2000.* **Sources: BR10, Co2, COL, Hi9, Si3, Va2, WI12.**

Chinook - *Source History: 3 in 1992; 1 in 2000.* **Sources: Nrs.**

Corum - Royal Anne type from Oregon. Yellow skin with red blush. Soft flesh is very sweet and suitable for canning. *Source History: 1 in 1988; 3 in 1992; 3 in 2000.* **Sources: Ea3, Gr4, Nrs.**

Craig's Crimson - Medium-large, dark red, firm fruit. Good flavor. Genetic semi-dwarf tree. If grown on GM 61/1 dwarfing rootstock, tree grows 8-12'; on Colt rootstock, 10-16'. Self-fruitful. Requires 800 hours of chilling. U.S. Plant Patent No. 7320. *Source History: 5 in 1992; 2 in 2000.* **Sources: Bay, WI4.**

Deacon - *Source History: 2 in 1992; 1 in 2000.* **Sources: Nrs.**

Early Purple Gean - Large, heart-shaped, shiny, purplish black fruit. Soft, tender, juicy flesh. Ripens very early. Sent by de Candolle to the Royal Horticultural Society of London where it was given its name. Introduced in 1822. *Source History: 1 in 1988; 1 in 1992; 1 in 2000.* **Sources: So5.**

Early Rivers - Seedling of Early Purple Gean. Large, unevenly-shaped, reddish black fruit with soft, dark flesh. Seldom cracks in wet weather. Ripens early. Long been regarded as one of the finest English cherries. Introduced in 1872 by the famous English nurseryman, Thomas Rivers. *Source History: 1 in 1988; 2 in 1992; 1 in 2000.* **Sources: So5.**

Early Ruby - Large, dark red fruit with sweet, purple flesh. Appreciated for its early, heavy production. Pollinate with Black Tartarian, Van or Royal Ann. Ripens in late May. Requires approximately 500 hours of chilling. U.S. Plant Patent No. 4150. *Source History: 2 in 1988; 2 in 1992; 1 in 2000.* **Sources: CO5.**

Ebony - *Source History: 2 in 1992; 1 in 2000.* **Sources: Nrs.**

Emperor Francis - Large, high quality sweet cherry of the White Oxheart type. Yellowish white color similar to that of Napoleon, but with more red blush. Also firmer, meatier and less subject to cracking. Outstanding flavor. Hardy, reliably productive tree. Ripens in June. One of the best main crop sweet cherries. *Source History: 9 in 1988; 11 in 1992; 13 in 2000.* **Sources: Ad2, Bo5, Co2, Cu4, Hi9, Mi1, Mo19, Nrs, Rai, St4, Va2, Wh4, Wor.**

Giant (Burbank Black Giant) - Large, very dark red fruit. Dark, blood-red flesh is very sweet and juicy. Fine, rich flavor. Ripens late. First grown by Luther Burbank and regarded by him as one of his best creations. Introduced in 1900. *Source History: 1 in 1988; 2 in 1992; 2 in 2000.* **Sources: Nrs, So5.**

Glacier - Large, attractive, mahogany, heart-shaped fruit. Blooms about the same time as Bing, but ripens 4-5 days earlier. Crack resistant. Self-fertile. Developed at Washington State University. Plant patent applied for. *Source History: 1 in 1992; 1 in 2000.* **Sources: Rai.**

Golden Heart, Jung's - Large, golden, heart-shaped fruits are blushed with red. Delicious tangy flavor. Crack resistant. Good yields. Not bothered by birds. Good pollinator for other sweet cherries. Zones 5-7. *Source History: 1 in 2000.* **Sources: Jun.**

Golden Sweet (Gold, Golden Cherry) - Small, firm fruits with crack resistant, light golden skin. Very sweet and juicy. Can be canned in light syrup. Used extensively for maraschino processing. Tree grows 20' tall. Well adapted to mechanical harvesting. Heavy producer. Excellent pollinator. Ripens in early June. Some folks claim birds go after red berries and leave the gold ones for the grower. *Source History: 5 in 1988; 10 in 1992; 14 in 2000.* **Sources: Bea, Bo5, Co2, Cu4, Ed5, Fi1, Hi9, MI5, Sc6, SIM, So5, Va2, Wh4, Wor.**

Goodman Gold - Clear yellow cherry. Flavor has a refreshing tanginess lacking in red types. Excellent for pies and canning. Slightly smaller than Bing and ripens two weeks later. Less bothered by birds because of its yellow color. *Source History: 1 in 1988; 1 in 1992; 1 in 2000.* **Sources: Gr4.**

Governor Wood - Large, pale yellow fruit with bright red cheeks. Softer, juicier flesh has the advantage of being less prone to cracking in wet weather. Rich, tangy flavor. Good table variety. Trees are noted for their vigor and productivity. Ripens early. Hardy in Zones 5-8. Seedling raised by Dr. Jared P. Kirtland of Cleveland, Ohio. Introduced in 1842. *Source History: 5 in 1988; 5 in 1992; 4 in 2000.* **Sources: Bar, Gr4, So5, TU5.**

Hardy Giant - Medium large, firm, reddish black fruits are highly resistant to cracking. Excellent flavor. Blooms early and bears heavily. Good pollinator for other sweet cherries, especially Lambert. Ripens in mid-July over a longer period than most cherries. Grown commercially in some areas. *Source History: 4 in 1988; 6 in 1992; 5 in 2000.* **Sources: Clo, Co2, Nrs, Rai, Va2.**

Hartland (New York 3308) - Open-pollinated Windsor type. Large, black fruits with small pits. Vigorous, spreading tree bears especially heavy annual crops. Self-fruitful. Trademarked. *Source History: 1 in 1988; 2 in 1992; 5 in 2000.* **Sources: Ad2, Bo5, Cu4, Hi9, WAF.**

Hedelfingen - Old European variety. Large, firm, black fruit of the Lambert type. More resistant to cracking than most. Exceptional quality. Used for fresh eating, freezing or canning. Vigorous, healthy, early bearing and reliably productive. Resembles Schmidt with which it is inter-fruitful. Ripens midseason. Hardy in Zones 5-7. *Source History: 10 in 1988; 14 in 1992; 12 in 2000.* **Sources: Ad2, Bo5, Co2, Cu4, Gr4, Hi9, Jun, Mel, Nrs, St4, Va2, Wh4.**

Hoskins - *Source History: 1 in 2000.* **Sources: Nrs.**

Hudson - Oswego x Giant. Medium large, black fruit with very firm, sweet flesh and good flavor. Crack resistant. Hangs well and keeps in good condition. Large, open, hardy, moderately productive tree. Ripens late. Introduced in New York in 1964. *Source History: 3 in 1988; 6 in 1992; 6 in 2000.* **Sources: Ad2, Bo5, Cu4, Hi9, Mo19, Sc6.**

Index - Dark red, medium to large size fruit with good firmness. Moderate rain cracking. Self-fertile. Ripens 5-7 days before Bing. U.S. Plant Patent No. 10,459. *Source History: 4 in 2000.* **Sources: BR10, Co2, COL, Si3.**

Kansas Sweet (Hansen) - Cross between sweet and sour cherry. Large, mahogany-red fruits. Sweet, firm, juicy flesh. Shapely tree grows 30' tall. Bing and Black Tartarian are good pollinators. Ripens in late June. *Source History: 2 in 1988; 4 in 1992; 2 in 2000.* **Sources: CO5, Rai.**

Kristin - European Francis x Gil Peck. Glossy, 1" diameter, purplish black fruit. Tender skin. Firm, meaty, juicy flesh. Sweet, richly aromatic flavor. Too dark for use in brining. Large, vigorous, winter hardy tree. Heavy cropping. Not compatible with Emperor Francis and NY 6476. Pollinate with NY 3308 and NY 11390. Ripens in mid-July. Proven winter hardy in Zone 5 and milder parts of Zone 4. Tested for 12 years in Norway, Montana and at the New York Agricultural Experiment Station in Geneva. Introduced in 1982. *Source History: 2 in 1988; 11 in 1992; 16 in 2000.* **Sources: Ad2, Bea, BO10, Bu7, Ch9, Clo, Cu4, Ed5, Fi1, Hi9, Mi1, Mo19, Nrs, On3, Rai, Sc6.**

Lambert - Dark red, heart-shaped fruit, slightly smaller than Bing. Strong, upright tree. Vigorous, hardy and heavy bearing. Susceptible to cracking in Eastern and Midwestern weather. Not as productive as Bing during first 12 years. More resistant to late spring frosts. Ripens 1-2 weeks later. Pollinate with Angela, Black Tartarian, Rainier, Sam, Stella or Van. Requires 800 hours of chilling. Hardy in Zones 5-7. Ranks second only to Bing as a commercial variety. Introduced in 1964. *Source History: 16 in 1988; 16 in 1992; 11 in 2000.* **Sources: Co2, Gur, Hi9, JOY, ME3, MI5, Nrs, Son, Va2, WI12, WI4.**

Lambert, Compact - Very large, dark reddish black fruit with solid flesh. Prone to cracking in damp summers. Genetic dwarf tree grows only 7-10' tall. Well suited for growing either in a pot or in the ground. Requires a pollinator. Ripens in mid-June. Hardy in Zones 5-7. *Source History: 2 in 1988; 4 in 1992; 1 in 2000.* **Sources: Gr4.**

Lamida - *Source History: 2 in 1992; 1 in 2000.* **Sources: Nrs.**

Lapins - Van x Stella. New Canadian introduction. Originally trialed as pollinators by commercial orchardists, and now becoming the replacement tree for Bings in much of the commercial cherry industry. Firm fruit as large as Bings. Excellent quality and rich flavor. Crack resistant. Heavy producer. Self-fertile. Resists late frosts. Ripens Late July. Requires 800 hours of chilling. Hardy in Zone 5. Introduced in 1983. *Source History: 1 in 1988; 18 in 1992; 30 in 2000.* **Sources: Ad2, Bay, Bea, BR10, Bu7, Clo, Co2, CO5, COL, Hi9, ME3, Mel, Mi1, MI5, Mo19, Nrs, On3, ORA, Pe2, Rai, Sc6, Si3, So5, Son, St4, STR, Va2, Wa3, WI12, WI4.**

Larian - *Source History: 2 in 1992; 1 in 2000.* **Sources: Nrs.**

Lyons - *Source History: 2 in 1992; 1 in 2000.* **Sources: Nrs.**

Merton Bigarreau - Knight's Early Black x Napoleon. Large, round, dark red fruit. Juicy, firm, light crimson flesh. Thin skinned. Superb quality. Heavy crops. Introduced in 1947 by Mr. M. B. Crane of the John Innes Horticultural Institute in England. *Source History: 1 in 1988; 3 in 1992; 1 in 2000.* **Sources: Nrs.**

Mona - *Source History: 2 in 1988; 3 in 1992; 2 in 2000.* **Sources: CO5, STR.**

Moreau - *Source History: 2 in 1992; 1 in 2000.* **Sources: Nrs.**

Napoleon (Royal Anne, Napoleon Wax, Emperor Francis Cultivar) - White Oxheart type. Pale yellow fruit with bright red cheeks. Firm, juicy flesh. Fine, very sweet flavor. One of the best for brining. Vigorous, well-shaped tree. Heavy crops. Pollinate with any sweet cherry except Bing or Lambert. Ripens from mid-

June to early July depending on location. Hardy in Zones 5-7. Recommended for home and commercial planting. *Source History: 8 in 1988; 6 in 1992; 5 in 2000.* **Sources: Hi9, Mel, Mi1, Nrs, Sc6.**

New Pioneer - Van x Bing. *Source History: 2 in 1992; 2 in 2000.* **Sources: Lee, Sav.**

New York 13791 - Gold x Stella. Late bloomer. Shiny, black fruit resists cracking. Shows considerable canker tolerance. Good pollenizer. Ripens early midseason. *Source History: 1 in 2000.* **Sources: Cu4.**

Olympus - Large, heart-shaped fruit with glossy, dark mahogany skin. Firm, dark red-black flesh. Low acid flavor. Ripens 5-7 days after Bing. Vigorous, spreading, productive tree. Pollinates with Sam and Lambert. Trademarked. U.S. Plant Patent No. 8033. *Source History: 1 in 2000.* **Sources: Hi9.**

Rainier - Van x Bing. Large, yellow fruit with a red blush similar to Royal Ann. Firm, clear to light yellow flesh. Fine texture and distinct flavor. Colorless juice. Lacks acidity to be as good a cooking cherry as Royal Ann. Vigorous, upright, spreading tree. Early bearing. Very productive. Sometimes tends to overbear, reducing fruit size but not quality. Exceptional holding ability after harvest. Resists cracking, spurs and doubles. Pollinate with Bing, Black Tartarian, Emperor Francis, Lambert, Mazzard, Montmorency, Napoleon, Sam, Stella or Van. Ripens midseason. Tolerates hot summers. Requires 700 hours of chilling. Zones 5-9. *Source History: 18 in 1988; 26 in 1992; 28 in 2000.* **Sources: Bay, Bea, BR10, Bu7, Ch9, Clo, Co2, CO5, COL, Ea3, Ed2, Gr4, Gur, Hi9, JOY, ME3, MI5, Nrs, On3, Pe2, Rai, Si3, So5, Son, STR, Va2, WI12, WI4.**

Rainier, Royal - Red blushed "white" variety with large, firm, yellow fruit. Holds well on the tree. Requires a pollinator. Zaiger introduction. Plant patent pending. *Source History: 1 in 2000.* **Sources: WI4.**

Regina - New variety from Germany. High quality, large dark red firm fruit. Mild sweet flavor. Tolerant to cracking. Ripens between Lapins and Sweetheart. Plant patent applied for. *Source History: 3 in 2000.* **Sources: Co2, COL, Va2.**

Ron's Seedling - *Source History: 1 in 2000.* **Sources: Nrs.**

Royal Ann (Napoleon, Napoleon Royal Ann, Royal Anne, Napolean Bigarreau) - Very old French variety. Large, firm, light yellow fruit with a beautiful rose blush. Firm, juicy, sweet flesh. Excellent fresh and for processing. Holds shape well. Considered one of the best for brining and canning. Often used for commercial maraschino cherries. Upright tree grows rapidly 20-25' tall. Heavy bearer when it misses the spring frosts. Ripens midseason. Pollinate with Black Tartarian, Montmorency, Sam, Stella, Van or Windsor, but not with Bing or Lambert. Requires 700 hours of chilling. Hardy in Zones 5-7. *Source History: 21 in 1988; 24 in 1992; 18 in 2000.* **Sources: Bay, Bea, Co2, CO5, COL, Gr4, Gur, JOY, Jun, Leu, ME3, MI5, ORA, SH8, STR, Va2, WI12, WI4.**

Royalton (NY 11390) - Chinook x open. Very large, black fruit. Resistant to fruit cracking caused by heavy spring rains. Ripens midseason; one week before Hedelfingen. Ulster, Emporer Francis, Kristin and Hartland are preferred pollinators. Zones 5-8. Plant patent applied for. *Source History: 1 in 1988; 2 in 1992; 4 in 2000.* **Sources: Ad2, Bo5, St4, WAF.**

Salmo - *Source History: 2 in 1992; 1 in 2000.* **Sources: Nrs.**

Sam - Medium large, firm, jet-black fruits. Large, vigorous, hardy, upright and spreading tree with a desirable framework. Blooms later than most sweet cherries and so may escape late spring frosts. Self-unfruitful, but a good pollinator. Pollinate with Bing, Montmorency, Royal Ann, Stella or Van. Shows some resistance to canker and cracking. Ripens early. Zones 5-9. Developed at Summerland, British Columbia. Introduced in 1953. *Source History: 11 in 1988; 16 in 1992; 13 in 2000.* **Sources: Bu7, Cu4, Gr4, Hi9, JOY, La3, Leu, ME3, Nrs, On3, Rai, WI4, Wor.**

Sandra Rose - Large, symmetrical dark red fruit with flat-round shape. Moderately short stem. Good flavor. Moderately firm flesh. Crack tolerant. Self-fertile. Ripens three days after Van. Introduced by the Summerland, British Columbia breeding program. Trademarked. Plant patent applied for. *Source History: 1 in 2000.* **Sources: COL.**

Saylor - Clear, bright yellow fruit with crisp, crunchy, juicy flesh. Very sweet; distinctive aftertaste. Ripens late. Origin unknown. *Source History: 1 in 1988; 2 in 1992; 2 in 2000.* **Sources: Nrs, So5.**

Schmidt (Schmidt's Bigarreau) - Large, deep mahogany fruits grow in clusters. Dark, fine grained flesh. Pleasingly sweet, rich flavor. Fresh market and commercial canning. Good shipper. Vigorous, hardy tree. Slow to come into bearing. Moderately productive. Good crack resistance. Requires a pollinator. Ripens in early July. Earliest of the large, hard fleshed sweet cherries, which makes it very profitable. *Source History: 10 in 1988; 12 in 1992; 9 in 2000.* **Sources: Ad2, Bo5, Hi9, Leu, Mi1, Nrs, Va2, Wh4, Wor.**

Schneider - Large, firm cherry. Resists cracking and bruising. Ripens late. Good pollinator for late sweet cherries. *Source History: 2 in 2000.* **Sources: Co2, Va2.**

Schneider Spate Knorpelkirshe - *Source History: 2 in 1992; 1 in 2000.* **Sources: Nrs.**

Seneca (Early Seneca) - *Source History: 2 in 1992; 1 in 2000.* **Sources: Nrs.**

Skeena - Large round fruit with dark red to black skin. Juicy, sweet, firm flesh. Shows good tolerance to rain-induced cracking. Self-fertile. Ripens about 14 days after Van. Introduced from the Summerland, British Columbia breeding program. Trademarked. Plant patent applied for. *Source History: 1 in 2000.* **Sources: COL.**

Somerset - Precocious black cherry. Tree grows 12-15'. Blooms early. Canker tolerant. Zones 4-7. Trademarked. *Source History: 4 in 2000.* **Sources: Cu4, Hi9, Wa16, WAF.**

Sonata - Large, black, kidney-shaped fruit with a dimpled blossom end. Firm, juicy flesh is moderately sweet. Shows moderate susceptibility to rain-induced cracking. Self-fertile. Ripens seven days after Van. Summerland, British Columbia breeding program introduction. Trademarked. Plant patent applied for. *Source History: 2 in 2000.* **Sources: COL, Va2.**

Sparkle - *Source History: 2 in 1992; 1 in 2000.* **Sources: Nrs.**

Star Stella - Deep wine-red, nearly black fruit. Firm and juicy. Larger than the 1" Lamberts. Tree bears younger than other sweet cherries. Requires cross-pollination. *Source History: 1 in 1988; 3 in 1992; 2 in 2000.* **Sources: Mi1, Nrs.**

Stark Gold (Thomas Cultivar) - Golden fruit with tangy flavor. Crack resistant. Pollinate with any other sweet cherry. Extremely disease resistant. Ripens in mid-June. Hardy to -30 degrees F. and in Zones 5-7. Trademarked. *Source History: 1 in 1988; 1 in 1992; 1 in 2000.* **Sources: St4.**

Starkrimson (Lapins Cultivar) - Extra large red fruit over 1" in diameter. Firm, juicy flesh. Tree grows 15-18' tall. Self-pollinating. Ripens in late June. Hardy in Zones 5-8. Trademarked. *Source History: 1 in 1988; 1 in 1992; 1 in 2000.*

Sources: St4.

Stella - Lambert type. Large, heart-shaped, dark red fruit. Sweet, juicy flesh. Rich flavor. Ideal for home orchard. Very vigorous, productive tree grows 25-30' tall. First self-fertile sweet cherry. Moderate crack resistance. Fine pollinator for other varieties. Ripens in mid-June. Fruit buds are relatively winter tender. Requires 700 hours of chilling. Hardy in Zones 5-8. Developed at Summerland, British Columbia. Introduced in 1968. *Source History: 26 in 1988; 37 in 1992; 31 in 2000.* Sources: Bay, Bo5, CO5, Fi1, GR26, Gr4, Gur, Hi9, Iso, Jo3, JOY, La3, Leu, ME3, Mel, MI5, Nrs, ORA, Pe2, Rai, Sc6, SH8, Si3, So5, Son, St4, STR, Va2, WI12, WI4, Wor.

Stella, Compact (Dwarf Stella) - Medium to large, heart-shaped, black fruit. Good texture and flavor. Genetic dwarf tree grows 7-9' tall, 40-60% of standard size. Sets fruit young with heavy, consistent crops. Good pollinator for other sweet cherries. Ripens from mid-June to early July depending on location. Requires 750 hours of chilling. Hardy in Zones 5-9. *Source History: 10 in 1988; 9 in 1992; 7 in 2000.* Sources: CO5, Ed2, Fi1, Gr4, Mi1, Nrs, Wh4.

Sue - Bing x Schmidt. Large, waxy yellow fruit with a pink or red blush. Firm flesh. Sweet, rich, vinous flavor. Very resistant to cracking. Prolific. Developed by J. H. Mann of the Summerland Station in British Columbia. Introduced in 1936. *Source History: 1 in 1988; 4 in 1992; 3 in 2000.* Sources: Bo5, So5, Wor.

Sugar Sweet - Van type. Medium size, ruby-red fruit. Has sweetness of Bing, but more crack resistance and better quality. Excellent pollinator, but not self-fertile. Heavy producer at an early age. *Source History: 3 in 1988; 2 in 1992; 1 in 2000.* Sources: Bu1.

Summit - Van x Sam. Large, 1.25" diameter, heart-shaped fruit. Small pit. Good flavor. Fairly resistant to cracking. Pollinate with any other sweet cherry. Ripens in mid-June. Hardy in Zones 5-8. Introduced in 1973. *Source History: 3 in 1988; 3 in 1992; 5 in 2000.* Sources: Ad2, Cu4, Hi9, Nrs, St4.

Sunburst - Stella x Van. Large fruit resembles Stella. Self-fertile. Good producer. Ripens mid-May. *Source History: 1 in 1988; 3 in 1992; 3 in 2000.* Sources: Hi9, Nrs, WI4.

Super Dwarf - The varieties Hedelfingen and Royal Ann are budded onto Gisela rootstock, a German development that produces a tree about half the size of regular sweet cherries which makes it easy to cover to protect from the birds. Begin bearing in 3 years. Very hardy and adapt to a wide variety of soil types. Very productive. Staking the tree helps suport the heavy load of fruit. *Source History: 1 in 2000.* Sources: Jun.

Surefire (NY 12716) - Borchert Black Sour x NY 6935 (Richmorency x Schattenmorelle). Bright red skin and flesh. High natural sugars make it excellent for fresh eating. Blooms late. Upright, open tree bears annually. Zone 4. Developed at the New York Agricultural Experiment Station, 1993. *Source History: 1 in 2000.* Sources: Fed.

Sweet Ann - Medium size, light yellow fruit. Sweeter than Royal Ann. Resists doubling and cracking. Resistant to X-disease (a mycoplasm) and cherry buckskin virus. Ripens midseason. Very cold hardy. Requires 700 hours of chilling. Introduced in 1981. *Source History: 4 in 1988; 2 in 1992; 2 in 2000.* Sources: Nrs, On3.

Sweet September - Medium size sweet red fruit. Ripens from August into September. *Source History: 2 in 1992; 2 in 2000.* Sources: Nrs, On3.

Sweetheart - Van x Newstar. Large, bright red fruit with good flavor. Precocious tree requires pruning to prevent size problems. Self-fertile. Matures 5-7 days after Lapins. Developed in Summerland, British Columbia. Trademarked. Plant patent applied for. *Source History: 1 in 1992; 5 in 2000.* **Sources: Co2, COL, Hi9, Va2, WI12.**

Sylvia - Large black fruit. Crack resistant. *Source History: 1 in 1992; 1 in 2000.* **Sources: Cu4.**

Tieton - Stella x Early Burlat. Resembles Bing but with larger size and firmer flesh. Vigorous, spreading tree is a consistent bearer. Blooms early. Ripens one week before Bing. Bred in Prosser, Washington. *Source History: 1 in 2000.* **Sources: WI12.**

Ulster - Schmidt x Lambert. Large, very dark red fruit. Firm, crisp, juicy, dark flesh. Sweet flavor. High quality. Too much color for brining. Resembles Schmidt, but is more productive, more crack resistant and ripens slightly later. Zones 5-7. Introduced in 1964. *Source History: 4 in 1988; 8 in 1992; 10 in 2000.* **Sources: Ad2, Bo5, Cu4, Ed2, Hi9, MI5, Nrs, Va2, Wh4, Wor.**

Utah Giant - Dark fruit is more flavorful than Bing or Lambert. Good canner. Does not double. Pollinate with Lambert and Sweet Ann. Partially resistant to X-disease. Ripens midseason. Requires 800 hours of chilling. Introduced in 1981. *Source History: 6 in 1988; 9 in 1992; 9 in 2000.* **Sources: Bay, CO5, Jo3, MI5, Nrs, Si3, Son, Va2, WI4.**

Valera - Medium size, good quality fruit. Recommended for fresh use. Vigorous tree. Bears early and consistently. Ripens early. *Source History: 1 in 1988; 4 in 1992; 2 in 2000.* **Sources: Bo5, Nrs.**

Van - Large, shiny, reddish black sweet cherry similar to Bing but firmer. Blocky shape with a short stem. Good flavor. Good fresh, cooked, canned or frozen. Commercial size and quality. Not a long distance shipper. Strong, vigorous, upright tree. Bears 1-3 years before Bing. Heavy, annual producer. Excellent pollinator. Pollinate with Bing, Lambert, Rainier, Royal Ann, Sam or Stella. Resistant to splitting. Ripens from mid-June to early July depending on location. Withstands harsher climatic conditions than other sweet cherries. 700 hours of chilling. Hardy in Zones 5-9. Introduced in 1944 by Summerland, British Columbia. *Source History: 26 in 1988; 35 in 1992; 27 in 2000.* **Sources: Bay, Bea, Bo5, BR10, Bu7, Ch9, Clo, Co2, CO5, COL, Gr4, Hi9, JOY, ME3, MI5, Nrs, ORA, Pe2, Si3, Son, St4, STR, Va2, Wa16, WI12, WI4, Wor.**

Van, Compact - Black fruit with excellent flavor. Tree can be maintained at under 10'. Compact form is still experimental. Good pollinator. *Source History: 1 in 1988; 3 in 1992; 1 in 2000.* **Sources: Nrs.**

Vega - Large, very attractive, sweet white cherry. Firm flesh. Small pit is easily removed. Good fresh. Recommended for brining, maraschinos and canning. *Source History: 1 in 1988; 3 in 1992; 1 in 2000.* **Sources: Nrs.**

Velvet - *Source History: 2 in 1992; 1 in 2000.* **Sources: Nrs.**

Venus - Large, shiny, purplish red fruit. Red flesh is less firm than Lambert and less subject to cracking. Vigorous, hardy, very productive tree. Ripens early. Introduced in 1967. *Source History: 2 in 1988; 3 in 1992; 1 in 2000.* **Sources: Nrs.**

Vic - Bing x Schmidt. Large, dark red cherry. Firm, sweet and crack resistant. Large, hardy, productive tree. Consistently heavy cropper. Sizes well in heavy crop years. Matures with Windsor in late June, but its fruit is larger and darker. *Source History: 2 in 1988; 4 in 1992; 2 in 2000.* **Sources: Hi9, Nrs.**

Victor - *Source History: 2 in 1992; 1 in 2000.* **Sources: Nrs.**

Viscount - Glossy, good quality, dark red fruit. Less cracking than Bing. Productive tree. Ripens midseason. Originated in Canada. Introduced in 1984. *Source History: 1 in 1988; 2 in 1992; 3 in 2000.* **Sources: Ad2, Ch9, Mo19.**

Vista - Hedelfingen x Victor. Large fruit. Firmer and earlier ripening than Black Tartarian. Vigorous, hardy, very productive tree. *Source History: 2 in 1988; 4 in 1992; 2 in 2000.* **Sources: Ad2, Nrs.**

Viva - Medium size, semifirm, dark red cherry of good quality. Moderately resistant to cracking and brown rot. Average picking date is one day later than Cavalier. *Source History: 1 in 1988; 3 in 1992; 3 in 2000.* **Sources: Cu4, Hi9, Nrs.**

Vogue - Large, shiny, black fruit. Firm, sweet flesh. Small pit. Very productive tree. Somewhat resistant to cracking. Requires careful spraying for brown rot control. Ripens midseason. Developed in Canada. Introduced in 1974. *Source History: 1 in 1988; 3 in 1992; 2 in 2000.* **Sources: Ad2, Nrs.**

Windsor - Large, almost black fruit. Firm, juicy, pinkish flesh is sometimes streaked. One of the best quality dark cherries. Excellent for canning and eating. Upright, vigorous tree. Rapid grower. Heavy yields. Used widely for pollination. *Source History: 8 in 1988; 6 in 1992; 5 in 2000.* **Sources: BO10, Hi9, Leu, Mi1, Nrs.**

Yellow Glass - Large, bright yellow fruits. Firm, juicy, sweet flesh. High quality. Heavy producer. Extremely hardy for a sweet cherry. Grows as far north as Des Moines, Iowa. Has withstood temperatures of -20 degrees F. *Source History: 2 in 1988; 3 in 1992; 3 in 2000.* **Sources: Bo5, Ed5, Nrs.**

Yellow Spanish - Napoleon type. Crimson and yellow fruit. Sweet, rich flavor. Very vigorous tree. Ripens late. One of the oldest known sweet cherries. Believed to have been described by the 1st century Roman naturalist, Pliny. Called Graffion by the early English writers. Brought to America in 1802 by Prince Nurseries of Long Island, New York. *Source History: 2 in 1988; 2 in 1992; 1 in 2000.* **Sources: Pi2.**

Cherry / Other

Prunus spp.

Autumn Cherry (Higan Cherry, Autumnalis Flowering Cherry) - *Prunus subhirtella.* Very spreading tree to 25'. Double white to pinkish white flowers in fall and early spring. Zone 6. *Source History: 2 in 1988; 3 in 1992; 4 in 2000.* **Sources: Big, We8, WI4, Wo2.**

Bird Cherry (Wild Sweet Cherry, European Bird Cherry, May Day Tree) - *Prunus padus* or *P. avium.* Small black, astringent fruit. Tree grows 30-50'. Excellent ornamental value. Attractive to birds. Zone 2. *Source History: 4 in 1988; 3 in 1992; 9 in 2000.* **Sources: Arb, Bea, CLI, FE7, Fo2, LA4, Mel, Sc2, SH8.**

Bitter Cherry (Oregon Cherry) - *Prunus emarginata.* Small, glossy, bright red bitter cherries. Large, deciduous shrub with shiny, reddish bark. White flowers. Suitable as rootstock for sweet and ornamental cherries in areas otherwise too wet for growing cherries. Hardy to Zone 4. Native to the West. *Source History: 5 in 1988; 3 in 1992; 4 in 2000.* **Sources: Bu7, Ca12, Fo2, No2.**

Black Beauty (Marasca di Ostheim) - Morello type. Glossy, reddish black fruits are almost as large as sweet cherries. Good for fresh eating, canning or freezing. Hybrid bush cherry grows 3-4' tall. No pollinator required. Hardy into Zone 3-8. *Source History: 1 in 1988; 2 in 1992; 1 in 2000.* **Sources: Jun.**

Capulin - *Prunus salicifolia.* Deep, glossy, maroon-purple, .5-.75" fruits. Pale

green flesh has a sweet, wild cherry flavor. Trees grow as much as 15' per year.
Native to the Mexican and Guatemalan highlands at 4,000-9,000'. Hardy. *Source
History: 1 in 1992; 4 in 2000.* **Sources: An4, Or2, Pa2, Po7.**

Carolina Cherry Laurel - *Prunus caroliniana.* Shiny, oval, .25" black fruits.
Evergreen tree grows 40' tall. Hardy in Zone 7. Native from North Carolina to
Texas. *Source History: 4 in 1988; 4 in 1992; 6 in 2000.* **Sources: Ca7, Fo2,
HI10, MIS, Sc2, Wo2.**

Catalina Cherry - *Prunus lyonii.* Nearly black, .5-1" fruits. Very drought toler-
ant. Hardy in Zone 8. Native to an island off the southern California coast. *Source
History: 5 in 1988; 5 in 1992; 7 in 2000.* **Sources: An4, Ca12, Ca7, Fo2, Las,
MIS, Or2.**

Chokecherry - *Prunus virginiana.* Heavy clusters of small, reddish black fruits.
Spicy flavor and aroma. Tree grows 25' tall. Ripens in July. Hardy to Zone 2.
Source History: 13 in 1988; 15 in 1992; 19 in 2000. **Sources: Abu, BA9, Bu7,
CLI, Co24, CR6, Fil, GR26, Gur, LA4, LI7, LOV, MIS, NA5, No2, Pl5, Pla,
Stl, Va5.**

Chokecherry, Amur (Amur Bird Cherry) - *Prunus maackii.* Chokecherry-like
flowers and fruits, usually eaten by the birds before fully ripe. Used in jelly and
wine. Tree to 25-40' with exfoliating bark like birch. Dark green leaves turn yellow
in the fall. Drought tolerant. Zone 3. *Source History: 4 in 1992; 11 in 2000.*
Sources: BA14, CLI, FE7, Fed, Fo2, Gr16, GR26, LA4, LI7, MEA, SH8.

Chokecherry, Black - *Prunus virginiana* var. *melanocarpa.* *Source History: 1
in 1988; 1 in 1992; 1 in 2000.* **Sources: Sc2.**

Chokecherry, Canada Red (Schubert, Redleaf, Red Flame) - *Prunus virginiana* var. *melanocarpa.* Canada Red selection by Schubert. Bluish purple fruits are
used for jellies and jams. Small tree or large shrub. Tendency to sucker. Bright
green spring leaves turn dark red by midsummer. White flowers. Ripens midsummer. Hardy through Zone 3. *Source History: 7 in 1988; 24 in 1992; 20 in 2000.*
**Sources: BA14, Bea, CLI, CO5, CR6, Cu4, Fo2, GR26, KAN, KEE, LA4, LI7,
Mc3, ME3, MEA, MI5, NA5, Sh14, SH8, Va5.**

Chokecherry, Garrington - *Prunus virginiana.* Bushes grow 6-8' tall; produce
up to 30 pounds of fruit. Hand or machine harvest. Pollinate with wild chokecherry. Developed in Alberta, Canada. *Source History: 1 in 2000.* **Sources: Stl.**

Chokecherry, Goldenbark - *Prunus maackii.* Hardy Asian chokecherry.
Known for its bright yellow, peeling bark and its 2-3" racemes of white flowers in
spring. Grows well in Zone 2. *Source History: 1 in 1988; 3 in 1992; 2 in 2000.*
Sources: CLI, Fo2.

Chokecherry, Western - *Prunus virginiana* var. *demissa.* Pendulous clusters
of dark red fruit. Used for jelly. Large shrub or small tree. Large, white flower
clusters. Foliage turns orange-red in the fall. Tendency to sucker. Hardy in Zone
4. Native from California to Washington and Idaho. *Source History: 3 in 1988; 3
in 1992; 3 in 2000.* **Sources: Ca12, Fo2, Las.**

Chokecherry, Western Black - *Prunus virginiana* var. *melanocarpa.* Black
fruit. Native from California to the Rocky Mountains. *Source History: 1 in 1988;
1 in 1992; 1 in 2000.* **Sources: Ca12.**

Chokecherry, Yellow - *Prunus virginiana flava.* Produces an abundant amount
of fruit which is cooked and made into jams, jellies and syrups. Mild flavor. Self-
fertile. Grows in any soil; tolerates shade. Hardy to -40 degrees F. *Source History:
2 in 2000.* **Sources: Oik, Va5.**

Dwarf Ground Cherry - *Prunus fruticosa*. Small, dark red, tart fruit used for making jam. Shrub grows 3-4' with beautiful bright green foliage and white flowers. At least two plants required for pollination. Good hedge plant. Extremely hardy. *Source History: 3 in 1992; 2 in 2000.* **Sources: LI7, Stl.**

Dwarfrich - *Prunus fruiticosa*. *Source History: 1 in 1992; 1 in 2000.* **Sources: Nrs.**

Fire Cherry - *Prunus pennsylvanica*. Named for its red spring twigs, red berries and red foliage color or its ability to reclaim fire-decimated land. Hardy to Zone 2. *Source History: 1 in 2000.* **Sources: Fo2.**

Grass Cherry - *Prunus humilis*. Dwarf species cherry grows only 4' tall and fruiting begins on 2 year plants when 1' tall. Used for preserves in northern China. So named because of its narrow grass-like leaves. Hardy to -35 degrees F. *Source History: 1 in 2000.* **Sources: Oik.**

Hansen's Bush Cherry - *Prunus besseyi*. Improved cultivar of Sand Cherry with purple-black fruit with tart, tangy flavor. Good for pies, preserves and sauces. Short, wide, 4-6' bush. Fast growing, hardy and drought tolerant with a 15-20 year life span. Small, white blossoms in the spring. Silvery green leaves turn crimson in the fall. Grows on sandy hills, rocky slopes and lakeshores in the North. Requires a minimum annual precipitation of 10". Excellent wildlife plant. Sometimes used as a dwarfing rootstock for cherries and other stone fruits. Ripens in early summer. Hardy to Zone 2. Developed by Dr. N. E. Hansen of the South Dakota Agricultural Experiment Station. *Source History: 18 in 1988; 14 in 1992; 11 in 2000.* **Sources: Bea, Ed5, Fi1, Gur, Int, La3, LOV, Mc3, Mel, Mi1, Or2.**

Holly-Leaved Cherry (Evergreen Cherry, Islay, Mountain Holly, Wild Cherry) - *Prunus ilicifolia*. Edible, thin fleshed fruit. Beautiful little tree often used as a formal or informal hedge. Has long been in cultivation. Adapts to many types of soil. White blossoms in spring are much appreciated by bees; fruit is eaten by birds and foragers. Hardy in Zone 8. *Source History: 5 in 1988; 5 in 1992; 6 in 2000.* **Sources: An4, Ca7, Co24, Las, MIS, Or2.**

Japanese Weeping Cherry - *Prunus subhirtella pendula*. *Source History: 2 in 1988; 1 in 1992; 3 in 2000.* **Sources: BO4, Sc2, SH8.**

Korean Bush Cherry - *Prunus japonica*. Bright to deep red, .4" cherries in late summer. Tart flavor. Very hardy, 3-5' shrub. White to pink flowers in spring. Hardy in Zone 2. Native to Asia. *Source History: 1 in 1988; 1 in 1992; 2 in 2000.* **Sources: Fo2, Oik.**

Mongolian Cherry - Makes fine jelly. Ornamental. *Source History: 1 in 1992; 1 in 2000.* **Sources: Va5.**

Nanking Cherry (Manchu Cherry, Chinese Bush Fruit, Bush Cherry, Hedge Cherry) - *Prunus tomentosa*. Heavy crops of short stemmed, .5" red fruits. Tart, tangy flavor, somewhat like that of sour cherries. Hold well on the plant 2-3 weeks after ripening. Fine for pies, jams and jellies. Vigorous, rounded, deciduous shrub grows 10'. Soft green foliage. White or pinkish blossoms in the spring. Used as a dwarfing rootstock for cherries. Good intermediate windbreak filler. Attracts birds and other wildlife. Widely adapted. Requires a minimum annual precipitation of 12". Ripens from July to August depending on location. Hardy to Zone 2. Native to temperate eastern Asia. *Source History: 30 in 1988; 44 in 1992; 33 in 2000.* **Sources: Bea, Ca7, Ca8, CLI, CR6, Ed2, Ed5, Fa1, Fed, Fi1, Fo2, Ga6, GR26, Gur, Hid, Jun, KAN, LA4, LI7, LOV, Mc3, MEA, No2, Pa2, Po2, Rai, Sc2, SH8, Stl, Va5, Wa13, Wa16, We8.**

Nanking Cherry, White - *Prunus tomentosa*. Sweetest of the Naking cherries.

Above average fruit size. Grows 6-8' tall. Does best in full sun; also good for pot culture. Zones 3-7. *Source History: 1 in 2000.* **Sources: Ed2.**

Pin Cherry, Jumping Pound - *Prunus pennsylvanica.* Shrub-like plant with a weeping habit. Fruit ripens 4-5 days before May Liss. Productive. Zones 2-7. *Source History: 2 in 2000.* **Sources: Rai, Stl.**

Pin Cherry, Mary Liss - *Prunus pennsylvanica.* Thin skinned fruit. Small tree grows 13-15'. Upright, sturdy trunk. Self-fertile. Produces three times that of wild types. Zones 2-7. *Source History: 2 in 2000.* **Sources: Rai, Stl.**

Prunus davidiana - Currently being trialed as an understock. Round, dry, 1" fruits. Peach-like tree grows 30'. White flowers. Hardy in Zone 3. Native to China. *Source History: 3 in 1988; 2 in 1992; 1 in 2000.* **Sources: Sc2.**

Prunus humulus - Soft pink flowers. Bright red, acid fruits. Zone 5. Native to China. *Source History: 1 in 2000.* **Sources: Fo2.**

Prunus mume - *Source History: 1 in 1992; 1 in 2000.* **Sources: Sc2.**

Sand Cherry (Western Sand Cherry, Great Plains Sand Cherry, Dwarf Sand Cherry, Western Bush Cherry, Hedge Cherry) - *Prunus besseyi.* Heavy bearer of sweet, fleshy, .6" purplish black fruits. Used for jams, jellies and pies. Deciduous shrub grows 4-6' tall. Shiny, leathery, silver green leaves. Fragrant, white blossoms in the spring. Attractive to birds. Adaptable to both drought and excessive moisture. Extremely hardy to Zone 2, but somewhat short-lived (5-10 years). Native to the Great Plains and the dunes on Lake Michigan. *Source History: 21 in 1988; 26 in 1992; 18 in 2000.* **Sources: CLI, Fa1, Fo2, Fo4, GR26, HI10, Int, LA4, LI7, Mel, MI5, No2, Oik, Pl5, Pla, Sc2, SH8, So5, Stl.**

Sand Cherry, Purpleleaf - *Prunus* x *Cistena.* Small, purplish black fruits in early May. Multi-stemmed bush reaches 6-8' tall with a slightly smaller spread. Intense reddish purple foliage throughout the season. Fragrant light pink to white flowers in late April. Adapts well to most well drained soils in sunny locations. Hardy in Zones 2-8. *Source History: 6 in 1988; 25 in 1992; 34 in 2000.* **Sources: Arb, BA14, Big, BO10, BO4, Bo5, BU12, CO3, CR6, Ed2, Fa1, Fi1, FO10, Fo2, Gir, GR26, HI10, HI7, IM2, Jun, KAN, KEE, LA4, LI7, Mc3, ME3, MEA, Mu2, Sav, SH8, TR19, Wa16, WA8, We8.**

Sargent Cherry - *Prunus sargentii.* Single, deep pink flowers. Bronze-red spring foliage turns dark green in summer and brilliant scarlet in autumn. Grows as wide as tall. Zone 6. *Source History: 2 in 1988; 3 in 1992; 5 in 2000.* **Sources: Big, KI3, Nrs, Sc2, We8.**

Sloe (Blackthorn) - *Prunus spinosa.* Bluish black .5" fruit with astringent flesh. Deciduous, multi-branched, 3-12' shrub. White flowers. Hardy in Zone 4. *SourceHistory: 1 in 1988; 2 in 1992; 3 in 2000.* **Sources: Fo2, Oik, Va5.**

Sloe Plum, Cole - *Prunus mexicana.* Delicious fruit makes an excellent jelly. Bears heavily. *Source History: 1 in 1992; 1 in 2000.* **Sources: Sh3.**

Sloe Plum, Krouse - *Prunus americana.* Delicious. Excellent aroma goes into jelly. Bears heavily. *Source History: 1 in 1992; 1 in 2000.* **Sources: Sh3.**

Texas Cherry - Semi-sweet, .4-.5" fruit. Native to Abilene, Texas area. *Source History: 1 in 1988; 1 in 1992; 1 in 2000.* **Sources: Sh3.**

Virginia Cherry - *Prunus virginiana.* Small tree grows 12-15' with white clusters of flowers in the spring. Red to purple fruit in the summer. Good for jelly and syrup. Drought and heat tolerant. Zones 2-9. *Source History: 2 in 2000.* **Sources: Co15, Mel.**

Wild Black Cherry (Black Cherry, Rum Cherry, Black Rum Cherry) - *Prunus*

serotina. Native black cherry forest tree of the East. Grows rapidly 50-100' tall; 20-50" trunk. Dense foliage green, lustrous, single, peach-shaped leaves turn yellow in fall. Fragrant, white flowers in May. Crimson-black fruits provide food for birds and many small animals. Makes a fine jelly. Dark timber prized for furniture making. Requires a minimum annual precipitation of 25". Hardy in Zones 3-9. *Source History: 14 in 1988; 18 in 1992; 24 in 2000.* **Sources: Ba3, Bea, BO10, Ca8, Ch9, CLI, Co15, Fa1, Fo2, Fra, JO4, KEE, LA4, LO6, Mc3, MEA, Mel, Mu2, Pi2, Sc2, SH8, Tri, TU5, WA8.**

Wild Red Cherry (Bird Cherry, Pin Cherry, Wild Red Cherry) - *Prunus pennsylvanica.* Fruits have thin, acid flesh. Tree to 30' with red spring twigs. Small red berries. Zone 2. *Source History: 3 in 1988; 1 in 1992; 1 in 2000.* **Sources: Sc2.**

Date
Phoenix spp.

Canary Island - *Phoenix canariensis.* Stout date growing 50' or more with a 3' diameter trunk. Dense crown with many leaves up to 20' long. Oblong yellow to reddish fruit is .75" long x .5" diameter. One of the hardiest and most massive palms when grown on fertile, moist soil. Hardy in the warmer parts of Zone 9. *Source History: 4 in 1988; 6 in 1992; 2 in 2000.* **Sources: Ba3, Sc2.**

Date Palm - *Phoenix dactylifera.* True, date bearing palm. Cylindrical, 1-3" long fruit. Thick, sweet flesh. Tall but slow growing tree to 100'. Hardy in warmer parts of Zone 9. Native to western Asia and northern Africa. *Source History: 4 in 1988; 6 in 1992; 3 in 2000.* **Sources: Ba3, Ca7, Sc2.**

Fig
Ficus carica

Adriatic (Verdone Adriatic, Strawberry Fig, Fico di Fragola) - Two crops of large greenish yellow figs. Red pulp. Very fine flavor. Good fresh and for jams, especially good dried. Consistent bearer. Fruits well near the coast or inland. Said to do well in Georgia. Originated in Italy. *Source History: 1 in 1988; 3 in 1992; 2 in 2000.* **Sources: Or2, Son.**

Alma - New light-colored fig from Texas A and M University. Medium size light yellow fruit. Very sweet, amber-tan flesh. Small eye. Seeds are very small. Excellent flavor. Good fresh or dried. Small tree. Light "breba" crop; heavy main crop. Requires long, warm summers. Ripens in late June. Well adapted to the Southeast. Quite frost sensitive; hardiness compares with Celeste. Zones 7-9. *Source History: 5 in 1988; 14 in 1992; 10 in 2000.* **Sources: Ed2, Jo3, Ju2, Or2, RA4, Sh3, Tri, VIR, Wel, Wom.**

Armenian - Very large, yellow fruit. Amber flesh. Mildly sweet flavor. Spreading; does well in pots. First ripe fruits set snugly in a tea cup. *Source History: 2 in 1988; 1 in 1992; 1 in 2000.* **Sources: Or2.**

Ballard's VO5 - Wild seedling from Dr. Ballard's collection that he named Volentier #5. Teardrop-shaped, smooth yellow fruit with thick skin. Tender, delicious, clear pulp. Fairly prolific second crop ripens midseason until heavy rains. *Source History: 1 in 2000.* **Sources: Or2.**

Bear's Black - *Source History: 1 in 2000.* **Sources: Sh3.**

Black Honey - *Source History: 1 in 2000.* **Sources: Sh3.**

Black Jack - Large to very large, purplish brown fruit. Small, spreading plant to

6'. Does well in pots. Self-fruitful. Needs protection in winter in cold areas. Ripens June to August. Requires 100 hours of chilling. Zones 3-9. *Source History: 1 in 1988; 3 in 1992; 9 in 2000.* **Sources: Bay, CO5, Ed2, Or2, ORA, Son, Tri, Ty2, WI4.**

Black Madeira - *Source History: 1 in 1988; 1 in 1992; 1 in 2000.* **Sources: Pa2.**

Black Mission (Franciscan Fig) - Medium to large, pear-shaped fruit with rough, purplish black skin. Sweet, strawberry-red flesh. Distinct rich flavor. Taste standard for figs. Finest quality. Favored for drying; good for fresh eating and canning. Heavy bearing, long-lived, large tree. Self-pollinating. Produces two crops per year in June and August-November. Requires 100 hours of chilling. Hardy in Zones 7-10. Produces almost everywhere in California except the high deserts. California's oldest, most popular shipping and drying fig. Owes its name to the Franciscan missionaries of Father Junipero Serra who planted it at the mission in San Diego. Introduced in 1769. *Source History: 13 in 1988; 23 in 1992; 15 in 2000.* **Sources: Bay, CO5, Gr4, Iso, MI5, MO10, ORA, Pa2, Pe2, SIM, Son, STR, Ty2, Wel, WI4.**

Black Spanish - Sweet, mahogany fruit. Fast grower; will produce two crops some years. Extremely hardy; Zones 7-9. Originated in Spain. *Source History: 1 in 1988; 3 in 1992; 1 in 2000.* **Sources: Ju2.**

Brown Turkey (Old Brown Turkey, Black Spanish, Texas Everbearing, English Brown Turkey) - Medium to large, elongated fruit with brownish maroon skin. Fine grained, sweet, juicy, firm, meaty flesh. Sugary, rich flavor. Excellent for jams, canning, drying or eating fresh. Handsome, low, bushy plants grow 10' tall. Can be pruned. Large, tropical, glossy green leaves. Self-pollinating. Selected for winter hardiness and fruit quality. Bears as far north as Zone 5 when grown in open ground; must be covered where temperature drops below 10 degrees F. Superb container plant further north. Everbearing beginning in early June. Requires 100 hours of chilling. *Source History: 34 in 1988; 46 in 1992; 39 in 2000.* **Sources: Bar, Bas, BO10, Bu7, CO5, Ea3, Ed2, Ga6, Gr4, Int, Iso, Jo3, Ju2, La3, Lee, Mi1, MI10, MI5, MO10, Or2, Pa2, Par, Pe2, PL2, RA4, Rai, Sav, Sh3, SIM, Son, St4, STR, Tex, Tr10, Ty2, VIR, Wa3, WA8, Wel.**

Brown Turkey Improved - Very large, bell-shaped, brownish purple fig. Sweet, light pink flesh. Rich flavor. Best as a table fruit. Small tree is self-fruitful. Prune to any shape. Bears twice a year. Widely adapted; coast or inland climate. Can produce throughout California. Requires 100 hours of chilling. *Source History: 2 in 1988; 3 in 1992; 4 in 2000.* **Sources: Bay, ORA, Sh3, WI4.**

Brown Turkey, Vern's - Two crops of fruit with dark brown skin. Sweet, amber flesh. Hardy in Zones 7-9. Originated in Texas. *Source History: 2 in 1992; 1 in 2000.* **Sources: On3.**

Burgess Dwarf - Trees reach 6'. Field grown stock will fruit the first year. Pot plants in twos. Where winter temperatures drop below 5 degrees F the trees need to be planted in tubs so they can be moved to shelter to both ripen the fruit and protect the top. Root is hardy anywhere, but the top will die back below 5 degrees F. *Source History: 1 in 1988; 1 in 1992; 1 in 2000.* **Sources: Bu1.**

Celeste (Sugar Fig, Blue Celeste, Malta, Honey) - Plump, small to medium size fruit. Tightly closed eye. Light violet to violet-brown skin. Firm, juicy, white flesh. One of the sweetest. Excellent quality. Resists spoilage. Hardy, self-pollinating tree grows 6-10' tall. Fruit will sometimes dry on the tree. Best to restrict roots in rich soil. Best adapted to cool areas of the South such as north and

FIG 208

central Georgia. Hardy to 0 degrees F. Grow outdoors in Zones 6-10. Tolerates lower temperatures than any fig except Brown Turkey. *Source History: 15 in 1988; 24 in 1992; 24 in 2000.* **Sources: Bas, BU12, Cla, Ed2, Hid, Iso, Jo3, Ju2, La3, Lee, Mi1, Or2, Pa2, RA4, Sav, Sh3, St4, Tex, Tr10, Ty2, VIR, WA8, Wel, Wom.**

Celeste, Golden - *Source History: 1 in 2000.* **Sources: Sh3.**

Celestial - Small to medium, purplish brown fruit. White flesh turns rose in the center. Sweet, excellent flavor. Prolific plant grows 10' tall. Self-fruitful. Large, tropical leaves. Can be pruned. Widely adapted. Thrives in most soils and produces the first season. Produces well everywhere in California except the high desert. Produces its first crop in early summer and second crop from late summer to early fall. Requires 100 hours of chilling. *Source History: 6 in 1988; 5 in 1992; 6 in 2000.* **Sources: Bay, CO5, ORA, Pe2, SIM, WI4.**

Chicago Black - *Source History: 1 in 2000.* **Sources: Sh3.**

Conadria - Adriatic x a capri fig. Medium to large fruit with thin, light green skin. Whitish pink flesh with an excellent rich, distinctive flavor. Good for table use or drying. Productive, very vigorous, long-lived tree. Self-fruitful. Resistant to spoilage and leaf mosaic. Capable of producing a profitable crop in its third year. Fruits twice a year. Early breba crop. Heavy crops both on the coast or inland. Does well as far north as Portland, Oregon. Requires 100 hours of chilling. Result of 28 years of breeding work begun by Professor Ira J. Condit. Conadria is a contraction of his name and Adriatic. Introduced in 1956. *Source History: 11 in 1988; 15 in 1992; 6 in 2000.* **Sources: Bay, CO5, Ju2, Or2, ORA, WI4.**

Deanna - One of Dr. Condit's hybrids developed to replace Calimyrna. Huge fruits with supple yellow skin. Clear white flesh. Bears a fair size first crop and a heavy second crop that continues until mid-November. *Source History: 1 in 1988; 1 in 1992; 2 in 2000.* **Sources: Or2, Sh3.**

Desert King - Large, dark green fruit. Strawberry-red flesh. Excellent for fresh eating; good dried. Bears consistently reliable crop. Produces one crop on second year wood. Ripens in late July. Good variety to plant in colder, wetter areas. *Source History: 4 in 1988; 5 in 1992; 9 in 2000.* **Sources: Bu7, Clo, Ea3, Er2, Gr16, On3, Rai, Son, WI4.**

Dr. O'Bar's Strawberry - *Source History: 1 in 2000.* **Sources: Sh3.**

Drop of Honey - *Source History: 1 in 1988; 1 in 2000.* **Sources: On4.**

Dwarf Fig - Sweet fruit. Good for canning, drying or baking. Field grown stock will fruit the first year; pot plants will fruit in two years. Root is hardy anywhere, but the top will die back below 5 degrees F. Not shipped to California. *Source History: 2 in 1988; 2 in 1992; 1 in 2000.* **Sources: Fa1.**

Early Violet - Very small chocolate-brown fruit. Strawberry-red flesh. Good quality. Very prolific; ripens three crops in a greenhouse. *Source History: 1 in 1988; 1 in 1992; 1 in 2000.* **Sources: Or2.**

Everbearing - Similar to Brown Turkey but bears smaller fruit over a longer period. Relatively small, good flavored, straw-colored fruit. Excellent for canning, jams or eating. Handsome, low, bushy plants. Begins bearing young, sometimes the first year. Hardy from the warmer portions of Zone 7 southward, but will grow and produce fruit outdoors as far north as Zone 5 if given winter protection. May not have time to ripen outdoors in areas with a short growing season. *Source History: 6 in 1988; 7 in 1992; 5 in 2000.* **Sources: Bar, Fi1, Or2, SIM, Tri.**

Excel - Yellow fruit with amber pulp. Sweet flavor. Resistant to splitting even

under adverse conditions. Superb, all-purpose fig. Introduced in 1975. *Source History: 1 in 1988; 4 in 1992; 3 in 2000.* **Sources: Ju2, Or2, Sh3.**

Fig - Medium to large fruit with coppery skin. White to amber flesh. Dwarf tree. Easy to grow in any soil. Cover before temperature reaches 10 degrees F. Patio container plant in colder climates. Hardy in Zone 5. *Source History: 2 in 1988; 6 in 1992; 4 in 2000.* **Sources: Fi1, Ga11, Gur, Mel.**

Flanders - Violet striped fruit with white flecks. Amber flesh; rich flavor. Highly productive. Resistant to splitting. Developed by Dr. Condit. Introduced in 1965. *Source History: 1 in 1988; 3 in 1992; 1 in 2000.* **Sources: Or2.**

Galbun - Large yellowish green fruit. Delicately sweet flesh. Does well in pots; fruitful. Obtained from Dr. Dunstan's collection. Zones 6-9. *Source History: 1 in 1988; 1 in 1992; 2 in 2000.* **Sources: Ed2, Or2.**

Genoa (White Genoa) - Green skinned fig with pale rose pulp. Delicious flavor. Favorite for eating fresh. Well adapted to cooler coastal areas. *Source History: 1 in 1988; 2 in 1992; 1 in 2000.* **Sources: Son.**

Gillette - Sweet, yellow fruit. Fine for fresh eating, canning or drying. Produces one large crop during July and August. Frost tolerant. Grown commercially in Oregon and Washington in the 1930s. *Source History: 1 in 1992; 1 in 2000.* **Sources: Or2.**

Green Ischia (Verte, Green Ischau) - Small to medium, thin skinned, greenish yellow fruit. Strawberry-red flesh. Fine flavor. Excellent quality. Fairly tight eye. Excellent fresh or dried. Somewhat of a dwarf tree. Does very well in pots. Heavy bearer. Good breba crop (first crop from previous season's growth). Fruit is resistant to spoiling by weather or insects. Birds do not find its green color very attractive. Very old cultivar. Zones 8-10. *Source History: 3 in 1988; 9 in 1992; 6 in 2000.* **Sources: Ed2, Ju2, Or2, Son, Tri, Ty2.**

Guilbeau - *Source History: 1 in 2000.* **Sources: Sh3.**

Hardy Chicago - Medium to small, black fruit. Sweet, very rich flavor. Became aware of this plant from a Chicago man. For years he protected the fig every year and it fruited for him. One year it was unprotected during the winter and the top growth died. The plant produced an abundant crop from the new growth without protection. Hardy in Zones 6-10. *Source History: 1 in 1988; 3 in 1992; 3 in 2000.* **Sources: Ed2, HA12, Or2.**

Hartwell Cook's Jack Lilley - Dwarf yellow. *Source History: 1 in 2000.* **Sources: Sh3.**

Hollier - Large, sweet fruit with excellent flavor. *Source History: 1 in 1992; 1 in 2000.* **Sources: Sh3.**

Italian Everbearing - Large, flavorful fruit. Prolific bearer. *Source History: 1 in 1988; 2 in 1992; 1 in 2000.* **Sources: CO5.**

Italian Honey (Florentine) - Green skinned fruit with honey colored, sweet flesh. Bears two crops. Self-fertile. Grows slower than other figs. Hardy outdoors from Maryland south; excellent container plant further north. Hardy in Zones 7-10. *Source History: 3 in 1992; 4 in 2000.* **Sources: Par, Sh3, Tr10, Wa3.**

Janice Seedless - Large, light green-yellow fruit with few seeds. Sweet flavor. Ripens from August to November. Self-fruitful. Can be pruned to any shape. Requires 100 hours of chilling. U.S. Plant Patent No. 8254. *Source History: 2 in 2000.* **Sources: Bay, WI4.**

Jelly (Marylane Seedless) - Long necked, yellow fig with seedless, flavorful flesh that looks like clear apple jelly. *Source History: 3 in 1992; 1 in 2000.* **Sources:**

FIG 210

Ju2.

<u>Jenkins Estate</u> - Possible variation of Brown Turkey. Red fig. Produces two crops. *Source History: 1 in 2000.* **Sources: Ea3.**

<u>Kadota</u> - Medium size fruit. Thin, tough, light greenish yellow skin. White to amber flesh tinged with pink. Rich, sweet, flavorful, all-purpose fig. Great for canning, fresh eating or preserving. The leading commercial canning variety. Long-lived, vigorous plant. Rampant grower; very productive. Bears twice a year. Self-fruitful. Fruit needs hot weather to ripen. Not recommended for Pacific Northwest. Often dries on the tree. Requires 100 hours of chilling. Very ancient variety praised by Pliny (23-79 A.D.) as an excellent drying fig. Zones 7-9. *Source History: 9 in 1988; 14 in 1992; 12 in 2000.* **Sources: Bay, Ed2, MI5, MO10, Or2, ORA, PL2, RA4, Sh3, STR, Tr10, WI4.**

<u>King</u> (Desert King) - Large, good quality green fruits with amber flesh. Very good flavor. Good fresh, canned or dried. Rampant grower; heavy yielding. One large spring crop; sometimes has a small second crop. Self-fruitful. Ripens in late July. Requires 100 hours of chilling. Hardier than Brown Turkey. *Source History: 5 in 1988; 4 in 1992; 3 in 2000.* **Sources: Bay, CO5, Or2.**

<u>L.S.U. Everbearing</u> - Large, dark purple fig with sweet, white-amber flesh. Will produce fruit on first year's growth. *Source History: 1 in 1992; 4 in 2000.* **Sources: Cla, Hid, RA4, Sh3.**

<u>L.S.U. Gold</u> - *Source History: 1 in 2000.* **Sources: Sh3.**

<u>L.S.U. Purple</u> - Purple fruit is larger than Celeste. Reliable, prolific producer of early to late figs, producing early figs as soon as growth starts. Bears two crops. Excellent for containers. Well adapted to the fluctuating weather of the South. Zones 7-9. Released by Louisiana State University. *Source History: 1 in 1992; 2 in 2000.* **Sources: Ed2, Wom.**

<u>Lattarula</u> (Italian Honey Fig) - Greenish yellow fruit. Sweet, amber, honey colored flesh. Good for fresh eating, canning or drying. Produces fruit on new wood. Ripens two crops in most years during July and September. Well adapted and widely grown in many areas west of the Cascades. One of the most widely planted figs in the Northwest. Zones 7-10. *Source History: 3 in 1988; 5 in 1992; 4 in 2000.* **Sources: Bu7, Ea3, On3, Rai.**

<u>Lemon</u> - Large, yellowish green fruit. Light pink flesh with the flavor of maple syrup. Very good quality. Tree bears quite young. Ripens early August. *Source History: 1 in 1988; 2 in 1992; 1 in 2000.* **Sources: Ju2.**

<u>Lola Martin</u> - *Source History: 1 in 2000.* **Sources: Sh3.**

<u>Long Island</u> - Sweet green fig found on Long Island, New York. Zones 7-9. *Source History: 1 in 2000.* **Sources: Ed2.**

<u>Magnolia</u> - Large, pear-shaped fruit with reddish brown skin. Strawberry-pink flesh. Tolerably rich and sweet. Grown as a preserving fig. Good fresh or preserved, but poor dried. Fruit tends to spoil after cool fall rains in November. Not suitable for forcing. Very hardy tree known to survive temperatures as low as 5 degrees F. Has large "hand" or "okra" shaped leaves; very ornamental. First crop is small but with very large fruit up to 4" long; second crop figs are medium size, copper brown with nearly seedless, sweet, rich pulp. Good for short summer areas. *Source History: 3 in 1988; 2 in 1992; 3 in 2000.* **Sources: Ea3, Hid, Or2.**

<u>Marseilles</u> (Latturula) - Large, almost round fruits. Pale green to yellow skin; slightly ribbed. Translucent flesh; rich and succulent. Good hardy variety for walls or forcing. At Jefferson's Monticello, Marseilles bears abundant crops. *Source*

History: 1 in 1988; 1 in 1992; 2 in 2000. **Sources: Ed2, Sh3.**

Mary Lane (Seedless Jelly Fig) - Yellow skin, sweet white flesh. Nearly seed-less. Sweet and delicious. Becoming popular in California. *Source History: 2 in 1988; 2 in 1992; 1 in 2000.* **Sources: Or2.**

Mediterranean Black - *Source History: 1 in 2000.* **Sources: Tr10.**

Mission - Commercially grown black fig. Large tree; very prolific. Two crops in warm spots. Ripens midseason. *Source History: 2 in 1988; 1 in 1992; 1 in 2000.* **Sources: Or2.**

Mystery X - Discovered on an old Georgia plantation many years ago; fig enthusi-asts cannot agree on its identity. Extra sweet and tasty. Hardy in Zones 8-10. *Source History: 1 in 1992; 1 in 2000.* **Sources: Ty2.**

Negronne (Violette de Bordeaux) - Small jet-black fruits. Deep red pulp. Very fine flavor fresh or dried. Excellent Mission-type fig for cooler areas. Vigorous and extremely hardy. Zones 7-10. Produces two crops each year. Originated in Spain. *Source History: 1 in 1988; 3 in 1992; 9 in 2000.* **Sources: Bu7, Clo, Ea3, Ed2, Gr16, On3, Or2, Rai, Son.**

Nero (Nero Caesar) - Large, wine colored fruit. Hardy tree. Bears young; holds fruit in its first year. Ripens in late July. Hardy in Zones 7-10. Originated in Italy. *Source History: 1 in 1988; 3 in 1992; 2 in 2000.* **Sources: Or2, Ty2.**

Neveralla (Osborne Prolific) - Very large fruit with dark reddish brown skin; somewhat striped. Peach or honey colored flesh; almost seedless. Very sweet fla-vor. Good for fresh eating; makes superior fig jam. Hardy, heavy bearing tree does best in cool, short summer areas. Produces fruit on new wood. Very productive; bears two crops in most years. *Source History: 4 in 1988; 3 in 1992; 3 in 2000.* **Sources: Ea3, Or2, Rai.**

New York City - Propagated from a tree growing in New York city. Good qual-ity fruit. Bears two crops annually. Winter hardy. *Source History: 1 in 2000.* **Sources: Tri.**

Osborne Prolific (Neveralla) - Medium to large, thin skinned, dark reddish brown fruit. Very sweet, white to amber flesh. Trees withstand cold temperatures. Self-fruitful. Bears twice a year. Long-time favorite in cool coastal areas. Adapt-able to cool short summers. Produces well in southern California and other coastal areas. Popular in England. Also does well against walls and sunny locations on the East Coast. Requires 100 hours of chilling. Zones 8-10. *Source History: 6 in 1988; 10 in 1992; 8 in 2000.* **Sources: Bay, CO5, Ed2, Ju2, ORA, Pa2, Son, WI4.**

Panache (Striped Tiger, Tiger) - Unusual, small to medium, yellow fruit with green stripes and strawberry flesh. Best eaten fresh. Branches are somewhat varie-gated. Likes long warm growing season. Ripens late. Very old variety. Zones 8-10. *Source History: 1 in 1988; 4 in 1992; 3 in 2000.* **Sources: Or2, Pa2, Son.**

Pasquale (Vernino) - Small, dark purple-black fruit. Dark strawberry flesh. Very sweet, rich flavor. Excellent fresh or dried. Heavy bearer. Ripens first crop in mid-July. Second crop ripens later than all other figs in California, extending harvest into December. *Source History: 2 in 1988; 5 in 1992; 2 in 2000.* **Sources: Ju2, Or2.**

Patrick's Super Giant - Fruit weighs up to one-half pound, thus causing excess weight on lower limbs; daily harvesting recommended. Soft, sesame-like seeds. Hardy in Zones 8-9. *Source History: 1 in 1992; 1 in 2000.* **Sources: Ty2.**

Peter's Honey Fig - Beautiful, shiny, greenish yellow fruit when ripe. Very

FIG   212

sweet, dark amber flesh. High quality. Superb for fresh eating; should be good for drying and canning. Warm location with a southern exposure is required for ripening fruit in maritime Northwest. Originated in Sicily. *Source History: 2 in 1988; 3 in 1992; 5 in 2000.* **Sources: BU12, MO10, On3, Rai, Ty2.**

Petite Negri - Large, black fruit with rich, red, jam-like flesh. Dwarf plant fruits very well in pots. Self-fertile. Bears two crops. Fruit is similar to Black Mission, but the plant is more hardy and bears two crops. Hardy in Zones 7-10. *Source History: 3 in 1992; 5 in 2000.* **Sources: Gr16, On3, Or2, Par, Rai.**

Royal Vineyard - Large purplish brown fruit. Bears good breba crop before the main crop. Hardy in Zones 6-10. Obtained from the collection of Dr. Dunstan, fruit breeder from Gainesville, Florida. One of his favorites. Originally from the Royal Vineyard in England. *Source History: 1 in 1988; 3 in 1992; 1 in 2000.* **Sources: Or2.**

Rutara - Yellow skinned fruit with peach colored flesh. Top quality. Ripens consistently in the Northwest. Needs reflected heat. *Source History: 1 in 2000.* **Sources: Ea3.**

Saint Anthony - Medium to large soft yellow fruits with prominent ridges. Sweet tender flesh. Well liked in California. Rare. *Source History: 1 in 1988; 1 in 2000.* **Sources: Or2.**

San Piero - *Source History: 1 in 2000.* **Sources: RA4.**

Smith - *Source History: 1 in 2000.* **Sources: Sh3.**

Tena - Light green fruit. Amber to pink flesh. Heavy crops. Excellent fresh or dried. Produces high quality fruit under poor conditions. *Source History: 1 in 1988; 4 in 1992; 2 in 2000.* **Sources: Ju2, Or2.**

Tennessee Mountain - Sugar content is high enough for dried use. Parent tree was obtained in 1979 from Dr. Silas Harmon at the Coastal Plains Experiment Station in Tifton, Georgia, who received his original cuttings from a government worker in the 1940s. Has survived the bitter cold of the Tennessee Mountains. Recommended for outdoor growing in marginal areas. Zones 7-9. *Source History: 1 in 1988; 1 in 1992; 3 in 2000.* **Sources: Hid, Or2, Ty2.**

Texas Everbearing (English Brown Turkey) - Medium to large, brownish mahogany to purple fruit. High quality, amber flesh. Has closed eye which helps reduce fruit spoilage. Excellent for preserves. Self-pollinating. Fruits continuously over a 60-70 day period from early in the season until the end of the summer. Fruiting habit includes a light first crop followed almost immediately by a heavy second crop that ripens early. Well adapted to cool areas of the South. Produces excellent crops in the Southwest and short growing season areas. Very hardy tree recommended for borderline areas. Will resprout and bear after a freeze kills back the top. Hardy in Zones 7-10. *Source History: 11 in 1988; 17 in 1992; 9 in 2000.* **Sources: CO5, Iso, Lee, ORA, Sav, Tex, WA8, Wel, Wom.**

Ventura (Strawberry Fig) - Large, flat, green fig. Ruby red flesh with natural strawberry jam flavor. Small, compact trees are more cold hardy than most. Ripens in August. *Source History: 2 in 1992; 1 in 2000.* **Sources: Ju2.**

White Genoa - Medium large fruit. Thin, greenish yellow skin. Amber to yellow flesh. Fair flavor. Good for eating fresh. Flesh poor when dried. Self-fruitful. Bears twice a year. Well adapted to cooler areas of the West. Produces well in coastal areas, particularly southern California. Requires 100 hours of chilling. *Source History: 6 in 1988; 5 in 1992; 3 in 2000.* **Sources: CO5, ORA, WI4.**

White Kadota - Medium size lemon-yellow fruit with thick skin. Amber flesh with few seeds. Good for canning or drying. Extremely vigorous fig tree. Self-pollinating. Commercial canning variety. Requires 100 hours of chilling. Hardy in Zones 7-10. *Source History: 2 in 1988; 5 in 1992; 2 in 2000.* **Sources: CO5, Pe2.**

White King - Yellow-skinned fruit with amber-pink, sweet flesh. Resists fruit rot. *Source History: 1 in 1992; 1 in 2000.* **Sources: Ju2.**

White Marseilles (Italian Honey Fig, Lattarula) - Greenish yellow fruit. Very sweet, honey colored flesh with high sugar content. Strong grower withstands very low temperatures. Never fails to ripen its fruit; July to November 1. Popular in France as drying fig. Very common in the Northwest. *Source History: 1 in 1988; 1 in 1992; 1 in 2000.* **Sources: Or2.**

Wild Turkey - Small sweet fig most in demand as a preserving fig. Zones 8-10. *Source History: 1 in 2000.* **Sources: Ty2.**

Yellow Honey - *Source History: 1 in 2000.* **Sources: Sh3.**

Jujube

Ziziphus spp.

29-16 TOC - Russian cultivar. *Source History: 1 in 2000.* **Sources: Me2.**

Abbeville - Prolific plant bears many small, elongated fruit. Originated in Louisiana. *Source History: 1 in 2000.* **Sources: Me2.**

Admiral Wilkes - Large, dark mahogany, oblong fruit. Sweet flavor. Very old seedling plant in Washington, D.C. Very late ripening. One of the progeny from the Wilkes expedition to the South Seas in 1842. *Source History: 1 in 1992; 3 in 2000.* **Sources: Me2, On3, Pa6.**

Ant Admire - Elongated fruit. Ripens late season. Excellent. *Source History: 1 in 2000.* **Sources: Me2.**

Chinese - *Source History: 1 in 2000.* **Sources: Ga11.**

Edhegard - Virtually thornless plant. Fruit resembles Lang. Originated in Alabama. *Source History: 1 in 1992; 1 in 2000.* **Sources: Me2.**

Fitzgerald No. 1 - Originated in Georgia. *Source History: 1 in 1992; 1 in 2000.* **Sources: Me2.**

GA 866 - Originally from the Chinese introductions at Chico, California. *Source History: 1 in 1992; 1 in 2000.* **Sources: Me2.**

GI 7-62 - Originally from the Chinese introductions at Chico, California. *Source History: 1 in 1992; 1 in 2000.* **Sources: Me2.**

GI 1183 - Originally from the Chinese introductions at Chico, California. *Source History: 1 in 1992; 1 in 2000.* **Sources: Me2.**

Globe - Large, round fruit best when dried. *Source History: 1 in 2000.* **Sources: Me2.**

Himalayan - *Ziziphus recurva.* Semi-evergreen tree grows 30-40' tall. Bears .5" mahogany drupelets with seedy flesh and sweet-tart flavor. Ripens in late autumn. Trademarked. *Source History: 1 in 2000.* **Sources: Or2.**

Honey Jar - Chinese cultivar. Small fruit with sweet taste fresh or dried. *Source History: 1 in 2000.* **Sources: Me2.**

Indian (Cottony Jujube) - *Ziziphus mauritiania.* Round, .5" fruits. Shrub or small tree. Twigs and bottoms of leaves are white. Well adapted to hot, dry climates. Hardy in Zone 10. Native to India. This unusual accession was collected in Mauritania, West Africa. *Source History: 1 in 1988; 3 in 1992; 2 in 2000.* **Sources: Ga11, Or2.**

Jin - Excellent fresh or dried. *Source History: 1 in 2000.* **Sources: Me2.**

Jujube (Chinese Date, Chinese Jujube, Common Jujube) - Bears large sweet, egg-shaped fruit profusely and at an early age. Fruit eaten fresh, dried or brandied. Oil is also extracted from the seed in southern India. Trees reach 25' with showy foliage. Hardy; blooms late. Disease and insect free. Needs warm inland summers to ripen. Give winter protection until trees are 3-4' tall in cold areas. Ripens in late September. *Source History: 4 in 1988; 11 in 1992; 9 in 2000.* **Sources: Ban, Ca7, Fra, Hud, LO6, Pa2, Sc2, Sh14, Wo2.**

Kitaiski No. 2 - Russian cultivar. *Source History: 1 in 2000.* **Sources: Me2.**

Kitaiski No. 60 - Russian cultivar. *Source History: 1 in 2000.* **Sources: Me2.**

Lang - Large, pear-shaped, reddish brown fruit, 1.5-2" long x .75" wide. Can be eaten fresh, dried or candied. Beautiful, no care ornamental with striking, gnarled, light grey branches when dormant. Pollinate with Li. Ripens in September or October. Native to China. Zones 5-10. *Source History: 5 in 1988; 7 in 1992; 10 in 2000.* **Sources: Bay, CO5, Me2, On3, Or2, ORA, Pa6, Rai, Ty2, WI4.**

Li - Large mahogany-brown fruit, often 2" in diameter; almost round with small pit. Sweet, crisp flesh. Glossy, small, ovate, green leaves in the summer. Self-fruitful. Ripens in September or October. Low chilling requirement. Hardy in Zones 5-10. *Source History: 6 in 1988; 8 in 1992; 13 in 2000.* **Sources: An4, Bay, Bu7, CO5, Ed2, Me2, On4, Or2, ORA, Pa6, Rai, Ty2, WI4.**

Oo Sene Hun - *Source History: 1 in 2000.* **Sources: Me2.**

Red Date - Fruit is used fresh or dried. Hardy, drought tolerant tree. *Source History: 1 in 1992; 1 in 2000.* **Sources: So12.**

Redlands No. 4 - Large, sweet, round fruit with crisp flesh. Collected at an old homestead in Redlands, California. *Source History: 1 in 2000.* **Sources: Me2.**

September Late - Use fresh or dried. Ripens mid to late season. *Source History: 1 in 2000.* **Sources: Me2.**

Sherwood - Large fruit is of extraordinary quality for the Deep South. Narrow upright tree with leaves with a weeping habit. *Source History: 1 in 1988; 3 in 1992; 4 in 2000.* **Sources: CO5, Me2, Pa6, Sh3.**

Shui Men - Elongated fruit. Excellent fresh or dried. Possibly the same as Sui Men. Originally from the TVA, Tennessee. *Source History: 1 in 1992; 1 in 2000.* **Sources: Me2.**

Sihong - Chinese cultivar. Excellent, large round fruit. Ripens midseason. *Source History: 1 in 2000.* **Sources: Me2.**

Silverhill (Silverhill Round) - Plum-shaped, light mahogany colored fruit. White flesh with date-like flavor. Ripens in September. *Source History: 1 in 1988; 2 in 1992; 2 in 2000.* **Sources: Ju2, Me2.**

So - Round, sweet fruit with crisp, apple-like flavor. Beautiful tree with zig-zag branching. Ripens in August. *Source History: 1 in 1988; 1 in 1992; 2 in 2000.* **Sources: Ju2, Me2.**

Sovetskii - Russian cultivar. *Source History: 1 in 2000.* **Sources: Me2.**

Suan Tzao (Sour Date) - *Ziziphus spinosa.* Long-lived, drought tolerant tree to 12'. Bears small mahogany-brown fruits. Crisp and tasty when fresh but very tart. Invasive plant spreads by suckers. Trademarked. *Source History: 1 in 2000.* **Sources: Or2.**

Sugar Cane - Spiny plant bears small to medium size fruit. Round to slightly elongated shape. Extremely sweet, crunchy flesh. *Source History: 1 in 2000.* **Sources: Me2.**

Sweet Meaty - Seedling that produced very round, meaty fruit. Excellent flavor. Very thorny. Last to ripen in the season. *Source History: 1 in 1992; 1 in 2000.* **Sources: Me2.**

Ta Yan Tsao - Probably Lang. *Source History: 1 in 2000.* **Sources: Me2.**

Texas Tart - Tart fruit with high acid content dries into a small, very sweet raisin-like fruit. Originated in Lubbock, Texas. *Source History: 1 in 1992; 1 in 2000.* **Sources: Me2.**

Thai - Container grown plant will bear huge fruit. Flesh is crisp like a green apple. Delicious. *Source History: 1 in 2000.* **Sources: Na13.**

Thornless - Possibly Lang. Virtually thornless. *Source History: 1 in 1992; 2 in 2000.* **Sources: Me2, Pa6.**

Tigertooth (Tigers Tooth) - Long, thin fruit looks like dates ripening on the tree. Harvest when crinkly brown. Probably the same as Silverhill. *Source History: 2 in 1992; 2 in 2000.* **Sources: Ju2, Me2.**

Topeka - Crispy sweet fruit. Late harvest. Collected in Kansas. *Source History: 1 in 1992; 1 in 2000.* **Sources: Me2.**

Tsao - Fruit is pointed at both ends. Tsao is the Chinese name for jujube (date). *Source History: 1 in 1992; 1 in 2000.* **Sources: Me2.**

Yu - Elongated fruit. Yu is the Chinese name for tooth. *Source History: 1 in 1992; 1 in 2000.* **Sources: Me2.**

Nectarine

Prunus persica var. nucipersica

Arctic Glo - Large, firm, white flesh fruit. Well balanced, acid flavor. Vigorous, productive tree. Self-fertile. Ripens in late June or early July; about six days before Redhaven. Requires 400-500 hours of chilling. Hardy to -20 degrees F. U.S. Plant Patent No. 7884. *Source History: 1 in 1992; 6 in 2000.* **Sources: Ad2, Bay, Bea, Hi9, Va2, WI4.**

Arctic Gold - Large fruit with 80% bright red over white skin color. Firm white freestone flesh. Non-acid. Vigorous tree. Subject to stem pulling. Requires 800-900 hours of chilling. U.S. Plant Patent No. 9406. *Source History: 1 in 2000.* **Sources: WI4.**

Arctic Jay - Attractive fruit with firm white flesh. Freestone. Rich flavor has a good balance of sugar and acid. Ripens in July, between Arctic Glo and Heavenly White. Self-fruitful. Requires 900-1000 hours of chilling. U.S. Plant Patent No. 9908. *Source History: 2 in 2000.* **Sources: Bay, WI4.**

Arctic Pride - White flesh clingstone with good color. Non-acid. Subject to June drop. Ripens mid-August. Requires 800-900 hours of chilling. U.S. Plant Patent No. 8450. *Source History: 1 in 2000.* **Sources: WI4.**

Arctic Queen - Medium to large fruit with firm, white flesh. Nice crunchy texture when firm ripe; extremely sweet when soft ripe. Freestone. Excellent dessert quality. Resembles Arctic Rose but ripens 3-4 weeks later. Requires 900-1,000 hours of chilling. U.S. Plant Patent No. 8094. *Source History: 3 in 2000.* **Sources: Ad2, Bay, WI4.**

Arctic Rose - Medium size fruit with white, sub-acid flesh. Freestone. Very sweet flavor. Crunchy texture when firm; extremely sweet when soft ripe. Self-fruitful. Ripens in late June to mid-July. Requires 900-1,000 hours of chilling. U.S. Plant Patent No. 7889. *Source History: 1 in 1992; 3 in 2000.* **Sources: Ad2, Bay, WI4.**

Arctic Snow - Large fruit with firm, sweet, white flesh. Non-acid. Ripens in late August. Requires 900-1,000 hours of chilling. U.S. Plant Patent No. 7920. *Source History: 1 in 2000.* **Sources: WI4.**

Arctic Star - Semi-freestone with snow-white flesh and beautiful dark red skin. Sweet flavor is low in acid with no tartness. Self-fruitful. Ripens mid to late June. Requires 550-650 hours of chilling. U.S. Plant Patent No. 9332. *Source History: 4 in 2000.* **Sources: Bay, On4, Pa2, WI4.**

Arctic Sweet - Medium to large fruit with 80-90% bright red over white skin color. Firm white flesh is non-acid with sweet flavor. Clingstone. Ripens in the second week of June. Requires 800-900 hours of chilling. U.S. Plant Patent No. 9542. *Source History: 1 in 2000.* **Sources: WI4.**

August Glo - U.S. Plant Patent No. 8039. *Source History: 1 in 2000.* **Sources: WI4.**

Boston Red - Yellow fruit with red cheek. Yellow, freestone flesh. Fine, sweet flavor. Ripens in late summer. *Source History: 1 in 1988; 1 in 1992; 1 in 2000.* **Sources: Wel.**

Carolina Red - Yellow flesh. Ripens 39 days before Elberta. Requires 750 hours of chilling. *Source History: 2 in 1988; 2 in 1992; 2 in 2000.* **Sources: Cum, Nrs.**

Cavalier - Flower buds show more frost tolerance than Redbud. *Source History: 1 in 1992; 2 in 2000.* **Sources: MI5, WI4.**

Cherokee - Medium size, blemish-free, highly colored, yellow-red fruit. Firm, juicy, yellow, freestone flesh. Vigorous, productive tree. Self-pollinating. Brown rot resistant. Ripens early. Requires 850 hours of chilling. Hardy in Zones 5-8. *Source History: 4 in 1988; 5 in 1992; 2 in 2000.* **Sources: GI3, Nrs.**

Columbia - Red fruit. Yellow, freestone flesh. Ripens in mid-July. Requires 850 hours of chilling. *Source History: 2 in 1988; 4 in 1992; 2 in 2000.* **Sources: Bas, Nrs.**

Crimson Baby - Ripens in late May. *Source History: 2 in 2000.* **Sources: AG2, Nrs.**

Crimson Gold, Stark (Zaiger Cultivar) - Large, bright red fruit. Non-browning flesh. Semi-freestone. Used fresh and for desserts. Extremely productive. Ripens in mid-July. Winter hardy; grows well in Zones 5-8 and in the cooler parts of Zone 9. Developed by Floyd Zaiger. U.S. Plant Patent No. 5228. *Source History: 1 in 1988; 1 in 1992; 1 in 2000.* **Sources: St4.**

Crimson Snow, Stark (Bradcrim Cultivar) - Firm, melting, white flesh. Free-stone. Sub-acid, sweet flavor. Excellent quality. Cold hardiness approaches that of Redhaven. Bacterial spot tolerance compares to Summer Pearl (TM) or White Lady. Ripens about 5 days after Redhaven. The first white-fleshed nectarine suitable for Midwestern conditions. U.S. Plant Patent No. 8461. *Source History: 2 in 2000.* **Sources: AG2, St4.**

Crystal Belle - Large round fruit with firm, juicy white flesh. Skin color is 90% red over cream background. Ripens early. Licensed by W. A. McCullough Inc. Plant Patent applied for. *Source History: 1 in 2000.* **Sources: AG2.**

Crystal Red - Excellent shipping variety with bright red covering over 90% of the fruit. Round to oblong shape. Ripens mid-June. U.S. Plant Patent No. 9099.

Source History: 1 in 2000. **Sources: AG2.**

Crystal Rose - Large size fruit with 90% red overcolor. Fruit has a tendency to be oblong in shape with slight tip occurring in years of inadequate chilling. Ships well. Ripens 10 days after Crystal Red. U.S. Plant Patent No. 9107. *Source History: 1 in 2000.* **Sources: AG2.**

Desert Dawn - Solid red fruit; medium size when thinned. Firm, juicy, sweet, yellow, semifreestone flesh. Aromatic with a rich, distinctive flavor. Self-fruitful. Susceptible to peach leaf curl, brown rot and Oriental fruit moth. Proven heavy producer in warm winter western climates. Ripens in mid to late May. Requires 150-250 hours of chilling. Developed by Floyd Zaiger. *Source History: 4 in 1988; 1 in 1992; 3 in 2000.* **Sources: Bay, MI5, WI4.**

Desert Delight - Large yellow fruit. Freestone. Yellow flesh. Ripens in mid-June, a few days after Desert Dawn. Self-fruitful. Requires 100-200 hours of chilling. U.S. Plant Patent No. 7891. *Source History: 2 in 1992; 5 in 2000.* **Sources: Bay, MI5, ORA, Pa2, WI4.**

Double Delight - Dark red fruit. Yellow, freestone flesh. Sweet, rich flavor. Superb quality. Heavy-bearing tree. Showy pink double flowers. Self-fertile. Susceptible to peach leaf curl, brown rot, Oriental fruit moth. Ripens midseason. Requires 500-650 hours of chilling. Developed by Floyd Zaiger. Plant patent applied for. *Source History: 2 in 1988; 4 in 1992; 3 in 2000.* **Sources: Bay, Pe2, WI4.**

Durbin - Semifreestone fruit with larger size and excellent color. Medium textured, yellow flesh. Very good flavor. More disease resistant than other varieties. Ripens 30 days before Elberta in mid-August. Requires 850 hours of chilling. Hardy in Zones 5-9. Developed in North Carolina. *Source History: 5 in 1988; 6 in 1992; 5 in 2000.* **Sources: Bar, Cum, Ho5, Iso, Nrs.**

Earliglo - Highly colored medium-large fruit. Firm yellow flesh. Vigorous, productive tree. Low chilling requirement of 150-250 hours. U.S. Plant Patent No. 7402. *Source History: 1 in 2000.* **Sources: WI4.**

Earliscarlet - Good size fruit; 80% scarlet over gold background. Yellow flesh with excellent firmness. Vigorous, productive tree. Ripens 28 days before Elberta, about July 21. Requires 850 hours of chilling. Developed at the USDA's Appalachian Fruit Research Station in Kearneysville, West Virginia. *Source History: 3 in 1988; 4 in 1992; 3 in 2000.* **Sources: Ad2, Cum, Nrs.**

Early Blaze - *Source History: 1 in 1992; 1 in 2000.* **Sources: Bo5.**

Early King - Yellow flesh. Ripens early. Requires 450 hours of chilling. *Source History: 1 in 1992; 1 in 2000.* **Sources: Tex.**

Easternglo - Medium to large size, highly colored fruit with dark red skin. Ripens about two weeks before Red Haven. U.S. Plant Patent No. 7890. *Source History: 2 in 2000.* **Sources: Ad2, Hi9.**

Fantasia - Gold King x Red King seedling. Large, egg-shaped, freestone fruit with very smooth skin; 70% bright red overlaid on brilliant yellow. Firm, smooth textured, yellow flesh of excellent quality. Can be harvested firm-ripe and tangy or soft-ripe and sweet. Fairly small, vigorous, productive tree is a reliable producer. Self-fertile. Susceptible to peach leaf curl, brown rot, Oriental fruit moth and bacterial leaf spot. Equal in quality to Flavortop, maturing 7-10 days later. Ripens 16 days before Elberta and 21 days after Red Haven; in late July or early August in central California. Requires 500-600 hours of chilling. USDA introduction from California in 1969. *Source History: 13 in 1988; 25 in 1992; 22 in 2000.* **Sources: Ad2, AG2, Bay, Bo5, Cla, Co2, CO5, Cum, Hi9, Ho5, JOY, Nrs, ORA, Sc6, Si3, So5, Son, St4, STR, Va2, WI4, Wor.**

Firebrite - Smooth, medium size, semifreestone fruit; should be thinned for optimum size. Dark cherry-red over a golden yellow background. Firm, smooth textured, yellow flesh. Excellent flavor. Moderately vigorous, highly productive tree; only medium hardy. Good resistance to bacterial spot. Early maturing, about August 1. *Source History: 5 in 1988; 6 in 1992; 3 in 2000.* **Sources: AG2, Co2, Va2.**

Firecracker - Freestone. Genetic dwarf tree. *Source History: 1 in 1988; 1 in 1992; 1 in 2000.* **Sources: STR.**

Flame Glo - Very large size fruit. Deep red color covers nearly the entire fruit. Yellow flesh. Good flavor. Moderately vigorous tree. Ripens early July. Requires 900-1,000 hours of chilling. U.S. Plant Patent No. 6408. *Source History: 1 in 2000.* **Sources: WI4.**

Flamekist - Large, firm, high quality, clingstone fruit; red over yellow skin. Self-fruitful. Popular fresh market variety. Ripens in late August or early September. Requires 500-700 hours of chilling. *Source History: 1 in 1988; 6 in 1992; 2 in 2000.* **Sources: AG2, WI4.**

Flavortop - Medium to large, egg-shaped fruit; mostly red over a bright yellow background. Firm, smooth textured, yellow, freestone flesh of excellent quality. Vigorous, productive, self-fertile tree. Large, showy blossoms. Susceptible to bacterial spot. Good shipper. Ripens in mid-July in central California, between Independence and Fantasia. Requires 650 hours of chilling. Tender to winter cold; Zone 5. USDA introduction from California. *Source History: 12 in 1988; 16 in 1992; 12 in 2000.* **Sources: Ad2, Co2, COL, Hi9, Ho5, JOY, MI5, Nrs, STR, Va2, Wh4, Wor.**

Garden Beauty - Yellow, clingstone fruit. Fairly good flavor; unusually sweet. Genetic dwarf tree grows only 4-5.5' tall. Spectacular springtime display of dark pink, double blossoms that completely cover the tree. Self-fertile. Yields up to a half bushel each year. Leaf curl susceptible. Ripens from late August to early September. Requires 500-600 hours of chilling. Developed by Floyd Zaiger. *Source History: 5 in 1988; 5 in 1992; 2 in 2000.* **Sources: Mi1, ORA.**

Garden Delight - Large, freestone fruit; yellow skin blushed with red. Sweet, juicy, yellow flesh. Sweet, orange-like flavor. Genetic dwarf tree grows 4-6' tall. Dense foliage. Beautiful spring display of dark pink, double blossoms that solidly cover the branches. Self-fertile. Heavy bearing. Ripens in mid-August in central California. Requires 500-600 hours of chilling. Hardy in Zones 5-9. Developed by Floyd Zaiger. *Source History: 5 in 1988; 9 in 1992; 4 in 2000.* **Sources: Bay, MI5, ORA, WI4.**

Garden Nectar - Large, clingstone fruit; sweet and delicious. Self-fertile. Ripens in late August. Requires 400 hours of chilling. *Source History: 1 in 1988; 1 in 1992; 1 in 2000.* **Sources: ORA.**

Garden State - Large fruit; thin, smooth, plum-like, fuzzless skin. Extra sweet, juicy, mellow, firm, yellow, freestone flesh. High quality. Good for slicing, canning and freezing. Very productive, self-fruitful tree. Ripens from mid-August to early September. Hardy in Zones 5-9. *Source History: 4 in 1988; 5 in 1992; 7 in 2000.* **Sources: Bar, Lee, Mel, Nrs, Sav, TU5, WA8.**

Garden Supreme - Large, freestone fruit. Sweet, white flesh. Patio-type variety; 5-6' at maturity. Heavy producer. Self-fertile. Ripens in mid-August. Requires 400 hours of chilling. *Source History: 1 in 1988; 2 in 1992; 1 in 2000.* **Sources: ORA.**

Gialla di Padova - Golden yellow skin and flesh color. Melting, juicy, sweet flesh with flavor resembling apricot. May need high heat to ripen satisfactorily. Ancient Roman fruit introduced to the U.S. and renamed Gold in 1832. *Source History: 1 in 2000.* **Sources: Son.**

Gold Flame - Freestone. Genetic dwarf tree. *Source History: 1 in 1988; 1 in 1992; 1 in 2000.* **Sources: STR.**

Golden Prolific - Medium to large fruit with yellow, freestone flesh. Genetic dwarf tree grows 5' tall. Ripens from mid to late August. Requires 900 hours of chilling. Good for cold areas. *Source History: 1 in 1988; 2 in 1992; 1 in 2000.* **Sources: CO5.**

Goldmine - Small to medium size fruit; red blush over white skin. Aromatic, sweet, juicy, white, freestone flesh. Vigorous, productive, self-fruitful tree. Ripens in midseason, usually during August. Requires 400-500 hours of chilling. Long-time favorite in California and western Oregon. Hardy to Zone 5. *Source History: 9 in 1988; 14 in 1992; 7 in 2000.* **Sources: CO5, MI5, On4, ORA, SIM, STR, WI4.**

Gran Sun - U.S. Plant Patent No. 8255. *Source History: 1 in 2000.* **Sources: AG2.**

Harblaze - Medium to large size fruit with 90% bright red blush. Firm flesh. Freestone when ripe. Vigorous, productive, cold hardy tree shows good resistance to bacterial spot and brown rot. Ripens about three days before Redhaven. *Source History: 1 in 2000.* **Sources: Hi9.**

Hardired - Lexington x NJN 32. Smooth skin with 90% red color. Medium firm, 2.25-2.5", yellow, freestone flesh; good texture and flavor. Tree is vigorous and very productive; must be heavily thinned to attain size. Self-fruitful. Resistant to brown rot and bacterial leaf spot. Ripens uniformly in early August. Hardiness comparable to Reliance peach. Hardy to almost -30 degrees F. Grows well in Zones 5-8. Developed by the Canadian Agricultural Research Station in Harrow, Ontario, 1974. *Source History: 8 in 1988; 5 in 1992; 4 in 2000.* **Sources: Fed, Fi1, Hi9, Nrs.**

Harko - Medium size, 2.5", roundish, 90% bright red fruit; almost freestone. Good quality, melting, medium firm, yellow flesh; good texture and flavor. Medium size, spreading, productive tree. Self-fertile. Very reliable. Tolerant to bacterial spot and brown rot. Ripens four days after Red Haven peach in mid-August. Hardier than Red Haven; compares with Madison and Veteran. *Source History: 3 in 1988; 5 in 1992; 4 in 2000.* **Sources: Bea, Clo, ME3, Nrs.**

Harvest Sun - U.S. Plant Patent No. 7012. *Source History: 1 in 1992; 1 in 2000.* **Sources: AG2.**

Heavenly White - Large fruit; dark red blush over creamy white skin. Very firm, white, freestone flesh. Aromatic, very rich, sweet flavor. Peak quality when soft-ripe. Self-fertile. Susceptible to peach leaf curl, brown rot and Oriental fruit moth. Ripens in late July or early August; mid-July in central California. Requires 600-700 hours of chilling. Developed by Floyd Zaiger. Patented. *Source History: 2 in 1988; 6 in 1992; 3 in 2000.* **Sources: Bay, Pe2, WI4.**

Honey Blaze - Large fruit with 80-90% bright red over yellow skin color. Sweet, low to non-acid yellow flesh. Ripens in early June. Requires 900-1000 hours of chilling. U.S. Plant Patent No. 10,350. *Source History: 1 in 2000.* **Sources: WI4.**

Honey Kist - Large fruit with 80% maroon-red over yellow skin color. Rich, sweet flavor. Low to non-acid, yellow flesh. Ripens mid-June, after Honey Blaze. Requires 900-1,000 hours of chilling. U.S. Plant Patent No. 9333. *Source History: 2 in 2000.* **Sources: WI4.**

Honeyglo, Stark (Anderhone Cultivar) - Medium size fruit. Gourmet quality. Dwarf tree grows 4-6' tall. Ripens in early August. Hardy in Zones 5-8. Trademarked. U.S. Plant Patent No. 4789. *Source History: 1 in 1988; 1 in 1992; 1 in 2000.* **Sources: St4.**

Hunter - Large, freestone to semifreestone fruit. Juicy, sweet, tender flesh. Very good quality. *Source History: 1 in 1988; 1 in 1992; 1 in 2000.* **Sources: Leu.**

Independence - Large, oval fruit is almost completely dark red over a yellow background. Firm, yellow, freestone flesh. Rich, tangy-sweet flavor; one of the best. Productive, moderately vigorous tree. Self-fruitful. Susceptible to peach leaf curl, brown rot and Oriental fruit moth. Ripens in early July in central California. Requires 700 hours of chilling. Tree and blossom buds are fairly hardy to winter cold; almost as hardy as Red Haven. Hardy to Zone 5. Introduced in 1965. *Source History: 9 in 1988; 12 in 1992; 7 in 2000.* **Sources: Bay, COL, MI5, ORA, STR, Va2, WI4.**

John Rivers - *Source History: 2 in 1988; 4 in 1992; 3 in 2000.* **Sources: Nrs, STR, WI4.**

Jolly Red Giant - Bright orange-red over yellow skin color. Fruit to 3.5" with proper thinning. Yellow flesh. Freestone. Self-fruitful. Requires 600 hours of chilling. Ripens in July. U.S. Plant Patent No. 7947. *Source History: 2 in 1992; 2 in 2000.* **Sources: Bay, WI4.**

June Glo (Juneglo) - Medium to large fruit with almost full red color over a yellow background. Firm, yellow flesh; clingstone to semifreestone. Superb flavor and aroma. Excellent eating and shipping qualities. Heavily productive tree; self-fertile. Some resistance to bacterial spot. Susceptible to peach leaf curl, brown rot and Oriental fruit moth. Earliest top quality nectarine; ripens in early June, 7-10 days before Independence, 30 days before Fantasia and 15 days before Redhaven. Requires 700 hours of chilling. Good for late frost areas. Developed by Floyd Zaiger. U.S. Plant Patent No. 5228. *Source History: 3 in 1988; 7 in 1992; 5 in 2000.* **Sources: Bay, Hi9, Rai, St4, WI4.**

Juneprincess - Round-oblong shaped fruit. Skin color is 80-90% red. Freestone yellow flesh with some red in pit cavity. Good texture and flavor. Reliable cropper. Ripens with Karla Rose and Sunfre. Requires 850 hours of chilling. *Source History: 1 in 2000.* **Sources: Cum.**

Karla Rose - White flesh freestone with deep red skin color. Ripens 35 days before Elberta. Requires 600-700 hours of chilling. Recommended for cooler parts of the Gulf Coast and northward. *Source History: 2 in 1988; 4 in 1992; 5 in 2000.* **Sources: Cla, Cum, Ho5, Iso, Ty2.**

Kreibich - Self-fertile. Quite resistant to leaf curl and other diseases. Discovered by Roland Kreibich in western Washington. *Source History: 1 in 2000.* **Sources: On3.**

Le Grand - Firm juicy fruit is great fresh or canned. *Source History: 3 in 1988; 7 in 1992; 4 in 2000.* **Sources: CO5, MI5, ORA, STR.**

Le Grand, Late - *Source History: 2 in 1988; 3 in 1992; 2 in 2000.* **Sources: ORA, WI4.**

Liz's Late - Red over yellow skin color. Freestone. Yellow flesh with an intense, spicy flavor. Self-fruitful. Ripens late August, early September. Requires 600-700 hours of chilling. PVP. *Source History: 3 in 2000.* **Sources: Bay, Son, WI4.**

Mayfire - Small to medium size clingstone with firm, flavorful, yellow flesh. Ripens 63 days before Elberta. Requires 650 hours of chilling. *Source History: 2 in*

1988; 5 in 1992; 4 in 2000. **Sources: AG2, Cla, Cum, Ho5.**

Maygrand - *Source History: 1 in 1992; 1 in 2000.* **Sources: AG2.**

Mericrest - Nectacrest x Merideth. The hardiest nectarine. Medium size fruit with smooth, dark red skin. Sweet, juicy, firm, yellow, freestone flesh. Rich, tangy flavor. Excellent quality. Self-fruitful; blooms late. Bears 2-3 years after planting. Resistant to brown rot and bacterial leaf spot. Tremendous for roadside markets. Ripens with Glohaven peach in mid to late August. Requires 800 hours of chilling. Very cold hardy; withstands winter temperatures of -20 degrees F. Grows well in Zones 5-8. Hardy south of Shenandoah, Iowa; worth a try as far north as Des Moines. Developed by Professor E. M. Meader at the New Hampshire Station. *Source History: 8 in 1988; 11 in 1992; 11 in 2000.* **Sources: Bay, Bea, Bu7, Fi1, Gur, Hi9, Mi1, Pe2, So5, St4, WI4.**

Mono - Genetic dwarf. U.S. Plant Patent No. 4078. *Source History: 1 in 1992; 1 in 2000.* **Sources: STR.**

Morton (NY 884) - Selfed seedling of a cross between New Boy x Schumaker. Small to medium fruit; thick green skin, almost solidly covered when fully ripe with bright red and dark red. Luscious, juicy, slightly coarse, medium firm, greenish white, semiclingstone flesh. Good quality. Ripens in mid-August. Hardy tree. Introduced in 1965. *Source History: 2 in 1988; 1 in 1992; 1 in 2000.* **Sources: So5.**

Nectacrest - Medium to large fruit with bright red cheeks that shade to pink. Sweet, pure white, freestone flesh with melting texture. Vigorous tree grows 6-8' tall. Self-fertile. Ripens in early September. Hardy to -15 degrees F. Developed at the New Jersey Agricultural Experiment Station. Introduced in 1947. *Source History: 2 in 1988; 1 in 1992; 1 in 2000.* **Sources: Mi1.**

Nectar Babe - Large fruit with bright red skin. Sweet, yellow, freestone flesh. Rich, delicious flavor. Heavily productive genetic dwarf tree grows less than 6' tall. Pollinate with Honey Babe or Garden Sun. Leaf curl susceptible, but easy to cover. Grow in a pot or in the ground. Ripens in mid-July. Requires 500-600 hours of chilling. Hardy in Zone 9. Developed by Floyd Zaiger. Plant patent applied for. *Source History: 5 in 1988; 10 in 1992; 3 in 2000.* **Sources: Bay, ORA, WI4.**

Nectar Zee (Necta Zee) - Large fruit with beautiful red skin. Firm, yellow, clingstone flesh. Strong, vigorous, genetic dwarf tree grows only 6' tall. Self-fruitful. Ripens very early; 35 days before Nectar Babe; in early June in central California. Requires 500 hours of chilling. Developed by Floyd Zaiger. U.S. Plant Patent No. 6283. *Source History: 1 in 1988; 7 in 1992; 4 in 2000.* **Sources: Bay, ORA, Rai, WI4.**

Nectared 3 - *Source History: 1 in 1992; 1 in 2000.* **Sources: Nrs.**

Nectared 7 - *Source History: 1 in 1992; 1 in 2000.* **Sources: Nrs.**

Nectarina, Genetic Dwarf - Yellow fleshed freestone; red at pit cavity. Ripens in July. Requires 400 hours of chilling. *Source History: 1 in 1992; 2 in 2000.* **Sources: CO5, MI5.**

Nectarine - Bright red fruit with smooth, fuzzless skin. Excellent quality, freestone flesh. Vigorous, early bearer. Self-fruitful. As hardy as the peach and requires the same culture. *Source History: 2 in 1988; 3 in 1992; 1 in 2000.* **Sources: Bu1.**

Nectarose - *Source History: 1 in 1992; 1 in 2000.* **Sources: Nrs.**

Ovation, Stark (Pollock Cultivar) - U.S. Plant Patent No. 9263. *Source History: 1 in 2000.* **Sources: St4.**

Panamint - Medium to large fruit with rich, red skin. Golden yellow, freestone flesh. Sweet, aromatic flavor. Vigorous, productive tree. Self-fruitful. Ripens in early to mid-July. Excellent for warm winter climates of southern California because of the low chilling requirement of 150-250 hours. *Source History: 4 in 1988; 9 in 1992; 7 in 2000.* **Sources: Bay, CO5, Nrs, ORA, Pa2, Son, STR, WI4.**

Pocahontas - Medium to large, highly colored, red fruit. Good quality. Vigorous, productive tree. Large, showy blossoms. Resists brown rot. Ripens in early June. Requires 850 hours of chilling. *Source History: 3 in 1988; 6 in 1992; 3 in 2000.* **Sources: GI3, Po2, Tex.**

Quetta - *Source History: 2 in 1992; 1 in 2000.* **Sources: Nrs.**

Red Chief - Good size, highly colored fruit. White, freestone flesh. Good quality. Keeps well in storage. Self-fruitful. Good resistance to brown rot. Matures late, just before Elberta. Requires 850 hours of chilling. *Source History: 4 in 1988; 7 in 1992; 4 in 2000.* **Sources: GI3, Iso, Mel, Nrs.**

Red Diamond - U.S. Plant Patent No. 3165. *Source History: 1 in 1992; 1 in 2000.* **Sources: AG2.**

Red Gold (Andosa Cultivar, Stark's Red Gold) - Large to very large, blemish-free, glossy, almost all red fruit; good size if properly thinned. Firm, juicy, deep yellow, freestone flesh is red around the pit. Excellent color and flavor. High quality. Has the ability to hold its firmness, making it excellent for storage and shipping. Good shelf life. Vigorous, exceptionally productive tree grows 12-15' tall. Crack resistant. Self-fertile. Susceptible to bacterial spot and mildew. Ripens 14 days before Elberta, near the end of August. Requires 850 hours of chilling. Fairly hardy. Grows well in Zones 5-8. Originated in California. Introduced in 1960. *Source History: 14 in 1988; 22 in 1992; 20 in 2000.* **Sources: Ad2, AG2, Bar, Bo5, Cla, Co2, COL, Cum, Hi9, Ho5, Jo3, ME3, Mel, MI5, Nrs, Si3, St4, Va2, Wom, Wor.**

Red Grand - *Source History: 1 in 1992; 1 in 2000.* **Sources: AG2.**

Red Sunset - Large fruit with highly colored red skin. Firm, juicy, yellow, freestone flesh. Genetic dwarf tree grows 5' tall. Self-fertile. Excellent producer. Ripens in mid-June. Requires 600 hours of chilling. U.S. Plant Patent No. 6982. *Source History: 1 in 1988; 2 in 1992; 1 in 2000.* **Sources: CO5.**

Redbud - Bright red skin color. White, freestone flesh is firm with a medium texture. *Source History: 1 in 2000.* **Sources: MI5.**

Redglobe - *Source History: 1 in 2000.* **Sources: Nrs.**

Rose - *Source History: 1 in 2000.* **Sources: WI4.**

Rose Princess - Firm white flesh. Freestone. Somewhat tart. High yields. Disease resistant. Ripens 21 days before Elberta. Requires 850 hours of chilling. Zones 5-8. Originated in Byron, Georgia. *Source History: 3 in 1992; 4 in 2000.* **Sources: Cla, Cum, Iso, St4.**

Royalglo - Large, highly colored fruit. Yellow flesh. Vigorous, productive tree. Ripens in late May, between Mayglo and May Grand. Requires 300-400 hours of chilling. U.S. Plant Patent No. 8281. *Source History: 1 in 2000.* **Sources: WI4.**

Ruby Grand - *Source History: 1 in 1988; 1 in 1992; 1 in 2000.* **Sources: CO5.**

Ruby Sun - Ripens mid to late July. Plant patent applied for. *Source History: 1 in 2000.* **Sources: AG2.**

Scarlet Sun - Ripens in June. U.S. Plant Patent No. 9264. *Source History: 1 in 2000.* **Sources: AG2.**

September Free - Ripens in late August. *Source History: 2 in 2000.* **Sources:**

AG2, Nrs.

Silverlode - Medium size fruit is red over creamy yellow with red dots. Freestone flesh is white, sweet, and fine grained with little fiber. Rich flavor. Self-fertile. Ripens in late June. Requires about 400 hours of chilling. *Source History: 3 in 1988; 3 in 1992; 4 in 2000.* **Sources: CO5, Nrs, ORA, STR.**

Snowqueen - White freestone flesh. Ripens early; 2-3 weeks before Babcock. Self-fruitful. Requires 250-300 hours of chilling. U.S. Plant Patent No. 3733. *Source History: 1 in 1992; 3 in 2000.* **Sources: Bay, Son, WI4.**

Southern Belle - Very large, yellow fleshed freestone. Very productive, genetic dwarf tree grows 5' tall. Blooms very early. Ripens in early August. Requires 300 hours of chilling. U.S. Plant Patent No. 3758. *Source History: 2 in 1988; 2 in 1992; 3 in 2000.* **Sources: CO5, On4, Pa2.**

Stribling's Giant Freestone - *Source History: 1 in 1988; 1 in 1992; 1 in 2000.* **Sources: STR.**

Stribling's White Freestone - *Source History: 1 in 1988; 1 in 1992; 1 in 2000.* **Sources: STR.**

Summer Beaut, Stark (Anderbeaut Cultivar) - Medium size fruit with 75-85% red color. Freestone. Good firmness. Excellent quality. Vigorous, spreading tree is a reliable cropper. Matures four days after Red Haven. Highly recommended to precede Sunglo. *Source History: 1 in 1992; 3 in 2000.* **Sources: Ad2, Hi9, St4.**

Sun Grand - Medium-large, yellow fruit with red blush. Yellow, freestone flesh. Fruit holds well on the large, productive tree. Ripens in mid-July. *Source History: 2 in 1988; 4 in 1992; 1 in 2000.* **Sources: AG2.**

Sun Red - Red and yellow flesh; delicious fresh. Likes the warmer climates of the Deep South. Ripens during June. Requires 150-500 hours of chilling. Hardy in Zones 5-9. *Source History: 4 in 1988; 10 in 1992; 5 in 2000.* **Sources: CO5, Ho5, RA4, SIM, Wel.**

Sunblaze - Yellow flesh. Ripens early. Requires 250 hours of chilling. Released by the University of Florida to replace Sunred. *Source History: 1 in 1992; 2 in 2000.* **Sources: AG2, RA4.**

Suncoast - Large fruit with good color and shape. Retains firmness. Ripens in May. Zones 5-9. *Source History: 3 in 2000.* **Sources: RA4, SIM, Ty2.**

Sundollar - Yellow clingstone. Bright when ripe. Ripens 60 days before Elberta. Requires 400 hours of chilling. *Source History: 2 in 1992; 2 in 2000.* **Sources: Ho5, Ju2.**

Sunfire - Ripens in early June. *Source History: 1 in 2000.* **Sources: AG2.**

Sunfre - Thin skin is 75% red over creamy yellow. Sweet, juicy yellow flesh with a creamy texture. Semifreestone. Ripens 35 days before Elberta; late May thru early June. Requires 525 hours of chilling. *Source History: 3 in 1988; 6 in 1992; 4 in 2000.* **Sources: Cum, Ho5, Ju2, STR.**

Sungem - Armking x FL3-4N. Large red fruit with firm, melting yellow flesh. Semifreestone. Extremely disease resistant. Ripens 54 days before Elberta; early to mid-May. Requires 425 hours of chilling. Developed by the University of Florida. *Source History: 2 in 1988; 3 in 1992; 2 in 2000.* **Sources: Ho5, Ju2.**

Sunglo (Andup Cultivar, Stark Sunglo) - Sun Grand x (Le Grand x Hale Haven). Large, 3", smooth skinned, high quality fruit; 75% red over golden yellow background. Firm, meaty, juicy, deep yellow, semiclingstone flesh. Sweet flavor. Long storage and shelf life. Excellent for the packed or retail market, shipping and roadside markets. Ripens 23 days before Elberta and 10-14 days after Red Haven, in early August. Requires 850 hours of chilling. Hardy in Zones 5-8. Developed in California. Introduced in 1962. *Source History: 6 in 1988; 16 in 1992; 13 in 2000.* **Sources: Ad2, Cla, Co2, Cum, Hi9, Ho5, MI5, Nrs, Si3, St4, Tex, Wh4, Wor.**

Sungold - Yellow freestone with milder flavor than most nectarines. Ripens 26 days before Elberta. Requires 550 hours of chilling. Hardy in Zones 5-9. *Source History: 1 in 1988; 6 in 1992; 5 in 2000.* **Sources: Ju2, MI5, Nrs, SIM, Wom.**

Sunhome - Clingstone. Excellent flavor. Requires thinning for better fruit size. Ripens 38 days before Elberta. Requires 300 hours of chilling. Does best in the warmer areas of the Gulf Coast. *Source History: 1 in 1992; 2 in 2000.* **Sources: RA4, SIM.**

Sunlite - *Source History: 1 in 1992; 1 in 2000.* **Sources: Nrs.**

Sunmist - White flesh. *Source History: 1 in 2000.* **Sources: RA4.**

Sunraycer - *Source History: 2 in 2000.* **Sources: Ho5, RA4.**

Sunrich - *Source History: 1 in 1992; 1 in 2000.* **Sources: Nrs.**

Sunsplash - Yellow flesh. Requires 450 hours of chilling. Ripens 54 days before Elberta. *Source History: 1 in 2000.* **Sources: Cum.**

Sure Crop - Large, round, bright red fruit with thin, smooth, plum-like, fuzzless skin. Sweet, juicy, mellow, white, freestone flesh. Rich flavor and good quality. Vigorous, productive tree. Self-fertile. Ripens during late July or early August. Hardy in Zones 5-9. *Source History: 7 in 1988; 11 in 1992; 8 in 2000.* **Sources: Bar, Fi1, Lee, Leu, MI5, Tex, TU5, Wel.**

Sweet Scarlett - *Source History: 1 in 1992; 1 in 2000.* **Sources: COL.**

Tasty Gold - Excellent size fruit, almost full red. Yellow, freestone flesh. Good eating and shipping qualities. Vigorous, upright tree has shown adequate cold hardiness in eastern tests. Susceptible to bacterial spot. Ripens with Red Haven. U.S. Plant Patent No. 5623. *Source History: 1 in 1988; 1 in 1992; 1 in 2000.* **Sources: Hi9.**

White Tiger - Medium size, red skinned fruit. Juicy, aromatic, sweet, white flesh. Low chill requirement. *Source History: 1 in 1992; 1 in 2000.* **Sources: Son.**

Yellow Nectarine - *Source History: 1 in 1992; 1 in 2000.* **Sources: Nrs.**

Zee Glo - Large, firm, highly colored fruit. Yellow flesh. Very good flavor. Ripens the last week of July, between Fantasia and Royal Giant. Requires 850-950 hours of chilling. Patented. *Source History: 1 in 2000.* **Sources: WI4.**

Zee Grand - Highly colored, large fruit with excellent flavor. Ripens mid to late June. Requires 800-900 hours of chilling. U.S. Plant Patent No. 7475. *Source History: 1 in 1992; 1 in 2000.* **Sources: WI4.**

Pawpaw

Asimina triloba

Belle - Grafted type. *Source History: 1 in 2000.* **Sources: To7.**

Broad - Large fruit with aromatic light flesh. Originated in Tennessee. *Source History: 1 in 2000.* **Sources: Hid.**

Campbell NC-1 - *Source History: 1 in 1988; 1 in 1992; 2 in 2000.* **Sources: Gor, Pa6.**

Cawood - Firm, cream-yellow colored flesh. Ripens late. *Source History: 1 in 2000.* **Sources: Hid.**

Convis - Grafted type. *Source History: 1 in 2000.* **Sources: To7.**

Davis - Fruit is 4" long with green skin and yellow flesh. Somewhat smaller fruit than Sunflower, otherwise similar. Hardy to -25 degrees F.; Zone 4. Originally from Michigan. Introduced in 1961. *Source History: 1 in 1988; 2 in 1992; 8 in 2000.* **Sources: Ed2, Hid, Nol, On3, Or2, Pa6, Sh3, To7.**

Dwarf Pawpaw - *Asimina parviflora.* Similar to but smaller than *A. triloba.* Originated in Florida. *Source History: 1 in 1988; 2 in 1992; 1 in 2000.* **Sources: Wo2.**

Estil - *Source History: 1 in 2000.* **Sources: Sh3.**

Greenriver Belle - *Source History: 1 in 2000.* **Sources: Nol.**

IXL - Davis x Overleese cross developed by Corwin Davis. Very large fruit. Originated in Michigan. *Source History: 1 in 1992; 2 in 2000.* **Sources: Nol, To7.**

Kristen - *Source History: 1 in 1992; 1 in 2000.* **Sources: Sh3.**

LA Native - Medium size fruit. Yellow flesh with a hint of caramel. Originated in Louisiana. *Source History: 1 in 2000.* **Sources: Hid.**

Lady-D - Grafted type. *Source History: 1 in 2000.* **Sources: To7.**

Little Paw - Possible natural hybrid. Slow growing dwarf form with small fruit. *Source History: 1 in 2000.* **Sources: Oik.**

Lynn's Favorite - Grafted type. *Source History: 1 in 2000.* **Sources: To7.**

Mango - Reported to be excellent. Originated in Georgia. *Source History: 2 in 1992; 2 in 2000.* **Sources: Hid, Sh3.**

Mary Foos Johnson - Large, sweet fruit. Yellow flesh with a few large seeds. Good flavor. Possibly self-fertile. *Source History: 1 in 1988; 2 in 1992; 3 in 2000.* **Sources: Hid, Or2, Pa6.**

Mitchell - Large, oval to round fruit. Good flavor. Ripens mid to late September. Hardy to Zone 5. *Source History: 2 in 1992; 4 in 2000.* **Sources: Hid, On3, Pa6, Sh3.**

Overleese - Large, oval to round fruit with superior flavor. Creamy yellow-orange flesh with few seeds. Annual bearer. Zone 4. Originated in Indiana. *Source History: 1 in 1988; 3 in 1992; 10 in 2000.* **Sources: Bu7, Gor, Hid, Nol, On3, Or2, Pa6, Rai, Sh3, To7.**

Pawpaw (Banana Tree, Custard Banana, Hardy Banana Tree, Michigan Banana Tree, Nebraska Banana) - Greenish yellow fruit is almost black when ripe; 3-5", 8 oz., 3-7 per cluster. Soft, yellow pulp. Banana custard flavor. Eaten fresh or used in cookies, cakes, pies, preserves, puddings, ice cream. High in unsaturated fats, proteins, carbohydrates; very high in amino acids. Multistemmed, deciduous, thicket grower; can train to 30' pyramidal tree. Drooping, oval, 12 x 4", dark green leaves; yellow fall foliage. Fragrant, tulip-shaped, purple flowers. Pest and disease free. Lives 30-80 years. Native to rich, moist soil along shaded river banks in central U.S. Thrives in the South, but subzero hardy; Zones 5-9. Shipped to England in 1736. *Source History: 27 in 1988; 40 in 1992; 48 in 2000.* **Sources: Arb, Ba3, Ban, BO10, BO4, Bu1, BU12, Car, Co24, Ed2, Fi1, FO10, Fo2, Fo4, Ga8, Gur, HA12, HI7, In5, Int, Ju2, Jun, KEE, Lee, LO6, LOV, Me2, Mel, Oik, Or2, Pa2, Par, Po2, Po7, Rai, Sav, Sc2, Sh10, Sh14, St4, Tr10, Tri, TU5, Ty2, Wa13, Wa3, WA8, We18, Wo2.**

Pawpaw Seedlings - Grown from seed of superior varieties. Good pollenizers for the grafted varieties. Plant at least two, or one with a grafted variety, for cross pollination. *Source History: 2 in 1988; 4 in 1992; 4 in 2000.* **Sources: Clo, Ed2, On3, Pa6.**

Pennsylvania Golden - Medium to large fruit with very sweet flavor. Ripens early. Good variety to try in cooler regions. *Source History: 1 in 1992; 7 in 2000.* **Sources: Bu7, Clo, Gor, Gr16, On3, Pa6, Sh3.**

Prolific - Yellow-fleshed fruit. Late blooming. Productive and reliable. Ripens mid-October. Hardy to Zone 4. Originated in Michigan. *Source History: 2 in 1992; 10 in 2000.* **Sources: Bu7, Clo, Hid, Nol, On3, Pa6, Rai, Son, To7, WI4.**

Prolific x Davis Seedling - Hand-pollinated cross. Variable fruit quality. *Source History: 1 in 2000.* **Sources: Hid.**

Rebecca's Gold - Large size fruit with thin skin. Yellow flesh with few and small seeds. Productive. Late ripening. Originated in California. *Source History: 8 in 2000.* **Sources: Bu7, Hid, On3, Or2, Pa6, Sh3, Son, WI4.**

Sibley - Grafted type. *Source History: 1 in 2000.* **Sources: To7.**

Sue - Yellow fleshed, 4-6 oz. fruit. Flavorful and productive. Discovered by Don Munich. Originated in south Indiana. *Source History: 1 in 2000.* **Sources: Nol.**

Sun-Glo - Grafted type. *Source History: 1 in 2000.* **Sources: To7.**

Sunflower - Especially large, thick, sweet, flavorful fruits. Flavor of bananas and texture of custard. Good fresh and in pies, puddings and preserves. Small, deciduous, pyramidal tree. Oval leaves, 5" long. Annual bearer. Pollinate with Davis. Ripens late. Zone 4. *Source History: 3 in 1988; 7 in 1992; 12 in 2000.* **Sources: Bu7, Clo, Gr16, Hid, Nol, On3, Or2, Pa6, Rai, Son, To7, WI4.**

Sweet Alice - Large fruits with orange-yellow flesh. Good flavor with no aftertaste. Hardy in Zone 5. Originated in Ohio. *Source History: 1 in 1988; 3 in 1992; 4 in 2000.* **Sources: Hid, Or2, Pa6, Sh3.**

Sweet Virginia - Grafted type. *Source History: 2 in 2000.* **Sources: Pa6, To7.**

Taylor - Small fruit with green skin and yellow flesh. Grows in clusters of up to seven. Hardy in Zone 5. *Source History: 2 in 1992; 7 in 2000.* **Sources: Bu7, Nol, On3, Pa6, Sh3, To7, Wh3.**

Taytoo - Medium size fruit. Exceptionally superior flavor resembling vanilla custard. Prolific, annual bearer. *Source History: 1 in 1988; 1 in 1992; 6 in 2000.* **Sources: Gor, Nol, Or2, Pa6, Sh3, To7.**

Tollgate - Grafted type. *Source History: 2 in 2000.* **Sources: Pa6, To7.**

Well's Delight - Large fruit with excellent flavor. *Source History: 1 in 2000.* **Sources: Ed2.**

Wells - Large, tasty fruit. Plant two plants for cross pollination and fruit production. Hardy to Zone 4. *Source History: 8 in 2000.* **Sources: Bu7, Gr16, On3, Or2, Pa6, Rai, Sh3, WI4.**

Wilson - Medium size, sweet, flavorful, yellow fruit. *Source History: 2 in 1992; 2 in 2000.* **Sources: Low, Pa6.**

Zimmerman - Selected for quality fruit. Discovered in an orchard that was established in the early 1900s. *Source History: 2 in 1988; 1 in 1992; 1 in 2000.* **Sources: Gor.**

Peach

Prunus persica

19-4-40 - Firm, clingstone fruit. Good quality canner. Tree similar to Loadel. Ripens mid-July. *Source History: 1 in 1992; 1 in 2000.* **Sources: AG2.**

Admiral Dewey - *Source History: 1 in 1992; 1 in 2000.* **Sources: Nrs.**

Allgold - Yellow clingstone flesh. Ripens 25 days before Elberta. Requires 750 hours of chilling. *Source History: 1 in 1988; 1 in 1992; 1 in 2000.* **Sources: Nrs.**

Allstar (FA-80) - Red blush covers 90-100% of skin surface. Firm fruit stores well. Good shipping qualities. Trademarked. U.S. Plant Patent No. 10,549. *Source History: 3 in 2000.* **Sources: AG2, Hi9, St4.**

Ambergen - *Source History: 1 in 1992; 1 in 2000.* **Sources: Nrs.**

Amsden - Medium size fruit. Green-yellow skin with dark red blush on sun side. Soft, juicy, white flesh. Freestone. Originated in Illinois. Dates back to 1868. *Source History: 1 in 2000.* **Sources: Son.**

Andross - Early ripening clingstone. Excellent canning variety. Medium size, semi-upright tree. Ripens early August. *Source History: 2 in 1988; 4 in 1992; 3 in 2000.* **Sources: AG2, Si3, WI4.**

Angelus - Large, round, yellow fruit overlaid with bright red. Firm, yellow, freestone flesh. Mild, subacid flavor. Outstanding shipping quality. Vigorous tree usually bears 3-4 years after planting. Ripens just after Elberta. Hardy to 35 degrees F. Originated as a seedling of J. H. Hale in California. *Source History: 3 in 1988; 8 in 1992; 6 in 2000.* **Sources: AG2, Co2, COL, Si3, St4, Va2.**

Arctic Gem - Freestone with white flesh. Good size, color and shape. Moderately acid flavor. Stores and ships well. Self-fertile. Ripens late August. Zone 5. U.S. Plant Patent No. 7065. *Source History: 1 in 1992; 2 in 2000.* **Sources: Bea, Va2.**

Arctic Supreme - Large clingstone with white flesh. Red over cream colored skin. Sweet flavor with a hint of tanginess. Good for slicing. Self-fruitful. Peak quality reached shortly after picking. Ripens in late July to early August. Requires 700 hours of chilling. Patented. *Source History: 2 in 1992; 3 in 2000.* **Sources: Bay, Pe2, WI4.**

Arkansas No. 9 - Large yellow clingstone with small pit. Yellow skin color with red cheek. Consistent cropper. A favorite for processing. Ripens one week before Babygold. Bacterial spot resistant. *Source History: 3 in 2000.* **Sources: Co2, Hi9, Va2.**

August Etter - Medium size fruit with yellow skin and flesh. Texture is a little fibrous. Good flavor. Good for fresh eating and jam. Not for canning, but excellent frozen. Ripens in late August. *Source History: 1 in 1988; 1 in 1992; 1 in 2000.* **Sources: Gr4.**

August Pride - Yellow freestone with sweet, aromatic flavor. Tart skin. Self-fruitful. Ripens mid to late season. Low chilling requirement of 300 hours or less. Developed by Floyd Zaiger. *Source History: 1 in 1988; 3 in 1992; 3 in 2000.* **Sources: Bay, Pa2, WI4.**

August Sun - U.S. Plant Patent No. 5140. *Source History: 1 in 2000.* **Sources: AG2.**

Autumn Glo (NJ 232) - Large, greenish yellow fruit overlaid with red. Firm, yellow, freestone flesh. Very good quality. Hangs well. Can be picked in one or two pickings. Will stay solid on the tree about a week after ripening. Vigorous, productive tree. Ripens midseason. Compares in hardiness to Cresthaven or Hale Haven. Susceptible to bacterial leaf spot. Requires 850 hours of chilling. *Source History: 4 in 1988; 3 in 1992; 3 in 2000.* **Sources: Ad2, Cum, Ho5.**

Autumn Red - Medium to large fruit. Deep yellow, freestone flesh. *Source History: 1 in 1992; 2 in 2000.* **Sources: AG2, Nrs.**

Autumnprince - Skin color is 50-60% dull red over yellow background. Yellow freestone flesh. Red pit cavity. Dry to melting texture. Good flavor. Requires 750-800 hours of chilling. Ripens 22 days after Elberta. *Source History: 1 in 2000.* **Sources: Cum.**

Aztec Gold - *Source History: 1 in 2000.* **Sources: RA4.**

Babcock - Medium size, round fruit. Almost fuzzless skin, slightly blushed with red. Firm, juicy, white, semifreestone flesh turns red around the pit. Sweet, aromatic flavor. Heavy bearing, self-fruitful tree. Susceptible to peach leaf curl, brown rot, Oriental fruit moth and peach twig borer. Ripens from late June to July, depending on location. Requires only 250-300 hours of chilling. Long time favorite. *Source History: 6 in 1988; 12 in 1992; 9 in 2000.* **Sources: Bay, CO5, On4, ORA, Pa2, Pe2, Son, STR, WI4.**

Babcock, Giant - Babcock x July (Kim) Elberta. Larger than Babcock with predominant red skin color. Ivory to pale yellow, freestone flesh. Excellent dessert quality. Very productive. Self-fruitful. Ripens about two weeks after Babcock. Requires 500 hours of chilling. *Source History: 1 in 1988; 4 in 1992; 3 in 2000.* **Sources: ORA, Si3, WI4.**

Babygold - Clingstone. Good for canning. Tree hardiness compares to Redhaven. Ripens mid-August. *Source History: 1 in 2000.* **Sources: Sc6.**

Babygold No. 5 - Excellent quality, good size processing peach. Non-melting, yellow, clingstone flesh, a little red around the pit. Vigorous, upright, productive tree. Susceptible to bacterial spot. Ripens 20 days before Elberta. Requires 850 hours of chilling. *Source History: 4 in 1988; 9 in 1992; 7 in 2000.* **Sources: Ad2, Co2, Hi9, Ho5, Nrs, Va2, Wor.**

Babygold No. 6 - *Source History: 1 in 1992; 1 in 2000.* **Sources: Nrs.**

Babygold No. 7 - Processing variety similar to Babygold No. 5. Yellow, clingstone flesh. Tree is less vigorous than No. 5. Susceptible to bacterial spot. Ripens 7-10 days later than No. 5 and six days before Elberta. Requires 750 hours of chilling. *Source History: 4 in 1988; 6 in 1992; 4 in 2000.* **Sources: Ad2, Hi9, Ho5, Nrs.**

Babygold No. 8 - Yellow, clingstone flesh. Ripens with Elberta. Requires 950 hours of chilling. *Source History: 1 in 1988; 2 in 1992; 2 in 2000.* **Sources: Ho5, Nrs.**

Babygold No. 9 - *Source History: 1 in 1992; 1 in 2000.* **Sources: Nrs.**

Bai Ning Tao - Extremely sweet, white fleshed peach from China. Small seed is less than one-third the size of common peaches. *Source History: 1 in 2000.* **Sources: Cla.**

Beekman - Large, 2.5-3" fruit. Medium thick skin with 75% to 100% full red color. Very firm, fine grained, freestone flesh. Quite uniform in ripening without soft sutures. Usually harvested in two pickings. Excellent shipper. Hardy, upright tree becoming spreading. Numerous fruit buds require some thinning. Large, showy, self-fruitful flowers. Very productive. Ripens around August 21. Developed from an open-pollinated seedling of Sunhigh. *Source History: 1 in 1988; 1 in 1992; 1 in 2000.* **Sources: Ad2.**

Bellaire - Round, almost fuzzless, yellowish orange fruit overlaid with a brilliant red blush. Firm, clear, yellow, non-browning, freestone flesh. Good flavor. Excellent shipper. Strong, vigorous, easily trained tree. Resistant to bacterial spot. Ripens uniformly, soon after Red Haven. Trademarked. *Source History: 1 in 1988; 1 in 1992; 1 in 2000.* **Sources: Hi9.**

Belle of Georgia - Old-time favorite. Large, creamy white fruit with a bright red cheek. Firm, white, freestone flesh tinged with red. Highly flavored. Drops when ripe. Bruises easily. Excellent for fresh eating, desserts and canning. Vigorous, self-fertile tree. Very bud hardy. Reliable producer. Very resistant to bacterial spot; slightly resistant to brown rot. Ripens late August; three days before Elberta. Requires 800-850 hours of chilling. Hardy in Zones 5-8. Originated in Georgia around 1870 as a seedling of Chinese Cling. *Source History: 31 in 1988; 46 in 1992; 36 in 2000.* **Sources: Bar, Bas, Bo5, Cla, CO5, Cu4, Cum, Ed2, Fed, Fi1, FO10, Gur, Hi9, Ho5, Iso, Jo3, Lee, Leu, Mel, MI10, MI5, Na4, Nrs, Sav, Sc6, SIM, So5, Tex, TU5, Ty2, Va2, WA8, Wel, Wh4, Wom, Wor.**

Berenda Sun - Medium to large, attractive fruit. Yellow background color is covered with an overall red blush. Superb flavor. Juicy flesh with firm texture makes it an excellent shipper. Ripens in July in California; mid-August in Washington. U.S. Plant Patent No. 5297. *Source History: 1 in 1992; 1 in 2000.* **Sources: AG2.**

Bicentennial - Round, yellow fruit with a red blush. Yellow, clingstone flesh. Ripens in late May, 47-51 days before Elberta. Requires 700-750 hours of chilling. Introduced by Louisiana State University. *Source History: 4 in 1988; 6 in 1992; 4 in 2000.* **Sources: Ho5, Nrs, SIM, Wel.**

Biscoe - Raritan Rose x Redskin. Medium size, round, yellow fruit half covered with a bright red blush. Firm, fine textured, yellow, freestone flesh. Good flavor. Medium size, well formed tree. Vigorous and productive. Tests show good bud hardiness. Highly resistant to bacterial spot. Ripens 3 days before Elberta. Requires 850 hours of chilling. NC/AES. *Source History: 4 in 1988; 8 in 1992; 6 in 2000.* **Sources: Bo5, Cu4, Hi9, Ho5, Nrs, St4.**

Blake - Large, bright yellow fruit with a bright red blush. Bright yellow, freestone flesh with red around the pit cavity. Excellent quality. Hangs well on the tree. Ripens three days before Elberta. Too bud tender for the Midwest; grown widely in the East. Requires 750 hours of chilling. *Source History: 4 in 1988; 4 in 1992; 3 in 2000.* **Sources: Cum, Ho5, Nrs.**

Blazeprince - Large fruit to 2.75" when properly thinned. 90% red surface with attractive background color. Firm yellow freestone flesh. Fruit hangs on the tree well. Good eating quality. Ripens with Majestic. Requires 500 hours of chilling. *Source History: 1 in 2000.* **Sources: Ho5.**

Blazingstar (FA-12) - Round fruit; 90% bright red blush. Good quality, non-browning, yellow flesh. Freestone. Good shipper. Hardy tree resists bacterial spot. Shows good bud hardiness. Trademarked. U.S. Plant Patent No. 10,555. *Source History: 3 in 2000.* **Sources: Co2, Hi9, St4.**

BlushingStar (FA-18) - Skin color is 80% deep pink-red. Very fim white flesh is tinged with pink. Freestone. Distinctive flavor. Excellent shipping and storage qualities. Heavy producer. Very hardy. Trademarked. U.S. Plant Patent No. 10,554. *Source History: 5 in 2000.* **Sources: AG2, Co2, COL, Hi9, St4.**

Bonanza (Bonanza Miniature) - Medium to large, yellow fruit with red blushes. Highly aromatic, yellow, freestone flesh. Good flavor. Genetic dwarf grows only 4-5' tall. Thrives in tubs or containers. Often fruits the first year. Heavy crops. Large, pink, self-fertile flowers. Ripens from early to mid-June. Requires 250-500 hours of chilling. U.S. Plant Patent No. 2213. *Source History: 4 in 1988; 4 in 1992; 6 in 2000.* **Sources: Bay, CO5, MI10, MI5, ORA, WI4.**

Bonfire - Shrub-type tree grows to 6' tall. Pink blooms. Attractive red leaves retain color all season. Sweet fruit with white flesh streaked with red. Ripens late. Zones 5-9. U.S. Plant Patent No. 8509. *Source History: 4 in. 2000.* **Sources:**

CO5, Ed2, MI10, MI5.

Bonita - Medium large, yellow fruit with a red blush. Sweet, subacid, freestone flesh. Self-fruitful tree. Adapted to inland or coastal climates. Ripens late July in southern California. Requires 150-250 hours of chilling. *Source History: 4 in 1988; 6 in 1992; 5 in 2000.* **Sources: Bay, CO5, Nrs, ORA, WI4.**

Bounty - Large, firm, yellow fleshed freestone. Rapidly becoming an important commercial variety. Ripens 12 days before Elberta. Recommended as a replacement for Loring. Requires 800 hours of chilling. Developed at the USDA Peach Breeding Program at Kearneysville, West Virginia. *Source History: 5 in 1992; 8 in 2000.* **Sources: Ad2, Cum, Hi9, Ho5, Nrs, St4, Tex, Wel.**

Bowen - Medium to large clingstone fruit. Large, spreading tree. Ripens the first week of August, just ahead of Andross. *Source History: 2 in 1988; 3 in 1992; 2 in 2000.* **Sources: Si3, WI4.**

Boyer No. 178 - *Source History: 1 in 2000.* **Sources: Bo5.**

Brighton - Medium size, round, yellow fruit nearly covered with a bright red blush. Medium firm, juicy, slightly fibrous, yellow, semifreestone flesh, slow to oxidize. Sweet, rich flavor. Attains high quality while still quite firm and maintains it well. Vigorous, productive tree. Ripens 33 days before Elberta. Requires 750 hours of chilling. Medium hardy. Developed in New York State. *Source History: 3 in 1988; 3 in 1992; 1 in 2000.* **Sources: Nrs.**

Brittney Lane - Yellow flesh clingstone with 80-90% red blush over yellow skin color. Very good flavor. Ripens with Gem Free with better quality. Requires 350-450 hours of chilling. U.S. Plant Patent No. 10,286. *Source History: 1 in 2000.* **Sources: WI4.**

Cal Red - Freestone. U.S. Plant Patent No. 3977. *Source History: 1 in 1988; 3 in 1992; 1 in 2000.* **Sources: AG2.**

Camden - Yellow fruit covered with a red blush. Yellow, clingstone flesh. Ripens 58-60 days before Elberta. Requires 850 hours of chilling. *Source History: 3 in 1988; 3 in 1992; 2 in 2000.* **Sources: Cum, Ho5.**

Canadian Harmony - Sun Haven x Redskin. Medium to large, round, yellow fruit, 50-80% covered with a red blush. Moderately firm, yellow, freestone flesh, slightly red at the pit. Slow to brown. Must be picked before it reaches full color if it is to be shipped a long distance. Good freezer. Vigorous, upright, spreading tree. Heavy bearer. Ripens mid to late August, 12 days after Red Haven. Hardiness comparable to that of Red Haven. Developed at Harrow, Ontario. *Source History: 7 in 1988; 10 in 1992; 9 in 2000.* **Sources: Ad2, Co2, Cu4, Hi9, Nrs, Sc6, St4, Va2, WI4.**

Candoka - *Source History: 1 in 1992; 1 in 2000.* **Sources: Nrs.**

Candor - Red Haven x Erly-Red-Fre. Small to medium, round to oval, yellow fruit, 75-80% covered with red at maturity. Medium firm, juicy, slightly coarse, yellow, semifreestone flesh. Non-browning. Moderately vigorous, productive tree. Self-fertile. Resistant to bacterial spot. Ripens 48 days before Elberta. Requires 350-900 hours of chilling. Buds are tolerant to winter cold and frost. Originated in North Carolina. Introduced in 1965. *Source History: 5 in 1988; 7 in 1992; 6 in 2000.* **Sources: Ad2, Cu4, Cum, Hi9, Ho5, Nrs.**

Cardinal - Yellow, clingstone flesh. Ripens 47 days before Elberta. Requires 950 hours of chilling. Cold hardy. *Source History: 2 in 1988; 3 in 1992; 1 in 2000.* **Sources: Ho5.**

Carogem - Freestone fruit with yellow flesh. Ripens 17 days before Elberta. Requires 850-900 hours of chilling. *Source History: 1 in 1992; 2 in 2000.* **Sources: Cum, Ho5.**

Carolina Belle - Freestone with white flesh. Skin color is bright red over creamy white. Rich, sweet flavor especially when tree ripened. Ripens 18 days before Elberta. Requires 750 hours of chilling. Zones 5-8. Developed at North Carolina State University. *Source History: 4 in 1992; 5 in 2000.* **Sources: Cu4, Ho5, Nrs, St4, Ty2.**

Carolyn G (Orange Cling) - Large, firm, clingstone fruit. Large, vigorous tree. Ripens mid-August. Requires 800 hours of chilling. *Source History: 1 in 1988; 3 in 1992; 1 in 2000.* **Sources: WI4.**

Carson - Firm clingstone fruit. Very good canning quality. Willowy tree with upright growth habit. Somewhat prone to invisible split pits. Ripens late July. *Source History: 2 in 1988; 4 in 1992; 3 in 2000.* **Sources: AG2, Si3, WI4.**

Cary Mac - Sweet, freestone yellow flesh. Fine for fresh eating and freezing. Ripens 20 days before Elberta. Requires 750 hours of chilling. Zones 5-9. U.S. Plant Patent No. 3965. *Source History: 1 in 1992; 2 in 2000.* **Sources: Ho5, La3.**

Champagne - U.S. Plant Patent No. 4865. *Source History: 1 in 2000.* **Sources: WI4.**

Champion - Large, white fruit, almost covered with bright red. Very tender, juicy, white, freestone flesh. Sweet, delicate flavor. Strong, hardy, vigorous, self-fertile tree. Reliable producer. Leading white variety for commercial use; also one of the best for the home garden. Ripens midseason before Belle of Georgia. Hardy in Zones 5-8. Originated as a seedling of Oldmixon Free discovered in Illinois in 1880. *Source History: 6 in 1988; 9 in 1992; 9 in 2000.* **Sources: Mel, Mi1, Na4, Nrs, Po2, Sav, So5, Son, TU5.**

Charlotte - Old, rediscovered variety. Large, tasty freestone fruit. Shows strong resistance to peach leaf curl. Ripens late August. *Source History: 1 in 2000.* **Sources: On3.**

Cherry Gold - Yellow, clingstone flesh. Ripens 47 days before Elberta. Requires 550 hours of chilling. *Source History: 2 in 1988; 2 in 1992; 1 in 2000.* **Sources: Ho5.**

Comanche - *Source History: 1 in 1992; 1 in 2000.* **Sources: Nrs.**

Common Peach - Uncultivated type that is produced from seed. Produces small 2" yellow-green fruit. Coarse flesh with sweet flavor. Hardy to -20 degrees F. Native to China. *Source History: 1 in 2000.* **Sources: Oik.**

Compact Flavorette - Genetic semi-dwarf. Yellow freestone fruit with red-streaked orange flesh. Rich, tangy flavor. Heavy bearing, naturally small tree grows 10-12' tall; easily kept to 8' with light annual pruning. Fruiting area is larger than that of a genetic dwarf. Self-fruitful. Ripens late July-early August. Requires 600-700 hours of chilling. U.S. Plant Patent No. 8071. *Source History: 2 in 2000.* **Sources: Bay, WI4.**

Contender - Large round fruit with 70% red blush over a yellow background. Firm yellow flesh resists browning. Freestone. Blooms late. Consistent cropper. Ripens 9 days before Elberta. Requires 1,050 hours of chilling. Developed at North Carolina State University. *Source History: 4 in 1992; 8 in 2000.* **Sources: Cla, Cu4, Cum, Hi9, Ho5, Nrs, St4, Wom.**

CoralStar (FA-59) - Large fruit with 80% coral-red blush. Ripens over a long period; holds well on the tree. Multiple pickings required. Trademarked. U.S. Plant Patent No. 10,547. *Source History: 3 in 2000.* **Sources: AG2, Hi9, St4.**

Corona - Clingstone. Vigorous tree may have some pre-harvest drop. Ripens early September. *Source History: 2 in 1988; 3 in 1992; 2 in 2000.* **Sources: AG2, Si3.**

Coronet - Yellow, semifreestone flesh. Ripens 34 days before Elberta. Requires 700 hours of chilling. *Source History: 2 in 1988; 3 in 1992; 3 in 2000.* **Sources: Cum, Ho5, Nrs.**

Correll - Yellow fleshed clingstone. Ripens 51 days before Elberta. Requires 850 hours of chilling. Cold hardy. *Source History: 2 in 1988; 3 in 1992; 2 in 2000.* **Sources: Cum, Ho5.**

Crawford, Baby - Small, yellow fleshed freestone with intense flavor. Golden orange skin with slight blush. Self-fruitful. Ripens late July. Requires 800 hours of chilling. *Source History: 3 in 2000.* **Sources: Bay, Son, WI4.**

Crawford, Early - Very large, golden yellow fruit, splashed and mottled with bright red and dark brownish red by the sun. Juicy, yellow, marbled flesh with red rays at the pit. Pleasing aroma. Rich flavor. Surpasses other early varieties in fruit quality.Tree is not a heavy bearer. Ripens in mid-July. Raised from seed in the orchard of William Crawford of Middletown, New Jersey in the early 1880s. Companion to Late Crawford. *Source History: 3 in 1988; 4 in 1992; 2 in 2000.* **Sources: Gr4, Nrs.**

Crawford, Late - Once the mainstay of American peach culture and the standard of excellence among yellow varieties. Beautiful red and yellow fruit. Firm, tender, yellow, freestone flesh. Rich, sweet but sprightly flavor. Vigorous, upright, spreading tree with dark green foliage and pink blossoms in the spring. Ripens in late September. *Source History: 2 in 1988; 1 in 1992; 1 in 2000.* **Sources: So5.**

Cresthaven - Kalhaven x S.H. 309. Medium to large, nearly round, golden yellow fruit with a bright red blush. Very smooth, tough skin. Firm, juicy, clear, bright yellow, freestone flesh with considerable red around the pit. Resists browning. Hangs well on the tree, but can crack under certain weather conditions. Good canner, freezer and shipper. Vigorous, medium large, productive tree. Tends to overset. Fair tolerance to bacterial spot. Ripens in August three days before Elberta. Requires 850 hours of chilling. Above average bud hardiness. Hardy in Zones 5-8. Introduced by the Michigan Agricultural Experiment Station in Southhaven in 1963. *Source History: 10 in 1988; 15 in 1992; 14 in 2000.* **Sources: Ad2, AG2, Co2, Cu4, Cum, Hi9, Ho5, Jo3, Nrs, Si3, St4, Va2, WI12, Wor.**

Curlfree (Oregon Curl-Free) - Yellow firm, tender, juicy flesh. Vigorous growing tree resists peach-leaf curl. Ripens in mid-August; one week before Red Haven. Winter hardy. Does well in the Northwest and areas where peach leaf curl is a problem. *Source History: 1 in 1992; 1 in 2000.* **Sources: Mi1.**

CVN-2 - Yellow flesh freestone. Ripens 20 days before Elberta. Requires 750 hours of chilling. *Source History: 1 in 1992; 1 in 2000.* **Sources: Cum.**

CVN-3 (Big Red) - Yellow fleshed freestone. Ripens 22 days after Elberta. Requires 750 hours of chilling. *Source History: 1 in 1992; 1 in 2000.* **Sources: Cum.**

CVN-4 - Freestone with yellow flesh. Ripens six days after Elberta. Requires 850 hours of chilling. *Source History: 1 in 1992; 1 in 2000.* **Sources: Cum.**

David Sun (20-75-5) - Semifreestone with 90% red blush over yellow. Firm, juicy, yellow flesh. Excellent flavor. No split pits. Hangs well on the tree. Ripens five days after Kern Sun. Developed in California in 1975. U.S. Plant Patent No. 5874. *Source History: 1 in 1992; 1 in 2000.* **Sources: AG2.**

Dee-Six (D615W) - Good size, clingstone fruit of good quality. Produces heavily. Tendency toward biennial bearing. Ripens extra early. *Source History: 2 in 1992; 1 in 2000.* **Sources: WI4.**

Delicious, Starking (Smith Cultivar) - Medium firm, golden, freestone flesh; 2.75" in diameter. Excellent dessert peach. Also good for canning and freezing because its skin slips so easily. Strong, vigorous tree. Heavy bearer. Ripens in mid-July. Hardy in Zones 5-8 and cooler parts of Zone 9. Trademarked. *Source History: 1 in 1988; 1 in 1992; 1 in 2000.* **Sources: St4.**

Delp Hale - Proven variety in Washington's Yakima Valley. Very large fruit does not split. Yellow freestone flesh with some red around the pit. Excellent shipper. Ripens one week ahead of J. H. Hale. *Source History: 1 in 1988; 2 in 1992; 1 in 2000.* **Sources: Va2.**

Delta - Yellow clingstone flesh. Ripens 49 days before Elberta. Requires 550 hours of chilling. *Source History: 2 in 2000.* **Sources: Ho5, Nrs.**

Denman - Large, round, yellow fruit. Firm, yellow, freestone flesh. Excellent for commercial production. Tree blooms later and over a longer period than most. Ripens eight days before Elberta. Requires 800 hours of chilling. Introduced by Texas A and M University. An open-pollinated seedling of Red Globe. *Source History: 4 in 1988; 8 in 1992; 2 in 2000.* **Sources: Ho5, Wom.**

Derby - Yellow, semifreestone flesh. Ripens 45-47 days before Elberta. Requires 850 hours of chilling. Cold hardy. *Source History: 2 in 1988; 3 in 1992; 3 in 2000.* **Sources: Bo5, Cum, Ho5.**

Desert Gold - Medium size, round, yellow fruit. Firm, yellow, semifreestone flesh. Good flavor and sweetness for such an early variety. Self-fruitful, heavy bearing tree. Ripens from late April to mid-May depending on location. Requires 250 hours of chilling. Hardy in Zones 8-9. *Source History: 5 in 1988; 7 in 1992; 7 in 2000.* **Sources: Bay, CO5, MI5, ORA, Pa2, STR, WI4.**

Dixie Red - Round, deep red fruit. Sweet, juicy, yellow, clingstone flesh. Good quality for an early variety. Fruit will hang on the tree for days after it is firm ripe. Productive, self-fertile tree. Bears at a young age. Ripens 41 days before Elberta. Requires 900-950 hours of chilling. Hardy in Zones 5-8. *Source History: 11 in 1988; 16 in 1992; 8 in 2000.* **Sources: Bar, Cum, Ho5, Lee, Na4, Sav, TU5, Wom.**

Dixieland - Yellow, freestone flesh. Ripens three days before Elberta. Requires 750 hours of chilling. Recommended for the cooler parts of the Gulf Coast and northward. *Source History: 3 in 1988; 5 in 1992; 4 in 2000.* **Sources: Cum, Ho5, Tex, Wom.**

Dixon - One of the earliest, best flavored, yellow clingstones. Self-fruitful. Ripens in August. Requires 800 hours of chilling. *Source History: 1 in 1992; 1 in 2000.* **Sources: WI4.**

Double Jewel - Large, freestone fruit. Excellent flavor. Good keeper. Showy, double pink flowers. Good for home orchard and landscape. Self-fruitful. Ripens in late June or early July. Requires 800 hours of chilling. U.S. Plant Patent No. 6410. *Source History: 1 in 1992; 2 in 2000.* **Sources: Bay, WI4.**

Dr. Davis (Davis) - Good quality, clingstone fruit resists bruising and discoloration. Stores well. Ripens mid-August. Introduced by the University of California in 1982. U.S. Plant Patent No. 4661. *Source History: 3 in 1988; 5 in 1992; 3 in 2000.* **Sources: AG2, Si3, WI4.**

Earligal - Yellow, clingstone flesh. Ripens 60-61 days before Elberta. Requires

550-650 hours of chilling. *Source History: 2 in 1988; 2 in 1992; 1 in 2000.* **Sources: Ho5.**

Earliglo, Stark (Roxburgh Cultivar) - Bright red fruit with firm, juicy, freestone flesh. Unique flavor. Ripens in mid-July. Hardy in Zones 5-8. Recommended for colder areas. Trademarked. *Source History: 1 in 1988; 1 in 1992; 1 in 2000.* **Sources: St4.**

Earligrande - Large, yellow fruit with a red blush. Moderately firm, yellow, semiclingstone flesh. Ships well. Very vigorous, productive tree. Self-fruitful. Particularly adapted to southern Texas. Ripens 55 days before Elberta. Requires 200-275 hours of chilling. Developed by the Texas Agricultural Experiment Station. *Source History: 6 in 1988; 12 in 1992; 10 in 2000.* **Sources: AG2, CO5, Ho5, ORA, Pa2, RA4, STR, Wel, WI4, Wom.**

Earlihale - Large, bright yellow fruit overlaid with a brilliant red blush. Yellow, freestone flesh. Medium texture. Good flavor. Upright tree. Requires a pollinator. Productive when well pollinated. Ripens two weeks ahead of J. H. Hale, but very similar in other respects. *Source History: 1 in 1988; 3 in 1992; 1 in 2000.* **Sources: Nrs.**

Earlired - Red Haven cross. Medium size, round, yellow fruit 85% covered with a bright red blush at maturity. Firm but melting yellow flesh. Clingstone when firm ripe and semiclingstone in the soft stage. Medium texture. Good flavor. Vigorous tree. Dependable bearer. Self-fertile. Requires heavy, early thinning for best size. Ripens 48 days before Elberta. Requires 850 hours of chilling. Cold hardy. *Source History: 4 in 1988; 5 in 1992; 3 in 2000.* **Sources: Bo5, Ho5, Nrs.**

Earlirich - Very large, extra firm, yellow flesh fruit. Deep red over yellow skin color. Resembles Rich Lady in fruit characteristics. Exceptionally vigorous, productive tree. Requires 750-850 hours of chilling. U.S. Plant Patent No. 9002. *Source History: 1 in 2000.* **Sources: WI4.**

Earlitreat - Medium size fruit with attractive red blush over yellow skin. Yellow flesh has nice acid-sugar balance. Flavor and sweetness compares to midseason ripening varieties. Highly recommended for home orchards. Self-fruitful. Ripens early May. Requires 350-450 hours of chilling. U.S. Plant Patent No. 9842. *Source History: 3 in 2000.* **Sources: Bay, Pa2, WI4.**

Early Amber - Semifreestone fruit. Very good commercial variety for southern Texas and other coastal regions. Ripens in early May. Requires 250 hours of chilling. U.S. Plant Patent No. 2458. *Source History: 2 in 1988; 3 in 1992; 3 in 2000.* **Sources: CO5, Tex, Wel.**

Early White Giant, Stark (Geheb Cultivar) - Largest of the white peaches. Fiery red skin splashed with white. White flesh. Favored for pies, cobblers and fresh eating. Vigorous tree. Heavy bearer. Tolerant to bacterial spot. Ripens in July. Hardy in Zones 5-8. Trademarked. *Source History: 1 in 1988; 1 in 1992; 1 in 2000.* **Sources: St4.**

Eden - Large, roundish, creamy white fruit, 60% covered with a red blush at maturity. Thick, firm, juicy, white, freestone flesh. Slow to brown for a white fleshed peach. Sweet, rich flavor. Vigorous, productive tree. Ripens midseason. Hardiness equals that of Red Haven. Introduced in 1972. *Source History: 1 in 1988; 1 in 1992; 1 in 2000.* **Sources: Nrs.**

Elberta - Most popular variety in America. Large, yellow fruit with a crimson blush. Juicy, yellow, freestone flesh. High quality. Favorite for the home garden. Excellent for desserts, canning, freezing and jam. Excellent shipper. Vigorous, compact, self-fruitful tree. Hardier in bud than many and therefore a more uniform cropper. Excellent pollenizer. Leading commercial processing peach. Ripens from late July to early August in central California; up to four to six weeks later in colder climates. Requires 800-950 hours of chilling. Hardy in Zones 5-9. Commonly grown in Utah and Colorado. Originated in Georgia in 1870 from a seed of Chinese Cling. *Source History: 41 in 1988; 62 in 1992; 46 in 2000.* **Sources: Bar, Bas, Bay, BO10, Bu1, Co2, CO5, Cum, Fi1, FO10, Fo4, GI3, Gur, Hi9, Ho5, Iso, Jo3, La3, Lee, Leu, Mel, Mi1, MI10, MI5, Na4, Nrs, ORA, Pi2, Po2, Sav, SH8, SIM, So5, STR, Tex, TU5, Ty2, Va2, Wa16, WA8, Wel, Wh4, WI12, WI4, Wom, Wor.**

Elberta Queen, Stark
(Jordan Cultivar) - Larger version of Elberta. Firm, sweet fruit. Ripens in late August. Preferred for canning and freezing. Hardy in Zones 5-8. Trademarked. *Source History: 1 in 1988; 1 in 1992; 1 in 2000.* **Sources: St4.**

Elberta, Burbank July
- Bright red fruit with the smallest pit-to-fruit ratio. Fine grained, succulent, yellow flesh. Sweet flavor. Well adapted to a variety of growing regions. Ripens early. Hardy in Zones 5-8; also bears well in the cooler sections of Zone 9. Trademarked. *Source History: 1 in 1988; 1 in 1992; 1 in 2000.* **Sources: St4.**

Elberta, Early
(Improved Early Elberta, July Elberta, July Early Elberta, July Kim Elberta, Kim Early Elberta) - Early sport of Elberta. Large, oblong, yellow fruit with a light red blush. Fine grained, yellow, freestone flesh. Sweet, rich flavor. Excellent canning variety; also good for fresh use and freezing. Vigorous, self-fruitful tree. Ripens a week before Elberta. Requires 500-750 hours of chilling. Hardy in Zones 5-8; also bears well in cooler sections of Zone 9. *Source History: 14 in 1988; 22 in 1992; 14 in 2000.* **Sources: CO5, COL, GI3, JOY, Mi1, MI5, Nrs, ORA, SIM, STR, Tex, WA8, Wel, WI4.**

Elberta, Fantastic
- Bud sport of Fay Elberta. Large, yellow fruit. Firm, juicy, subacid, freestone flesh. High quality. Good for fresh use, canning, drying and freezing. Keeps well. Self-fruitful tree. Beautiful, pink, double blossoms in the spring. Susceptible to brown rot, peach leaf curl, Oriental fruit moth and peach twig borer. Ripens on August 1 in central California. Requires 700-750 hours of chilling. U.S. Plant Patent No. 3806. *Source History: 2 in 1988; 2 in 1992; 2 in 2000.* **Sources: Bay, WI4.**

Elberta, Fay
(Fay Late Elberta, Late Elberta) - Yellow fruit with firm, fine grained, yellow, freestone flesh. Excellent flavor. Good fresh or frozen. Self-fertile tree with showy, pink flowers in the spring. Blooms earlier than Elberta. Prolific bearer. Needs thinning. Ripens 1-6 days after Elberta. Requires 700-850 hours of chilling. *Source History: 8 in 1988; 12 in 1992; 9 in 2000.* **Sources: AG2, CO5, Cum, Ho5, ORA, Si3, Son, STR, WI4.**

Elberta, Gleason
(Gleason Early Elberta, Golden Elberta, Improved Elberta, Lemon Elberta) - Early sport of Elberta. Medium to large, oblong fruit. Brighter golden color than Elberta with little or no red blush. Firm, yellow, freestone flesh with no red around the pit. Excellent quality. One of the best canners; also good for fresh use and freezing. Self-fertile tree. Does well in Utah and the Pacific Northwest. Ripens 8-10 days before Elberta. Zone 5. Requires 800 hours of chilling. *Source History: 6 in 1988; 6 in 1992; 8 in 2000.* **Sources: Bay, Co2, CO5, ME3, Si3, STR, Va2, WI4.**

Elberta, Johnson
- Yellow fruit with a red blush. Yellow, freestone flesh. Good flavor. Good quality. Ripens a few days ahead of Early Improved Elberta. Originated in Utah. *Source History: 1 in 1988; 1 in 1992; 1 in 2000.* **Sources: Co2.**

Elberta, Kim (July Elberta, Early Elberta) - Yellow freestone. Sweet and flavorful. Used for canning, freezing or fresh. July harvest. Self-fruitful. Requires 500 hours of chilling. *Source History: 1 in 1988; 3 in 1992; 3 in 2000.* **Sources: Bay, ORA, Pe2.**

Elberta, Redskin (Redskin) - Red Haven x Elberta. Yellow, freestone flesh. Good for all uses. Vigorous, spreading, self-fertile tree. Good producer. Resistant to bacterial spot. Ripens at the same time as Elberta; around August 1in central California. Requires 800-850 hours of chilling. Frost hardy. *Source History: 2 in 1988; 3 in 1992; 1 in 2000.* **Sources: WI4.**

Eldorado (Eldorado Miniature) - Genetic dwarf tree is self-fruitful. Red blushed skin. Rich flavor. Freestone. Does well in the ground or container grown. Self-fruitful. Ripens in late June. Requires 500 hours of chilling. *Source History: 3 in 2000.* **Sources: Bay, Rai, WI4.**

Elegant Lady - Freestone. U.S. Plant Patent No. 4399. *Source History: 1 in 1988; 1 in 1992; 2 in 2000.* **Sources: AG2, Si3.**

Emery - Large fruit with firm, yellow, freestone flesh. Tree has excellent winter cold resistance. Ripens seven days before Elberta. Requires 900 hours of chilling. Developed in North Carolina. *Source History: 3 in 1988; 1 in 1992; 1 in 2000.* **Sources: Nrs.**

Empress - Large, highly colored, pink to red fruit. Juicy, yellow, clingstone flesh. Sweet flavor. Genetic dwarf tree grows only 4-5' tall. Ripens 49-52 days before Elberta. Requires 650-850 hours of chilling. *Source History: 3 in 1988; 4 in 1992; 4 in 2000.* **Sources: Cla, CO5, Cum, Ho5.**

Encore, Stark (N. J. 260 Cultivar) - Autumnglo x New Jersey seedling cross from Rutgers University. Medium large fruit with firm, juicy, sweet flesh. Good for fresh eating or canning. Flower buds resist cold very well. Very resistant to bacterial leaf spot. Ripens in early September, 35 days after Redhaven. Required 850 hours of chilling. Hardy in Zones 5-8. Trademarked. U.S. Plant Patent No. 4572. *Source History: 1 in 1988; 1 in 1992; 3 in 2000.* **Sources: Ad2, AG2, St4.**

Envoy - *Source History: 2 in 1992; 1 in 2000.* **Sources: Nrs.**

Erly-Red-Fre - Probably the best early white peach. Large, creamy white fruit develops a bright red blush on one side well before harvest time. White, semifreestone flesh. Good quality. Sturdy, vigorous tree. Heavy bearer. Bud hardy. Resistant to bacterial spot. Ripens in mid-July. Zones 5-8. Originated in Virginia. Introduced in 1938. *Source History: 2 in 1988; 5 in 1992; 3 in 2000.* **Sources: Ad2, Ed2, Wor.**

Ernie's Choice (N.J. 275) - Medium to large, attractive fruit. Yellow flesh with some red around the pit. Exceptional color and firmness. Productive tree is resistant to bacterial leaf spot. Cold hardy. Ripens about 12 days after Red Haven. Developed at the New Jersey Experiment Station. *Source History: 1 in 1992; 2 in 2000.* **Sources: Ad2, St4.**

Eva - *Source History: 1 in 2000.* **Sources: On4.**

Eva's Pride - Large, firm, yellow freestone. Self-fruitful. Ripens between May Pride and Mid-Pride. Requires 100-200 hours of chilling. U.S. Plant Patent No. 7751. *Source History: 3 in 2000.* **Sources: Bay, Pa2, WI4.**

Evert - Clingstone. *Source History: 2 in 1992; 1 in 2000.* **Sources: Si3, WI4.**

Fairhaven - Large, smooth, nearly round, bright golden fruit with a red blush. Firm, fine textured, yellow, freestone flesh. Good flavor. Good for fresh use, canning and freezing. Hardy, productive tree. Ripens after Redhaven. *Source History:*

3 in 1988; 3 in 1992; 3 in 2000. **Sources: COL, Nrs, Va2.**

Fairtime - Very large fruit with yellow, freestone flesh. Excellent flavor. Self-fruitful tree. Blooms early. Ripens 35 days after Elberta; mid-September in central California. Fine variety for the very late season. Requires 650-750 hours of chilling. *Source History: 4 in 1988; 9 in 1992; 7 in 2000.* **Sources: AG2, Cla, Cum, Ho5, Si3, STR, WI4.**

Fallate - *Source History: 2 in 1992; 1 in 2000.* **Sources: Bo5.**

Fayette - Large, round, yellow fruit with little fuzz and a bright red blush. Very firm, smooth, yellow, freestone flesh. Good quality. Vigorous tree. Ripens in early September, about 7 days after Elberta. Requires 850 hours of chilling. Fruit buds may be susceptible to low winter temperatures. USDA introduction from California. *Source History: 2 in 1988; 5 in 1992; 4 in 2000.* **Sources: Cum, Hi9, Ho5, Nrs.**

Fingerlakes S. H. - Round, red fruit with juicy, yellow, freestone flesh. Resists browning. Sweet flavor. Good for fresh eating and canning. Very hardy tree. Ripens in early to mid-August depending on location. *Source History: 1 in 1988; 1 in 1992; 1 in 2000.* **Sources: Mi1.**

Fireprince - Yellow, freestone flesh. Ripens 17-20 days before Elberta. Requires 850 hours of chilling. *Source History: 2 in 1988; 3 in 1992; 3 in 2000.* **Sources: Cum, Ho5, Nrs.**

Flamecrest - Large, bright yellow fruit with almost no fuzz and a bright red blush. Firm, yellow, freestone flesh. Smooth texture. Ideal for canning and freezing. Vigorous, self-fertile tree. Heavy bearer. Market acceptance has been favorable. Ripens approximately 28 days after Redhaven. *Source History: 3 in 1988; 7 in 1992; 1 in 2000.* **Sources: Co2.**

Flameprince - *Source History: 3 in 2000.* **Sources: Cum, Nrs, St4.**

Flamin' Fury PF 1 - Medium size, partial clingstone with very little split pit. Skin color is 90% red over yellow background. Tolerates bacterial spot. Winter hardy. Ripens 20 days before Redhaven. Recommended for trial. Developed by the Paul Friday Peach Breeding Program. Trademarked. U.S. Plant Patent No. 9192. *Source History: 7 in 2000.* **Sources: Ad2, AG2, Bo5, Co2, Hi9, Ho5, St4.**

Flamin' Fury PF 5B - Highly colored, medium size fruit lacks the firmness necessary for commercial packing but is worthy of trial in the early season. Freestone. Ripens about two weeks before Red Haven. Trademarked. U.S. Plant Patent No. 9850. *Source History: 6 in 2000.* **Sources: Ad2, AG2, Bo5, Hi9, Si3, St4.**

Flamin' Fury PF 7 - Few split pits. Ripens in the Garnet Beauty season; about 10 days before Red Haven. Developed by the Paul Friday breeding program. Trademarked. U.S. Plant Patent No. 10,490. *Source History: 2 in 2000.* **Sources: Ad2, Hi9.**

Flamin' Fury PF 8 - Ripens mid-June. Plant patent applied for. *Source History: 1 in 2000.* **Sources: AG2.**

Flamin' Fury PF 9 - Plant patent applied for. *Source History: 1 in 2000.* **Sources: AG2.**

Flamin' Fury PF 12A - Medium size freestone. Skin is mostly red over yellow ground color. Hardy. Crops well. Tolerates bacterial spot. Matures 3-5 days after Red Haven. Requires 800 hours of chilling. Developed by the Paul Friday Peach Breeding Program. Trademarked. U.S. Plant Patent No. 8950. *Source History: 5 in 2000.* **Sources: Ad2, AG2, Co2, Hi9, Ho5.**

Flamin' Fury PF 12B - Red blush covers 70-80% of skin surface. Firm flesh.

Freestone. Few split pits. Productive. Ripens 3 days after Redhaven. Requires 750 hours of chilling. Trademarked. Plant patent applied for. *Source History: 3 in 2000.* **Sources: Hi9, Si3, St4.**

Flamin' Fury PF 15A - Large fruit with 80% red blush over yellow ground color. Freestone. Heavy cropper. Ripens 8 days after Redhaven. Resists bacterial spot. Developed by the Paul Friday Peach Breeding Program. Trademarked. U.S. Plant Patent No. 8978. *Source History: 7 in 2000.* **Sources: Ad2, AG2, Co2, Hi9, Ho5, Si3, St4.**

Flamin' Fury PF 17 - Large, firm fruit with 70% red skin color. Freestone. Hardy. Ripens just before Loring; 17 days after Redhaven. Requires 800 hours of chilling. Requires two pickings. Developed by the Paul Friday Peach Breeding Program. Trademarked. U.S. Plant Patent No. 8169. *Source History: 6 in 2000.* **Sources: Ad2, AG2, Co2, Hi9, Ho5, St4.**

Flamin' Fury PF 20 - Large freestone. Few split pits. Harvests in two pickings. Shows resistance to bacterial spot. Ripens 20 days after Redhaven. Trademarked. *Source History: 1 in 2000.* **Sources: Hi9.**

Flamin' Fury PF 20-007 - Freestone. Trademarked. *Source History: 1 in 2000.* **Sources: Si3.**

Flamin' Fury PF 23 - Medium-large, highly colored fruit of good quality. Freestone. Moderately susceptible to bacterial spot. Ripens 24 days after Red Haven. May be bud tender. Requires 700 hours of chilling. Developed by the Paul Friday Peach Breeding Program. Trademarked. U.S. Plant Patent No. 8164. *Source History: 7 in 2000.* **Sources: Ad2, AG2, Co2, Hi9, Ho5, Si3, St4.**

Flamin' Fury PF 24-007 - Large, firm freestone with good color. Productive tree requires very little fruit thinning to achieve good size. Ripens three days before Cresthaven; 26 days after Redhaven. Requires 750 hours of chilling. Trademarked. U.S. Plant Patent No. 9939. *Source History: 4 in 2000.* **Sources: Ad2, Hi9, Ho5, St4.**

Flamin' Fury PF 25 - Highly colored fruit. Ripens with Redskin. Trademarked. U.S. Plant Patent No. 9940. *Source History: 1 in 2000.* **Sources: Bo5, Hi9.**

Flamin' Fury PF 26 - Plant patent applied for. *Source History: 1 in 2000.* **Sources: AG2.**

Flamin' Fury PF 27A - Large, very firm fruit is highly colored. Vigorous, productive tree shows good resistance to bacterial spot. Recommended for commercial planting. Ripens a month later than Red Haven. Trademarked. U.S. Plant Patent No. 9895. *Source History: 3 in 2000.* **Sources: Ad2, Hi9, St4.**

Flavorcrest - Medium size, round, yellow fruit, 60-80% covered red at maturity. Exceptionally firm, yellow, semifreestone flesh. Self-fertile tree. Heavy fruit set. Good shipper. Ripens 33 days before Elberta. Requires 750 hours of chilling. Appears to be winter bud hardy. Early maturing variety from California. *Source History: 8 in 1988; 10 in 1992; 6 in 2000.* **Sources: AG2, Co2, Cum, Ho5, Nrs, Si3.**

Flordabelle - Flavorful, yellow flesh freestone. Ripens mid-late season. Requires 150 hours of chilling. Hardy in Zones 8-9. *Source History: 2 in 1992; 2 in 2000.* **Sources: RA4, SIM.**

Flordacrest - Yellow flesh, cling to semifreestone fruit. Ripens 47 days before Elberta. Requires 400-450 hours of chilling. *Source History: 1 in 1988; 2 in 1992; 4 in 2000.* **Sources: Ho5, RA4, SIM, Ty2.**

Flordadawn - Clingstone with yellow flesh. Long bloom period. Ripens 67 days before Elberta. Requires 300 hours of chilling. Released by the University of

Florida. *Source History: 3 in 1992; 4 in 2000.* **Sources: Cum, Ho5, RA4, Ty2.**

Flordaglo - White, semifreestone flesh. Ripens in late April. Requires 150 hours of chilling. *Source History: 1 in 1988; 3 in 1992; 4 in 2000.* **Sources: AG2, Ho5, RA4, SIM.**

Flordaglobe - Clingstone. Better shape and color than Flordaking with fewer split pits; ripens 3-5 days earlier. Requires 475 hours of chilling. *Source History: 2 in 1992; 2 in 2000.* **Sources: Ho5, RA4.**

Flordagold - Yellow, clingstone flesh. Ripens 34 days before Elberta. Requires 450 hours of chilling. *Source History: 3 in 1988; 5 in 1992; 1 in 2000.* **Sources: RA4.**

Flordagrande - Yellow flesh fruit. Ripens 37 days before Elberta. Requires 75-100 hours of chilling. *Source History: 2 in 1988; 1 in 1992; 3 in 2000.* **Sources: Ho5, RA4, Ty2.**

Flordahome - Yellow fruit half blushed with red. White, freestone flesh. Attractive ornamental tree. Nematode resistant. Ripens from May to June depending on location. Requires 300 hours of chilling. Warm weather variety hardy in Zones 8-9. *Source History: 2 in 1988; 4 in 1992; 3 in 2000.* **Sources: GI3, SIM, Wel.**

Flordaking - Large, yellow fruit with a red blush. In areas with chilling hours below 450, the fruit has a pronounced tip; above 450, the fruit is roundish. Firm, yellow, clingstone flesh. High quality. Vigorous, self-fruitful tree. Heavy producer. Well adapted to the Deep South. Ripens 57 days before Elberta. Hardy in Zones 8-9. Introduced by the Florida Agricultural Experiment Station at Gainesville. *Source History: 10 in 1988; 16 in 1992; 16 in 2000.* **Sources: Bas, Cum, Ed2, GI3, Ho5, Iso, Ju2, ORA, RA4, SIM, Tex, Ty2, WA8, Wel, WI4, Wom.**

Flordaprince - Medium large, round, yellow fruit with red blush and stripes. Firm, yellow, cling or semiclingstone flesh. High quality. Vigorous, self-fruitful tree. Good producer. Tolerant of desert heat. Ripens 55 days before Elberta. Requires 150 hours of chilling. Recently developed in Florida. Many acres being planted in southern California and Arizona. *Source History: 7 in 1988; 13 in 1992; 12 in 2000.* **Sources: AG2, Bay, CO5, Ho5, On4, ORA, Pa2, RA4, SIM, STR, Ty2, WI4.**

Flordaqueen - Low chill peach. Hardy in Zones 8-9. *Source History: 1 in 1988; 2 in 1992; 1 in 2000.* **Sources: SIM.**

Flordared - White flesh freestone with good size and flavor. Ripens 30 days before Elberta. Requires 100 hours of chilling. Recommended for southern Florida area. *Source History: 1 in 1992; 1 in 2000.* **Sources: RA4.**

Flordastar - Semifreestone with yellow flesh. Ripens 34 days before Elberta. Requires 225 hours of chilling. *Source History: 3 in 1992; 3 in 2000.* **Sources: Nrs, ORA, RA4.**

Flordasun - Low chill requirement. Hardy in Zones 8-9. *Source History: 2 in 1988; 2 in 1992; 1 in 2000.* **Sources: SIM.**

Flordawon - *Source History: 1 in 1988; 1 in 1992; 1 in 2000.* **Sources: SIM.**

Flory - Large, double, red flowers. Small fruit; white, freestone flesh. Genetic dwarf patio variety. Self-fertile. Ripens in July. Requires about 200 hours of chilling. *Source History: 2 in 1988; 3 in 1992; 3 in 2000.* **Sources: CO5, ORA, STR.**

Fortyniner - Similar to its parent, J. H. Hale. Large, yellow, freestone flesh. Excellent dessert quality. Good keeper. Self-fruitful tree. Ripens in late July in central California. Requires 700 hours of chilling. *Source History: 4 in 1988; 6 in 1992; 3 in 2000.* **Sources: Si3, STR, WI4.**

Frank - Large, yellow fruit almost covered with red at maturity. Yellow, cling-stone flesh. Good flavor. Excellent quality. One of the best for home and market use. Tree bears very young; good crop at 2 years old. Ripens 30 days after Elberta. Requires 750-800 hours of chilling. *Source History: 4 in 1988; 4 in 1992; 2 in 2000.* **Sources: Tex, Wom.**

Frost - Medium to large, fuzzy, yellow fruit with green shoulders. Soft, yellow, semifreestone flesh. Flavor similar to locally grown Red Havens. Resistant to split pit, about 17%. Good for drying and fresh eating; fair for canning. Self-fertile tree. Showy blooms in the spring. Very heavy fruit set; must be thinned. One of the most resistant varieties to leaf curl disease. Although not immune, its resistance seems to increase with maturity. Ripens in mid-August. Requires 700 hours of chilling. Zone 6-9. Recently introduced from western Washington. Patented. *Source History: 5 in 1988; 13 in 1992; 15 in 2000.* **Sources: Bay, Bu7, Clo, CO5, Ea3, Fo2, Gr16, JOY, ME3, Mel, Pe2, Rai, Son, Va2, WI4.**

GaLa - Yellow freestone flesh. Ripens 34 days before Elberta. Requires 750 hours of chilling. *Source History: 3 in 2000.* **Sources: Ho5, Nrs, Ty2.**

Garden Gold - Fist-sized, yellow fruit with a slight red blush. Soft, melting, yellow, freestone flesh. Good flavor. Genetic dwarf tree grows 5-6' tall. More vig-orous than other miniatures. Also blooms a week later, so less susceptible to frost damage. Self-fruitful. Bears up to a half bushel of fruit each year. Well adapted to poor soils. Ripens in August, 14 days after Elberta. Requires 600 hours of chilling. Developed by Floyd Zaiger. Plant patent applied for. *Source History: 4 in 1988; 6 in 1992; 4 in 2000.* **Sources: Bay, Mi1, ORA, WI4.**

Garden Parade - Yellow fruit with a red blush. Heavy bearing tree. Self-fertile. Requires 300 hours of chilling. Ripens in late August. *Source History: 1 in 1988; 1 in 1992; 1 in 2000.* **Sources: ORA.**

Garden Pride - Yellow, freestone fruit with a red blush. Good flavor. Self-fertile. Ripens in early July. Requires 500 hours of chilling. *Source History: 1 in 1988; 1 in 1992; 1 in 2000.* **Sources: ORA.**

Garden Sun - Large fruit with juicy, yellow, freestone flesh. Very sweet, subacid flavor. Genetic dwarf tree grows 4-6' tall. Highly ornamental in the spring, covered with pink, self-fruitful blossoms. Exceptionally heavy crops. Especially recom-mended for the lower South. Ripens seven days after Elberta. Requires 500-600 hours of chilling. Hardy in Zones 7-9. Developed by Floyd Zaiger. *Source History: 4 in 1988; 5 in 1992; 1 in 2000.* **Sources: WI4.**

Garnet Beauty - Bud mutation of Red Haven. Medium to large, slightly elon-gated, almost fuzzless, red fruit, similar to its parent. Firm, yellow, semifreestone flesh streaked with red. Smooth, fine texture. Resistant to split pits, which com-monly occurs in early varieties. Excellent for pies, cobblers and preserves. Also good for canning and freezing. Vigorous, productive tree. Ripens in late July, 30-32 days before Elberta, 8-10 days before Red Haven. Requires 850 hours of chill-ing. Quite bud hardy. Discovered in the Garnet Bruner Orchard in Ontario. Intro-duced in 1958. *Source History: 8 in 1988; 9 in 1992; 8 in 2000.* **Sources: Ad2, Cum, Hi9, Ho5, Nrs, Sc6, Si3, Wor.**

Gemfree - *Source History: 1 in 1992; 1 in 2000.* **Sources: AG2.**

General (P417-86) - *Source History: 1 in 2000.* **Sources: Cu4.**

George IV - Small, greenish white, freestone fruit with slight pinkish blush. When well thinned, the fruit is of good size with attractive gold and brownish red markings. Juicy, aromatic, white flesh is richly flavored. One of America's oldest peaches, first obtained from a Mr. Gill in New York City in 1820. *Source History: 1 in 1988; 2 in 1992; 2 in 2000.* **Sources: So5, Son.**

Georgia Belle - White flesh freestone with exceptional flavor. *Source History: 1 in 1988; 3 in 1992; 2 in 2000.* **Sources: GI3, La3.**

GF305 - *Source History: 1 in 2000.* **Sources: Nrs.**

Glenglo (GW 115) - Discovered as a limb sport of Loring by W. Glenn Welsh of Martinsburg, West Virginia. Attractive, medium-large fruit with firm flesh. Plant patent applied for. *Source History: 1 in 2000.* **Sources: Ad2.**

Glohaven - Uniformly large, nearly round, attractive yellow freestone fruit. Very tough, mostly red skin is practically fuzzless with deep yellow ground color. Firm yellow flesh is resistant to browning. Superior canning and freezing qualities. Tree is vigorous and productive; average or above in wood and bud hardiness. Excellent quality for fresh market and commercial processing. Keeps and ships very well. Can be pitted by mechanical means. Ripens 14 days before Elberta. Requires 850 hours of chilling. Introduced by the South Haven Experiment Station. *Source History: 10 in 1988; 13 in 1992; 13 in 2000.* **Sources: Ad2, BO10, Bo5, Co2, Cu4, Cum, Hi9, Ho5, Nrs, Si3, St4, Va2, Wor.**

Glory - Yellow freestone. Ripens 7 days ahead of Elberta. Requires 800 hours of chilling. *Source History: 2 in 2000.* **Sources: Ho5, Nrs.**

GlowingStar (FA-17) - Large fruit with 70% bright red blush. Firm, freestone flesh. Stores well. Ripens in early Cresthaven season. Strong, vigorous tree. Trademarked. U.S. Plant Patent No. 10,556. *Source History: 3 in 2000.* **Sources: AG2, Hi9, St4.**

Gold Crest - Freestone with yellow flesh. Ripens 61 days before Elberta. Requires 650 hours of chilling. USDA introduction. *Source History: 2 in 1988; 4 in 1992; 3 in 2000.* **Sources: AG2, Ho5, Nrs.**

Gold Dust - Yellow, semifreestone flesh; exceptional flavor. Self-fruitful; all-purpose. Superb for eating fresh. Ripens from mid to late June in central California. Requires 550 hours of chilling. *Source History: 4 in 1988; 5 in 1992; 4 in 2000.* **Sources: Bay, CO5, STR, WI4.**

Gold Prince - Large clingstone with yellow flesh and bright red skin. Highly productive. Ripens 47 days before Elberta. Requires 650 hours of chilling. Developed at the Byron, Georgia Research Station. *Source History: 2 in 1992; 3 in 2000.* **Sources: Cla, Cum, Ho5.**

Golden Gem - Resembles Rio Oso Gem. Large freestone with yellow skin. Yellow flesh turns red near pit. Firm flesh with good texture and excellent flavor. Genetic dwarf patio variety with pink flowers. Ripens in June. *Source History: 2 in 1988; 2 in 1992; 2 in 2000.* **Sources: ORA, STR.**

Golden Glory - Very large fruit; yellow freestone flesh with good flavor. Genetic dwarf tree grows 5' tall. Good for cold areas. Ripens from mid to late August. Requires 700 hours of chilling. *Source History: 1 in 1988; 2 in 1992; 1 in 2000.* **Sources: CO5.**

Golden Jubilee - Abundant yields of medium to large, oblong, freestone fruit with soft, yellow skin blushed with red. Fine grained, tender, juicy, light yellow flesh of highest quality. A favorite of orchardists and home gardeners throughout the U.S. Excellent for home use, canning, freezing and preserves. Hardy, self-fruitful, productive tree. One of the best early commercial canning sorts. Also fine for roadside markets. Ripens 21-25 days before Elberta. Requires 850 hours of chilling. Known for its ability to survive in cold climates. Zones 5-8. New Jersey Experiment Station introduction. *Source History: 19 in 1988; 22 in 1992; 15 in 2000.* **Sources: COL, Fi1, FO10, JOY, Lee, Leu, Mel, Mi1, Na4, Nrs, Sav, SIM, TU5, Va2, WI4.**

Golden Monarch - Similar to Red Haven in color, quality and appearance. Semiclingstone, but freestone when fully ripe. Firm, smooth flesh with very little fiber. Resistant to flesh browning when frozen. Good canning and freezing peach. Retains good appearance and flavor after processing. Ripens 12 days before Redhaven. *Source History: 1 in 1988; 1 in 1992; 1 in 2000.* **Sources: Va2.**

Goldilocks - Clingstone with yellow flesh. Ripens 21 days before Elberta. Requires 750 hours of chilling. *Source History: 1 in 1988; 1 in 1992; 1 in 2000.* **Sources: Nrs.**

Goldprince - *Source History: 1 in 2000.* **Sources: Nrs.**

Gum's Mango - Redhaven x Alexander cross developed by Stewart Gum. Grainy flesh with excellent flavor. Strong, vigorous grower. *Source History: 1 in 2000.* **Sources: Ea3.**

Hale Haven - J. H. Hale x South Haven. Large, oval, orangish yellow freestone fruit overlaid with a deep carmine blush. Tough skin stands up to handling and prevents bruising. Sweet, juicy, yellow flesh is firm yet tender. Good color several days before it is fully ripe. Exceptional quality. One of the finest for home use or roadside markets. Excellent for canning and freezing. Vigorous, productive, hardy tree is dependable and high yielding. Ripens 15 days before Elberta. Requires 850-900 hours of chilling. Hardy in Zones 5-8. Developed in Michigan. *Source History: 30 in 1988; 47 in 1992; 30 in 2000.* **Sources: Bar, Bu1, CO5, Fi1, FO10, Fo4, GI3, Gur, Ho5, JOY, La3, Lee, Leu, Mel, Mi1, MI10, MI5, Na4, Nrs, ORA, Pi2, Sav, SIM, STR, Tex, TU5, Ty2, Va2, Wel, WI4.**

Hale, Yakima - Yellow, freestone fruit is 65% covered with scarlet blush. Firm, yellow flesh. Excellent for shipping. Self-fertile. Ripens about 28 days after Redhaven. Hardy to 27 degrees F. *Source History: 1 in 1988; 5 in 1992; 1 in 2000.* **Sources: Va2.**

Halford - Large, firm, clingstone fruit. Very good for canning. Leading commercial variety. Large, vigorous, semiupright tree. Consistent heavy yields. Ripens late August. Requires 800 hours of chilling. *Source History: 5 in 1988; 9 in 1992; 5 in 2000.* **Sources: AG2, Nrs, Si3, STR, WI4.**

Halloween - *Source History: 1 in 1988; 3 in 1992; 1 in 2000.* **Sources: CO5.**

Harbelle – Large, 2.5-2.75", nearly smooth, deep yellow, semifreestone fruit with bright red blush. Medium, firm, juicy, melting, rich yellow flesh is slow to oxidize. Good quality. Tree has medium vigor and is medium hardy. Ripens 42 days before Elberta. Requires 850 hours of chilling. Developed in Ontario, Canada. Introduced in 1968. *Source History: 4 in 1988; 5 in 1992; 1 in 2000.* **Sources: Wor.**

Harbinger - Semi-freestone fruit colors 80% bright red over yellow ground. Size averages 2-2.25". Yellow, melting flesh of good quality. Flower buds are as hardy as Redhaven and mature 33 days sooner. Ripens 55 days before Elberta. Requires 850 hours of chilling. *Source History: 2 in 1988; 2 in 1992; 1 in 2000.* **Sources: Bo5.**

Harbrite - Sister variety of Harken and very similar. Freestone fruit with 80-90% brilliant red over yellow background. Fruit size averages 2.5". Medium firm yellow flesh of good quality. Great potential for canning and freezing. Tree is vigorous, hardy and very productive with medium resistance to bacterial spot. Ripens 26 days before Elberta. Requires 850 hours of chilling. *Source History: 5 in 1988; 7 in 1992; 2 in 2000.* **Sources: Ad2, Nrs.**

Harcrest (H.W. 225) - Redskin x H4219. Medium size fruit with 60% red over yellow background. Firm, freestone flesh. Spreading tree is vigorous and productive. Some resistance to perennial canker, brown rot and bacterial spot. Requires 950 hours of chilling. Ripens with Elberta. More hardy than Cresthaven. Developed at the Harrow Research Station, Canada. Introduced in 1983. *Source History: 3 in 1992; 3 in 2000.* **Sources: Ad2, Cum, Hi9.**

Harken - Brilliant, red over yellow skin is highly colored and non-fuzzy. Medium firm, good quality flesh. Generally freestone with small pit. Resistance to split pit runs about 18%. Shows good potential for canning and freezing. Tree is average bearing with non-showy bloom. Moderately susceptible to leaf curl; more resistant than most varieties, but needs spraying. Resistant to bacterial spot. Ripens 25 days before Elberta; early August. Requires 850 hours of chilling. Zone 5. Introduced by the Harrow Research Station, Canada. *Source History: 5 in 1988; 10 in 1992; 7 in 2000.* **Sources: Bea, Bo5, Ho5, ME3, Nrs, Rai, WI4.**

Harmony - Freestone with yellow flesh. Excellent for fresh eating. Ripens 11 days before Elberta. Requires 850 hours of chilling. Cold hardy. *Source History: 2 in 1988; 4 in 1992; 2 in 2000.* **Sources: Ho5, Wor.**

Harrow Beauty - Smooth, bright yellow fruit with bright red blush. Smooth textured, firm, bright yellow flesh with red around the pit. Excellent flavor. High quality. Open, spreading tree with medium vigor. Requires early thinning to achieve adequate size. Resists bacterial spot. Cold hardy. Introduced in 1983. *Source History: 1 in 1988; 1 in 1992; 2 in 2000.* **Sources: Ad2, Hi9.**

Harrow Diamond (HW 213) - Medium size fruit, yellow ground color with 70% red blush. Freestone when picked ripe. Moderately vigorous, productive tree. Cold hardy. Resists bacterial spot and brown rot; moderately tolerant to perennial canker. Ripens about 24 days before Redhaven. *Source History: 1 in 1992; 5 in 2000.* **Sources: Ad2, Cu4, Hi9, Sc6, St4.**

Harson (H 781) - Redskin x Sun Haven. Medium to large size fruit. Freestone. Firm, sweet, juicy flesh is slow to oxidize. Tree is equal to Redhaven in bud and wood hardiness; more resistant to bacterial spot. Released from the Harrow Station, Canada. Introduced in 1982. *Source History: 1 in 1988; 3 in 1992; 1 in 2000.* **Sources: Nrs.**

Harvester - Firm, highly colored, freestone fruit with yellow flesh. Excellent quality; becoming very popular with commercial growers. Ripens 21 days before Elberta. Requires 750 hours of chilling. Hardy in Zones 5-8. *Source History: 6 in 1988; 13 in 1992; 11 in 2000.* **Sources: Bas, CO5, Cum, GI3, Ho5, MI5, Nrs, Tex, Ty2, Wel, Wom.**

Havis - Freestone with yellow flesh. Ripens three days after Elberta. Requires 850 hours of chilling. *Source History: 2 in 1988; 2 in 1992; 2 in 2000.* **Sources: Ho5, Nrs.**

Hawthorne - Freestone with yellow flesh. Ripens 17 days before Elberta. Requires 600 hours of chilling. *Source History: 2 in 1992; 1 in 2000.* **Sources: Ho5.**

Hesse - Clingstone. Very productive tree. Ripens uniformly for minimum pickings. No tendency to split pits. U.S. Plant Patent No. 8332. *Source History: 2 in 2000.* **Sources: Si3, WI4.**

Honey Babe - Large, sweet, freestone fruit. Deep red over yellow skin. Rich, firm, orange flesh speckled with red. Superb flavor; excellent for fresh eating. Genetic dwarf; grows very slowly into a wide, ornamental bush 3-5' tall. Showy, pink blossoms. Bears when young, usually same year planted. Very susceptible to leaf curl, but can be avoided if covered with plastic from mid-December thru February. Light winter and summer pruning required for best quality. Self-fertile, but yields better if pollinated with Nectar Babe. Ripens in mid-July. Requires 500-600 hours of chilling. Hardy in Zones 6-9. Developed by Floyd Zaiger. U.S. Plant Patent No. 5276. *Source History: 6 in 1988; 13 in 1992; 3 in 2000.* **Sources: Bay, ORA, WI4.**

Idlewild - Semifreestone. Sweet, spicy yellow flesh is speckled with splashes of red. Ripens 34 days before Elberta. Requires 550 hours of chilling. *Source History: 3 in 1988; 5 in 1992; 2 in 2000.* **Sources: Ho5, Ju2.**

Indian Blood (Indian Blood Cling, Indian Red Cling) - Old-fashioned Indian peach. Large, clingstone fruit with dark crimson skin and flesh. Distinctive, tart flavor when fully ripe. Makes beautiful and delicious pickled peaches. Also excellent for eating fresh, pies and preserves. High yielder; dependable. Requires a pollinator. Withstands bacterial leaf spot and brown rot. Ripens two days before Elberta. Requires 750-900 hours of chilling. Hardy in Zones 5-9. *Source History: 16 in 1988; 22 in 1992; 19 in 2000.* **Sources: Bar, Bay, Cla, CO5, Cum, Fi1, Gur, Ho5, Iso, Jo3, La3, Nrs, ORA, Po2, SIM, Tex, Wel, WI4, Wom.**

Indian Free (Indian Blood Free) - Developed from the Indian heirloom cling peach. Large, freestone fruit with firm, red flesh. Tart until fully ripe, then rich, sweet, distinctive flavor. Excellent fresh or for canning. Resistant to peach leaf curl. Susceptible to brown rot, Oriental fruit moth, peach twig borer. Needs cross-pollination. Ripens late season. Requires 700-900 hours of chilling. *Source History: 5 in 1988; 8 in 1992; 3 in 2000.* **Sources: Bay, Bou, Son, WI4.**

Iron Mountain - *Source History: 1 in 1992; 1 in 2000.* **Sources: Wor.**

J. H. Hale - Old variety; still one of the best. Exceptionally large, round, uniform, freestone fruit is golden yellow overlaid with carmine. Skin is smooth and almost fuzzless. Firm, fine grained, deep yellow flesh is free from stringiness and has delicious flavor. Good for home canning and fresh use; outstanding handling and shipping peach. Hangs well; excellent keeper. Tree not as vigorous and is one of the few peach cultivars requiring pollination. Consistent producer; requires good soil. Susceptible to peach leaf curl, brown rot, Oriental fruit moth, peach twig borer. Winter tender. Requires 800-900 hours of chilling. Hardy in Zones 5-8. *Source History: 26 in 1988; 41 in 1992; 25 in 2000.* **Sources: Ad2, Bar, Co2, CO5, FO10, GI3, Lee, ME3, MI10, MI5, Na4, ORA, Po2, Sav, Si3, SIM, Son, STR, Tex, TU5, Va2, WA8, Wel, WI4, Wor.**

J. M. Mack - Freestone, pure creamy white flesh to the stone with no hint of red; very small stone. Flavor is distinctive from, but equal to Champion. Same tender, melting flesh. Ripens just after Champion. *Source History: 1 in 1988; 1 in 1992; 1 in 2000.* **Sources: So5.**

Jayhaven - Medium large, round, freestone fruit achieves bright color at full maturity. Melting, yellow flesh. Tree has medium vigor with strong scaffolds. Bud hardy, promising larger and more consistent crops. More resistant to bacterial spot than Redhaven. Ripens 18 days before Elberta. Requires 850 hours of chilling. *Source History: 3 in 1988; 5 in 1992; 3 in 2000.* **Sources: Cum, Hi9, Nrs.**

Jefferson - J. H. Hale x Valiant. Medium large, freestone fruit with 50% red blush on bright yellow background; yellow flesh. Excellent quality approaches that of J. H. Hale. Noted for exceptional color, attractive appearance, above average size, firmness, desirable texture, flavor and quality. Tree is moderately vigorous. Blossom buds are moderately resistant to mid-winter cold; have shown outstanding hardiness to blossoming season frosts. Fruit seems to be much less susceptible to

brown rot than J. H. Hale. Requires 850 chilling hours. Ripens 2-3 days after Elberta. Developed in Canada. Introduced in 1960. *Source History: 6 in 1988; 6 in
1992; 6 in 2000.* **Sources: Cla, Cum, Ho5, Iso, Wel, Wom.**

Jersey Queen (N. J. 216) - Large, bright red fruit. Firm, yellow flesh; excellent
mild dessert quality. Resembles M. A. Blake in size and appearance, but ripens 5-6
days later and the color is a little darker red. Vigorous tree, but generally a shy
cropper. Tender buds are subject to winter kill. Large, showy flowers with good
pollen. Introduced as a replacement of Elberta, however its biggest competition will
be Redskin. Ripens same time as Elberta. Requires 850 hours of chilling. Developed and introduced by the New Jersey Agricultural Experiment Station at Rutgers
University; mixed parentage. *Source History: 5 in 1988; 7 in 1992; 5 in 2000.*
Sources: Ad2, Cum, Ho5, So5, Wor.

Jerseydawn (N. J. 246) - Very attractive, semifreestone fruit. Good color, quality, size and firmness. Few split pits. Tree is strong and productive. Good bacterial
spot resistance. Hardiness and bud survival records to date have been excellent.
Ripens July 26. *Source History: 2 in 1988; 3 in 1992; 2 in 2000.* **Sources: Hi9,
Nrs.**

Jerseyglo (N. J. 244) - Medium to large, round, freestone fruit with lots of red
blush over golden background. Firm, attractive fruit with yellow flesh. Vigorous
tree is easy to manage, with medium hardiness. Excellent storage qualities. Leaves
and fruit are very resistant to bacterial spot. Ripens with Elberta. Developed by the
New Jersey Agricultural Experiment Station. Introduced in 1979. *Source History:
3 in 1988; 5 in 1992; 3 in 2000.* **Sources: Ad2, Hi9, Wor.**

Jerseyland (N. J. 135) - Large, firm, attractive, semifreestone fruit with yellow
flesh. Hangs well to the tree; excellent shipper. Tree is productive and early. Ripens 30 days before Elberta. Requires 850 hours of chilling. *Source History: 2 in
1988; 3 in 1992; 1 in 2000.* **Sources: Ho5.**

Jim Dandee - Fruit size is better than Redhaven with similar color and appearance. Freestone fruit with yellow flesh and red pit cavity. Excellent firmness and
shipping quality. Hardy, spreading tree with medium vigor. Slightly susceptible to
bacterial spot. Ripens eight days after Redhaven and has equally hardy buds.
Trademarked. U.S. Plant Patent No. 5223. *Source History: 1 in 1988; 1 in 1992; 1
in 2000.* **Sources: Hi9.**

Jim Wilson - *Source History: 1 in 2000.* **Sources: Bo5.**

John-Boy (Clendening Strain) - Large, firm fruit of high quality. Vigorous, productive tree. Resists bacterial leaf spot. Discovered by Ed Clendening in 1981 as a
complete limb sport of Loring. U.S. Plant Patent No. 6827. *Source History: 1 in
1992; 1 in 2000.* **Sources: Ad2.**

July Sun - U.S. Plant Patent No. 5139. *Source History: 1 in 1992; 1 in 2000.*
Sources: AG2.

June Gold - Large, firm, slightly red, clingstone fruit with yellow flesh and fine
texture. Number one peach in Texas. Strong market acceptance. Tree is vigorous
and disease resistant. Ripens 47 days before Elberta. Requires 650 hours of chilling. Hardy in Zones 5-9. *Source History: 10 in 1988; 14 in 1992; 10 in 2000.*
Sources: Bas, CO5, Cum, Ho5, Nrs, SIM, Tex, WA8, Wel, Wom.

June Lady - Ripens mid to late June. *Source History: 1 in 2000.* **Sources: AG2.**

June Pride - Large, firm, yellow freestone with exceptional flavor. Perhaps the
best flavored peach for its season. Ripens early to mid-July. Requires 600-700
hours of chilling. Patented. *Source History: 1 in 1992; 1 in 2000.* **Sources: Bay.**

June Sun - U.S. Plant Patent No. 5873. *Source History: 1 in 1992; 1 in 2000.* **Sources: AG2.**

Juneprince - Semifreestone with yellow flesh. Ripens 35-38 days before Elberta. Requires 650 hours of chilling. *Source History: 2 in 1988; 3 in 1992; 3 in 2000.* **Sources: Cum, Ho5, Nrs.**

Kaweah - Large, firm freestone. Ripens in early August. Requires 900-1000 hours of chilling. U.S. Plant Patent No. 10,177. *Source History: 1 in 2000.* **Sources: WI4.**

Kern Sun (108-1) - Large, round, semifreestone fruit with 90% red blush over yellow background. Extremely firm, yellow flesh with slight reddening at the pit. Excellent shipping qualities. Ripens with Spring Lady. Developed in California in 1975. U.S. Plant Patent No. 4980. *Source History: 1 in 1992; 1 in 2000.* **Sources: AG2.**

Keystone - Good size freestone fruit with attractive mottled skin. Delicious, golden yellow flesh. Ripens 23 days before Elberta. Requires 750 hours of chilling. *Source History: 2 in 1988; 2 in 1992; 1 in 2000.* **Sources: Tex.**

Klamt - Clingstone fruit lacks good color and firmness. Fairly uniform fruit ripening. Large, semiupright tree. Ripens early August. *Source History: 2 in 1988; 4 in 1992; 2 in 2000.* **Sources: Si3, WI4.**

La Feliciana - Freestone fruit, 2.5-2.75". Yellow skin with a good red blush. Yellow flesh has excellent flavor for fresh eating or freezing. High quality. Tree is an abundant producer and disease resistant. Self-fruitful. Adapted to warmer areas; good for the lower South. Ripens 22 days before Elberta. Requires 550-600 hours of chilling. Hardy in Zones 8-9. Originated in Los Angeles. *Source History: 7 in 1988; 11 in 1992; 9 in 2000.* **Sources: Bas, CO5, Cum, Ho5, RA4, SIM, Tex, Wel, Wom.**

La Festival - Large, sweet freestone with yellow flesh. Tangy flavor. Ripens 20 days before Elberta; late June to early July. Requires 450 hours of chilling. Developed at Louisiana State University. *Source History: 2 in 1988; 5 in 1992; 4 in 2000.* **Sources: Cum, Ho5, Ju2, Nrs.**

La Gold - Freestone with yellow flesh. Ripens 25 days before Elberta. Requires 700 hours of chilling. *Source History: 1 in 1988; 2 in 1992; 1 in 2000.* **Sources: Cum.**

La Jewell - Red Globe x Prairie Rose. Freestone with yellow flesh. Ripens 15 days after Elberta. Requires 850 hours of chilling. Developed by the LSU's Calhoun Research Station. *Source History: 2 in 1988; 2 in 1992; 1 in 2000.* **Sources: Ho5.**

La Pecher - Semifreestone with yellow flesh. Ripens 39 days before Elberta. Fruit ripens in waves for over a month from late May to late June. Requires 450 hours of chilling. *Source History: 2 in 1988; 3 in 1992; 2 in 2000.* **Sources: Ho5, Ju2.**

La Premier - Freestone with yellow flesh. Ripens 12 days before Elberta. Requires 1,050 hours of chilling. Cold hardy. *Source History: 2 in 1988; 2 in 1992; 1 in 2000.* **Sources: Ho5.**

La White - White skin is overlayed with rose-pink and red blush. Freestone, white flesh is flecked with rose-red. Great canner. Ripens 27 days before Elberta; mid to late June. Requires 650 hours of chilling. *Source History: 2 in 1988; 4 in 1992; 3 in 2000.* **Sources: Cum, Ho5, Ju2.**

Lady Nancy - Discovered as a limbsport of Jerseyqueen. Shows a faint yellow streak through the white flesh. Ripens late; 31 days after Redhaven. U.S. Plant Patent No. 7069. *Source History: 1 in 2000.* **Sources: Ad2.**

Last Chance - *Source History: 1 in 2000.* **Sources: STR.**

Late Glow - Large, high quality fruit. Ripens mid-September. *Source History: 1 in 2000.* **Sources: Wor.**

Laurol - Attractive, large fruit with red skin and firm yellow flesh. Ripens about 40 days after Redhaven. Discovered in Richwood, New Jersey. Licensed exclusively to Adams County Nursery. U.S. Plant Patent No. 8558. *Source History: 1 in 2000.* **Sources: Ad2.**

Legend - Firm, good quality fruit. Freestone. Excellent productivity. Tree sets high number of flower buds that are resistant to freeze injury. Moderate resistance to bacterial spots. Ripens late; about 16 days after Elberta. Requires 850-950 hours of chilling. Released from North Carolina State. *Source History: 2 in 1992; 3 in 2000.* **Sources: Cla, Ho5, Nrs.**

Lemon Free - High quality yellow freestone. Slight red blush on yellow skin. Excellent canner. Vigorous, hardy, productive tree. *Source History: 2 in 1992; 2 in 2000.* **Sources: Nrs, Wh4.**

Loadel - Medium to large, firm, clingstone fruit. High quality canner. Large, vigorous, spreading tree. Ripens early to mid-July. *Source History: 2 in 1988; 4 in 1992; 3 in 2000.* **Sources: AG2, Si3, WI4.**

Lola Queen - Medium size, pale, greenish white, freestone fruit with pink and red blush. White, juicy flesh of Champion quality but more sprightly flavor. Has disappeared from cultivation. Too tender for commercial use but, because of its superb quality, has been preserved all these years at the Arkansas Agricultural Experiment Station. Originated in Mexia, Texas by J. W. Stubenrauch, who named it after his daughter. Introduced in 1876. *Source History: 1 in 1988; 1 in 1992; 1 in 2000.* **Sources: So5.**

Loring - Frank x Halehaven. Medium to large, smooth, nearly round, freestone fruit. Bright red blush over a yellow ground. Yellow, firm, high quality flesh. Excellent for processing, fresh market, canning, preserves. Fruit hangs well to the tree; holds up well after picking. Has good handling and holding qualities. Self-fruitful. Trees are sturdy, vigorous, heavy croppers; somewhat bud tender. Blooms early. Reliable producer even when weather during bloom is cool and wet. Susceptible to peach leaf curl, brown rot, Oriental fruit moth and peach twig borer. Ripens 10-12 days before Elberta. Requires 750 hours of chilling. Hardy in Zones 5-8. *Source History: 20 in 1988; 29 in 1992; 27 in 2000.* **Sources: Ad2, AG2, Bar, Bay, Bo5, Cla, Co2, CO5, Cu4, Cum, GI3, Hi9, Ho5, Iso, Nrs, Pe2, Sc6, SIM, St4, Tex, TU5, Va2, Wel, Wh4, WI4, Wom, Wor.**

Loring, Early - Mutation of Loring with more intense red blush. Ripens 3-5 days after Redhaven. *Source History: 1 in 2000.* **Sources: Hi9.**

Loring, Stark Early (Beyer Cultivar) - Trademarked. U.S. Plant Patent No. 4170. *Source History: 1 in 1992; 1 in 2000.* **Sources: St4.**

Louisiana Pecher - *Source History: 1 in 1992; 1 in 2000.* **Sources: Nrs.**

Louisiana White - *Source History: 1 in 1992; 1 in 2000.* **Sources: Nrs.**

Lovell - Freestone. *Source History: 1 in 2000.* **Sources: Si3.**

Low Chill Red Skin (Special Strain) - Scarlet red skin; firm, melting, yellow, freestone flesh. Hardy in Zones 5-8. *Source History: 1 in 1992; 1 in 2000.* **Sources: Ty2.**

M. A. Blake (N. J. 117) - Medium to large, freestone fruit with bright red blush over yellow background. Very firm, bright yellow flesh with contrasting red around the pit. Excellent flavor. Fruit hangs well to the tree and remains firm for several days after the ground color has turned bright yellow. Medium size, vigorous tree tends to be a shy cropper. Resistant to bacterial spot. Bud tender for Midwest but still grown in volume in the East. *Source History: 3 in 1988; 5 in 1992; 3 in 2000.* **Sources: Ad2, Co2, Va2.**

Madison - Ideal x Redhaven. Medium size, bright red freestone fruit. High quality, slightly fibrous, firm, orange-yellow flesh with contrasting pinkish red near the pit. Mild, rich flavor. Flesh is slow to soften; skin peels easily. Excellent canning peach. Tree is hardy, vigorous, frost resistant and self-pollinating. Blossom buds have considerable resistance to spring frosts. Recommended for Northern climates. Ripens in late August; seven days before Elberta. Requires 850 hours of chilling. Hardy in Zones 5-8. Shows exceptional tolerance to frosts during blossoming season. Released by the Virginia Station in 1963. *Source History: 9 in 1988; 10 in 1992; 10 in 2000.* **Sources: Ad2, Cu4, Cum, Fed, Hi9, Jun, Sc6, St4, Va2, Wh4.**

Majestic - Freestone with yellow flesh. Ripens 16 days before Elberta. Requires 800 hours of chilling. Louisiana State University release. *Source History: 2 in 1988; 3 in 1992; 4 in 2000.* **Sources: Cum, Ho5, Tex, Wom.**

Marland - *Source History: 1 in 1992; 1 in 2000.* **Sources: Nrs.**

Marqueen - Good size, well colored, freestone fruit. Bright red over yellow skin and yellow flesh. Vigorous, productive tree. Ripens 11 days after Elberta. Requires 750 hours of chilling. Recently introduced by the University of Maryland. *Source History: 3 in 1988; 3 in 1992; 2 in 2000.* **Sources: Cum, Ho5.**

Marsun - Freestone with yellow flesh. Ripens 24 days after Elberta. Requires 950 hours of chilling. Cold hardy. *Source History: 1 in 1988; 2 in 1992; 2 in 2000.* **Sources: Ho5, Nrs.**

May Pride - Larger fruit size than other early peaches. Self-fruitful. Ripens with Desert Gold in May. Requires 175-200 hours of chilling. Plant patent applied for. *Source History: 2 in 1992; 2 in 2000.* **Sources: Bay, WI4.**

May Sun - U.S. Plant Patent No. 6992. *Source History: 1 in 1992; 1 in 2000.* **Sources: AG2.**

Mayflower - Medium to large, red fruit. Excellent flavored white flesh. Has 10-15% rate of leaf infection. Ripens in late June. *Source History: 1 in 1988; 3 in 1992; 3 in 2000.* **Sources: Gr4, Nrs, Po2.**

Maygold - Freestone with yellow flesh. Ripens 39 days before Elberta. Requires 650 hours of chilling. Hardy in Zones 5-9. *Source History: 3 in 1988; 6 in 1992; 5 in 2000.* **Sources: Nrs, SIM, TU5, Ty2, WA8.**

McKay - Very large, yellow and dark red fruit. Orange, freestone flesh with fine flavor. Hardy; high quality. Ripens from mid to late August. Discovered on the Balmer farm near Waterloo, Wisconsin. For years it was propagated in Faribault, Minnesota as the only proven hardy peach for that area. *Source History: 1 in 1988; 2 in 1992; 3 in 2000.* **Sources: GR26, Mc3, Wa16.**

McNeely - *Source History: 1 in 1992; 1 in 2000.* **Sources: Nrs.**

Melba - Older white fleshed variety. Medium size fruit with sweet flesh. Bruises easily. Good home orchard variety. Requires 800 hours of chilling. *Source History: 1 in 1988; 3 in 1992; 1 in 2000.* **Sources: Wom.**

Mid-Pride - Yellow, freestone fruit with red blush. Exceptional orange-like flavor; dessert quality. Good for canning. Heavy-bearing tree blooms early and is self-fruitful; heavy annual bearer. Susceptible to peach leaf curl, brown rot, Oriental fruit moth, peach twig borer. Best yellow freestone for warm winter climates of southern California, Phoenix, Houston and the San Francisco Bay area. Requires 150-250 hours of chilling. Developed by Floyd Zaiger. *Source History: 4 in 1988; 3 in 1992; 4 in 2000.* **Sources: Bay, Pa2, Son, WI4.**

Monaco - Clingstone with good size, color and firmness. Large, upright spreading tree produces heavily. Ripens around August 19. *Source History: 1 in 1988; 1 in 1992; 2 in 2000.* **Sources: Si3, WI4.**

Monroe - Rio-Oso-Gem x Unnamed VPI Peach. Large fruit with bright, medium red skin over orangish yellow background. Firm, mild flavored, good quality, freestone yellow flesh. Trees are reliable producers and have shown above average tolerance to blossoming season frost. Ripens 6-11 days after Elberta. Requires 850 hours of chilling. Cold hardy. *Source History: 4 in 1988; 6 in 1992; 5 in 2000.* **Sources: Co2, Cu4, Cum, Ho5, Wom.**

MP 1 - Yellow, semi-freestone flesh. Great for canning, pies, poached or eaten fresh. Ripens in mid-July. Discovered as a chance seedling in 1981 in Issaquah, Washington by Margaret Proud and will be named in honor of her father, Donald Croft. Patent pending. *Source History: 1 in 2000.* **Sources: Rai.**

Muir - Large freestone with rich, yellow flesh. Unattractive green-yellow skin color. Excellent for drying because of the sweetness and density of the flesh. Good producer. Self-fruitful. Resistant to peach leaf curl. Requires 600-700 hours of chilling. Originated as a chance seedling at the home of John Muir in California. *Source History: 2 in 1992; 2 in 2000.* **Sources: Bay, WI4.**

NC 152 - *Source History: 1 in 2000.* **Sources: Nrs.**

Nectar - Medium to large, cream colored fruit with dark pink blush. White, freestone flesh with great taste, aroma and texture. Susceptible to bruising when ripe. Self-fertile tree with exceptional vigor, dense foliage and above average frost hardiness. Susceptible to peach leaf curl, brown rot, Oriental fruit moth and peach twig borer. Ripens 22 days before Elberta. Requires 800 to 1,050 hours of chilling. Cold hardy. *Source History: 8 in 1988; 9 in 1992; 6 in 2000.* **Sources: CO5, Cu4, Cum, Ho5, Nrs, WI4.**

Newhaven (New Haven) - Freestone with yellow flesh. Has all the qualities of Redhaven plus added brightness and sizing ability. Excellent for freezing. Tree is strong, spreading, productive, very resistant to bacterial leaf spot; moderately resistant to leaf curl; slightly resistant to brown rot. Reliable cropper; cold hardiness equal to Redhaven. Starts to ripen midway in the Redhaven season; can be harvested with fewer pickings. Ripens 24 days before Elberta. Requires 950 hours of chilling. *Source History: 4 in 1988; 9 in 1992; 10 in 2000.* **Sources: Cum, Hi9, Ho5, Jo3, Nrs, Rai, Si3, St4, Va2, Wh4.**

NJC 92 - *Source History: 1 in 2000.* **Sources: Nrs.**

Norman - Midseason variety with round fruit that is 80% dark red over yellow background. Semifreestone with yellow flesh. Tree is vigorous, winter hardy and resistant to bacterial spot. Ripens 28 days before Elberta. Requires 850-900 hours of chilling. Cold hardy. *Source History: 4 in 1988; 5 in 1992; 3 in 2000.* **Sources: Cum, Ho5, Nrs.**

O'Henry - Large, firm, yellow freestone with full red skin and superb flavor. Strong, vigorous, heavy bearing, self-fruitful tree. Ripens from early to mid-August in central California. Popular fresh market variety. Requires 750 hours of chilling. Hardy to 36 degrees F. U.S. Plant Patent No. 2964. *Source History: 3 in 1988; 12 in 1992; 14 in 2000.* **Sources: AG2, Bay, Co2, COL, Cum, Ho5, Nrs, ORA, Pe2, Si3, Son, STR, Va2, WI4.**

Oldmixon Free - Variant of Oldmixon Cling. White flesh freestone that ripens in September. Believed to have been introduced to America from a stone planted during a visit to this country in the early part of the 18th century by Sir John Oldmixon, an English historian. *Source History: 1 in 1988; 1 in 1992; 1 in 2000.* **Sources: So5.**

Orange - Clingstone. *Source History: 2 in 1988; 3 in 1992; 2 in 2000.* **Sources: Nrs, STR.**

Oregon Curl-Free - Large fruit with sweet, juicy, firm, yellow-orange flesh. Semi-freestone. Excellent for cooking and preserving. Ripens mid-August. Recommended for the Northwest and other areas where peach leaf curl is a problem. *Source History: 1 in 2000.* **Sources: On3.**

Ouchita Gold - Medium size, round freestone with yellow flesh. Does not ship well due lack of firmness. Ripens nine days after Elberta; 49 days after Redhaven. Requires 800 hours of chilling. Originated in Louisiana. *Source History: 2 in 1988; 4 in 1992; 4 in 2000.* **Sources: Ad2, Cum, Ho5, Nrs.**

Parade - Large fruit with red over a bright yellow ground color. Freestone, firm yellow flesh. Ripens 18-20 days after Elberta. Requires 800-850 hours of chilling. *Source History: 2 in 1988; 4 in 1992; 5 in 2000.* **Sources: Ad2, AG2, Cum, Ho5, Wom.**

Patio Peach - Genetic dwarf white peach. Grows to 5' tall. Self-fertile. Disease resistant. Zones 5-8. *Source History: 1 in 2000.* **Sources: Ed2.**

Peento (Saucer Peach, Peentau, Doughnut) - Doughnut-shaped fruit with sunken center and plump outer edge. Sweet, juicy, white, clingstone flesh with overtones of almond and honey. Fairly hardy and self-fruitful. Big, dependable yields. Ripens in late August. *Source History: 1 in 1988; 1 in 1992; 1 in 2000.* **Sources: Jo3, Son.**

Pekin - Semifreestone with yellow flesh. Ripens 31 days before Elberta. Requires 950 hours of chilling. Cold hardy. *Source History: 1 in 1988; 1 in 1992; 1 in 2000.* **Sources: Nrs.**

Peregrine - Seedling of Spencer nectarine. Brilliant red skin is thin and fuzzless. Almost as smooth as a nectarine, making it excellent for eating fresh. White flesh is very juicy and richly flavored like George IV. Ripens in early September. Originated in England. Introduced to the U.S. in 1906. *Source History: 1 in 1988; 3 in 1992; 3 in 2000.* **Sources: Nrs, So5, Son.**

Pl 3232 - *Source History: 1 in 2000.* **Sources: Nrs.**

Pix Zee Miniature - Delicious, firm, yellow, clingstone fruit with beautiful red skin. Strong, vigorous, self-fruitful tree grows 6' tall. Ripens in mid-June in central California. Requires 500 hours of chilling. Hardy to Zone 5. Developed by Floyd Zaiger. U.S. Plant Patent No. 6364. *Source History: 1 in 1988; 6 in 1992; 4 in 2000.* **Sources: Bay, MI5, ORA, WI4.**

Polar - *Source History: 1 in 1992; 1 in 2000.* **Sources: Nrs.**

Polly - Seedling of Hill's Chili. Medium to large, white skinned, freestone fruit overlaid with a rich crimson blush. Tender, juicy, sweet, high quality, white flesh. Flavor resembles George IV. Ripens from mid to late August. Bred for hardiness and productivity. Withstands winter temperatures to -20 degrees F. Developed in Glenwood, Iowa by S. A. Beach in 1920. *Source History: 5 in 1988; 7 in 1992; 4 in 2000.* **Sources: CO5, MI5, So5, WI4.**

Prairie Rambler - *Source History: 1 in 1992; 1 in 2000.* **Sources: Nrs.**

Prairie Rose - *Source History: 1 in 1992; 1 in 2000.* **Sources: Nrs.**

Prairie Sunrise - *Source History: 1 in 1992; 1 in 2000.* **Sources: Nrs.**

President Monroe - Large, golden yellow, freestone fruit. Sweet, yellow flesh with red highlight around the pit. Excellent for fresh eating, canning, freezing, pies or preserves. *Source History: 1 in 1988; 1 in 1992; 1 in 2000.* **Sources: Ga6.**

Q 1-8 (Washington State Q1-8) - Semifreestone with little fuzz; white flesh. Fine, sweet flavor. Great for fresh eating but too soft for canning. Moderate but regular bearer with showy blossoms. Leaf curl resistant. Self-fertile. Ripens in early August. Zones 5-8. Released by Washington State University. *Source History: 1 in 1988; 2 in 1992; 3 in 2000.* **Sources: Bay, Bu7, Ed2, ME3, Rai.**

Ranger - Medium to large, bright red blushed, freestone fruit. High quality, medium firm, yellow flesh with good flavor. Excellent variety for freezing and canning. Flesh is firm and will remain so for days after harvesting. Usually free of skin blemishes. Tree is vigorous and productive,with an abundance of dark green foliage. Ripens 24 days before Elberta. Requires 750-900 hours of chilling. Cold hardy. One of the best peaches where spring frost is a problem. *Source History: 11 in 1988; 16 in 1992; 13 in 2000.* **Sources: Cla, CO5, Cum, GI3, Ho5, Iso, MI5, ORA, STR, Tex, WA8, Wel, Wom.**

Raritan Rose (N. J. 97) - J. H. Hale x Cumberland. Large, round, freestone fruit is bright red over very light creamy white background. White flesh is melting, tender, juicy and aromatic with rich honeysweet flavor. Extremely high quality. Excellent early white peach for the roadside trade and for freezing. Tree is very vigorous, strong and productive with hardy blossom buds. Ripens 22 days before Elberta. Requires 950 hours of chilling. Developed by the New Jersey Agricultural Experiment Station. Introduced in 1936. *Source History: 4 in 1988; 8 in 1992; 8 in 2000.* **Sources: Ad2, Bo5, Hi9, Nrs, Ro3, So5, Wh4, Wor.**

Rayon - Freestone with yellow flesh. Ripens in early May. Requires 175 hours of chilling. *Source History: 1 in 1988; 1 in 2000.* **Sources: RA4.**

Red Baron - Large, yellow fleshed fruit up to 3" in diameter. Freestone. Sweet juicy flesh. Self-fruitful. Ripens in mid-July to mid-August. Requires 250-400 hours of chilling. Zones 5-9. U.S. Plant Patent No. 4195. *Source History: 2 in 1992; 5 in 2000.* **Sources: Bay, CO5, Ed2, WI4, Wom.**

Red Fremont - Apparent seedling of Red Gold peach. Fruit is slightly larger than Redhaven. Deep red color over 90% of the fruit. Freestone. Yellow flesh with red pigments coming from the stone. Some resistance to browning. Cold hardy. Trademarked. *Source History: 2 in 2000.* **Sources: Co2, Mel, Va2.**

Red Globe - Large, round, freestone fruit is highly blushed red over golden yellow background. Firm, yellow flesh has excellent flavor. Bruise resistant; good shipper. Good quality. Adapted to Pacific Coast conditions and areas where Elberta is grown. Ripens 13 days before Elberta. Requires 850-950 hours of chilling. Hardy in Zones 5-8. *Source History: 10 in 1988; 17 in 1992; 13 in 2000.* **Sources: Bar, Co2, COL, Cum, GI3, Ho5, Iso, Mi1, Si3, Tex, Va2, Wel, Wom.**

Red Lady - Medium size fruit. Solid red skin color. Firm, bright yellow flesh. Red coloring near the pit extends slightly into the flesh. Good flavor. Freestone. Vigorous tree is heavy bearing. *Source History: 1 in 1988; 2 in 1992; 1 in 2000.* **Sources: Co2.**

Red Leaf Patio - Sweet, white, freestone flesh. Self-fertile. Maroon leaves on genetic dwarf tree. Perfect for container growing. Requires 650-850 hours of chilling. *Source History: 1 in 1988; 2 in 1992; 1 in 2000.* **Sources: Wel.**

Red Rose - Medium size, red peach with white flesh. Quality is tops for a white peach. Vigorous, hardy tree. Ripens in mid-August. *Source History: 2 in 1988; 2 in 1992; 1 in 2000.* **Sources: Ad2.**

Red Sun - U.S. Plant Patent No. 7829. *Source History: 1 in 1992; 1 in 2000.* **Sources: AG2.**

Red Top - High quality, very firm, yellow freestone with attractive full red blush. Ripens in early July in central California. Self-fruitful. Requires 600-800 hours of chilling. *Source History: 3 in 1988; 7 in 1992; 3 in 2000.* **Sources: Nrs, Pr6, Si3.**

Redcap - Clingstone with yellow flesh. Ripens 42 days before Elberta. Requires 750 hours of chilling. *Source History: 2 in 1988; 2 in 1992; 1 in 2000.* **Sources: Ho5.**

Redhaven (Red Haven) - Hale Haven x Kalhaven. The standard for early peaches. Medium, nearly fuzzless fruit; bright all-over red. Firm, yellow flesh becomes freestone as it ripens. Excellent for dessert, canning and freezing. Vigorous, strong growing, self-fertile tree bears young. Tolerates handling well; flesh resists browning. Abundant fruit set; requires early, thorough thinning. Tolerant to leaf spot. Susceptible to leaf curl, brown rot, Oriental fruit moth and twig borer. Dislikes warm winters; best for the lower Midwest. Ripens 28-31 days before Elberta. 800-950 hours chilling. Hardy in Zones 5-8. Introduced by Michigan Station in 1940. *Source History: 53 in 1988; 66 in 1992; 53 in 2000.* **Sources: Ad2, AG2, Bar, Bay, Bea, Bo5, Bu1, Co2, CO5, COL, Cu4, Cum, Ed2, Fed, Fi1, FO10, Fo4, GI3, Hi9, Ho5, Iso, JOY, Lee, Leu, ME3, Mel, Mi1, MI10, MI5, ORA, Pe2, Pi2, Sav, Sc6, SH8, Si3, So5, Son, St4, STR, Tex, TU5, Ty2, Va2, Wa16, WA8, Wel, Wh4, WI12, WI4, Wom, Wor, ZEL.**

Redhaven, Com-Pact (Pratt Strain Com-Pact Red Haven) - Medium to large, freestone fruit with almost fuzzless skin. Yellow, firm flesh of excellent quality. Bears heavily on compact tree structure with close fruit spurs. Hardy variety recommended to gardeners in northern and central areas. Ripens in late July. Hardy in Zones 5-8. U.S. Plant Patent No. 3217. *Source History: 2 in 1988; 2 in 1992; 1 in 2000.* **Sources: St4.**

Redhaven, Early - Mutation of Redhaven which ripens about 14 days earlier than its parent. Brilliant red, semiclingstone fruit with firm, yellow flesh; more round at the apex. Ripens 34 days before Elberta. Requires 950 hours of chilling. Cold hardy. U.S. Plant Patent No. 3342. *Source History: 6 in 1988; 12 in 1992; 9 in 2000.* **Sources: Co2, Cu4, Cum, Hi9, Ho5, ME3, Nrs, Va2, WI12.**

Redkist - Medium size, freestone fruit with prominent red blush over bright yellow. High quality flesh is very firm and holds well, making it an outstanding shipper. Tree is vigorous but upright, and resistant to bacterial spot. Blossom buds are moderately hardy. Sets heavily, requiring careful early thinning. Trademarked. U.S. Plant Patent No. 4055. *Source History: 1 in 1988; 1 in 1992; 1 in 2000.* **Sources: Hi9.**

Redqueen - *Source History: 1 in 1992; 1 in 2000.* **Sources: Nrs.**

Redskin - J. H. Hale x Elberta. Large, freestone fruit. Red blush covers most of its yellow background, even in shaded areas. Firm, yellow, non-browning flesh. Exceptionally high quality for eating, canning, freezing or shipping. Vigorous, fast growing tree must be carefully trained and pruned. Produces good crops even under frosty conditions because of long blossom period. Heavy producer; shows resistance to bacterial spot. Very dependable bearer. Ripens two days before Elberta. Requires 700-800 hours of chilling. Hardy in Zones 5-9. Developed by Maryland Experiment Station. Introduced in 1931. *Source History: 22 in 1988; 29 in 1992; 25 in 2000.* **Sources: Ad2, Bar, Bo5, Co2, CO5, Cum, GI3, Hi9, Ho5, Iso, Jo3, La3, Leu, Nrs, Si3, So5, St4, Tex, TU5, Va2, WA8, Wel, Wh4, Wom, Wor.**

RedStar (FA-52) - Red blush covers 80% of skin surface. Flesh clings slightly to the pit. Few split pits. Good shipping quality. Trademarked. U.S. Plant Patent No. 10,546. *Source History: 3 in 2000.* **Sources: AG2, Hi9, St4.**

Regal - Yellow, semifreestone fruit. Requires 700 hours of chilling. Ripens 56 days before Elberta. *Source History: 2 in 2000.* **Sources: Cum, Ho5.**

Regina - Round, nearly fuzzless, yellow fruit covered with red blush. Yellow freestone flesh. Self-fruitful. Ripens with Redhaven. Requires 700-800 hours of chilling. *Source History: 2 in 1988; 7 in 1992; 3 in 2000.* **Sources: Co2, Si3, WI4.**

Reliance - Open-pollinated seedling of Meredith x Minn. PHO 4559. Medium size fruit has dull red blush over yellow background. Bright yellow, medium soft, juicy, sweet flesh. Freestone even in coldest, driest seasons; small pit. Good for canning, freezing and fresh market. Vigorous, fast growing tree; self-fruitful and bears when young. Showy blossoms. Very bud hardy. Best choice for severely cold winters and springs. Ripens late July; 14-21 days before Elberta. Requires 950-1,000 hours of chilling. Hardy throughout Zones 5-8; withstands temperatures of -25 degrees F. if preceding weather is favorable. Developed by Professor Meader at the New Hampshire Agricultural Experiment Station in 1964. *Source History: 29 in 1988; 33 in 1992; 28 in 2000.* **Sources: Ad2, Bea, CO5, Cum, Fed, Fi1, Gur, Hi9, Ho5, Jo3, Jun, La3, Mc3, ME3, Mel, Mi1, MI5, Sc6, SH8, So5, St4, STR, Ty2, Va2, Wa16, WI4, Wor, ZEL.**

Rich Lady - Extra large fruit. Yellow clingstone flesh. Low acid. Highly productive tree. Ripens the third week of June. Requires 750-850 hours of chilling. U.S. Plant Patent No. 7290. *Source History: 1 in 2000.* **Sources: WI4.**

Rich May - Large, highly colored fruit with excellent flavor. Clingstone. Ripens mid-May, between Goldcrest and Maycrest. Requires 800-900 hours of chilling. U.S. Plant Patent No. 7432. *Source History: 1 in 2000.* **Sources: WI4.**

Richaven - Cross of Hale Haven, Redhaven and J. H. Hale. Freestone with yellow flesh. Ripens 15 days before Elberta. Requires 950 hours of chilling. Withstands temperatures of -19 degrees below zero. Developed at Michigan State University. *Source History: 2 in 1988; 3 in 1992; 3 in 2000.* **Sources: Ho5, Mi1, TU5.**

Rio Grande - Large, freestone peach with yellow flesh. Requires 450-950 hours of chilling. Ripens midseason. Excellent peach for warmer regions of Texas. Patent expired. *Source History: 3 in 1988; 8 in 1992; 6 in 2000.* **Sources: CO5, Ho5, Ju2, ORA, Tex, Wel.**

Rio Oso Gem (Rio Oso) - Large, round, yellow, freestone fruit with bright red blush. Firm, yellow flesh turning red at the pit. Excellent flavor for fresh eating and freezing. Noted for excellent quality, high color, firmness in shipping. Self-fertile tree is relatively small but productive; showy bloom. Outstanding commercial value. Similar to J. H. Hale; makes a good pollinator for J. H. Hale. Susceptible to peach leaf curl, brown rot, Oriental fruit moth and peach twig borer. Main fault is its relative lack of vigor and shorter life span. Ripens six days after Elberta. Requires 800-850 hours of chilling. Needs a cold climate. California origin. *Source History: 15 in 1988; 22 in 1992; 15 in 2000.* **Sources: Ad2, Bay, Bo5, CO5, Fi1, Gur, Hi9, Ho5, Nrs, ORA, Si3, Son, STR, Va2, WI4.**

Risingstar (FA-47) - High quality semi-freetone. Skin color is 80% bright orange-red with a slight stripe. Firm flesh has a pleasing sugar-acid ratio. Trademarked. U.S. Plant Patent No. 10,545. *Source History: 4 in 2000.* **Sources: AG2, COL, Hi9, St4.**

Rizzi - Clingstone with excellent storage capability, making it attractive to canneries for extending the processing season. U.S. Plant Patent No. 8394. *Source History: 2 in 2000.* **Sources: Si3, WI4.**

Rochester - Crawford type. Yellow freestone fruit overlaid with mottled red. Thick, firm, juicy flesh, marbled yellow with tint of red at the pit. Vigorous, productive tree flourishes over a wide range of soils. Ripens early. Introduced in 1912. *Source History: 1 in 1988; 1 in 1992; 1 in 2000.* **Sources: Mi1.**

Rosa (Roza) - Large, round, freestone fruit with a faintly streaked medium red blush over 75% of its surface. Firm, deep yellow flesh with slightly coarse texture and excellent flavor. Good for fresh market, canning and shipping. Tree is vigorous, productive and self-fertile. Ripens ten days after Redhaven. Developed at Prosser, Washington. *Source History: 5 in 1988; 5 in 1992; 3 in 2000.* **Sources: Co2, Si3, Va2.**

Roseprince - *Source History: 1 in 2000.* **Sources: Nrs.**

Ross (Ross Cling) - Large, uniform, firm clingstone fruit with good color and flavor. Large tree is slightly spreading and highly productive. Ripens mid to late August. U.S. Plant Patent No. 4863. *Source History: 3 in 1988; 5 in 1992; 3 in 2000.* **Sources: AG2, Si3, WI4.**

Royal Gold - Yellow, cling to semifreestone flesh. Very sweet and flavorful. Superb fresh peach for the very early season. Self-fruitful. Ripens in late May in Southern California. Requires 500 hours of chilling. Developed by Floyd Zaiger. *Source History: 1 in 1988; 1 in 1992; 1 in 2000.* **Sources: WI4.**

Royal May - *Source History: 1 in 1992; 1 in 2000.* **Sources: CO5.**

Roza - *Source History: 1 in 1992; 1 in 2000.* **Sources: Nrs.**

Rubidoux - Freestone. *Source History: 2 in 1988; 1 in 1992; 1 in 2000.* **Sources: CO5.**

Rubired - Semifreestone with yellow flesh. Ripens 40-42 days before Elberta. Requires 800-950 hours of chilling. *Source History: 2 in 1988; 2 in 1992; 3 in 2000.* **Sources: Cum, Ho5, Nrs.**

Rubyprince - Medium fruit is 2.25-2.5" with proper thinning; 80-90% red with attractive background color. Clingstone with good texture and flavor. Flesh softens slowly on the tree. Ripens with Derby. Requires 850 hours of chilling. *Source History: 1 in 2000.* **Sources: Ho5.**

Rustin Red - Freestone with yellow flesh. Ripens five days before Elberta; early July. Requires 850-900 hours of chilling. Cold hardy. *Source History: 2 in 1988; 2 in 1992; 5 in 2000.* **Sources: Cum, Ho5, Tex, Wel, Wom.**

Ryan Sun (28-24) - Highly colored fruit. Ripens mid to late season. Developed in California in 1975. U.S. Plant Patent No. 5103. *Source History: 1 in 1992; 1 in 2000.* **Sources: AG2.**

Salem - Complete tree sport of Loring. Excellent color, firmness and size. Original tree has been very productive. Shows resistance to winter cold and bacterial spot. Ripens two weeks ahead of Loring, about August 7. U.S. Plant Patent No. 6267. *Source History: 1 in 1988; 1 in 1992; 1 in 2000.* **Sources: Ad2.**

Sam Houston - Medium size, yellow, freestone fruit with good quality, yellow flesh and small pit. If planted on deep, coarse, sandy soils, bacterial spot will likely be a problem. Recommended especially for southern areas. Ripens 15 days before Elberta. Requires 500-650 hours of chilling. Introduced by Texas A and M. *Source History: 7 in 1988; 13 in 1992; 8 in 2000.* **Sources: Bas, GI3, MI5, Nrs, SIM, Tex, Wel, Wom.**

Santa Barbara - Sport of Ventura. Large, yellow fruit with red blush. Yellow flesh freestone; red near pit. Excellent flavor and quality. Does not keep well. Self-fruitful. Ripens mid-July. Requires 250-300 hours of chilling. *Source History: 1 in 1992; 5 in 2000.* **Sources: Bay, CO5, ORA, Pa2, WI4.**

Saturn - Fruiting and flowering variety bears large, double, dark pink blooms. Large, yellow, freestone fruit. Sweet, low-acid, juicy flesh. Self-fruitful. Ripens mid-July. Requires 360-300 hours of chilling. *Source History: 3 in 2000.* **Sources: Bay, Ed2, Pa2.**

Saturn, Stark (N. J. F-2, Donut) - White fleshed fruit. Sweet, almond-like flavor. When pit is removed, peach looks like a doughnut. Spreading tree is vigorous and resistant to bacterial leaf spot. Self-fruitful. Ripens in late June or early July. Requires 400-500 hours of chilling. Hardy in Zones 5-8. Trademarked. U.S. Plant Patent No. 5123. *Source History: 2 in 1988; 4 in 1992; 8 in 2000.* **Sources: Bay, CO5, On3, On4, ORA, Pa2, Rai, St4.**

Scarlet Pearl - Semifreestone with white flesh. Ripens 47 days before Elberta. Requires 750 hours of chilling. *Source History: 3 in 1992; 3 in 2000.* **Sources: Ho5, Nrs, St4.**

Sensation, Stark (Andergen Cultivar) - Juicy, firm fruit. Used for fresh eating, canning, freezing. Dwarf tree grows 4-6' tall. Ripens in mid-July. Hardy in Zones 5-8; will grow well in Zone 4 if potted and protected during winter. Trademarked. U.S. Plant Patent No. 5124. *Source History: 1 in 1988; 1 in 1992; 1 in 2000.* **Sources: St4.**

Sentinel - Hale Haven x Dixie Gem. Medium size, roundish, semiclingstone fruit is 80% dark red blush on yellow background. Medium firm, juicy, slightly coarse, yellow flesh with sweet flavor and good texture. Trees are vigorous, productive, self-fertile and resistant to bacterial leaf spot. Blossom bud survival in winter has been rather erratic, but generally seems to set good crops. In years of light crops it tends to have many split pits. Ripens 34 days before Elberta. Requires 650-850 hours of chilling. Released from the USDA in Georgia. Introduced in 1966. *Source History: 7 in 1988; 11 in 1992; 7 in 2000.* **Sources: Cum, GI3, Ho5, Nrs, Tex, Wel, Wom.**

Sentry - Loring x Sentinel. Semifreestone with firm, highly colored flesh. Excellent size for an early maturing variety. Vigorous tree is resistant to bacterial leaf spot. Ripens about July 19. Introduced in 1980 by the USDA in Beltsville, Maryland. *Source History: 1 in 1988; 3 in 1992; 7 in 2000.* **Sources: Ad2, Bo5, Hi9, Nrs, Rai, St4, Wh4.**

September Snow - Large white freestone with good coloring. Non-acid, sweet flesh. Ripens in late August. Requires 900-1,000 hours of chilling. U.S. Plant Patent No. 8003. *Source History: 1 in 2000.* **Sources: WI4.**

September Sun (20-79-13) - Fruit has 70% red blush over yellow-orange ground color. Firm flesh with good texture; excellent flavor. Ripens in September. Developed in California. U.S. Plant Patent No. 6008. *Source History: 1 in 1992; 1 in 2000.* **Sources: AG2.**

Shepherd's Beauty - Clingstone with yellow flesh. Ripens 42 days before Elberta. Requires 650 hours of chilling. *Source History: 1 in 1988; 1 in 1992; 1 in 2000.* **Sources: Ho5.**

Shippers Late Red (Big Red) - Very hardy Hale type. Large, attractive, red, freestone fruit with yellow flesh. Excellent quality; good shipper. Bears young and heavily. Beauty and size make it a good marketing peach. Fruit may be allowed to remain on the tree much longer than most. Ripens a few days after Elberta. *Source*

History: 2 in 1988; 2 in 1992; 2 in 2000. **Sources: Mel, TU5.**

Sierra Lady - Freestone. U.S. Plant Patent No. 6045. *Source History: 1 in 1988; 1 in 1992; 1 in 2000.* **Sources: Si3.**

Silver Logan - Large fruit with white-green skin. White, freestone flesh of excellent flavor and melting texture. Productive, vigorous tree. Ripens mid-July. Originated in California, 1965. *Source History: 1 in 1992; 1 in 2000.* **Sources: Son.**

Sims - Large, golden yellow fruit with a faint blush. Clingstone flesh is clear yellow to the small pit. Excellent for canning. Self-fertile. Ripens in mid-August to September. Requires 700 hours of chilling. *Source History: 3 in 1988; 2 in 1992; 1 in 2000.* **Sources: ORA.**

Slappy (Slappey) - Large, yellow, freestone fruit with yellow flesh and distinctive flavor. Thin, almost fuzzless skin. Delicious, clean, pine-like flavor, reminiscent of the purity of flavor of the Newtown Pippin apple. A favorite for home canning. Older variety that bears well. Ripens in late August. *Source History: 2 in 1988; 6 in 1992; 1 in 2000.* **Sources: Bo5.**

Slaybaugh Special - Large, firm freestone. Excellent shipper. Planted commercially in New Jersey for many years. *Source History: 2 in 2000.* **Sources: Ad2, Bo5.**

Snow Flame - Dark red fruit with white, flavorful flesh. Good for fresh eating or canning. Good shipper. Ripens in June. Requires 900 hours of chilling. PVP. *Source History: 1 in 1992; 1 in 2000.* **Sources: ORA.**

Snow Giant - Creamy white fuzzy skin with attractive red blush. Firm, sweet white flesh with sub-acid flavor. Clingstone. Productive tree. Self-fruitful. Ripens in late August. Requires 600-900 hours of chilling. U.S. Plant Patent No. 8085. *Source History: 3 in 2000.* **Sources: Ad2, Bay, WI4.**

Snow King - Large, red skinned fruit with white flesh. Freestone. Self-fruitful. Ripens between Sugar Giant and Snow Giant. Requires 900-1,000 hours of chilling. U.S. Plant Patent No. 8415. *Source History: 3 in 2000.* **Sources: Ad2, Bay, WI4.**

Snow Prince - Medium to large fruit with 90% dark red blush on white background. Firm, clingstone flesh. Non-acid. Very good flavor. Requires 750-850 hours of chilling. U.S. Plant Patent No. 9873. *Source History: 1 in 2000.* **Sources: WI4.**

Snowbrite - Medium to large white fruit with good color. Firm, non-acid flesh. Sweet flavor. No leaf curl resistance. Ripens mid-June. Requires 900-1,000 hours of chilling. U.S. Plant Patent No. 8195. *Source History: 2 in 2000.* **Sources: Ea3, WI4.**

Southern Flame - Large, yellow fruit overspread with red. Firm, crisp, melting, yellow, freestone flesh. Good aroma; good eating quality. Genetic dwarf tree grows 5' tall. Ripens in late July. Requires approximately 400 hours of chilling. U.S. Plant Patent No. 3620. *Source History: 1 in 1988; 2 in 1992; 1 in 2000.* **Sources: CO5.**

Southern Pearl - Fruit can reach 2.75" with proper thinning; 60-70% red on a cream colored background. White flesh with firm texture. Freestone. Good eating quality. Not recommended for shipping. Ripens with Garnet Beauty, 12 days after Redhaven. Requires 650 hours of chilling. *Source History: 3 in 2000.* **Sources: Cu4, Ho5, Ty2.**

Southern Rose - Large, yellow fruit with red blush. Firm, yellow, freestone flesh. Good eating quality. Genetic dwarf tree grows 5' tall. Blooms early. Compares favorably with commercial peaches. Ripens in early August. Requires approximately 300 hours of chilling. U.S. Plant Patent No. 3476. *Source History: 2 in 1988; 2 in 1992; 3 in 2000.* **Sources: CO5, On4, Pa2.**

Southern Sweet - Medium size, freestone fruit with yellow flesh. Good flavor. Genetic dwarf, very prolific, 5' tree. Ripens from early to mid-June. Requires approximately 500 hours of chilling. U.S. Plant Patent No. 3757. *Source History: 1 in 1988; 1 in 1992; 1 in 2000.* **Sources: CO5.**

Southland - Freestone with yellow flesh. Ripens 18 days before Elberta. Requires 750 hours of chilling. *Source History: 2 in 1988; 3 in 1992; 1 in 2000.* **Sources: Ho5.**

Spartan Cling - *Source History: 1 in 1992; 1 in 2000.* **Sources: Nrs.**

Spotlight - *Source History: 1 in 2000.* **Sources: Nrs.**

Spring Baby - Ripens mid-May. *Source History: 2 in 2000.* **Sources: AG2, Nrs.**

Spring Gem - Ripens late May. *Source History: 1 in 2000.* **Sources: AG2.**

Spring Snow - Large fruit with 90% maroon-red over white skin color. White flesh. Clingstone. Non-acid. Very good flavor. Ripens late May to early June. Requires 750-850 hours of chilling. U.S. Plant Patent No. 9883. *Source History: 1 in 2000.* **Sources: WI4.**

Springbrite - Yellow, semi-cling fruit. Ripens 52 days before Elberta. Requires 650 hours of chilling. *Source History: 1 in 1988; 2 in 1992; 1 in 2000.* **Sources: Iso.**

Springcrest - Clingstone with yellow flesh. Ripens 51-52 days before Elberta. Requires 650 hours of chilling. Hardy in Zone 5. *Source History: 3 in 1988; 7 in 1992; 4 in 2000.* **Sources: AG2, GI3, Ho5, ME3.**

Springold - Round, clingstone fruit at maturity is 80-90% covered with bright red blush and striping over yellow background. Relatively firm, yellow flesh is non-melting with good flavor. Tree is productive and as resistant to low winter temperatures as Redhaven. Less prone to split pits than most early varieties. Ripens 55 days before Elberta. Requires 750-850 hours of chilling. Introduced in 1966. *Source History: 5 in 1988; 10 in 1992; 7 in 2000.* **Sources: Cla, Cum, GI3, Ho5, Tex, Wel, Wom.**

Springprince - Medium to large size fruit is 80-90% bright red. Yellow clingstone flesh with red pit cavity. Non-melting texture. Good flavor. Requires 650 hours of chilling. Ripens 52 days before Elberta. *Source History: 1 in 2000.* **Sources: Cum.**

St. John - *Source History: 1 in 1992; 1 in 2000.* **Sources: Nrs.**

Stagg - Freestone with yellow flesh. Ripens seven days before Elberta. Requires 850 hours of chilling. Cold hardy. *Source History: 1 in 1988; 1 in 1992; 1 in 2000.* **Sources: Cum.**

Stanislaus - Extra early clingstone ripens around July 22. Zaiger introduction. U.S. Plant Patent No. 8376. *Source History: 1 in 2000.* **Sources: WI4.**

StarFire (FA-11) - Fayette x Newhaven. Firm yellow flesh with some red around the small pit. Freestone. Heavy annual cropper requires several pickings. Good shipping qualities. Ripens 5 days after Redhaven. Trademarked. U.S. Plant Patent No. 10,548. *Source History: 5 in 2000.* **Sources: AG2, Co2, COL, Hi9, St4.**

Starlite - Very early, semifreestone peach. Firm, sprightly flavored, aromatic, white flesh. Ripens 55 days before Elberta; early May. Requires 650 hours of chilling. Hardy in Zones 6-9. *Source History: 3 in 1988; 3 in 1992; 3 in 2000.*

Sources: Cum, Ho5, Ju2.

Starn - Large, firm clingstone fruit with good color. Good canner. Large, semi-upright tree is highly productive. Very popular late season variety. *Source History: 2 in 1988; 4 in 1992; 3 in 2000.* **Sources: AG2, Si3, WI4.**

Strawberry Cling - Large, creamy white, freestone fruit mottled with red. White, juicy flesh has strawberry marbling and rich flavor. Good for canning. Self-fertile. Susceptible to peach leaf curl, brown rot, Oriental fruit moth and peach twig borer. Ripens in September. *Source History: 5 in 1988; 3 in 1992; 2 in 2000.* **Sources: Nrs, STR.**

Strawberry Free - Light cream fruit with pink blush. Early season freestone with white flesh. Very sweet, aromatic and flavorful. Self-fruitful. Old favorite in northern California, especially the San Francisco Bay area. Ripens late June or early July. Requires 400-500 hours of chilling. *Source History: 4 in 1988; 7 in 1992; 6 in 2000.* **Sources: Bay, CO5, Ga20, Nrs, ORA, WI4.**

Stump-the-World - Oldmixon type. Almost lost to cultivation. Appearance is not flattering. Pale green skin with reddish blush in the sun. White flesh is juicy, melting, tender, sparkling and richly flavored. Freestone. Ripens in late September. Originated in New Jersey in 1876. *Source History: 1 in 1988; 2 in 1992; 1 in 2000.* **Sources: Son.**

Sugar Giant - Large, very firm fruit with nearly full, solid red color. White free-stone flesh. Compares with White Lady. Ripens about 24 days after Redhaven. Requires 800-900 hours of chilling. Zaiger selection. U.S. Plant Patent No. 8442. *Source History: 2 in 2000.* **Sources: Ad2, WI4.**

Sugar Lady - White flesh freestone with cream colored skin with dark red blush. Sweet, slightly tangy flavor. Self-fertile. Ripens 12 days after Redhaven. Requires 700 hours of chilling. U.S. Plant Patent No. 7532. *Source History: 4 in 1992; 4 in 2000.* **Sources: Ad2, Bay, ORA, WI4.**

Sugar May - Medium to large, highly colored, firm fruit. White flesh. High quality with low incidence of split pits. Ripens three weeks before Redhaven. Zaiger Genetics development. U.S. Plant Patent No. 8034. *Source History: 1 in 2000.* **Sources: Ad2.**

Sugarsweet - Semifreestone. Sweet flavor. Ripens with Sentinel; 32 days before Elberta. Requires 800 hours of chilling. *Source History: 1 in 1992; 1 in 2000.* **Sources: Ho5.**

Sullivan No. 4 - Clingstone fruit. Medium to large, semi-upright tree. Good production; ripens uniformly. Ripens late August. *Source History: 1 in 1988; 2 in 1992; 2 in 2000.* **Sources: Si3, WI4.**

Summer Breeze (HB 110) - Large, firm, high quality fruit. Yellow freestone flesh. Ripens 4 days after Loring; 24 days after Redhaven. Discovered as a seedling by Donald Hollabaugh of Biglerville, Pennsylvania. Trademarked. Plant patent applied for. *Source History: 1 in 2000.* **Sources: Ad2.**

Summer Pearl, Stark (N. J. 252 Cultivar) - Medium to large fruit with firm, white flesh. Moderate resistance to bacterial leaf spot. Released by the New Jersey Agricultural Experiment Station. Trademarked. *Source History: 1 in 1992; 2 in 2000.* **Sources: Ad2, St4.**

Summer Serenade - Sport of Garnet Beauty. Medium to large size fruit. Red blush covers 70-80% of skin surface. Semi-cling, firm yellow flesh. Few split pits. Trademarked. *Source History: 1 in 2000.* **Sources: Hi9.**

Summer Sun - U.S. Plant Patent No. 6007. *Source History: 1 in 1992; 1 in*

2000. **Sources: AG2.**

Summer Sweet - White flesh fruit. Sweet, non-acid flavor. Not recommended for large scale planting at this time. Ripens 27 days after Redhaven. Requires 650-750 hours of chilling. U.S. Plant Patent No. 8070. *Source History: 2 in 2000.* **Sources: Ad2, WI4.**

Summer Zee - Large, very firm freestone. Skin color is 80% deep red over yellow. Ripens in early July. Requires 900-1,000 hours of chilling. U.S. Plant Patent No. 9529. *Source History: 1 in 2000.* **Sources: WI4.**

Summerglo (N. J. 233) - Large, yellow freestone. Firm, well colored flesh. Tree is vigorous and productive, showing above average cold hardiness. Ripens about August 11. *Source History: 1 in 1988; 2 in 1992; 1 in 2000.* **Sources: Nrs.**

Summergold - Freestone with yellow flesh. Ripens 10 days before Elberta. Requires 750 hours of chilling. *Source History: 2 in 1988; 3 in 1992; 2 in 2000.* **Sources: Cum, Ho5.**

Summerprince - Yellow flesh. Requires early and hard thinning to size properly. Semi-freestone. Tree shows moderate resistance to bacterial spot. Ripens 42 days before Elberta. Requires 850 hours of chilling. *Source History: 3 in 2000.* **Sources: Hi9, Ho5, Nrs.**

Summerset - Large, round, yellow freestone with red blush. Firm, flavorful, high quality flesh. Used for fresh, canning and freezing. Self-fertile tree is vigorous and productive with showy flowers. Susceptible to peach leaf curl, brown rot, Oriental fruit moth and peach twig borer. Ripens in late September or early October depending on location. Requires 700 hours of chilling. *Source History: 6 in 1988; 10 in 1992; 3 in 2000.* **Sources: Bay, Si3, WI4.**

Sun Grande - Freestone with yellow flesh. Ripens 25 days before Elberta. Requires 450 hours of chilling. *Source History: 1 in 1988; 2 in 1992; 1 in 2000.* **Sources: Cum.**

Sun Haven - Seedling of Redhaven. Large, round, bright red, freestone fruit with yellow-gold cheeks. Firm, sweet, juicy flesh with rich flavor. Resists browning when cut. Excellent for pies. Vigorous, productive tree is very hardy. No injury to the tree after -19 degree temperatures, though buds were damaged. Self-fertile. Ripens in late July or early August. Introduced by Michigan State University. One of the best flavored of all early peaches. *Source History: 5 in 1988; 6 in 1992; 3 in 2000.* **Sources: BO10, Mi1, Nrs.**

Sun Haven, Late - Mutation of Sun Haven. Medium to large, round, brightly colored, freestone fruit. Very firm; handles well. Hardy, productive tree is resistant to bacterial spot. Larger than Sun Haven and more desirable. Ripens just after Redhaven and 31 days before Elberta. Requires 850-900 hours of chilling. Released from the Michigan Station in 1960. *Source History: 3 in 1988; 5 in 1992; 5 in 2000.* **Sources: Ad2, Bo5, Cu4, Cum, Ho5.**

Sunapee - Very hardy, yellow freestone with good flavor. Larger but not so well colored as Reliance. Ripens in late August. Developed by Professors Meader and Yeager of the New Hampshire Agricultural Experiment Station in Durham. Introduced in 1955. *Source History: 1 in 1988; 2 in 1992; 1 in 2000.* **Sources: Nrs.**

Sunbright, Stark (751 Cultivar) - *Source History: 1 in 1992; 1 in 2000.* **Sources: St4.**

Sunbrite - Semifreestone with yellow flesh. Ripens 49 days before Elberta. Requires 750 hours of chilling. *Source History: 2 in 1988; 3 in 1992; 3 in 2000.* **Sources: Cum, Ho5, Nrs.**

Suncling - *Source History: 1 in 1992; 1 in 2000.* **Sources: Nrs.**

Suncrest - Alamar x Gold Dust. Large, round freestone that colors to about 80% bright red blush over yellow background. Flesh is yellow and exceptionally firm with good texture and flavor. Vigorous, self-fruitful, productive trees have good hardiness record where tested in Eastern sites. Susceptible to bacterial spot. Good shipper that is proving to be a good commercial market peach. Ripens about August 25. Requires 700 hours of chilling. Originated in Fresno, California. Introduced in 1959. *Source History: 7 in 1988; 14 in 1992; 11 in 2000.* **Sources: Ad2, Bay, Co2, COL, Hi9, Nrs, Si3, Son, St4, Va2, WI4.**

Sunhigh (N. J. 82) - Large, oblong, freestone fruit is pointed at the tip. Bright red blush over an orange background; colors well before it ripens. Melting, sweet, mild, fragrant flesh with distinctive flavor. Firm shipper. Valuable commercial variety that is also excellent for canning and roadside markets. Moderately hardy tree is susceptible to bacterial leaf spot. Ripens in mid-August, 15 days before Elberta, and has comparable hardiness. Requires 750-800 hours of chilling. Originated at the New Jersey Agricultural Experiment Station in New Brunswick as a seedling of J. H. Hale. Introduced in 1938. *Source History: 9 in 1988; 9 in 1992; 9 in 2000.* **Sources: Ad2, Bo5, Cum, Ho5, Nrs, Pi2, So5, Wh4, Wor.**

Sunland - Freestone with yellow flesh. Ripens 23 days before Elberta. Requires 750 hours of chilling. *Source History: 2 in 1988; 3 in 1992; 3 in 2000.* **Sources: Cum, Ho5, Nrs.**

Sunprince - Freestone with yellow flesh. Ripens two days before Elberta. Requires 800 hours of chilling. *Source History: 2 in 1988; 4 in 1992; 3 in 2000.* **Sources: Cum, Ho5, Nrs.**

Sunsplash - *Source History: 1 in 2000.* **Sources: Nrs.**

Super Rich - Medium to large yellow clingstone with 70-80% red over yellow skin color. Productive tree. Ripens the second week of May. Requires 700-800 hours of chilling. U.S. Plant Patent No. 9860. *Source History: 1 in 2000.* **Sources: WI4.**

Surecrop - Semifreestone with yellow flesh. Reliable cropper. Ripens 43 days before Elberta. Requires 950 hours of chilling. Cold hardy. *Source History: 4 in 1988; 7 in 1992; 5 in 2000.* **Sources: Cla, Cu4, Cum, Ho5, Wel.**

Suwanee - Large, yellow freestone fruit with a red blush. Yellow flesh with medium texture. Suited to the lower South. Ripens 22 days before Elberta. Requires 650 hours of chilling. Hardy in Zones 7-9. *Source History: 7 in 1988; 11 in 1992; 6 in 2000.* **Sources: GI3, Ho5, Iso, Ju2, SIM, Ty2.**

Suzi Q (Trisha) - Semifreestone with yellow flesh. Ripens 50-52 days before Elberta. Requires 650 hours of chilling. *Source History: 2 in 1988; 2 in 1992; 2 in 2000.* **Sources: Cum, Ho5.**

Sweeney - Clingstone. *Source History: 1 in 1992; 1 in 2000.* **Sources: AG2.**

Sweet Gem - U.S. Plant Patent No. 7952. *Source History: 1 in 2000.* **Sources: WI4.**

Sweet Scarlet - Highly colored, large fruit. Clingstone. Very good flavor; low to non-acid. Vigorous, productive tree. Requires 800-900 hours of chilling. U.S. Plant Patent No. 9695. *Source History: 1 in 2000.* **Sources: WI4.**

Sweet September - Firm, sweet, sub-acid flesh. Freestone. Ripens in mid-September. Requires 800-900 hours of chilling. U.S. Plant Patent No. 9964. *Source History: 1 in 2000.* **Sources: WI4.**

Sweet Sue - Similar but superior to Rio-Oso-Gem. Large and has smoother suture. Brighter red blush over strong yellow ground color. Tree is as hardy and also stronger, more vigorous and less susceptible to bacterial spot. Heavy producer; ripens uniformly with excellent storage and long distance shipping. Not recommended for areas that cannot grow and mature Rio Oso Gem satisfactorily. Ripens late. U.S. Plant Patent No. 4451. *Source History: 1 in 1988; 1 in 1992; 1 in 2000.* **Sources: Hi9.**

Sweethaven - Medium size, oblong, freestone fruit with 80% bright red over yellow background. Yellow, juicy, slightly fibrous, soft, melting flesh. Tree is vigorous and productive. Blossom buds are as hardy as Redhaven. Ripens 42 days before Elberta. Requires 850 hours of chilling. *Source History: 4 in 1988; 4 in 1992; 3 in 2000.* **Sources: Cum, Ho5, Nrs.**

Tasty Giant - Extremely large, yellow freestone fruits weigh up to one pound each. Flavor has good sugar-acid balance. Highly recommended for home planting. Self-fruitful. Ripens in August. Requires 500 hours of chilling. Plant patent applied for. *Source History: 2 in 1992; 2 in 2000.* **Sources: Bay, WI4.**

Tejon - Medium size, yellow fruit blushed with red. Slightly fuzzy skin. Yellow freestone flesh. Good for fresh eating. Self-fertile. Ripens in mid-July. Requires 300-400 hours of chilling. *Source History: 3 in 1988; 2 in 1992; 2 in 2000.* **Sources: ORA, SIM.**

TexRoyal - Medium to large fruit with red blush covering 80% of skin surface. Firm, yellow, freestone flesh with melting texture. Flavor similar to Harvester. Good tolerance to late spring frosts. Ripens in early June, 34 days before Elberta. Requires 600 hours of chilling. Patented. *Source History: 3 in 1992; 3 in 2000.* **Sources: Cum, Ho5, Wom.**

Texstar - Sets heavy crops of semiclingstone fruit with yellow flesh. Ripens 43 days before Elberta. Requires 450 hours of chilling. Developed at Texas A and M University. *Source History: 5 in 1988; 8 in 1992; 5 in 2000.* **Sources: Cum, Ho5, Nrs, Tex, Wom.**

Topaz - Very attractive, large, round, freestone with light fuzz. Color is 100% red over bright yellow background. Flesh is yellow, non-browning, very firm, high quality and good texture. Fruit hangs well. Tree is vigorous, upright, strong, resistant to bacterial spot and tender to winter cold. Ripens 20 days before Elberta. Requires 850 hours of chilling. *Source History: 4 in 1988; 7 in 1992; 5 in 2000.* **Sources: Cum, Hi9, Ho5, Si3, Va2.**

Tra-Zee - Large, firm, highly colored fruit. Freestone flesh. Good flavor. Self-fruitful. Ripens late August. Requires 700 hours of chilling. Zaiger introduction. U.S. Plant Patent No. 6847. *Source History: 3 in 1992; 2 in 2000.* **Sources: Bay, WI4.**

Triogem (N. J. 70) - Medium size, oval, attractive, red all over fruit; firm, yellow, freestone flesh. Very good shipper. One of the finest sorts for freezing. Tree is vigorous and productive. Quite popular, due to heavy yields and good marketing traits. Ripens 20-25 days before Elberta. Hardy. *Source History: 2 in 1988; 3 in 1992; 1 in 2000.* **Sources: Wor.**

Tropi-Berta - U.S. Plant Patent No. 4014. *Source History: 1 in 1988; 1 in 1992; 1 in 2000.* **Sources: CO5.**

Tropic Beauty - Semifreestone. Ripens late April. Requires 150 hours of chilling. *Source History: 3 in 1992; 3 in 2000.* **Sources: AG2, Ho5, RA4.**

Tropic Snow - Creamy white freestone flesh with superb flavor. Self-fruitful. Ripens during May. Requires 200 hours of chilling. Good for deep south Texas. *Source History: 4 in 1992; 10 in 2000.* **Sources: AG2, Bay, CO5, Ho5, On4,**

ORA, Pa2, RA4, SIM, WI4.

Tropic Sweet - Yellow flesh freestone. Good yields. Ripens 42 days before Elberta. Requires 150-175 hours of chilling. Hardy in Zones 8-9. *Source History: 2 in 1988; 5 in 1992; 3 in 2000.* **Sources: AG2, Ho5, RA4.**

Tulip - *Source History: 1 in 1992; 1 in 2000.* **Sources: Nrs.**

Tuolumne - Clingstone. Ripens with or slightly ahead of Andross but with firmer fruit. Zaiger introduction. Patent pending. *Source History: 1 in 2000.* **Sources: WI4.**

Tyler - Freestone with yellow flesh. Ripens six days after Elberta. Requires 950 hours of chilling. Cold hardy. *Source History: 2 in 1988; 4 in 1992; 3 in 2000.* **Sources: Cu4, Cum, Ho5.**

Tzim Pee Tav - *Source History: 1 in 1992; 1 in 2000.* **Sources: Nrs.**

UF Gold - *Source History: 1 in 2000.* **Sources: RA4.**

Valleyfire - Semifreestone. Ripens 12 days before Redhaven. Requires 800-850 hours of chilling. Originated in Georgia. *Source History: 1 in 1992; 1 in 2000.* **Sources: Ho5.**

Vedoka - *Source History: 1 in 1992; 1 in 2000.* **Sources: Nrs.**

Ventura - Medium size, yellow, freestone fruit with red blush. Yellow, firm flesh. Good for fresh eating. Grows well in mild and coastal areas. Ripens in early July. Low chill requirement. *Source History: 4 in 1988; 4 in 1992; 3 in 2000.* **Sources: CO5, ORA, STR.**

Veteran - Early Elberta x Vaughn. Round, good quality, medium to large, golden yellow fruit with slight red blush. Freestone when fully ripe. Yellow, firm flesh with coarse grain; easy to peel. Excellent fresh, canned or frozen. Self-fruitful tree is a vigorous grower and bears early with consistent yields. Ornamental, with large, pale pink blooms. Reliable producer in cold, wet weather. One of the cold hardiest varieties. Sets crops when other peach blossoms are killed by frosts. Ripens 8-10 days before Elberta. Requires 1,000+ hours of chilling. Zone 5. Originated in Canada. Introduced in 1928. *Source History: 8 in 1988; 13 in 1992; 11 in 2000.* **Sources: Bea, Bu7, Cu4, Ea3, JOY, ME3, Nrs, Son, Va2, WI4, Wom.**

Vista - Large, highly colored fruit. Firm, clingstone flesh. Productive tree. Ripens with Rich Lady. Requires 700-800 hours of chilling. U.S. Plant Patent No. 9549. *Source History: 1 in 2000.* **Sources: WI4.**

Vivid - Medium to large, attractive, bright red, freestone fruit. Tree is medium hardy and productive. Ripens early. Introduced in 1974. *Source History: 1 in 1988; 1 in 1992; 1 in 2000.* **Sources: Hi9.**

Washington - Sunhigh x VIP 15. Large, attractive, high quality, yellow freestone fruit with yellow flesh and excellent flavor. Outstanding qualities of size, color, firmness of flesh, texture and flavor. Highly recommended for home and commercial use. Tree is vigorous, hardy and productive. Ripens 21 days ahead of Elberta. Requires 950 hours of chilling. Superior hardiness. *Source History: 3 in 1988; 4 in 1992; 2 in 2000.* **Sources: Nrs, Po2.**

White - White flesh with melting characteristics similar to Belle of Georgia. Excellent for fresh eating. Ripens late August. *Source History: 1 in 2000.* **Sources: Sc6.**

White Champion - Large, firm, freestone with white flesh and excellent fresh flavor. Tree is highly productive and very dependable. Bred for disease resistance. Ripens in mid-September. Moderately hardy. Bears well in Zone 4 if given some winter protection. *Source History: 1 in 1988; 1 in 1992; 1 in 2000.* **Sources: Fi1.**

White English - Clingstone with white flesh. Ripens six days after Elberta. Requires 750 hours of chilling. *Source History: 1 in 1988; 1 in 2000.* **Sources: TU5.**

White Hale - J. H. Hale x Belle. Large, firm, freestone fruit that is very similar to J.H. Hale except that it has white flesh. Very attractive; very good quality. Tree is hardy, vigorous and productive. Ripens four days after Elberta. Requires 750 hours of chilling. Released by the New Jersey Station. Introduced in 1932. *Source History: 5 in 1988; 8 in 1992; 4 in 2000.* **Sources: Bo5, Ho5, So5, Wh4.**

White Heath (White Heath Cling) - Medium to large, creamy white, clingstone-fruit with red blush. Juicy, melting, white flesh with rich, unique flavor. Great for canning. Tree is self-fruitful, hardy, disease resistant and vigorous. Ripens in late August or September, depending on location. Requires 500-600 hours of chilling. *Source History: 4 in 1988; 4 in 1992; 3 in 2000.* **Sources: Bay, STR, WI4.**

White Lady - Medium-large, red skinned fruit. Firm, white flesh. Freestone. Good storage quality. Self-fertile. Ripens during July. Highly recommended for commercial use. Requires 850-950 hours of chilling. Developed by Zaiger Genetics, Modesto, California. U.S. Plant Patent No. 5821. *Source History: 4 in 1992; 6 in 2000.* **Sources: Ad2, Bay, Hi9, ORA, St4, WI4.**

Wild Rose - *Source History: 2 in 1992; 1 in 2000.* **Sources: Bo5, Bo5, Ho5, Wor.**

Winblo - Freestone with yellow flesh. Ripens 15 days before Elberta. Requires 850 hours of chilling. Cold hardy. *Source History: 2 in 1988; 3 in 1992; 3 in 2000.* **Sources: Cum, Ho5, Nrs.**

Wisconsin Balmer - Large, golden, freestone fruit with an unusually small pit. Rich sweet flavor. Exceptional quality. Excellent for canning and fresh eating. Ripens in September. Hardy in Zones 4-9, much farther north than most. Discovered as a chance seedling in Wisconsin. *Source History: 1 in 1988; 1 in 2000.* **Sources: Fi1.**

Wiser - Clingstone. *Source History: 1 in 1988; 2 in 1992; 1 in 2000.* **Sources: WI4.**

Yellow Yunan - *Source History: 1 in 1992; 1 in 2000.* **Sources: Nrs.**

Yosemite - Genetic dwarf tree. U.S. Plant Patent No. 4075. *Source History: 1 in 1988; 1 in 1992; 1 in 2000.* **Sources: STR.**

Yukon King (Autumn Snow Cultivar) - Very large size fruit. White skin with 80% red blush. Extra firm flesh. Freestone. Ripens from mid to late August. Requires 750-850 hours of chilling. Trademarked. U.S. Plant Patent No. 9872. *Source History: 1 in 2000.* **Sources: WI4.**

Zee Diamond - Large, firm clingstone fruit with 90% red over yellow skin color. Productive, vigorous tree. Ripens in late May with Spring Lady. Requires 850-950 hours of chilling. U.S. Plant Patent No. 9673. *Source History: 1 in 2000.* **Sources: WI4.**

Zee Lady - Large, round fruit. Very firm, freestone flesh. Excellent flavor. Potentially good freezer variety. Ripens mid-August. Requires 900-1,000 hours of chilling. U.S. Plant Patent No. 5832. *Source History: 1 in 1992; 1 in 2000.* **Sources: WI4.**

Peach / Flowering

Prunus spp.

Bonfire - Genetic dwarf tree. Showy double pink flowers. Red foliage. *Source History: 1 in 2000.* **Sources: Cu4.**

Crimson Cascade - Ornamental tree with weeping form. Double red flowers. Dark maroon spring foliage fades to green in summer. Small fruit. *Source History: 1 in 2000.* **Sources: GR26.**

Desert Peach - *Prunus andersonii.* Medium large, spiny, heavily branched shrub is covered with pale to deep rose flowers in late spring. Bears round, .5" fruits. Hardy to Zone 5. Wild species native to eastern California and western Nevada. *Source History: 1 in 2000.* **Sources: Ca12, Fo2, Las.**

Helen Borchers - Large, double pink flowers. Blooms late. *Source History: 4 in 2000.* **Sources: CO5, ORA, STR, WI4.**

Late Pink - *Source History: 1 in 2000.* **Sources: ORA.**

Peppermint - Showy variegated flowers are red, pink and white striped. Blooms midseason. Tree grows to 20'. *Source History: 3 in 2000.* **Sources: Bay, GI3, WI4.**

Pink Flowering - *Source History: 2 in 2000.* **Sources: Bo5, GI3.**

Pink, Early - Large double, bright pink flowers. Tree grows to 20'. *Source History: 5 in 2000.* **Sources: Bay, CO5, On4, ORA, WI4.**

Prunus persica - Deep purple-red blooms. Hardy to Zone 5. *Source History: 1 in 2000.* **Sources: Fo2.**

Red Flowering - *Source History: 4 in 2000.* **Sources: Bo5, GI3, MI5, STR.**

Red, Double - *Prunus persica.* Beautiful ornamental tree grows 15-18'. Blooms in early spring. Prune after it blooms to encourage strong blooming the following year. Hardy in Zones 5-8. *Source History: 1 in 2000.* **Sources: Mel.**

Red, Early - Bright purple-red flowers. Blooms late. Small, sweet, light green fruit. *Source History: 5 in 2000.* **Sources: Bay, CO5, On4, ORA, WI4.**

Red, Late - Large double red flowers. Blooms late. Tree grows to 20'. *Source History: 4 in 2000.* **Sources: Bay, CO5, ORA, WI4.**

Variegated - Pink and white striped, double blooms. *Source History: 2 in 2000.* **Sources: CO5, ORA.**

White Flowering - *Source History: 2 in 2000.* **Sources: GI3, MI5.**

White Icicle - Large double flowers. *Source History: 2 in 2000.* **Sources: CO5, STR.**

White, Double - Large, double, snow-white flowers. Grows to 20' tall. *Source History: 2 in 2000.* **Sources: Bay, CO5, ORA, WI4.**

Pear

Pyrus communis

Abbe Fetel (Abate Fetel) - Elongated Bosc-shaped fruit. Yellow skin with pink cheek in sun exposed areas. Occasional russeting around the stem end. Excellent flavor and quality. Pollinate with Bartlett. Ripens with Anjou. Originated in Italy. *Source History: 1 in 1988; 3 in 1992; 3 in 2000.* **Sources: Co2, Nrs, So5.**

Amire Joannet - Small fruit is waxy, deep yellow washed with pale rose when mature. Semifine, tender, juicy, white flesh is sugary with a musty perfume. Large tree that requires cross-pollination. Ripens about June 24. Originated in France in 1660. *Source History: 1 in 1988; 1 in 1992; 1 in 2000.* **Sources: Son.**

Anderson - *Source History: 1 in 2000.* **Sources: Er2.**

Aniversarea - *Source History: 1 in 2000.* **Sources: Ed5.**

Anjou (Beurre d'Anjou) - Favorite European winter eating pear a century ago. Large, conical, short-necked fruit; remains light green when ripe with slight brown russeting. Mild, fine textured, melting, white flesh with a delicate aroma. Develops best quality after two months in cold storage; keeps until late spring. Large tree is vigorous, hardy, very productive and an early bearer. Requires a pollinator; plant with Bosc or Bartlett. Good pollinator for Bartlett. Moderately resistant to fire blight; more cold tolerant than Bartlett. Ripens in late September. Requires 800 hours of chilling. Hardy to Zone 5. Originated in France prior to 1800. *Source History: 25 in 1988; 33 in 1992; 29 in 2000.* **Sources: Ad2, Bay, Bea, Bo5, BR10, Co2, CO5, COL, Ea3, Fo2, Hi9, Jo3, JOY, Leu, ME3, Mi1, MI5, Nrs, ORA, Pe2, Sc6, So5, Son, St4, STR, Va2, Wh4, WI4, Wor.**

Anjou, Columbia Red (Euwer Cultivar) - D'Anjou parentage. Medium size fruit with exceptional internal quality. Good storage life. Originally discovered as a mutation in the Eugene Euwer Orchard in Hood River, Oregon. U.S. Plant Patent No. 6194. *Source History: 1 in 2000.* **Sources: BR10, Va2, WI12.**

Anjou, Red (Gebhard Strain) - Sport of Anjou with same shape, texture, flavor and flesh coloring, but with a deep red surface color. Red deepens as fruit is re-moved from storage for ripening. Sweet, mild flavor reaches peak two weeks after picking. Keeps well in storage for up to eight months. Highly ornamental tree with reddish tint to bark, leaves and leaf veins. Not as vigorous as regular Anjou; grows more slowly because of red tinted leaves. Pollinate with Bartlett, Max Red Bartlett, Comice, Seckel or Bosc. Take care to control all mildew and pear psylla problems, especially the first year. Ripens in September. Hardy. *Source History: 10 in 1988; 11 in 1992; 3 in 2000.* **Sources: Co2, Gur, Mi1.**

Apple Pear, Carne's - Good eating and cooking pear. Sweet crunchy flesh is free of grit cells. *Source History: 1 in 2000.* **Sources: Ju2.**

Araganche - Round yellow fruit. Ripens mid-July. Originated in Yugoslavia. *Source History: 1 in 2000.* **Sources: Rai.**

Atlantic Queen - Immense, yellow-green fruit up to 1.5 lbs. Fine, firm, melting, very juicy, sweet flesh. Distinctive, delicious aroma. Prolific bearer. No trace of fire blight. Has thrived under the most adverse conditions: salt water, poor soil and intense summer heat. Ripens in September. Old French pear discovered in a New York garden close to the seashore. Imported with other varieties 30 years ago. *Source History: 1 in 1988; 1 in 1992; 1 in 2000.* **Sources: Leu.**

Aurora - Marguerite Marillat x Bartlett. Large fruit is bright yellow, lightly over-laid with russet and frequently slightly blushed; regular pear shape. Smooth, melt-ing, juicy flesh with sweet, aromatic flavor. High quality dessert pear. Keeps well in cold storage until December. Tree is vigorous and spreading, but not resistant to fire blight. Ripens just before Bartlett. Developed at the New York Agricultural Experiment Station in Geneva. Introduced in 1964. *Source History: 3 in 1988; 4 in 1992; 3 in 2000.* **Sources: Cu4, Nrs, So5.**

Ayers (Ayer's Sugar Pear, Ours Ayers) - Small to medium size, high quality, yel-low fruit with a red blush. Sweet flesh is subacid and almost free of grit cells. Ex-cellent fresh eating quality. Pollinator required. Resistant to fire blight. One of the highest quality pears that can be grown in the South. Ripens in mid-August. Hardy in Zones 6-9. *Source History: 6 in 1988; 7 in 1992; 10 in 2000.* **Sources: Bar, Cla, Cum, GI3, Ho5, MI5, Tex, WA8, Wel, Wom.**

Baldwin - Medium to large, oblong, semihard fruit. Light green skin lightly overlaid with russet. Good fresh or processed. Moderately resistant to fire blight and leaf spot. Good variety for the Deep South. Ripens in mid-October. Requires 150 or less hours of chilling. Hardy in Zones 8-9. *Source History: 3 in 1988; 6 in 1992; 6 in 2000.* **Sources: Iso, Ju2, RA4, SIM, Ty2, WA8.**

Bantam - *Source History: 1 in 1992; 1 in 2000.* **Sources: Nrs.**

Barland - Perry pear used for cider. *Source History: 1 in 2000.* **Sources: Cid.**

Barnet - Perry pear used for cider. *Source History: 1 in 2000.* **Sources: Cid.**

Bartlett (Williams Bartlett, Williams Bon Cretien) - Standard for pears; 75% of all U.S. and Canadian production. Large, golden yellow fruit blushed with brownish red; classic shape. Smooth, juicy, white flesh; pleasant touch of tartness. Good for fresh eating, canning or preserves. Ripen off the tree for a few weeks to develop famous musky flavor. Keeps for three months. Medium size, compact, upright tree ideal for dense plantings; vigorous, highly productive, long-lived and bears early. Self-fruitful in the arid West; needs pollination elsewhere. Susceptible to fire blight. Ripens from mid-August to mid-September. 800 hours of chilling. Hardy in Zones 5-7. Introduced from England in 1797. *Source History: 59 in 1988; 79 in 1992; 64 in 2000.* **Sources: Ad2, Amb, Bar, Bas, Bay, BO10, Bo5, BR10, Bu1, Co2, CO5, COL, Cu4, Cum, Ea3, Fed, Fi1, FO10, Fo2, Fo4, GI3, GR26, Gr4, Hi9, Ho5, Iso, Jo3, JOY, Jun, LA4, Leu, Mc3, ME3, Mel, Mi1, MI10, MI5, Na4, Nrs, ORA, Pe2, Pi2, Po2, Sav, Sc2, Sc6, SH8, Si3, SIM, So5, Son, St4, STR, Tex, TU5, Va2, Wa16, WA8, Wel, Wh4, WI12, WI4, Wor.**

Bartlett, Giant - Golden yellow skin with a rosy pink blush. Ripens in August. Hardy in Zones 4-8. *Source History: 1 in 1988; 1 in 2000.* **Sources: Gur.**

Bartlett, Max Red - Bud sport of Bartlett with solid red skin. As the underlying green skin turns yellow, the fruit develops a bright red cast. Firm, white flesh is sweeter than the regular Bartlett; 10% fructose. Excellent dessert qualities. Tree is a vigorous grower that bears young and abundantly, usually three years after planting. Older trees will need apple tree thinning to let in light for coloring. Pollinate with Bosc, Anjou or Winter Nellis. Slightly more fire blight resistant than Bartlett. Ripens in August or September depending on location. Requires 800 hours of chilling. Winter hardy to -20 degrees F. Originated in Europe. *Source History: 6 in 1988; 6 in 1992; 4 in 2000.* **Sources: CO5, Mi1, MI5, ORA.**

Bartlett, Nye Russet - Sport of Bartlett. Attractive russet with sweeter, more spicy flavor than Bartlett. Very good dessert quality. Originated in Oregon, 1937. *Source History: 2 in 1992; 1 in 2000.* **Sources: Son.**

Bartlett, Red Sensation - Red skinned Bartlett strain. Similar to Max Red Bartlett, but reports indicate that it has more color stability. Fruit shape, quality and ripening features similar to Bartlett. Tender, juicy, white flesh is dessert quality. Good fresh, dried or canned. Fair to good keeper. Fruit ripens without cold storage, but off the tree. Tree is somewhat slower growing. Self-fruitful or pollinate with Anjou. Poor fire blight resistance. Requires 700 hours of chilling. Winter hardy to -20 degrees F. Originated in Australia. *Source History: 19 in 1988; 27 in 1992; 17 in 2000.* **Sources: Ad2, Bay, Bea, Bo5, Co2, CO5, COL, Cu4, Fi1, Hi9, Mel, Nrs, Son, STR, Va2, WI4, Wor.**

Bartlett, Russett - Unknown origin. Fruit tuns a smooth, golden yellow-russet color as it matures. Buttery smooth, juicy flesh with excellent flavor. Excellent for fresh eating. Medium size tree comes into bearing later than some. Ripens late summer, early fall. *Source History: 1 in 1992; 1 in 2000.* **Sources: Fed.**

Bartlett, Winter - Resembles Bartlett in appearance and flavor, but is firmer and has coarser flesh. Exceptional quality when canned; best pear for preserves. Grows vigorously into a spreading, loose, unusually large tree. Ripens later than Bartlett. *Source History: 2 in 1988; 3 in 1992; 1 in 2000.* **Sources: Gr4.**

Beirschmitt - Originated as a seedling of Bartlett in Iowa. Medium large, yellow fruit; dries well. Excellent flavor with mild, tender, very sweet, grit-free flesh. Tender, easily bruised skin. Because it is not overly juicy, the flesh does not turn brown when cut, making a fine salad pear. Can be picked when ripe in September or harvested in late August for indoor ripening. Spreading, moderately vigorous tree is a dependable, heavy producer. Slightly more resistant to fire blight than Bartlett. Highly recommended by the late NAFEX member Robert Kurle. Hardy to Zone 4. *Source History: 3 in 1988; 3 in 1992; 1 in 2000.* **Sources: Gr4.**

Bell - Very hard fruit is stored until soft. Old-time favorite for canning, preserving and fresh eating. *Source History: 1 in 1992; 1 in 2000.* **Sources: La3.**

Bella di Guigno - Red blushed 3" fruit with excellent flavor. Ripens late June, early July. Originated in Italy. *Source History: 1 in 1992; 1 in 2000.* **Sources: Rai.**

Belle Angevine (Pound Belle Angevine, Uvedales St. Germain) - Very old variety. Enormously large cooking pear, not infrequently three pounds in weight. Ripens very late. *Source History: 1 in 1988; 1 in 1992; 1 in 2000.* **Sources: So5.**

Belle Lucrative - Small, greenish yellow fruit with small russet dots. Flesh and flavor are nearly perfect. Precocious tree is disease resistant with above average hardiness. Particularly well suited for the home orchard. Ripens in October. Flemish origin from the late 1800s. *Source History: 1 in 1988; 2 in 1992; 1 in 2000.* **Sources: Leu.**

Belle Picard - Very large winter pear with orange-red skin that is speckled on the sunny side. Melting, sugary, white flesh with pleasant flavor. Must be carefully ripened off the tree. Cooks to beautiful light pink; good for dessert. French pear that was introduced in 1850. *Source History: 1 in 1988; 1 in 1992; 1 in 2000.* **Sources: So5.**

Bennett - Strain of Clapp's Favorite. Medium to large, very smooth skinned, yellowish green fruit with red blush. Buttery flesh has full, sweet flavor. Ripens well on the tree. Pick early for storage to prevent breakdown. Tree is moderately productive and very reliable. Pollinate with another pear. Highly scab resistant. Ripens in late August. Zones 5-8. Developed in Whatcom County. *Source History: 3 in 1988; 3 in 1992; 4 in 2000.* **Sources: Bu7, Clo, Nrs, Rai.**

Bere Obtjabra - *Source History: 1 in 2000.* **Sources: Ed5.**

Beurre Gris - One of the oldest known pears; described by Oliver de Serres in 1608. Greenish yellow fruit varying to gold, grey and red. Buttery, juicy flesh is well flavored. *Source History: 1 in 1988; 1 in 1992; 1 in 2000.* **Sources: So5.**

Beurre Hardy (French Butter Pear) - Medium to large fruit with green-yellow russet. Sweet, juicy flesh with a touch of astringency. Hardy, productive tree. Moderate disease resistance. Hardy to Zone 4. Originated in France around 1820. *Source History: 3 in 1992; 3 in 2000.* **Sources: Ed5, Nrs, Son.**

Beurre Superfin - Round, conical, medium-sized green pear with flesh tapering to the short stout stem. Sweet, melting, juicy, perfumed flesh. Can be brought to ripeness in about 30 days. Ripens in late September. Originated near Angers, France in the middle of the 19th century. *Source History: 1 in 1988; 2 in 1992; 2 in 2000.* **Sources: Fed, So5.**

Blakeney Red - Perry pear used for cider. *Source History: 1 in 2000.* **Sources: Cid.**

Bonne d'Ezee - *Source History: 1 in 1992; 1 in 2000.* **Sources: Nrs.**

Bordeaux - Medium to large, yellow fruit. Sweet, juicy flesh. Similar to Duchess. *Source History: 1 in 2000.* **Sources: Leu.**

Bosc (Beurre Bosc, Fall Russet) - Medium to large, dark yellow fruit with brownish russeted skin and long, gourd-shaped neck. Tender, aromatic, juicy, smooth textured, white flesh. Rich, slightly acid flavor. Fine for eating, baking and drying. Keeps six months; ripens better at room temperature than in cold storage. Ready to eat when russet-bronze. Large, upright, slow growing, late blooming tree; very productive and reliable. Somewhat difficult to train because of leggy growth. Requires a pollinator. Susceptible to fire blight in warm, moist climates. Ripens in early to mid-October; 800-900 hours of chilling. Hardy in Zones 5-8. Introduced from Belgium in 1807. *Source History: 30 in 1988; 37 in 1992; 35 in 2000.* **Sources: Ad2, Amb, Bay, BO10, Bo5, Bu7, Clo, Co2, CO5, Cu4, Ea3, Fed, Fo2, Gr4, Hi9, JOY, Leu, ME3, Mel, Mi1, Mo19, Nrs, ORA, Pe2, Rai, SH8, Si3, So5, Son, St4, STR, Wh4, WI12, WI4, Wor.**

Bosc, Bronze Beauty (Wimmers Cultivar) - Sport of Beurre Bosc with solid, heavy russet over the entire fruit that takes on a rich bronze color when ripe. Medium to large size fruit with typical Bosc shape. Flesh is yellow-white, very slightly granular, and juicy with a sweet flavor when properly ripened at room temperature. Large tree is vigorous with a spreading habit. U.S. Plant Patent No. 7485. *Source History: 3 in 1992; 1 in 2000.* **Sources: Co2.**

Bosc, Golden Russet (Fukui Cultivar) - Oblong-shaped fruit changes from green to yellow, maturing to a golden color with a fine, net-like russet. Excellent dessert quality. Moderately vigorous tree with an upright growth habit. Partially self-fertile. U.S. Plant Patent No. 5243. *Source History: 2 in 2000.* **Sources: BR10, WI12.**

Bosc, Noble Russet - Smooth russet skin. Fruit size and shape resembles standard Bosc. Begins to russet the first of July; almost solid russet by harvest time. Trademarked. *Source History: 3 in 2000.* **Sources: Co2, COL, Hi9.**

Brandy - Small fruit with some russet and attractive red blush. Makes a medium acid, low tannin pear cider. *Source History: 2 in 2000.* **Sources: Cid, Son.**

Burford Pear - Fine home orchard variety. Annual bearer. Originated in the Blue Ridge Mountains and introduced to the public by Tom Burford. *Source History: 1 in 2000.* **Sources: Or9.**

Butirra Precoce Morettini - Bartlett x Coscia. Medium size, greenish yellow fruit blushed with red. Pyriform, but not as uniform as Bartlett. Melting, juicy, sweet, white flesh has excellent flavor. Stores longer than Bartlett. One of the best early pears. Vigorous tree is a regular, heavy cropper. Ripens 19-21 days before Bartlett. Fruit drops readily as it approaches maturity. Originated in Italy. *Source History: 3 in 1988; 5 in 1992; 5 in 2000.* **Sources: Ea3, Ed5, Nrs, Rai, Son.**

Butirra Rosata Morettini - *Source History: 1 in 1992; 1 in 2000.* **Sources: Nrs.**

Butt (Norton Butt) - Perry pear. *Source History: 1 in 2000.* **Sources: Cid.**

California - Max Red Bartlett x Comice. Yellowish green with red blush. Peak quality when ripened after 2-3 months in cold storage. Self-fruitful commercial variety for the Fresno-Bakersfield area in California. Matures in August. Requires

700 hours of chilling. U.S. Plant Patent No. 3599. *Source History: 1 in 1988; 3 in 1992; 2 in 2000.* **Sources: Bay, WI4.**

Capitol - *Source History: 1 in 1992; 1 in 2000.* **Sources: Nrs.**

Carrick - One of the best for canning and preserving. Bears young and is blight resistant. *Source History: 1 in 1988; 1 in 1992; 1 in 2000.* **Sources: La3.**

Cascade - Max Red Bartlett x Comice. Very large, bright red fruit. Same texture, flavor and juiciness as Comice; tartness of Bartlett. Stores well. Slight tendency to alternate bearing. Developed at Medford Agricultural Experiment Station in Oregon. U.S. Plant Patent No. 6245. *Source History: 1 in 1988; 1 in 1992; 2 in 2000.* **Sources: Va2, WI12.**

Chapin - Seedling of Seckel, but larger. Flesh is juicy, melting and smooth with sweet, aromatic flavor. Highest quality. Regularly productive. Ripens in mid-August. Developed at the New York State Agricultural Experiment Station. *Source History: 1 in 1988; 2 in 1992; 1 in 2000.* **Sources: So5.**

Clairgeau (Beurre Clairgeau) - Large, smooth fruit is a rich orangish yellow at maturity. Granular flesh is firm at first, but becoming tender and melting at maturity. Excellent dessert quality. Very good for cooking. Does not keep as long as other winter varieties. Tree is very healthy and productive. Ripens in October. Originated in France. *Source History: 2 in 1988; 2 in 1992; 3 in 2000.* **Sources: Gr4, Leu, Son.**

Clapp's Favorite - Very large, elongated, long necked, lemon-yellow fruit with dull red cheek and russet specks. White flesh is high quality, fine grained, very sweet and highly flavored. Dessert and fresh eating pear that is also good for canning. Not a keeper. Should be picked when full size but still green; do not leave on the tree. Fruit will break down at the core if picked too late. Strong, sturdy, very hardy, vigorous tree. Very susceptible to fire blight. Ripens early August; 7-14 days before Bartlett. Hardy to Zone 4. *Source History: 20 in 1988; 23 in 1992; 19 in 2000.* **Sources: Ad2, Amb, Bea, Bo5, Ed5, Fed, Fi1, Hi9, Jun, Leu, Mel, Mi1, Pi2, Sc6, SH8, So5, TU5, Wa16, Wor.**

Clapp's Favorite, Red (Red Clapp, Kalle) - Yellow fruit with bright red cheek. Excellent variety to ship before Bartlett. Productive, winter hardy tree is susceptible to fire blight. Ripens about ten days before Bartlett; early September. Zone 5. *Source History: 3 in 1988; 8 in 1992; 6 in 2000.* **Sources: Bea, BR10, COL, ME3, Nrs, Son.**

Clara-Frijs (Comptesse Clara Frijs) - Nineteenth century German pear. Medium-large, Bartlett-type fruit. Exceptional dessert quality. Does not store well. Hardy tree; annual bearer. Fungus resistant. Zone 4. Popular pear of good reputation in Denmark and spread further throughout western Europe and Nova Scotia. *Source History: 2 in 1992; 1 in 2000.* **Sources: Fed.**

Clark - Hard fruit about the size of Bartlett. Good for culinary use. Fire blight and scab resistant. Grafts well and is a vigorous grower. Not a good keeper. Ripens all at once in early September. Hardy to -50 degrees F. *Source History: 1 in 1988; 1 in 1992; 1 in 2000.* **Sources: Stl.**

Colette (Everbearing Colette) - Rich, waxy, yellow skin with pink cheeks. Sweet, juicy, fine, firm, white flesh is smooth textured and entirely free of grit. Rich, aromatic, spicy flavor. Short, broad, shapely tree that is very hardy. Everbearing; keeps blooming and setting fruit all summer. Bartlett size. Hardy in Zones 4-8. *Source History: 3 in 1988; 4 in 1992; 5 in 2000.* **Sources: Fi1, Mi1, Mo19, Ro3, Wh4.**

Comice (Doyenne du Comice) - Large, broad based, narrow necked, greenish yellow fruit with red blush and light russet. Rich, juicy, firm, sweet, finely textured flesh. Premium dessert pear; too delicate for cooking. Needs a month of cool storage for good ripening. Large, very vigorous tree comes into bearing slowly; erratic cropper. Requires pollination from Sugar, Beurre d'Anjou, Starking Delicious, Moonglow or Bartlett. Good fire blight resistance. Primarily grown in Oregon and California where it excels. Matures one month after Bartlett. Requires 600 hours of chilling. Outstanding winter pear that originated in Angers, France. Zone 5. *Source History: 25 in 1988; 28 in 1992; 27 in 2000.* **Sources: Bay, BR10, Bu7, Ch9, Clo, Co2, CO5, COL, Ea3, Ed5, Gr4, JOY, Leu, ME3, MI5, Mo19, Nrs, ORA, Pe2, Rai, Si3, So5, Son, St4, STR, Va2, WI4.**

Comice, Red (Scarlet Comice) - Red sport of Doyenne du Comice. Similar in shape, flesh, texture and flavor. Deep red surface color with broad stripes. Tree is not as vigorous as regular Comice; attractive reddish tinge to the foliage in spring and autumn. Ripens in early October. Discovered in Medford, Oregon. *Source History: 3 in 1988; 2 in 1992; 2 in 2000.* **Sources: Cu4, Nrs.**

Comice, Taylor's Gold - Natural mutation of Doyenne du Comice. Russeted skin. Yellow-white flesh. Originated in New Zealand. U.S. Plant Patent No. 8308. *Source History: 1 in 2000.* **Sources: WI12.**

Concorde - Conference x Comice. Large green fruit with prominent lenticels. Green skin is flushed with pink. Tender, juicy flesh. Very good flavor and aroma. Bears early. U.S. Plant Patent No. 9192. *Source History: 6 in 2000.* **Sources: BR10, Co2, COL, Er2, Va2, WI12.**

Conference - Medium to large, slightly long, gourd-shaped fruit. Smooth, green skin tinted with russet. Pale yellow flesh with slight pink tinge; sweet, melting and very juicy. Medium size tree requires cross-pollination. Fruit keeps until January. Poor fire blight resistance. Ripens late September. Originated in England in 1894. *Source History: 1 in 1988; 3 in 1992; 7 in 2000.* **Sources: Clo, Ed5, Er2, Mo19, Nrs, Rai, Son.**

Dabney - *Source History: 1 in 1992; 1 in 2000.* **Sources: Nrs.**

Dana Hovey (Winter Seckel Dana Hovey) - Small greenish yellow fruit covered with a thin russet, ripening to golden. Delicious, high quality dessert pear with juicy, sweet, rich flesh. Similar to Seckel, but ripens later with larger, more uniform fruit; less productive. Good keeper. Large tree requires cross pollination. Poor fire blight resistance. Developed from Winter Seckel, a European pear, that was raised by Francis Dana, a Massachusetts breeder. Introduced in 1854. *Source History: 2 in 1988; 3 in 1992; 3 in 2000.* **Sources: Ed5, So5, Son.**

David - Thin skinned fruit. Flesh holds firmness. Good for cooking and processing. Fire blight resistant. Ripens in September. Hardy to -50 degrees F. *Source History: 1 in 1988; 1 in 1992; 2 in 2000.* **Sources: Stl, Va5.**

Dawn - *Source History: 1 in 1988; 1 in 1992; 1 in 2000.* **Sources: Nrs.**

Delicious, Starking (Cook Cultivar) - Extra large, golden fruit with creamy white flesh. Good fresh, cooked, or canned; keeps well refrigerated. Bartlett quality. Pick when yellowish green and ripen at 70-75 degrees F. for 5-10 days for peak flavor. Strong pollinator. Resistant to fire blight. Ripens in early September. Hardy in Zones 5-8. Trademarked. *Source History: 1 in 1988; 2 in 1992; 2 in 2000.* **Sources: Nrs, St4.**

Des Urbanistes - Roundish, pyriform, pale yellow, lightly russeted fruit. Fine grained, melting, buttery, white flesh with delicious flavor. Ripens late. Originated in the gardens of the religious order of Urbanistes in Belgium after the order was suppressed. New seedlings sprung up from the uncultivated land, one of which attracted the attention of a Belgian pomologist. First grown in the U.S. in Massachusetts in the early part of the 19th century. Introduced in 1783. *Source History: 1 in 1988; 1 in 1992; 1 in 2000.* **Sources: So5.**

Devoe - *Source History: 1 in 1992; 1 in 2000.* **Sources: Nrs.**

Docteur Jules Guyot - Richer flavor than Bartlett; also colors more and has more delicate flavor and aroma. Must be picked green and ripened indoors to avoid core rot. Originated in France in 1883. *Source History: 2 in 1992; 2 in 2000.* **Sources: Nrs, Son.**

Douglas - Golden yellow fruit with sweet, juicy, white flesh. Best when used fresh. Often produces one year after planting. Blight proof and disease resistant. Hardy in Zones 4-8. *Source History: 2 in 1988; 3 in 1992; 1 in 2000.* **Sources: Gur.**

Doyenne Gris - Smaller version of Bosc with perfectly smooth, unblemished, golden brown, russet skin. Melting, juicy, buttery flesh with sweet, spicy flavor. Ripens in late September. Ready to eat within a few weeks, but will keep longer. Originated in the Chartreux Monastery in Paris. Introduced in 1750. *Source History: 1 in 1988; 1 in 1992; 1 in 2000.* **Sources: So5.**

Duchess - High yields of very large, greenish yellow russet fruit with pink cheek. Crisp, firm flesh; excellent quality and fine flavor. Delicious for eating fresh or canning. Tree is self-fruitful and bears two to three years after planting. Makes a good pollinator for Bartlett. Ripens in early October. Hardy in Zones 5-9. Originated in France. *Source History: 7 in 1988; 6 in 1992; 3 in 2000.* **Sources: Fil, Gur, SH8.**

Duchess Bronzee - Sport of the famous Duchess d'Angouleme, an old French variety with fruits from large to enormous size and melting, juicy, sweet flesh of very high quality. Found in a garden in Dijon, France, 1870. *Source History: 1 in 1988; 2 in 1992; 2 in 2000.* **Sources: So5, Son.**

Duchess d'Angouleme - Enormous fruit with buttery, melting flesh and rich delicious flavor. Large tree bears regularly and has good fire blight resistance. Ripens in late October or early November depending on location. Originated in France in 1808. *Source History: 2 in 1988; 3 in 1992; 4 in 2000.* **Sources: Ed5, Leu, Nrs, Son.**

Duchess de Brissac - *Source History: 1 in 1992; 1 in 2000.* **Sources: Nrs.**

Dumont (Beurre Dumont) - Oblong, conical, green and brown with white fruit. Firm, juicy, smooth, very fine grained, sweet flesh with rich, perfumed flavor. Stores until the end of December. Tree is productive, but old trees tend to bear in alternate years. Moderately susceptible to fire blight. Ripens late. Belgian pear that is still regarded in the Geneva Station as one of the best winter pears. *Source History: 2 in 1988; 2 in 1992; 1 in 2000.* **Sources: So5.**

El Dorado - Medium to large fruit with yellow-green skin even when ripe. Sweet, smooth, melting texture and flavor. Very good to excellent quality. Good canning pear. Very long storage life; will keep until January or February. Requires a pollinator. Ripens from mid to late October. Originated in El Dorado County, California. *Source History: 2 in 1988; 1 in 1992; 2 in 2000.* **Sources: La3, Nrs.**

Fan-Stil - Bell-shaped, yellow fruit with slight red blush. Crisp, juicy, white flesh. Consistent bearer. Self-fruitful. Highly resistant to blight. Ripens in August. Requires 150-500 hours of chilling. Trademarked. *Source History: 2 in 1988; 2 in 1992; 2 in 2000.* **Sources: Bay, CO5.**

Farmingdale - *Source History: 1 in 1992; 1 in 2000.* **Sources: Nrs.**

Fertility - *Source History: 1 in 1992; 2 in 2000.* **Sources: Ch9, Nrs.**

Flemish Beauty - Originally known as Fondante de Boise, "Sweetmeat of the Woods." Large, roundish pear, uniform in size and shape. Thick, clear yellow skin with a dotted and marbled red blush. Firm, yellowish white flesh, becoming melting and tender; sweet and aromatic with slightly musky flavor. Favorite for slicing and drying because of its round shape. Hardy, strong growing, vigorous, productive tree; early and abundant bearer. Requires cross-pollination; good pollinator. Susceptible to fire blight. Ripens from mid-September to early October depending on location. Hardy to -45 degrees F. Leading commercial variety at one time. Originated in Belgium around 1830. *Source History: 8 in 1988; 14 in 1992; 8 in 2000.* **Sources: Cu4, Ed5, Er2, Jun, So5, Son, Stl, Va2.**

Flordahome - Tender, thin, green skin. Juicy, fine textured, white flesh. Excellent for fresh eating or canning. Good producer. Ripens from mid to late July. Requires 150-300 or less hours of chilling. Grown extensively in Florida; hardy in Zones 8-10. *Source History: 5 in 1988; 9 in 1992; 8 in 2000.* **Sources: GI3, Ho5, ORA, Pa2, RA4, SIM, Ty2, WI4.**

Flordahope - Similar to Bartlett with extra fine canning quality. Holds white color for months. Ripens mid-July. *Source History: 1 in 1992; 1 in 2000.* **Sources: Ju2.**

Fondante d'Automne (Belle Lucrative) - Medium size fruit is round, conical and dull green-yellow. Sugary, buttery flesh with musky taste and perfume. Ripens in September or October. Ready to eat within a few weeks. Flemish pear brought to this country by Robert Manning of Salem, Massachusetts. Originated in Belgium around 1825. *Source History: 1 in 1988; 2 in 1992; 3 in 2000.* **Sources: Nrs, So5, Son.**

Forelle - Small to medium winter pear; considered a specialty fruit. The highly colored fruit turns a golden yellow with bright red blush and trout-like specklings. High quality flesh. Tree is quite susceptible to fire blight. Forelle is German for trout. Originated in Germany around 1800. *Source History: 3 in 1992; 4 in 2000.* **Sources: BR10, Ed5, Nrs, Son.**

Garber - Large, almost round fruit with firm flesh. Fine for canning, preserving or eating fresh. One of the best for pear cider or "perry." Tree is vigorous and reliable. Very hardy and blight resistant. Ripens in August or September. *Source History: 4 in 1988; 5 in 1992; 1 in 2000.* **Sources: Wel.**

Gelbmostler - Perry pear used for cider. *Source History: 1 in 2000.* **Sources: Cid.**

Giffard (Beurre Giffard) - Old French pear. Medium size, light green fruit turning pale yellow with pink blush. Crisp, tender, juicy flesh with delicious, refreshing flavor. Medium size, hardy tree requires cross-pollination. Poor keeper. Ripens in early August. Originated in France in 1825. *Source History: 2 in 1988; 2 in 1992; 4 in 2000.* **Sources: Ed5, Leu, So5, Son.**

Gin - Perry pear used for cider. *Source History: 1 in 2000.* **Sources: Cid.**

Glen's Giant - Large fruit holds on the tree until late in the season. Good fresh when fully ripe; makes fine preserves. Good for wildlife planting. *Source History: 1 in 2000.* **Sources: La3.**

Golden Boy - Good disease resistance. Perfect pear shape. Very sweet flesh. Ripens in August. Discovered at an old homesite in Wakulla County, Florida. *Source History: 1 in 1992; 1 in 2000.* **Sources: Ju2.**

Golden Russet, Japanese - *Source History: 1 in 2000.* **Sources: Ed5.**

Golden Spice - Fruit is good for eating fresh and for home processing. Not a keeper. Tree is a vigorous grower. Good pollinator. Ripens during October. Hardy to -50 degrees F. *Source History: 2 in 1992; 2 in 2000.* **Sources: Ed5, Stl.**

Gorham - Bartlett x Josephine de Malines. Large pear resembling Bartlett. Smooth, bright yellow fruit has slight russet around the stem. Flesh is fine, juicy and melting, with sweet flavor. Keeps in cold storage 1.5 months longer than Bartlett; ripens 14 days later. Tree requires heavier nitrogen fertilization than Bartlett and is slightly more resistant to fire blight. Developed at the New York State Agricultural Experiment Station. Introduced in 1923. *Source History: 2 in 1988; 4 in 1992; 4 in 2000.* **Sources: Bo5, Cu4, Nrs, So5.**

Gourmet - SD F15 x Ewart. Medium size fruit with green-yellow skin. Crisp, yellowish flesh like the Asian varieties. Sweet taste. Good dessert pear. Trees are moderately productive, upright, medium size and winter hardy. Ripens in September. Introduced by the South Dakota Agricultural Experiment Station at Brookings, 1988. *Source History: 3 in 1988; 6 in 1992; 3 in 2000.* **Sources: Ed5, Fed, SH8.**

Hardee - Medium to large fruit with excellent quality flesh. Hardy in most of Wisconsin. *Source History: 1 in 1992; 1 in 2000.* **Sources: Mc3.**

Hardy Wisconsin, Jung's - Medium size fruit with a small core. Thin, golden, russeted skin. Picked before the first frost; stores well under cool conditions. Softens for eating after a few days at room temperature. Can be used for canning, but best when eaten fresh. Cross-pollination from another variety recommended for best production. Very hardy; Zone 4. Discovered as a tree on a Wisconsin farm that Jung's purchased in the early 1940s. *Source History: 1 in 1988; 1 in 1992; 1 in 2000.* **Sources: Jun.**

Harrow Delight (HW 603) (Old Home x Early Sweet) x Bartlett. Medium size fruit with attractive red blush over yellow background. Flesh is high quality and very smooth with no grit cells. Similar to Bartlett, but slightly smaller and 14-28 days earlier. Hardy, productive tree shows impressive resistance to fire blight that ranks with Bartlett and Kieffer. Cross-fertile with Bartlett, Anjou, Moonglow or Starking Delicious. Ripens in mid-August. Hardy in Zones 5-7. Introduced in 1982 by Agriculture Canada Research Station in Harrow, Ontario. *Source History: 8 in 1988; 9 in 1992; 15 in 2000.* **Sources: Bu7, Ch9, Cla, Cu4, Ed5, Gr4, Hi9, Mo19, Nrs, Rai, Ro3, Sc6, St4, Wh4, WI4.**

Harrow Sweet - Fruit size compares to Bartlett when properly thinned. Yellow with red blush. Sweet, juicy flesh. Keeps well in cold storage for about 10 weeks. Medium size, hardy tree with good fire blight resistance. Trademarked. Plant patent applied for. *Source History: 1 in 2000.* **Sources: Hi9.**

Harvest Queen (HW 602) - Michigan 572 x Bartlett. Similar to Bartlett but hardier and matures a week earlier. Fruit has a shorter neck than Bartlett and is .5" smaller in diameter. Flesh and processing qualities are similar in every respect. Pollen-compatible with all common varieties except Bartlett. As productive and equal to Kieffer in fire blight resistance. Hardy to Zone 4. Introduced in 1982 by the Agriculture Canada Research Station in Harrow, Ontario. *Source History: 5 in 1988; 6 in 1992; 9 in 2000.* **Sources: Ch9, Cla, Cu4, Ed5, Gr4, Hi9, Hid, Nrs, Ro3.**

Hendre Huffcap - Perry pear used for cider. *Source History: 1 in 2000.* **Sources: Cid.**

Herman Last - Medium to large size fruit. Good for eating and cooking. Resistant to fire blight. Ripens on the tree in mid-September. Hardy to -50 degrees F. with occasional winter injury. *Source History: 1 in 1988; 1 in 2000.* **Sources: Stl.**

Highland - Bartlett x Doyenne de Comice. Large, fairly smooth, greenish yellow fruit covered with light russet. Melting, juicy, smooth textured flesh with rich, sweet flavor. Very high quality dessert pear. Develops better quality if stored about one month before ripening. Will keep in storage until January. Tree is moderately vigorous, productive and as susceptible to fire blight as Bartlett. Pollinate with any other pear. Ripens 28 days after Bartlett. Zone 5. Introduced in 1974 by the New York State Agricultural Experiment Station. *Source History: 6 in 1988; 7 in 1992; 8 in 2000.* **Sources: Bu7, Cu4, Hi9, ME3, Mo19, Nrs, Rai, So5.**

Honeysweet, Stark - Firm fruit with smooth, creamy flesh. Flavor is similar to Seckel. Use for fresh eating or canning. Vigorous tree is blight resistant. Self-pollinating, but for larger crops pollinate with Starking Delicious or Moonglow. Ripens in early September. Hardy in Zones 5-8. U.S. Plant Patent No. 4379. *Source History: 1 in 1988; 1 in 1992; 2 in 2000.* **Sources: Ro3, St4.**

Hood - Large size fruit with smooth, yellow-green skin. Buttery textured flesh with a few small stone cells. Sweet, mild flavor. Upright, spreading tree. High resistance to fire blight; moderate resistance to leaf spot. Ripens mid-July. Requires 100-200 hours of chilling. Hardy in Zones 6-9. *Source History: 4 in 1988; 10 in 1992; 10 in 2000.* **Sources: Bay, CO5, Cu4, GI3, Ju2, Pa2, RA4, SIM, Ty2, WI4.**

Hoskins - *Source History: 1 in 1992; 1 in 2000.* **Sources: Nrs.**

Hudar - Yellow pear with sweet, juicy flesh. Good size, about equal to Bartlett. Good for eating fresh. Ripens in late July. Hardy to -50 degrees F. with occasional winter injury. *Source History: 1 in 1988; 1 in 1992; 2 in 2000.* **Sources: Ed5, Stl.**

Hybrid Pear - *Pyrus x pyrifolia*. Oikos Seed Orchard has developed a new generation of pear hybrids that combine the best of fruit production and the best of disease and insect resistance. The gritty fruit is not suitable for human consumption but the wildlife eats it as soon as it hits the ground. Hardy to -35 degrees F. *Source History: 1 in 2000.* **Sources: Oik.**

Ilinka - Very hardy pear from the former Soviet Union being tested in the U.S. *Source History: 1 in 2000.* **Sources: Ed5.**

Johantorp - Pear from Sweden being tested in the northern U.S. *Source History: 1 in 2000.* **Sources: Ed5.**

John - *Pyrus communis x P. ussuriensis*. Yellow fruit with thin skin and mellow, juicy flesh. Fair eating quality; better if grown in the far north and eaten when perfectly ripe. Preserves very well. Very hardy tree. Fire blight resistant. *Source History: 2 in 1992; 2 in 2000.* **Sources: Stl, Va5.**

Jubilee - *Pyrus ussuriensis x P. communis*. Small to medium size fruit. Good for canning or fresh eating. Not a keeper. Ripens in September. Extremely hardy; down to -50 degrees F or colder. *Source History: 1 in 1992; 2 in 2000.* **Sources: Stl, Va5.**

Jules d'Airolles - *Source History: 1 in 1992; 1 in 2000.* **Sources: Nrs.**

June Sugar - Fruit has excellent eating quality. Tree blooms relatively late. Reported to have good blight resistance. Ripens early. Heirloom variety from Georgia. *Source History: 1 in 1988; 2 in 1992; 1 in 2000.* **Sources: Gr4.**

Kalebasa Plocka - Hardy cultivar from Poland being tested in the United States. *Source History: 1 in 2000.* **Sources: Ed5.**

Kalle (Kalle Red Clapps) - Red sport of Clapp's Favorite that is a natural semidwarf. Large reddish purple fruit with sweet flavor. Hangs like jewels from the tree.

Not a keeper. Ripens in late August. *Source History: 1 in 1988; 3 in 1992; 2 in 2000.* **Sources: Cu4, Va2.**

Karl's Favorite (Ewart Cultivar) - Yellow skin with slight russet. Tender, melting flesh. Exceptional flavor and quality. Shows moderate resistance to fire blight. Excellent pollinator for Bartlett. Ripens 10-20 days after Bartlett. Zones 4-7. Originated in Ohio. Introduced in 1928. *Source History: 1 in 1992; 1 in 2000.* **Sources: Jun.**

Kieffer (Kieffer Hybrid) - *Pyrus communis x P. pyrifolia.* Large, long, golden yellow fruit with a crimson blush. Crisp, juicy, coarse textured, white flesh with musky aroma. Excellent for canning and baking. Good variety for pear honey and preserves. Pick fruit while still hard and store in a cool place; reaches peak flavor when fruit gives slightly to the touch. Hardy, vigorous tree bears young; dependable crops. Self-fruitful. Practically immune to blight. Tolerates hot climates; grows well in all parts of the country. Extra hardy. Ripens from mid-September to mid-October. Requires 350 hours of chilling. Hardy in Zones 4-9. *Source History: 28 in 1988; 46 in 1992; 36 in 2000.* **Sources: Bar, Bas, Bay, Bu1, Ch9, Cla, CO5, Cum, Ed5, Fi1, FO10, Fo4, GI3, Ho5, Iso, Jo3, Lee, Leu, MI10, MI5, Mo5, Na4, Nrs, ORA, Po2, Sav, SIM, St4, STR, Tex, TU5, Ty2, WA8, Wel, WI4, Wom.**

Lacock 6 - *Source History: 1 in 1992; 1 in 2000.* **Sources: Nrs.**

Le Conte - *Pyrus communis x P. pyrifolia.* Attractive, bell-shaped, creamy yellow fruit with slight blush. Medium soft flesh. Vigorous, upright growing tree bears consistently. Fire blight resistant. Requires pollinator. Hardy in Zones 8-9. *Source History: 6 in 1988; 12 in 1992; 5 in 2000.* **Sources: GI3, SIM, Tex, Ty2, Wel.**

Lincoln - Big, golden fruits. Tree is exceptionally hardy and reliable. Ripens in September. Hardy in Zones 4-8. Good choice for northern growers. Originated as a seedling around 1835. *Source History: 1 in 1988; 2 in 1992; 3 in 2000.* **Sources: La3, Nrs, Wh4.**

Louise Bonne d'Avaranche (Louise Bonne de Jersey) - Long, red and yellow fruit with juicy flesh. Sweet vinous flavor. First quality. Strong tree with upright growth; very productive. Ripens in October. Originated in Avaranches, France, 1780. *Source History: 1 in 1988; 1 in 1992; 1 in 2000.* **Sources: Son.**

Luscious - SDE31 x Ewart. Medium size, bright yellow fruit with a red blush. Juicy, pleasant, sweet flavor is similar to but more intense than Bartlett. Flesh is melting but firm; remains firm to the core when ripe. Excellent dessert pear; not well suited for canning. Vigorous, very hardy, upright to spreading tree. Glossy, green foliage turns red in the fall. Requires a pollinator such as Patten or Parker. Resistant but not immune to fire blight. Ripens in late September. Hardy into Zone 4. Developed at South Dakota State University especially for the northern Great Plains. Introduced in 1967. *Source History: 10 in 1988; 19 in 1992; 13 in 2000.* **Sources: Bea, Ed5, Fa1, Fed, Hi9, Mc3, MI5, Nrs, SH8, Stl, Va5, Wa16, ZEL.**

Madeleine - *Source History: 1 in 1992; 1 in 2000.* **Sources: So5.**

Magness - Seckel x Comice. Medium size, short, oval, greenish yellow fruit with dark spots and light russet. Tough skin reduces insect damage and contributes to long storage life. Soft, juicy flesh is almost free of grit cells. Sweet flavor and high quality. Stores well. Moderately vigorous, spreading tree. May take six years to come into bearing. Does not produce good pollen. Requires nearby pollen source such as Maxine, Harrow Delight or many of the Asian varieties. Resistant to fire blight. Matures seven days after Bartlett; early September. Hardy in Zones 6-9. Developed by the USDA in Beltsville, Maryland. Introduced in 1960. *Source His-*

tory: 9 in 1988; 17 in 1992; 16 in 2000. **Sources: Ad2, Bar, Bea, Bo5, Ch9, Cu4, Ed2, Gr4, Ho5, Leu, Nrs, Ro3, Sc6, So5, Son, Wom.**

Manning-Miller - Firm, melting flesh is sweet when green or ripe and stands up well to processing. Tree grows strongly, yields abundant crops and is self-fruitful. Ripens in early September. Hardy to -40 degrees F. *Source History: 1 in 1988; 1 in 1992; 2 in 2000.* **Sources: Ed5, Stl.**

Marks - Small fruit similar to Seckel, but has exceptionally good flavor and texture. Attractive, yellow, russet skin. Origin of the variety is unknown but its parent was a pear sent to the New York State Agricultural Experiment Station in the early 1930s. *Source History: 1 in 1988; 2 in 1992; 1 in 2000.* **Sources: So5.**

Maxine (Starking Delicious) - Bartlett type. Large, golden yellow fruit with firm, crisp, juicy, snow-white flesh that is free from grit cells. Reminiscent of the Asian pears which are sweet but not rich. Good for eating fresh, canning and preserves. Tree is vigorous, hardy, productive and upright in habit; fire blight resistant. Ripens from mid to late September. Hardy in Zones 4-8. Developed in Ohio and introduced in 1923. *Source History: 8 in 1988; 11 in 1992; 9 in 2000.* **Sources: Ch9, Cum, Jo3, La3, Nrs, Ro3, Sc6, So5, Wom.**

Mericourt - Seckel x Late Faulkner. Short, medium size fruit is green to greenish yellow blushed with dark red. Flesh is creamy white and buttery, with excellent sweet, subacid, sprightly flavor. Developed at the Tennessee Agricultural Experiment Station. Introduced in 1938. *Source History: 1 in 1988; 1 in 1992; 1 in 2000.* **Sources: So5.**

Michelmas Nelis - Yellowish green fruit covered with cinnamon dots and netting. Melting, juicy, sweet flesh with excellent flavor. Leaves turn beautiful scarlet in fall. Superior to its parent as a garden pear because of its larger size and capability to ripen well. Ripens in late September. Winter Nelis seedling introduced by the English nursery, Bunyard and Co. in 1900. *Source History: 1 in 1988; 1 in 1992; 1 in 2000.* **Sources: So5.**

Micherin - *Source History: 1 in 1992; 1 in 2000.* **Sources: Va5.**

Monica Harris - *Source History: 1 in 1988; 1 in 2000.* **Sources: Ed5.**

Monterey - Very large, high quality fruit with yellow-green skin. Apple shape. Crisp, smooth, high quality flesh with sweet flavor. Fine for canning or eating fresh. Tree is very hardy and blight resistant. Requires 150-300 hours of chilling. *Source History: 3 in 1988; 3 in 1992; 4 in 2000.* **Sources: Bay, CO5, Pa2, Wom.**

Moonglow - Comice seedling. Medium-large, dull yellow fruit with pink blush. Mildly juicy, soft, white flesh with smooth texture. Excellent, mild flavor and almost no grit cells. Excellent for fresh use or canning; stores well. Spur-type tree is fire blight resistant. Requires pollination. Good variety for commercial production or home gardens. Matures 10-14 days earlier than Bartlett; from early August to mid-September depending on location; ripens to peak flavor in cool storage 10-15 days later. Requires 700 hours of chilling. Hardy in Zones 5-8. Introduced in 1960. *Source History: 29 in 1988; 44 in 1992; 38 in 2000.* **Sources: Bar, Bas, Bay, Bea, Bo5, Ch9, CO5, Cum, Ed5, Fi1, GI3, GR26, Gur, Hi9, Ho5, Iso, Jo3, Lee, Leu, ME3, Mel, Mi1, MI10, MI5, Nrs, Sav, SIM, So5, St4, Tex, TU5, Ty2, Wa16, WA8, Wel, WI4, Wom, Wor.**

Morettini, Early - *Source History: 1 in 2000.* **Sources: So5.**

Nain Vert - *Source History: 1 in 1992; 1 in 2000.* **Sources: Nrs.**

Normannischen Ciderbirne - Perry pear used for cider. *Source History: 1 in 2000.* **Sources: Cid.**

Nouveau Poiteau (PI 322035) - *Source History: 1 in 1992; 1 in 2000.*
Sources: Nrs.

Nova - Large, round, good quality fruit with melting juicy flesh. Can be used green or ripe. Hangs well without premature drop. Appears to have some fire blight resistance. Ripens in mid-September. Hardy to -50 degrees F. Discovered in northern New York state. *Source History: 3 in 1988; 5 in 1992; 3 in 2000.* **Sources: Ed5, Fed, Stl.**

Orcas - Yellow fruit with carmine blush. Large, flavorful pear that is well suited for home orchards and processing. Very versatile; good for fresh eating, canning or drying. Very little core breakdown has been seen in ripe fruit, which can be a problem in slightly overripe pears. Tree has vigorous, open, spreading habit. Both tree and fruit show good resistance to pear scab. Ripens in early September. Discovered by Joe Long on Orcas Island, Washington. *Source History: 2 in 1988; 4 in 1992; 4 in 2000.* **Sources: Clo, Nrs, On3, Rai.**

Orient - Large, firm, smooth, shiny, round, yellow fruit with red cheek; known for its intense beauty. Thick skin; juicy, melting, creamy white flesh with good texture and mild flavor. Used mainly for canning. Large, vigorous tree bears heavy crops and is blight resistant. Not self-fertile; use Kieffer or Moonglow as a pollinator. Dependable producer; needs little pruning. Ripens from mid-August to mid-September depending on location. Requires 350 hours of chilling. Hardy in Zones 5-8. Originated in California. *Source History: 15 in 1988; 26 in 1992; 20 in 2000.* **Sources: Bar, Bas, CO5, Cum, FO10, GI3, Ho5, Iso, Jo3, MI10, Na4, Po2, SIM, Tex, TU5, Ty2, WA8, Wel, WI4, Wom.**

Packham's Triumph - Bartlett type. Fruit has bumps but is plumper on the bottom. Good keeper; needs cold storage to ripen. Medium size tree is vigorous and early bearing. Requires cross-pollination. Susceptible to fire blight. Ripens late. The number one eating pear grown in Australia, where it originated. *Source History: 2 in 1988; 4 in 1992; 3 in 2000.* **Sources: Co2, Nrs, Son.**

Parker - Considered the same as the old Belgian pear, Flemish Beauty. Medium to large, yellow-bronze fruit with fine grained, tender, sweet, juicy flesh. Visible grit cells soften at maturity. Susceptible to scab. Large upright, moderately spreading tree. Use Patten for pollinator. Ripens in early September. Hardy for the North; Zone 3. Seed from Manchuria. Released by the University of Minnesota for the southern half of Minnesota and similar latitudes. *Source History: 3 in 1988; 9 in 1992; 6 in 2000.* **Sources: BA14, Ed5, Fa1, Fed, Nrs, SH8.**

Passe Crassane - Large to very large fruit with fat, roundish, cylindrical shape that tapers at the stem. Rough, greenish brown skin becomes yellowish brown when ripe and is often covered with brilliant purple and red spots. Flesh is white and juicy. Regarded by the French to be their finest winter pear. *Source History: 1 in 1988; 4 in 1992; 3 in 2000.* **Sources: Nrs, So5, Son.**

Passe Crassane Rouge - *Source History: 1 in 1992; 1 in 2000.* **Sources: Nrs.**

Patten - Orel 15 x Anjou. Medium large, good quality, yellow fruit that resembles Bartlett. Very tender and juicy. Good for eating, fair for canning. Should be picked about seven days before ripe and then allowed to ripen. Good pollinator. Ripens in mid-September. Hardy to -50 degrees F. with occasional winter injury. Developed by the University of Minnesota for southern Minnesota and for trial in favorable locations farther north. Originated in Charles City, Iowa. Introduced in 1922. *Source History: 5 in 1988; 9 in 1992; 6 in 2000.* **Sources: Ed5, Fa1, Fed, Nrs, SH8, Stl.**

Pepi - *Pyrus ussuriensis* cross. Small fruit is good for canning. Lacks the eating quality of European pears. Immune to fire blight. Extremely cold hardy; down to -50 degrees F. or colder. *Source History: 1 in 2000.* **Sources: Stl.**

Pineapple - Large, yellow fruit blushed with red. Crisp flesh with unusual pineapple-like flavor. Fine for canning, preserving or eating fresh. Tree grows 15-20' tall. Bears large crops at an early age. Self-fruitful but sets heavier crop if a second variety is planted. Fire blight resistant. Good for the Deep South. Ripens in August. Requires 150 or less hours of chilling. Hardy in Zones 8-9. *Source History: 12 in 1988; 14 in 1992; 13 in 2000.* **Sources: Bas, CO5, Cum, GI3, Ho5, Iso, Jo3, Ju2, RA4, SIM, Tex, Ty2, Wel.**

Ping Ding Li 7 - *Source History: 1 in 1992; 1 in 2000.* **Sources: Nrs.**

Potomac (US 62537-048) - Moonglow x Buerre D'Anjou. Fruit averages 2.5". Ripens to a light green. Flesh texture is moderately fine and buttery. Pleasingly subacid flavor with mild aroma. Moderately vigorous tree shows more resistance to fire blight than Seckel. Developed by the USDA and Ohio State University. *Source History: 7 in 2000.* **Sources: Ad2, Bo5, Cu4, Hid, Nrs, Ro3, Sc6.**

Red Horse - Perry pear used for cider. *Source History: 1 in 2000.* **Sources: Cid.**

Reimer (Reimer Red) - Red Bartlett x Comice. Fruit has red flush on sunny side. Buttery, melting, flavorful flesh. Small tree is a shy bearer. Originated in Oregon. U.S. Plant Patent No. 6245. *Source History: 1 in 1988; 2 in 1992; 2 in 2000.* **Sources: Nrs, Son.**

Rescue - Large to very large, elongated, pyriform fruit; yellow skin, 35-50% covered by vivid orange and red stripes and blush. Creamy, smooth, buttery flesh; mild, sweet flavor. Ripens in September; slightly later than Aurora. Rescued in Washington State. *Source History: 1 in 1988; 3 in 1992; 7 in 2000.* **Sources: Ea3, Nrs, On3, Rai, So5, Son, WI4.**

Rogue Red - *Source History: 1 in 1992; 1 in 2000.* **Sources: Nrs.**

Romania Perry - Perry pear used for cider. *Source History: 1 in 2000.* **Sources: Cid.**

Rousselet de Reims (Late Catherine, Musk Pear, Spice Pear) - Small to medium size, oval to turban-shaped pear. Greenish yellow fruit sometimes with a red cheek and spotted with small gray dots. Extremely sweet, spicy or musky flavor causing it to be called Musk or Spice Pear in early America. Ripens in early September. Believed to be of ancient origin; a favorite of Louis XIV. LaQuintinye, the king's gardener at Versailles, wrote in 1688 that no garden should be without it. *Source History: 1 in 1988; 1 in 1992; 1 in 2000.* **Sources: So5.**

Saint Andre - Variably shaped, green-yellow fruit with some gray or green dots. Melting, juicy flesh. Pleasant flavor. First observed in 1829. *Source History: 1 in 1992; 1 in 2000.* **Sources: Son.**

Sanguinole - Maroon-red skin. Red flesh is transparent, semi-breaking, juicy, semi-fine. Somewhat musky, acid flavor. Does not keep. Cold hardiness unknown. Originated in Switzerland prior to 1500. *Source History: 2 in 2000.* **Sources: Ed5, Ro3.**

Santa Claus - Medium size, long stemmed, conical, dessert pear. Russeted fruit is reddish brown with pale yellowish, melting, good flavored flesh. Leaves turn a rich claret-red in the fall. Ripens late. Brought to notice by a Col. Brymer of Dorchester, England. Introduced in 1905. *Source History: 1 in 1988; 1 in 1992; 1 in 2000.* **Sources: So5.**

Sauvignac - Very sweet, juicy pear with few grit cells. Ripens in September.

Hardy to -50 degrees F. with occasional winter injury. Brought to our attention by Henri Bernard, this 150-year-old tree deserves to be propagated more widely. Originated near Quebec City, Canada in a very cold area. *Source History: 1 in 1988; 1 in 1992; 1 in 2000.* **Sources: Stl.**

Savannah - New dessert pear found growing in Savannah, Georgia. Similar to Maxine. Good for eating, canning and freezing. Highly resistant to fire blight. Ripens in August. Hardy in Zone 5. *Source History: 1 in 1988; 1 in 1992; 1 in 2000.* **Sources: Jo3.**

Seckel (Honey Pear) - Commonly called Sugar Pear. Not very pretty, but a connoisseur's delight. Small, yellowish brown fruit with pale russet and russet red cheek. Fine grained, smooth, extremely sweet, very juicy flesh. Distinctive, spicy, rich, aromatic flavor, mostly in the skin. Excellent dessert pear; ideal for pickling, spicing and canning whole. Productive, slow growing, naturally semidwarf, 15-20' tree; widely adaptable, reliable and heavy setting. Self-fertile, but benefits from cross-pollination. Some fire blight resistance. Ripens during September. 500-800 hours of chilling. Hardy in Zones 5-8. Introduced from Europe in 1790. *Source History: 34 in 1988; 43 in 1992; 39 in 2000.* **Sources: Ad2, Bay, Bea, Bo5, Bu7, Ch9, Cla, Co2, CO5, Cu4, Ed2, Ed5, Fed, Fi1, Gr4, Gur, Hi9, Hid, Jo3, La3, Leu, Mel, Mi1, MI5, Nrs, Pe2, Pi2, Rai, Ro3, Sc6, SIM, So5, Son, St4, TU5, Va2, WA8, WI4, Wor.**

Shannon - Resembles Seckle in size, habits and sweetness, but with more consistent yields. *Source History: 1 in 2000.* **Sources: Ea3.**

Sheldon - Medium to large, uniform, symmetrical, green fruit thickly covered with fine russet dots turning a fawn gold when fully ripe. Very juicy, melting, sweet, white flesh. Delicious, delicately spicy flavor. Good dessert quality. Keeps well. Ready for eating as soon as flesh yields to firm pressure. Ripens in October. *Source History: 2 in 1988; 2 in 1992; 1 in 2000.* **Sources: So5.**

Shipova - Mountain Ash x European Pear. Medium size, round, yellow fruit. Firm, flavorful flesh. Scab resistant. Ripens during August. Zones 4-9. *Source History: 1 in 1992; 2 in 2000.* **Sources: Bu7, Or2.**

Siberian (Harbin) - *Source History: 1 in 2000.* **Sources: Ch9.**

Sirrine - Good size Bartlett seedling. Green and yellow fruit with Bartlett shape. Juicy, melting flesh with sweet, rich flavor. Tree is a regular, heavy bearer. Hardy to Zone 4. *Source History: 1 in 1988; 3 in 1992; 3 in 2000.* **Sources: Mo19, Nrs, So5.**

Sommer Blutbirne - Tasty red flesh. Compact tree. *Source History: 1 in 2000.* **Sources: Son.**

Southworth - Good flavored pear with very few grit cells; about the same size as Bartlett. Self-fertile tree is a strong, vigorous grower. Ripens mid to late September. Hardy to -50 degrees F. with occasional winter injury. Originated in northern New York. *Source History: 1 in 1988; 1 in 1992; 2 in 2000.* **Sources: Ed5, Stl.**

Spadona - European pear. Medium size fruit. White flesh. Ripens before Bartlett. Originated in Italy, 1790. *Source History: 1 in 2000.* **Sources: Son.**

Spalding - Yellow fruit with white, mellow flesh. Combines the mellow complex flavor of a European pear and the crunchy sweetness of an Asian pear. Ripens during August. Released in Spalding County, Georgia. *Source History: 1 in 1988; 3 in 1992; 3 in 2000.* **Sources: Iso, RA4, Rai.**

Spina Carpi - *Source History: 1 in 1992; 1 in 2000.* **Sources: Nrs.**

Stacey - Original tree is 108" in circumference at 4' above the ground and is at least 250 years old, growing near Staceyville, Maine. Brought to our attention by Clarke Nattress and collection developed by Jack Kertesz. Stacey has shown itself to grow vigorously here. The fruit is small but very sweet. Ripens in early September. Hardy to -50 degrees F. with occasional winter injury. *Source History: 1 in 1988; 1 in 1992; 2 in 2000.* **Sources: Ed5, Stl.**

Stacyville - Round, teardrop-shaped fruit is light yellow with a beautiful orange to solid gray-red blush. Delicious citrusy aftertaste. Self-pollinating. Disease resistant. Extremely hardy. Zone 3. Rare. *Source History: 1 in 2000.* **Sources: Fed.**

Starkrimson (Kalle Cultivar) - *Source History: 1 in 1992; 1 in 2000.* **Sources: St4.**

Sucre de Montlucon - Oval, conical, pure green fruit. White flesh is very juicy, buttery, lightly acidulous and delicately perfumed. Grows in clusters if not thinned. Ripens in late October. Found in a hedge in Montlucon in central France. Introduced in 1812. *Source History: 1 in 1988; 1 in 1992; 1 in 2000.* **Sources: So5.**

Sucre Verte - *Source History: 1 in 2000.* **Sources: Ed5.**

Sug Soft - So named by Just Fruits Nursery because of the rich sweet juicy flesh. Ripens in August. *Source History: 1 in 2000.* **Sources: Ju2.**

Sugar - Nearly round, bright yellow fruit with red russet blushes. Sweet flavor. Vigorous tree bears early. Self-fertile. Ripens in August. Requires 400 hours of chilling. Hardy in Zones 6-9. *Source History: 3 in 1988; 6 in 1992; 5 in 2000.* **Sources: Bar, CO5, GI3, ORA, Ty2.**

Summer Blood Birne - Named 300 years ago for its red flesh and juice. Ripens early August. *Source History: 1 in 2000.* **Sources: Ea3, On3.**

Summer Crisp (MN 33201) - Unknown parentage. Medium size, 3.5" long fruit with sweet, crisp flesh. Harvest when still green with red blush. Will keep up to two months. Tree is an annual bearer and fire blight resistant. Ripens in mid-August. Hardy in Zone 4. Found in Caledonia, Minnesota in 1933. Introduced by the University of Minnesota in 1986. *Source History: 4 in 1988; 9 in 1992; 8 in 2000.* **Sources: BA14, Bea, Ed5, Fed, Nrs, Ro3, SH8, Stl.**

Sun Pear - *Pyrus phaecarpa.* Excellent drought resistant species with pear-shaped, 1" fruits and brown skin with light spots. Hardy to -35 degrees F. *Source History: 1 in 2000.* **Sources: Oik.**

Superfin (Beurre Superfin) - Medium to large, round-oval fruit with a pointed neck like Bosc. Smooth, green-yellow skin with an occasional blush. Very fine flesh is extremely juicy and free of grit cells. Sweet with vinous spicy flavor. Vigorous spreading tree. Too soft for commercial operations but does well in home orchards. Originated in France in 1837. *Source History: 1 in 1992; 2 in 2000.* **Sources: Nrs, Son.**

Surecrop - *Source History: 1 in 1988; 1 in 1992; 1 in 2000.* **Sources: CO5.**

Tayton Squash - Perry pear used for cider. *Source History: 1 in 2000.* **Sources: Cid.**

Tenn's Soft - Thin-necked fruit with a red cheek. Buttery, sweet, tender flesh. Heavy bearer. *Source History: 1 in 2000.* **Sources: Ju2.**

Thorn - Perry pear used for cider. *Source History: 1 in 2000.* **Sources: Cid.**

Turnbull (Turnbull Giant) - Huge fruits up to 3 pounds. Immature, green fruits taste tart and apple-like; make delicious pie. Fully ripe fruits have creamy, smooth texture and sweet pear flavor. Long blooming period with very heavy fruit set. Self-fruitful. Resistant to fire blight and most foliage diseases. Hardy in Zones 4-9. U.S. Plant Patent No. 4616. *Source History: 1 in 1988; 2 in 1992; 2 in 2000.*

Sources: Fi1, Hid.

Turner Shade - Brown, round fruit. Pleasant, crunchy flesh; coarse but not gritty. Good for baking. Blight resistant. Does well in complete shade. Irregular bearer; starts to bear very young. Ripens in late November. Originated in North Carolina. *Source History: 1 in 1992; 1 in 2000.* **Sources: Ed5.**

Tyson - Known as the Early Sugar Pear. Medium size, yellow fruit with juicy, spicy-sweet flavor. Excellent for early eating and local market. Hardy tree is a heavy producer and fire blight resistant. Pollinate with Starking Delicious or Moonglow. Ripens in early August. Hardy in Zones 5-8. Known since 1794. *Source History: 3 in 1988; 4 in 1992; 4 in 2000.* **Sources: Cla, Ed5, Fed, Stl.**

Ubileen - Bartlett-size fruit with attractive red blush. Buttery-textured flesh. Vigorous and disease resistant. Ripens early to mid-July. Originated in Bulgaria. *Source History: 2 in 1992; 6 in 2000.* **Sources: Cla, Clo, Ea3, On3, Or2, Rai.**

Ure - Offspring of *Pyrus ussuriensis*. Rhymes with "pure." Greenish yellow fruit. Sweet, very juicy flesh. Excellent for eating and canning. Ripens in mid-September. Hardy in Zone 3. Introduced by the Morden Research Station in 1978. *Source History: 8 in 1992; 2 in 2000.* **Sources: Ed5, SH8.**

Vermont Beauty - Pale yellow fruit covered with numerous conspicuous dots; broad, brilliantly blushed cheek with pinkish red dots. Texture is tender and juicy; rich flavor. Ripens seven days later than Seckel. Supposed to have originated in the Macomber Nursery at Grand Isle, Vermont in the late 19th century. *Source History: 1 in 1988; 2 in 1992; 3 in 2000.* **Sources: Fed, Nrs, So5.**

Vicar of Winkfield (Viker) - Large, unrusseted, clear greenish yellow fruit. Strong, musky aroma. Excellent keeper with fine cooking potential. Trees are more vigorous and healthier than Bosc; can reach very large size. *Source History: 2 in 1988; 2 in 1992; 2 in 2000.* **Sources: Gr4, So5.**

Warren - Medium to large, long necked, drop-shaped fruit is faded green with an occasional red blush in full sun. Varies in size and shape. Flavor is rated equal to Magness by many. Sweet, very juicy, buttery, smooth flesh with no grit. Self-fruitful tree is spreading with pyramidal shape and thick, smooth branches. Never blighted in extreme heat and humidity. Cold hardy to -21 degrees F. Discovered by T. O. Warren in Mississippi some years ago. *Source History: 5 in 1988; 12 in 1992; 13 in 2000.* **Sources: Bu7, Ch9, Cla, Cu4, Cum, Hid, Ho5, Jo3, Rai, Son, Tex, WI4, Wom.**

Washington State - Medium size tree bears dark grey-brown russeted fruit. Slightly grainy, firm flesh. Less juice than others. Retains white color and firmness when canned. Makes excellent pear cider. Discovered many years ago on a Washington State University field trip in the mountains of Washington or Oregon. *Source History: 1 in 2000.* **Sources: Fed.**

Waterville - Large pear with coarse, sweet flesh. Vigorous tree. Ripens in September. Keeps well. Hardy to -50 degrees F. Originated in Waterville, Vermont. Brought to our attention by David Fried. *Source History: 1 in 1988; 1 in 1992; 2 in 2000.* **Sources: Ed5, Stl.**

White Doyenne - Medium to small, roundish pear; pale yellow russeted skin with small, bright red blush on exposed cheek. Flesh is juicy and sweet with rich, aromatic flavor and melting texture when fully ripe. Large tree is fire blight resistant. This ancient and world renowned pear came from France via Italy where it was described in 1550 as the old Roman pear, Sementinum. Introduced in 1559. *Source History: 1 in 1988; 1 in 1992; 2 in 2000.* **Sources: Ed5, Son.**

Whitehouse - *Source History: 1 in 1992; 1 in 2000.* **Sources: Nrs.**

Winnals Longdon - Perry pear used for cider. *Source History: 1 in 2000.*
Sources: Cid.

Winter Nelis - Medium size, roundish, roughly russeted, dark brown and dull green fruit. Unattractive in appearance, but ripens into one of the most delicious for late winter use. Juicy, aromatic, sweet, fine flavored flesh. Keeps well. Tree is blight resistant; somewhat difficult to train when young. Partially self-fruitful, but more productive when planted with any other pear variety. Good pollinator for Bartlett. Resistant to fire blight. Ripens in October or November depending on location. Requires 700 hours of chilling. Originated in Belgium during the early 19th century. *Source History: 9 in 1988; 10 in 1992; 5 in 2000.* **Sources: Gr4, Nrs, So5, Son, STR.**

Worden Seckel - Large Seckel-type fruit with red blush. Dessert quality. Blight resistant. *Source History: 1 in 1992; 3 in 2000.* **Sources: Cu4, Nrs, Wh4.**

Yellow Huffcap - Perry pear used for cider. *Source History: 1 in 2000.*
Sources: Cid.

Pear / Asian

Pyrus pyrifolia or *P. ussuriensis* var. *ovoidea*

20th Century (Apple Pear, Nijisseiki) - *Pyrus pyrifolia.* Best known Asian pear; actually, it's Japanese. Medium size, round, lopsided, long stemmed, yellow fruit with greenish mottling. Thin, tender skin. Extremely juicy, crisp flesh; bland, mild flavor. Excellent quality. Stores through January. Ornamental, medium size, drooping tree with large, glossy leaves. Partly self-fertile; pollinate with Chojuro, Hosui, Bartlett or Shinseiki. Productive to a fault; thin to one fruit per spur. Susceptible to many diseases, especially blackspot. Tolerates drought and heat. Requires 450-500 hours of chilling. Hardy to 20 degrees F. and in Zones 6-9. Chance seedling from Matsudo City, Chiba Prefecture, Japan, 1898. Introduced in 1898. *Source History: 32 in 1988; 49 in 1992; 37 in 2000.* **Sources: Ad2, Bay, Bo5, Bu7, Clo, CO5, Cu4, Ea3, Fed, Ga20, Gr4, Iso, Jo3, JOY, Ju2, ME3, Mel, MI5, Nrs, On3, On4, Or2, ORA, Pa2, Pe2, SH8, SIM, So5, Son, St4, STR, Tex, Va2, Wel, WI12, WI4, Wom.**

Asian, Early - Unknown origin. Yellow fruit with sweet crisp taste. Disease resistant, mid-size tree. Ripens 3 weeks earlier than any other Asian pears. *Source History: 1 in 2000.* **Sources: Cla.**

Chinese Pear (Sand Pear) - *Pyrus ussuriensis* var. *ovoidea.* Oval, long stemmed, apple-shaped, crisp-textured pear; shape and size of a baseball. Yellowish tan skin with small dots; sweet, delicious flavor. Flesh is firm and crisp, breaking like an apple. Good fresh, canned or preserved. Tree is long bearing, up to 75 years or more. Must be thinned to one pear per cluster, otherwise all flowers may set and as many as seven tiny fruits can result from each spur. Does well in all southern states. Ripens in July. *Source History: 5 in 1988; 3 in 1992; 1 in 2000.* **Sources: Sc2.**

Chojuro (Old World Chojuro) - *Pyrus pyrifolia.* Medium to large, flattened, brown russeted greenish fruit with thick skin. White flesh is crisp like an apple when ripe; mild, slightly aromatic flavor. Keeps in cool storage until February. Medium size, spreading, vigorous, early bearing tree; reliable annual bearing tree with somewhat drooping habit. Somewhat prone to overbearing; needs some thinning. Pollinate with Nijisseiki, Shinseiki, Bartlett, Hosui, 20th Century or Shinko. Poorer quality fruit in dry climates. Ripens during September. 450-500 hours of chilling. Some of the best new varieties are crosses of Chojuro x Nijiseiki (20th Century). Zone 5. *Source History: 24 in 1988; 32 in 1992; 23 in 2000.* **Sources: Bay, Bea, Bu7, Clo, CO5, Cu4, Ea3, Gr16, Gr4, JOY, ME3, Mel, Mo19, Nrs, On3, Or2, ORA, Ro3, So5, Son, Tex, Wel, WI4.**

Daisui Li - Asian pear. Large to very large, obovate fruit with medium green skin color. White flesh is slightly coarse and crisp. Very juicy, sweet flavor with a trace of tartness. Stores 5-6 months. Ripens during September. U.S. Plant Patent No. 6075. *Source History: 1 in 1988; 1 in 1992; 2 in 2000.* **Sources: Gr16, On3.**

Doitsu - *Source History: 1 in 1992; 1 in 2000.* **Sources: Nrs.**

Giant Asian - Pale gold, apple-like fruit shape with crisp texture even when ripe. Smooth pear flavor. Weigh 2-3 lbs. Stores well. Self-pollinating. Zones 4-9. *Source History: 1 in 2000.* **Sources: Gur.**

Hamese No. 1 - Medium size, yellow-skinned fruit with superior flavor. Sweet, crisp flesh. Ripens mid-August. Productive tree bears large crops. *Source History: 1 in 2000.* **Sources: Rai.**

Hardy Giant, Starking (Olympic Cultivar) - Large round fruit weighs 26-30 oz. Skin color is a beautiful russetted fawn-brown color. Keeps for 9 months when refrigerated. Resists pear leaf spot. Ripens mid-October. Zones 4b-8. Trade-marked. *Source History: 1 in 2000.* **Sources: St4.**

Hosui (Much Water) - *Pyrus pyrifolia.* (Kikusui x Yakumo) x Yakumo. Medium large, brownish orange fruit. Juicy, sweet, fine grained, crisp, off-white flesh; 12% sugar content. Stores through December. Large round fruit with medium thick skin covered with yellow-brown russet and numerous russet dots. Firm, crisp, fine textured flesh. Produces tart tasting fruit in cooler climates with mild, short summers. Favorite in several taste tests. Exceptionally vigorous tree with floppy, spreading, loose growth habit. Vigorously develops lots of flower bud spurs. Pollinate with Chojuro, 20th Century, Bartlett, Shinseiki or Shinko. Susceptible to pseudomonas during cold, wet springs. Best adapted to the Willamette Valley. Ripens from mid-August to late September depending on location. 450-500 hours of chilling. Zone 6-9. Developed at the National Horticultural Research Station, Tsukuba, Japan, 1972. *Source History: 20 in 1988; 39 in 1992; 30 in 2000.* **Sources: Ad2, Bay, Bea, Bo5, Bu7, Cla, CO5, Cu4, Cum, Ed2, Fed, Ga20, Gr16, Iso, Jo3, ME3, Mi1, Nrs, On3, On4, Or2, ORA, Pe2, Son, St4, Va2, Wel, WI12, WI4, Wom.**

Ichiban Nashi - Medium size, lightly golden russet skin. Light yellow flesh is tender, crisp, juicy and sweet. Moderately vigorous, productive, spur bearing tree. Stores about 6 weeks. Ripens from late June to early July. Requires a pollinator. 400 hours of chilling. Name means "number one" in Japanese since it is the earliest ripening commercial Asian pear variety. *Source History: 1 in 1992; 5 in 2000.* **Sources: Bay, Clo, Ga20, Rai, WI4.**

Ishiiwase - *Pyrus pyrifolia.* Large, russeted, juicy fruit. Sweet, subtle, flavorful, refreshing flesh is crisp like an apple when ripe. Pollinate with Kikusui or 20th Century. Ripens from early to mid-August in central California. Requires 450-500 hours of chilling. *Source History: 5 in 1988; 5 in 1992; 2 in 2000.* **Sources: Bay, WI4.**

Iwate Mukaku - Small fruit the size of a golf ball is easily shaken from the tree. Spicy, tart flavor. Makes good juice or syrup. *Source History: 1 in 2000.* **Sources: Hid.**

Japanese Golden Russet (Japanese Golden Pear, Taihe Japanese Golden Russet) - Asian pear with medium size, dark brown russeted fruit and juicy, sweet flesh. Among the favorites in the Oregon State University test orchards. Ripens in late

September. *Source History: 4 in 1988; 2 in 1992; 1 in 2000.* **Sources: So5.**

Kamenashi - Large, sweet fruit. Ripens late. *Source History: 1 in 2000.* **Sources: Hid.**

Kikusui (Kikisui) - *Pyrus pyrifolia.* Medium size, smooth fruit. Thin, greenish yellow skin remains greenish when ripe; no russet and faint aroma. Flesh is white, sweet, tart, juicy, crisp. Rapidly loses its color after harvest. Keeps well. Not suitable for shipping. Tree is a medium size, slightly drooping, widespreading grower; very productive, vigorous and early to bear. Pollinate with Chojuro, 20th Century or Bartlett. Ripens from mid-August to mid-September depending on location. Requires 450 hours of chilling. *Source History: 12 in 1988; 18 in 1992; 10 in 2000.* **Sources: Bay, Ch9, Gr16, Nrs, ORA, Pe2, Rai, SIM, Son, WI4.**

Korean Giant (A-Ri-Rang, Dan Bae, Muk Gul, Olympic Giant) - *Pyrus pyrifolia.*Very large, round, dark brown russet fruit weighs up to a pound or more. Excellent, crisp flavor. Juicy flesh with a high sugar content. Precocious, productive tree. Requires a long growing season. Ripens late October-November. Pollinate with Singo. Zone 5. Fruits have sold for $5 each in Japan. *Source History: 4 in 1988; 8 in 1992; 10 in 2000.* **Sources: Bea, Bo5, Bu7, Cla, Fed, ME3, Or2, Rai, Ro3, Wh4.**

Kosui - Small to medium, faded yellow fruit with slight bronze russet. Crisp, crunchy, juicy flesh. Exceptional, sweet taste. Stores through September. Tree is a strong grower and moderate yielder. Ripens from mid-July to early August depending on location. *Source History: 4 in 1988; 13 in 1992; 5 in 2000.* **Sources: Clo, Ea3, Ju2, Nrs, On3.**

Megietsu (Megeitsu) - Medium-large, round fruit. Medium-brown skin color. Super sweet and aromatic. Vigorous tree. Ripens early September. Stores well through December. *Source History: 2 in 1988; 1 in 2000.* **Sources: Ro3.**

Meigetsu - Ripens in October. *Source History: 1 in 2000.* **Sources: Ea3.**

Mishirasu - Large oval fruit with brown skin looks like a European pear. Crisp, crunchy flesh with excellent flavor. Ripens mid to late September. *Source History: 1 in 2000.* **Sources: Rai.**

Niitaka - *Pyrus pyrifolia.* Large, attractive, greenish fruit with brown russet. Mild, sweet, crisp, juicy flesh. Fruit quality is good to excellent. Ripen on the tree. One of the best keepers of all Asian pears. Sweetens with storage. Very productive tree. Not a pollinator. Ripens from mid-September to mid-October depending on location. Requires 500 hours of chilling. *Source History: 9 in 1988; 13 in 1992; 5 in 2000.* **Sources: Ad2, Nrs, On3, ORA, Ro3.**

Okusankichi (Late Korean, Nihon Nashi, Bansankichi) - Large, round, greenish tan fruit. Slightly tart, very juicy flesh with relatively few stone cells. Not the best for quality. Good keeper. Tree is very vigorous and productive. Fruit thinning recommended to avoid excessive fruit set. Overbearing causes much poorer production the following year. Susceptible to pear scale disease. Ripens in late September. *Source History: 5 in 1988; 7 in 1992; 2 in 2000.* **Sources: Cu4, ORA.**

Olympic - Korean pear. Attractive, very large, orange-brown russeted, round fruit. Firm, crisp, juicy, sweet flesh. Large, upright, winter hardy tree. Stores for eight to nine months. Requires a pollinator. Ripens during October. *Source History: 2 in 1992; 4 in 2000.* **Sources: Ad2, COL, Cu4, Ed2.**

Seigyoku - *Pyrus pyrifolia.* Large fruit with clear, yellow skin. Excellent quality, juicy, flavorful, white flesh. Central leader tends to droop. Winding branch growth creates very interesting though somewhat difficult to manage tree; somewhat spreading growth habit. Not a good pollinator. Ripens in mid-September. Requires

500 hours of chilling. *Source History: 5 in 1988; 7 in 1992; 3 in 2000.* **Sources: Bay, Nrs, WI4.**

Seuri - Large, round fruit. Yellow skin mottled greenish brown and partially russeted. Crisp, fine textured, juicy flesh with aromatic flavor. Stores through October. Tree is strong, vigorous and heavy yielding. Ripens from mid-September to mid-October depending on location. Zone 5. *Source History: 7 in 1988; 12 in 1992; 6 in 2000.* **Sources: Ea3, ME3, Nrs, On3, Or2, Son.**

Shin Li - Large to very large, light-green, russeted fruit. Firm, white flesh with sweet-tart flavor. Ripens mid-September. Can be stored up to 6 months. Developed by the University of California. U.S. Plant Patent No. 6076. *Source History: 1 in 1988; 1 in 1992; 2 in 2000.* **Sources: Gr16, On3.**

Shinko - *Pyrus pyrifolia.* Medium size, oval, brownish green fruit. Firm crisp, apple-like flesh with rich, sweet, distinctive flavor. One of the best keeping Asian varieties; keeps until spring in cool storage. Tree is a precocious, annual bearer. Pollinate with Chojuro, 20th Century, Bartlett, Kikusui or Hosui. Susceptible to fire blight and codling moth. Ripens from early to mid-October depending on location. Requires 450-500 hours of chilling. Zone 5. *Source History: 11 in 1988; 25 in 1992; 25 in 2000.* **Sources: Bay, Bu7, Cla, CO5, Cu4, Cum, Ea3, Ed2, Ga20, Gr16, Hid, Iso, Jo3, Ju2, La3, ME3, Nrs, On3, Or2, ORA, Pa2, Son, Tex, Wh4, WI4.**

Shinseiki (New Century, New Generation) - Nijisseiki x Chojuro. Round, medium to large, yellow fruit with little or no russet. Crisp, creamy white flesh; mild, sweet flavor. Tastes best when tree ripened. Retains quality longer than any midseason variety. Hangs on the tree in good condition for 4-6 weeks. Stores through January; keeps well under refrigeration. Larger tree than other Japanese varieties; vigorous and spreading. Usually bears second year. Pollinate with Bartlett, Chojuro, Nijiseiki or Hosui. Highly resistant to pseudomonus. Moderate fire blight resistance. Ripens during August in Zone 9. Requires 350-450 hours of chilling. Hardy in Zones 5-9. Originated in Japan, 1945. *Source History: 29 in 1988; 42 in 1992; 39 in 2000.* **Sources: Ad2, Bay, Bea, Bo5, Bu7, Cla, Clo, CO5, Cu4, Ea3, Ed2, Fed, Ga20, Gr16, Gr4, Jo3, JOY, ME3, Mel, MI5, Mo19, Nrs, On3, On4, Or2, ORA, Pa2, RA4, Rai, Ro3, SIM, So5, Son, St4, STR, Va2, We8, WI12, WI4.**

Shinsui - Asian pear with small to medium, yellow-brown, russeted fruit. Crisp, tender, juicy flesh. Very sweet; approximately 15% sugar. Can be pollinated by all other Asian varieties except Niitaka and Kikusui. Ripens in early July. Requires 400 hours of chilling. Hardy to Zone 5. *Source History: 2 in 1988; 6 in 1992; 8 in 2000.* **Sources: Bay, Bea, Mo19, Nrs, ORA, Rai, Ro3, WI4.**

Singo - Yellow-tan fruit. White, tender, juicy flesh. Keeps until spring. Vigorous tree has productive upright habit. Ripens mid-October. Excellent pollinator for Korean Giant. Considered to be hardy to Zone 4 but needs Zone 5 to ripen. *Source History: 1 in 1988; 1 in 1992; 1 in 2000.* **Sources: Bea.**

Tarusa Crimson (Tamared) - Possible cross of European and Asian pear. Attractive, reddish fruit. Crisp when first ripe, eventually developing a smooth texture, similar to a European pear. Storage enhances the flavor. Ripens in late October. *Source History: 2 in 1992; 1 in 2000.* **Sources: Son.**

Tsu Li - *Pyrus pyrifolia.* Chinese variety. Medium to large, oval, light green to yellow fruit with thick, semiglossy skin. White flesh tinted with yellow is sweet, crisp and juicy with slightly tart, mild flavor. Stores through January. Large, vigorous tree is productive. Early bloom; pollinator for Ya Li in warm winter climates.

Ripens from early to mid September. Requires 150-500 hours of chilling. Tolerates temperatures into the low 20s; Zone 5. *Source History: 12 in 1988; 15 in 1992; 15 in 2000.* **Sources: Bay, CO5, Ea3, Ed5, Gr16, JOY, Me2, Nrs, On3, Or2, ORA, Pa2, So5, Son, WI4.**

Ya Li (Duckbill Pear, Yali) - *Pyrus pyrifolia.* Chinese variety that is pear-shaped rather than round like other Asian pears. Large, smooth, dull to semiglossy, light greenish yellow fruit. Crisp, white flesh is moderately sweet with trace of tartness and fragrant aroma. Very good to excellent eating quality. Tree is large, upright, very vigorous, dense and productive. Beautiful wine-red foliage in the fall. Earliest to bloom, latest to ripen. Will not consistently ripen in the coolest areas. Pollinate with Tsu Li or Bartlett. Ripens from early September to late October depending on location. Very low chilling requirement of 150-500 hours. Hardy in Zones 6-8. *Source History: 14 in 1988; 19 in 1992; 13 in 2000.* **Sources: Bay, CO5, Cu4, Gr16, Me2, Mi1, On3, Or2, ORA, RA4, SIM, Son, WI4.**

Yakumo - *Pyrus pyrifolia.* Oblong to oval, smooth, shiny, pale yellow fruit with crisp, very juicy flesh. Sweet and delicious with subtle melon taste. Crisp like an apple when ripe. Pollinate with any Asian pear or Bartlett. Will keep for months in cold storage. Grown as market fruit in Japan. Ripens during August. Requires 450 hours of chilling. *Source History: 5 in 1988; 9 in 1992; 7 in 2000.* **Sources: Bea, Bu7, Ed5, Gr16, ME3, So5, WI4.**

Yoinashi - Round fruit with light brown, russeted skin with gold undertones. Flesh has finer texture than most Asian pears. Sweet flavor. Ripens mid to late August. Requires 400 hours of chilling. Trademarked. *Source History: 1 in 1992; 3 in 2000.* **Sources: Bay, Rai, WI4.**

Yongi - Large apple-shaped fruit with juicy flesh. Beautiful caramel color skin. Crisp, sweet flesh. Best eaten when peeled. Ripens early September. Zone 5. *Source History: 1 in 1988; 3 in 2000.* **Sources: ME3, Mo19, Rai.**

Pear / Flowering

Pyrus spp.

Aristocrat - White flowers in early spring. Grows 25-50' tall. Brilliant purple-red to orange foliage color in the fall. Zones 4-8. U.S. Plant Patent No. 3193. *Source History: 23 in 2000.* **Sources: Arb, Bay, Big, BO10, CO5, FE7, GR26, HI7, IM2, KAN, KEE, KI3, ME3, MI10, MI5, ORA, SH8, St4, STR, TR19, We8, Wel, WI4.**

Autumn Blaze - White spring blossoms. Bright red fall color. Hardy to Zone 4. U.S. Plant Patent No. 4591. *Source History: 7 in 2000.* **Sources: Arb, CO5, FE7, Fo2, GR26, KI3, SH8.**

Bradford - Ornamental, non-fruiting tree. Bears masses of white flowers in spring. Tree grows to 30'. Glossy green foliage turns crimson in the fall. Well adapted to atmospheric pollution. Disease resistant. Zones 4-8. *Source History: 39 in 2000.* **Sources: Bay, Big, BO10, BO4, Bo5, CO5, Fi1, FO10, Gur, HI7, Hi9, Ho5, IM2, IN7, KAN, KEE, KI3, La3, Lee, Leu, Mel, MI10, MI5, MO10, Na4, ORA, RA4, Sav, Sc2, SIM, St4, STR, Tex, TR19, TU5, Ty2, We8, Wel, WI4.**

Bradford, New (Improved Bradford) - More disease resistant than Bradford. Profuse spring blooms. Orange to purple-red fall color. Zone 5. *Source History: 2 in 2000.* **Sources: FE7, Ro3.**

Burgundy Snow - Well branched pyramidal tree to 40'. Crisp green foliage.

White flowers with burgundy centers. Zone 4. Trademarked. *Source History: 1 in 2000.* **Sources: FE7.**

Capital - Sport of Bradford with a more narrow crowned form. White blooms. Thornless. Purple-orange foliage color in the fall. Disease resistant. Hardy to Zone 4. *Source History: 9 in 2000.* **Sources: Arb, Bo5, CO5, HI7, ME3, ORA, St4, We8, WI4.**

Chanticleer - *Pyrus calleryana.* Clusters of single white blossoms. Glossy dark green leaves change to maroon in the fall. Fruitless. Strong upright branches create a narrow, pyramidal tree. Zone 5. U.S. Plant Patent No. 2489. *Source History: 16 in 2000.* **Sources: Big, BO10, CO5, FE7, Fo2, GR26, HI7, KAN, KI3, LI7, ME3, MI5, ORA, SH8, STR, We8.**

Cleveland - Zones 4-8. *Source History: 1 in 2000.* **Sources: KEE.**

Cleveland Select - *Pyrus calleryana.* Conical-shaped tree rarely produces fruit. White flowers. Dark, glossy green foliage turns brilliant red and purple in the fall. Zone 4. *Source History: 17 in 2000.* **Sources: Arb, BO4, CO5, HI7, Ho5, IM2, IN7, Mc3, MI10, MI5, MO10, SH8, SIM, St4, TR19, Ty2, WI4.**

Dancer - The most blight resistant of the flowering pears. Medium size tree with silver-gray foliage that matures to a light green color. Leaves appear to "dance" in the wind because the leaf petioles are extensive and flexible. White flowers with bright purple-red stamens. Blooms 3 weeks after Bradford. Zone 5. U.S. Plant Patent No. 7033. *Source History: 3 in 2000.* **Sources: BO10, CO5, ORA.**

Dusky Pear - Resembles Callery Pear. Zone 4. *Source History: 1 in 2000.* **Sources: Arb.**

Early Red - Formerly Simpson Red. Shows early red fall color. Zone 5. *Source History: 1 in 2000.* **Sources: Arb.**

Edgewood - Spring foliage has a purple tint; summer foliage is silver-green; red-purple in the fall. White blossoms. Small pea size fruit. Upright, spreading tree is fire blight resistant. Zone 5. U.S. Plant Patent No. 10,151. *Source History: 2 in 2000.* **Sources: CO5, FE7.**

Jack - White flowers. Glossy, dark green foliage. Dwarf tree grows 15-20'. Compact branching structure gives it a dense look. Produces .5" fruit. Trademarked. *Source History: 1 in 2000.* **Sources: Hi9.**

Korean Sun - Compact, rounded tree form. Great red fall color. Grows 15-20' tall. Hardy to Zone 4. *Source History: 2 in 2000.* **Sources: FE7, GR26.**

Mordak (Prairie Gem Pear) - Hardy to Zone 3. Trademarked. *Source History: 1 in 2000.* **Sources: SH8.**

Oleaster Pear - *Pyrus elaeagrifolia.* Small tree with attractive gray foliage. *Source History: 1 in 2000.* **Sources: Arb.**

Pendula - *Pyrus salicifolia.* Drooping branches with gray-green, willow-like leaves. White flowers. Hardy to -20 degrees F. *Source History: 2 in 2000.* **Sources: BO10, Gr16.**

Prairie Gem - *Pyrus ussuriensis.* Upright, oval tree becomes rounded with age. Most hardy ornamental pear. Developed in North Dakota. *Source History: 2 in 2000.* **Sources: Arb, GR26.**

Rancho - Pyramid form. Excellent flowering. Zone 4. *Source History: 1 in 2000.* **Sources: Arb.**

Redspire - *Pyrus calleryana.* Pyramidal tree shape. Yellow to red fall color. Grows 30-35' tall. Very adaptable to city conditions. Zone 4-5. U.S. Plant Patent

No. 3815. *Source History: 16 in 2000.* **Sources: Big, CO5, FE7, Fo2, GR26, HI7, IM2, KAN, ME3, MI5, ORA, SH8, STR, TR19, We8, WI4.**

<u>Robinson</u> - Dwarf tree. Zone 4. *Source History: 1 in 2000.* **Sources: HI7.**

<u>Stone Hill</u> - Dense, upright growth habit. Summer color is dark green; brilliant orange in the fall. Grows to 30'. Zone 5. *Source History: 3 in 2000.* **Sources: Bo5, CO5, GR26.**

<u>Trinity</u> - Light green foliage turns purple and red in the fall. Grows to 35'. U.S. Plant Patent No. 4530. *Source History: 2 in 2000.* **Sources: ORA, We8.**

<u>Valiant</u> - Trademarked. *Source History: 1 in 2000.* **Sources: Bo5.**

<u>Weeping Willow-Leaved</u> - *Pyrus salicifolia* 'Pendula'. Gracefully drooping branches are covered with white blossoms in late spring. Insignificant fruit. Grows 15-20'. Zone 4. *Source History: 2 in 2000.* **Sources: Bay, CO5.**

<u>Whitehouse</u> - *Pyrus calleryana*. White blooms. Purple-red fall color. Tree grows to 40'. Narrow pyramidal crown form allows its use in tight spaces. Hardy in Zones 4-8. *Source History: 4 in 2000.* **Sources: Arb, MO10, ORA, Wel.**

<u>Willow Leaf Pear</u> - *Pyrus salicifolia*. Attractive silver-gray foliage. Stake when young. Pendant habit. Zone 4. *Source History: 1 in 2000.* **Sources: Arb.**

Pear Rootstock

Pyrus spp. (and *Cydonia spp.*)

<u>Bartlett Seedling</u> - *Source History: 2 in 1988; 4 in 1992; 1 in 2000.* **Sources: WI12.**

<u>European Pear Seedling</u> (Standard, Common Pear) - *Pyrus communis*. Widely used for commercial understock. Produces a hardy deep rooted tree with good anchorage. This strain is from northern seed sources. Hardy to Zone 4. *Source History: 1 in 1988; 1 in 1992; 1 in 2000.* **Sources: Bea.**

<u>French Pear Seedling</u> - Rootstock for standard, full size trees. Can grow as tall or taller than apples, but are more upright and less spreading. Where fire blight is a major problem, an interstem of Old Home pear can be used to form a blight resistant framework. *Source History: 1 in 1988; 1 in 1992; 1 in 2000.* **Sources: Va2.**

<u>Harbin Pear</u> - *Pyrus ussuriensis*. Wild Manchurian pear. Some resistance to fire blight. Excellent hardy rootstock for Asian pears. Hardier than *P. calleryana* or *P. betulifolia*. Will not die out at 20-30 years like the Asians on common pear rootstock. Hardy to Zone 4. *Source History: 3 in 1988; 3 in 1992; 2 in 2000.* **Sources: Bea, LA4.**

<u>OH X F 40</u> - Currently being tested. U.S. Plant Patent No. 5412. *Source History: 1 in 1992; 1 in 2000.* **Sources: WI12.**

<u>OH X F 51</u> - *Source History: 1 in 1992; 1 in 2000.* **Sources: Nrs.**

<u>OH X F 87</u> - Semi-dwarf tree. Produces a slightly smaller tree than Bartlett on Bartlett seedling rootstock. Known for its tolerance to blight and decline. Excellent producer. U.S. Plant Patent No. 6362. *Source History: 1 in 1992; 2 in 2000.* **Sources: Va2, WI12.**

<u>OH x F 97</u> (Old Home x Farmingdale 97) - Standard rootstock for European and Asian pears. Trees will be vigorous or near standard size. Productive and well anchored. Good candidate for weaker growing Asian varieties such as Hosui. *Source History: 2 in 1988; 4 in 1992; 7 in 2000.* **Sources: Bay, Ea3, MEA, Nrs, Ro3, Va2, WI12.**

OH x F 333 (Brooks Selection, Old Home x Farmingdale No. 333) - Recently developed in Oregon. Yielded a range of dwarfing rootstock that overcomes the incompatibility and cold tenderness of previously used dwarfing rootstocks for pears. Classed as a semidwarf. Will reduce final tree size to 50-70% of standard. Should be hardy into all pear growing zones. Resistant to fire blight and pear decline. Does not sucker. Hardy, well anchored and productive. Does well on a variety of soils. Superior selection over quince. *Source History: 7 in 1988; 7 in 1992; 4 in 2000.* **Sources: Bay, Ea3, MEA, Ro3.**

OH x F 513 (Old Home x Farmingdale 513) - Developed in Oregon. Semidwarf rootstock for pears that overcomes the incompatibility and cold tenderness of previously used dwarfing rootstocks. Reduces tree size to 50-70% of standard. Compatible with other Zone 4 pear varieties. Resistant to fire blight and pear decline. Does not sucker. Recommended as the best by the Medford Pear Experiment Station. *Source History: 3 in 1992; 5 in 2000.* **Sources: Ea3, MEA, Nrs, On3, Rai.**

Old Home - Hardy, blight resistant variety that is primarily used for understock. Healthy, vigorous grower. *Source History: 2 in 1988; 3 in 1992; 2 in 2000.* **Sources: Nrs, Va2.**

Pyrus betulifolia (Birch-Leaved Pear) - Hardy Asian rootstock immune to pear decline and resistant to fire blight. Exceptional vigor; recommended for marginal land. Adapts well to difficult soil conditions, making a vigorous standard tree. While Asian pears can be dwarfed by grafting on common domestic rootstock, the dwarfing is a result of genetic incompatibility. Such trees will become unproductive after a few years. *P. betulifolia* used on Asian varieties produces a tree 15-20' tall. Used on European pears it makes a huge tree of 30' or more. Can suffer damage in climates consistently below -10 degrees F. More cold hardy and larger trees than *P. calleryana*. *Source History: 12 in 1988; 10 in 1992; 9 in 2000.* **Sources: Bay, Ea3, Fo8, LA4, MEA, Nrs, Sh14, Si3, WI4.**

Pyrus betulifolia, Hardy - Possibly the most hardy *P. betulifolia*. Has withstood -40 degrees. May take the place of *P. ussuriensis* and *P. communis* in many situations due to its compatability, disease resistance, soil adaptability and vigor. Asian pears topworked onto this *P. betulifolia* may be able to survive in much colder climates. Zone 3. *Source History: 1 in 2000.* **Sources: Ed5.**

Pyrus calleryana (Callery Pear) - Rootstock for all pear species, including flowering pears and Asian pears. Asian pear varieties are slightly dwarfed. Heavy bearing at a young age. Strong, vigorous root system. Tolerates wet soils. Most strains not winter hardy. Lacks uniformity. Somewhat susceptible to pear decline. *Source History: 5 in 1988; 9 in 1992; 11 in 2000.* **Sources: Bay, KAN, LA4, LO6, MEA, MIS, Nrs, RA4, Sh14, TU5, WI4.**

Pyrus communis - The species of pear which is the source of all cultivated pears. Produces fruits that are barely edibe by humans. Tree grows to 50'. Hardy to -35 degrees F. *Source History: 2 in 1992; 4 in 2000.* **Sources: Nrs, Oik, Sc2, Sh14.**

Pyrus fauriei - Pyramidal tree grows 30-40'. Fall color changes from yellow to red. Zones 5-8. *Source History: 2 in 1992; 2 in 2000.* **Sources: Arb, GR26, KI3, Nrs.**

Pyrus pyrifolia - *Source History: 3 in 1992; 2 in 2000.* **Sources: Nrs, Sc2, Sh14.**

Pyrus regelii bucharia - *Source History: 1 in 1992; 1 in 2000.* **Sources: Nrs.**

Pyrus serrulata - *Source History: 1 in 2000.* **Sources: Sh14.**

Pyrus syriaca - *Source History: 1 in 1992; 1 in 2000.* **Sources: Nrs.**

Pyrus ussuriensis - Dark green, glossy foliage. Shades of red to purple fall color. Small, sparse fruit. More hardy than Callery pear. *Source History: 5 in 1992; 4 in 2000.* **Sources: GR26, Nrs, Sc2, Sh14.**

Pyrus veitchii - *Source History: 1 in 2000.* **Sources: Nrs.**

Quince - Rootstock used for dwarfing some European pear varieties. Semi-dwarf, approximately 60% of full size. Some compatibility problems. Limited compatibility with Asians. Tolerant of wet soil. Hardy to -10 degrees F. *Source History: 3 in 1988; 2 in 1992; 1 in 2000.* **Sources: Nrs.**

Quince Interstem - Produces the same size tree as pear grafted directly to Quince but the interstem overcomes incompatibility. *Source History: 1 in 2000.* **Sources: Ro3.**

Quince, A - The true Angers Quince widely used to dwarf pears. More tolerant of wet soil than Provence Quince. *Source History: 4 in 1992; 2 in 2000.* **Sources: LA4, WI12.**

Quince, EMLA A - Dwarfing rootstock for pears. Produces heavy crops of large fruit. More winter hardy than EMLA Quince C. Resistant to pear decline, crown gall, mildew, nematodes and root aphids. Susceptible to fire blight. *Source History: 4 in 1988; 4 in 1992; 3 in 2000.* **Sources: MEA, So5, TR8.**

Quince, EMLA C - In the late 1950s and early 1970s, Dr. Ian Campbell of the Long Ashton Research Station in England developed an extensive indexing program for pears. From that program of testing and thermotherapy, the East Malling - Long Ashton (EMLA) pear rootstock EMLA Quince C was released in 1973. More dwarfing and precocious than EMLA Quince A. Heavier yields and greater fruit size. Resistant to pear decline, crown gall, mildew, nematodes, root aphids. Not compatible with all pears; may require a bridging interstem with some varieties. Old Home, Magness and Maxine make good interstems. Performs well in trellised or espalier systems. Introduced in 1973. *Source History: 2 in 1988; 3 in 1992; 2 in 2000.* **Sources: Ro3, TR8.**

Quince, Provence - Quince rootstock is currently used for dwarfing pears, but lacks hardiness for northern areas. Provence Quince is the best stock available at the present time, yielding a tree about half the size of standard. Some varieties can be budded direct; some are not compatible. Bosc, Spartlett and Clapp's Favorite require a compatible interstem between the pear variety and the quince rootstock. *Source History: 4 in 1988; 5 in 1992; 2 in 2000.* **Sources: LA4, Nrs.**

Quince, Provence BA 29-C - Virus-free selection from Le Page Series C. More resistant to calcareous soil types. More compatible with some Bartlett selections than Le Page Series C. Produces trees from 50%-65% the size of standard pear trees. Incompatible with some pear varieties, resulting in the use of an interstem between the scion variety and the understock. Most commonly used interstems are Old Home and Hardy. *Source History: 1 in 1988; 1 in 1992; 3 in 2000.* **Sources: MEA, On3, TR8.**

Quince, Provence Series C (LePage Series C) - Selected from *Cydonia oblonga* by the Institute National de la Recherche Agronomique (INRA) in France. Produces trees anywhere from 50-65% of standard size pear trees. Precocious and very high yielding. Resistant to pear decline, crown gall, nematodes and root aphids. Susceptible to fire blight. Not compatible with Bartlett, Bosc, Clapp and Seckel, so requires an interstem to form a strong union. The most commonly used interstems are Hardy and Old Home. Anjou, Comice, Flemish Beauty and Swiss Bartlett are compatible. More winter hardy than EMLA Quince A. *Source History: 1 in 1988; 1 in 1992; 1 in 2000.* **Sources: MEA.**

Standard Pear Seedling (Common Pear Seedling, Domestic Pear Seedling) - *Pyrus communis*. Seedlings grown from common pear seed which are used for rootstock. Standard pear trees are usually grown on Bartlett or Winter Nelis. They produce a standard size, 20-25' tree with good longevity, durability and productiveness. The trees are full size, vigorous and tolerant of drought or wetter soils. *Source History: 7 in 1988; 7 in 1992; 5 in 2000.* **Sources: Bay, Ca7, LA4, MEA, Sc2.**

Persimmon / American

Diospyros virginiana

American - Sweet, 1-2, yellowish orange fruit with reddish cheek; usually seeded. Astringent until soft ripe; then eaten fresh or in spiced fruit bread or steamed pudding. Round headed, widely spreading, 35-50' deciduous tree; hard, durable wood. Greyish brown bark; glossy, 6" leaves. New leaves are reddish; yellow and red fall foliage. For best results, plant two trees. Native to eastern U.S. Adapted to wide range of soils and climates. Grows as far north as southern shores of the Great Lakes. Drought resistant. Ripens in fall. Frequently hangs on the tree until midwinter. Hardy to -25 degrees F. Zones 4-8. *Source History: 12 in 1988; 12 in 1992; 14 in 2000.* **Sources: Ba3, Bar, Bea, BO4, Ed5, Fo2, Lee, Lo7, Mel, Pa6, Po2, Sav, TU5, WA8.**

Begole - Large fruit; very good flavor. Prolific. Ripens early. *Source History: 1 in 1988; 2 in 1992; 1 in 2000.* **Sources: Nol.**

Black Persimmon (Texas Persimmon) - *Diospyros texana*. Sweet, 1" black fruits. Shrubby, often multi-stemmed, deciduous tree. Peeling, mottled bark. Small, lustrous leaves. Native to the Southwest. Hardy in Zone 7. *Source History: 3 in 1988; 4 in 1992; 2 in 2000.* **Sources: Ca12, Sc2.**

Blue - Blue, prune-shaped fruit matures late. Originated in southern Indiana, 1978. *Source History: 1 in 2000.* **Sources: Nol.**

Campbell 10 - *Source History: 1 in 1992; 1 in 2000.* **Sources: Nol.**

Cemetary - *Source History: 1 in 1992; 1 in 2000.* **Sources: Nol.**

Craggs - Yellow-orange skin with red blush. High quality pulp. Ripens in late October. Originated in Illinois. *Source History: 1 in 1988; 1 in 1992; 1 in 2000.* **Sources: Nol.**

Delight - Round, orange, 1.5" fruit with few seeds. Excellent quality. Originated in southern Indiana. *Source History: 1 in 2000.* **Sources: Nol.**

Early Golden - Large, sweet fruit with large seeds; very good flavor. Wood hardens early. Often self-fertile, but plant with a seedling for best results. Meader is also a good pollinator. Hardy to Zone 4. Superior to native seedlings for fruit production or useful rootstock. Commercially grown in Indiana for fruit pulp canning. The hardiest, along with John Rick; many varieties have been bred from them. *Source History: 7 in 1988; 7 in 1992; 8 in 2000.* **Sources: Bu7, Gr16, Nol, Oik, On3, Or2, Rai, Tri.**

Eastern Persimmon - *Source History: 1 in 1988; 1 in 1992; 1 in 2000.* **Sources: Ca12.**

Elmo - Hand-pollinated cross of Golden Supreme x Garretson, a male seedling which is a member of the Early Golden family. Orange fruit with no black spots on the skin. Slightly larger than a golf ball. Unsurpassed flavor with a slightly firm texture. Fruit drops to the ground when ripe. Tree has almost no insect pests. Jersey Persimmon Farm introduction. *Source History: 1 in 2000.* **Sources: Jer.**

Evelyn - Large, deep orange, sweet fruit. Usually seedless. Heavy crops. Originated in New York. *Source History: 1 in 1988; 2 in 1992; 2 in 2000.* **Sources: Gor, Nol.**

Florence - Medium size fruit. Excellent flavor. Prolific. Ripens midseason. *Source History: 1 in 1988; 1 in 1992; 1 in 2000.* **Sources: On3.**

Gailey - Small, conical, astringent fruit. Sets abundant male flowers; excellent pollinator. *Source History: 1 in 1988; 1 in 1992; 1 in 2000.* **Sources: RA4.**

Garretson - Seedling of Early Golden. Excellent fruit with medium size seeds. Excellent flavor. High quality. Tree structure is somewhat contorted, giving interesting winter lines. Good producer. Ripens early October. Zones 4-8. *Source History: 4 in 1988; 4 in 1992; 4 in 2000.* **Sources: Bu7, Nol, On3, Or2.**

Geneva Long - Bred at the Experiment Station in Geneva, New York. *Source History: 1 in 1992; 2 in 2000.* **Sources: Gor, Nol.**

Golden Supreme - Extra large fruit. Good flavor. Prolific. Ripens late. *Source History: 1 in 1988; 1 in 1992; 2 in 2000.* **Sources: Nol, On3.**

Hess - *Source History: 1 in 1992; 1 in 2000.* **Sources: Gor.**

Janet - *Source History: 1 in 1992; 1 in 2000.* **Sources: Nol.**

John Rick - Largest and latest fruit. Very fine flavor. Wood hardens early. Pollinate with Yates. Ripens early. Hardy to Zone 4. Superior to native seedlings for fruit production or useful rootstock. Most widely grown variety of North American persimmon. Commercially grown in Indiana for fruit pulp canning. John Rick and Early Glow are the hardiest American persimmons; many varieties have been bred from them. *Source History: 6 in 1988; 3 in 1992; 4 in 2000.* **Sources: Nol, On3, Or2, Son.**

Keener - *Source History: 1 in 2000.* **Sources: Neb.**

Killen - Possibly seedling of Early Golden. High quality fruit. Most productive. Originated in Delaware. *Source History: 3 in 1988; 3 in 1992; 1 in 2000.* **Sources: Nol.**

King - *Source History: 1 in 2000.* **Sources: Or2.**

Lena - Large fruit. Very good flavor. Prolific. Ripens early. *Source History: 1 in 1988; 1 in 1992; 1 in 2000.* **Sources: Or2.**

Lindy's Giant - Huge fruit can grow to 7" long. Astringent. Excellent flavor. *Source History: 1 in 2000.* **Sources: Ju2.**

Male - Non-fruiting, medium size tree with yellow fall foliage. Good pollinator for most American persimmons. *Source History: 1 in 1992; 6 in 2000.* **Sources: Bu7, Gr16, Hid, On3, Rai, Son.**

Meader - Fruit is shaped like small tomatoes, about 1.5" in diameter; apricot-colored with red blush. Outstanding, very sweet flavor. Excellent quality. Tree shape is narrow, similar to a pear. Large, ornamental, dark green leaves. Self-fertile; unique in that it will set heavy crops of usually seedless fruit year after year without a pollinator. Outperforms all others. Probably the most advanced of the new varieties. Ripens over a long time during September and October. Hardy to -35 degrees F. Selected by Professor Elwyn Meader in New Hampshire. *Source History: 6 in 1988; 11 in 1992; 11 in 2000.* **Sources: Bu7, Clo, Ed2, Hid, Jun, Mi1, Neb, Nol, On3, Or2, Rai.**

Miles - Heavy annual producer of small seedless orange fruit. Ripens through October-November. Originated in Tennessee. *Source History: 1 in 2000.* **Sources: Nol.**

Miller - Sets rather soft fruit without a pollinator. Ripens early. *Source History: 1 in 1988; 1 in 1992; 1 in 2000.* **Sources: Nol.**

Missouri - Orange, golf ball size fruit. Sugar sweet after a hard autumn frost. Small, ornamental tree with lustrous, tropical looking foliage and deeply fissured bark. Will thrive under the most difficult conditions. Hardy. *Source History: 2 in 1988; 1 in 1992; 1 in 2000.* **Sources: KEE.**

Mitchellena - *Source History: 1 in 2000.* **Sources: Oik.**

Morris Burton - Average size fruit. High quality. Yields well. Ripens late. *Source History: 3 in 1988; 2 in 1992; 2 in 2000.* **Sources: Hid, Nol.**

NC-10 - *Source History: 1 in 1988; 1 in 1992; 1 in 2000.* **Sources: Gor.**

NC-21 - Medium size fruit with super sweet flavor. Ripens in October. *Source History: 1 in 2000.* **Sources: Gor.**

Ormand - Astringent flesh. *Source History: 1 in 2000.* **Sources: RA4.**

Persimmon (Common Persimmon, Hardy Persimmon, Native Persimmon) - Round, fleshy, 1-2", yellowish orange fruit is edible after a good frost, which develops its sweetness and best flavor. Bread and beer are made from the fruits. Pyramidal, spreading tree grows 40-60' tall and 30-40' across. Life span of 30-80 years; begins bearing at 10, continues for over 50 years. Large, dense, 6" dark green leaves turn yellow in fall. Lovely bark pattern. Plant two trees for proper pollination and maximum yields. Good bee plant. Prefers well drained to moist soil. Native from Nebraska to Connecticut. Hardy in Zones 5-10 and maybe milder parts of Zone 4. *Source History: 13 in 1988; 12 in 1992; 21 in 2000.* **Sources: Arb, Ban, BO10, Ca7, Ca8, Fi1, FO10, Fra, Gur, HI7, KEE, LO6, LOV, Mel, RA4, Sc2, Sh10, Sh14, Wa12, Wo2, Wom.**

Pieper - Small fruit. Astringent flesh. Dwarf tree. Hardy in Zone 7. *Source History: 1 in 1988; 3 in 1992; 1 in 2000.* **Sources: Gor.**

Pipher - Commercially grown in Indiana for fruit pulp canning. Not self-pollinating. *Source History: 1 in 1988; 1 in 1992; 2 in 2000.* **Sources: Hid, Oik.**

Prok - Jumbo size fruit. Ripens some of its crop in October. *Source History: 1 in 2000.* **Sources: Gor.**

Ruby - Fine flavored, sweet fruit. Vigorous and productive tree. Somewhat self-fertile, but a seedling or Meader will help produce better crops. Zones 5-8. *Source History: 1 in 1988; 1 in 1992; 2 in 2000.* **Sources: Ed2, Nol.**

Slate - *Source History: 1 in 1988; 1 in 1992; 1 in 2000.* **Sources: Gor.**

Szukis - Medium-large fruit. Tree requires trimming of its many male branches to increase energy to its female branches for bigger fruit size. Pollinates all other persimmons. Ripens Sept.-Oct. *Source History: 1 in 1988; 1 in 1992; 2 in 2000.* **Sources: Gor, Nol.**

Tatum - Early Golden type fruit. Originated in the Tatum orchard near Gravel Switch, Kentucky. *Source History: 1 in 1992; 1 in 2000.* **Sources: Hid.**

Velvet Apple - *Diospyros discolor.* Apple-shaped fruit with brown velvet skin. Tasty but with a pungent, musky odor. Medium size tree. *Source History: 2 in 1992; 1 in 2000.* **Sources: Ga11.**

Wabash - High quality, small fruit with seedless tendencies. Matures early. Leaves turn red in autumn. From Illinois. *Source History: 1 in 1988; 1 in 1992; 1 in 2000.* **Sources: Nol.**

Weber - Large fruit; excellent flavor. Prolific. Ripens early. *Source History: 1 in 1988; 2 in 1992; 1 in 2000.* **Sources: Nol.**

Woolbright - *Source History: 1 in 2000.* **Sources: Nol.**

Yates (Juhl, Jewel) - Large fruit grows up to 2.25" in diameter; fine flavor. Seedless if grown without a pollinator. Prolific bearer. Ripens very early. Originated in Indiana. *Source History: 3 in 1988; 6 in 1992; 5 in 2000.* **Sources: Gor, Hid, Neb, Nol, Oik.**

Persimmon / Oriental

Diospyros kaki (and Diospyros spp.)

Chinese Ebony - *Diospyros docluxii.* Fast growing tree bears orange-brown fruits; semi-dried right off the tree. Fruits store for years. Deep green leaves change to orange then red. Hardy to Zone 5. Trademarked. *Source History: 1 in 2000.* **Sources: Or2.**

Chocolate - Small to medium, oblong cylindrical fruit with rounded apex and bright red skin. Sweet, spicy, firm, juicy, dark flecked, chocolate brown flesh. Astringent until soft ripe. Superb flavor; the choice of connoisseurs. Self-fruitful. Very productive. Requires 200 hours of chilling. Hardy in Zones 7-10. *Source History: 6 in 1988; 9 in 1992; 6 in 2000.* **Sources: Bay, CO5, ORA, Rai, Son, WI4.**

Date Plum (False Lote Tree) - *Diospyros lotus.* Small, .5" tomato-like, yellow fruit on the female trees; turns black when ripe. Black currant-like aroma. Attractive, deciduous tree; varies in size from rather small to 45' tall. Reddish or greenish, .3" flowers and 5" leaves. Native to Asia and Japan; much prized by the Afghans. Hardy in Zone 7 and into the North Central U.S. *Source History: 9 in 1988; 7 in 1992; 5 in 2000.* **Sources: Arb, Ban, Ca7, Or2, Sc2.**

Eureka - Japanese persimmon. Large, reddish orange fruits that hang on the tree until soft and ripe; sometimes seedless. Delicious flavor. Beautiful, very hardy tree, known for its consistent, heavy bearing. Bears young, about the third year. Ripens during September. Recommended for Zones 7-9. *Source History: 6 in 1988; 13 in 1992; 6 in 2000.* **Sources: Iso, Or2, Tex, Ty2, Wel, Wom.**

Fuji - Firm, sweet, dark, non-astringent flesh. *Source History: 1 in 1992; 1 in 2000.* **Sources: Wel.**

Fuyu (Apple Persimmon, Jiro Fuyu, Jiro, Fuyugaki) - Medium to large, round, flattened, glossy, orangish red fruit. Light orange, firm, crunchy, rich, sweet, mild flesh; non-astringent when firm ripe. Can be peeled and eaten fresh like an apple, dried or frozen. Keeps for several months in a cool room. Hardy, attractive tree; practically pest-free. Self-fruitful. Better for cool summer climates than Hachiya. Fall harvest. Requires 200 hours of chilling. Hardy in Zones 8-10. *Source History: 14 in 1988; 28 in 1992; 20 in 2000.* **Sources: Bay, CO5, CO5, Ed2, Gr16, Ju2, Lo7, Me2, On4, Or2, ORA, Pa2, RA4, Rai, Son, STR, Tex, Ty2, WI4, Wom.**

Fuyu Imoto, Giant - *Source History: 1 in 1992; 1 in 2000.* **Sources: Me2.**

Fuyu, Giant - Very large, round, flattened, reddish orange fruit; approximately 40% larger and not as flat as regular Fuyu. Sweeter, juicier, smooth textured, reddish yellow flesh. Non-astringent; may be eaten while still firm. Good for fresh eating, dried, frozen or cooked fresh in pastry, jams and jellies. Self-fruitful. Easy to grow in cool or hot climates. Fall harvest. Ripens in late October. Requires 200 hours of chilling. Hardy in Zones 8-9. *Source History: 6 in 1988; 11 in 1992; 8 in 2000.* **Sources: Bay, CO5, Me2, On4, ORA, Pa2, Pe2, WI4.**

Fuyugaki (Winter Persimmon) - Tomato-shaped fruit with few seeds. Dark red skin develops a blue blush when fully ripe. Light colored, firm textured, non-astringent flesh; can be eaten like an apple even before fully ripe. Excellent in all respects. Self-pollinating. Favorite commercial cultivar in Japan. Ripens in late fall. Hardy in Zones 7-9. *Source History: 5 in 1988; 5 in 1992; 5 in 2000.* **Sources: Bas, BO10, Ed2, Iso, SIM.**

Gionbo - Giant, conical fruit, weighing up to one pound. Excellent, astringent taste. Very productive. Hardy in Zones 8-10. *Source History: 1 in 1988; 3 in 1992; 4 in 2000.* **Sources: Ju2, Lo7, Or2, RA4.**

Great Wall - Chinese variety discovered by the explorer J. Russell Smith. Small, square, flattened, very sweet, orange fruit; low percentage are seedless. Astringent flesh. Abundant producer. Ripens very early. Very cold hardy. Hardy in Zones 6-10. *Source History: 2 in 1988; 7 in 1992; 2 in 2000.* **Sources: Ju2, Or2.**

Hachiya - Large, acorn-shaped, flattened fruit; has few seeds when planted apart from other persimmons. Orange flesh; astringent until fully ripe. Sweet, even when crisp and firm; more so when fully ripe. Usually softened off the tree. Excellent quality. Used for drying when firm ripe. Medium to large, vigorous, spreading, highly ornamental tree with red, bronze and yellow autumn color. Self-fruitful. Insect and disease free. Grows best in well-drained, light soil. Leading U.S. commercial variety; widely planted in California. Ripens in late fall. 200 hours of chilling. Hardy in Zones 6-10. *Source History: 15 in 1988; 23 in 1992; 20 in 2000.* **Sources: Bas, Bay, CO5, Ju2, Lo7, On3, On4, Or2, ORA, Pa2, RA4, Rai, SIM, Son, STR, Tex, Ty2, Wel, WI4, Wom.**

Hana-Fuyu (Winter Flower) - Very large, reddish orange, obliquely rounded fruit. Non-astringent flesh. Wonderful flavor and quality. Dwarf tree. Ripens in mid-October. Hardy in Zones 7-10. *Source History: 1 in 1988; 5 in 1992; 3 in 2000.* **Sources: Ju2, Or2, RA4.**

Hana-Gosho (Flower of the Imperial Palace) - Large, flat, quadranted, orange fruit. Non-astringent flesh. Excellent taste and quality. Ripens late. Hardy in Zones 7-10. *Source History: 1 in 1988; 2 in 1992; 2 in 2000.* **Sources: Ju2, RA4.**

Hira Tanashi (Flat Seedless, Hira Tenenaeshi) - Medium size, flat, seedless, very sweet, orange fruit; no cracks in the skin. Astringent until ripe. Medium vigorous, spreading tree. Second most popular variety in Japan behind Fuyu. Ripens over a six week period. When fully dormant it has withstood -40 degree F. Siberian cold in northern Japan, but because of the East Coast's fluctuating springtime temperatures and late frosts, this variety should not be considered north of Philadelphia. Hardy in Zones 6-10. *Source History: 2 in 1988; 2 in 1992; 3 in 2000.* **Sources: Arb, Cla, Or2.**

Hiyakume - Large, 3" fruits vary from roundish oblong to roundish flat. Buff yellow to orange skin. Juicy, dark cinnamon flesh. Good flavor; can be eaten right off the tree. *Source History: 1 in 1988; 4 in 1992; 1 in 2000.* **Sources: Or2, ORA.**

Honan Red - Astringent flesh until soft. Ripens midseason. *Source History: 1 in 1988; 2 in 1992; 3 in 2000.* **Sources: Ju2, Lo7, Or2.**

Ichi-Ki-Kei-Jiro - Large, flat, orange fruit. Non-astringent flesh. Very good flavor. Dwarf tree grows 10-15' tall. Self-fertile. Hardy in Zones 6-10. Name translates "First life from Jiro." *Source History: 1 in 1988; 4 in 1992; 5 in 2000.* **Sources: Ed2, Or2, RA4, Rai, St4.**

Izu - Medium size fruit with good taste. Non-astringent flesh. Dwarf tree. Bears only female flowers. Good disease resistance. Good fruit set. Ripens in September. Requires 100 hours of chilling. Zones 6-10. *Source History: 1 in 1988; 6 in 1992; 16 in 2000.* **Sources: Bay, Bu7, Clo, CO5, Ju2, Me2, On3, On4, Or2, ORA, Pa2, RA4, Rai, Son, WI4, Wom.**

Jiro - Large, sweet, orange-red fruit. Upright tree. Ripens mid to late October. Cold hardy. Second most popular non-astringent cultivar in Japan. Hardy in Zones 6-10. *Source History: 4 in 1992; 6 in 2000.* **Sources: Bu7, Gr16, Iso, On3, Or2, RA4.**

Kaki (Date Plum, Japanese Persimmon, Japanese Plum, Keg Fig) - Variably shaped, 3" orange to reddish fruit. Orange flesh. Tree grows 40' tall. Many cultivars of this species are widely grown in Japan and China. *Source History: 4 in 1988; 5 in 1992; 4 in 2000.* **Sources: Ban, BO10, Ca7, Sc2.**

Korean - Medium size, flat, orange fruit. Astringent flesh; sweet taste. Productive bearer. Hardy to Zone 7. *Source History: 1 in 1988; 2 in 1992; 1 in 2000.* **Sources: Or2.**

Maru - Medium size, broad, orangish red fruit with a rounded apex. Sweet, rich, dark cinnamon flesh. Excellent quality. Self-fruitful. Requires 200 hours of chilling. *Source History: 2 in 1988; 5 in 1992; 3 in 2000.* **Sources: ORA, Pa2, WI4.**

Matsumoto - Similar to Fuyu. Large fruit with sweet flavor. Prolific. Disease resistant. Ripens two weeks ahead of Fuyu. Hardy in Zones 7-10. *Source History: 1 in 1992; 2 in 2000.* **Sources: Or2, RA4.**

Matsumoto Wasefuyu - Tasty orange fruit with non-astringent flesh. Ripens two weeks before Jiro. *Source History: 1 in 1992; 1 in 2000.* **Sources: ORA.**

Meakawa Jiro - *Source History: 1 in 2000.* **Sources: ORA.**

Midia - Non-astringent flesh. *Source History: 1 in 1988; 1 in 1992; 1 in 2000.* **Sources: RA4.**

Nishimura Wase - Bud sport developed in Japan. Medium to large, almost round fruit. Sweet, juicy, chocolate-brown flesh. Non-astringent. Ripens mid-September to mid-October; earliest known variety to ripen in California. Requires a pollinator and 100 hours of chilling. *Source History: 4 in 2000.* **Sources: Bay, Or2, ORA, WI4.**

Oku-Gosho - Medium size, round, orange fruit. Astringent flesh; inconsistent astringency loss. Good taste. Medium size tree. Older variety. Ripens in early September. *Source History: 1 in 1988; 2 in 1992; 1 in 2000.* **Sources: RA4.**

Oriental - Plump, nearly seedless, orangish gold fruit. Can be eaten before fully ripe; also good dried. Tree grows 10-15' tall. Self-fruitful and an excellent pollinator for other varieties. Resists blight and foliage diseases. Thrives even in frost-free areas of the Deep South. Ripens during September. *Source History: 1 in 1988; 1 in 1992; 1 in 2000.* **Sources: Arb.**

Russian Kaki - Small, pointed, gold fruits with soft, melting flesh. Excellent flavor. Astringent until fully ripe. Ripens very early. Hardy. *Source History: 1 in 1992; 1 in 2000.* **Sources: Or2.**

Saijo (Mr. Elegant) - Small, conic, elongated, yellowish orange fruit. No cracks; high seedlessness. Flesh is astringent and is not eaten fresh until soft ripe; very sweet, wonderful flavor. Very good quality. Can be dried while firm; drying process removes the astringency. Dried fruit is very sweet with texture like dates. Stores well. Highly vigorous, medium size, upright, spreading tree. Heavy annual bearer; consistent producer. Self-pollinating. Hardy in Zones 6-9. Old Japanese variety; original tree is 600 years old. Known in Japan as "The very best one." *Source History: 4 in 1988; 9 in 1992; 7 in 2000.* **Sources: Ed2, Ju2, Lo7, Mi1, Or2, RA4, Rai.**

Sheng - Medium to large, flat, four-lobed, orange fruit; high quality. Non-astringent flesh. Low percentage of seedless fruit. Dries well. Open, widespreading tree with irregular branches; very similar to Hana-Gosho, but is a smaller, dwarf tree.   Medium crop load; medium vigor.   Ripens during October.   Zones 6-10. *Source History: 2 in 1988; 5 in 1992; 3 in 2000.* **Sources: Ed2, Ju2, Or2.**

Suruga - Recently developed cross of Hanagosho and Okugosho. Large, red fruit. Non-astringent flesh. Recommended for warmer climates. Ripens during November. Hardy in Zones 8-10. *Source History: 1 in 1988; 3 in 1992; 3 in 2000.* **Sources: Ju2, ORA, RA4.**

Tamopan - Large, flat, reddish orange fruit with a very flat, deep constriction near the stem end.   Not as good tasting as other varieties.   Ripens in November.   Requires 200 hours of chilling. *Source History: 3 in 1988; 11 in 1992; 5 in 2000.* **Sources: CO5, Or2, RA4, Tex, Wel.**

Tamopan, Giant - Extremely large, 3-5" reddish orange fruit with distinctive shape like a flat acorn cap on the stem end; usually quadrangular with prominent crease below the middle.   Often weighs up to one pound.   Light reddish orange, very juicy, astringent flesh. Thick skin; often eaten with a spoon from the half shell. Not as good tasting as some varieties.   Ripens in November or December.   Hardy in Zones 8-10.   Very large strain of Tamopan that was bred using colchicine by R. T. Dunstan. *Source History: 3 in 1988; 3 in 1992; 1 in 2000.* **Sources: ORA.**

Tanenashi (Tani Nashi) - Large to very large, long, round conic fruit; light yellow ripening to light orangish red. Melting, yellow flesh is astringent until fully ripe; almost always seedless. Delightful flavor; finest quality. Tree grows 40' tall; self-pollinating. Bears prolifically, even when quite young; holds its fruit into late fall and winter. Ripens in September and October. Excellent variety for home or commercial use. One of the earliest introductions into the U.S. from Japan. Hardy in Zones 8-10. *Source History: 11 in 1988; 18 in 1992; 14 in 2000.* **Sources: Bas, CO5, Fi1, Gur, Iso, Ju2, Lo7, Or2, ORA, RA4, SIM, St4, Tex, Wel.**

Yamagaki - Non-astringent fruit. Good pollinator. Hardy. Zones 6-9. *Source History: 1 in 1992; 1 in 2000.* **Sources: Ed2.**

Yamato Hyakume - Elongated, conical, very pretty fruit. Flesh turns chocolate with pollination. Astringent until fully ripe. Upright tree. *Source History: 1 in 1988; 2 in 1992; 2 in 2000.* **Sources: Ju2, RA4.**

Plum

Plum / European – *Prunus domestica*

Plum / Japanese – *Prunus salicina*

and *Prunus spp.*

Abundance - *Prunus salicina*; Japanese plum. Medium size, dark red fruit with a purple blush. Tender, juicy, light yellow, clingstone flesh. Good quality but softens rapidly. Vigorous, fast growing tree. Comes into bearing quite young. Biennial bearing tendency. Yields abundantly. Ripens midseason. Hardy to Zone 5. *Source History: 5 in 1988; 7 in 1992; 4 in 2000.* **Sources: FO10, Leu, TU5, WA8.**

Ace (Red Ace) - *Source History: 1 in 1992; 1 in 2000.* **Sources: Ch9.**

Alabaster - *Prunus domestica*; European plum. Almost round fruit with clear, pale yellow skin entirely covered with a heavy white bloom. Firm, juicy, sweet flesh. Regular, heavy crops. Ripens in mid-August. Comes from a chance seedling originating under a tree carrying grafts of Pearl and McLaughlin. *Source History: 1 in 1988; 1 in 1992; 1 in 2000.* **Sources: So5.**

Alace - *Source History: 1 in 1992; 1 in 2000.* **Sources: Nrs.**

Alderman - Japanese x American plum. Large, burgundy fruit. Medium soft, yellow, clingstone flesh. Sweet, slightly astringent flavor. Excellent quality. Fresh eating or preserves. Requires a pollinator; Premier does well. Ripens in mid-August. Hardy at -50 degrees F. with occasional winter injury. *Source History: 1 in 1988; 6 in 1992; 8 in 2000.* **Sources: Ed5, Fed, Hi9, Mc3, Nrs, Ro3, SH8, Stl.**

All Red - Purple fruit with red, freestone flesh. Slightly tart flavor. Small tree to 12' with purple leaves. Self-fertile. Hardy in Zones 5-9. *Source History: 6 in 1992; 2 in 2000.* **Sources: Ed2, Nrs.**

Ambra - Medium size, red-purple fruit. Sweet flesh. Requires a pollinator. Ripens late May to mid-June. *Source History: 1 in 1992; 1 in 2000.* **Sources: Ju2.**

Angeleno - Dark purple-black fruit with firm, amber flesh with fair to good flavor. Holds and stores well. Pollinate with Santa Rosa or Wickson. Ripens during September. *Source History: 3 in 1992; 1 in 2000.* **Sources: AG2.**

Assiniboine - Seedling of *Prunus nigra* from South Dakota. Medium size fruits with bright red skin. Extremely hardy tree; Zone 3. Ripens late August. *Source History: 1 in 1992; 2 in 2000.* **Sources: Bea, Nrs.**

Au Amber - Medium size, red-purple fruit with amber flesh of very good eating quality. Ripens about 4-5 days before Methley. Released by Auburn University. *Source History: 5 in 1992; 6 in 2000.* **Sources: Cla, Cum, Ho5, Iso, Nrs, Ty2.**

Au Cherry - Small, red fruit of good eating quality. Large, productive tree. Good choice for home gardeners. *Source History: 4 in 1992; 1 in 2000.* **Sources: Cla.**

Au Homeside - Very large plum with orange skin; cream flesh. Released by Auburn University. *Source History: 1 in 1992; 1 in 2000.* **Sources: Ty2.**

Au Producer - Japanese plum. Medium size, round fruit with moderately firm, juicy, red flesh. High flavor. Ripens in early July. Introduced by Auburn University. *Source History: 3 in 1988; 4 in 1992; 4 in 2000.* **Sources: Cla, Cum, Ho5, Iso.**

Au Roadside - Japanese plum. Very large, high quality fruit with magenta skin and red flesh. Slight resistance to brown rot; shows good resistance to all other major plum diseases. Named for Auburn University where it was developed. *Source History: 3 in 1988; 5 in 1992; 3 in 2000.* **Sources: Cum, Ho5, Nrs.**

Au Rosa - Japanese plum. Santa Rosa hybrid. Red fruit with firm, sweet yellow flesh. Fruit size reaches 2" with proper thinning. Ripens a few days later than Santa Rosa and is a healthier tree. Zones 5-9. Released by Auburn University. *Source History: 2 in 1992; 5 in 2000.* **Sources: Cum, Iso, Jo3, Nrs, Ro3.**

Au Rubrum - Methley hybrid. Fruit is maroon with red flesh. Similar to Morris with a healthier tree. Self-fruitful. Ripens early to mid July. Zones 5-9. Released by Auburn University. *Source History: 3 in 1992; 5 in 2000.* **Sources: Cla, Cum, Ho5, Jo3, Ty2.**

Autumn Beaut - Medium size, dark red fruit. Firm, juicy flesh with good flavor. Very productive, spreading tree requires pollination. Ripens in mid-September. Requires 800-900 hours of chilling. U.S. Plant Patent No. 8189. *Source History: 1 in 2000.* **Sources: WI4.**

Autumn Pride - Maroon skin color. Firm flesh. Good flavor. Ripens in mid-September and holds well on the tree. Requires 800-900 hours of chilling. U.S. Plant Patent No. 7843. *Source History: 1 in 2000.* **Sources: WI4.**

Autumn Rosa - Purple-red fruit with amber cast. Red streaked, yellow flesh. Excellent flavor. Holds well on the tree. Heavy producer. Self-fruitful; good pollinator for Mariposa. Ripens over a long period in September. Requires 500 hours of chilling. *Source History: 1 in 1988; 2 in 1992; 2 in 2000.* **Sources: Bay, CO5.**

Autumn Sweet - European plum. Large, firm sweet fruit. Blooms late. Requires a pollinator. Developed at Washington State University at Prosser. *Source History: 1 in 2000.* **Sources: COL.**

Aycock - Red fleshed fruit on small, spreading 12' tree. Hardy in Zones 5-8. *Source History: 1 in 1992; 1 in 2000.* **Sources: Ed2.**

B69158 - Prune type with sweet, amber-colored flesh. Deep purple skin. Clingstone. Thinning is beneficial in years of heavy fruit set. Ripens about ten days before Stanley. *Source History: 1 in 2000.* **Sources: Ad2.**

Beauty - Japanese plum. Santa Rosa type, but more widely adapted. Medium size, reddish purple fruit. Amber flesh streaked with red. Excellent flavor. Does not keep. Self-fruitful. Consistently heavy crops. Ripens from June to early August depending on location. Requires 250-500 hours of chilling. Zone 5. *Source History: 7 in 1988; 14 in 1992; 11 in 2000.* **Sources: Bay, Bu7, CO5, ME3, Mo19, Nrs, On3, ORA, Pa2, Rai, WI4.**

Betty Anne - Large, bright red fruit. Productive, spreading tree requires a pollinizer. Chilling requirement of 750-850 hours. U.S. Plant Patent No. 8471. *Source History: 1 in 2000.* **Sources: WI4.**

Big Blue - Chicken egg size fruit. Sweet and juicy. Good for fresh eating, canning or preserves. Early, heavy bearer. Ripens in mid-September. *Source History: 1 in 1988; 1 in 1992; 1 in 2000.* **Sources: Mi1.**

Black Amber - Japanese plum. Round, firm, dark purple fruit closely resembles Friar, but ripens 10-12 days earlier. High quality. Rapid growing, heavy bearing tree. Needs a pollenizer. *Source History: 5 in 1988; 10 in 1992; 4 in 2000.* **Sources: AG2, Bo5, Nrs, STR.**

Blackruby - Yellow fleshed fruit with reddish black skin color. Ripens late. Zones 5-9. *Source History: 3 in 2000.* **Sources: Cum, Nrs, Ty2.**

Blue Damson (Shrop Improved) - European plum. Small, round, blue fruits in clusters. Very tart, green, freestone flesh. Excellent for jams, jellies and preserves. Vigorous, heavy producer, a little larger than most plum trees. Widely adapted. Self-fruitful. Ripens from late August to late September depending on location. Requires 800 hours of chilling. Hardy to central Iowa; Zone 5. *Source History: 15 in 1988; 15 in 1992; 12 in 2000.* **Sources: Bar, Bu1, Fi1, FO10, Fo4, JOY, ORA, Pe2, Son, STR, Ty2, WI4.**

Blue Giant - Very large fruit up to one-half pound. Firm, sweet-tart flesh. Ripens in July. Requires 600 hours of chilling. Plant patent applied for. *Source History: 2 in 1992; 1 in 2000.* **Sources: ORA.**

Bluebyrd - European plum. Deep blue fruit with sweet, amber colored flesh. Developed in Kerneysville, Virginia. *Source History: 1 in 2000.* **Sources: Ro3.**

Bluefree (Bluefre) - Stanley x President seedling from Missouri. European plum. Large, blue fruit with firm, yellow, freestone flesh. Excellent, sweet flavor. Hangs to the tree well, but has a tendency toward split pits. Retains color well when processed. Vigorous, extremely hardy tree bears early and heavily. Partially self-fruitful. Sets well with pollen of Stanley. Ripens 3-7 days after Stanley. *Source History: 3 in 1988; 5 in 1992; 3 in 2000.* **Sources: Ad2, Nrs, Sc6.**

Briceland Damson - Small, bluish purple fruit with a heavy bloom. Yellow flesh with a spicy, somewhat astringent flavor. Best for canning. Semidwarf, upright tree. Well adapted. Ripens in September. Originated in Damascus, then spread progressively to continental Europe, England America. *Source History: 1 in*

1988; 1 in 1992; 1 in 2000. **Sources: Gr4.**

Brompton - *Source History: 1 in 1992; 1 in 2000.* **Sources: Nrs.**

Brookgold - *Source History: 1 in 1992; 1 in 2000.* **Sources: Nrs.**

Brooks - European plum. Large, purplish black fruit with sweet, yellow flesh. Excellent for eating, canning and drying. Self-pollinating according to one source. Another recommends pollinating with Green Gage, Italian or Peach Plum. Hardy to Zone 5. Originated in Oregon. *Source History: 6 in 1988; 7 in 1992; 7 in 2000.* **Sources: Ea3, Gr16, JOY, ME3, Nrs, On3, WI4.**

Bruce - Large, brilliant, wine-red fruit. Very good for canning. Early, heavy bearer. Requires a pollinator, usually Methley. Ripens mid to late May. Well suited to northern Texas and Oklahoma. Good plum for commercial use. Hardy in Zones 5-9. *Source History: 10 in 1988; 21 in 1992; 14 in 2000.* **Sources: Bar, Bas, FO10, GI3, Ho5, Ju2, MI10, MI5, SIM, Tex, TU5, Ty2, Wel, Wom.**

Burbank - Japanese plum. Large, purplish red fruit. Sweet, meaty, amber yellow, clingstone flesh. Excellent flavor. Best when picked before fully ripe. Excellent for eating fresh and canning. Low growing, flat topped, somewhat drooping tree. Bears early and sets heavily. Widely adapted. Good for commercial production and shipping. Ripens in early August in Michigan, mid-July in the West and South. Requires 400 hours of chilling. Hardy in Zones 5-9. Developed by Luther Burbank of Santa Rosa, California. *Source History: 22 in 1988; 31 in 1992; 21 in 2000.* **Sources: Bar, Bay, Ch9, Ea3, FO10, GI3, Hi9, Ho5, Lee, Leu, Mel, MI10, Na4, Nrs, Sav, SIM, TU5, WA8, Wel, WI4, Wor.**

Burbank, Grand Prize - European plum. Round-ovate, purple-blue fruit. Juicy, yellow, freestone flesh of excellent quality. Ripens 14 days before Stanley. Developed by Luther Burbank in Sebastopol, California. *Source History: 2 in 1992; 1 in 2000.* **Sources: Nrs.**

Burbank, Red Ace - Crimson fruit with sweet, semifreestone flesh. Natural semidwarf tree, 12-15' tall. Pollinate with Ozark Premier, Redheart or Shiro. Ripens in mid-August. Hardy in Zones 5-9. Trademarked. *Source History: 1 in 1988; 2 in 1992; 1 in 2000.* **Sources: St4.**

Burgundy - Japanese plum. Medium size, cherry red fruit with sweet, mellow red flesh. Very productive. Self-fruitful. Ripens from July to August depending on location. Requires 150-500 hours of chilling. *Source History: 4 in 1988; 6 in 1992; 6 in 2000.* **Sources: Bay, CO5, On4, Pa2, STR, WI4.**

Burton - *Source History: 1 in 2000.* **Sources: Nrs.**

Byron Gold - Japanese plum. Large, pretty, yellow fruit. Golden yellow flesh. Requires pollination. Ripens 16 days after Methley; late June to early July. Originated in Byron, Georgia. *Source History: 1 in 1988; 3 in 1992; 4 in 2000.* **Sources: Cu4, Ju2, Nrs, Ty2.**

California Blue - Large, blue, nearly freestone fruit. Somewhat tart flavor. Good quality. Ripens with Shiro. Gaining popularity in Ontario. *Source History: 1 in 1988; 2 in 1992; 1 in 2000.* **Sources: Nrs.**

Cambridge Gage - European plum. Seedling of Green Gage thought to have originated in Cambridge, England. Similar to Green Gage, but more yellow and not quite as rich in flavor. Consistent bearer. *Source History: 1 in 1988; 2 in 1992; 2 in 2000.* **Sources: Rai, So5.**

Casselman - Skin color is crimson with yellow flecking. Firm, yellow flesh with rich, sweet flavor. Heavy producer. Self-fruitful. Ripens midseason. *Source History: 3 in 1988; 4 in 1992; 3 in 2000.* **Sources: AG2, CO5, ORA.**

Castleton - European plum. Valor x Iroquois cross. Blue, slightly ovate fruit resembles Stanley. Non-fragmenting stone. Spreading tree is a consistently heavy producer. Thinning is recommended. Ripens 2-3 weeks before Stanley. Trade-marked. U.S. Plant Patent No. 9638. *Source History: 5 in 2000.* **Sources: Ad2, Co2, Cu4, Hi9, St4.**

Catalina - Japanese plum. Large, black, fresh market plum. Good variety for home planting. Vigorous, productive tree. Self-fruitful. Ripens from early to mid-July in central California, 10-14 days after Santa Rosa. Requires 400-500 hours of chilling. *Source History: 1 in 1988; 7 in 1992; 4 in 2000.* **Sources: AG2, Bay, Va2, WI4.**

Cocheco - Red blushed fruit. Hardy in Zones 4-9. Released from New Hamp-shire. *Source History: 1 in 1992; 1 in 2000.* **Sources: Mo19.**

Coe's Golden Drop - Medium to large fruits with yellow skin and golden flesh. Sweet and juicy flesh with an apricot-like flavor. Freestone. Ripens in October. Requires a pollinator. Introduced at Bury St. Edmunds, England in 1800. *Source History: 1 in 2000.* **Sources: Rai.**

Convoy - *Source History: 1 in 1992; 1 in 2000.* **Sources: Nrs.**

Count Althan's Gage - Dark crimson-purple plum shaded with brown and cov-ered with a bluish bloom. Sweet, juicy, rich golden flesh. Raised by the gardener of Count Althann in Swoyschitz, Bohemia. Introduced in 1867. *Source History: 1 in 1988; 2 in 1992; 2 in 2000.* **Sources: So5, Son.**

Crimson - Japanese plum. Round fruit with crimson red skin and flesh. Excellent quality. Good for fresh eating, jams and jellies. High yielding. Highly disease re-sistant. Ripens from early June to mid-July depending on location. Hardy in Zones 6-9. *Source History: 4 in 1988; 5 in 1992; 2 in 2000.* **Sources: Cu4, Ho5.**

Damson - European plum. Small to medium, oval, bluish purple fruit. Tart, juicy, golden yellow flesh. Excellent for home canning. Vigorous, self-fertile tree. Heavy crops. Used commercially in some parts of the U.S. Ripens from August to early September. Hardy in Zones 5-7. *Source History: 9 in 1988; 15 in 1992; 9 in 2000.* **Sources: Cla, Co2, MI5, Na4, Nrs, Oik, Po2, SIM, St4.**

Delicious - *Source History: 1 in 2000.* **Sources: Ch9.**

Double Cross French Prune - European plum. Dark blue fruit. Just as rich and sweet as Petite but larger and it shrinks far less when drying. Excellent for drying into prunes. Hardy tree is sport of Petite. Partially self-fruitful; benefits from a pollinator. Early, heavy crops. Good shipper. Hardy to Zone 5. *Source History: 2 in 1988; 2 in 1992; 1 in 2000.* **Sources: Bea.**

Duarte - Japanese plum. Large, heart-shaped, deep red fruit. Firm, juicy, sweet, blood-red flesh. Excellent quality for fresh eating or canning. Tree is vigorous, hardy and somewhat self-fruitful. For best production cross-pollinate with another variety. Good pollinator for others, especially Santa Rosa. *Source History: 2 in 1988; 3 in 1992; 2 in 2000.* **Sources: Va2, Wor.**

Duarte Improved - Japanese plum. Extra large, heart-shaped fruit. Solid, meaty, blood-red flesh. Excellent quality. *Source History: 1 in 1988; 1 in 1992; 2 in 2000.* **Sources: Bo5, Co2.**

Dura - *Source History: 1 in 1992; 1 in 2000.* **Sources: Nrs.**

Earliblue (Earliblue Prune Plum) - European plum. Purplish blue fruit. Resem-bles Stanley, but is softer and has shorter shelf life. Good quality and appearance. One of the best tasting of its type. Very sturdy, upright tree, rather slow to come into production. Late blooming. Moderate crops, but sufficient for home use and roadside market. Ripens in July. Hardy in Zones 5-8. *Source History: 3 in 1988; 3 in 1992; 1 in 2000.* **Sources: St4.**

EarliMagic - Large, dark red-purple plum with firm, yellow, freestone flesh. Good flavor. Cracks less than Methley. Hangs well on the tree. Trademarked. *Source History: 1 in 2000.* **Sources: Hi9.**

Early Golden - Japanese plum. Medium size, round, yellow fruit with red blush. Freestone. Fair quality. Requires a pollinator. Ripens in July; two weeks before Shiro. Hardy in Zones 5-9. Introduced in 1946. *Source History: 2 in 1988; 4 in 1992; 2 in 2000.* **Sources: Hi9, Rai.**

Early Italian (Early Italian Prune, Goodman Strain, Richards) - European plum. Large, oblong, purple fruit. Greenish yellow, freestone flesh. Used for canning, drying or fresh eating. Excellent commercial variety. Good shipper. Self-fertile, but more productive when pollinated by another European variety. Resembles Italian Prune in shape and color, but ripens 10-14 days earlier. *Source History: 3 in 1988; 5 in 1992; 6 in 2000.* **Sources: Bu7, Gr16, Gr4, ORA, Va2, WI4.**

Early Italian, Milton - Excellent variety with fruiting habits and qualities the same as Italian but with less firmness. Ripens 10-14 days before Italian. *Source History: 1 in 2000.* **Sources: WI12.**

Early Italian, Richard's Strain - European plum. Resembles Italian Prune from which it developed as a bud sport. Fruit is not quite as firm, but still considered a good shipper. Tree is more productive, but less vigorous. Ripens 10-14 days earlier. Introduced in 1950. *Source History: 3 in 1988; 3 in 1992; 2 in 2000.* **Sources: Co2, Nrs.**

Early Laxton - Tasty old European variety. Bright pinkish orange fruit dotted with rose and violet. Juicy, sweet, freestone flesh, high in vitamin C. Refreshing flavor. Partially self-fertile. Very heavy bearer. Must be thinned or the branches will be weighted down with fruit clustered like grapes. Ripens in mid-July. Introduced by the Laxton Nursery of Bedford, England. *Source History: 2 in 1988; 2 in 1992; 4 in 2000.* **Sources: Bea, Mo19, Rai, So5.**

Ebony Sun - Large, conical, black fruit. Firm, juicy, non-melting, yellow flesh. Holds well on the tree and in storage. No sign of cracking even after rain. Moderately vigorous tree requires thinning. Pollinate with Anna Sun plum. Ripens in August. Developed in California. U.S. Plant Patent No. 6153. *Source History: 1 in 1992; 1 in 2000.* **Sources: AG2.**

Elephant Heart (Burbank Elephant Heart) - Japanese plum. Large, heart-shaped fruit with thick, bronze green skin that turns reddish purple when completely ripe. Juicy, blood-red, freestone flesh. Rich, distinctive flavor. Good for fresh eating, canning and freezing. Vigorous, hardy tree. A favorite for home orchards on dwarf rootstock. Self-fruitful, but produces best when cross-pollinated. Pollinate with Beauty, Redheart or Santa Rosa. Does well in northern, central and inland areas of southern California. Ripens over a 14 day period in midseason. Good shipper. Requires only 500 hours of chilling. Zone 5. *Source History: 15 in 1988; 19 in 1992; 15 in 2000.* **Sources: Bay, Cla, CO5, Gr16, Hi9, ME3, Nrs, ORA, Pe2, So5, Son, STR, Ty2, Va2, WI4.**

Elma's Special - Small, round, purple-red fruit about 1.5" in diameter. Amber, freestone flesh with good flavor. Outstanding for drying. Makes good jam. Vigorous tree with dense foliage. Ripens in late July. Originally from Whatcom, Washington. *Source History: 1 in 1988; 1 in 1992; 1 in 2000.* **Sources: Clo.**

Ember - Large, golden yellow fruit with orange-red blush. Sweet, firm flesh. Delicious fresh, cooked or canned. Pollinate with Underwood. Heavy crops even after severe winter cold. Ripens in mid-August. Hardy in Zones 4-8. *Source History: 1 in 1988; 3 in 1992; 2 in 2000.* **Sources: Mc3, Nrs.**

Emerald Beaut - Light green skin. Green-yellow to orange, freestone flesh. Sweet, distinctive, pleasing flavor. Crunchy when ripe. Ripens late August through early October. Holds well on the tree for up to two months. Requires a pollinator and 600-900 hours of chilling. U.S. Plant Patent No. 9162. *Source History: 2 in 2000.* **Sources: Bay, WI4.**

Empress - President x Emily. European plum. Fruit is larger than President and deeper blue. Firm, fine textured, yellow flesh. Good shipper. Strong, vigorous, productive, upright tree. Cross-pollinates well with President. Very popular in Idaho. Ripens in early September, seven days ahead of President. *Source History: 6 in 1988; 6 in 1992; 5 in 2000.* **Sources: Cla, Co2, Cu4, Hi9, Nrs.**

Ersinger - European plum. Medium-small blue fruit is not large enough for packing but excellent for home use. Elegant flavor. Ripens just before Castleton. *Source History: 1 in 2000.* **Sources: Cu4.**

Ewing Blue - European plum. Excellent prune type. Similar to Todd but larger and slightly higher in quality. The tree is somewhat more tender to cold. Vigorous grower. Ripens in early September. Hardy to -40 degrees F. *Source History: 1 in 1988; 1 in 2000.* **Sources: Stl.**

Excelsor - *Source History: 1 in 1988; 1 in 1992; 1 in 2000.* **Sources: SIM.**

Explorer - Sweet, juicy, reddish black fruit. Ripens midseason. Developed at the Georgia Agricultural Experiment Station. *Source History: 4 in 1988; 5 in 1992; 2 in 2000.* **Sources: Cla, Ho5.**

Fellemberg - European prune plum. Large, oval, purple freestone. Firm, tender, fine grained, yellow flesh. Sweet, delicious flavor. Fruits hang on the tree for two weeks after ripening. Good for fresh eating, cooking, canning, preserves and drying. Flesh turns burgundy red when cooked. Hardy, spreading, moderately productive tree. Self-fertile. Ripens in September. *Source History: 4 in 1988; 3 in 1992; 2 in 2000.* **Sources: Ch9, Mi1.**

Formosa - Japanese plum. Large, oval, greenish yellow fruit overlaid with red. Firm, sweet, juicy, melting, pale yellow flesh. Stone is slightly clinging. Tree is prolific but tends to be a biennial bearer. Poor pollinator. May be pollinated with other Japanese varieties. Ripens midseason. Introduced in 1907. *Source History: 2 in 1988; 3 in 1992; 1 in 2000.* **Sources: Ad2.**

Fortune - Japanese plum. Large fruit with red skin. Moderately vigorous, upright to slightly spreading tree requires a pollinator. Ripens the last week of July. *Source History: 1 in 1992; 3 in 2000.* **Sources: AG2, Cu4, WI4.**

French Improved - European prune plum. Medium size, dark blue fruit. Tender, fine textured flesh. Very sweet, rich flavor. Suitable fresh, canned or dried. California's leading prune. Long-lived tree. Self-fruitful. Shows good canker resistance. Ripens from August to September. Requires 600-800 hours of chilling. A Gillet introduction. *Source History: 6 in 1988; 8 in 1992; 7 in 2000.* **Sources: Bay, CO5, ORA, Pe2, STR, WI12, WI4.**

French Petite - European prune plum. Very old variety propagated because of its fine flavor. The California French Prune of commerce. Small to medium, long, oval fruit, tapered toward the stem. Delicate, violet-purple skin. Greenish yellow, nearly freestone flesh. Mild, sugary flavor. Very high quality when dried. Also one of the best for dessert and canning. Reliable, heavy producer. Ripens during September. Zone 5. *Source History: 2 in 1988; 4 in 1992; 2 in 2000.* **Sources: Gr4, ME3.**

French Prune - Small, medium red to purplish black prune plum. Very sweet, mild flavor. Good for canning and drying. Self-fertile. Ripens midseason. *Source History: 4 in 1988; 7 in 1992; 3 in 2000.* **Sources: Nrs, Si3, STR.**

Friar - Japanese plum. Large, round, dark purple fruit turns almost black when fully mature. Sweet, firm, amber, freestone flesh. Good quality. Tends to over-bear, so it requires early, heavy thinning. Partially self-fruitful, but produces better if pollinated by another variety such as Black Amber, Queen Ann, Santa Rosa, Simka or Wickson. Resistant to cracking. Requires 400 hours of chilling. *Source History: 10 in 1988; 12 in 1992; 9 in 2000.* **Sources: AG2, Bay, Bo5, Co2, Mel, Nrs, Va2, WI12, WI4.**

Frontier - *Source History: 2 in 1988; 4 in 1992; 1 in 2000.* **Sources: Nrs.**

Full Moon - Round, yellow fruit. High yields. Ripens midseason. *Source History: 1 in 1992; 1 in 2000.* **Sources: Iso.**

General Hand - Japanese plum. Solid, golden yellow fruit with good flavor. Frequently attains the size of the largest Japanese plums. Ripens in early September. First fruited on the home place of General Hand near Lancaster, Pennsylvania. *Source History: 1 in 1988; 1 in 1992; 1 in 2000.* **Sources: So5.**

Gold - *Source History: 1 in 1988; 4 in 1992; 2 in 2000.* **Sources: GI3, SIM.**

Golden Nectar - Large yellow dessert plum with thin, amber skin. Firm, sweet amber flesh. Small pit. Excellent both fresh and dried. Good keeper. Self-fertile. Ripens in late July. Requires 500 hours of chilling. U.S. Plant Patent No. 4977. *Source History: 1 in 1988; 4 in 1992; 3 in 2000.* **Sources: Bay, CO5, WI4.**

Golden Transparent Gage - European plum. Seedling of Transparent Gage. Large, round, golden yellow fruit dotted with red. Rich, juicy, sugary flesh, almost like candied fruit. Reportedly self-fertile. Ripens in September. Introduced in 1894. *Source History: 1 in 1988; 2 in 1992; 4 in 2000.* **Sources: Rai, So5, Son, Stl.**

Gracious - Open-pollinated seedling of Emerald. Oval to round, yellow-orange and coral-red mottled skin. Yellow-orange, firm, juicy sweet flesh. Freestone. Excellent for fresh eating, sauce and jam. Upright spreading tree. Zone 3. Rare. Developed at the Northern Great Plains Field Station, Mandan, North Dakota, 1957. *Source History: 2 in 2000.* **Sources: Ed5, Fed.**

Grand Duke - *Source History: 1 in 1992; 1 in 2000.* **Sources: Nrs.**

Grand Prize - European plum. Large, high quality purple fruit. Ripens late midseason. Moderately vigorous tree. Luther Burbank introduction from the 1930s. *Source History: 1 in 2000.* **Sources: Cu4.**

Green Egg - Spicy flavor is refreshing to those who like to cleanse the palate after a heavy meal. Hardy in Zones 5-9. *Source History: 1 in 1992; 1 in 2000.* **Sources: Ty2.**

Green Gage (Reine Claude Green Gage, Reine Claude) - European plum. Famous "Reine Claude" named after the wife of Francis I of France. Imported into England in the 18th Century by Sir Thomas Gage who provided its English name. An American favorite since the time of Jefferson. Small to medium, oval, yellowish green fruit. Juicy, smooth textured, amber freestone flesh. Rich, confectionary flavor. Considered the ideal dessert plum in Europe. Also good cooked, canned, or preserved. Typically a rather small, low branched, round headed tree with attractive blossoms and deep green foliage. Productive. Self-fertile. Susceptible to brown rot. Requires 500-800 hours of chilling. Hardy to central Iowa. *Source History: 28 in 1988; 29 in 1992; 31 in 2000.* **Sources: Ad2, Bea, Bu7, Ch9, Cla, CO5,**

Cu4, Ea3, Ed5, Fed, Fi1, Gr4, Gur, JOY, La3, Leu, ME3, Mel, Mi1, MI5, On4, ORA, Pa2, Pe2, Sc6, So5, Stl, STR, Va2, WI12, WI4.

Green Gage, Bavay's - Superior selection of gage type European plums. Small to medium size fruit with sweet, richly flavored flesh. Excellent for canning, cooking and fresh eating. Relatively small tree. More productive in moderate winter climates than Green Gage. Self-fruitful. Requires 600 hours of chilling. Originated in Belgium in the 19th century. *Source History: 2 in 2000.* **Sources: Bay, Son.**

Gulf Beauty - Japanese plum. *Source History: 1 in 2000.* **Sources: RA4.**

Gulf Blaze - Japanese plum. *Source History: 1 in 2000.* **Sources: RA4.**

Gulf Ruby - Japanese plum. Early ripening red plum for the warmer parts of the Gulf Coast. *Source History: 1 in 1992; 2 in 2000.* **Sources: RA4, SIM.**

Hanska - High quality medium size fruit. Red skin color. Yellow flesh. Great for canning. *Source History: 2 in 1988; 1 in 1992; 2 in 2000.* **Sources: MI5, Nrs.**

Hazel - *Source History: 1 in 1992; 1 in 2000.* **Sources: Nrs.**

Herrenhausen Mirabel - European plum. *Source History: 1 in 2000.* **Sources: Cu4.**

Hiromi Red - Large firm fruit. Red over yellow skin color. Excellent size, color and flavor. Upright to spreading tree. Multiple pollenizers recommended. Ripens in late June. Requires 800-900 hours of chilling. U.S. Plant Patent No. 9858. *Source History: 1 in 2000.* **Sources: WI4.**

Hollywood (Hollywood Purple-Leaf) - Japanese plum. Large red fruit used for fresh eating and jelly making. Ornamental tree with pink blossoms and dark purple leaves. Ripens in August. Zones 5-9. *Source History: 2 in 1992; 3 in 2000.* **Sources: Ed2, Mo19, Rai.**

Homeside - Japanese plum. *Source History: 1 in 1988; 3 in 1992; 1 in 2000.* **Sources: Nrs.**

Howard Miracle - Japanese plum. Large, yellow fruit with a handsome red blush. Yellow flesh with a tart, pineapple flavor. Requires a pollinator. Ripens midseason. Requires 400 hours of chilling. *Source History: 3 in 1988; 5 in 1992; 3 in 2000.* **Sources: ORA, Son, WI4.**

Howard Sun - Very large fruit, 4 x 4" or larger. Similar to Friar in skin color, but its flesh is more yellow. Bears early and heavily. Holds well on the tree and in storage. Ripens mid to late September. Developed in California. U.S. Plant No. 6006. *Source History: 1 in 1988; 1 in 1992; 1 in 2000.* **Sources: AG2.**

Hungarian Type - *Source History: 1 in 1992; 1 in 2000.* **Sources: Nrs.**

Imperial Epineuse - Mottled dark and light purplish red skin. Meaty, greenish yellow, clingstone flesh. Rich, sweet flavor. Highest quality. Ripens mid-September. Used at the National Fruit Trials in England as a standard of comparison for other plums, although it is mentioned nowhere in European pomological literature. Found in 1870 as a chance seedling near Clairoc, the famous French prune district. Brought to the U.S. in 1883. Once widely grown in California for large prunes. *Source History: 2 in 1988; 3 in 1992; 7 in 2000.* **Sources: Ad2, Clo, Leu, Mo19, Rai, So5, Son.**

Imperial Gage (Reine Claude Imperiale) - Small, round, dull green fruit, sometimes tinged red in the sun and usually covered with a whitish bloom. Tender, juicy, transparent flesh with a fine aroma. Sweet, refreshing taste. Ripens in mid-September. From a planting of 25 quarts of Green Gage plum seeds at the famous William R. Prince Nursery in Flushing, Long Island. Introduced in 1790 as White Gage and later called Prince's Imperial Gage. *Source History: 1 in 1988; 1 in*

1992; 1 in 2000. **Sources: So5.**

Italian PR-H-1 - Medium to large, dark purple fruit. Greenish yellow, freestone flesh turns a dark wine color when cooked. Excellent for fresh eating, canning or drying. Profitable commercial variety. *Source History: 1 in 1988; 1 in 1992; 1 in 2000.* **Sources: Co2.**

Italian Prune (Italian) - European prune plum. Medium to large, oval, purplish black fruit. Juicy, greenish yellow, freestone flesh turns red when cooked. Distinctive, rich, sweet flavor. Good for both canning and drying. Vigorous, cold hardy tree. Early, reliable producer. Sometimes overbears and needs to to be thinned. Self-fruitful, but production improved with pollination from another European variety. Excellent shipper. Ripens from August to September. Requires 800 hours of chilling. Hardy in Zone 4. German origin. *Source History: 14 in 1988; 25 in 1992; 17 in 2000.* **Sources: Bay, Bea, BO10, Cla, CO5, JOY, Leu, ME3, Mel, MI5, Nrs, On3, Pe2, Son, STR, Va2, WI12.**

Italian Prune, Sehome Strain - Large, purple plum from Bellingham, Washington. Yellow green flesh. Seems to split less than other Italian prunes. A favorite for drying and canning. Makes a classic plum tart. Partially self-fruitful. Heavy setting. *Source History: 1 in 1988; 1 in 1992; 1 in 2000.* **Sources: Rai.**

Italian, Early - European plum. Medium large, oblong, purple fruit. Greenish yellow, freestone flesh. Excellent for fresh eating, canning or drying. Vigorous, productive tree. Ships well. Ripens in mid-August. Zone 5. *Source History: 1 in 1988; 2 in 1992; 2 in 2000.* **Sources: COL, ME3.**

Italian, Late - European plum. Same as Early Italian in all respects except that it ripens later (early to mid-September). Excellent shipper. Good for canning and drying. *Source History: 1 in 1988; 1 in 1992; 1 in 2000.* **Sources: COL.**

Japanese Plum - *Prunus salicina.* Pointed, yellow or light red fruit. Tree grows to 25'. White flowers. Native to China. Cultivated in Japan. Hardy in Zone 8. *Source History: 2 in 1988; 1 in 1992; 1 in 2000.* **Sources: Sc2.**

Jefferson - Large, golden yellow fruit with a beautiful pinkish red cheek and a thin, white bloom. Juicy, meaty, deep orange flesh. Rich, delicious flavor. Raised from a seed by Judge Buel of Albany, New York. Introduced in 1825. *Source History: 1 in 1988; 1 in 1992; 1 in 2000.* **Sources: So5.**

Joanna Red - Very large fruit. Red over yellow skin color. Productive, vigorous, moderately spreading tree; multiple pollenizers suggested. Ripens late July to early August. Requires 750-850 hours of chilling. Plant patent pending. *Source History: 1 in 2000.* **Sources: WI4.**

K. V. Plum - *Source History: 1 in 1992; 1 in 2000.* **Sources: GI3.**

Kahinta - Luther Burbank's Apple Plum (*Prunus salicina*) x Terry Plum (*P. americana*). Large yellow fruit overlaid with speckled red and bluish bloom. Sweet yellow flesh has a spicy, refreshing, nectar-like flavor. Tends toward splitting some years. Ripens in September. Zone 3. Rare. *Source History: 3 in 1992; 4 in 2000.* **Sources: Ch9, Ed5, Fed, Nrs.**

Kelsey - Large, thin skinned, greenish yellow fruit with a red blush. Firm, freestone flesh when fully mature. Rich, aromatic flavor. Small pit. Keeps well. Vigorous, heavy bearing tree. Pollinate with Beauty, Santa Rosa or Wickson. Requires 400 hours of chilling. *Source History: 4 in 1988; 8 in 1992; 3 in 2000.* **Sources: AG2, Pa2, WI4.**

Kirke's Blue - Large, dark purple fruit. Green-yellow, juicy, freestone flesh. Good quality. Shy bearer. Requires a pollinator. Originated in England. Introduced in 1830. *Source History: 1 in 1992; 1 in 2000.* **Sources: Rai.**

La Crescent (Golden La Crescent, Golden Minnesota) - *Prunus americana* x *P. salicina.* Small fruit with tender, yellow skin, sometimes blushed light red. Yellow, melting, freestone flesh. Sweet, aromatic flavor. Excellent quality for fresh eating. Very good for jam; fair to good for jelly. Vigorous, fast growing tree. Produces best with a pollinator such as Toka. Ripens in late summer. Hardy to -50 degrees F. with occasional winter injury. Developed by the University of Minnesota. Introduced in 1919. *Source History: 2 in 1988; 8 in 1992; 5 in 2000.* **Sources: Ch9, Ed5, Fed, Stl, Wa16.**

Laroda - Santa Rosa x Gaviota. Japanese plum. Dark red, almost black fruit covered with tiny light dots. Pale, violet-red flesh, yellow near the stone. Rich, wine-like flavor. Pollinate with another Japanese plum. Requires 400 hours of chilling. Developed under Dr. C. O. Hesse at the Agricultural Experiment Station at Davis, California. *Source History: 3 in 1988; 8 in 1992; 2 in 2000.* **Sources: Bay, WI4.**

Lewis Gold - *Source History: 1 in 2000.* **Sources: Ch9.**

Longjohn - European plum named after the late John Watson, Geneva plum breeder. Large, long, teardrop-shaped, blue fruit. Freestone. Iroquois type. Upright, spreading tree with somewhat willowy growth. Crops early; self-thinning. *Source History: 3 in 2000.* **Sources: Ad2, Cu4, Nrs.**

Majestic Damson - *Source History: 1 in 1992; 1 in 2000.* **Sources: Nrs.**

Mammoth Cardinal - *Source History: 2 in 1992; 1 in 2000.* **Sources: Wor.**

Manor - *Source History: 1 in 1992; 1 in 2000.* **Sources: Nrs.**

Mansan - *Source History: 1 in 1992; 1 in 2000.* **Sources: Nrs.**

Mariposa (Improved Satsuma) - Japanese plum. Large, green fruit mottled pink and light purple. Juicy, firm, maroon, nearly freestone flesh surrounding a small pit. Sweet, rich, aromatic flavor. Excellent quality. Use fresh or cooked. Pollinate with Beauty, Nubiana or Santa Rosa. Ripens midseason. Requires 250 hours of chilling. *Source History: 6 in 1988; 11 in 1992; 9 in 2000.* **Sources: AG2, Bay, Cla, Ju2, ORA, Pa2, Son, STR, WI4.**

Methley - Medium to large, reddish purple fruit. Juicy flesh with a sweet, mild, distinctive flavor. Fine quality. Good for fresh eating or jelly. Growth habit and fruit character very similar to Japanese plums. Handsome, vigorous, upright tree does well on most soils. Early blooming. A good pollinator for early bearing varieties such as Bruce, Santa Rosa and Shiro. Heavy, annual crops. One crop requires several pickings. Good shipper. Self-fruitful. Ripens from late May to mid-July depending on location. Requires 150-250 hours of chilling. Bud hardy in Zones 5-9. *Source History: 25 in 1988; 39 in 1992; 39 in 2000.* **Sources: Ad2, Bar, Bas, Bay, Bea, Bo5, Bu7, Clo, CO5, Cum, Ea3, FO10, GI3, Hi9, Ho5, Iso, Jo3, Lee, ME3, Mel, MI10, MI5, Mo19, Na4, Nrs, On4, Pa2, Po2, Rai, Sav, SIM, St4, Tex, TU5, WA8, Wel, Wh4, WI4, Wom.**

Methley, Improved - An improved wonderful old standby. Purple fruit with sweet, melting, amber flesh. Very good pollinator. *Source History: 2 in 1992; 1 in 2000.* **Sources: Ju2.**

Middelburg - Very large, dark and light purple prune type with a heavy bloom. Juicy, light yellow flesh with a sweet, vinous flavor. Excellent for tarts. *Source History: 1 in 1988; 1 in 1992; 1 in 2000.* **Sources: So5.**

Midnight Sun - Black fruit. Firm, amber flesh. Excellent flavor. Ripens in August. Introduced in 1986. U.S. Plant Patent No. 6044. *Source History: 1 in 1992; 1 in 2000.* **Sources: AG2.**

Mirabelle - Small, round, yellow fruit with yellow dots. Firm, tender, yellow, freestone flesh. Not beautiful, but sweet and mild. Good for jams, tarts, compotes and canning. Spreading tree is very productive. Much grown and highly esteemed in Europe, especially France where it is prized for making brandy. Ripens in late August. Introduced in 1790. *Source History: 2 in 1988; 2 in 1992; 2 in 2000.* **Sources: Leu, Rai.**

Monitor - Probably a cross of Burbank x *Prunus americana.* Large, juicy, bright red fruit. Very sweet. Prolific bearer. Ripens in late August. Hardy in Zone 4. Developed in Minnesota. *Source History: 2 in 1988; 1 in 1992; 3 in 2000.* **Sources: Ch9, Ed5, Nrs.**

Morris - Japanese plum. Medium to large, red to purple fruit. Flesh red to the pit. Excellent quality. May require pollination. Slight resistance to brown rot; resistant to other major diseases. Ripens from early to mid-June. Recent Texas A and M release. *Source History: 6 in 1988; 14 in 1992; 9 in 2000.* **Sources: Cum, GI3, Ho5, Iso, MI5, Nrs, Tex, Wel, Wom.**

Mount Royal - European plum. Medium to large, round, bluish black freestone. Meaty, tender, sweet, juicy flesh. Good for fresh eating, jam and preserves. Excellent for canning and freezing. Can be dried to make prunes. Vigorous, productive tree. Makes an exceptionally good pollinator for wild plums and other European varieties. A chance seedling found near Montreal, Canada. Ripens from midseason to late August. Hardy in northern Wisconsin and Minnesota; Zone 4. *Source History: 7 in 1988; 13 in 1992; 14 in 2000.* **Sources: BA14, Ed5, Fa1, Fed, GR26, Hi9, Jun, Mc3, Ro3, SH8, Stl, Wa16, WI12, ZEL.**

Moyer Prune - Similar to the Italian Prune, but can grow to three times the size. Slight tendency to biennial bearing. Ripens in mid-September. Originated in Douglas County, Oregon. *Source History: 1 in 1988; 2 in 1992; 2 in 2000.* **Sources: Gr4, Si3.**

Murietta - Medium size fruit with black over red skin. Amber flesh. Low acid. Freestone. Moderately vigorous, spreading tree. Ripens early June. Requires 600-700 hours of chilling. U.S. Plant Patent No. 9568. *Source History: 1 in 2000.* **Sources: WI4.**

New York 77.602.1 (NY 21) - Large European prune-plum shows promise for wholesale fresh market. *Source History: 1 in 2000.* **Sources: Cu4.**

Newport - *Source History: 3 in 1992; 1 in 2000.* **Sources: GI3, GR26, Ty2.**

Nubiana - Sister of Laroda (Gaviota x El Dorado). Large, reddish purple fruit. Firm, light yellow flesh. At full maturity it has a pleasant, mild flavor. Excellent for fresh market and home orchard. Good pollinator for Laroda. Self-fruitful to a substantial degree. Ripens in late July in central California. Requires 400-500 hours of chilling. Developed at the Agricultural Experiment Station at Davis, California. *Source History: 4 in 1988; 8 in 1992; 3 in 2000.* **Sources: Bay, Nrs, WI4.**

October Sun - Late season red plum. Similar in appearance to Casselman. Very sweet and juicy. Ripens in September. Developed in California. Licensed by the University of California. Plant patent applied for. *Source History: 1 in 1992; 1 in 2000.* **Sources: AG2.**

Opal - Oullins x Early Favorite. European plum. Reddish fruit with yellow flesh. Excellent cropper. Self-fertile. Ripens seven days before Oullins. Swedish variety raised at Alnarp. Introduced in 1948. *Source History: 1 in 1988; 2 in 1992; 2 in 2000.* **Sources: Ed5, So5.**

Opata - *Source History: 1 in 1992; 1 in 2000.* **Sources: Nrs.**

Oullins (Reine Claude d'Oullins) - European plum. One of the largest and most attractive of the Gage types. Almost cylindrical, green fruit turns greenish white and pale gold with a fine white blush when mature. Clear, greenish yellow flesh is sweet, tender and succulent. Exceptional quality. Hangs on a long stem. Self-fertile. Moderately vigorous tree tends toward biennial bearing when left un-thinned. Susceptible to brown rot. Ripens in mid-August. French origin. Intro-duced in 1846. *Source History: 2 in 1988; 2 in 1992; 3 in 2000.* **Sources: Ad2, Cu4, So5.**

Ozark Premier - Burbank x Methley. Japanese plum. Fruit is larger than either of its parents. Tough, bright red skin. Juicy, yellow, clingstone flesh with a small pit. Mildly tart flavor. Vigorous, reliably productive tree. Self-fertile according to some sources; requires cross-pollination according to others. Cross-pollinates well with other oriental varieties, at any rate. Requires several pickings. Does well in the Midwest but best in the South. Ripens in late summer over an extended period. Requires 700-800 hours of chilling. Hardy in Zones 5-9. Developed in Mountain Grove, Missouri. Introduced in 1946. *Source History: 20 in 1988; 24 in 1992; 20 in 2000.* **Sources: Ad2, Bas, Bo5, Ch9, CO5, Cum, Fed, Hi9, Ho5, Iso, La3, MI5, Nrs, St4, Tex, TU5, WA8, Wel, Wom, Wor.**

Peach Plum - Large, round, brownish or purplish red fruit. Juicy, yellow flesh with good flavor. Excellent for fresh eating or canning. Partially self-fertile. Polli-nate with Brooks, Green Gage or Italian. Ripens early to midseason. Zone 5. *Source History: 6 in 1988; 6 in 1992; 1 in 2000.* **Sources: ME3.**

Pearl - Deep yellow fruit specked with red dots. Tender, sweet, melting, deep yellow flesh. Incomparable flavor. Ripens in September. Developed by Luther Burbank in 1898. Believed to be the progeny of Prune d'Agen and one of the Reine Claude group. *Source History: 1 in 1988; 3 in 1992; 3 in 2000.* **Sources: Ro3, So5, Son.**

Pembina - Red June x Manitoba wild plum. Red fruit with yellow, freestone flesh. Thick skin. Excellent eating quality and good for preserves. Ripens mid to late August. Hardy in Zone 3. Introduced by N. E. Hansen, South Dakota Station in 1923. *Source History: 5 in 1992; 5 in 2000.* **Sources: Bea, Ch9, Ed5, Fa1, Fed.**

Pipestone - Burbank x (*Prunus salicina* x Wolf). Large fruit with tough, red skin that peels easily. Sweet, juicy, golden yellow, clingstone flesh. Excellent quality. Vigorous, productive tree. Pollen sterile. Requires cross-pollination with another red variety. One of the best for Northern growers. Ripens from early August to early September depending on location. Hardy to -50 degrees F. Developed at the Minnesota Fruit Breeding Farm. Introduced in 1942. *Source History: 8 in 1988; 12 in 1992; 11 in 2000.* **Sources: Bea, Ch9, Ed5, Fed, Jun, Mc3, SH8, Stl, Va5, Wa16, WI12.**

Pocegaca - *Source History: 1 in 1992; 1 in 2000.* **Sources: Nrs.**

Polly - European plum. Pretty, purple-red fruit with unique kidney shape. Free-stone. Mild flavor. Ripens with Stanley. Self-fruitful; also considered a universal pollinator. Tree self-thins, producing a consistent crop of large fruit. Ripens with Stanley. *Source History: 3 in 2000.* **Sources: Cu4, Hi9, Nrs.**

Prairie Egg - *Source History: 1 in 2000.* **Sources: Ed5.**

President - Latest maturing of the European plums. Large, round to oblong, blue-black fruit. Fine textured, yellow, freestone flesh. Good commercial variety. Vig-orous, upright tree. Heavy producer. Pollinate with other Europeans like Bluefree, Empress, Peach Plum and Stanley. Keeps and ships well. Ripens from early to mid-September. *Source History: 10 in 1988; 9 in 1992; 6 in 2000.* **Sources: Ad2, Bo5, Ch9, COL, MI5, Va2.**

Prune d'Agen - Long, oval fruit tapered at the stem. Dark blue or violet-purple skin covered with a thin bloom. Firm, sugary sweet, greenish yellow flesh. One of the best dessert plums. Ripens in late September. Of ancient origin. Brought to their Abbey on the River Lot by Benedictine monks returning from the Crusades in Persia. Known commercially in the U.S. as the "French prune" of California. *Source History: 1 in 1988; 1 in 1992; 1 in 2000.* **Sources: So5.**

Prune-Plum, Stark Blue Ribbon (Aldrich Cultivar) - Large, purple-blue freestone. Good fresh, canned or dried. Heavy crops. Ripens in early September. Hardy in Zones 5-8. Trademarked. U.S. Plant Patent No. 4053. *Source History: 1 in 1988; 1 in 1992; 1 in 2000.* **Sources: St4.**

Purple - Purple fruit with cream colored flesh. Excellent flavor. Ripens in mid-July. *Source History: 1 in 1988; 4 in 1992; 1 in 2000.* **Sources: GI3.**

Purple Gage (Reine Claude Violette) - European plum. Dark purple fruit, usually furrowed or pitted towards the stem. Same round shape as Green Gage, but larger. Yellow, juicy flesh with sweet, rich flavor. Hang on the tree until almost shriveled. Richest flavor at the prune stage. Ripens in mid-September. Old French variety brought to America early in the 19th century. *Source History: 1 in 1988; 1 in 1992; 1 in 2000.* **Sources: Son.**

Purple Heart - Japanese plum. Small, 1-1.5" deep purple fruit with crisp, sweet, clingstone flesh. Vigorous, hardy, spreading tree. Easily pollinated by Toka or Underwood. Hardy to -25 degrees F. Probable origin is New Hampshire. *Source History: 1 in 1988; 2 in 1992; 1 in 2000.* **Sources: Fed.**

Queen Ann - Large, purple semifreestone. Amber flesh streaked red. Superb flavor. Fine dessert plum. Small tree. Pollinate with Friar, Santa Rosa or Wickson. Ripens in late July in central California. Requires 500 hours of chilling. *Source History: 2 in 1988; 4 in 1992; 1 in 2000.* **Sources: Nrs.**

Queen Rosa - Dark purple skin and juicy, red-streaked flesh. Superb flavor. Pollinate with Catalina, Laroda or Santa Rosa. Ripens between Santa Rosa and Laroda. Requires 400 hours of chilling. *Source History: 4 in 1992; 1 in 2000.* **Sources: Ad2.**

Raribank - *Source History: 1 in 2000.* **Sources: Ch9.**

Red Ace - *Source History: 1 in 2000.* **Sources: Nrs.**

Red Beaut - *Source History: 1 in 1988; 1 in 1992; 1 in 2000.* **Sources: AG2.**

Red Diamond - American plum. Red-purple, thick fleshed fruit. Disease resistant. Hardy in Zone 3. Developed in Minnesota. U.S. Plant Patent No. 4285. *Source History: 1 in 1992; 1 in 2000.* **Sources: Ch9.**

Red Glow - Large, firm clingstone. Minnesota Fruit Breeding Farm introduction. *Source History: 3 in 1992; 2 in 2000.* **Sources: Ed5, Mc3.**

Red Heart - Japanese plum. Medium to large, semifreestone fruit with somewhat tough, dark red skin. Firm, juicy, blood-red flesh. Good for fresh eating, canning, preserves and jellies. Good quality. Holds well on the tree. Vigorous, hardy, productive tree. Self-unfruitful but one of the best pollinators for other Japanese varieties. Suggested pollinators are Elephant Heart, Ozark Beauty, Shiro and Starking Delicious. Ripens from early to mid-August. Requires 500 hours of chilling. Hardy in Zones 5-9. *Source History: 3 in 1988; 5 in 1992; 8 in 2000.* **Sources: Bay, Bo5, Ch9, Cla, Hi9, St4, WI4, Wor.**

Red June - Large, bright red fruit. Firm, high quality flesh. Heavy bearing. Thin fruits to avoid dropping of excess fruit known as June Drop. One of the best for Southern planting. Ripens early. *Source History: 3 in 1988; 5 in 1992; 4 in 2000.* **Sources: Bar, GI3, Po2, TU5.**

Redcoat - *Source History: 1 in 1992; 1 in 2000.* **Sources: Ed5.**

Robusto - Red fruit. Sweet, spicy flavor. Requires pollination. Ripens midseason. *Source History: 3 in 1988; 6 in 1992; 2 in 2000.* **Sources: Ju2, Nrs.**

Rosa Grande - *Source History: 1 in 1988; 1 in 1992; 1 in 2000.* **Sources: STR.**

Roysum - Japanese plum. Medium to large, red-blue fruit, with juicy, aromatic, light yellow flesh. Very flavorful. Vigorous, spreading tree. Pollinate with Santa Rosa. Ripens very late. *Source History: 1 in 1988; 2 in 1992; 1 in 2000.* **Sources: AG2.**

Ruby Sun - *Source History: 1 in 2000.* **Sources: AG2.**

Ruby Sweet (Rubysweet) - Japanese plum. Reddish bronze fruit with firm, dark red freestone flesh. Good quality. Ripens early to midseason. Released by Dr. Dick Okie, USDA, Byron, Georgia. *Source History: 2 in 1992; 6 in 2000.* **Sources: Cla, Cu4, Cum, Iso, Nrs, Ty2.**

Saint Anthony - *Source History: 1 in 1992; 1 in 2000.* **Sources: Nrs.**

Sannois - European plum from France. Small, reddish purple fruit. Firm, extremely sugary flesh. Ripens in late September. *Source History: 2 in 1988; 1 in 1992; 1 in 2000.* **Sources: So5.**

Santa Rosa - Japanese plum. Very large, round to round oval, purplish red fruit covered with light dots and a thin bloom. Fragrant, fine textured, clingstone flesh, purplish near the skin, yellow streaked pink near the pit. Highest quality. Excellent fresh or canned. Large, vigorous, fast growing tree. Prolific, annual bearer in the West, but shy under Eastern conditions. Partially self-fertile, but production improved when planted with other Japanese varieties. Susceptible to bacterial spot. Keeps and ships well. Ripens midseason. Requires 300 hours of chilling. Hardy in Zones 5-9. Developed by Luther Burbank of Santa Rosa, California. Introduced in 1906. *Source History: 44 in 1988; 68 in 1992; 48 in 2000.* **Sources: Ad2, AG2, Bar, Bas, Bay, BO10, Bo5, Ch9, Co2, CO5, COL, Cum, Ea3, Fi1, FO10, GI3, Gr16, Hi9, Ho5, Iso, Jo3, JOY, Lee, Leu, ME3, Mel, Mi1, MI10, MI5, Nrs, ORA, Pa2, Pi2, Sav, SIM, So5, Son, St4, STR, Tex, Va2, WA8, Wel, Wh4, WI12, WI4, Wom, Wor.**

Santa Rosa, July - *Source History: 1 in 1992; 1 in 2000.* **Sources: AG2.**

Santa Rosa, Late - Japanese plum. Large, oval, dark red fruit with a blue bloom. Firm, yellow flesh, dark red near the skin. Rich, tart flavor. Excellent for fresh eating. Self-fertile. Ripens from early to mid-August, about 30 days later than regular Santa Rosa. Requires 500 hours of chilling. *Source History: 3 in 1988; 8 in 1992; 5 in 2000.* **Sources: Bay, ORA, Pa2, Pe2, WI4.**

Santa Rosa, Late Dwarf - Natural dwarf tree. *Source History: 1 in 1988; 1 in 1992; 1 in 2000.* **Sources: CO5.**

Santa Rosa, Late Improved - *Source History: 1 in 1988; 1 in 1992; 1 in 2000.* **Sources: STR.**

Santa Rosa, Weeping - Japanese plum. Fruit similar to regular Santa Rosa. Tree grows 8-10' tall, developing long, slender limbs with a beautiful weeping habit. Excellent for espalier or as a free standing specimen. Needs to be staked for two years. Attractive, white flowers bloom in early spring, five days after regular Santa Rosa. Self-fertile. Fruits ripen 14 days after Santa Rosa. Requires only 150-400 hours of chilling. U.S. Plant Patent No. 4338. *Source History: 3 in 1988; 8 in*

1992; 7 in 2000. **Sources: Bay, CO5, ORA, Pa2, Rai, Son, WI4.**

Sapa - *Source History: 1 in 1992; 1 in 2000.* **Sources: Nrs.**

Satsuma (Blood Plum Satsuma) - Japanese plum. Medium to large, nearly round, dark red fruit with a small pit. Firm, meaty, juicy flesh, red to the pit. Sweet, lively flavor. Excellent for fresh eating, cooking, canning or preserves. Upright tree is partially self-fruitful. Pollinate for improved production with such Japanese varieties as Beauty, Shiro, Santa Rosa and Wickson. Ripens from mid to late summer depending on location. Requires 300 hours of chilling. Hardy in Zones 5-9. Developed by Luther Burbank in 1899. *Source History: 16 in 1988; 22 in 1992; 14 in 2000.* **Sources: Ad2, Bay, Bo5, Bu7, CO5, Ga6, JOY, ME3, MI5, ORA, Pa2, Son, WI12, WI4.**

Satsuma Improved - *Source History: 1 in 1988; 1 in 1992; 1 in 2000.* **Sources: STR.**

Segundo - Yellow-red fruit with yellow-red flesh. *Source History: 2 in 1992; 1 in 2000.* **Sources: Nrs.**

Seneca - European plum. Italian Prune x Prinlew. Large, reddish blue fruit. Crisp, yellow, freestone flesh. Very sweet. High dessert quality. Good for fresh eating, canning or drying. Vigorous, upright tree. Regular bearer. Resistant to brown rot and gum pockets. Crack resistant. Ripens from early to mid-September. Zone 5. Developed by the New York State Agricultural Experiment Station in Geneva. Introduced in 1972. *Source History: 5 in 1988; 7 in 1992; 11 in 2000.* **Sources: Ad2, Bu7, Clo, Cu4, Ea3, Er2, ME3, Mo19, Nrs, Rai, WI4.**

September King - Ripens mid to late September. U.S. Plant Patent No. 6008. *Source History: 1 in 2000.* **Sources: AG2.**

Shirley - Japanese plum. *Source History: 3 in 1988; 2 in 1992; 2 in 2000.* **Sources: Cum, Ho5.**

Shiro - Japanese plum. Medium to large, round, yellow fruit with a pink blush. Juicy, translucent yellow, clingstone flesh. Mild, sweet flavor. Excellent for fresh eating, cooking, canning, preserves and dessert. Spreading tree. May need thinning to attain good size. Consistent bearer. Excellent pollinator for early Japanese varieties. Pollinate with Early Golden, Methley, Ozark Premier, Redheart, Santa Rosa or Satsuma. Thrives in full sun and well drained soil. Fine shipper. Ripens midseason. Requires 150-500 hours of chilling. Hardy in Zones 5-9. Originated in California in 1899. *Source History: 22 in 1988; 25 in 1992; 27 in 2000.* **Sources: Ad2, Bo5, Bu7, Ch9, Clo, Co2, COL, Cu4, Ea3, Fil, Hi9, JOY, ME3, Mi1, Mo19, Nrs, On3, Pa2, Pi2, Rai, Ro3, Son, St4, Va2, Wh4, WI4, Wor.**

Shropshire Damson - European plum. An improved Blue Damson, larger than the old type. Small to medium, oval, dark purple, clingstone fruits grow in clusters. Favorite for home use, especially preserves. Growing in demand commercially as well. Vigorous, hardy tree. Early bearer. Late bloomer. Consistently heavy producer. Self-fruitful. Ripens in late August. *Source History: 4 in 1988; 3 in 1992; 3 in 2000.* **Sources: Fed, Leu, Nrs.**

Silver Prune - Teardrop-shaped fruit. Skin shows a lavender cast with heavy bloom. Excellent flavor. Good fresh or dried. More productive than French prunes. *Source History: 1 in 2000.* **Sources: Son.**

Simka - Japanese plum. Large, uniform, purplish red fruit. Very firm, sweet, yellowish white flesh. Tends to be partially self-thinning and to drop throughout the season. Ships and stores well. Ripens 5-7 days ahead of Friar with which it is interfruitful. *Source History: 4 in 1988; 4 in 1992; 4 in 2000.* **Sources: AG2, Co2, Hi9, Va2.**

<u>Six Weeks</u> - *Source History: 2 in 1988; 1 in 1992; 1 in 2000.* **Sources: Ty2.**

<u>South Dakota</u> - Japanese plum x American plum. Medium size, oval fruit. Tough, yellow skin with a red blush. Medium firm, sweet, yellow, clingstone flesh. Fine for fresh eating and processing. Vigorous, productive, cold hardy tree. Useful as a pollinator for other Japanese-American hybrids which are difficult to pollinate. Ripens from late August to early September. Hardy in Zone 4. Developed by Dr. N. E. Hansen at the South Dakota Agricultural Experiment Station. Introduced in 1949. *Source History: 3 in 1988; 6 in 1992; 5 in 2000.* **Sources: Bea, Ch9, Ed5, Fed, Nrs.**

<u>Standard</u> - *Source History: 1 in 1992; 1 in 2000.* **Sources: Nrs.**

<u>Stanley</u> - Agen x Grand Duke. European plum. Medium to large, oval, dark blue fruit with a thick bloom. Firm, tender, fine grained, yellowish green, freestone flesh. Sweet, rich flavor. Excellent for fresh eating, canning, preserves and drying. Flesh turns purplish red when canned. Large, vigorous, spreading tree. Early bearer. Late bloomer. Heavy, annual producer. Self-fertile, but yields more heavily when pollinated with another variety. Most widely planted European plum in the East, Midwest and South. Ripens early September. Requires 800-900 hours of chilling. Hardy in Zones 4-8. Introduced by the Geneva Station in 1926. *Source History: 51 in 1988; 61 in 1992; 49 in 2000.* **Sources: Ad2, Bar, Bay, Bea, BO10, Bo5, Bu1, Cla, Clo, Co2, CO5, COL, Ed2, Er2, Fa1, Fed, Fi1, Fo4, Gur, Hi9, Jo3, Jun, Lee, Leu, ME3, Mel, Mi1, MI5, Nrs, ORA, Pi2, Po2, Sav, Sc6, SH8, SIM, So5, St4, STR, TU5, Va2, Wa16, WA8, Wel, Wh4, WI12, WI4, Wom, Wor.**

<u>Starking Delicious</u> (Johnson Cultivar) - Japanese plum. Bears very large clingstone fruit if thinned to 4" apart early in the season. Pollinate with Ozark Premier, Redheart or Shiro. Disease resistant. Ripens early August. Hardy in Zones 5-9. Trademarked. *Source History: 1 in 1988; 1 in 1992; 1 in 2000.* **Sources: St4.**

<u>Sugar Prune</u> - European prune plum. Medium size, reddish purple fruit with greenish yellow flesh. Very sweet and highly flavored. Used fresh and for canning. Biennial. Self-fruitful. Lower chilling requirement than other European prune plums; 550-800 hours. *Source History: 7 in 1988; 10 in 1992; 5 in 2000.* **Sources: Bay, Nrs, ORA, WI12, WI4.**

<u>Superior</u> (MN 194) - Japanese x American hybrid selected for extreme size, vigor and hardiness. Large, golden fruit turns pink, then develops a deep red blush. Peels like peach skin. Firm, fine textured, clingstone flesh. Good fresh and for preserves. Tree grows faster and larger than most. Bears early, often setting fruit in the nursery row. Good pollinator. Ripens in August-September. One of the hardiest jumbos, but not for the far North. Hardy in Zone 4. *Source History: 7 in 1988; 9 in 1992; 14 in 2000.* **Sources: BA14, Bea, BO10, Ch9, Ed5, Fed, Fi1, GR26, Gur, Mc3, Mi1, MI5, SH8, Wa16.**

<u>Surprise</u> - *Source History: 1 in 1992; 1 in 2000.* **Sources: Ed5.**

<u>Tecumseh</u> - Japanese Plum (*Prunus salicina*) x Wild Plum (*P. americana*). Medium size, dark red fruit with a bluish cast. Firm, juicy, yellow, clingstone flesh. Sweet, distinctive flavor. Excellent quality. Good for fresh eating, jam, jelly or sauce. Vigorous, widely adapted tree. Consistent bearer. Ripens in August. One of Dr. N. E. Hansen's first introductions from the breeding program he began in 1895 at the South Dakota Agricultural Experiment Station. *Source History: 2 in 1988; 2 in 1992; 4 in 2000.* **Sources: Ch9, Ed5, Fed, Nrs.**

<u>Timme</u> - *Source History: 1 in 1992; 1 in 2000.* **Sources: Nrs.**

<u>Toka</u> - Wild Plum (*Prunus americana*) x Apricot Plum from China (*P. simonii*).

Medium to large, tapered, reddish bronze fruit with a blue bloom. Firm, yellow, aromatic, freestone flesh. Rich, spicy, sweet flavor. Excellent for fresh eating. Erect, vase-shaped tree. Moderately vigorous. Heavy bearer. One of the best pollinators for American, Japanese and hybrid plums. Ripens from late August to September. Hardy to -50 degrees F. with occasional winter injury. Developed by Dr. N. E. Hansen at the South Dakota Experiment Station. Introduced in 1911. *Source History: 11 in 1988; 16 in 1992; 13 in 2000.* **Sources: BA14, Ch9, Ed5, Fa1, Fed, Jun, Mc3, ME3, MI5, SH8, Stl, Wa16, WI12.**

Underwood - Shiro x *Prunus americana*. Santa Rosa type. Large, smooth, dark red fruit with a small, long pit. Juicy, pale amber, clingstone flesh. Mild, sweet flavor. Good quality for fresh use and jam; fair for jelly. Vigorous, long-lived tree. Early, annual, productive bearer. Toka and Ember recommended as pollinators for maximum yield. Ripens over a long season starting from early July to mid-August depending on location. Hardy to -50 degrees F. with occasional winter injury. Developed by the Minnesota Fruit Breeding Farm. Introduced in 1921. *Source History: 11 in 1988; 14 in 1992; 7 in 2000.* **Sources: Bea, Ch9, Ed5, Fa1, Fed, Nrs, Stl.**

Unika - *Source History: 1 in 2000.* **Sources: Ed5.**

V66071 - European plum. High quality blue fruit. Ripens one week ahead of Castleton. *Source History: 1 in 2000.* **Sources: Cu4.**

V77031 - European plum. High quality, large blue fruit. Ripens 10 days before Castleton. Excellent for early fresh market. *Source History: 1 in 2000.* **Sources: Cu4.**

Valor - Imperial Epineuse x Grand Duke. European prune plum. Larger fruit than Italian Prune. Dark purple skin with some speckling. Greenish yellow, freestone flesh. Excellent eating quality. Vigorous, productive tree is self-fertile. Ripens midseason just after Italian Prune. Introduced in 1967. *Source History: 2 in 1988; 2 in 1992; 1 in 2000.* **Sources: Rai.**

Vanier - Japanese plum. Wickson x Burbank. Red, medium size fruit. Clingstone, yellow flesh. Upright, vigorous tree habit. Productive. Good keeper. Ripens one week after Wickson. *Source History: 1 in 1988; 1 in 1992; 2 in 2000.* **Sources: Ad2, Hi9.**

Victor Large - *Source History: 1 in 1992; 1 in 2000.* **Sources: Si3.**

Victoria - European plum. Large, pink to rose fruit with red dots and a blue bloom. Sweet, golden yellow, freestone flesh. Good but not rich flavor. Excellent variety for canning. Chance seedling found in London. Introduced in 1840. *Source History: 1 in 1988; 1 in 1992; 2 in 2000.* **Sources: Rai, Ro3.**

Victory - European plum. Large, attractive fruit. Semi-freestone. Good quality. Ripens 5 days after Stanley. *Source History: 2 in 2000.* **Sources: Cu4, Hi9.**

Vision - European plum. Very large blue freestone. Excellent quality. Ripens one week before President. Consistent cropper. *Source History: 1 in 1988; 1 in 1992; 1 in 2000.* **Sources: Hi9.**

Voyageur - European plum. Medium size, light purple fruit. Firm, flavorful flesh. Ripens three weeks before Stanley. Originated in Ontario. *Source History: 1 in 1992; 1 in 2000.* **Sources: Cu4.**

Wade - Large, deep red fruit with somewhat flattened shape. Red streaked, yellow flesh. Requires pollinator. Ripens late May to mid-June. Zones 7-10. *Source History: 2 in 1988; 2 in 1992; 4 in 2000.* **Sources: Cum, Jo3, Ju2, Nrs.**

Waneta - Terry (*Prunus salicina*) x Apple Plum (*P. americana*). Largest of all hybrid plums. Yellow skin washed with dark red. Small pit. Juicy, deep yellow, clingstone flesh. Good quality. Fine for fresh use and processing. Highly fertile tree bears at an early age. Heavy, annual producer. Pollinate with Toka. Ripens from late August to early September. Hardy to -50 degrees F. with occasional winter injury. One of the best for severe winter areas. Developed by Dr. N. E. Hansen at the South Dakota Agricultural Experiment Station. Introduced in 1913. *Source History: 10 in 1988; 12 in 1992; 8 in 2000.* **Sources: Bea, Ch9, Ed5, Fa1, Fed, Gur, SH8, Stl.**

Weatherspoon - *Source History: 1 in 1992; 1 in 2000.* **Sources: Nrs.**

Weaver - *Source History: 1 in 1992; 1 in 2000.* **Sources: Nrs.**

Whitaker - *Source History: 1 in 1992; 1 in 2000.* **Sources: Nrs.**

Wickson - Japanese plum. Large, heart-shaped, greenish yellow fruit. Firm, very sweet, translucent flesh. Very popular for fresh eating. Self-fruitful, but will set heavier crops with a pollinator; Friar, Kelsey, Nubiana and Queen Ann are suggested. Ripens midseason, 21 days after Santa Rosa. Requires 400-500 hours of chilling. *Source History: 8 in 1988; 12 in 1992; 7 in 2000.* **Sources: AG2, Bay, Nrs, ORA, Pa2, Son, WI4.**

Yakima - European plum. Very large, oval, red fruit. Firm, smooth grained, clear, golden yellow flesh. *Source History: 2 in 1988; 4 in 1992; 3 in 2000.* **Sources: Ch9, Ed5, Fed.**

Yellow Egg (Pershore) - European plum selected for outstanding quality. Large, oval, golden yellow fruit. Firm, juicy, yellow, semifreestone flesh. Somewhat tart flavor until fully ripe when it becomes rich and sweet. Good for fresh use or canning. Vigorous, fast growing tree. Tall, spreading habit. Very productive. Self-pollinating. Ripens from late August to mid-September depending on location. Zone 5. *Source History: 5 in 1988; 7 in 1992; 5 in 2000.* **Sources: Clo, Gr4, ME3, Mi1, WI12.**

Plum / Flowering

Prunus spp.

Blireiana - *Prunus x blirieana.* Large, pale pink, double flowers. Little or no fruit. Spreading tree with copper-purple leaves. Grows to 20'. Zone 5. *Source History: 7 in 2000.* **Sources: Bay, CO5, Fo2, ME3, ORA, STR, WI4.**

Krauter Vesuvius - *Prunus cerasifera.* Purple leaves throughout the growing season. Light pink spring flowers. Little or no fruit. Heat and cold resistant 20' tree. Zone 4. *Source History: 11 in 2000.* **Sources: Bay, CO5, FE7, Fo2, ME3, MI5, ORA, SIM, STR, TR19, WI4.**

Newport - *Prunus cerasifera.* Leaves retain red-purple color throughout the growing season. Single light blue-pink blossoms are sometimes followed by purple fruit. Grows 15-20' tall. Zone 4. *Source History: 11 in 2000.* **Sources: Bo5, CO5, FE7, Ho5, KAN, LI7, ME3, MI5, SH8, STR, TR19.**

Princess Kay - Hardy to Zone 2. *Source History: 2 in 2000.* **Sources: GR26, SH8.**

Prunus pissardi - *Source History: 1 in 2000.* **Sources: ORA.**

Purple Leaf - *Prunus cistena.* Red-leaved flowering plum holds its deep rich color all season. Pink blossoms in early spring. Bright red fruits. Grows 8-10' tall. *Source History: 4 in 2000.* **Sources: Gir, MI10, Na4, TU5.**

Purple Pony - Single pale pink blooms. Tree grows 10-12' tall. Outstanding purple foliage retains its color. Sterile. Zone 5. Trademarked. *Source History: 3 in 2000.* **Sources: Bay, CO5, FE7.**

Purple Princess - Blooms early. Produces dessert quality, freestone fruit. Red skin. Dark red flesh. Ripens mid-June. U.S. Plant Patent No. 5926. *Source History: 2 in 2000.* **Sources: Bay, CO5.**

Plum / Other

Prunus spp.

All Red - Probably *Prunus cerasifera.* Japanese Cherry Plum. Maroon-red fruit. Tender, dark red, freestone flesh. Sweet and juicy. Good for preserves. Beautiful, ornamental shade tree. Fruit, flower buds, foliage and bark are all the same red color. *Source History: 3 in 1988; 4 in 1992; 3 in 2000.* **Sources: CO5, Tex, Wel.**

American Plum (Native Plum, Wild Plum) - *Prunus americana.* Native Eastern plum. Abundant, 1" red and yellow fruit. Excellent food for wildlife. Suitable for humans as well. Especially good for jam, jelly and preserves. Small, graceful tree. Beautiful fall color. Fragrant, white flowers bloom profusely. Widely used as a rootstock for American or American-Japanese hybrid plums. Adapted to light soils. Ripens in late summer. Hardy in Zone 2. (For other sources, see *Prunus americana* in the Stone Fruit Rootstock section.) *Source History: 16 in 1988; 23 in 1992; 29 in 2000.* **Sources: BO10, Ca8, Co15, CR6, Fi1, Fo2, GR26, Gur, KEE, KI3, LA4, LI7, LO6, LOV, Mc3, MEA, Mel, No2, Oik, Pi2, Pl5, Pla, Sc2, Sh10, Sh14, SH8, Stl, Tri, Va5.**

Beach Plum (Shore Plum) - *Prunus maritima.* Heavily bloomed, 1" diameter fruit. Color varies from black, blue, red or yellow. Widely used by the early settlers for fresh eating, canning, jams, jellies and sauces. Still delightful for all these purposes. Straggling, stiff, thorny bush. Grows to 6-10' high and 6' wide. Fragrant, white flowers in June. Shrub grows well in the poorest soil. Ripens in late summer. Requires a minimum annual precipitation of 25". Hardy in Zones 4-8. Native to the sand dunes along the Atlantic Coast. *Source History: 10 in 1988; 12 in 1992; 11 in 2000.* **Sources: Big, BO10, BU12, Fed, Fo2, Mi1, Oik, Sc2, So5, Tri, We8.**

Beach Plum, Jersey - *Prunus maritima.* Tasty red fruit ripens in June. Good for jelly and sauces. Plant two varieties for fruit production. Zones 4-8. *Source History: 1 in 2000.* **Sources: Rai.**

Beach Plum, Premier - *Prunus maritima.* Grafted cultivar. Tasty fruit. Tree grows 15' tall. Bears heavily some years and light in others, as with all beach plums. *Source History: 1 in 2000.* **Sources: Rai.**

Chickasaw Plum (Sand Plum) - *Prunus angustifolia.* Fruit is good for jelly; enjoyed by wildlife. Hardy in Zones 4-9. *Source History: 2 in 1992; 3 in 2000.* **Sources: Fo2, LO6, Wo2.**

Flatwoods Plum - *Prunus umbellata.* Small tree with rough bark. Small sour purple plums are used for jelly. Native to southern U.S. Zones 6-9. *Source History: 1 in 2000.* **Sources: Wo2.**

Klamath Plum (Sierra Plum) - *Prunus subcordata.* Yellow and red fruit, 1" in diameter. Famous for wild plum preserves. Medium to large shrub or small tree. Fragrant, white flowers. Orange-red fall foliage. Hardy in Zone 5. Native to the western U.S. *Source History: 2 in 1988; 1 in 1992; 2 in 2000.* **Sources: Ca12, Fo2.**

Thundercloud (Cherry Plum, Myrobalan Plum, Newport Plum, Purple Leaf Plum, K.V.) - *Prunus cerasifera.* Sporadic crops of tasty, red plums. Vigorous, upright tree rapidly grows 12-20' tall. Dark, reddish purple leaves with bright red tips hold their color all season. Covered in May with small, fragrant, pink flowers. Hardy in Zones 3-9. *Source History: 7 in 1988; 21 in 1992; 24 in 2000.* **Sources: Big, Bo5, CO5, Cu4, FE7, FO10, Fo2, GI3, Gir, Gir, Ho5, IN7, ME3, MI5, MO10, Na4, Nrs, ORA, SH8, SIM, STR, TR19, We8, WI4.**

Wild Goose Plum (Flatwoods Plum) - *Prunus umbellata.* Small spreading tree to 20'. Dark red, .5" fruit for jams and jellies. Also enjoyed by the wild geese of the lower Carolina Piedmont. Native to the river swamps. Zone 7. *Source History: 1 in 2000.* **Sources: Fo2.**

Quince / Common

Cydonia oblonga

Aromatnaya - Medium size, round, yellow fruit with pineapple-like flavor. Excellent eaten fresh. Picked in October to ripen and soften like a pear. Flesh softens after it is harvested. Disease resistant. Self-fertile. Originated in the Black Sea region of Russia and Turkey. *Source History: 3 in 2000.* **Sources: Clo, On3, Rai.**

Boyer - Deciduous tree up to 12' tall. Fruit has a pleasant spicy flavor when cooked. Used for desserts, jelly and preserves. Self-fertile. Ripens in the fall. Zones 5-8. *Source History: 2 in 2000.* **Sources: Bo5, Ed2.**

Champion - Sweet, golden yellow fruit. Tree grows 12-15' tall. Big, white flowers. Ripens during October. Extremely hardy and reliable. Zones 5-9. *Source History: 1 in 1988; 1 in 1992; 1 in 2000.* **Sources: Son.**

Chinese Quince - *Cydonia sinensis.* Deciduous shrub or tree grows 10' tall. Flaking bark; makes a nice ornamental. Pink flowers are 1-1.5" diameter. Needs a long season to ripen its fruit properly. Hardy in Zones 6-9. Native to China. *Source History: 3 in 1988; 5 in 1992; 1 in 2000.* **Sources: Ba3.**

Common Quince - Large, round or pear-shaped, golden yellow fruit. Excellent for jelly or fruit candy; also used with apples for pie or sauce. Deciduous tree grows 12-20' tall. White to pink flowers in spring. Self-fertile. *Source History: 7 in 1988; 3 in 1992; 4 in 2000.* **Sources: Fo2, Mel, Oik, Sh14.**

Cook's Jumbo (Jumbo) - Very large, pear-shaped, yellowish green fruit with white flesh. Used for preserves, jelly and baked like an apple. Ripens in September. Hardy in Zones 5-10. Originated in Turkey. *Source History: 3 in 1988; 4 in 1992; 4 in 2000.* **Sources: CO5, Ju2, La3, Or2.**

Meech's Prolific - Selected in the early 1800s. Originated in Connecticut. *Source History: 1 in 2000.* **Sources: Hid.**

Orange - Large to very large, round, smooth skinned, bright yellow fruit, frequently exceeding one pound. Orangish yellow flesh. Excellent aroma and flavor. Best for culinary use. Self-fruitful. Low chill requirement. Ripens early. Hardy in Zones 5-10. Very old variety. *Source History: 8 in 1988; 10 in 1992; 9 in 2000.* **Sources: Bay, CO5, Gr4, On3, Or2, ORA, Rai, Ty2, WI4.**

Orange, Dwarf - Large, golden yellow fruit. Excellent quality. Good for jams, jellies, preserves and flavoring. Low, bushy tree grows 10-15' tall; may be grown as a tree or a bush. Abundant, annual bearer. Self-pollinating. Ripens in early September. *Source History: 3 in 1988; 2 in 1992; 2 in 2000.* **Sources: Mel, Mi1.**

Patrick's Jumbo - Extremely large, pear-shaped fruit. About twice the size of other known grafted varieties. White flesh. Ripens in September. *Source History: 1 in 2000.* **Sources: Ty2.**

Perfume - Waxy skinned, fragrant fruit. Compares in size to Smyrna quince. Hardy. *Source History: 1 in 2000.* **Sources: Or2.**

Pineapple - Large, smooth, round, light golden yellow fruit. Tart, slightly aromatic, white flesh. Great for jellies, preserves, baking, fresh eating, winemaking and as a zesty addition to applesauce. Ornamental tree grows 10-25' tall. Can be trained as a small tree or bush. Large, white flowers tinted pink. Blooms late, so less subject to frost damage. Self-fertile. Tolerates wet soils; subject to some pest problems of apple and pear. Requires 200-300 hours of chilling. Ripens mid-September. Cold hardy; Zones 5-9. Named by Luther Burbank for the pineapple-like flavor it imparts to jelly. It took Burbank 15 years and 15,000 crosses to develop this cultivar. *Source History: 12 in 1988; 17 in 1992; 12 in 2000.* **Sources: Bay, Bu7, CO5, Hid, Ju2, On3, Or2, ORA, Pa2, Son, Ty2, WI4.**

Portugal - Fruit turns red when cooked. Ripens early. Prefers a pollinator. *Source History: 1 in 2000.* **Sources: Hid.**

Smyrna - Large to very large, furrowed, oblong, pear-shaped fruit; golden yellow skin covered with tiny brown hairs. Mild, aromatic, tender, light yellow flesh. Superb quality. Great for cooking; favored for desserts, preserves and jellies. Excellent keeper. Small but vigorous tree; large, thick green leaves; widely adapted. Self-fruitful. Requires 200-300 hours of chilling. Hardy in Zones 5-10. Brought from Smyrna, Turkey by G. C. Roeding of Fresno, California, son of Fred Roeding who introduced the Smyrna fig to this country. Introduced in 1897. *Source History: 10 in 1988; 10 in 1992; 14 in 2000.* **Sources: Bay, Clo, CO5, Hid, La3, ME3, On3, Or2, ORA, Rai, So5, Son, Ty2, WI4.**

Soyuznaya - Large, attractive yellow fruit. Sweet-tart flavor. Can be eaten fresh. Small to medium size tree shows no pest or disease problems. Originated in Russia. *Source History: 1 in 2000.* **Sources: On3.**

Van Damen (Van Daman) - Large, somewhat oblong, bright yellow fruit. Pleasing, spicy flavor. Used in cooking and jelly. Heavy bearing tree or shrub grows 10-25'. Considered among the hardiest varieties. It took 700 crosses of Orange x Portugal Quince for Luther Burbank to develop this variety. Introduced in 1891. *Source History: 1 in 1988; 3 in 1992; 2 in 2000.* **Sources: On3, Rai.**

Quince / Flowering

Chaenomeles spp.

Cameo - Double peach flowers followed by yellow, edible fruits. Thornless variety grows to 4'. Hardy in Zone 4. *Source History: 1 in 1988; 6 in 1992; 3 in 2000.* **Sources: Or2, SH8, We8.**

Chaenomeles cathayensis - Tree/shrub grows to 15-20'. Spiny branches. Bears huge apple-green fruit, 6 x 4". Used for quince jelly. *Source History: 1 in 2000.* **Sources: Fo2.**

Contorted - *Chaenomeles japonica.* Hardy deciduous shrub blooms early. Pink-white flowers on twisted branches. Grows to 6' tall. Hardy to Zone 4. *Source History: 2 in 2000.* **Sources: On3, Rai.**

Double Pink - Creamy pink flowers. Large edible fruit. Can grow to 6'. Zones 4-9. *Source History: 1 in 2000.* **Sources: On3.**

Flowering Quince (Japanese Quince) - Spicy fruits make fine jelly. Low growing shrub with dark green foliage. Bright orange-red flowers from April to May. Withstands drought well. Hardy to -30 degrees F. *Source History: 1 in 1988; 3 in 1992; 4 in 2000.* **Sources: Mel, Oik, Sav, TU5.**

Jet Trail - White flowering sport of Texas Scarlet. Nearly thornless, low, spreading shrub bears lemon-scented, yellow fruits which are good for jelly. *Source History: 2 in 2000.* **Sources: Or2, We8.**

Minerva - *Source History: 1 in 2000.* **Sources: ORA.**

Salmon - Large, soft orange flowers followed by large, yellow, edible fruit. Can bloom all summer. Grows 5-6'. Zones 4-9. *Source History: 1 in 2000.* **Sources: On3.**

Scarlet Japanese - Tree grows 4' tall. Masses of fiery red blooms in early spring before shiny green leaves appear. Plant in sun or partial shade. Hardy in Zones 4-9. *Source History: 1 in 1988; 5 in 1992; 2 in 2000.* **Sources: BO10, SH8.**

Spitfire - Bright red flowers. *Source History: 1 in 1988; 1 in 2000.* **Sources: Hid.**

Texas Scarlet - Fruit about 3" in diameter; one of the best for canning. Compact, spreading plant. Hardy in Zones 5-10. *Source History: 10 in 1992; 12 in 2000.* **Sources: Big, Bo5, BU12, GR26, Mc3, MEA, Mel, Or2, ORA, Rai, We8, ZEL.**

Toyo Nishiki - Japanese variety. White and pink flowers. Apple size fruits may be used for jelly. Ripens late summer. Hardy in Zone 4. *Source History: 1 in 1988; 3 in 1992; 6 in 2000.* **Sources: Bay, Hid, Mel, Or2, Rai, We8.**

Victory - *Chaenomeles japonica.* Scarlet red flowers in March produce large yellow fruit which hangs on the plant until late October. Used to make syrup or preserves. Will keep for several months when kept in cool conditions or under refrigeration. *Source History: 1 in 2000.* **Sources: On3.**

Stone Fruit Crosses

Prunus spp.

Aprium, Flavor Delight - Apricot-plum hybrid created by crossing a plumcot back to an apricot. Distinctive flavor all its own with lingering, pleasant aftertaste. Better production when pollinated with another apricot. Ripens in early June. Requires 600 hours of chilling. Zones 6-9. Zaiger introduction. Trademarked. U.S. Plant Patent No. 7090. *Source History: 7 in 1992; 3 in 2000.* **Sources: Bay, St4, WI4.**

Cherry Plum - Bite size, bright red, tasty fruit. *Source History: 1 in 2000.* **Sources: Ju2.**

Compass - *Prunus besseyi x P. hortulan cv. Mineri.* Medium size, oval, purplish red fruit. Juicy, tart, yellow flesh. Clingstone. Excellent for canning, jams, jellies, juice, sauces, preserves and pies. Attractive, flowering, shrubby tree grows 5-8' tall. Reliably productive bearer. Best pollinator for all cherry-plum hybrids. Good pollinator for Sapalta. Reliably productive bearer. Ripens in late August. Hardy to -50 degrees F. Developed in Minnesota and introduced in 1896. *Source History: 4 in 1988; 10 in 1992; 5 in 2000.* **Sources: Ch9, Ed5, Fa1, Nrs, SH8.**

Delight - St. Lucie cherry (*Prunus mahaleb*) x Japanese Plum (*P. salicina*). Floyd Zaiger's cherry-plum companion to Sprite. Dark colored, clingstone fruit. Rich flavor; tart at the skin. Tangier than Sprite. Good for jams and preserves. Pollinate with Sprite, Santa Rosa, Weeping Santa Rosa or other early bloomers. Ripens from July to early August depending on location. Reqires 300-400 hours of chilling. Hardy in Zones 6-9. *Source History: 6 in 1988; 4 in 1992; 3 in 2000.* **Sources: Bay, Pa2, WI4.**

Hiawatha - Cherry plum cross. Small, almost black fruit. Bush habit rather than upright growth. Ripens mid to late June. *Source History: 1 in 1988; 2 in 1992.* **Sources: Nrs, Wom.**

Kaga - Wild Plum (*Prunus americana*) x Apricot Plum from China (*P. simonii*). Small, crimson fruit. Firm, amber, clingstone flesh. Sweet, aromatic flavor. Excellent quality. Small, productive tree. Strong pollinator for other varieties. Ripens in August. Very hardy. Bred by Dr. N. E. Hansen at the South Dakota Agricultural Experiment Station around 1900. *Source History: 3 in 1988; 3 in 1992; 4 in 2000.* **Sources: Bea, Ch9, Ed5, Gur, Nrs.**

Massida - Apricot-plum cross from Israel. Medium size fruit with bronzed skin. Slightly tart, blood-red flesh has an unusual pleasing flavor. *Source History: 1 in 2000.* **Sources: Cla.**

Mesch-Mesch Amrah - *Prunus dasycarpa*. Cross between a Japanese plum (*Prunus salicina*) and Mesch-Mesch apricot. Possibly a plumcot. Mesch Mesch means apricot in Arabic and Hebrew. Very dark red fruit with sweet yellow flesh. Sweet to tart, raspberry-like flavor; variable from season to season. Obtained by the USDA from Tripoli, Libya. *Source History: 1 in 1988; 1 in 1992; 1 in 2000.* **Sources: Rai.**

Oka - Sand Cherry (*Prunus besseyi*) x Japanese Plum (*P. salicina*). Plum size fruit, larger than any other bush cherry. Almost black skin. Purplish red, clingstone flesh. Sweet and juicy. Ripens late August. Hardy into Zone 3. Bred by Dr. N. E. Hansen at the South Dakota Agricultural Experiment Station around 1900. *Source History: 2 in 1988; 2 in 1992; 3 in 2000.* **Sources: Ed5, Fi1, Gur.**

Peach Plum - Peach x plum. Peach size fruit with smooth, reddish purple skin and juicy, golden yellow flesh. Sweet, plum-like flavor. Use Stanley as a pollinator. Ripens mid to late August. Originally bred in British Columbia, but all records of its parentage have disappeared. May be the only successful peach-plum cross ever developed. *Source History: 1 in 1988; 1 in 2000.* **Sources: Clo.**

Peachcot - Peach x apricot. Large, yellow fruit with a good peach-like flavor. Tree has all apricot characteristics. Self-fruitful. Ripens in June. Requires about 550-600 hours of chilling. *Source History: 2 in 1988; 4 in 1992; 4 in 2000.* **Sources: Bay, Bea, CO5, STR.**

Plumcot - Plum x apricot. Large, round, yellow fruit with golden yellow flesh. Aromatic, apricot-like flavor. Tree form favors its plum parent. Ripens June to July. Requires about 400 hours of chilling. *Source History: 4 in 1988; 4 in 1992; 4 in 2000.* **Sources: Bea, CO5, ORA, STR.**

Plumcot, Burbank - Burgundy-purple fruit with gold-yellow flesh. Small pit. Resembles a plum more than an apricot. Obtained from Luther Burbank's Santa Rosa garden. *Source History: 1 in 1992; 1 in 2000.* **Sources: Son.**

Plumcot, Flavorella - Medium size fruit with translucent gold skin blushed with light red. Firm, juicy flesh. Spreading tree requires a pollinator. Ripens late May to early June. Requires 250-350 hours of chilling. U.S. Plant Patent No. 8470. *Source History: 1 in 2000.* **Sources: WI4.**

Plumcot, Flor Ziran (Tlor Tsiran, Black Apricot) - Dark purple skin. Tender, juicy, orange flesh suffused with red. Hardy and vigorous. Originated in Turkey. *Source History: 1 in 2000.* **Sources: Son.**

Plumcot, Plum Parfait - Plum x apricot. Medium size, pinkish orange fruit. Red and amber marbled, freestone flesh. Unique flavor with no tartness at the skin. A connoisseur's delight. Naturally semidwarf tree grows 10-14' tall. Requires annual pruning. Self-fertile. Does well wherever apricots thrive. Good ornamental. Fragrant, white flowers bloom early. Ripens in July. Requires 350-400 hours of chilling. Hardy in Zones 4-8. Developed by Floyd Zaiger. U.S. Plant Patent No. 4338. *Source History: 6 in 1988; 4 in 1992; 4 in 2000.* **Sources: Bay, Fi1, Gur, WI4.**

Plumcot, Spring Satin - Apricot x plum cross. Red-black skin; red flesh has 33% sugar content. Self-fertile. Zones 6-9. *Source History: 1 in 2000.* **Sources: Ty2.**

Pluot, Dapple Dandy - Plum-apricot hybrid. Freestone with creamy white and red flesh with plum-apricot flavor. Green-yellow skin with red spots that turn maroon with a yellow dapple when ripe in August. Requires 400-500 hours of chilling. Flavor Supreme is a good pollinator. Zone 6. U.S. Plant Patent No. 9254. *Source History: 6 in 2000.* **Sources: Bay, Gr16, Pa2, Rai, Son, WI4.**

Pluot, Flavor King - Plum-apricot cross. Red-purple skin. red flesh. Excellent quality fruit with sweet, plum-like flavor with an apricot aftertaste. Ripens in July. Requires 500-900 hours of chilling. Zones 6-9. U.S. Plant Patent No. 8026. *Source History: 5 in 2000.* **Sources: Bay, Pa2, Rai, Son, WI4.**

Pluot, Flavor Queen - Japanese plum x plumcot (plum x apricot). Green-yellow fruit with plum shape. Sweet, juicy flavor with apricot aftertaste. Pollinate with Santa Rosa, Methley or other early blooming Japanese plums. Ripens midseason. Requires 500-600 hours of chilling. Zones 6-9. Zaiger introduction. U.S. Plant Patent No. 7420. *Source History: 8 in 1992; 6 in 2000.* **Sources: Bay, ORA, Pa2, Rai, Son, WI4.**

Pluot, Flavor Supreme - Plum-apricot hybrid. Marbled purple skin color. Flavorful, firm, red flesh. No tartness. Ripens very early; mid-June to early July. Pollinate with Flavor Queen Pluot or another Japanese plum. Requires 500-600 hours of chilling. Zone 6-9. Trademarked. U.S. Plant Patent No. 6763. *Source History: 8 in 1992; 9 in 2000.* **Sources: Bay, Gr16, ORA, Pa2, Pe2, Rai, Son, St4, WI4.**

Pluot, Flavorich - Large fruit with dark purple skin. Firm, sweet, yellow-orange flesh. Vigorous, upright tree. Ripens late August to early September. Requires 800-900 hours of chilling. Needs a pollinator. U.S. Plant Patent No. 8546. *Source History: 2 in 2000.* **Sources: Bay, WI4.**

Red Diamond - Cherry x plum cross. Fruit to 1.5" diameter with tender, deep maroon skin. Firm, ruby red flesh and a small pit that is almost freestone. High sugar content. Good for fresh eating or preserves. Compact bush reaches a maximum height of 6'. Pollinate with Hansen's Bush Cherry or Compass. Bears the second year after transplanting. Winter hardy throughout Minnesota; Zone 3. U.S. Plant Patent No. 4285. *Source History: 3 in 1988; 5 in 1992; 2 in 2000.* **Sources: Ed5, Fa1.**

Sapalta - Open-pollinated cross of *Prunus besseyi*. Resembles Sapa, but sweeter and less clingstone. Large cherry-plum with purple skin and flesh. Sweet and juicy. Excellent for eating, pies, preserves, juice and canning. Ripens slightly earlier than Compass with which it is interfruitful. Dependable cropper. Hardy to -50 degrees F. Introduced in the early 1900's from Brooks, Alberta, Canada. *Source History: 3 in 1988; 8 in 1992; 2 in 2000.* **Sources: Fa1, Nrs.**

Sprite - St. Lucie cherry (*Prunus mahaleb*) x Japanese Plum (*P. salicina*). Companion to Delight. Small, round, purplish black fruit. Amber yellow, freestone flesh. Unmistakable cross of cherry and plum flavor with a lingering, mild sweetness. No tartness at the skin. Good for all uses. Small, vigorous tree. Dependable, heavy bearer. Pollinate with Delight, Santa Rosa and other early bloomers. Holds on the tree 3-4 weeks after ripening. Ripens from July to August depending on location. Requires 300-400 hours of chilling. Hardy in Zones 6-9. Developed by

Floyd Zaiger. *Source History: 6 in 1988; 6 in 1992; 4 in 2000.* **Sources: Bay, Gr16, Pa2, WI4.**

Tlor-Tsiran - *Prunus dasycarpa*. Naturally occuring hybrid of apricot (*P. armeniaca*) and Myrobalan plum (*P. cerasifera*). Dark purple, oval fruit with fuzzy skin. Blooms later than other apricots. Marbled red and yellow flesh. Self-fertile. Somewhat brown rot resistant. Very hardy. Originated in central Asia. *Source History: 1 in 2000.* **Sources: Rai.**

Stone Fruit Rootstock

Prunus spp.

283-1 (WA 1230) - Selection from California. *Source History: 1 in 2000.* **Sources: Nrs.**

290-1 (WA 107) - Selected by Dr. E. C. Blodgett, Prosser, Washington. *Source History: 1 in 2000.* **Sources: Nrs.**

421-3 (Ohio 2) - Selection made at USDA, Cheyenne, Wyoming. *Source History: 1 in 2000.* **Sources: Nrs.**

624-4 (Ohio 3) - Selection made at USDA, Cheyenne, Wyoming. *Source History: 1 in 2000.* **Sources: Nrs.**

Bailey Seedling - *Prunus persica*. Rootstock for peaches. Cold hardy. Adapts to sandy and sandy loam soils. Develops an abundant root system. Resistant to root lesion nematodes. Hardy to Zone 4. Originated in Iowa. *Source History: 1 in 1988; 2 in 1992; 2 in 2000.* **Sources: LA4, Nrs.**

Boone County Seedling - Small freestone fruits. Produces good seedlings. *Source History: 1 in 1992; 1 in 2000.* **Sources: Nrs.**

Brompton Plum - *Prunus domestica*. Semi-dwarfing rootstock for apricot, peach and plum. Provides good compatibility and vigor. Shows some tolerance of wet soils. Zone 4. *Source History: 1 in 2000.* **Sources: LA4.**

Chui Lum Tao Peach - *Prunus persica*. Vigorous, cold hardy rootstock provides good anchorage and compatibility. Nematode susceptible. Selected from the coldest native range of peach in Northern China. Useful in hybridization work. Hardy to Zone 3. *Source History: 1 in 2000.* **Sources: LA4.**

Cistena Plum - *Prunus cistena*. Used as dwarfing rootstock for plums. Hedge plant with purple foliage. Light pink, fragrant blossoms. Occasionally produces purple fruit. Hardy to Zone 2. *Source History: 1 in 1992; 4 in 2000.* **Sources: FE7, HI7, Rai, ZEL.**

Citation - Peach-plum hybrid rootstock for dwarfing stone fruits. Reduces tree size 50-66% of standard on peaches and nectarines; 75% of standard on apricots and plums. Nematode resistant. Tolerant of wet soils. Induces early dormancy and cold hardiness. Induces early and heavy bearing, often in the second year. Does not sucker. Tree life expectancy comparable to standard. Strong and well anchored. Excellent compatibility. Zone 4. Developed by Floyd Zaiger. U.S. Plant Patent No. 5112. *Source History: 3 in 1988; 5 in 1992; 4 in 2000.* **Sources: Bay, Ea3, MEA, WI4.**

EMLA Colt (Colt) - *Prunus avium x P. pseudocerasus*. Mazzard-type cherry rootstock developed by England's East Malling Station in 1958. Bred for reduced tree size, improved disease resistance, earlier cropping and uniformity. Trees on Colt give larger crops of good quality fruit earlier in the life of the tree. Trees are well anchored and well branched with wide angles. Has shown resistance to bacterial canker, crown gall and cherry replant disease. Compatible with most popular sweet, sour and ornamental varieties. Tree size is 70-80% of those on Mazzard. Not as hardy as cherries on standard roots. Will survive -10 degrees F. U.S. Plant Patent No. 4059. *Source History: 7 in 1988; 5 in 1992; 3 in 2000.* **Sources: Bay, MEA, TR8.**

European Dwarf Ground Cherry - *Prunus fruticosa.* Dwarfing understock
for sweet cherry. Dark red, tart fruit is edible. Also used as an ornamental. Hardy in Zone 3. *Source History: 2 in 1988; 2 in 1992; 1 in 2000.* **Sources: LA4.**

Ferris Strain - Similar to Boone County. *Source History: 1 in 2000.* **Sources: Nrs.**

G. M. 61 - *Prunus dawyckensis.* Latest of the truly dwarfing cherry rootstocks
from Gembloux, Belgium. Produces a tree that is 50% of standard size. Should be maintainable at 20' tall or less. First time it has been made available to the backyard gardener. Tested with cross section of common cherry varieties and found to be compatible. Does well on a variety of soils. Hardy to -10 degrees F. *Source History: 2 in 1988; 3 in 1992; 4 in 2000.* **Sources: Bay, Ea3, On3, Rai.**

G. M. 61/1 - Selection of *Prunus dawyckensis* from the Fruit and Vegetable Sta-
tion at Gembloux, Belgium. Scions are 35-50% the size of scions on F 12/1 ex-presssed in trunk section. Trees are less bushy, more open, moderately vigorous, few or no suckers, frost resistant, and show good growth. Thrives in heavier soils. Does well under both sweet and tart cherries. Induces greater fruit size, higher color and earlier fruiting. Reduced development of the crowns facilitates the drying out of fruit for easier harvest. More productive than F 12/1. Disease resistance unknown. Density from 150-230 trees per acre. U.S. Plant Patent No. 5803. *Source History: 3 in 1988; 2 in 1992; 1 in 2000.* **Sources: MEA.**

Gisela 5 - Tree size is 45% of Mazzard. Precocious and productive with very little
suckering and better tolerance to virus infection than Mazzard or Mahaleb. Moderate anchorage; requires support. Adaptable to all soil types. Shows no variety incompatibilities. U.S. Plant Patent No. 9622. *Source History: 1 in 2000.* **Sources: WI12.**

Gisela 6 - Semi-dwarfing rootstock produces a tree 60-70% of Mazzard. No vari-
ety incompatibilities. Adapts to a wide range of soil conditions; does well in heavy soil. Shows good resistance to Bacterial Canker and a tolerance to viruses equal to that of Mazzard or Mahaleb. U.S. Plant Patent No. 8954. *Source History: 1 in 2000.* **Sources: WI12.**

Gisela 7 - Semi-dwarfing rootstock is 50% of Mazzard. Precocious and heavy
bearing. Excellent hardiness. Bears heavy crops. Anchorage is recommended but not necessary. Benefits from annual training. Some suckering. Adapts to a wide range of soils. No compatibility problems. U.S. Plant Patent No. 8852. *Source History: 1 in 2000.* **Sources: WI12.**

Gisela 12 - Produces a semi-dwarf tree about 55% of a Mazzard seedling with an
open, spreading habit. Very precocious and productive. Wide soil adaptability. Good virus resistance. No suckering. Well anchored but benefits from support to carry its heavy crop. U.S. Plant Patent No. 9631. *Source History: 1 in 2000.* **Sources: WI12.**

Harrow Blood - *Source History: 1 in 1992; 1 in 2000.* **Sources: Nrs.**

Himalayan Peach - Hardy seedling peach from high elevation in the Himalayan
Mountains in Nepal. Cold hardiness and rootstock merits unknown but worthy of trial. *Source History: 1 in 2000.* **Sources: LA4.**

Japanese Dwarf Blood - *Source History: 1 in 1992; 1 in 2000.* **Sources: Nrs.**

Lovell (Lovell Seedling) - Very dependable standard rootstock. Compatible with all *Prunus* species. Provides good anchorage, a higher degree of disease resistance than some and a potentially longer life. More tolerant of wet soils and more cold hardy than Nemaguard. Susceptible to nematodes in sandy soils. Equal in performance to Halford as a standard peach stock. *Source History: 8 in 1988; 11 in 1992; 7 in 2000.* **Sources: Bay, Ea3, Fo8, LA4, Nrs, Si3, WI4.**

Mahaleb - *Prunus mahaleb.* Standard rootstock for sour cherries. Slightly dwarfing rootstock for sweet cherries. Best for sweet cherries on lighter soils. Hardier than Mazzard and more tolerant of drought and sandy soils, but shorter lived. Requires well drained soil. Hard to grow in areas of high rainfall. Resists crown gall, bacterial canker and some nematodes. Well anchored. Widely adaptable. Makes a good bird cherry. Hardy to Zone 4. *Source History: 13 in 1988; 14 in 1992; 10 in 2000.* **Sources: Bay, Bea, Ca7, Fo8, LA4, MEA, Sc2, Va2, WI12, WI4.**

Manchurian (Manchurian Plum) - *Prunus armeniaca* var. *Mandshurica.* Extremely hardy rootstock for Asian and Asian hybrid plums. Shiny, red and yellow fruit. Sweet, juicy flavor. Good for fresh eating, preserves, jam, sauce and pie. Bushy, compact tree grows 10-15' tall. White blooms. Starts bearing within a year or two. Hardy to Zone 2-3. Native to Manchuria. Cultivated for centuries in Japan. Usable fruit without grafting. Excellent as naturalized plum thickets for wildlife habitat. *Source History: 4 in 1988; 3 in 1992; 5 in 2000.* **Sources: Bea, LA4, MI5, Stl, Va5.**

Mariana 26-24 - Rootstock for plums, prunes, apricots and most almonds. Slightly dwarfing for apricots and plums. Shallow rooting. Much more tolerant of wet soils than Lovell or Nemaguard. Resists armillaria (oak root fungus), some nematodes and brown line. *Source History: 5 in 1988; 6 in 1992; 6 in 2000.* **Sources: Bay, MEA, Nrs, Rai, Si3, WI4.**

Mariana GF 8-1 - *Source History: 1 in 1992; 1 in 2000.* **Sources: MEA.**

Mazzard - *Prunus avium.* Wild cherry rootstock best suited for sweet or tart cherries planted on heavier soils. Makes a larger tree than *P. mahaleb.* More tolerant of wet soils, but still requires good drainage. More compatible with various sweet cherry varieties. Especially well anchored. Very hardy, but not quite as hardy as *P. mahaleb.* Resistant to rootknot nematodes and oak root fungus. *Source History: 9 in 1988; 14 in 1992; 11 in 2000.* **Sources: Arb, Bay, Bea, Ch9, Fo8, LA4, MEA, Sc2, Va2, WI12, WI4.**

Mazzard F 12/1 - Very vigorous rootstock for cherry production. Trees can be kept to a reasonable height if trained to a multi-leader system. Resistant to bacterial canker. *Source History: 4 in 1988; 1 in 1992; 1 in 2000.* **Sources: Nrs.**

Mazzard, Wild - *Prunus avium sylvestris.* Gum flux resistant, silver bark strain from wild trees. *Source History: 1 in 1988; 1 in 1992; 1 in 2000.* **Sources: Sc2.**

Montclar Peach - *Prunus persica.* Rootstock for peaches, plums, apricots and almonds. Shows good vigor and hardiness to Zone 4. Introduced and tested by the INRA Research Station in France. *Source History: 1 in 2000.* **Sources: LA4.**

Myrobalan (Cherry Plum, Myro Plum) - *Prunus cerasifera.* Widely used rootstock for European plum varieties and also somewhat for peaches. Compatible with a wide range of cultivars. Excellent anchorage. Particularly adaptable to heavier soils. Susceptible to oak root fungus. Lacks nematode resistance. Hardy to Zone 4. *Source History: 8 in 1988; 8 in 1992; 7 in 2000.* **Sources: Bea, Fed, Fo8, LA4, MEA, So5, WI12.**

Myrobalan 29-C (Myrobalan H-29-C) - *Prunus cerasifera.* Vigorous rootstock for prunes and plums. Trees will be vigorous and nearly standard size. Shallow rooting. Resistant to armillaria root rot (oak root fungus) and nematodes. Adaptable to varied soil types. *Source History: 5 in 1988; 5 in 1992; 4 in 2000.* **Sources: Bay, MEA, Si3, WI4.**

Myrobalan B - *Source History: 1 in 1992; 1 in 2000.* **Sources: Nrs.**

Myrobalan, Virus Certified - *Prunus myrobalan. Source History: 1 in 1988; 1 in 1992; 1 in 2000.* **Sources: Sc2.**

Nemaguard - *Prunus persica.* Compatible with all *Prunus* species. Very vigorous. Excellent for well drained soils. Should be planted on a hill where soil is heavy or poorly drained, as it is extremely susceptible to wet feet. Nematode resistant. Poor anchorage in some soils. Suspected physiological effects on some varietal types. *Source History: 8 in 1988; 10 in 1992; 9 in 2000.* **Sources: Bay, Ca7, Fo8, LA4, Nrs, RA4, Sc2, Si3, WI4.**

Nemared - *Source History: 1 in 1992; 1 in 2000.* **Sources: Fo8, Nrs.**

Prunus americana (American Plum, Wild Plum) - Native Eastern plum. Rootstock for American or for American x Japanese hybrid plums. Excellent for wildlife habitat. Does well on thin soil. Hardy in Zone 3. (For other sources, see American Plum in the "Plum / Other" section.) *Source History: 2 in 1988; 4 in 1992; 3 in 2000.* **Sources: Bea, Fed, Sc2.**

Prunus armeniaca (Common Apricot) - Used for apricots where hardiness is not a major concern. Seed from California. Hardy in Zone 5. *Source History: 1 in 1992; 2 in 2000.* **Sources: LA4, Oik, Sh14.**

Prunus besseyi (Sand Cherry, Western Sand Cherry) - Used as a dwarf rootstock for cherries and other stone fruits. Has some compatibility problems with peaches and nectarines. Very hardy, but prone to suckering. Well anchored and adaptable to a wide range of soils. Dwarfs plum cultivars 60-80% of standard size. Tree life not as long as standards. (For other sources of cherry rootstocks, also see Hansen's Bush Cherry, Sand Cherry and Nanking Cherry in the "Cherry / Other" section.) *Source History: 2 in 1988; 5 in 1992; 3 in 2000.* **Sources: Mel, Sh14, So5.**

Prunus Pumiselect - Precocious, dwarfing rootstock for peach and nectarine. Hardy to Zone 2. Trademarked. Patented. *Source History: 1 in 2000.* **Sources: MEA.**

Prunus tomentosa - *Source History: 1 in 1992; 1 in 2000.* **Sources: Sh14.**

Rutgers Red Leaf - *Source History: 1 in 1992; 1 in 2000.* **Sources: Nrs.**

Siberian C (Siberian C Seedling) - Very cold hardy. Induces earlier defoliation, earlier hardening-off plus 10-15% dwarfing. Earlier bearing and maturing. Tree life, suckering and anchorage have developed as problems on some sites, particularly on heavier soils. Not resistant to nematodes. Used for peach and apricot root stock. Hardy to Zone 5. *Source History: 3 in 1988; 3 in 1992; 3 in 2000.* **Sources: Bea, LA4, Nrs.**

St. Julian - *Prunus insititia.* Seedlings from St. Julian A. Slightly dwarfing plum understock. Also used as a rootstock for cherries, peaches, almonds and nectarines. Tolerates a wide variety of soil conditions. Shows great resistance to crown gall and chlorosis. Hardy in Zone 4. *Source History: 2 in 1988; 4 in 1992; 5 in 2000.* **Sources: Bea, LA4, Nrs, Sh14, So5.**

St. Julian A (St. Julian A EMLA) - Semidwarf rootstock. Produces a medium size tree 10-15' tall. Precocious in bearing and productive. Will tolerate a wide variety of soils. Seems to be compatible as an understock for apricot, peach, nectarine or almond as well as plum. Resists chlorosis; tolerant of crown gall. *Source History: 5 in 1988; 4 in 1992; 6 in 2000.* **Sources: Bay, Ea3, MEA, Nrs, On3, Ro3.**

St. Julian GF-655-2 - Plum rootstock from a clonal selection of St. Julian. Well known for its semidwarfing, anchorage, hardiness and disease resistance. Does well on heavy soils. Resistant to bacterial canker. Does not sucker readily. *Source History: 1 in 1988; 2 in 1992; 1 in 2000.* **Sources: MEA.**

Stockton Morello - *Source History: 5 in 1992; 2 in 2000.* **Sources: Nrs, Va5.**

Tennessee Natural - *Source History: 1 in 1992; 1 in 2000.* **Sources: Nrs.**

Tzim Pee Tao Peach - Cold hardy rootstock useful in hybridization work. Produces uniform, vigorous, well anchored trees on well drained soils. Shows some resistance to root lesion nematodes. Selected from the coldest native range of peach in Northern China. Zone 3. *Source History: 1 in 2000.* **Sources: LA4.**

Winter Nelis - Apricot rootstock. *Source History: 1 in 1988; 1 in 1992; 1 in 2000.* **Sources: MEA.**

Blackberry

Rubus spp.

Amity - Bears two crops of large, dark red, firm berries with classic taste. Superior quality. Used for fresh eating, canning or freezing. Good disease resistance. Zone 5. Selected by the Oregon Agricultural Extension. *Source History: 1 in 2000.* **Sources: Fo2.**

Apache - Large, firm fruit. Thornless, erect canes. Good flavor. Shows good cold hardiness and excellent disease resistance. Ripens in July. Originated in Arkansas. Patented. *Source History: 3 in 2000.* **Sources: Bos, Ced, Pe3.**

Arapaho - Large, short-conic, firm glossy black fruit. Small seed size. Erect, thornfree canes. Good flavor. Heat tolerant. Hardy. First harvest around July 20. Earliest ripening thornless blackberry. Zones 5-9. Originated in Arkansas. U.S. Plant Patent No. 8510. *Source History: 20 in 2000.* **Sources: Bo5, Bos, Bu2, BU12, Ced, Ed2, Eno, Gur, HA12, In5, Pe3, Rai, RAM, Sh3, St4, Ty2, VIR, Wel, Wom, ZEL.**

Black Butte - Very large, extra firm berries on trailing vines. Requires a trellis. Good early market variety. Ripens mid-June. Moderate winter hardiness. Zones 7-9. Developed by the Oregon State USDA-ARS program. *Source History: 6 in 2000.* **Sources: Bos, Ced, CO5, On3, Wbn, We4.**

Black Douglass - Large fruit with medium firmness. Trailing vines. First harvest in mid-July. Moderately hardy. *Source History: 1 in 2000.* **Sources: Ced.**

Black Satin (Black Satin Thornless, SIUS 64-21-11) - *Rubus lanciniatus.* Thornfree x Darrow cross. Large, firm, oblong, 1.5-2" glossy black berries; shine fades during ripening. Delicious, sweet flavor. Excellent quality for jams, jellies, pies, fresh eating. Good keeper. Heavy yielding, semierect, thornless vines. Does not sucker. Self-fruitful; more productive with a second variety. Highly resistant to septoria leaf spot and anthracnose; mildew tolerant. Thoroughly tested by USDA; released on East Coast. Excellent in Pacific Northwest. Winter hardy in Midwest and South. Not for coastal plains or Gulf Coast. Ripens in July. Hardy to -15 degrees F. and in Zones 6-9. Introduced in 1973. *Source History: 27 in 1988; 37 in 1992; 29 in 2000.* **Sources: Ba8, Ba8, Bar, Bay, Bo5, Bos, Co12, CO3, CO5, Fi1, Fo2, GR26, Gur, HI10, In5, Iso, Ju2, La3, MO10, Par, Pe3, RAM, Rid, STR, Ty2, Wbn, We4, Wel, ZEL.**

Boysenberry (Nectarberry) - *Rubus ursinus* var. *loganobaccus* cv. Boysen. Extremely large, practically seedless, non-shiny, dark maroon berries; 2-2.5" long and 1" across. Soft, very juicy flesh. Distinctive, rich, tangy flavor and delightful aroma. Excellent quality. Excellent for eating fresh, juice, freezing, canning, desserts and preserves. Harvest when drops from vine at slightest touch; use immediately, does not keep well. Vigorous, trailing vines; fruit is borne on previous season's canes. Hardy to -14 degrees F. without protection; Zones 5-9. Introduced in 1923. *Source History: 12 in 1988; 22 in 1992; 20 in 2000.* **Sources: Bar, Bay, Bea, Clo, Co12, CO5, GR26, HI10, Jo3, Mel, On3, Pe3, Rai, Rid, Son, STR, Ty2, Wbn, We4, ZEL.**

Boysenberry, Clone 43 - Large, firm fruit. Thorny canes. Ripens in early July. Winter hardy. *Source History: 1 in 1992; 1 in 2000.* **Sources: Ced.**

Boysenberry, Thornless - Thornless strain; less vigorous with lower yields than regular boysenberry. Extremely large, almost seedless, juicy, sweet berries, 1.5-2.5" long and 1" wide. Juicy, full-bodied flavor; more flavor than blackberry.

Good for eating fresh, jam, preserves, pie, fruit juice, syrup and wine. Good for freezing; too soft to ship. Vigorous plant grows 5' tall; easy to transplant. Bears the first year after planting. Self-pollinating. Heavy producer for a period of two months during the summer; ripens during May and June. Hardy in Zones 5-9. Requires winter protection below -5 degrees F. Developed by Dr. Boysen in California. *Source History: 20 in 1988; 27 in 1992; 21 in 2000.* **Sources: Bos, Bu1, BU12, Co12, CO5, Fi1, Fo4, Gur, Iso, Ju2, MI5, MO10, Pe3, RAM, SH8, Shu, St4, Wbn, We4, Wel, Wom.**

Brazos - *Rubus lanciniatus.* Big clusters of large, fairly firm, sweet, juicy fruits. High quality. Vigorous, fairly erect to trailing, thorny canes are extremely productive. One of the leading varieties in commercial blackberry plantings. Thrives farther south than any other blackberry because of its disease resistance. Recommended for Texas and the Gulf Coast area. Outyields all others in eastern Texas. Being grown commercially in the Southwest. Ripens in mid-May. Hardy in Zones 4-9. Developed by Texas A and M University. *Source History: 9 in 1988; 14 in 1992; 6 in 2000.* **Sources: Bar, Co12, CO5, SIM, Wel, Wom.**

Brison - Developed by the Texas Agricultural Experiment Station. *Source History: 1 in 1988; 1 in 1992; 1 in 2000.* **Sources: Wom.**

Cascade - Medium size fruit. Thorny canes. Ripens in July. Requires a pollinator. *Source History: 1 in 1992; 1 in 2000.* **Sources: Ced, Rai.**

Cascade, Wild - Medium size berries on trailing vines. Moderately hardy. First harvest around July 1. Requires a male pollinator. *Source History: 1 in 2000.* **Sources: Ced.**

Cherokee - Medium-large, firm, very sweet, good quality berries. Good for freezing, canning, pies, jellies and jams. Strong, vigorous, moderately thorny, very erect canes; dependable and highly productive. Fruit is borne high; more accessible to machine harvest. Separates freely from the plant. Produces a good frozen or canned pack. Ripens in late July. Hardy in Zones 5-8. Developed at the University of Arkansas. *Source History: 8 in 1988; 7 in 1992; 3 in 2000.* **Sources: Co12, CO5, In5, La3, Pa2, Pe3, Po7, Wel.**

Chester (Chester Thornless, SIUS 68-6-17) - Thornless variety very similar to Hull; better resistance to cane blight, slightly hardier. Large, very sweet, high quality fruit. Good flavor, even when firm. Excellent for fresh use, jams, jellies and baked products. Flowers with Hull Thornless, but ripens 10 days later. Most resistant to cane blight caused by *Botryosphaeria dothidea.* Hardiest and most productive thornless blackberry tested at Urbana, Illinois; also tested by USDA in Ohio and Maryland with great success. Performs well in the Deep South; will not soften, leak or lose color on hot, sunny days. Ripens in July. Hardy in Zones 5-7; worth a try in Zones 8-9. Introduced in 1985. *Source History: 13 in 1988; 25 in 1992; 21 in 2000.* **Sources: Al2, Ced, Cla, Clo, Ed2, Fi1, HA12, Hid, In5, Iso, Jun, Mi1, Nou, Pe3, RAM, Sh2, St4, VIR, We4, Wh4, ZEL.**

Cheyenne - Large, very sweet, firm berries grow to the size of a quarter. Excellent quality. Great for pies, jams and frozen packs. Upright, moderately thorny canes that can be mechanically harvested. Also good for processing, Pick Your Own and home gardens. Ripens midseason. Developed and released by the University of Arkansas, 1976. *Source History: 9 in 1988; 15 in 1992; 7 in 2000.* **Sources: Bos, CO5, Iso, La3, Pe3, Va5, Wel.**

Chickasaw - Large, firm cylindrical berries on erect thornless canes. High yields. Winter hardy. Excellent disease resistance. First harvest around June 25. Originated in Arkansas. Patented. *Source History: 3 in 2000.* **Sources: Bos, Ced, Pe3.**

Choctaw - Arkansas 526 x Roseborough. Medium size fruit with mild flavor. Smaller seeds than most blackberries. Good yields. Ripens very early. Hardy in Zone 5. Released by Dr. Moore at the University of Arkansas. Introduced in 1988. U.S. Plant Patent No. 6678. *Source History: 1 in 1988; 15 in 1992; 6 in 2000.* **Sources: Bos, In5, Iso, Pe3, Ty2, Wel.**

Comanche - Large, high quality fruit is somewhat soft; better for eating fresh than for processing. Very good quality. Good for freezing, canning, pies and jams. Canes are moderately thorny with vigorous, erect growth habit. Ripens early June. Recommended from Maryland westward through Arkansas and the central U.S. Hardy in Zones 4-9. Developed at the University of Arkansas. Introduced in 1974. *Source History: 4 in 1988; 8 in 1992; 3 in 2000.* **Sources: Bar, Pe3, Ty2.**

Darrow (Eldorado x Brewer) x Hedrick. Firm, high quality, long conic, 1 x .75" glossy black berries. Subacid, wild blackberry taste; rich, fruity aroma. Good quality. Good for fresh eating, pies, jams and jellies. Tall, upright plants with very strong, 4-5' canes. Space plants 4' apart in rows that are 7-8' apart. Fully productive at a young age; exceptionally large crops. Self-pollinating. A top variety in the Northeast; also a good choice for the Midwest. Ripens early; may produce a second crop in late September. Extremely winter hardy; withstands -22 degrees F. in Zones 4-9. Introduced at the Geneva Station in 1958. *Source History: 25 in 1988; 24 in 1992; 16 in 2000.* **Sources: BA14, Bar, Bu1, BU12, Co12, CO3, Fi1, Fo4, Ga6, Gur, Led, Mel, RAM, Rid, SH8, VA3.**

Dirksen (Dirksen Thornless) - Big, thick clusters of 20 large, very sweet, glossy, black berries. Excellent for fresh eating, pie, jam, jelly, juice and blackberry cobbler. Exceptionally vigorous, highly productive, thornless plants with erect canes. Self-pollinating, but makes a good companion for Black Satin. Resistant to leaf spot, mildew and anthracnose. Similar to Black Satin; matures a week earlier, during July. Not recommended for northern climates; sustains damage unless protected by adequate snow cover. Hardy in Zones 6-10. Developed by the USDA. Introduced in 1973. *Source History: 11 in 1988; 14 in 1992; 4 in 2000.* **Sources: Co12, CO5, Fi1, La3.**

Ebony King - Large, long purplish black berries. Delicious, very sweet, blackberry flavor. Good fresh, canned or frozen. Sturdy, upright canes. Bears dependably, annually and early, before hot weather sets in. Hardy to -20 degrees F. *Source History: 2 in 1988; 3 in 1992; 3 in 2000.* **Sources: Co12, Gur, RAM.**

Eldorado - Large, black, glossy fruit. Sweet, tangy flavor. Upright grower. Resistant to orange rust. Hardy to Zone 4. *Source History: 1 in 1992; 1 in 2000.* **Sources: SH8.**

Evergreen (Evergreen Thornless, Oregon Evergreen Thornless) - Large, firm berries with large seeds; high sugar content. Somewhat bland flavor. Good quality. Excellent for pie, jelly and jam. Canes are green during winter. Very high yields. Thornless, so picking is easy. Not recommended for coastal plain and gulf coast areas. Ripens during August. *Source History: 8 in 1988; 7 in 1992; 3 in 2000.* **Sources: Bar, CO5, St6.**

Flordagrand (Florida Grand) - Large tasty berries. High yields. Well adapted to dry soils. Hardy in Zones 8-10. Developed at the University of Florida. *Source History: 1 in 1988; 2 in 1992; 1 in 2000.* **Sources: SIM.**

Hull (Hull Thornless, SIUS 68-6-6) - Selected from the same cross that produced Black Satin. Large to very large, firm, flavorful, sweet fruit; does not soften, leak or lose color on hot, sunny days. Delicious flavor. Good for fresh eating, jams, jellies baked products and juice. Great keeping quality. Highly vigorous, semierect, thornless canes. Yields about twice as much as most thorned types; up to half a bushel per vine. Good for Pick Your Own. Ripens a few days after Black Satin, during July. Hardy in Zones 5-8. East Coast release; performs very well in the Pacific Northwest. Introduced in 1982. *Source History: 14 in 1988; 24 in 1992; 17 in 2000.* **Sources: Al2, Bay, Bea, Bu2, Ced, Cla, Co12, CO5, In5, Iso, Jo3, La3, Pe3, Po2, Wbn, We4, Wel.**

Illini Hardy - NY 95 x Chester. Shiny fruit with a delicious, wild blackberry flavor. Slightly acidic. Erect, thorny canes. More vigorous than Darrow. Ripens in early August. Hardy to -24 degrees F.; does well in northern areas. Developed by the University of Illinois. U.S. Plant Patent No. 8333. Introduced in 1990. *Source History: 5 in 1992; 5 in 2000.* **Sources: In5, Mi1, Nou, Shu, St4.**

Jumbo, Stark (Shawnee Cultivar) - Very large, tasty fruit up to 1.5" long are produced over a longer time than most. Recommended for Zones 6-8 and warmer areas of Zone 5. *Source History: 1 in 1992; 1 in 2000.* **Sources: St4.**

Kiowa - Large, firm fruit with good flavor. Thorny canes are not as erect as Shawnee but are self-supporting. Winter hardy. Long harvest season; first harvest in mid-July. Zones 6-9. Developed at the Arkansas breeding program. U.S. Plant Patent No. 9861. *Source History: 8 in 2000.* **Sources: Bos, Ced, Eno, HA12, In5, Pe3, Rai, Wel.**

Kotata - Large, firm, tasty fruit. Good for canning. Good keeping qualities. Thorny but easy to pick because fruit protrudes outwards from the cane. May need mulching to protect from winter damage in colder areas. Recommended for fresh market. West Coast variety. Ripens during July. *Source History: 3 in 1988; 3 in 1992; 3 in 2000.* **Sources: Ced, Wbn, We4.**

Lawton - Medium to large, firm, very sweet fruit. True blackberry flavor. Excellent processing qualities. Very strong bush with erect canes that bear fruit well off the ground. Dependable. Winter hardy. An old favorite. *Source History: 2 in 1988; 6 in 1992; 2 in 2000.* **Sources: Co12, MI5.**

Loch Ness - Firm, medium size fruit with rich tart flavor. Thornless, semi-erect canes. High yields. Ripens midseason. Zones 5-9. Developed in Scotland. U.S. Plant Patent No. 6782. *Source History: 2 in 1992; 5 in 2000.* **Sources: Bos, HA12, Rai, Wbn, We4.**

Loganberry (Logan, Thornless Logan, Thornless Loganberry) - *Rubus ursinus* var. *oganobaccus* cv. Logan. Thought to be a wild cross between a blackberry and a red raspberry. Large, light red berries that do not darken when ripe. Unique, tart flavor that is highly prized; many people prefer its flavor over all others. Makes an excellent loganberry wine and pies. Thornless canes; average yields. Ripens in June. Hardiness is similar to Boysenberry; Zones 5-9. *Source History: 11 in 1988; 11 in 1992; 10 in 2000.* **Sources: Bay, Ced, Clo, Co12, CO5, On3, Rai, Son, Wbn, We4.**

Marion (Marionberry) - Medium to large, medium firm, sweet, bright, shiny black berries. Medium to firm flesh. Faint wild blackberry flavor. Excellent quality. Excellent for fresh eating; particularly recommended for desserts. Vigorous, thorny plant with a few long, slightly upright, strong canes; thrifty cane production. Higher yields over a longer picking period than Boysenberry. Developed for western Washington and Oregon, where it is now a major commercial variety. Named after Marion County, Oregon where it was tested extensively. Ripens midseason. Similar to Olallie in size and quality, but better adapted to Pacific Northwest. Zones 6-9. *Source History: 9 in 1988; 12 in 1992; 9 in 2000.* **Sources: Bay, Ced, Clo, CO5, On3, Rai, St6, Wbn, We4.**

Mora de Amarillo - Wild yellow *Rubus* collected in the cool mountains of Ecuador. Viney plant reaches 8'. Bears clusters of small sweet pale yellow fruits with fair quality. *Source History: 1 in 2000.* **Sources: Or2.**

Mora de Castilla (Andean Blackberry) - *Rubus glaucus.* Light purple-red fruits. Rich, tart flavor. Technically a blackberry, though it resembles a raspberry in flavor and plant form. Excellent for fresh eating, jams and jellies. Canes grow 9-13' long. Grown in the Andes Mountains. *Source History: 1 in 1992; 1 in 2000.* **Sources: Or2.**

Mora de Monte - *Rubus roseus* var. *rocota.* Deep purple-red to black, medium size berries. Acid-sweet flavor. Size and flavor resembles raspberries. Second most popular species after Mora de Castilla. *Source History: 1 in 2000.* **Sources: Or2.**

Navaho (Navajo) (Thornfree x Brazos) x (AR 550 x Cherokee). Very small berries with possibly the best flavor of any blackberry. Thornless canes. Shows moderate resisistance to anthracnose. Ripens seven days after Shawnee. Hardy in Zones 5-10. Developed by Dr. Moore at the University of Arkansas. Introduced in 1988. U.S. Plant Patent No. 6679. *Source History: 1 in 1988; 23 in 1992; 26 in 2000.* **Sources: Bay, Bo5, Bos, Ced, Cla, Co12, CO5, Ed2, Eno, Gur, HA12, In5, Iso, Jo3, Ju2, Pa2, Par, Pe3, Sh3, St4, Ty2, VIR, Wa3, Wel, Wh4, Wom.**

Nectarberry (Nectar) - Sweeter than Boysenberry; very similar in size and growth habits. An old-time favorite. *Source History: 1 in 1988; 1 in 2000.* **Sources: CO5.**

Olallie - *Rubus argutus.* Large, shiny, firm, black berries; 1.5" long and .75" wide. Sweeter and less tart than others; some wild blackberry flavor. Vigorous, productive, trailing, thorny canes. Developed in Oregon, but does extremely well in California, where the lack of daylength and cold tends to limit the productivity of some blackberry varieties. Ripens during July. Zones 4-11. *Source History: 6 in 1988; 10 in 1992; 7 in 2000.* **Sources: Bay, Ced, CO5, Pa2, Son, Wbn, We4.**

Pacific, Variegated - *Rubus ursinus.* Dark green leaves with white edge. White flowers produce edible red fruit that matures to dark purple. Upright plant becomes vine-like with maturity. Zones 5-9. *Source History: 1 in 2000.* **Sources: Gr16.**

Rosborough (Rosebrough) - Extra large, sweet, shiny, black berries. Similar to Brazos, but with improved flavor and firmness. Vines hold up well under extreme heat and dryness. Upright canes bear heavy crops that are easily harvested. Ripens in mid to late May. Hardy in Zones 5-9. Developed at the Texas A and M University. *Source History: 6 in 1988; 11 in 1992; 6 in 2000.* **Sources: Bos, Iso, Pe3, St4, Wel, Wom.**

Shawnee - Cherokee x (Thornfree x Brazos). Large, high quality, sweet, juicy, flavorful, shiny, black fruit. Excellent flavor and firmness. Fast growing, erect, thorny canes; no need to trellis. Noted for consistently high yields. Good for fresh market, processing, home gardens and Pick Your Own. Long fruiting season; produces heavily for several weeks. Berry size is maintained throughout the season. Probably the largest fruit and the most productive of all thorny varieties. Immune to orange rust; moderate resistance to anthracnose; susceptible to rosette. Ripens late. Hardy to -9 degrees F. Developed at the University of Arkansas. Introduced in 1984. U.S. Plant Patent No. 5686. *Source History: 9 in 1988; 21 in 1992; 9 in 2000.* **Sources: BA14, Ced, Cla, In5, Iso, Ju2, Pe3, Ty2, Wel.**

Siskiyou - Very large, extra firm berries on trailing vines. First harvest June 15; good for very early fresh market. Moderate hardiness. *Source History: 3 in 2000.* **Sources: Ced, On3, We4.**

<u>Smooth Stem</u> (Smooth Stem Thornless) - Large, firm, luscious, jet-black berries, 35-40 on each stem. Good flavor. Erect growth habit; needs no support. Completely thornless; plants will not sucker. Extremely vigorous and disease free. Consistent, heavy producer. Hardy in the Midwest and South; must be protected with mulch in the North. Ripens 14 days after Black Satin and seven days after Thornfree, in very early August. Released by the USDA as a companion for Thornfree. *Source History: 3 in 1988; 4 in 1992; 2 in 2000.* **Sources: Bu1, Fo4.**

<u>Sylvan</u> - Boysenberry x Marionberry. Large, shiny, black fruit. Mild, very sweet flavor. Very high quality fruit similar to Marionberry. Vigorous, highly productive, thorny, trailing vines. Disease and rot resistant. Excellent tolerance to heavy soils, wind and drought. Imported from Australia, but its parents are from the Pacific Northwest. Developed for the fresh market trade. *Source History: 4 in 1988; 7 in 1992; 2 in 2000.* **Sources: Ced, We4.**

<u>Tayberry</u> - Loganberry x black raspberry. Juicy, cone-shaped, deep purple fruit up to 1.5" long; 50% larger than Loganberry. Firm core like a blackberry. Strong, slightly tart flavor like Loganberry. Fine for jam, jelly or homemade wine. Prickly vines grow 6-7' tall; require strong support. Huge yields up to 12 tons per acre. Vigorous even in difficult weather and bad soil. Ripens late. Hardy in Zones 5-8; needs protection below -15 degrees F. Named after the Tay River in Scotland. Introduced by Scottish Horticultural Research Institute in Perthshire and National Seed Development Organization in Cambridge. U.S. Plant Patent No. 4424. *Source History: 14 in 1988; 14 in 1992; 9 in 2000.* **Sources: Bea, CO5, Gur, La3, Lin, On3, Rai, Wbn, We4.**

<u>Thimble Cap Mora</u> - Commercially grown variety from the cool regions of Colombia. Pink-red berries with excellent flavor that is similar to Oregon's thimbleberries. Look like small strawberries with tender inconspicuous seeds. *Source History: 1 in 2000.* **Sources: Or2.**

<u>Thornfree</u> - Medium-large to large, blunt, firm, glossy, dark black fruit; 1-1.5" long and 20-30 per stem. Good, tangy-tart flavor. Strong, vigorous, completely thornless canes are generally trailing the first year after planting, but semiupright thereafter. Disease free. Does best in fertile soil; will not sucker. Fruits are very similar to Darrow and Black Satin. Ripens a little earlier than Darrow, and about 14 days later than Black Satin, in late July or early August. Hardy in Zones 5-9. New thornless variety released by the USDA. *Source History: 18 in 1988; 17 in 1992; 8 in 2000.* **Sources: Bar, Bo5, Bos, Co12, Mel, SH8, Shu, St4.**

<u>Thornless</u> - Giant berries over .5" long. Fruit ripens over a long period. Hardy to sub-zero temperatures. *Source History: 1 in 1992; 2 in 2000.* **Sources: Lee, WA8.**

<u>Trailing Blackberry</u> - *Rubus ursinus*. Choice native blackberry. *Source History: 1 in 1988; 1 in 1992; 2 in 2000.* **Sources: Abu, ALD.**

<u>Triple Crown</u> - Carbondale 47 x Arkansas 545. Named for its three crowning attributes--flavor, productivity and vigor. High yielding, semi-trailing, thornless vines can grow to 15' long. Bears large, firm, flavorful berries. Self-pollinating. First harvest is in early August. Winter hardy; Zones 5-9. Joint release from Beltsville, Maryland and the Pacific West Agricultural Research Service. *Source History: 11 in 2000.* **Sources: Bos, Ced, In5, Jun, Nou, Pe3, Rai, St4, VIR, Wbn, We4.**

<u>Waldo</u> (Waldo Thornless) - Produces high yields of highly flavored, easy to pick blackberries. Remains thornless, even from the suckers. Named after Dr. George Waldo. Bred at Oregon State University at Corvallis. Introduced in 1945. *Source*

History: 2 in 1988; 4 in 1992; 2 in 2000. **Sources: Ced, We4.**

Wild Blackberry - *Rubus ursinus. Source History:* 1 in 1988; 1 in 1992; 1 in 2000. **Sources: No2.**

Womack - Average size berry with some disease resistance. *Source History:* 1 in 1992; 1 in 2000. **Sources: Wel, Wom.**

Youngberry (Thornless Youngberry) - *Rubus ursinus* var. *loganobaccus* cv. Young. Berries are purplish black when ripe. Fruit size is the same as Boysenberry, about 1.5 x 1.25", but a little firmer, shiny and less acid. Excellent flavor. Good for fresh eating, canning or freezing. Makes refreshing wine-colored juice. Growth habit is similar to Boysenberry. Canes are immune to disease. Capable of surviving adverse weather conditions. Ripens 10 days earlier than Boysenberry, but produces about 20% less. Very hardy. *Source History:* 7 in 1988; 8 in 1992; 4 in 2000. **Sources: Co12, CO5, Wbn, We4.**

Blueberry

Vaccinium spp.

1613-A (Hardyblue) - Medium size, light blue berries are very sweet. Small scar. Erect, open bush; very productive. Ripens midseason. Open cluster and twice pick characteristic make it desirable for mechanical harvesting. Not suitable for long distance fresh shipping. *Source History:* 2 in 1992; 2 in 2000. **Sources: FAL, OR1.**

Alaska - *Vaccinium alaskense.* Deciduous Northwest native to 2-3'. Purplish twigs. Large, sweet berries. Zone 4-5. *Source History:* 1 in 2000. **Sources: Co24, Fo2.**

Aliceblue - *Vaccinium ashei*; rabbiteye blueberry, so called for the pink color of its ripening berries. Medium to large berries; 70-75 per cup. Tall, spreading, 6-10' bush; 7-14 pounds per bush on well irrigated plantings. Good for Pick Your Own, fresh or processed markets. Does well in the lower South. Ripens about May 20. Hardy in Zones 6-9. *Source History:* 3 in 1988; 4 in 1992; 2 in 2000. **Sources: Fi4, Ju2.**

Atlantic - Large, light blue berries. Delicious quality. Vigorous, productive bush. Heavy producer. Ripens midseason. *Source History:* 2 in 1988; 2 in 1992; 1 in 2000. **Sources: Mi1.**

Avonblue (Southern Highbush Avonblue) - *Vaccinium corymbosum*; highbush blueberry. Large berries; 75-80 per cup. Well proportioned, 4-5' bush; 7-14 pound yields on well kept, irrigated plantings. Good for fresh market and Pick Your Own operations. Ripens mid to late May. Hardy in Zones 6-9. *Source History:* 3 in 1988; 3 in 1992; 3 in 2000. **Sources: Hi2, Ju2, VIR.**

Baldwin - *Vaccinium ashei*; rabbiteye. Medium size, dark blue fruit with small dry stem scars. Vigorous, upright plants. Ripens mid to late season; late July. *Source History:* 1 in 1988; 3 in 1992; 2 in 2000. **Sources: Fi4, Ju2.**

Beckyblue - *Vaccinium ashei*; rabbiteye. Medium to large, sweet, light blue fruit; 70-75 per cup. Tall, upright, spreading, 6-10' bush; 8-22 pounds per bush on well irrigated plantings. Produces in high and low winter chilling. Ripens about May 20. Hardy in Zones 6-9. Released by the University of Florida. Introduced in 1977. *Source History:* 4 in 1988; 6 in 1992; 3 in 2000. **Sources: Fi4, HA12, Ju2.**

Berkeley - *Vaccinium corymbosum*; highbush. Large, rather open, loose clusters. Large, firm, pale powder blue berries; 70 per cup. Small scar; no cracking. Medium flavor; some aroma. High dessert quality; good freezer. Vigorous, productive, open, spreading bush with heavy, yellow canes. Large, dark green leaves. White flowers in early spring. Needs good air drainage and light, well drained, sandy loam. Inconsistent yields; 5 pound average. Not for mechanical harvest, due to spreading habit and brittle canes. Recommended for home gardens and midseason Pick Your Own. Susceptible to spring frosts. Hardy in Zones 4-8. Introduced in 1949. *Source History: 24 in 1988; 25 in 1992; 18 in 2000.* **Sources: AMM, BU12, Co12, CO5, De2, DYK, FAL, Fi4, HA12, Led, Mo8, Pe2, TOW, VA3, Wbn, We4, Wh4, Wor.**

Bladen - *Vaccinium corymbosum*; highbush. Vigorous upright plants. Light blue, medium size fruit. Ripens early. *Source History: 1 in 2000.* **Sources: Fi4.**

Bloodstone - Selected from a native stand of *Vaccinium sempervirens*. Lowbush, creeping variety that only grows 5-8" tall. Trailing effect as it spreads, making it a good ground cover. Evergreen; leaf size and texture reminiscent of periwinkle. Susceptible to Phytopthera cinnamonii and anthracnose, so it will not do well in conditions of excessive soil moisture, high temperatures and humidity. Ripens in late July. Hardy in Zones 7-9. Developed at North Carolina State University. *Source History: 1 in 1988; 1 in 1992; 3 in 2000.* **Sources: BR2, Sis, Wo2.**

Blue Chip - *Vaccinium corymbosum*; highbush. Large, light blue fruit borne in loose clusters with medium size stems; 65 berries per cup average. Small to no picking scar. Upright plant; never spreading. Consistent yields; 10-20 pounds per bush average. Late blooming, so not bothered by bud mite. Resistant to all canker prevalent in North Carolina. Susceptible to septoria leaf spot. Can be adapted for mechanical harvest. Ripens in mid-June. Hardy in Zones 6-7. Developed at North Carolina State University. *Source History: 1 in 1988; 2 in 1992; 1 in 2000.* **Sources: Fi4.**

Blue Ridge - *Vaccinium pallidum*. Excellent fruit. Very desirable ornamental shrub grows 2-7' tall. Ripens early midseason. *Source History: 1 in 1988; 3 in 1992; 3 in 2000.* **Sources: Fi4, Ga8, VIR.**

Bluebelle - *Vaccinium ashei*; rabbiteye. Large, dark berries. Excellent flavor and quality extending over a relatively long period of time. Upright plant; moderately vigorous and productive. Recommended for home plantings. Excellent Pick Your Own variety. Ripens over a long period of 3-4 weeks. Hardy in Zones 6-10. *Source History: 6 in 1988; 8 in 1992; 3 in 2000.* **Sources: Bar, Fi4, Ju2.**

Bluecrop - Standard of excellence; leading commercial highbush cultivar. Open, medium-large clusters. Large to very large, firm, bright light blue berries; 65 per cup. Small scar; crack resistant. Good subacid flavor. Good for fresh eating, preserves, baking and freezing. Vigorous, upright, 4-6' bush with slender, light red canes. Foliage somewhat sparce; fiery red in autumn. Overbears unless properly pruned. Yields 12-20 pounds per bush. Suited for mechanical harvest. Bears for over one month; maintains good size. Moderately drought resistant. Ripens in mid-July. Withstands spring frosts. 600-100 hours of chilling. Hardy to -25 degrees F. Introduced in 1952. *Source History: 47 in 1988; 50 in 1992; 57 in 2000.* **Sources: Al2, AMM, BA10, Ba8, Bay, Be4, Bo5, Bos, BR2, Bu7, BU12, Car, Cla, Clo, Co12, CO3, CO5, De2, DYK, Ed2, FAL, Fed, Fi1, Fi4, Fo2, Gur, HA12, Hi2, In5, Je2, KR3, Mel, Mi1, MI5, Mo8, Nou, On3, OR1, Pe2, Pe3, Pi2, Rai, RAM, Rid, Roh, SH8, Son, St4, TOW, VIR, Wa16, Wbn, We4, We8, Wh4, WI4, Wor.**

Bluegem - *Vaccinium ashei*; rabbiteye. Large berries; 75-80 per cup. Spreading, vigorous, 6-10' bush. Yields 10-25 pounds per bush on well kept irrigated plantings. Good for early Pick Your Own. Ripens about June 5. *Source History: 1 in 1988; 1 in 1992; 1 in 2000.* **Sources: Ju2.**

Bluegold - Blue Haven x (Ashworth x Bluecrop). Late season, highbush variety from the USDA. Medium size, light blue, firm fruit. Small dry scar. High quality. Pruning is important to encourage upright growth and to reduce crop load. Zones 4-7. Introduced in 1989. *Source History: 11 in 1992; 7 in 2000.* **Sources: BA10, De2, HA12, Hi2, Stl, TOW, VIR.**

Bluehaven - *Vaccinium corymbosum x V. angustifolium.* Originated from the same cross as Northland (Berkeley x 19-H). Large, round, very firm, light blue fruit; 60 berries per cup. Small, dry scar. Good flavor. Lowbush-highbush type. Vigorous and more upright; 4' tall. Inconsistent yields; 5-20 pounds per bush. Susceptible to mummy berry. Good for fresh market and Pick Your Own. Ripens about July 12. Hardy in Zones 5-7. Developed at Michigan State University. *Source History: 4 in 1988; 7 in 1992; 2 in 2000.* **Sources: De2, VIR.**

Bluejay - *Vaccinium corymbosum*; highbush. Open, loose clusters on outer periphery of plant. Medium to large, firm, smooth, light blue fruit; 76 berries per cup. Mild, slightly tart flavor. Good dessert quality. Tiny dry scar; will not drop, crack or bleed. Medium size, upright bush with yellow wood; slightly spreading. Unusually vigorous; moderate yields. Retains quality on bush until 80% ripe. Long stems and loose clusters; well adapted to mechanical harvest by vibration. Pollinate with Northland. Resistant to both phases of mummy disease. Fresh market and processing. Ripens in early July. Hardy in Zones 4-7. Developed at the Michigan Experiment Station. *Source History: 16 in 1988; 18 in 1992; 23 in 2000.* **Sources: AMM, BA10, Bo5, Bos, BR2, Bu2, Bu7, Car, Co12, De2, FAL, Fi1, Fi4, HA12, Hi2, In5, Mi1, OR1, Pe3, TOW, VIR, Wbn, We4.**

Blueray - *Vaccinium corymbosum*; highbush. Small, tight clusters. Large, medium blue fruit; small scar; 60 berries per cup. Soft, firm skin resists cracking. Very sweet, slightly tart, aromatic flavor; excellent quality. Vigorous, slender, multicaned, very productive, 4-6' bush. Waxy green leaves; brilliant red in the fall. Consistent yields of 12-20 pounds per bush. Self-fruitful. Tight clusters discourage machine harvest. Fine pollinator for Bluecrop and Northblue. Good for home gardens and Pick Your Own. Good shipper. Excels in marginal blueberry areas, especially hot climates. Early-midseason. 800 hours of chilling. Hardy to -25 degrees F. Developed at the New Jersey Station. Introduced in 1955. *Source History: 47 in 1988; 57 in 1992; 56 in 2000.* **Sources: Al2, AMM, BA10, Ba8, Ba8, Bay, Be4, Bea, Bo5, Bos, BR2, Bu1, Bu2, Car, Cla, Co12, CO5, De2, DYK, FAL, Fed, Fi4, Fo2, Fo4, Gir, Gr16, HA12, Hi2, In5, Int, Jun, Lee, Leu, Mel, Mi1, MI5, Mo8, Nou, Pe3, Pi2, RAM, Rid, Sav, Sh2, Sh2, SH8, Shu, Son, TOW, VIR, Wa16, We4, We8, Wh4, WI4, Wor.**

Bluetta - *Vaccinium corymbosum*; highbush. Medium size, firm, sweet, light blue fruit; 71 berries per cup. Crack resistant. Fair quality and flavor. Excellent for fresh eating. Broad stem scar; unattractive as a fresh pack berry. Short, compact, spreading, medium vigorous plants. Self-fruitful. Produces heavily and consistently, even at a young age. Tolerates close planting. Does not like heavy, wet ground with poor drainage. Performs well in hot climates. Resistant to spring frosts. Ripens very early. Requires 800 hours of chilling. Hardy in Zones 5-7. Developed at the New Jersey Agricultural Experiment Station. *Source History: 16 in 1988; 19 in 1992; 10 in 2000.* **Sources: Co12, FAL, Fi4, Gr16, HA12, TOW, VA3, Wbn, We4, WI4.**

Bonita - *Vaccinium ashei*; rabbiteye. Medium to large, light blue fruit; 70-75 berries per cup. Excellent quality. Vigorous, mostly upright, 6-10' bush. Yields of 8-22 pounds per bush on well irrigated plantings. Good for fresh use, processing markets or Pick Your Own. Ripens early. University of Florida release. *Source*

History: 3 in 1988; 3 in 1992; 2 in 2000. **Sources: Fi4, HA12.**

Bonus - Mid-late variety with very large size berries. *Source History: 1 in 2000.* **Sources: De2.**

Bounty - Highbush type. Very large, light blue fruit. Excellent firmness and flavor. Ripens early midseason. *Source History: 1 in 1992; 1 in 2000.* **Sources: Fi4.**

Brightwell - *Vaccinium ashei*; rabbiteye. Medium to large, sweet, light blue fruit; 75-80 berries per cup. Small dry stem scars. Good flavor. Upright, vigorous, 8-12' bush. Yields of 8-14 pounds per bush on well kept, irrigated plantings. Good for midseason Pick Your Own, fresh market or processing. Ripens about June 7. Hardy in Zones 7-9. *Source History: 5 in 1988; 8 in 1992; 8 in 2000.* **Sources: BA10, Fi4, HA12, Iso, Jo3, Ju2, Ty2, Wel.**

Brigitta (Brigitta Blue) - Medium-large, light blue, slightly tart, firm berries; 65 per cup. Small dry scar. Vigorous, upright bush. Heavy bud set. Ripens late; between Bluecrop and Elliott. Yields of from 4-9 pounds per bush. Superior shelf life; ships well. Shows potential for outstanding machine harvestability. Zone 5-8. Recommended for continued trial. Introduced from Australia. *Source History: 11 in 2000.* **Sources: Al2, BA10, De2, FAL, Fo2, HA12, On3, OR1, Rai, TOW, We4.**

Briteblue - *Vaccinium ashei*; rabbiteye. Some clusters may be 12" long. Medium to large, firm, very sweet, light frosty blue berries; 75-80 per cup. Excellent flavor and quality. Very firm; fine for shipping. Vigorous, low, spreading plant. Yields of 8-12 pounds per bush on well kept, irrigated plantings. Good for late Pick Your Own, fresh market or processing. Rabbiteye varieties are native to the South where they do much better than highbush varieties; need less winter chilling to induce flowering. Tolerates a wide range of growing conditions, heat and drought. Ripens from mid-June to mid-August depending on location. Hardy in Zones 6-10. *Source History: 7 in 1988; 6 in 1992; 4 in 2000.* **Sources: Bar, Fi4, Ty2, WA8.**

Brunswick - Clone of the wild lowbush blueberry, *Vaccinium angustifolium*. Forms a dense ground cover that grows 6-8" tall. Pea size blue fruit has the wild blueberry flavor. Orange to crimson fall foliage. Originated in Nova Scotia, Canada. *Source History: 2 in 2000.* **Sources: Clo, Rai.**

Burlington - *Vaccinium corymbosum*; highbush. Small, loose clusters of medium-small fruit; 75 berries per cup. Small scar. Crack resistant. Very firm; excellent shipper. Vigorous, upright, bushy, spreading, 5-7' bush with a wide crown. Yields of 5-10 pounds per bush; not consistent in colder climates. Ripens about August 24. Hardy in Zones 5-7. *Source History: 5 in 1988; 5 in 1992; 3 in 2000.* **Sources: Gir, HA12, Hi2.**

Cape Fear - Low-chill southern highbush variety. Heat tolerant. Plant two varieties for better production. Ripens early to midseason. Requires 500-600 hours of chilling. Hardy in Zones 6-10. *Source History: 5 in 1992; 6 in 2000.* **Sources: Bay, CO5, Fi4, Pa2, VIR, WI4.**

Centurion - *Vaccinium ashei*; rabbiteye. Medium to large fruit; darker than most rabbiteyes. Good quality. Good for fresh eating; outstanding for jam, jelly and on ice cream. Generally upright plants are easy to manage. Thick foliage; makes a nice hedge. Ripens in late August. Hardy in Zones 6-9. *Source History: 4 in 1988; 6 in 1992; 2 in 2000.* **Sources: Fi4, Ju2.**

Chaucer - *Vaccinium ashei*; rabbiteye. Medium to large fruit; 75-80 berries per cup. Vigorous, spreading, 8-12' bush. Yields of 12-25 pounds per bush on well irrigated plantings. Good for early Pick Your Own or processing. Plant in areas of low frost damage. Ripens in early-midseason. Hardy in Zones 6-9. *Source History: 2 in 1988; 2 in 1992; 1 in 2000.* **Sources: Fi4.**

Chippewa - Medium-large, very light blue, firm fruit with very sweet flavor. Compact, upright bush to 4' tall. Ripens midseason. Production and fruit size compares to Northblue; 90 berries per cup. Very cold hardy. Parentage includes some of the most cold hardy selections known. Zones 3-8. A 1996 release from Minnesota. PVP. *Source History: 11 in 2000.* **Sources: Ag4, BA14, BR2, Clo, De2, FAL, HA12, On3, Rai, TOW, We4.**

Choice - *Vaccinium ashei*; rabbiteye. Medium size, darker blue fruit; 80-90 berries per cup. Vigorous, upright, 8-12' bush with some spreading. Yields of 8-12 pounds per bush on well kept, irrigated plantings. Good for late Pick Your Own, fresh market or processing. Will grow well in the South. Ripens mid-late. Hardy in Zones 6-9. *Source History: 2 in 1988; 4 in 1992; 2 in 2000.* **Sources: Fi4, Ju2.**

Climax - *Vaccinium ashei*; rabbiteye. Medium to large, sweet, medium dark blue fruit; 75-80 berries per cup. Small stem scars. Good flavor. Upright, 6-10' plant with a spreading, open growth habit. Yields of 8-22 pounds per bush on well irrigated plantings. Plant two varieties for better pollination. Berries tend to ripen uniformly. One of the very best for mechanical harvesting. Also good for Pick Your Own, fresh use or processed markets. Ripens early. Hardy in Zones 7-9. *Source History: 15 in 1988; 23 in 1992; 17 in 2000.* **Sources: Bar, Bas, Cla, Ed2, Fi4, HA12, Hid, In5, Iso, Jo3, Ju2, La3, Lee, Sav, St4, Ty2, Wel.**

Collins - *Vaccinium corymbosum*; highbush. Medium size, long, rather tight, grape-like clusters. Medium to large, firm, light blue fruit; 70 berries per cup. Small scar. Highly flavored; sweet to mildly subacid. Good quality. Berries do not drop or crack. Moderately spreading, 4-6' bush with strong canes and red wood; somewhat slow growing. Early, long lasting fall color. Moderately productive; yields of 10-15 pounds per bush. Excellent for both hand-picking and mechanical harvest. Ripens midseason. Hardy in Zones 5-7. Developed by the USDA. Introduced in 1959. *Source History: 18 in 1988; 19 in 1992; 7 in 2000.* **Sources: AMM, Bos, Co12, HA12, Hi2, Leu, Pe3.**

Cooper - *Vaccinium corymbosum*. Moderately vigorous, upright bush is productive. Ripens early. *Source History: 1 in 1992; 1 in 2000.* **Sources: Fi4.**

Coville - *Vaccinium corymbosum*; highbush. Open, loose clusters. Large to very large, firm, medium blue fruit; 65 berries per cup. Not subject to cracking. Good, aromatic flavor, but tart until fully ripe. Excellent for freezing and jellies. High quality fruit hangs well, even when fully ripe. Extremely vigorous, productive, upright, 4-6', slightly spreading bush. Ornamental waxy green leaves; brilliant red in the fall. Pollinate with Jersey or Bluecrop. Susceptible to anthracnose. Adapts well to mechanical harvest. Used to extend Pick Your Own season. Ripens late. Hardy in Zones 5-8. Introduced by the USDA in 1949. *Source History: 24 in 1988; 26 in 1992; 17 in 2000.* **Sources: AMM, Bu1, Co12, CO3, DYK, Fo4, HA12, Hi2, Int, Je2, KR3, Leu, Mel, Mo8, Roh, We8, Wor.**

Croatan - Northern highbush type. Medium-firm fruit hangs in loose cluster. Early ripening. *Source History: 1 in 2000.* **Sources: Fi4.**

Darrow - *Vaccinium corymbosum*; highbush. Medium size, loose fruit cluster. Large, firm, light blue fruit; 57 berries per cup. Medium size scar. Tart until completely ripe, then excellent flavor. Vigorous, upright, slightly spreading, 5-7' bush. Yields average 8-15 pounds per bush. Consistently productive in mild climates. Good choice in the Pacific Northwest. Does not appear suitable for mechanical harvesting. Ripens in early August. Hardy in Zones 5-7. Named after George Darrow, a pioneer in blueberry breeding during the 1950s and 1960s. Introduced in 1965. *Source History: 5 in 1988; 10 in 1992; 11 in 2000.* **Sources: AMM, Bu7, Clo, CO5, FAL, Fo2, HA12, Rai, Son, VIR, We4.**

Delite - *Vaccinium ashei*; rabbiteye. Medium to large, round, firm, light blue fruit with red undercolor sometimes showing through even when ripe; 75-80 berries per cup. Dry stem scars. Fine texture. High sugar content; excellent flavor. Good quality. Upright, moderately vigorous, well proportioned, multistemmed, 6-10' bush. Lacks density of foliage; tends to have thin leaf canopies. Yields of 8-15 pounds per bush on well kept, irrigated plantings. Fine for home gardens and late Pick Your Own because the fruit may be eaten greener than most. Good variety to close out the season. Ripens late. Hardy in Zones 6-10. *Source History: 12 in 1988; 15 in 1992; 8 in 2000.* **Sources: Bar, Fi4, Jo3, Ju2, La3, Ty2, WA8, Wel.**

Duke - *Vaccinium corymbosum*; highbush. Medium size, firm, light blue berries. Good color and small, dry scar. Mild flavor. Good quality. Vigorous, very productive, open, stocky, multicaned, upright, 4-6' bush. Consistently high yields. Used for fresh market and processing. Ripens early. Hardy in Zones 4-7. Developed by the New Jersey Agricultural Experiment Station and the USDA. Selected in 1972 from crosses of Earliblue, Ivanhoe, Berkeley, Coville and Atlantic. Introduced in 1986. *Source History: 2 in 1988; 11 in 1992; 23 in 2000.* **Sources: AMM, BA10, Bos, BR2, Bu2, Bu7, Clo, De2, Ed2, FAL, Fed, Fi4, HA12, Hi2, Mel, Mo8, Nou, On3, OR1, TOW, VIR, Wbn, We4.**

Earliblue - *Vaccinium corymbosum*; highbush. Stanley x Weymouth. Medium size, long, open, loose clusters. Medium to large, firm, light blue berries; 65-75 per cup. Small picking scar; crack resistant. Excellent, mild, sweet, full flavor. Vigorous, erect, 4-6' bush; heavy, bright red canes. Large, heavy leaves. Fairly consistent yields of 8-15 pounds per bush. Pollinate with Jersey or Bluecrop. Susceptible to phomopsis canker; hard to control. Average quality; does not hold up. Machine harvests well. Avoid poorly drained soils. Ripens early. Best in northern areas. Hardy to -25 degrees F. and in Zones 5-7. Developed at the New Jersey Agricultural Experiment Station. Introduced in 1962. *Source History: 29 in 1988; 28 in 1992; 29 in 2000.* **Sources: Al2, AMM, Be4, Bo5, Bu7, BU12, CO5, DYK, FAL, Fo2, Gir, HA12, Je2, Led, Lee, Leu, Mel, Mo8, OR1, Pi2, Roh, Sav, SH8, St4, TOW, We4, We8, Wh4, Wor.**

Early Sweet - *Vaccinium angustifolium* var. *laevifolium*. Generally regarded as producing the best fruit of the lowbush varieties. Deciduous shrub, usually 1-1.5' tall. Spreads by means of its root system to form a nearly solid cover. Productive, low maintenance ground cover. Native to the eastern and central U.S. Ripens early. Hardy in Zones 2-7. *Source History: 1 in 1988; 1 in 1992; 1 in 2000.* **Sources: Tri.**

Elliott's Blueberry - *Vaccinium elliottii*. Small to medium, firm, light blue berries; 75 per cup. Small, dry scar; will not crack or drop. Good, mild flavor when fully ripe; very tart until 60% of the berries are ripe. Vigorous, very upright, slightly spreading, 5-8' bush with red wood. Good ornamental; bluish green leaves, late blooming flowers. Self-fruitful. Consistently yields 10-20 pounds per bush. Suitable for mechanical harvesting; 70-80% of the berries can be picked at one time. Not a good choice for Zone 5 coastal areas of the Pacific Northwest. Ripens from late August until frost. Requires 800 hours of chilling. Hardy in Zones 4-7. Introduced in 1973. *Source History: 15 in 1988; 19 in 1992; 22 in 2000.* **Sources: AMM, BA10, Ba3, Bay, Bu2, Bu7, Car, De2, FAL, Fi4, Fo2, HA12, In5, Mel, Mi1, OR1, RAM, TOW, VIR, Wbn, We4, WI4.**

Friendship - Medium size fruit. Slight flavor of wild lowbush. Yields 4-8 pounds per bush. Late season. Hardy in Zones 3-7. Selected from native wild blueberries found in Friendship, Wisconsin. Introduced in 1990. PVP. *Source History: 5 in 1992; 8 in 2000.* **Sources: BA14, De2, HA12, Jun, Stl, TOW, VIR, We8.**

Garden Blue - *Vaccinium ashei*; rabbiteye. Medium size, firm, light blue fruit. Fine flavor. Good quality. Upright, vigorous plant is consistently productive. Plant two varieties for better pollination. Ripens early-midseason. Hardy in Zones 6-9. *Source History: 2 in 1988; 3 in 1992; 3 in 2000.* **Sources: Fi4, Lee, Sav.**

Georgiagem (Georgia Gem) - Low chilling Southern Highbush with consistently good yields. Grows 5-6' tall. Medium to large, very firm fruit with small scar; 80 berries per cup. Excellent flavor and color. Bush appearance resembles that of its parent, Bluecrop. Tolerates higher pH than others. Good for fresh market. Early to midseason ripening. Requires 200-500 chilling hours. Hardy in Zones 7-9. University of Georgia and USDA release. *Source History: 6 in 1992; 15 in 2000.* **Sources: Bay, CO5, FAL, Fi4, Fo2, HA12, HI10, Jo3, Ju2, Pa2, Sh2, Son, Wbn, We4, WI4.**

Gulfcoast - Highbush type with growing qualities comparable to Cooper. Superior fruit quality. Blooms late; ripens early. *Source History: 3 in 1992; 2 in 2000.* **Sources: Fi4, Ju2.**

Hardiblue (16-13-A) - Medium size, sweet berry with superior flavor. Heavy yields in midsummer. Tolerates heavy clay soil. Zones 4-8. *Source History: 1 in 1988; 1 in 1992; 1 in 2000.* **Sources: Bu7.**

Herbert - *Vaccinium corymbosum*; highbush. Loose clusters of large, flat, nearly 1", not firm, dark blue berries; 65 per cup. Outstanding color. Known for its fine, sweet-tart, blueberry flavor. Large picking scar will leak, making the fruit an unattractive black color. Vigorous, productive, slightly spreading, slightly dwarf, 4-6' bush. Blooms in late spring. Yields 5-8 pounds per bush. Hangs well on the bush without dropping. Tip bearer, so easy to pick. Good for home gardens, local sales and Pick Your Own. Recommended for commercial use. Not good for shipping. Ripens late. Hardy in Zones 4-7. *Source History: 10 in 1988; 13 in 1992; 8 in 2000.* **Sources: Al2, AMM, Co12, DYK, HA12, Mi1, Pe2, We4.**

Highbush Blueberry (Swamp Blueberry, Whortleberry) - *Vaccinium corymbosum*. Bluish black, bloomy fruits. Deciduous bushes grow 6-15' tall. White or pinkish flowers in May. Red foliage in autumn. Native to the eastern U.S. Ripens from June to August. *Source History: 3 in 1988; 3 in 1992; 4 in 2000.* **Sources: Big, BO10, HI10, We8.**

Home Bell - *Source History: 1 in 1988; 1 in 1992; 1 in 2000.* **Sources: SIM.**

Ivanhoe - Large to very large, medium blue berries. Firm, crisp flesh. Excellent, delightful, sweet-tart flavor. High dessert quality; resistant to cracking. Very vigorous, tall, upright bush. Heavy, annual bearer. Ripens midseason. *Source History: 4 in 1988; 3 in 1992; 1 in 2000.* **Sources: Mi1.**

Jersey - *Vaccinium corymbosum*; highbush. Long, loose clusters. Small to medium, juicy, light blue berries; 110 per cup. Small scar; crack resistant. Mild, fairly good flavor. Vigorous, fast growing, semiupright bush, 5-7' tall. Open, spreading, yellow canes. Large, glossy, waxy, green leaves; brilliant yellow in autumn. Pollinate with Earliblue or Bluecrop; closely related to Earliblue. Yields 7-10 pounds per bush. Suitable for mechanical harvest. Excellent for fresh shipping, processing, local sales and home gardens. Leading midseason berry in southwestern Michigan. Ripens from mid-August until frost. Hardy to -30 and in Zones 5-8. Introduced in

1928. *Source History: 36 in 1988; 36 in 1992; 38 in 2000.* **Sources: Al2, AMM, BA10, Be4, Bo5, BR2, Bu1, BU12, Car, Co12, De2, FAL, Fed, Fi4, Fo4, Gur, HA12, In5, Int, KR3, Led, Leu, Mi1, Mo8, Nou, Pi2, Rai, RAM, Rid, SH8, Shu, St4, TOW, VA3, VIR, Wbn, We4, Wor.**

John Blue (Jonblue) - *Vaccinium darrowi*. Blue leaves. Hardy in Zone 8. Selected at the North Carolina State University. *Source History: 2 in 1988; 2 in 1992; 1 in 2000.* **Sources: Wo2.**

Late Blue - *Vaccinium corymbosum*; highbush. Medium size clusters. Firm, small berries; 94 per cup. Small stem scars. Highly flavored. Erect, vigorous, wide crowned, 5-7' bush. Consistently yields 9-12 pounds per bush. Simultaneous ripening in hot weather. Ripens about August 15. Hardy in Zones 4-7. *Source History: 3 in 1988; 4 in 1992; 2 in 2000.* **Sources: AMM, We8.**

Legacy - Evergreen variety bears heavy yields of medium to large, flavorful fruit. Ripens in August. Orange foliage over winter. Grows to 6 ft. Zones 5-9. *Source History: 6 in 2000.* **Sources: Bu7, Clo, On3, Rai, Wbn, We4.**

Lowbush Blueberry - *Vaccinium angustifolium*. Native, dense growing, 18-24" tall, spreading ground cover with edible berries in summer. Powder blue to black color fruit. Brilliant red autumn foliage. Prefers sandy, acid soils. Excellent for naturalizing and wildflower gardens. Harvested commercially in Maine and eastern Canada. Hardy in Zones 2-7. *Source History: 4 in 1988; 2 in 1992; 12 in 2000.* **Sources: Bea, Big, BO10, Bu7, Fed, Fo2, HA12, Or2, Sh14, VIR, We18, We8.**

Marimba - Large, sweet berries with great flavor. Long ripening season. Excellent for Pick Your Own or home gardens. University of Florida release. *Source History: 1 in 2000.* **Sources: Ju2.**

Meader - *Vaccinium corymbosum*; highbush. Medium to large, medium blue fruit; 65 berries per cup. Small, dry scar. Exceptional quality. Berries do not crack, drop or soften in hot weather. Good for fresh use or processing. Vigorous, upright, open, slightly spreading, 5-7' bush. Holds its size and remains firm throughout the season. Consistently high yields. Recommended for severe winter areas. Ripens in mid-July. Hardy to -15 degrees F. Developed by Professor Elwyn Meader at the New Hampshire Agricultural Experiment Station in Durham. *Source History: 4 in 1988; 4 in 1992; 2 in 2000.* **Sources: Fa1, HA12.**

Misty (Challenger, 2-1, Mistyblue) - *Vaccinium ashei*; rabbiteye. Large, firm berries; 65 per cup. Excellent flavor. Firm with little to no picking scar. Evergreen bush is erect with narrow crown at maturity. Shape of the bush lends itself to mechanical harvest. Used to pollinate Sharpblue. Requires 150-300 hours of chilling. Ripens in early May. Zones 5-9. University of Florida release, 1989. *Source History: 3 in 1992; 10 in 2000.* **Sources: Ed2, FAL, Fi4, HA12, Ju2, Pa2, Rai, Son, Wbn, We4.**

Mortino - *Vaccinium floribundum*. Wild blueberry species collected from moist volcanic slopes in Ecuador and Colombia. Deep green evergreen foliage covers the 2-5' tall bushes. *Source History: 1 in 2000.* **Sources: Or2.**

Nelson - Bluecrop x Berkeley. Excellent fruit quality. Small scar. Exceptional flavor. Vigorous, upright bush; 5-6' tall. High yields; 13-18 pounds per plant. Hand or machine harvest. Late season variety from the USDA. Hardy in Zones 4-7. Introduced in 1988. *Source History: 7 in 1992; 13 in 2000.* **Sources: BA10, BR2, De2, FAL, Fed, Fo2, HA12, In5, Nou, OR1, TOW, Wa16, We4.**

Northblue - *Vaccinium corymbosum* x *V. angustifolium*. (G65 x Ashworth) x U53. Plump, firm, sweet, .5" navy blue fruit. Excellent, wild blueberry flavor that is superior to most highbush cultivars; very good to excellent quality. Stores well with refrigeration. Bush grows 20-30" tall. Unusually large, glossy, dark green leaves turn dark red in autumn. Yields 3-7 pounds per plant, if adequate snow cover. Self-fertile but yields improve when planted with Northcountry. Easy to pick. Good for fresh use, Pick Your Own, local sales or commercial processing. Ripens in mid-July. Hardy to -35 and in Zones 3-7. Introduced by University of Minnesota in 1983. PVP. *Source History: 16 in 1988; 20 in 1992; 22 in 2000.* **Sources: Ag4, BA14, BR2, Clo, De2, Ed5, Fa1, FAL, Fi1, Fo2, Gr16, Gur, HA12, Jun, Lin, Mi1, Or2, SH8, Stl, TOW, Wbn, We4.**

Northcountry - *Vaccinium corymbosum* x *V. angustifolium*. (G65 x Ashworth) x R2P4. Medium size, .5" diameter, sky blue fruit. Little to no picking scar. Sweet to mild, wild blueberry flavor. Good quality. Tough, vigorous plants grow 18-24" tall and 30-40" wide. Sky blue flowers. Yields of 2-7 pounds per bush. Production is maximized when snow protection is adequate. Begins ripening five days before Northblue, about July 19; continues for 2-3 weeks. Recommended for commercial fruit production. Hardy to -35 degrees F. Developed at the University of Minnesota. Introduced in 1983. PVP. *Source History: 8 in 1988; 15 in 1992; 17 in 2000.* **Sources: Ag4, BA14, BR2, Clo, De2, Fa1, Fo2, HA12, In5, Lin, Or2, SH8, Stl, TOW, Wbn, We4, We8.**

Northland - *Vaccinium corymbosum* x *V. angustifolium*. Inherited more lowbush traits than Bluehaven, its sister. Long, loose clusters. Small, round, medium firm, dark blue berries; 136 per cup. Medium scar; small and dry if picked soon after ripe. Wild blueberry flavor. Vigorous, moderately spreading, 3-4' bush; pliable, limber branches withstand weight of heavy snow. Blossoms tolerate light frost. Requires pollination. Extremely productive; consistent yields of 15-20 pounds in one main picking. Larger bush than similar crosses; heavier yields but not quite as hardy. Ripens early July. Hardy to -25 degrees F; Zones 3-7. Developed at Michigan State University. *Source History: 19 in 1988; 22 in 1992; 27 in 2000.* **Sources: Ag4, Al2, AMM, Bea, Bu7, Car, Clo, Co12, De2, Ed2, Ed5, Fa1, FAL, Fed, Fi4, Fo2, HA12, Hi2, Jun, Mi1, Mo8, Nou, Stl, TOW, Wbn, We4, We8.**

Northsky - *Vaccinium corymbosum* x *V. angustifolium*. (G65 x Ashworth) x R2P4. Small to medium, sky blue fruit with dusty bloom; smaller than Northblue. Excellent wild blueberry flavor, superior to most highbush cultivars. Low, spreading plant with dense foliage; 10-18" tall and 24-36" wide. Small, glossy, dark green leaves turn dark red in the fall. Yields 1-2 pounds per bush. Harvested by hand or with a special berry rake. Home garden variety for northern Minnesota and similar areas with severely cold winters, but abundant snow cover. The hardiest, surviving -40 degrees F. Grows well in Zones 3-7. Developed at the University of Minnesota. PVP. *Source History: 11 in 1988; 12 in 1992; 19 in 2000.* **Sources: BR2, De2, Ed5, Fa1, Fo2, Gr16, HA12, In5, Mi1, On3, Or2, Rai, SH8, Stl, TOW, Wbn, We4, We8, ZEL.**

Nui - Extremely large, light blue, firm fruit with outstanding flavor and superior keeping quality. Spreading bush with medium to low vigor and average productivity. Medium to light production in northern zones with better performance in southern areas. Tolerates both moderate chilling and high summer heat. Ripens early to midseason. U.S. Plant Patent No. 6699. *Source History: 1 in 2000.* **Sources: FAL.**

O'Neal (O'Neill) - Early, low-chilling southern highbush. Large, attractive fruit with little or no picking scar. Suitable for fresh or process markets. High temperatures do not deteriorate fruit quality. Requires 150-500 hours of chilling. Does best where soil pH is kept below 5.5. Hardy in Zones 7-9. Developed by the USDA. Introduced in 1987. *Source History: 10 in 1992; 19 in 2000.* **Sources: BA10,**

Bay, CO5, Ed2, FAL, Fi4, Fo2, Gr16, HA12, Hi2, Jo3, Pa2, Sh2, Son, VIR, Wa16, Wbn, We4, WI4.

Olympia - Large, loose clusters of medium to large, medium to dark blue fruit. Thin skin; small scar. Won't drop or crack. Superb, distinctive, very sweet flavor and aroma. Spreading, vigorous bush with strong canes and light red wood. Prune severely to force upright growth and best quality. Requires pollination. Well suited for process frozen packs because of its high sugar content and uniform size. Good for fresh shipping if the weather is not too hot. Adapts well to most types of soil. Ripens midseason with Bluecrop. Named for Olympia, Washington where it was developed. Hardy in Zones 5-7. *Source History: 5 in 1988; 6 in 1992; 10 in 2000.* **Sources: Bu7, Clo, FAL, Fo2, Gr16, Rai, Son, Wbn, We4, WI4.**

Ornablue - *Vaccinium corymbosum* x *V. angustifolium*. Heavy bearer of small, dark blue fruits; 120 berries per cup. Bush is 3' tall and spreads to 5' diameter at maturity. Dense, but very slender foliage; long lasting, red color in autumn. Blooms profusely. Hardy in Zones 4-7. Developed at the West Virginia Agricultural Experiment Station. *Source History: 2 in 1988; 3 in 1992; 3 in 2000.* **Sources: Car, HA12, We8.**

Ozarkblue - Large, firm, high quality fruit. Vigorous, upright bush. Consistently outyields Bluecrop with higher quality berries. Shows better vigor, yields and spring frost resistance than all other southern highbush varieties. Ripens midseason. Released from the University of Arkansas blueberry program along with the USDA. U.S. Plant Patent No. 10,035. *Source History: 2 in 2000.* **Sources: FAL, Hi2.**

Patriot - *Vaccinium corymbosum*; highbush. US3 x Earliblue. Tight clusters of large, slightly flat, medium blue berries; 49 per cup early in harvest, 60 per cup later. Firm, if weather is not too hot. Small, dry, recessed scar. Above average flavor. Moderately upright, open, very vigorous, 4-6' bush; red wood. Yields 10-20 pounds per bush, depending on site. Usually picked twice; first picking yields 80%. Shows "red back" if picked too early. Only variety resistant to Phytophthora cinnamomi, widely distributed soil fungus that causes root rot. Tolerates wet or clay soils well. Ripens early July. Hardy to -29 degrees F.; Zones 3-7. Developed at the University of Maine. *Source History: 18 in 1988; 26 in 1992; 33 in 2000.* **Sources: AMM, BA10, Bea, Bos, BR2, Bu7, Clo, CO3, De2, Ed5, FAL, Fed, Fi1, Fi4, Gr16, Gur, HA12, Hi2, In5, Jun, Mi1, Mo8, Nou, Pe3, Rai, Sh2, Stl, TOW, VIR, Wa16, Wbn, We8, Wh4.**

Pemberton - Loose clusters of large, firm berries. Holds flavor during processing. Good dessert quality. Fine for eating fresh, canning and freezing. Prolific and vigorous. *Source History: 4 in 1988; 3 in 1992; 2 in 2000.* **Sources: Fi1, Gir.**

Polaris - Medium size, very firm, light blue fruit. 70 berries per cup. Small scar. Highly aromatic flavor. Upright 4' bush. Ripens early. Requires a pollinator. Hardy in Zones 3-7. 1996 release from Minnesota. PVP. *Source History: 10 in 2000.* **Sources: Ag4, BA14, BR2, Clo, De2, FAL, Gr16, HA12, TOW, We4.**

Powder Blue - *Vaccinium ashei*; rabbiteye. Medium to large, sweet, dark blue fruit; 75-80 berries per cup. Vigorous, upright, 8-12' plant with good foliage. Highly productive; yields of 8-14 pounds on well kept, irrigated plantings. Recommended for home use, fresh market, processing and mid to late Pick Your Own. Hardy in Zones 6-9. North Carolina State University release. *Source History: 4 in 1988; 7 in 1992; 5 in 2000.* **Sources: Ed2, Fi4, HA12, Iso, Ju2.**

Premier - *Vaccinium ashei*; rabbiteye. Large, light blue fruit; 75-80 berries per cup. Small stem scar. High quality. Vigorous, fairly upright, 6-10' plants with good foliage. Very productive; yields of 8-16 poundsper bush on well irrigated plantings. Stores well. Disease resistant. Good for home use, fresh market, processing and early Pick Your Own. Hardy in Zones 7-9. *Source History: 7 in 1988; 16 in 1992; 7 in 2000.* **Sources: Bas, Fi4, HA12, In5, Iso, Ju2, Ty2.**

Putte - True lowbush variety developed in Sweden using material from the Nova Scotia breeding program. Blue-black berry is sweet. Plants grow 12-18" tall. Has survived -40 degrees F. in Sweden. *Source History: 1 in 2000.* **Sources: Stl.**

Rabbiteye Blueberry - *Vaccinium ashei*. Upright plant growth. Hardy to Zone 4. *Source History: 1 in 1988; 1 in 1992; 2 in 2000.* **Sources: MI5, SIM.**

Rancocas - *Vaccinium corymbosum*; highbush. Medium size fruit; 130 berries per cup. Good flavor. Poor quality. Large picking scar; noted for stems staying with berries when picked. Will crack during a heavy rainfall when ripe. Upright, spreading, 5-7' bush. Small, slender, glossy, dark green leaves turn red in fall. Consistent yields of 10-20 pounds per bush; usually comes through every season with good crop. Used for mechanical harvesting and the processing market only. Ripens about July 18. Hardy in Zones 3-7. *Source History: 3 in 1988; 4 in 1992; 2 in 2000.* **Sources: Ha12, KR3.**

Reka - Medium size, medium blue, firm fruit. Small scar. Adaptable; grows well in light sandy soils, peat, and heavier clay soil. Upright, vigorous bush is extremely productive. Ripens between Earliblue and Bluecrop. Successful for fresh market and process growers; superior machine harvestability. New Zealand introduction. U.S. Plant Patent No. 6700. *Source History: 1 in 2000.* **Sources: FAL.**

Reveille - *Vaccinium corymbosum*; highbush. Medium size, medium blue, extremely firm berries. Pleasing crunchy texture; excellent flavor. Fruit color at harvest may be inconsistent with many red-backs, but will turn blue after harvest if held for a day at room temperature. Upright, narrow, 6-7' bush is vigorous and productive. Currently the best southern highbush variety for mechanical picking, sorting and fresh sales. Ripens late midseason. Requires 500 hours of chilling. Zones 4-9. Released from North Carolina. *Source History: 9 in 2000.* **Sources: BA10, Bay, CO5, FAL, Fi4, HA12, Wa16, Wbn, We4.**

Rubel - *Vaccinium corymbosum*; highbush. Long clusters of small, firm, light blue fruit; 132 berries per cup. Medium size picking scar. Very good, tart, flavor. Bushy, 5-7' plants. Long, slender foliage turns reddish in autumn. Average yields of 8-10 pounds per bush. Best for the processing market, because of its small size. Ripens about July 27. Tends to be stemmy during a drought or if not harvested on time. Hardy in Zones 4-7. *Source History: 6 in 1988; 4 in 1992; 5 in 2000.* **Sources: BA10, FAL, Ha12, Lee, Sav.**

Sharpblue - *Vaccinium corymbosum*; highbush. Large fruit; 75-80 berries per cup. Well proportioned. Yields of 8-16 pounds per bush on well kept, irrigated plantings. Most adaptable of the low chill types; performs well from heavy soils of coastal Australia to the sandy soils of Florida. Good for fresh use and Pick Your Own. Requires frequent harvesting to retain high quality in hot weather. Ripens early. Recommended in areas with winter chilling under 500 hours but will grow where there are practically no chilling hours. Hardy in Zones 5-10. Developed at the University of Florida, 1984. *Source History: 1 in 1988; 8 in 1992; 4 in 2000.* **Sources: FAL, Fi4, HA12, Ju2.**

Sierra - Very large berries; 50 per cup. Small dry scars; good quality. Yields 10-20 pounds per bush. Early to midseason; slightly ahead of Bluecrop. Highly recommended for trial for Pick Your Own or fresh market operations. Hardy in Zones 4-7. Developed by the USDA, 1989. *Source History: 5 in 1992; 10 in 2000.* **Sources: Al2, AMM, BA10, De2, FAL, HA12, Mo8, OR1, Rai, TOW.**

Snowflake - One of the first blueberries to ripen; bred for the commercial market. Great flavor. Good yield. University of Florida release. *Source History: 1 in 2000.* **Sources: Ju2.**

South Moon - Southern low chilling highbush. Grows 6-10' tall. Large, firm berries with very little picking scar. Plants are resistant to root and fungal diseases. Zones 7-9. Developed by the University of Florida, 1996. *Source History: 1 in 2000.* **Sources: HA12.**

Southland - *Vaccinium ashei*; rabbiteye. Medium to large, firm, light blue fruit with waxy bloom; 80-90 berries per cup. Good flavor. Good quality throughout the season, but many develop a tough skin during the last picking. Moderately vigorous, compact, upright bush grows 8-12' tall. Dense foliage turns red in autumn. Yields of 8-16 pounds per bush on well kept, irrigated plantings. Good for home use, late Pick Your Own or commercial processing. Ripens about June 21. Hardy in Zones 6-10. *Source History: 8 in 1988; 10 in 1992; 4 in 2000.* **Sources: Bar, Fi4, Lee, Sav.**

Spartan - *Vaccinium corymbosum*; highbush. Open clusters of large to very large, firm, powdery light blue fruit; 60 berries per cup. Medium size, dry, picking scar. Excellent flavor. Superb fresh or in pies. Vigorous, upright, open, productive bush with red wood. Partially resistant to both phases of mummy berry disease which attacks shoots and fruit. Can turn chlorotic in the field; needs a properly fertilized soil with good drainage and the right pH. Very site specific, preferring light, well drained soil. Machine harvest in one or two pickings. Excellent for early ripening Pick Your Own. Very winter hardy; Zones 5-7. Appears to be frost resistant. *Source History: 13 in 1988; 12 in 1992; 18 in 2000.* **Sources: AMM, BA10, BR2, Bu7, De2, FAL, Fi4, Fo2, HA12, In5, On3, OR1, Rai, TOW, Wa16, Wbn, We4, Wh4.**

St. Cloud - Medium to large fruit with superior firmness and flavor; 70 berries per cup. Upright growth habit; 4' tall. Hand or machine harvest. Requires pollination. Ripens midseason. Hardy in Zones 3-7. Developed by the University of Minnesota, 1990. PVP. *Source History: 6 in 1992; 7 in 2000.* **Sources: BA14, BR2, De2, Fed, HA12, Stl, TOW.**

Stanley - Large, sweet berries. Good quality. Vigorous, upright, productive bush. *Source History: 3 in 1988; 2 in 1992; 1 in 2000.* **Sources: Gir.**

Star - Southern low chilling highbush. Mature bush is 6-10' tall. Large fruit with excellent firmness. Small scar. Calyx of the fruit resembles the shape of a star so is very attractive for fresh market. Resists root and leaf diseases and stem blight. Zones 7-9. Developed at the University of Florida, 1996. *Source History: 1 in 2000.* **Sources: HA12.**

Sunrise - Medium size, medium blue fruit of good quality. Early, highbush from the USDA. Released as an alternate to Earliblue and Bluetta; fruit is said to be superior to both. Machine harvest adaptability unknown. Hardy in Zones 5-7. Introduced in 1978. *Source History: 6 in 1992; 3 in 2000.* **Sources: BR2, TOW, We8.**

Sunshine Blue - Southern highbush cultivar. Firm berries; 80 per cup. Yields of 5-10 pounds per bush. Good fruit quality. Ripens May 10 through June 15 at Gainesville, Florida. More tolerant of high pH soil than other Southern highbush and rabbiteye types. Ripens midseason. Hardy in Zones 5-10. Originated in Florida. *Source History: 1 in 1988; 1 in 1992; 11 in 2000.* **Sources: Bu7, Clo, Ed2, Gos, Gr16, HA12, On3, Par, Rai, Wbn, We4.**

Thin Leaved - *Vaccinium membranaceum*. Black fruit. Native from Michigan and Ontario to British Columbia, and south to northern California. *Source History: 1 in 1988; 1 in 1992; 1 in 2000.* **Sources: Abu.**

Tiftblue - *Vaccinium ashei*; present standard among rabbiteye blueberries. Medium to large, firm, light powder blue fruit with heavy, waxy bloom; 75-80 berries per cup. Color turns blue before fully mature; harvest when all reddish color around stem disappears. Sweet and highly flavored. Good to excellent quality holds throughout season. Vigorous, upright, 8-14' bush with dense foliage canopy. Yields of 8-15 pounds. Pollinate with Woodard. Good for Pick Your Own, fresh market or processing. Best commercial variety from the standpoint of appearance. Ripens midseason. Most cold hardy rabbiteye. Grows well in Zones 7-9. *Source History: 18 in 1988; 28 in 1992; 16 in 2000.* **Sources: Bas, Cla, Ed2, Fi4, HA12, Hid, Iso, Jo3, Ju2, La3, Lee, Sav, SIM, St4, WA8, Wel.**

Tophat - Lowbush dwarf variety; primarily ornamental. Medium-large, firm, sweet, bright, light blue berries that last for several weeks. Good flavor. Spherical bush matures in 3-4 years to a height of 16-24" and 12-24" across. Completely covered with white, bell-shaped flowers lasting for several weeks. Foliage turns blazing crimson in the fall. Self-fruitful. Perfect for growing in a pot on the patio or indoors in a sunny window. Hardy in Zones 3-7. Developed by Dr. James Moulton and Stanley Johnston at the Michigan State University Agricultural Experiment Station at South Haven. *Source History: 7 in 1988; 9 in 1992; 18 in 2000.* **Sources: BR2, Bu1, Clo, Co12, Fa1, Fi1, Fi4, Fo2, Ga6, Gur, HA12, Hi2, Or2, Rai, Sis, Spr, VIR, We4.**

Toro - Early to midseason, highbush variety of commercial quality from the USDA. Medium to large, attractive blue fruit; 60 berries per cup. Excellent firm quality. Ripens midseason. Harvest may be completed in two pickings. Tolerates fluctuating temperatures. Fall foliage and winter wood is an attractive red color. Hardy in Zones 4-7. Introduced in 1988. *Source History: 9 in 1992; 15 in 2000.* **Sources: AMM, BA10, BR2, Bu7, Clo, De2, FAL, Fi4, HA12, Mo8, OR1, Rai, TOW, Wbn, We4.**

Upright Maine Wild Blueberry - Upright bushes grow 2-3' tall. Blueberry size fruit with outstanding flavor. *Source History: 1 in 2000.* **Sources: Rai.**

Vaccinium angustifolium - Wild lowbush cultivar. Medium size berries with wild blueberry flavor. Spreading plant grows 6-18". Native to northeastern U.S. Hardy in Zones 3-7. *Source History: 1 in 1992; 3 in 2000.* **Sources: Bu7, Gr16, HA12.**

Vaccinium myrsinites (Evergreen Blueberry) - Bush grows 24' tall with many branches. Small, black fruit. Native from North Carolina to Florida and Louisiana. Hardy in Zone 7. *Source History: 1 in 1988; 1 in 1992; 1 in 2000.* **Sources: Wo2.**

Vaccinium nummularia - Small shrub with bristly stems and thick, hairy small rounded leaves. Dense clusters of white-tipped rose-red flowers are followed by black edible fruits. Hardy in Zones 7-9. Good for container culture. Native from the Himalayas to Burma. *Source History: 1 in 2000.* **Sources: Sis.**

Vaccinium ovalifolium - Blooms early. Small blue-black fruit. Grows 2-8'. Hardy to Zone 4. *Source History: 1 in 2000.* **Sources: Fo2.**

Vaccinium vacillans - Ornamental landscape plant is 12-36". Spreads by branching and rhizomes. Powdery blue berries appear late in the season. Leather foliage is bright green in summer; orange and burgundy fall color. Vigorous and adaptable. *Source History: 1 in 2000.* **Sources: HA12.**

Velvet-Leaved Blueberry - *Vaccinium myrtilloides*. Grows in moist woods and bogs from Newfoundland south to New England. Small berries. Hardy to Zone 3. *Source History: 1 in 2000.* **Sources: Fo2.**

Walcott - Northern highbush type. Medium-blue, medium size fruit. Ripens midseason. *Source History: 1 in 1988; 2 in 2000.* **Sources: Fi4, We8.**

Well's Delight - *Vaccinium crassifolium*. Creeping blueberry that grows only 5-8" tall. Trailing effect as it forms a nearly solid evergreen ground cover. Leaf size and texture are reminiscent of Japanese holly. Excellent low maintenance ground cover for any ornamental landscape. Ripens in late July. Hardy in Zones 6-9. Selected from a native stand of *V. crassifolium* at North Carolina State University. *Source History: 3 in 1988; 6 in 1992; 8 in 2000.* **Sources: BR2, Fo2, Gos, Gr16, Hi2, VIR, We18, Wo2.**

Weymouth - Ripens extremely early. *Source History: 3 in 1988; 2 in 1992; 1 in 2000.* **Sources: Gir.**

Woodard - *Vaccinium ashei*; rabbiteye. Large to very large, light to medium blue fruit with large stem scar; 70-75 berries per cup. Medium to firm flesh. One of the best flavored rabbiteyes; aromatic with just a touch of tartness. Good quality when fully ripe. Plants are medium size, moderately vigorous and spreading; will sprout out over an area of 3-4' in 6-8 years. Yields of 8-16 pounds on well kept, irrigated plantings. Young plants tend to fruit heavily. Pollinate with Tifblue. Excellent for the home garden; good for midseason Pick Your Own or processing. Does not do well in the mountains of Georgia. Ripens early. Hardy in Zones 7-9. *Source History: 12 in 1988; 18 in 1992; 7 in 2000.* **Sources: Fi4, Ju2, Lee, Sav, SIM, WA8, Wel.**

Cranberry / Bush

Viburnum spp.

Alfredo - *Viburnum trilobum* cv. Alfredo. Dense, broad form. Good summer foliage and excellent fall color. Sparse flowers and fruit. Zones 2-7. *Source History: 4 in 1988; 9 in 1992; 6 in 2000.* **Sources: BA14, CR6, GR26, MEA, SH8, Wa16.**

American Cranberry Bush (Cranberry Tree, Grouseberry, Highbush Cranberry, Squawbush) - *Viburnum trilobum*. Handsome native shrub; not the bog cranberry used for cranberry sauce. Large clusters of bright scarlet fruit that remain on the branches until spring. Fruit varies considerably. All are suitable for jelly or sauce; some are less tart and may be enjoyed out of hand. Neat, compact, nearly symmetrical growth habit; 6-12' tall and 4-6' wide. Excellent ornamental plant with showy blooms and attractive fruit clusters. Leaves turn scarlet in the fall. Heavy bearer. Fine wildlife food crop. Thrives in poor soil but favors moisture. Requires annual precipitation of 25". Ripens in the fall. Hardy in Zone 2-4. *Source History: 13 in 1988; 25 in 1992; 28 in 2000.* **Sources: Bea, Big, Ca8, CR6, Fa1, GR26, HA12, Jun, KAN, LA4, Lit, LOV, Mc3, MEA, Mi1, MI5, Mu2, Sc2, SH8, So5, Stl, TR19, VIR, Wa12, Wa16, WA8, We8, ZEL.**

American Cranberry Bush Dwarf (Bailey Compact) - *Viburnum trilobum* cv. *Compactum.* Edible fruits. Compact shrub grows 4-5'. Same fine qualities of the American highbush. Hardy in Zone 2-7. *Source History: 2 in 1988; 18 in 1992; 12 in 2000.* **Sources: BA14, CO3, GR26, Jun, KAN, LI7, MEA, MO10, SH8, Va5, We18, ZEL.**

European Cranberry Bush (Guelder Rose, Whitten Tree) - *Viburnum opulus*. Scarlet berries much like the cranberry. Eaten in northern countries; spirits are distilled from them. Valuable food for birds. Shrub grows 13' tall. White, .75" flowers in 4" clusters from May to June. Hardy in Zone 3. The bark is reputed to be a uterine sedative, hence the name Cramp Bark. (**Hud** is offering seed.) *Source History: 7 in 1988; 13 in 1992; 19 in 2000.* **Sources: Big, Ca7, Co24, CO3, Fed, FO10, GR26, HI7, Hud, IN7, KAN, LA4, MI5, Oik, Or2, Sc2, Sh14, SH8, WA8.**

European Cranberry Bush Dwarf - *Viburnum opulus* cv. *Compactum.* Bright

red berries ripen in early autumn and persist into the winter. Dense plant, 4-6' tall in an arching, mounded form. Large, white flowers in May. Adaptable to most soils, even those that are wet. Best in full sun, but tolerant of light shade. Very effective in masses, for screening or as a shrub border. Hardy in Zones 3-8. *Source History: 3 in 1988; 12 in 1992; 15 in 2000.* **Sources: BA14, CO3, CR6, Fo2, Gos, GR26, KAN, LI7, Mc3, MEA, SH8, Va5, Wa3, We18, ZEL.**

European Cranberry Bush Dwarf, Hahs - *Viburnum trilobum.* Similar to *V.*

trilobum '*Compactum*' except has larger fruit. Good selection for the Midwest. Grows to 6'. Zones 2-8. *Source History: 1 in 2000.* **Sources: We18.**

Flava - *Viburnum trilobum.* Northern form is a slow grower. Upright growth

habit. Small bright yellow fruit with mild flavor. Hardy to -40 degrees F. *Source History: 1 in 2000.* **Sources: Oik.**

Highbush Cranberry - *Viburnum trilobum.* Not a true cranberry, but used as a

substitute. Large clusters of scarlet fruits are edible but somewhat bitter. Makes delicious, tart jellies, sauces, preserves, syrups and wines. Grows 8-12' tall. Covered with showy white blossoms in spring. Grows well in any moist, loamy soil. Shade tolerant. Beautiful vivid red fall color. Ripens in late July. Fruit hangs on all winter. Attractive to birds. Hardy to Zone 2. *Source History: 7 in 1988; 10 in 1992; 9 in 2000.* **Sources: Co15, Fed, Fi1, Fro, Gur, Rai, St6, Tri, Win.**

Highbush Cranberry, Ukraine - *Viburnum opulus.* Snowy white flowers pro

duce bright red fruit and beautiful yellow and red fall colors. Ukraine is known for its productivity and large, superior quality fruit. Selected at the Main Botanic Garden in Kiev. Trademarked. *Source History: 1 in 2000.* **Sources: On3.**

Nanum - *Viburnum opulus* cv. *Nanum.* Compact, non-flowering form of larger

European Cranberry Bush; smaller leaves. Grows only 18-24' tall. Very dense mound of overlapping green foliage in summer turns golden yellow in fall. A mass of twiggy, crimson branches for the remaining six months. Fine dwarf shrub for bonsai, rock gardens, borders and foundation plantings. Zones 4-8. *Source History: 6 in 1988; 9 in 1992; 6 in 2000.* **Sources: CO3, CR6, Fo2, Gr16, SH8, Va5.**

Phillips Clone - *Viburnum trilobum.* Pendulous clusters of shiny, red fruit in

autumn. This strain selected for freedom from bitter qualities, so fruit can be made into jellies and jams. Berries remain on the bush throughout the winter. Rapid growing; somewhat rangy in habit. Some use it as an ornamental. Hardy in Zone 3. *Source History: 1 in 1988; 2 in 1992; 3 in 2000.* **Sources: Fed, Hid, Oik.**

Sargent Cranberry Bush - *Viburnum sargentii.* Large scarlet fruit. Plant grows

10-12' tall. Sometimes larger than *V. opulus*; darker, thicker bark. Creamy white flowers in flat clusters. *Source History: 3 in 1988; 5 in 1992; 3 in 2000.* **Sources: Mc3, MEA, SH8.**

Stevens - Leading commercial variety for the Northwest. The robust thick vines

and large dark green leaves form a heavy mat with bright bronze fall color. Medium large, dark glossy red fruit. Hardy in Zones 2-7. *Source History: 1 in 2000.* **Sources: Gr16.**

Wentworth - *Viburnum trilobum* cv. Wentworth. Large, bright scarlet edible

berries about .5" in diameter. Used as a cranberry substitute in preserves, syrup and wine. Red fall foliage. Hardy in Zone 3. *Source History: 5 in 1988; 16 in 1992; 14 in 2000.* **Sources: BA14, CO3, CR6, Fed, Fo2, GR26, KAN, KEE, LI7, LOV, MEA, MO10, SH8, Stl.**

Cranberry / True

Viburnum macrocarpon

A. J. - Originated in Chatsworth, New Jersey. *Source History: 1 in 1992; 1 in 2000.* **Sources: HA12.**

Beckwith - McFarlin x Early Black. Large-medium red fruit with good flavor. Ripens late. *Source History: 1 in 1992; 2 in 2000.* **Sources: De2, HA12.**

Ben Lear - Large to medium, deep red berries; 70-90 per cup. Good production. Ripens early. Zones 3-7. Wild clone from Wisconsin selected in 1901. *Source History: 1 in 1992; 5 in 2000.* **Sources: De2, Ed2, HA12, Mel, VIR.**

Bennett - Egg-shape fruit. Originated in Michigan. *Source History: 1 in 1992; 1 in 2000.* **Sources: HA12.**

Bergman - *Source History: 1 in 2000.* **Sources: De2.**

Cranberry (American Cranberry, Bog Cranberry, Commercial Cranberry, True Cranberry) - True bog-type cranberry. Large, tart, red berries. Slender, wiry, prostrate, trailing stems with tiny evergreen leaves and small, pink flowers. Requirements for successful commercial cultivation are exacting and difficult to meet. As a home garden plant, will produce some fruit in moist, acidic, sandy or peaty soil. Plant 2' apart in full sun; spreads fairly quickly. Can be quite productive, especially if protected from late spring frosts while blossoming. Ripens in the fall. Hardy in Zones 3-7; thrives even in areas with short growing season. *Source History: 5 in 1988; 3 in 1992; 14 in 2000.* **Sources: Big, Clo, Fed, Fi1, Fo2, Gur, In5, Lin, Par, Sh14, Stl, Tri, Wa3, We4.**

Cropper - McFarlin x Prolific. Large, deep red fruit is resistant to softening after harvest. Good processing variety. Ripens midseason. Adapted to the Pacific Northwest. *Source History: 1 in 1992; 1 in 2000.* **Sources: HA12.**

Crowley - *Source History: 1 in 2000.* **Sources: De2.**

Early Black - *Source History: 1 in 2000.* **Sources: De2.**

Franklin - *Source History: 1 in 2000.* **Sources: De2.**

Hamilton - Miniature plant from the Arnold Arboretum. Non-vining. Very slowly forms a cushion covered in spring with typical, dainty, pink flowers and later with red fruits. *Source History: 1 in 1988; 2 in 1992; 2 in 2000.* **Sources: Rai, Wbn.**

Honkers - Huge berries. Productive. *Source History: 1 in 1992; 1 in 2000.* **Sources: HA12.**

LeMunyon - Best producer in Wisconsin and New Jersey. *Source History: 1 in 1992; 1 in 2000.* **Sources: HA12.**

McFarlin - Old commercial variety still widely grown. Large fruits with extra fine flavor. Low growing, spreading evergreen ground cover with wiry stems and pink flowers. Will grow in peat, sandy or clay soil if it is acidic with adequate moisture. Resistant to false blossom. *Source History: 2 in 1992; 1 in 2000.* **Sources: HA12.**

N. J. 35 - Originated in Chatsworth, New Jersey. *Source History: 1 in 1992; 1 in 2000.* **Sources: HA12.**

Olson's - Good production of huge berries. Originated in Chatsworth, New Jersey. *Source History: 1 in 1992; 1 in 2000.* **Sources: HA12.**

Pilgrim - Plant makes a useful ground cover that spreads quickly. Small pink flowers followed by large red fruit with traditional tart cranberry flavor. Can be quite productive. Self-fertile. Best grown in loamy soil with regular irrigation. *Source History: 1 in 1992; 3 in 2000.* **Sources: Ag4, De2, On3.**

Stevens - Exceptionally large, deep red berries; 50-55 per cup. Self-fertile. Ripens midseason. Keeps well in storage. Zones 3-7. Leading cultivar being planted in the Northwest; also planted in Wisconsin and Massachusetts. Introduced in 1950. *Source History: 9 in 2000.* **Sources: Ag4, Bu7, De2, Ed2, Fo2, HA12, Mel, Rai, VIR.**

Thunderlake - Forms a solid carpet of plants up to 12" tall and 3-4' wide. Fuchsia-pink flowers are followed by bright red, juicy berries. Ripen September to October. Yields up to 2 pounds per plant. Thrives in blueberry-type soils. Winter hardy from Newfoundland to the Carolinas. Self-pollinating. Does well in hanging baskets. *Source History: 1 in 2000.* **Sources: Mi1.**

Wilcox - *Source History: 1 in 2000.* **Sources: De2.**

WSU 61 - *Source History: 1 in 2000.* **Sources: De2.**

Currant

Ribes spp.

Alpine Currant (Mountain Currant) - *Ribes alpinum.* Bright scarlet fruits. Dense shrub; small, rich green foliage and densely branched, symmetrical growth habit. Small greenish yellow flowers. Blooms in May. Requires little pruning or clipping. Ideal as a sheared or natural hedge, or as a specimen. One of the few plants thriving in deep shade. Extremely rugged and hardy; Zone 2. *Source History: 10 in 1988; 20 in 1992; 15 in 2000.* **Sources: BA14, CO3, CR6, GR26, HI10, Jun, KAN, LI7, Mc3, MEA, Sh14, SH8, Va5, We8, ZEL.**

Alpine Currant, Schmidt - *Source History: 1 in 1992; 1 in 2000.* **Sources: Va5.**

Ben Alder - Black currant. *Source History: 1 in 2000.* **Sources: Ag4.**

Ben Lomond - Compact, upright bush to 5'. Popular commercial variety in Scotland because of the traditional strong pungent flavor. The "Ben" series is named after the mountains of Scotland are easy to grow and produce the highest quality black currants in the world. Ripens mid-July. *Source History: 1 in 1992; 2 in 2000.* **Sources: Rai, Wh3.**

Ben More - Black currant. *Source History: 1 in 1992; 1 in 2000.* **Sources: Wh3.**

Ben Nevis - *Source History: 1 in 2000.* **Sources: Or2.**

Ben Sarek - Black currant. Compact growth habit is ideal for high density planting on Pick Your Own farms or in private gardens. Bears consistent crops of large fruit. Excellent for jams and jellies. Branches may need support; can be shaken to harvest the crop. Highly resistant to white pine blister rust. (No unauthorized propagation is allowed; contact Indiana Berry for details.) Originated in Scotland. *Source History: 1 in 1992; 6 in 2000.* **Sources: Ag4, In5, Nou, Rai, St4, Wh3.**

Black Currant (European Black Currant) - *Ribes nigrum.* Glossy, .5-.75" purplish black, fruit. Strong, sweet, musky currant flavor. Good quality. Make superb jelly, juice and liqueurs. Good for home use, bird forage and hedges. Open, upright, deciduous shrub grows 4-6' high and 2-4' wide. Rust resistant. Does best in semi-shade. Requires a minimum annual precipitation of 20". Hardy in Zone 4.

Source History: 4 in 1988; 4 in 1992; 5 in 2000. **Sources: Bea, CO3, GR26, LA4, So12.**

Black Currant Cross - Black Currant x Kerry x *Ribes ussuriense.* Immune to white pine blister rust. Recently exempted from the ban on black currants in New York State. Customers in other areas should consult their State or County Environmental Conservation Department. Very hardy. Developed at the Central Experiment Station in Ottawa, Canada. Introduced in the 1950s. *Source History:* 1 in 1988; 1 in 1992; 1 in 2000. **Sources: Stl.**

Black Down - Large, black fruit with distinctive, musky flavor. Excellent in juice, jellies and jams. Upright bush resists white pine blister, rust and mildew. Ripens in July. *Source History:* 3 in 1992; 4 in 2000. **Sources: Clo, On3, Or2, Wh3.**

Black Reward - Black currant. *Source History:* 1 in 1992; 1 in 2000. **Sources: Wh3.**

Black September - Large firm black currant. Mild flavor. Upright canes. Heavy bearer. Mildew resistant. Has five times the vitamin C content of oranges, by comparable weight. Ripens late. Hardy to -30 degrees F. *Source History:* 3 in 1988; 4 in 1992; 3 in 2000. **Sources: On3, Or2, Wh3.**

Blanca - White currant. Averages 30 pounds per bush. Late bloom time escapes spring frosts. Self-pollinating. Good shelf life for fresh market. Zones 4-7. Originated in Sweden. *Source History:* 1 in 1992; 3 in 2000. **Sources: Ed2, HA12, Wh3.**

Boskoop Giant (Black Booskoop) - Old black currant from Holland. Fruit is aromatic and acidic. Upright canes. Bears heavily. Not rust resistant. Mildew resistant. Has five times the vitamin C content of oranges, by comparable weight. Ripens in early July. Hardy to -30 degrees F. *Source History:* 4 in 1988; 3 in 1992; 2 in 2000. **Sources: Or2, Wh3.**

Brodtorp - Large, black, sweet berries on a short, spreading plant. Best for drying, either on the bush or after picking. Disease resistant. Ripens early. Originated in Scandinavia. *Source History:* 3 in 1992; 2 in 2000. **Sources: Or2, Wh3.**

Buffalo Currant - *Ribes odoratum.* Edible, black fruits. Medium size, somewhat suckering shrub. Pendulous clusters of yellow, clove scented flowers. Scarlet fall color. Native to the West. Hardy in Zone 4. Seedlings from a plant selected and carried by a pioneer to Oregon. *Source History:* 1 in 1988; 2 in 1992; 1 in 2000. **Sources: Fo2.**

Cascade - Slightly sweeter than most red currants. Excellent, pest resistant variety in the Northwest. Zones 2-8. *Source History:* 1 in 1988; 1 in 1992; 4 in 2000. **Sources: Bu7, Or2, Rai, Wh3.**

Chaparral Currant - *Ribes malvaceum.* Hardy in Zone 8. *Source History:* 1 in 1988; 1 in 1992; 1 in 2000. **Sources: Las.**

Cherry (Cherry Red) - *Ribes rubrum.* Large fruited, older variety; deep dark red. Acid flavor. High quality. Excellent for jam, jelly, sauce or fresh. Spreading bush. Grows 4-6' high and 2-5' wide. Make good hedges and ornamentals. Bears well, but attracts aphids. Appears to have resistance to powdery mildew. Commonly grown commercially. Hardiest and heaviest yielding currant released to date. Ripens in early September. Requires a minimum annual precipitation of 20". Hardy in Zone 3. Developed by the Washington State Department of Agriculture. *Source History:* 10 in 1988; 13 in 1992; 11 in 2000. **Sources: Bea, Clo, Ed2, Fo2, HA12, Mel, On3, Or2, Wbn, We4, Wh3.**

Clove Currant - *Ribes odoratum*. Grows 6-8' in an irregular arching form with bluish green foliage. Fragrant, clove scented, yellow flowers in early to mid-April. Hardy in Zones 4-7. *Source History: 1 in 1988; 4 in 1992; 2 in 2000.* **Sources: Gr16, SH8.**

Consort (Consort Black, Prince Consort) - Medium long clusters of somewhat soft, .5-.75" black berries. Prominent, sweet, unique, musky flavor. Good for jams, jellies, preserves, juice, wine and flavoring. Excellent dried. Heavy bearing shrub grows 4-6' tall by 3-5' wide. Self-fruitful; easy to care for. Resistant to white pine blister rust. Will naturalize. Excellent bird forage or windbreak shrub. Black currants are one of the highest sources of vitamin C. Requires minimum annual precipitation of 20". Hardy to -30 degrees F. Developed in Ottawa, Ontario. Introduced in 1950. *Source History: 9 in 1988; 15 in 1992; 18 in 2000.* **Sources: Bea, Bo5, Bos, Bu7, Clo, Ed2, Ed5, In5, KR3, Mi1, Or2, Rai, RAM, So5, VIR, Wbn, We4, Wh3.**

Crandall (Crandall Black, Clove Currant, Missouri Currant) - *Ribes odoratum*. Large black currants in clusters. Sweet-tart flavor. Excellent for jam, syrup and juice. Five times the vitamin C of oranges. Bush is upright, fast growing, and has dark green leaves. Very produtive. Ornamental yellow flowers with delightful fragrance lasting for up to two weeks in the spring. Ripens in mid-July. Zone 4. *Source History: 4 in 1988; 9 in 1992; 17 in 2000.* **Sources: Bea, Bu7, Clo, Ed2, Fo2, Gr16, Hid, In5, On3, Or2, Pe3, Rai, So5, Stl, Wbn, We4, Wh3.**

Crusader (Crusader Black) - *Ribes nigrum x R. ussuriense*. Loose clusters of large black fruits. Excellent dried, made into jams, jellies, juice and wine. Self-fruitful. Resistant to white pine blister rust. Developed in Canada for rust resistance along with Consort. Reported to have poor fruit set when planted alone. Somewhat later than Consort. Hardy in Zone 3-7. Introduced in 1950. *Source History: 2 in 1988; 3 in 1992; 5 in 2000.* **Sources: Bea, In5, SH8, Wa16, Wh3.**

Elk River - *Ribes sanguineum*. Vigorous, upright plant produces many bright red flowers. Zones 4-9. *Source History: 3 in 2000.* **Sources: Bu7, On3, Wh3.**

European White - White currant. *Source History: 2 in 2000.* **Sources: Or2, Wh3.**

Evergreen Currant - *Ribes viburnifolium*. Hardy in Zone 8. *Source History: 1 in 1988; 1 in 1992; 1 in 2000.* **Sources: Las.**

Fuschia Flowered Currant - *Ribes speciosum*. Hardy in Zone 8. *Source History: 1 in 1988; 1 in 1992; 1 in 2000.* **Sources: Las.**

Golden Currant (Missouri Currant) - *Ribes aureum*. Smooth, tasty, yellow to reddish black berries. Useful for food, wildlife, hedges, lower story windbreak and bees. Makes very good raisins if left to dry unpicked. Moderately spreading, thornless, deciduous shrub with graceful arching branches. Grows 4-7' tall and 2-4' wide. Small, leathery, maple-shaped, bright green leaves; nice autumn color. Fragrant, yellow flowers in May are excellent bee forage. Native to the northern Rockies. Ripens in early August. Requires minimum annual precipitation of 15". Hardy in Zone 2. *Source History: 8 in 1988; 16 in 1992; 15 in 2000.* **Sources: Bea, Bu7, Fo2, Gr16, GR26, LA4, Las, LI7, NA5, Oik, Pl5, Pla, Stl, Va5, Wh3.**

Green's Black - Large black berries hang in long clusters. Makes a superior jelly with a nice balance of acid and sweet flavors. Ripens midseason. *Source History: 2 in 1992; 1 in 2000.* **Sources: Wh3.**

Heros - Large, red fruit with good flavor. Upright bush. *Source History: 1 in 1992; 1 in 2000.* **Sources: Wh3.**

Hillside Currant - *Ribes californicum*. Hardy in Zone 6. *Source History: 1 in*

1988; 1 in 1992; 1 in 2000. **Sources: Las.**

Hilltop Baldwin - English variety. Black currant. Highest in vitamin C content. Excellent for jelly. Bears heavily. Mildew resistant. *Source History: 2 in 1992; 2 in 2000.* **Sources: Rai, Wh3.**

Invigo Black - Mildest flavor of all the black currants. Makes an excellent wine. Easily picked; good processor. New European release. *Source History: 1 in 1988; 3 in 1992; 1 in 2000.* **Sources: Wh3.**

Jhonkheer Van Tets - Large, red fruit. Fine flavor. Good for eating fresh, jellies or sauces. Bush has a spreading growth habit; best to be trained on a cordon. Excellent for espalier. Heavy producer. Mildew and aphid resistant. Appears somewhat less tolerant of summer heat than other reds. Zones 3-8. Imported from Holland in 1941. *Source History: 3 in 1988; 6 in 1992; 7 in 2000.* **Sources: Bu7, HA12, In5, Or2, Rai, So5, Wh3.**

Jostaberry - *Ribes nidigrolaria.* Complex cross of Black Currant x Gooseberry. Large clusters of nearly black berries; looks like a gooseberry until ripe. Mild, black currant flavor but larger berry size. Higher vitamin C content than gooseberries. Excellent for eating fresh, jam, juice and cordials. Thornless, gooseberry-like plant is more vigorous than either parent; grows over 5' by the second year. Bears sooner than either parent. Self-fertile. Heavy yields of up to 11 pound per plant. Completely resistant to powdery mildew, fungal dieback, currant bud mite and white pine blister rust. Cold hardy into Canada; Zones 3-8. Developed in Europe. *Source History: 6 in 1988; 18 in 1992; 20 in 2000.* **Sources: Bea, Bos, Clo, Ed2, Ed5, Fa1, HA12, Hid, In5, Jun, Lin, Mi1, On3, Rai, Shu, So5, Stl, Wbn, We4, Wh3.**

Jostaberry, Red - *Source History: 1 in 1992; 1 in 2000.* **Sources: Wh3.**

King Edward VII - *Ribes sanguineum.* Dense, low growing variety of red flowering currant that blooms later than species. Produces blue edible berries. Zones 4-9. *Source History: 5 in 2000.* **Sources: Bu7, Gr16, On3, Rai, Wh3.**

Laxton's Giant - Black currant. Heavy bearing, sweet dessert variety. *Source History: 2 in 1992; 1 in 2000.* **Sources: Wh3.**

Laxton's No. 1 - English variety. Bright red fruit. Free and strong growing; heavy cropping. *Source History: 1 in 1988; 3 in 1992; 1 in 2000.* **Sources: So5.**

Leningrad Giant - Black currant from Russia. Large, jet-black fruit with delicious black currant flavor. Vigorous plant with upright growth habit. *Source History: 1 in 1992; 1 in 2000.* **Sources: On3.**

Magnus - Black currant. *Source History: 1 in 1992; 1 in 2000.* **Sources: Wh3.**

Mason's - White currant. *Source History: 1 in 2000.* **Sources: Wh3.**

Mendip Cross - Black currant. Vigorous, heavy bearer. *Source History: 1 in 1988; 1 in 1992; 2 in 2000.* **Sources: So5, Wh3.**

Minnesota 52 - Red currant. *Source History: 1 in 2000.* **Sources: Wh3.**

Mopsy - Black currant. *Source History: 1 in 1992; 1 in 2000.* **Sources: Wh3.**

Mountain Pink Currant - *Ribes nevadensis.* Blue fruits. Rounded, medium size shrub. Pendulous clusters of pink flowers. Yellow fall color. Hardy in Zone 5. Native to the West. *Source History: 2 in 1988; 2 in 1992; 2 in 2000.* **Sources: Fo2, Las.**

Orus 8 - Appears to be a black currant x gooseberry cross. Dark purple, flavorful fruit used for fresh eating, jelly and wine. Large upright bush with leaves like a gooseberry. Some thorns. Disease and aphid resistant. Originated in Corvallis, Oregon. *Source History: 2 in 1992; 5 in 2000.* **Sources: Hid, Or2, Pe3, Rai,**

Wh3.

Otelo - Black currant used for commercial production. *Source History: 1 in 2000.* **Sources: Wh3.**

Perfection - Large, easy to pick clusters of large, good flavored, bright red berries. Good all-around quality. Prolific and heavy bearing. Zones 3-7. *Source History: 2 in 1988; 2 in 1992; 3 in 2000.* **Sources: Co12, Fi1, KR3.**

Pink Champagne - Red x white currant cross. Compact bush produces large clusters of light pink berries. Good for fresh eating, cooking and preserving. Resists mildew, rust and aphids. Easy to grow. *Source History: 2 in 2000.* **Sources: Rai, Sh2.**

Pink Flowered Currant - *Ribes sanguineum* var. *glutinosum.* Fruit edible but not delicious. Hardy in Zone 8. *Source History: 1 in 1988; 2 in 1992; 2 in 2000.* **Sources: Lar, Las.**

Pokey's Pink - *Ribes sanguineum.* Named for Portland gardener Pokey Balis. Said by many to be the best pink form of currant. *Source History: 1 in 1988; 1 in 2000.* **Sources: Wh3.**

Primus - White currant. Compact bushes bear long fruiting clusters; 20 pounds per bush. Very high vitamin C content. Flavor is the sweetest of the currants. Self-pollinating. *Source History: 4 in 2000.* **Sources: HA12, In5, Rai, Wh3.**

Purdy (Purdy Black) - Black currant. Vigorous. *Source History: 2 in 1988; 1 in 1992; 1 in 2000.* **Sources: Wh3.**

Red Currant (Common Currant, Garden Currant) - *Ribes sativum.* Dark red fruit. Good for eating fresh. Also used for desserts, preserves and wines. Large crops. *Source History: 1 in 1988; 1 in 2000.* **Sources: Lin.**

Red Flowered Currant - *Ribes sanguineum.* Blue berries. Deciduous, medium to large, upright shrub. Abundant bright pinkish red flowers in early spring. Yellow fall color. Enjoyed by hummingbirds and humans. Hardy in Zone 5 and to -10 degrees F. Native to the West. *Source History: 2 in 1988; 4 in 1992; 12 in 2000.* **Sources: Abu, BA9, Bu7, Clo, Co24, Ed2, Fo2, Fro, MO10, No2, Pl5, Wh3.**

Red Hollander - *Source History: 1 in 2000.* **Sources: So5.**

Red Jade - Abundant clusters of bright red translucent fruit. Great for fresh eating and preserves. Vigorous and disease resistant. Trademarked. *Source History: 1 in 2000.* **Sources: On3.**

Red Lake - Superior strain of *Ribes rubrum.* Compact clusters are medium to large, 4" long with 8-10 berries. Long stems for easy picking. Large, .4-.65" diameter, dark red berries. Excellent for jellies, preserves, tarts and muffins; makes sparkling red jelly. Strong, vigorous, upright bush with dense foliage; 4-6' tall and 2-5' wide. Early bearing; produces fruit on two-year and older wood. Long ripening season; holds well on the bushes. Remains productive in partial shade. Excellent bird forage and windbreak plant. Most widely grown red currant. Ripens during July. Hardy in Zone 2-8. Developed at the University of Minnesota. Introduced in 1933. *Source History: 31 in 1988; 44 in 1992; 36 in 2000.* **Sources: BA14, Bea, Bo5, Bos, Bu1, Clo, Co12, CO3, Ed5, Fa1, Fi1, GR26, Gur, HA12, In5, Jun, KR3, Led, Leu, LI7, Mc3, Mi1, Or2, Pe2, Pe3, RAM, SH8, Shu, Shu, So5, St6, Stl, VIR, Wa16, We4, Wh3.**

Red Versailles - *Source History: 1 in 2000.* **Sources: So5.**

Redstart (Malling Redstart) - Red Lake x *Ribes multiflorum x R. sativum.* Red currant. Consistent heavy yields of medium size berries. Flowers late, thereby avoiding frost damage. Harvest begins in early August. Machine harvestable. Ripe fruit retains quality on the bush for some time. Fresh fruit flavor is rather acid. Good for processing and fresh market. Developed at the East Malling Research Station, 1990. Propagation protected; contact Indiana Berry for details. *Source History: 1 in 1992; 5 in 2000.* **Sources: HA12, In5, Nou, Sh2, St4.**

Risager - Black currant. *Source History: 1 in 1992; 1 in 2000.* **Sources: Wh3.**

Rolan - Jhonkheer van Tets x Rosetta. Red fruit. Ripens midseason. *Source History: 1 in 1992; 2 in 2000.* **Sources: So5, Wh3.**

Rosetta - Jhonkheer van Tets x Heinemann's Rote Spatlese. Very productive. Ripens late. *Source History: 1 in 1992; 1 in 2000.* **Sources: So5.**

Rotet - Jhonkheer van Tets x Heinemann's Rote Spatlese. Red fruit. Ripens late season. *Source History: 1 in 1992; 2 in 2000.* **Sources: So5, Wh3.**

Rovada - Fay's Prolific x Heinemann's Rote Spatlese. Bears abundant long clusters of translucent red berries. Delicious eaten fresh and in jams and jellies. Vigorous and disease resistant. Late flowering escapes frost. Ripens late. Developed in the Netherlands. *Source History: 1 in 1992; 4 in 2000.* **Sources: Nou, On3, So5, Wh3.**

Silver Gieter - Black currant. Vigorous. *Source History: 1 in 1988; 2 in 1992; 2 in 2000.* **Sources: So5, Wh3.**

Squaw Currant - *Ribes cereum.* Red currant. Medium size shrub with light pink flowers. Yellow fall color. Grows best with good drainage. Hardy in Zone 4. Native to high elevations in the West. *Source History: 2 in 1988; 3 in 1992; 2 in 2000.* **Sources: Fo2, LI7.**

Strata - Very large, sweet, black fruit. Best for fresh eating. *Source History: 2 in 1992; 2 in 2000.* **Sources: Or2, Wh3.**

Swamp Black Currant - *Ribes lacustre.* Small, shiny black fruits with a strong taste. Somewhat lax currant grows 2-4' tall with lobed leaves and thorns. Hardy in Zone 4. *Source History: 1 in 1988; 1 in 1992; 2 in 2000.* **Sources: Fo2, Oik.**

Swedish Black - Black currant. Somewhat milder, sweeter flavor than others. Originated in Sweden. *Source History: 2 in 1988; 2 in 1992; 2 in 2000.* **Sources: On3, Wh3.**

Swedish White - One of the most productive white varieties. Long clusters of white berries. Ripen in mid-July. Disease resistant. *Source History: 1 in 2000.* **Sources: On3.**

Titania - Altajskaja Desertria x Consort x Kajaanin Mustal-Tarrias. Black currant. Shows good resistance to mildew; completely resistant to White Pine Blister Rust. Flowering and ripening seasons compare to Ben Lomond. Vigorous plants are well suited for machine harvest. Reaches full maturity in three seasons. (Variety propagation protected; contact Indiana Berry for details.) *Source History: 1 in 1992; 2 in 2000.* **Sources: In5, Nou.**

Topsy - Large black berries in medium clusters. Ripens early. *Source History: 1 in 1992; 1 in 2000.* **Sources: Wh3.**

Viola - Black currant. *Source History: 1 in 2000.* **Sources: Wh3.**

Wellington's XXX (Wellington) - English variety. Small clusters of large, black berries with a sweet, distinctive flavor. Upright, spreading bush is highly productive. *Source History: 3 in 1992; 2 in 2000.* **Sources: Clo, Wh3.**

Westwick - Black currant. *Source History: 1 in 2000.* **Sources: Wh3.**

White Cloud - White translucent fruit with sweet flavor. Upright growth habit. *Source History: 1 in 2000.* **Sources: On3.**

White Currant - *Ribes sanguineum album*. White form of our native currant. Upright growth habit. Superb when used with the red form. *Source History: 1 in 1988; 1 in 2000.* **Sources: Clo.**

White Dutch - *Source History: 2 in 1992; 1 in 2000.* **Sources: So5.**

White Flowered Currant - *Ribes indecorum*. Hardy in Zone 8. *Source History: 1 in 1988; 1 in 1992; 1 in 2000.* **Sources: Las.**

White Imperial - Loose clusters of beautiful, white, translucent fruit with pink blush; vary from medium to large. Seeds show through the flesh and skin, looking somewhat brownish in color. Richest and sweetest flavor of all currants. Similar to red currants in size and hardiness. Ripens in mid-July. Hardy in Zone 3. Very old variety of unknown origin. Introduced in 1895. *Source History: 3 in 1988; 6 in 1992; 8 in 2000.* **Sources: Bu7, In5, Or2, Rai, So5, Wbn, We4, Wh3.**

White Pearl - Large, spherical, pearl-shaped berries with translucent, pale yellow skin. Mild sweet flavor. Hardy in Zone 3. Believed to be the old White Pearl of Belguim described by Hovey in 1850 as "the best white variety in cultivation." Originated in Holland. *Source History: 1 in 1988; 3 in 1992; 2 in 2000.* **Sources: Mi1, So5.**

White Versailles - *Source History: 1 in 1992; 1 in 2000.* **Sources: So5.**

Wilder (Wilder Red) - *Ribes rubrum*. Large clusters of dark red fruit; a bit smaller than Red Lake. Sprightly, sweet-tart flavor. Very good quality. Healthy, vigorous, tall stemmed, heavy bearing bush grows 4-6' tall and 2-5' wide. Prune severely for best production. Resists anthracnose. Good market variety or for home use. Exceptionally hardy. Bears over a long season from July 1-20. Requires minimum annual precipitation of 20". Hardy in Zone 3. Originated in Indiana. Introduced in 1876. *Source History: 11 in 1988; 9 in 1992; 7 in 2000.* **Sources: Bea, Co12, CO5, Gur, Hid, Son, We4.**

Willoughby (Willoughby Black) - Older, rust resistant black currant. Vigorous. Performs well in Washington. Hardy in Zone 4. *Source History: 4 in 1988; 4 in 1992; 3 in 2000.* **Sources: Or2, So5, Wh3.**

Elderberry

Sambucus spp.

Adams (Adams No. 1) - *Sambucus canadensis*. Huge clusters of large, sweet, glistening, purplish black berries. Ideal for pie, jam, preserves, juice and wine. More vitamin C than an orange or grapefruit. Strong, vigorous, 6-10' shrub. Lovely autumn foliage. Beautiful, broad, white flowers in June; flowers also are excellent for wine. Requires cross-pollination with another variety. Productive and hardy; easy to grow. Not bothered by insects or disease. Grows in any soil in partial shade or full sun. Tolerates wet locations well. Ripens about August 1. Hardy in Zone 3. Originated in New York State. Introduced in 1926. *Source History: 11 in 1988; 21 in 1992; 16 in 2000.* **Sources: Bu1, BU12, Co12, CO3, Ed2, Fed, Fo2, Fo4, Jun, Led, Mel, Mi1, Or2, Pe3, SH8, Stl.**

American Elderberry (Common Elderberry, Elderberry, Sweet Elderberry) - *Sambucus canadensis*. Heavy clusters of edible, purplish black fruit. Rich aroma; full-bodied flavor. Good for pies, jellies and wines. Fast growing, short-lived shrub. Tiny white blossoms form huge flower clusters up to 10" across from June to July. Flowers used in teas. Plant two varieties to ensure pollination. Likes full sun and slightly acid soil; does well in wet sites. Ideal shrub for attracting songbirds. Ripens in late summer. Zones 3-9. *Source History: 12 in 1988; 12 in 1992;*

23 in 2000. **Sources: Arb, Bea, Big, BO4, Bo5, Bos, Fa1, Fi1, FO10, Gr16, Gur, HI7, LA4, Mel, Oik, Pi2, Sc2, SH8, Tri, Wa16, WA8, We18, We8.**

American Elderberry, Maxima - *Sambucus candensis.* Shrub to 10-15' with leaves up to 12-18" long. Bears huge flower clusters up to 10-18" across in summer, followed by black berries. Hardy to Zone 5. *Source History: 1 in 2000.* **Sources: Fo2.**

Black Elder - *Sambucus racemosa* var. *melanocarpa.* Shrub to 6'. *Source History: 3 in 1992; 5 in 2000.* **Sources: Co15, HA12, NA5, No2, Pl5.**

Blue Elderberry (Western Blue Elderberry) - *Sambucus caerulea.* Juicy, edible, dark blue berries covered with a waxy coating. Large, sometimes tree-like shrub grows 15-20' tall and 12-15' wide. Large, compound leaves. Flat-topped clusters of fragrant, creamy white flowers. Can be trained as a tree or shrub; makes a handsome, ornamental specimen tree. Requires a minimum precipitation of 15". Hardy in Zones 4-5. Native from British Columbia and Montana to California. *Source History: 10 in 1988; 11 in 1992; 14 in 2000.* **Sources: Abu, BA9, Bu7, Ca12, Co24, Fo2, Fro, LA4, MIS, NA5, No2, Pl5, Rai, Va5.**

Cut Leaf Elder - *Sambucus nigra.* Shrub grows 6-8' tall. Deeply cut, lobed leaves. Produces large heads of creamy white flowers followed by shiny black berries. Zones 3-9. *Source History: 3 in 2000.* **Sources: Ed2, GR26, We8.**

Elderberry - *Sambucus canadensis.* Fruit used for jelly and wine making. Canes reach 5-12'. Tolerates part shade. Hardy in Zones 3-9. *Source History: 5 in 1992; 11 in 2000.* **Sources: BO10, Dab, Ga8, HA12, In5, KI3, LO6, Po2, Sh10, So12, Win.**

European Black Elderberry (European Elderberry, Ellhorn, Pipetree) - *Sambucus nigra.* Large clusters of tasty, shiny, purplish black berries. Used for jam, pie and wine. Small tree grows 30' tall. Showy, flat-topped, 8" clusters of creamy white flowers from May to June. Plant two to ensure pollination. Highly regarded as a medicinal plant. Tea from its leaves is used as an insect repellant on crops and for humans, and as a blight cure for fruit trees. Strong tea with peppermint is used for colds and flu. Hardy in Zones 5-6. Native to Europe and western Asia. *Source History: 6 in 1988; 4 in 1992; 5 in 2000.* **Sources: Gr16, Ho8, Hud, LA4, Sc2.**

European Red Elderberry - *Sambucus racemosa.* Brilliant, scarlet fruit. Yellowish white flowers. Good background shrub for border planting. Attractive to the birds. Ripens in June. Hardy to Zone 3. Native to Europe and western Asia. Naturalized from Minnesota to the Northwest. *Source History: 7 in 1988; 8 in 1992; 7 in 2000.* **Sources: Arb, Fa1, Fro, LA4, LI7, No2, Sc2.**

European Variegated - *Sambucus nigra 'Marginata'.* Large shrub grows 15-20' tall. Green leaves have yellow margins that fade to white in the summer. Produces edible, shiny black berries in late summer. *Source History: 1 in 2000.* **Sources: LI7.**

Golden Elder, Aurea - Yellow leaved forms of *Sambucus canadensis* and *S. nigra.* Hardy, long-lived shrub grows rapidly to 12'. Tolerates a wide range of soils. Hardy in Zones 3-9. *Source History: 3 in 1988; 8 in 1992; 7 in 2000.* **Sources: CO3, CR6, Fo2, GR26, LI7, Mc3, SH8.**

Guincho Purple - *Sambucus nigra.* Shrub grows 10-15'. Deep red-purple leaf color in summer changes to red in the fall. Pinkish flowers. Purple-black fruit. Zone 5. *Source History: 2 in 2000.* **Sources: Fo2, Rai.**

Hidden Springs - Fruits ripen evenly. High in vitamin C. Hardy in Zones 5-9. *Source History: 1 in 2000.* **Sources: Hid.**

Johns - *Sambucus canadensis*. Huge clusters of large, sweet, tasty, purplish black berries. An excellent source of vitamin C. Good for pie, jam, jelly and homemade wine. Hardy, 6-10' shrub. Lovely fall foliage. Beautiful, broad, white flower clusters in June. Cross-pollination recommended. Not bothered by insects or disease. Will grow in any soil. More vigorous than Adams; slightly less productive, but has larger clusters and berries. Ripens about 14 days later than Adams, in mid-August. Zones 3-8. Originated in Canada. Introduced in 1926. *Source History: 9 in 1988; 13 in 1992; 14 in 2000.* **Sources: Bu1, Bu7, BU12, Co12, Ed2, Fo2, Fo4, Mel, Mi1, Or2, Pe3, Rai, Stl, Wh3.**

Madonna - *Sambucus nigra*. Multi-colored bush to 8' tall with beautiful foliage that is variegated with lime-green and lemon-yellow. Large clusters of black fruit ripens in September. Zone 5. *Source History: 3 in 2000.* **Sources: Fo2, Rai, Wa13.**

Marginata - Showy small tree to 15'. Compound leaves edged with white. Purple-black, edible berries. Zone 6. *Source History: 1 in 2000.* **Sources: Co24.**

Mexican Elderberry - *Sambucus mexicana*. Rare. Hardy in Zone 4. *Source History: 1 in 1988; 2 in 1992; 1 in 2000.* **Sources: Las.**

Mountain - *Sambucus caerulea*. *Source History: 1 in 1992; 1 in 2000.* **Sources: Las.**

Nova - *Sambucus canadensis*. Large, sweet fruit. Good for wine, pie and jelly. Hardy, productive, 6-8' bush. Pollinate with York. Ripens evenly and slightly earlier than York, during August. Hardy in Zones 4-8. Originated in Nova Scotia. Introduced in 1959. *Source History: 6 in 1988; 6 in 1992; 11 in 2000.* **Sources: Bea, Clo, CO3, Ed2, Mel, Or2, Pe3, St4, Stl, Wbn, We4.**

Red Elder - *Sambucus racemosa* var. *arborescens*. Shrub to 10'. Bears glossy red round fruit in summer. Zones 3-7. *Source History: 3 in 1992; 3 in 2000.* **Sources: Abu, Ca12, Gr16.**

Red Elderberry - *Sambucus pubens*. Clusters of bright red fruits. Edible but bitter. Shrub grows to 10-12' and is slightly smaller than blue elderberry. Native to northern Minnesota, Wisconsin and Michigan. Extremely hardy. *Source History: 4 in 1992; 14 in 2000.* **Sources: ALD, Arb, BA9, Bu7, Co24, CR6, GR26, LI7, Lit, MIS, Mu2, Pl5, SH8, Va5.**

Sambucus nigra purpurea - Variegated pink flowers followed by black fruit on a large multi-stemmed shrub that grows to 10'. Ripens in September. *Source History: 1 in 1992; 1 in 2000.* **Sources: Gr16.**

Variegated (Yellow Variegated Elderberry) - *Sambucus nigra*. Light green and white leaves on a 6-8' shrub. Large clusters of scented, white flowers followed by shiny, black berries. Good fresh or for cooking. Zones 5-8. *Source History: 6 in 2000.* **Sources: Clo, Ed2, Fo2, On3, Or2, Wa13.**

York (York Imperial) - *Sambucus canadensis*. Adams 2 x Ezyoff. Juicy, sweet, purplish black fruit. Largest berries of any cultivated elderberry; larger than Adams or Nova. Excellent source of vitamin C. Good for pie, jam, jelly, juice and wine. Hardy, vigorous, highly productive, 6-8' bush. Lovely fall foliage. Large, creamy white flowers in early summer. Pollinate with Nova. Should be planted 7-8' apart. Bears as early as the second year. Last to ripen. Hardy in Zones 4-8. Developed at the New York State Agricultural Experiment Station. Introduced in 1964. *Source History: 9 in 1988; 12 in 1992; 17 in 2000.* **Sources: Bea, Bu7, Clo, Fed, Fo2, Hid, Jun, Mc3, Or2, Pe3, Po2, Rai, St4, Stl, Wbn, We4, Wh3.**

Gooseberry

Ribes spp.

Achilles (Achilles Red) - Old English variety still grown in Northern Europe. Medium to large, elliptical, red berries. Sweet, delicious flavor. Small, unripe berries are used for compote and jelly; ripe fruit is used for fresh eating, jams, preserving. Bush droops. Ripens late. Zones 3-9. *Source History: 2 in 1988; 6 in 1992; 6 in 2000.* **Sources: Clo, Gr16, On3, Rai, So5, Wh3.**

Betty - *Source History: 1 in 2000.* **Sources: Wh3.**

Black (Coastal Black Gooseberry) - *Ribes divericatum.* Thorny shrub grows to 5' in sun or part shade. Produces tasty purple-black fruit. Northwest native. *Source History: 2 in 2000.* **Sources: Abu, Bu7.**

Black Velvet - *Ribes divaricatum* x gooseberry. Good market variety produces top quality sweet red berries. Superb flavor resembles blueberries. Mildew resistant. *Source History: 1 in 1992; 3 in 2000.* **Sources: HA12, Mel, Rai.**

Canyon Gooseberry - *Ribes menziesii. Source History: 1 in 1988; 1 in 1992; 1 in 2000.* **Sources: Las.**

Captivator - Spinefree x Clark. Hybrid of a European and an American species (*Ribes hirtellium*). Large, 1" sweet teardrop-shaped berries. Green when immature; pink to full red when ripe. Average flavor. Large, open bush; light bearer. Good disease resistance. Ripens in late July. Very winter hardy. Developed at the Central Experiment Farm in Ottawa, Canada. Introduced in 1949. *Source History: 7 in 1988; 9 in 1992; 11 in 2000.* **Sources: BA14, Bea, Bu7, Clo, Hid, ME3, Or2, So5, Wbn, We4, Wh3.**

Careless - Very large, white, hairy berry with tangy flavor. Mildew resistant, spineless plants. Hardy in Zones 3-7. *Source History: 1 in 1988; 6 in 1992; 3 in 2000.* **Sources: ME3, So5, Wh3.**

Catherina - Very large, egg-shaped, golden orange berry with a few marks and single green stripe. Sweet flavor. Best for eating fresh. Grows 4-5' tall. Most disease resistant of all the large fruiting types. Ripens late. Zones 4-7. In early days it was grown for exhibition; a specimen that weighed 1.5 oz. was reported by Hogg in 1852. *Source History: 1 in 1988; 4 in 1992; 6 in 2000.* **Sources: Ed2, HA12, On3, So5, VIR, Wh3.**

Champion (Champ) - Medium to large, oval berries; light green, turning pinkish red when ripe. Very sweet when ripe. Makes a delicious pie when picked green but full sized. Also good for jellies and canning. Vigorous, bushy, umbrella-shaped plant grows 5' tall. Hardy, prolific bearer. Grows best in partial shade, especially where summers are hot. Common in Western gardens. Ripens early. Hardy in Zones 4-8. Originated in Oregon. Introduced in 1880. *Source History: 4 in 1988; 5 in 1992; 3 in 2000.* **Sources: Bos, Mel, RAM.**

Clark - Roundish, very large, light copper-red berries. Excellent flavor. Medium size bush is vigorous and healthy. Originated in Canada. *Source History: 2 in 1988; 4 in 1992; 2 in 2000.* **Sources: So5, Wh3.**

Colossal - *Ribes hirtellium.* Large berries are egg-shaped and have green translucent skin. Some are up to 1.5" long. Mild flavored green flesh; sour skin. Heavy bearer. Ripens in mid-July. *Source History: 1 in 1988; 6 in 1992; 3 in 2000.* **Sources: On3, Rai, Wh3.**

Crownbob (Crown Bob) - Large, tasty, red berry. Spreading bush. Ripens late. *Source History: 2 in 1992; 1 in 2000.* **Sources: Wh3.**

Early Sulphur (Golden Ball, Yellow Lion) - Roundish-oval, hairy, medium size berries. Pale golden yellow flesh; excellent, delicate, sweet flavor. Slow growing bush. Early ripening. Old English dessert variety. Introduced in 1825. *Source History: 2 in 1988; 5 in 1992; 2 in 2000.* **Sources: So5, Wh3.**

Fredonia - *Ribes hirtellium.* Medium to large, pinkish green berries turn red when ripe. Excellent flavor when fully ripe. Good quality. Moderately vigorous, productive, spreading bush is very thorny. European-type gooseberry developed by the New York State Agricultural Experiment Station in Geneva. Introduced in 1927. *Source History: 4 in 1988; 3 in 1992; 2 in 2000.* **Sources: Or2, Wh3.**

Friedl - Reddish fruit with excellent flavor. Moderately vigorous plant. *Source History: 1 in 1992; 1 in 2000.* **Sources: Wh3.**

Friend - Thornless variety from the Ukraine. Medium to large green-yellow berries. Good fresh and for jam and pies. *Source History: 1 in 2000.* **Sources: On3.**

Glendale - Purplish red fruit. Fine flavor. Thorny plant grows 5-6' tall. Great vigor and productiveness. Zones 4-7. Stands hot summers better than other sorts. Derived from European and native American parents. *Source History: 1 in 1988; 2 in 1992; 1 in 2000.* **Sources: Ed2.**

Gooseberry - Fruit is deep pink when fully ripe. Hangs on slender stems below branches. Easy to pick. *Source History: 1 in 1988; 2 in 2000.* **Sources: La3, Lin.**

Hinnomaki Red - Dark red medium size fruit with tangy outer skin and sweet flesh. Upright plants; adaptable to various growing systems. Can be machine harvested. Favorite with home gardeners. Good mildew resistance. Ripens in July. Zones 4-8. *Source History: 5 in 2000.* **Sources: HA12, In5, Nou, St4, Wa16.**

Hinnomaki Yellow - Small, yellowish green berries. Delicate, sweet flavor with a hint of apricot aftertaste. Slow growing bush is mildew resistant and extremely winter hardy. Ripens in mid-July. Zones 2-9. Originated in Finland. *Source History: 2 in 1988; 5 in 1992; 6 in 2000.* **Sources: Bu7, ME3, Or2, Rai, So5, Wh3.**

Hoenings Earliest (Hoenings Frueheste) - Golden yellow, hairy fruit. Very tender, juicy flesh. Sweet, mild plum-like flavor. Ripens in early July. Raised by Julius Hoenings at an agricultural school in Neuss, Germany from a seed of an old English variety. Introduced in 1900. *Source History: 1 in 1988; 3 in 1992; 1 in 2000.* **Sources: Wh3.**

Howard's Lancer - Very large, oval berries. Almost transparent, pale green skin marked by prominent yellowish veins; no hairs. Excellent flavor. Ripens in early August. Old English variety. *Source History: 1 in 1988; 2 in 1992; 1 in 2000.* **Sources: Wh3.**

Invicta - Green culinary variety. Vigorous, spiny, spreading bush bears abundant crops of huge, sweet, white berries. Great for fresh eating, pies and preserves. Mildew resistant. Zones 4-7. Originated in England. *Source History: 1 in 1992; 10 in 2000.* **Sources: Bu7, Ed2, HA12, In5, Nou, On3, Rai, Sh2, St4, Wh3.**

Jahns Prairie - High yields of large red-pink fruit. Good resistance to powdery mildew and other diseases. Good for the home gardener and shows potential for the commercial market. Originated from the wild in Alberta, Canada. *Source History: 2 in 2000.* **Sources: On3, Wh3.**

Keepsake - Yellow dessert variety. *Source History: 1 in 1992; 1 in 2000.* **Sources: Wh3.**

Leepared (Lepaa Red) - *Ribes hirtellium.* Small to medium, sweet, dark red berry. One of the very best for cooking. Plant is very strong growing and productive; forms graceful arching branches. Disease and pest resistant. Ripens in late

June. Originated in Finland. *Source History: 2 in 1988; 7 in 1992; 4 in 2000.*
Sources: Or2, Rai, So5, Wh3.

Leveller - Large berry of unusual shape; wider at the base than at the stem, like a Bartlett pear. Dull green with yellow veins and some red dots near the stem. Luscious meaty texture; distinctive, mild, mellow, aromatic flavor. *Source History: 1 in 1988; 4 in 1992; 1 in 2000.* **Sources: Wh3.**

May Duke - *Source History: 1 in 1992; 1 in 2000.* **Sources: So5.**

Missouri Gooseberry - *Ribes Missouriensis.* Hardy to Zone 4. *Source History: 1 in 2000.* **Sources: CLI.**

Oregon Champion - Medium to large, pale yellowish green berries; holds its color well. Flavor sweetens as it ripens. Excellent for pies, jams, canning and wines. Very productive, healthy bushes grow 3-5' tall. Heavy yields; mildew resistant. Fruit holds well on the bush. Starts bearing in its second year; will produce for 20 years. Hardy in Zones 4-10. Best for the Northwest. Originated in Salem, Oregon before 1880. *Source History: 8 in 1988; 9 in 1992; 8 in 2000.* **Sources: Bea, CO5, ME3, Or2, So5, Son, We4, Wh3.**

Pixwell - *Ribes hirtellium.* Large, oval, light green berries turn rosy pink when fully ripe, when they are soft, juicy and high in sugar, with rich pink flesh. Makes excellent pies and preserves. Bush is a moderately vigorous, productive, upright grower with ornamental, glossy, dark green leaves; practically thornless. Fruits hang in clusters on long, slender stems 1" below the branches and any small thorns for easy picking, hence its name. Mildew resistant. Thrives in partial shade where summers are hot; drought resistant. Leaves turn purple in the fall; good choice as an edible ornamental. Hardy in Zones 3-9. Originated in North Dakota. Introduced in 1932. *Source History: 33 in 1988; 46 in 1992; 32 in 2000.* **Sources: BA14, Bar, Bea, Bo5, Bos, Bu1, BU12, Co12, CO3, Fi1, GR26, Gur, Hid, In5, Jun, KR3, Leu, LI7, Mc3, ME3, Mi1, MI5, Or2, Pe3, RAM, SH8, Shu, Stl, Wa16, Wbn, We4, ZEL.**

Poorman - *Ribes hirtellium.* Oval to somewhat pear-shaped, 1" berries are green but turn wine-red with lilac bloom when ripe; the largest of any American variety. Excellent, highly flavored, aromatic sweet table variety which can be eaten out of hand. Also fine in pies and jams. Plant is vigorous, healthy, quick growing and most reliably productive. Mildew resistant. Hardy in Zones 4-10. Old American variety esteemed for its quality. Considered by many to be the best American gooseberry. Originated in Utah. Introduced in 1888. *Source History: 12 in 1988; 10 in 1992; 12 in 2000.* **Sources: Bea, Bo5, Bos, Clo, Fo2, In5, ME3, Or2, Rai, So5, We4, Wh3.**

Red Jacket - Large, dull red berries. Excellent in both green and red stages. Good for pies, jams and jellies. Large, sturdy, nearly thornless bush. Very disease resistant. Developed at the Cheyenne Experiment Station, 1930. *Source History: 2 in 1988; 3 in 1992; 4 in 2000.* **Sources: Co12, GR26, Led, Wh3.**

Rocky Mountain Gooseberry - *Ribes montigenum.* Mounding thorned shrub produces small spiny red berries in the fall. Zone 4. *Source History: 1 in 2000.* **Sources: Fo2.**

Sabine - Formerly known as Canada 0273. Pear-shaped, medium size, copper-red berries. Highest quality. Good flavor. Large, open bush; light bearer. Relatively thornless. *Source History: 2 in 1988; 3 in 1992; 2 in 2000.* **Sources: So5, Wh3.**

Sebastian - *Source History: 1 in 2000.* **Sources: Wh3.**

Shulz - Large round bush bears sweet white berries. *Source History: 1 in 2000.* **Sources: Wh3.**

Sierra Gooseberry - *Ribes roezlii*. Large, spiny, dark red fruits. Low, thorny shrub. Dark red, fuchsia-like flowers. Red fall color. Hardy in Zone 5. *Source History: 1 in 1988; 1 in 1992; 1 in 2000.* **Sources: Fo2.**

Siskiyou - *Ribes lobbii*. Bush grows 3-4'. Prickled only at the nodes. Large, bright red fruit makes great jam. *Source History: 1 in 2000.* **Sources: Fo2.**

St. Fiacre - Large red berry with football shape. Twice the size of regular gooseberries. Disease resistant. Zones 4-7. Introduced by Elwood Fisher of Harrisonburg, Virginia. *Source History: 1 in 2000.* **Sources: Ed2.**

Stanbridge - *Source History: 1 in 2000.* **Sources: Wh3.**

Sutton - *Source History: 1 in 2000.* **Sources: Wh3.**

Sylvia - *Ribes hirtellium*. Round fruit about 1" in diameter; pinkish red blush over green. Flesh is sweet and aromatic; one of the most delicious flavored gooseberries. Disease resistant and easy to grow. Heavy bearer. Susceptible to mildew. Ripens in mid-July. Developed by William Sanders, one of the greatest Canadian horticulturists, at the Central Experiment Station in Ottawa, Canada. *Source History: 3 in 1988; 4 in 1992; 2 in 2000.* **Sources: So5, Wh3.**

Welcome - Medium to large, light green fruits with few spines turn pinkish red when fully ripe. Rich, juicy, pink flesh; sweet-tart flavor. Makes delicious red pies, jellies or jams. Extremely productive. Practically thornless. Bears over a long season from late June until late July. Adapted to the mid-Atlantic states. Hardy in Zones 4-7. *Source History: 8 in 1988; 10 in 1992; 7 in 2000.* **Sources: Co12, CO3, Ed2, Fa1, Fi1, Gur, ME3.**

Whinham's Industry - Claret-red fruit with light red stripes. Very sweet flavor. Productive bush. One of the best of the reds. *Source History: 1 in 1988; 4 in 1992; 2 in 2000.* **Sources: So5, Wh3.**

Whitesmith - *Ribes hirtellium*. Medium to large, oval, pale light green berry is tinged with yellow. Very sweet when fully ripe. Reportedly has a hint of grape flavor. Extraordinary fertility with huge crop every year. Ripens in mid-July. Old English variety. *Source History: 2 in 1988; 2 in 1992; 4 in 2000.* **Sources: On3, Rai, So5, Wh3.**

Whitestem - Dense, rounded shrub with whitish spiny stems maturing to red-brown. Produces pea-size red berries in late summer. *Source History: 2 in 2000.* **Sources: GR26, LI7.**

Yellow - *Ribes quercetorum*. Hardy in Zone 6. *Source History: 1 in 1988; 1 in 1992; 1 in 2000.* **Sources: Las.**

Grape

Vitis spp.

Agawam - American; *Vitis Labrusca*. Large, compact bunches of large red grapes. Rich, aromatic flavor. Superb for table or juice. Produces pink wine. Strong, vigorous vine. Ripens midseason. Hardy in Zone 4. *Source History: 3 in 1988; 1 in 1992; 2 in 2000.* **Sources: Fo3, Rom.**

Aglianico - *Source History: 1 in 2000.* **Sources: Fo8.**

Alachua - Black muscadine; *Vitis rotundifolia*. Self-fertile. Excellent for wine making or fresh eating. Very productive. *Source History: 1 in 1992; 1 in 2000.* **Sources: Ju2.**

Alden - American; *Vitis Labrusca*. Ontario x Grosse Guillaume. Large, loose clusters can weigh 1.5 pounds. Oval, reddish and purplish black fruits almost 1" long. Solid, crisp, juicy, sweet flesh. Delicate, distinctive, muscat flavor. Excellent quality. Meatier and more non-slipskin texture than any other American grape. Texture like California or European grapes. Keeps well in cold storage. Strong, vigorous vine. Requires close pruning and/or crop thinning, or overcropping will reduce quality, cause late ripening and sometimes biennial bearing. Ripe about two weeks before Concord. Hardy to -20 degrees F. Developed at the Geneva Station. Introduced in 1952. *Source History: 5 in 1988; 6 in 1992; 9 in 2000.* **Sources: Bea, Bo5, Do7, Fo8, Mi1, Rom, So5, So6, We4.**

Aleatico - Red fruited variety. *Source History: 1 in 1992; 2 in 2000.* **Sources: Fo8, So6.**

Alicante Bouschet - Red fruited variety. *Source History: 1 in 1992; 2 in 2000.* **Sources: Fo8, So6.**

Aligote - White grape. *Source History: 1 in 1992; 2 in 2000.* **Sources: Fo8, So6.**

Almeria - *Source History: 1 in 1992; 1 in 2000.* **Sources: Fo8.**

Alvarelhao - Red fruited variety. *Source History: 1 in 1992; 1 in 2000.* **Sources: So6.**

Alwood - American; *Vitis Labrusca.* Seeded variety. Tough, bluish black skin not subject to cracking. Good, sweet flavor. Resembles Worden or Concord in quality. Used mainly as a table grape. Tolerant to black rot, anthracnose, downy and powdery mildew. Ripens more evenly than Concord in southern areas. Hardy to -5 degrees F. Developed in Virginia. Introduced in 1967. *Source History: 3 in 1988; 3 in 1992; 4 in 2000.* **Sources: Bea, Do7, Fo3, We4.**

America - Munson hybrid. Black fruit is rich in sugar when fully ripe. Drought, rot and leaf roller resistant. Hardy to -27 degrees F. *Source History: 1 in 1992; 1 in 2000.* **Sources: Rom.**

Apache - The largest thornless, upright berry available. Sweet, cone-shaped berry of excellent quality. Cold hardy. High yields. Late season. University of Arkansas release. *Source History: 1 in 2000.* **Sources: Iso.**

Aramon - *Source History: 1 in 1992; 1 in 2000.* **Sources: Fo8.**

Arapaho - Excellent quality. Thornless. Cold hardy. Disease resistant. Ripens 11 days before Navaho. Patent pending. *Source History: 1 in 2000.* **Sources: Iso.**

Arneis - White grape. *Source History: 1 in 2000.* **Sources: So6.**

August Giant - American; *Vitis Labrusca.* Blue skin. Seeded. Midseason. *Source History: 1 in 2000.* **Sources: Rom.**

Aurore (Aurora, Seibel 5279) - French; *Vitis vinifera.* Long slender clusters. White fruits with a slightly pink blush. Tender, adherent skin; very sweet flesh. Delicious for fresh eating or juice; produces an excellent, delicate, light, neutral, white table wine. Vine is vigorous, moderately hardy; one of the most productive. Resistant to downy mildew and powdery mildew. Ripens 4-6 weeks before Concord. Hardy to -10 degrees F. Now the leading white wine variety in the Finger Lakes region of New York and other short season areas. Not well adapted to warm, humid conditions. *Source History: 13 in 1988; 7 in 1992; 9 in 2000.* **Sources: Do7, Fo3, Leu, ME3, Mel, Mi1, Pe3, Rom, So5.**

Autumn Black - *Source History: 1 in 1988; 2 in 1992; 2 in 2000.* **Sources: Fo8, So6.**

Autumn Royal - *Source History: 2 in 2000.* **Sources: Fo8, ORA.**

Auxerrois - *Source History: 1 in 2000.* **Sources: Fo8.**

Baco Blanc (22A) - *Source History: 1 in 1992; 1 in 2000.* **Sources: Fo8.**

Baco Noir (Baco No. 1) - Older French hybrid; *Vitis vinifera*. Small, long clusters of bluish black grapes. Produces a fine, red, fruity, light wine with a slight strawberry flavor. Ferments fast and clears early. Light body and high acid, so blends well with varieties of less color. Ultra-vigorous, heavily productive vines. Downy mildew resistant. Grows well even in heavy, poorly drained soils. Fine for areas with short growing season. Ripens 3-4 weeks before Concord. Hardy to 0 degrees F. and in Zones 5-7. Developed by Francois Baco. Introduced in 1902. Brought to the U.S. in 1951. *Source History: 11 in 1988; 9 in 1992; 6 in 2000.* **Sources: Do7, Fo3, Mel, Mi1, Rom, So5.**

Barbera - *Source History: 1 in 1988; 2 in 1992; 2 in 2000.* **Sources: Fo8, So6.**

Barry - American; *Vitis Labrusca*. Thick, full bunches. Tender, juicy flesh. Delicate, sweet flavor. To have it at its best, must not be picked when it first colors, but only after it matures to a jet black. Vine is highly productive and vigorous. Edward Rogers, son of a Salem, Massachusetts merchant fertilized flowers of a native grape, Carter, with pollen from two famous European grapes, Black Hamburg and White Chasselas. Forty-five of the resulting seeds germinated and eventually produced the high quality grapes known as Rogers Hybrids, thirteen of which were named. One of these was Barry (Rogers No. 43). Introduced in 1851. *Source History: 1 in 1988; 1 in 1992; 1 in 2000.* **Sources: Rom.**

Bath - American; *Vitis Labrusca*. Seedling of Fredonia with Mills and Chasselas Rose in its ancestry. Uniformly symmetrical bunches. Bluish black grape develops a fine powdery blue bloom. Sweet, juicy flesh. Pure, mild, clean flavor. Vine appears to be as hardy as Concord; very productive. Severe pruning or cluster thinning is necessary to prevent overbearing. Subject to mite damage. Ripens midseason. Developed at the Geneva Station. Introduced in 1962. *Source History: 2 in 1988; 3 in 1992; 2 in 2000.* **Sources: Rom, We4.**

Beaumont - American; *Vitis Labrusca*. Red skin. Table use, wines, jams, jellies. Good disease resistance. Ripens early midseason. *Source History: 1 in 2000.* **Sources: Rom.**

Beauty Seedless (Black Beauty) - Muscadine; *Vitis rotundifolia*. Black female. Very large, compact clusters of egg-shaped, bluish black, seedless berries. Tends to have slightly higher acid than some of the seedless grapes; not unpleasantly so, just more piquant in flavor. Makes interesting ebony raisins. Vigorous vine. Ripens in late August. U.S. Plant Patent No. 7592. *Source History: 2 in 1988; 3 in 1992; 4 in 2000.* **Sources: Fo8, Iso, Rom, So6.**

Beaver - American; *Vitis Labrusca*. Bluish black grape. Unique flavor makes delicious grape jelly. Very productive, vigorous vines. Always ripens well; ripens early. One of the best blues. Bred by Paul Shepard at the Missouri State Experiment Station. Introduced in 1945. *Source History: 1 in 1988; 1 in 1992; 1 in 2000.* **Sources: So5.**

Bell - American; *Vitis Labrusca*. Delaware x Elvira. Green grape; tender flesh. Very sweet, mild flavor. Ripens just before Concord. *Source History: 1 in 1988; 2 in 1992; 2 in 2000.* **Sources: Hid, Rom.**

Berckmans - American; *Vitis Labrusca*. Red skin. Table use. Ripens early midseason. *Source History: 1 in 2000.* **Sources: Rom.**

Beta - *Vitis riparia* x Concord. Small to medium, tart, slipskin, bluish black fruits. Tangy taste of a wild grape. Good quality. Not a table grape. Makes fine jelly and juice. Hardy, productive, vigorous vines grow 20' long. Should do well as an arbor vine. Always dependable; heavy crops every year. Will ripen fruit even in a cool summer of 110 days free of hard frost. Ripens from early to mid-September. Hardy to -40 degrees F. Developed in Minnesota in 1881. *Source History: 7 in 1988; 14 in 1992; 10 in 2000.* **Sources: CR6, Do7, Ed5, Fa1, Fed, La5, Mc3, SH8, Stl, Wa16.**

Black Corinth - European; *Vitis vinifera*. Black seedless grape. Table and raisin variety. Ripens midseason. Powdery mildew susceptible. *Source History: 1 in 1992; 3 in 2000.* **Sources: Fo8, Rom, So6.**

Black Malvoisie (Cinsaut) - Red fruited variety. *Source History: 1 in 1992; 2 in 2000.* **Sources: Fo8, So6.**

Black Monukka (Black Monukka Seedless) - European; *Vitis vinifera*. Clusters are large and long. Medium to large, oval, reddish black grapes; mostly seedless. Crisp flesh; sweet flavor. Excellent for all uses, especially fresh or raisins. Self-fruitful. Ripens in early September. Requires 100 hours of chilling. Hardiest of European varieties. Zones 6-9. *Source History: 9 in 1988; 12 in 1992; 9 in 2000.* **Sources: Bay, CO5, FAI, Fo8, HI10, ME3, So6, Son, Wel, WI4.**

Black Spanish (Lenoir Black Spanish) - American; *Vitis Labrusca*. Small to medium, bluish black fruit. Very popular for juice, jelly or wine. Vigorous, heavily productive vines. Ripens in August or September depending on location. *Source History: 2 in 1988; 3 in 1992; 2 in 2000.* **Sources: CO5, Wom.**

Blackrose - European; *Vitis vinifera*. Black table and raisin variety. Cracks badly. *Source History: 1 in 1992; 3 in 2000.* **Sources: Fo8, Rom, So6.**

Blanc Du Bois - Holds fruit quality and flavor while ripening and through fermentation. Makes a high quality, spicy-fruity flavored, white wine. Rated as one of the top ten wines produced in the Southeast. *Source History: 1 in 1988; 5 in 1992; 2 in 2000.* **Sources: Ju2, Wga.**

Blauer Portugieser - Red fruited variety. *Source History: 1 in 1992; 2 in 2000.* **Sources: Fo8, So6.**

Blue Eye - American; *Vitis Labrusca*. Ellen Scott x America. Large compact clusters. Large, bluish black berries. Sweet flavor. Makes excellent red juice. Ripens late. Developed at the Missouri Fruit Experiment Station. Introduced in 1947. *Source History: 1 in 1988; 1 in 1992; 1 in 2000.* **Sources: So5.**

Blue Lake - American; *Vitis Labrusca*. Dark blue grape with spicy, tart flesh. Good for jellies and juices. Disease resistant. Well suited to warm southern climates. Ripens in late June. Hardy in Zones 5-9. Cannot ship to Oregon, Idaho or Washington. *Source History: 3 in 1988; 6 in 1992; 2 in 2000.* **Sources: SIM, Wga.**

Blue Vernon - *Source History: 1 in 1992; 2 in 2000.* **Sources: Roh, VA3.**

Bluebell (MN 158) - Beta x unknown. Small Concord-type fruit. Blue-black color. Makes excellent juice. More hardy than Concord and ripens 2-3 weeks earlier. Hardy to -30 degrees F. Old University of Minnesota introduction that almost disappeared but now is having a revival. Introduced in 1944. *Source History: 2 in 1992; 7 in 2000.* **Sources: CR6, Do7, Ed5, Fed, Pe3, SH8, Stl.**

Blush Seedless - U.S. Plant Patent No. 4856. *Source History: 1 in 1988; 1 in 1992; 1 in 2000.* **Sources: So6.**

Bokay - American; *Vitis Labrusca*. Captain x Terret Monstre. Compact clusters. Large, meaty, yellow berries. Pleasing flavor regarded as resembling the Malaga. Keeps well. Ripens with Concord. Developed by Paul Shepard at the Missouri Fruit Experiment Station. *Source History: 1 in 1988; 1 in 1992; 1 in 2000.* **Sources: Rom.**

Brilliant - American; *Vitis Labrusca*. Delaware x Lindley; a Rogers hybrid. Large clusters of large red berries with thin bloom. Meaty, tender, melting, white flesh. Delicious flavor. Good for table use and wine. Mildew resistant. Ripens in late June. Hardy to -15 degrees F. Grandparent of Captivator. *Source History: 3 in 1988; 4 in 1992; 5 in 2000.* **Sources: CO5, Hid, Rom, So5, Wom.**

Bronx Seedless - American; *Vitis Labrusca.* Very long, large clusters of oval, red berries. Light, fruity flavor. Vine is quite productive and vigorous; tends to be rather light, yellowish green which is not harmful. Likes extra fertilizer compared to most grapes. Said to be susceptible to cracking during wet weather. At its best in dry weather. Ripens about one week before Concord. Old variety developed at the Geneva Station in New York. *Source History: 1 in 1988; 2 in 1992; 2 in 2000.* **Sources: Fo8, Rom.**

Buffalo - American; *Vitis Labrusca.* Herbert x Watkins. Concord type, but earlier. Medium size, bluish black grapes in medium to large, well filled, sometimes shouldered clusters. Juicy, sweet, melting flesh. Slipskin, but with spicy-sweet, vinous, non-foxy flavor. Marvelous grape aroma. Excellent for table use, jam, juice or wine. Stores well with some shriveling. Vine is quite vigorous. Heavy, regular bearer. Disease free; requires no spraying. Ripens about 25 days before Concord. Good hardiness; good secondary crop if frosted. Introduced in 1938. *Source History: 9 in 1988; 8 in 1992; 8 in 2000.* **Sources: Do7, ME3, Mi1, Mo8, Rom, Sc6, So5, We4.**

Burger - White fruited variety. *Source History: 2 in 1992; 2 in 2000.* **Sources: Fo8, So6.**

Burgrave - *Source History: 1 in 1992; 1 in 2000.* **Sources: Fo8.**

Cabernet Franc - European; *Vitis vinifera.* Similar to Cabernet Sauvignon, but more cold hardy and ripens slightly earlier. Used in France as a blending grape in wine production. One of three major grapes grown in the Bordeaux region. *Source History: 3 in 1988; 5 in 1992; 7 in 2000.* **Sources: Do7, FAI, Fo3, Fo8, ME3, So6, Wi21.**

Cabernet Ruby - European; *Vitis vinifera.* Round, black berries for red wines. Distinctive flavor. Self-fruitful. Ripens midseason. Requires 50 hours of chilling. Tolerates hot climates. Better than Cabernet Sauvignon for inland California. Developed by Dr. H. P. Olmo at Davis, California. *Source History: 2 in 1988; 2 in 1992; 2 in 2000.* **Sources: Fo8, So6.**

Cabernet Sauvignon – European; Vitis *vinifera.* Small to medium, round, purplish black berries. Strong flavor; makes distinctive, red Bordeaux-type wines. Vigorous, upright vine. Self-fruitful. Requires long growing season to mature entire crop. Ripens late. Requires 100 hours of chilling. Gillet introduction. *Source History: 12 in 1988; 18 in 1992; 15 in 2000.* **Sources: Bay, Bos, CO5, FAI, Fi1, Fo3, Fo8, ME3, Pa2, Rai, So6, Wel, Wi21, WI4, Wom.**

Caco - American; *Vitis Labrusca.* Large, full, shapely clusters of medium to large, fancy, red fruits. Very sweet, juicy flesh. Rich flavor. High quality grape. Upright, prolific vines. Good winter hardiness and medium vigor. Needs winter protection only in coldest climates. Highly productive even in the hottest weather. Ripens from mid to late September. *Source History: 12 in 1988; 11 in 1992; 7 in 2000.* **Sources: BU12, Led, Mc3, Pe3, RAM, We4, ZEL.**

Calmeria - European; *Vitis vinifera.* Similar to Lady Finger. Light green, seeded, elongated fruit. Excellent quality. *Source History: 1 in 1988; 3 in 1992; 2 in 2000.* **Sources: Fo8, STR.**

Calzin - *Source History: 1 in 1992; 1 in 2000.* **Sources: Fo8.**

Campbell's Early (Island Belle) - American; *Vitis Labrusca.* Large clusters of dark, purplish black, slipskin fruit with heavy bloom. High quality. Lacks foxy taste. Makes excellent fresh juice. Moderately vigorous vines. Moderately susceptible to powdery mildew; resists downy mildew. Needs time to ripen as it colors before it reaches full sweetness. Ripens 10-28 days before Concord. Hangs very well without shattering. Needs good, fertile soil, though well adapted to many climates. Excellent, early, larger Concord type where too cool for Concord. Zones 4-9. *Source History: 6 in 1988; 7 in 1992; 6 in 2000.* **Sources: Bea, Bu7, ME3, Rom, We4, WI4.**

Canadice (Canadice Seedless) - American; *Vitis Labrusca*. Bath x Himrod. Hardy, seedless, red, American grape derived from Himrod. Large, long, well filled, large shouldered clusters 6-8" long. Medium size, firm fruit. Excellent, spicy, grapey flavor, much like old Delaware. Outstanding quality. Excellent table grape; fine for juice, jelly and wine. Vigorous, reliably productive vines; crops well without a lot of manipulation. Medium resistance to black rot. Somewhat susceptible to mildews. Keeps long on the vine. Harvest from mid-August through September. Hardy to -15 degrees F. Hardy in Zones 5-7 and cooler areas of Zone 8. Introduced by the Geneva Station in 1977. *Source History: 33 in 1988; 45 in 1992; 36 in 2000.* **Sources: Bay, BO4, Bo5, Bu1, BU12, Clo, CO3, CO5, Do7, Ed2, Ed5, Fa1, FAI, Fed, Fi1, Fo3, Gur, KR3, Led, Leu, Mc3, ME3, Mel, Mi1, On3, Pe3, Rai, RAM, Rom, SH8, St4, VIR, We4, Wh4, WI4, Wor.**

Canandaigua - American; *Vitis Labrusca*. Red-blue skin color. Table use. Stores well. Ripens late. Resists cracking. *Source History: 1 in 2000.* **Sources: Rom.**

Canner - *Source History: 1 in 1992; 1 in 2000.* **Sources: Fo8.**

Captivator - American; *Vitis Labrusca*. Herbert x Brilliant. Large, seeded dessert grape, straggly bunches. Orange-red berries with lilac bloom. Does have some foxiness, but not overwhelming. Ranks tops in quality. Hardy, healthy vine. Ripens two weeks before Concord. Hardy to -5 degrees F. *Source History: 4 in 1988; 3 in 1992; 6 in 2000.* **Sources: Do7, Fo3, Hid, Mel, Sh2, So5.**

Cardinal - European; *Vitis vinifera*. Tokay x Ribier. Medium to large, dark red table grape. Crisp flesh with few seeds. Very vigorous, productive vine. Self-fruitful. Best in hot areas. Requires 100 hours of chilling. Earliest red table grape; ripens July-August. *Source History: 5 in 1988; 4 in 1992; 2 in 2000.* **Sources: Fo8, So6.**

Carignane - *Source History: 1 in 1988; 2 in 1992; 2 in 2000.* **Sources: Fo8, So6.**

Carlos - Muscadine; *Vitis rotundifolia*. Small clusters; picks with dry stem scar. Small to medium, bronze fruit; medium skin. Pleasing flavor. Very good quality. Good for eating fresh; valued for wine making. Vigorous, disease resistant vines; weeping growth. Self-fertile cross pollinator. Hangs well on the vines. Heavy to overproductive. Recommended for commercial plantings. Suitable for mechanical harvesting. Ripens midseason. Hardy in Zones 7-9. Developed by the North Carolina Agricultural Experiment Station and USDA. Introduced in 1970. *Source History: 10 in 1988; 16 in 1992; 8 in 2000.* **Sources: Bu1, Fo4, Iso, SIM, Tex, Ty2, VIR, Wel.**

Carman - American; *Vitis Labrusca*. Dark blue fruit. Developed by T.V. Munson. *Source History: 1 in 1988; 1 in 1992; 1 in 2000.* **Sources: Wom.**

Carmine - Red fruited variety. Patented. *Source History: 1 in 1992; 2 in 2000.* **Sources: Fo8, So6.**

Carnelian - Red fruited variety. U.S. Plant Patent No. 3625. *Source History: 1 in 1992; 2 in 2000.* **Sources: Fo8, So6.**

Cascade (Seibel 13053) - French; *Vitis vinifera.* Bluish black fruit. Vine is vigorous, moderately hardy to hardy, productive. Very reliable. Prune to short canes. Ripens early in the season. One of the best for short season areas. Blends well with other red wine hybrids like Baco Noir or Foch. By itself makes a fine rose or "blush" wine. *Source History: 3 in 1988; 3 in 1992; 2 in 2000.* **Sources: ME3, Rom.**

Catawba - American; *Vitis Labrusca.* Medium to large, well-formed clusters. Medium size, seedless, coppery red berries. Full, sweet flavor. Very good table grape. Makes highly prized jams and jellies. Widely used in New York and Ohio for Catawba wine and champagne. Keeps well after picking until late December. Exceptionally vigorous, hardy, productive vines. Mildew susceptible. Ripens two weeks after Concord, from September 25 to October 10. Hardy to -10 degrees F. and grows well in Zones 5-7 and cooler areas of Zone 8. Leading grape for American wine and juice. *Source History: 33 in 1988; 46 in 1992; 41 in 2000.* **Sources: Bar, BO4, Bo5, Bos, Bu1, BU12, Co12, CO3, CO5, Do7, FO10, Fo3, Fo4, Fo8, GI3, KR3, Led, Lee, ME3, Mel, Mi1, MI10, MI5, MO10, Pe3, Pi2, Po2, RAM, Sav, Sc6, SH8, SIM, So5, So6, TU5, Ty2, WA8, We4, Wel, Wh4, Wor.**

Cayuga (GW-3) - American; *Vitis Labrusca.* Seyve-Villard 5-276 x Schuyler. A white wine hybrid. Large, compact clusters. Makes wines with a clean, neutral, light, dry, palate-cleansing taste. Large, vigorous, very productive, moderately hardy vines. Excellent productivity. Late blooming. Good resistant to bunch rot. Ripens midseason with Concord. Hardy to -5 degrees F. Introduced in 1972. *Source History: 6 in 1988; 4 in 1992; 7 in 2000.* **Sources: Bo5, Bos, Fo3, In5, Mi1, Pe3, Rom.**

Centennial Seedless - Patented. *Source History: 1 in 1988; 2 in 1992; 2 in 2000.* **Sources: Fo8, So6.**

Centurion - Red fruited variety. U.S. Plant Patent No. 3870. *Source History: 1 in 1992; 2 in 2000.* **Sources: Fo8, So6.**

Chambourcin (Joannes Seyve 26-205) - French; *Vitis vinifera.* Bluish black fruit. Used to make very superior quality, tart, Claret-type red wine. Vine has only medium vigor. Relatively disease free, but spray treatments cannot be neglected. Short cane pruning. Ripens mid-late. Moderately hardy to 0 degrees F. Grown in the French Loire Valley and Savoie. *Source History: 3 in 1988; 3 in 1992; 6 in 2000.* **Sources: Bos, Do7, Fo3, Pe3, Rom, Wom.**

Champanelle (Champaniel) - Concord x *Vitis champini.* Loose bunch with not so many to the cluster. Large, black fruit. Used mainly for juice and jelly. Makes dark blue juice. Excellent grape to eat if allowed to fully ripen, about two weeks after it turns blue. Vigorous vines. Ripens in early July. *Source History: 3 in 1988; 6 in 1992; 4 in 2000.* **Sources: CO5, Sh3, Wel, Wom.**

Chancellor (Seibel 7053) - European; *Vitis vinifera.* Bluish black fruit. Good quality. Used to make a red wine with good body, tannin that ages well. Vigorous, compact vines. One of the heaviest producers. Early downy mildew must be controlled. Fine for short season climates. Ripens early-midseason. Hardy to -10 degrees F. Widely grown in southern France. *Source History: 5 in 1988; 4 in 1992; 4 in 2000.* **Sources: Do7, Fo3, Leu, Rom.**

Charbono - Red fruited variety. *Source History: 2 in 1992; 1 in 2000.* **Sources: So6.**

Chardonel (GW 9) - Seyval x Chardonnay. Medium size amber berries produce a high quality, white wine that develops a Chardonnay character when allowed to fully mature. Vines more hardy than Chardonnay; nearly as hardy as Seyval. Requires good disease control program. Ripens early October. U.S. Plant Patent No. 7860. *Source History: 1 in 1992; 5 in 2000.* **Sources: Bos, Do7, Leu, Mi1, Pe3.**

Chardonnay - European; *Vitis vinifera.* Outstanding white grape from France. Excellent quality fruit used in making Chablis to Burgundy type, dry white wines. Vigorous vines. One of the hardiest of wine grapes. Excellent in cooler regions; hardy to -5 degrees F. Gillet introduction. *Source History: 11 in 1988; 15 in 1992; 14 in 2000.* **Sources: Bay, Bos, Do7, FAI, Fo3, Fo8, ME3, On3, ORA, Pa2, So6, Wel, Wi21, WI4.**

Chasselas Dore - White wine grape. Mild flavor with full bodied fruitiness. Productive, disease resistant variety. *Source History: 1 in 1992; 3 in 2000.* **Sources: Clo, Fo8, So6.**

Chelois (Seibel 10 878) - French; *Vitis vinifera.* Large clusters of medium size, bluish black fruit. Good table wine that somewhat recalls Burgundy. Healthy, vigorous, productive vine. Growth starts relatively late in the spring, an advantage in frosty spots. Ripens midseason. Only moderately hardy, especially if overcropped. Can withstand temperatures to -5 degrees F. Already a standard in the Northeast. *Source History: 3 in 1988; 1 in 1992; 2 in 2000.* **Sources: Do7, Rom.**

Chenin Blanc - European; *Vitis vinifera.* Medium size, compact clusters. Medium size, oval, juicy, whitish green grapes. Used to make well-known white wine. Very vigorous vine is consistently productive. Self-fruitful. Ripens from late September to early October. Requires 100 hours of chilling. Best quality in cool to moderately warm climates. *Source History: 6 in 1988; 7 in 1992; 4 in 2000.* **Sources: Fo8, ME3, Pa2, So6.**

Chickasaw - Vigorous, thorny, upright canes bear large, sweet fruit. Long and slightly flattened shape. Size compares to Kiowa. Disease resistant. University of Arkansas release. *Source History: 1 in 2000.* **Sources: Iso.**

Chowan - Muscadine; *Vitis rotundifolia.* Large clusters of large, light brown fruit; medium skin. Sweet, but low in acid. Vigorous, productive vines. Self-fertile. Suitable for home use. Ripens early-midseason. *Source History: 1 in 1988; 6 in 1992; 2 in 2000.* **Sources: Tex, Wel.**

Christmas - American; *Vitis Labrusca.* Concord type with blue skin. Table use, jam, juice and jelly. Good for hot climates. *Source History: 1 in 1992; 2 in 2000.* **Sources: Rom, So6.**

Christmas Rose - Red fruit similar to Emperor but larger and more flavorful. Ripens in September. Patented. *Source History: 1 in 1988; 2 in 1992; 1 in 2000.* **Sources: So6.**

Clairette Blanche - *Source History: 1 in 1992; 1 in 2000.* **Sources: Fo8.**

Colobel (Seibel 8357) - French; *Vitis vinifera.* Bluish black fruit. Used for blending to deepen color of paler red wines; poor quality if made as a straight varietal. Healthy vines. Ripens mid-late to late. Moderately hardy to 0 degrees F. *Source History: 2 in 1988; 1 in 1992; 2 in 2000.* **Sources: Do7, Fo3.**

Colombard - White grape. *Source History: 1 in 2000.* **Sources: So6.**

Concord - American; *Vitis Labrusca.* Standard of quality for bluish black grapes. Large, well filled clusters of glossy, medium size, round, slipskin, bluish black berries overspread with bloom. Green, pulpy, seeded flesh. Excellent, distinctive flavor that virtually identifies bottled U.S. grape juice. Used for table, juice, jelly and wine. Vigorous, hardy, strong growing, productive vine. Self-fruitful. Susceptible to black rot. Ripens in late September; tends to ripen unevenly in warmer areas.

100 hours of chilling. Bud hardy into parts of Zone 4. Developed from wild grape seeds in Concord, Massachusetts. Introduced in 1843. *Source History: 66 in 1988; 82 in 1992; 64 in 2000.* **Sources: Bar, Bay, BO4, Bo5, Bos, Bu1, BU12, Co12, CO3, Do7, Ed2, Fa1, FAI, Fi1, FO10, Fo3, Fo4, Fo8, GI3, GR26, Gur, In5, Iso, Jo3, Jun, KR3, Led, Lee, Mc3, ME3, Mel, Mi1, MI10, MI5, MO10, Pa2, Pe3, Pi2, Po2, RAM, Rid, Rom, Sav, Sc6, SH8, Shu, SIM, So5, So6, Son, St4, STR, Tex, TU5, Ty2, VIR, Wa16, WA8, Wbn, We4, Wel, Wh4, WI4, Wor.**

Concord, California
(Pierce) - American; *Vitis Labrusca.* Large, oblong, seeded, bluish black grape. Sweet flavor. Good for table, juice and jelly. Not subject to Pierce's disease. Ripens during September. Good for mild coastal areas and cold winter areas. *Source History: 2 in 1988; 2 in 1992; 1 in 2000.* **Sources: CO5.**

Concord, Seedless
- American; *Vitis Labrusca.* Seedless sport of Concord. Slightly smaller clusters and berries than regular Concord. Occasionally a seed is present, but usually berries are seedless. Same color and flavor as Concord. Better and sweeter table grape. Highly regarded as a pie grape. Vigor and productivity improve as the vine becomes well established, though low at first. Ripens in mid-September, about one week earlier than Concord. Hardy in Zones 5-9. Introduced by the New York Experiment Station. *Source History: 22 in 1988; 26 in 1992; 29 in 2000.* **Sources: Bay, BO4, Bo5, Bu1, Bu2, CO3, Do7, Fed, Fi1, Fo3, Fo4, GR26, Gur, HI10, Iso, Jo3, ME3, Mel, Mi1, Pe2, Pe3, RAM, Sc6, SH8, So5, Wa16, We4, WI4, Wor.**

Concord, White
- American; *Vitis Labrusca.* White skinned, seeded variety with all Concord traits except skin and juice coloring. Excellent for all uses. Moderately susceptible to powdery mildew. Ripens in late September. Does best in areas with cool nights. Zones 5-8. *Source History: 2 in 1988; 1 in 2000.* **Sources: Fi1.**

Conquistador
- Florida's version of the Concord grape with Concord bred into it. Deep purple berries with light gray bloom hang in medium size, tight clusters. Pleasant, spicy flavor. Ripens mid to late July. *Source History: 4 in 1992; 2 in 2000.* **Sources: Ju2, Wga.**

Constantia
- *Vitis rupestris. Source History: 1 in 2000.* **Sources: Fo8.**

Corvina Veronese
- Red fruited variety. *Source History: 1 in 1992; 2 in 2000.* **Sources: Fo8, So6.**

Cowart
- Muscadine; *Vitis rotundifolia.* Very large clusters. Very large, black fruit. Excellent flavor. Good quality. Good for fresh eating, preserves, jellies and wines. Vigorous, productive vine. Largest self-fertile variety. Good disease resistance. Ripens in mid-September to early October depending on location. Hardy in Zones 7-9. Recommended for home and commercial plantings. Best quality of the large fruited varieties. *Source History: 6 in 1988; 17 in 1992; 8 in 2000.* **Sources: Cla, Iso, St4, Tex, Ty2, VIR, Wel, Wom.**

Crimson Seedless
- Late season, seedless grape. Very sweet flavor. Excellent quality. Ripens early October. Requires 100 chilling hours. Self-fruitful. *Source History: 3 in 1992; 4 in 2000.* **Sources: Bay, Fo8, So6, WI4.**

Cynthiana
(Norton) - American; *Vitis Labrusca.* Small to medium clusters. Small, firm, round, black berries covered with heavy bloom. Thin, tough, adherent, stringent, purple skin. Dark green flesh. Keeps well. Ripens very late. Makes the most expensive red wine among hardy varieties. Grown commercially in Arkansas and Missouri. Referred to as the "Cabernet of the Ozarks." *Source History: 1 in 1988; 1 in 1992; 3 in 2000.* **Sources: Bos, Do7, Wom.**

D. M. 8313-1 - European; *Vitis vinifera*. White muscat selection deriving its flavor from the German wine grape, Morio Muscat. Good sugar-acid balance. Ripens early-mid. So far has shown little winter injury. Selected by Dave McGregor. *Source History: 1 in 1992; 1 in 2000.* **Sources: La5.**

D. M. 8521-1 - E. S. 283 x (*Vitis riparia* x Merlot) x (*V. riparia* x Chambourcin). Very small berries and clusters. Sugar and acid are balanced though high. Compact grower that can be grown as a vertical cordon about a meter apart. Very early ripening. Zone 3B. *Source History: 1 in 2000.* **Sources: La5.**

D. M. P26-50 - D. M. P313 x D. M. P3-25. Low acid. Makes a white wine similar to Seyval. Hardy. Susceptible to disease. Zone 3-4. *Source History: 1 in 2000.* **Sources: La5.**

Darlene (Darling) - Muscadine; *Vitis rotundifolia*. Large, bronze fruit. Melting flesh. Picks with dry scar. Uniform size. Excellent quality. U.S. Plant Patent No. 7314. *Source History: 1 in 1992; 1 in 2000.* **Sources: Iso.**

Dattier de St. Vallier (Seyve-Villard 20-365) - French table grape; *Vitis vinifera*. Huge, heavy, loose clusters of large, oval, tapered grayish yellow to golden yellow grapes. Crisp, meaty texture; pure, sweet flavor. Must be short pruned or it will overbear and have poor quality. A gamble in humid, short season locations. Needs some winter protection. *Source History: 2 in 1988; 4 in 1992; 2 in 2000.* **Sources: Fo8, Rom.**

Dawn Seedless - Patented. *Source History: 1 in 1988; 1 in 1992; 2 in 2000.* **Sources: Fo8, So6.**

Daytona - Fruit turns pink when exposed to sunlight, light green when completely shaded. Superior bunch and grape size. Good for fresh eating. Resistant to Pierce's disease and downy mildew. Ripens in early August. Hardy in Zones 7-1C. Thrives in the deep South, even southern Florida. *Source History: 2 in 1988; 8 in 1992; 4 in 2000.* **Sources: Ju2, SIM, Ty2, Wga.**

De Chaunac (Seibel 9549) - French; *Vitis vinifera*. Bluish black fruits. Makes a superior red wine with a good, pleasant taste, good tannin and color, sometimes herbaceous. Extremely highly vigorous, productive vine. Disease resistant. Ripens midseason. Hardy to -10 degrees F. Widely planted in New York State. *Source History: 4 in 1988; 3 in 1992; 5 in 2000.* **Sources: Bos, Do7, Fo3, Mi1, Rom.**

Dearing - Muscadine; *Vitis rotundifolia*. Medium size clusters. Medium to small, bronze fruit with thin skin. Excellent quality but has very firm pulp. Heavily productive vines. Self-fertile. Ripens midseason. Good for commercial use. *Source History: 2 in 1988; 1 in 1992; 2 in 2000.* **Sources: SIM, WA8.**

Delaware - American; *Vitis Labrusca*. Standard of flavor in American grapes in times past. Small to medium size, compact, attractive clusters. Small, round, firm, light red berries with lilac bloom. Very sweet with only a touch of foxiness. Highly flavored. Excellent quality. Beautiful ornamental vines with decorative foliage. Medium vigor; may be planted closer than other varieties. Susceptible to powdery mildew; said to have good black rot resistance. More vigorous on good soils. Ripens two weeks before Concord, about September 15-25. Hardy to -10 degrees F. Still used for white wine in many areas of the East. *Source History: 12 in 1988; 8 in 1992; 6 in 2000.* **Sources: Do7, Fo3, Mi1, MO10, Rom, So5.**

Delicatessen - American; *Vitis Labrusca*. Well shouldered clusters. Round, dark, bluish black berries. Juicy, sprightly, delicate flavor. Ripens midseason. *Source History: 1 in 1988; 1 in 1992; 1 in 2000.* **Sources: Rom.**

Delight - European; *Vitis vinifera*. Good size clusters. Large, crisp, golden grapes. Slight muscat flavor when properly matured. One of the best seedless grapes for raisins. Also a good table grape. Odd, short-jointed growth habit gives it bushy look; can take extra time to establish. Very productive. Ripens about three weeks before Concord. Related to Perlette. Zones 6-9. *Source History: 5 in 1988; 6 in 1992; 5 in 2000.* **Sources: CO5, Fo8, Rom, So6, Son.**

Diamond (Moore's Diamond, White Diamond) - American; *Vitis Labrusca.* Concord x Iona. Old variety. Compact clusters of sweet, juicy, high quality, round grapes that ripen to golden yellow. Slightly aromatic, pleasantly tart flavor. Only light foxiness. Makes excellent white grape juice. Favored by American winemakers for white wines and domestic champagne. Fairly vigorous, very productive vine. Hardiness and disease resistance about equal to Concord; gets bunch rot in bad years. One of the best all-around grapes. Ripens about 10 days before Concord. Hardy to -10 degrees F. Developed by Jacob Moore. Introduced in 1870. *Source History: 6 in 1988; 5 in 1992; 8 in 2000.* **Sources: Do7, Fo3, Fo8, Mi1, Rom, So5, We4, ZEL.**

Dixie (Dixie Bronze) - Muscadine; *Vitis rotundifolia.* Medium size grapes, white ripening to bronze. Excellent flavor. Fine quality; very high yields. Vine is vigorous and rapid growing. Perfect flowered. Ripens midseason. Winter hardy. Introduced in 1976. *Source History: 4 in 1988; 5 in 1992; 1 in 2000.* **Sources: SIM.**

Dixie Red - Muscadine; *Vitis rotundifolia.* Very large clusters of 12-30 berries. Large, light red fruit. Very good quality. Vigorous, self-fertile vine. Ripens midseason. Because of its high yields, outstanding quality, fruit and cluster size, this grape may prove to be best of all introduced self-fertile varieties for home and commercial plantings. U.S. Plant Patent No. 4770. Introduced in 1976. *Source History: 1 in 1988; 1 in 1992; 1 in 2000.* **Sources: Iso.**

Dixieland - Muscadine; *Vitis rotundifolia.* Large bronze fruit. Excellent flavor. Similar to Fry in flavor, color and size. Production is not as great as Carlos and Cowart, but total returns per acre should be as good or better because of quality and size of fruit. Vigorous vine. Ripens mid-early. Recommended for home and commercial planting. Largest of all self-fertile grapes. U.S. Plant Patent No. 4771. Introduced in 1976. *Source History: 1 in 1988; 1 in 1992; 1 in 2000.* **Sources: Iso.**

Dobson - American; *Vitis Labrusca.* Blue skin color. Table use, jam, juice and jelly. Unusual flavor. Ripens early. *Source History: 1 in 2000.* **Sources: Rom.**

Dolcetto - Red fruited variety. *Source History: 1 in 1992; 2 in 2000.* **Sources: Fo8, So6.**

Dovine - Table and raisin variety. *Source History: 2 in 2000.* **Sources: Fo8, So6.**

Dutchess - American; *Vitis Labrusca.* White Concord x (Delaware or Walter). Pale green, crisp berries with distinctive dots. Pure flavored, refreshingly sweet table grape. Vine is variable in vigor; berries ripen unevenly. Named after Dutchess County, New York. Introduced in the 1890s. Exceedingly rare. *Source History: 1 in 1988; 2 in 1992; 2 in 2000.* **Sources: Fo8, Rom.**

E. S. 2-08-1 - Attractive red table and white wine grape. Low in acid with a neutral flavor. Early and vigorous. Hardy to -30 degrees F. Developed by Elmer Swenson. *Source History: 1 in 1992; 1 in 2000.* **Sources: La5.**

E. S. 2-12-8 - White pistillate grape that is good for eating and white wine. Medium size berries and production. Early ripening. One of the hardiest non-labrusca selections. Swenson introduction. *Source History: 1 in 1992; 1 in 2000.* **Sources: La5.**

E. S. 3-24-7 - Non-labrusca white wine selection from Elmer Swenson. Low vigor. Moderate production. Hardy to -40 degrees F. *Source History: 1 in 1992; 1 in 2000.* **Sources: La5.**

E. S. 4-9-12 - E. S. 2-11-14 x St. Croix. Resembles St. Croix in size, sugar-acid balance and early maturity. Shows more disease resistance. Lighter in pigment and flavor. Good red wine blending grape. Zone 4a. *Source History: 1 in 2000.* **Sources: La5.**

E. S. 5-3-78 - Large clusters. Makes a very nice smooth wine in the Beaujolais style. Hardy to -30 degrees F. Developed by Elmer Swenson. *Source History: 1 in 1992; 1 in 2000.* **Sources: La5.**

E. S. 5-4-16 - Huge compact clusters of large blue berries. Mild flavor. Healthy and vigorous. Crop size must be controlled. Zone 4A. *Source History: 1 in 2000.* **Sources: La5.**

E. S. 5-4-29 - E. S. 2-4-13 x E. S. 2-5-5 cross. Dual purpose white table and wine grape. Pleasing muscat and American flavor. Healthy, productive vines. Hardy. Ripens early. Zone 4b. *Source History: 1 in 2000.* **Sources: La5.**

E. S. 6-1-43 - Seedling of Edelweiss and E. S. 442. Large clusters of large golden grapes with a sweet, mild, fruity flavor. Good for eating, juice and wine. Healthy, vigorous, productive vine. Unlike Edelweiss, it does not develop a strong *Labrusca* flavor when fully mature. Hardy to -30 degrees F. Developed by Elmer Swenson. *Source History: 1 in 1992; 1 in 2000.* **Sources: La5.**

E. S. 6-4-47 - Kandiyohi x E. S. 24-52. Black seedless grape. Hardy, healthy and productive. Zones 4a-3b. *Source History: 1 in 2000.* **Sources: La5.**

E. S. 7-4-76 - Kay Gray x E. S. 2-12-13. White table and wine grape with somewhat meaty texture. Fresh juice has a flavor resembling pineapple juice, like grandparent Swenson Red. Hardy, healthy and productive. Matures early. Zones 4a-3b. *Source History: 1 in 2000.* **Sources: La5.**

E. S. 8-2-24 - Manitoba *Vitis riparia* No. 37 x S. V. 23-657. Better than average *V. riparia* x French hybrid. Acid runs somewhat high. Makes red wine. Healthy, hardy vines. Zone 3b. *Source History: 1 in 2000.* **Sources: La5.**

E. S. 8-2-43 - *Vitis riparia* hybrid x S. V. 23-657. Medium size berries and clusters. White grape with good muscat-like flavor. Zones 3b-4a. *Source History: 1 in 2000.* **Sources: La5.**

E. S. 9-2-74 - E.S. 2-8-23 x U. M. 1-7-47 cross. White wine and table selection. Makes a clean fruity white wine. Matures early. Zone 4a. *Source History: 1 in 2000.* **Sources: La5.**

E. S. 9-7-48 - Blue grape. Ripens early. *Source History: 1 in 2000.* **Sources: Ed5.**

E. S. 9-7-70 Blue Early 1 - Early ripening blue variety. *Source History: 1 in 2000.* **Sources: Ed5.**

E. S. 9-7-70 Blue Early 2 - *Source History: 1 in 2000.* **Sources: Ed5.**

E. S. 12-7-98 - Pink seedless grape. *Source History: 1 in 2000.* **Sources: Ed5.**

Early Burgundy (Arbouriou) - Red fruited variety. *Source History: 1 in 1992; 2 in 2000.* **Sources: Fo8, So6.**

Edelweiss - American; *Vitis Labrusca.* Minnesota 78 x Ontario. Medium to large, rather loose clusters can reach a pound or more. Medium size, slipskin, geenish white to pale gold fruit. High sugar content. Quite juicy with mild Niagara-type flavor. Primarily a table grape, but makes acceptable semisweet to dry wines. Vigorous, productive vines have withstood -35 degrees F. without protection. Hangs on the vine well; flavor becomes strong if left too long. Very good disease resistance; resistant to fungus. Ripens 5-6 weeks before Concord. Developed by Elmer Swenson and introduced by the University of Minnesota in 1980. Companion of Swenson Red. *Source History: 8 in 1988; 16 in 1992; 15 in 2000.* **Sources: BA14, Bu7, Do7, Fa1, Fed, Fo3, Gur, Hid, Jun, Mc3, Rom, Sh2, SH8, Stl, Wa16.**

Einset (Einset Seedless, New York 63.878.1) - American; *Vitis Labrusca.* Clusters are medium size, shouldered. Medium size, oval, seedless, bright red fruit. Tender to firm flesh. Fruity, mildly strawberry flavor. Adherent skin, resistant to cracking. Excellent storage potential. Vine is vigorous, moderately hardy. Resistant to botrytis. Susceptible to powdery mildew. Ripens early. Hardy to -5 degrees F. Introduced by the New York Fruit Testing Cooperative in 1985. U.S. Plant Patent No. 6160. *Source History: 4 in 1988; 8 in 1992; 10 in 2000.* **Sources: Bu7, Do7, Ed5, Fo3, ME3, On3, Pe3, Rai, Rom, We4.**

Elizabeth - American; *Vitis Labrusca.* Blue skin color. Ripens early. *Source History: 1 in 2000.* **Sources: Rom.**

Elvira - American; *Vitis Lubrusca.* White fruit. Used for wine. Mildew resistant. Hardy to -15 degrees F. Ripens midseason. *Source History: 1 in 1988; 1 in 1992; 3 in 2000.* **Sources: CR6, Do7, Fo3.**

Emerald Black - *Source History: 2 in 2000.* **Sources: Fo8, ORA.**

Emerald Riesling - White fruited variety. *Source History: 1 in 1992; 2 in 2000.* **Sources: Fo8, So6.**

Emerald Seedless - Table and raisin variety. *Source History: 2 in 1992; 2 in 2000.* **Sources: Fo8, So6.**

Emperor - European; *Vitis vinifera.* Large, red to purple table grape. Ripens in late September. *Source History: 3 in 1988; 3 in 1992; 1 in 2000.* **Sources: Fo8.**

Eona - American; *Vitis Labrusca.* Purple-red skin color. Table use, jam, jelly and juice. Ripens early. Hardy to -30 degrees F. *Source History: 1 in 2000.* **Sources: Rom.**

Erie - American; *Vitis Labrusca.* Good early Concord type with blue skin. Table use, jam, juice and jelly. Female flowers. *Source History: 1 in 2000.* **Sources: Rom.**

Espirit - French; *Vitis vinifera.* Villard Blanc seedling. Huge, compact clusters of firm, mildly fruity, white wine grapes. Makes excellent wine. Pleasant grapes to eat. Very vigorous vine. Good disease resistance. Ripens in mid-September. Needs winter covering in Minnesota. Elmer Swenson introduction. U.S. Plant Patent No. 5716. *Source History: 2 in 1988; 1 in 1992; 3 in 2000.* **Sources: Do7, La5, Rom.**

Exotic - Table and raisin variety. *Source History: 1 in 1992; 2 in 2000.* **Sources: Fo8, So6.**

Fantasy (Fantasy Seedless) - European; *Vitis vinifera.* Large, oval, blue-black fruit with pale green, translucent flesh. Good for table use and raisins. Ripens in August, just before Thompson Seedless. Zones 6-9. Released by the USDA in 1989. *Source History: 5 in 1992; 9 in 2000.* **Sources: Bay, CO5, Fo8, ORA, ORA, Rom, So6, Son, WI4.**

Farrer - Muscadine; *Vitis rotundifolia.* Black female. Large clusters of large, black fruit. Dry scar. High yields. Excellent quality. U.S. Plant Patent No. 7294. *Source History: 2 in 1992; 1 in 2000.* **Sources: Iso.**

Favorite - American; *Vitis Labrusca.* Seedling of Black Spanish. Medium size black grape. Very productive. *Source History: 1 in 1988; 1 in 1992; 1 in 2000.* **Sources: Wom.**

Fercal 103 - Patented. *Source History: 1 in 2000.* **Sources: Fo8.**

Ferdinand de Lesseps - *Source History: 1 in 1992; 1 in 2000.* **Sources: Fo8.**

Fern Munson - Dark, almost black, purple-red fruit borne in large clusters. Very juicy. *Source History: 1 in 2000.* **Sources: Hid.**

Fernao Pires - *Source History: 1 in 1992; 1 in 2000.* **Sources: Fo8.**

Fiesta (Fiesta Seedless) - European; *Vitis vinifera.* Large clusters of firm, meaty, oval, white berries. Good table or raisin grape. Vigorous, productive vines. Less prone to bunch rot than some *vinifera* grapes in rainy Pacific Northwest fall weather. Ripens one to two weeks before Concord. *Source History: 2 in 1988; 2 in 1992; 2 in 2000.* **Sources: Fo8, So6.**

Flame Seedless (Flame) - European; *Vitis vinifera.* Crisp, sweet, light red, seedless grapes on clusters loose enough that bunch rot is not a big problem. Fine flavor. Excellent for fresh use or raisins. Good vigor and productivity. Self-fruitful. Needs hot summer. Ripens from late July to early August. Requires 100 hours of chilling. Hardy in Zones 7-10. This is the red seedless grape found in most grocery stores. *Source History: 15 in 1988; 26 in 1992; 19 in 2000.* **Sources: Bay, CO5, Fo8, HI10, ME3, MI5, MO10, ORA, Pa2, Pe2, Rom, So6, Son, St4, STR, Ty2, We4, WI4, Wom.**

Flora - White fruited variety. *Source History: 1 in 1992; 2 in 2000.* **Sources: Fo8, So6.**

Florida Fry - Bronze muscadine; *Vitis rotundifolia.* Self-fertile. Good quality, disease resistant, vigorous. Excellent for fresh eating; 18% sugar. Ripens early-midseason. *Source History: 2 in 2000.* **Sources: Iso, Ju2.**

Foch (Kuhlmann 188-2, Marechal Foch) - French wine grape; *Vitis vinifera.* Small, long, loose clusters of small to medium, bluish black grapes. Makes cherry flavored fresh juice or excellent red wine. Used to produce an outstanding Burgundy-type red wine without blending; low tannin. Vine has medium vigor. Needs long pruning to get enough clusters to make good weight of crop. Ripens 30 days before Concord. Hardy. Good for areas with short growing seasons. Hardy to -15 degrees F. Developed by Eugene Kuhlman from Alsace, France. *Source History: 9 in 1988; 5 in 1992; 10 in 2000.* **Sources: Do7, Ed5, Fed, Fo3, In5, Mi1, Pe3, Rom, St4, VIR.**

Forestera - White fruited variety. *Source History: 1 in 1992; 2 in 2000.* **Sources: Fo8, So6.**

Fredonia (Early Concord) - American; *Vitis Labrusca.* Champion x Lucille. Similar to Concord but larger and two weeks earlier. Medium to large, compact clusters. Large, slipskin, dark blue to black berries covered with a beautiful blue bloom. Delicious, spicy flavor. Fine quality. Good for fresh use, jams and jellies, wine and juice. Very productive, vigorous, strong growing vines. Needs less pruning. Moderately susceptible to downy mildew. Thick skin resists brown rot and attack by bees. Firm, good shipper; favorite in home vineyards. Entire bunch ripens at once. Ripens mid-September. Hardy in Zones 4-9 and to -40 degrees F. Developed at the Geneva Station. *Source History: 32 in 1988; 39 in 1992; 35 in 2000.* **Sources: Bar, Bo5, Bos, BU12, Co12, CO5, Do7, Fa1, Fed, FO10, Fo3, Ga6, GI3, In5, Iso, Jun, KR3, Lee, Mc3, Mi1, MO10, Pe3, Pi2, Po2, Sav, Sc6, SH8, SIM, So5, Stl, Tex, Ty2, Wel, Wh4, Wor.**

Freisa - Red fruited variety. *Source History: 1 in 1992; 2 in 2000.* **Sources: Fo8,**

So6.

French Colombard - European; *Vitis vinifera*. Medium size, yellowish green fruit. Juicy, mild flesh. Fruity flavor and high acidity. Used in making fruity white wines. Vine is very vigorous with dense foliage. High yielding. Self-fruitful. Latest to ripen of white wine grapes. Requires 50 hours of chilling. Needs a long, warm to hot growing season for best quality. *Source History: 6 in 1988; 4 in 1992; 6 in 2000.* **Sources: Bay, CO5, Fo8, ME3, Pa2, WI4.**

Fresno Seedless (F32-68) - Table variety. *Source History: 1 in 1992; 1 in 2000.* **Sources: FAI.**

Frontenac - *Vitis riparia* x Landot 4511. American wine grape. Large, loose clusters of blue-black fruit. Makes a wine that is similar to St. Croix with a very nice finish. Resistant to common grape diseases. Hardy to -25 degrees. Ripens midseason. Developed at the University of Minnesota. *Source History: 7 in 2000.* **Sources: CR6, Do7, Ed5, Fed, Fo3, La5, Stl.**

Fry - Bronze muscadine; *Vitis rotundifolia*. Very large clusters of very large bronze fruit up to 1.25" in diameter. Superb flavor. Quality very good before fully ripe. High sugar content. Good for fresh eating. Winemaking ability is poor. Moderately vigorous, productive vine. Needs a perfect-flowered pollinator variety planted with it for pollination. Susceptible to black rot. Keeps well on the vine. Ripens in mid-September. Hardy in Zones 7-9. Do not plant where temperature falls below 10 degrees F. Developed by the Georgia Experiment Station. Introduced in 1970. *Source History: 8 in 1988; 19 in 1992; 8 in 2000.* **Sources: Bu1, Cla, Fo4, Iso, Ju2, SIM, St4, Ty2.**

Fry Seedless - Muscadine; *Vitis rotundifolia*. Medium size, red fruit. Erratic yields. Self-fertile, but plant with another self-fertile variety. Disease tolerant. U.S. Plant Patent No. 7296. *Source History: 1 in 1992; 1 in 2000.* **Sources: Iso.**

Fry, Black - Muscadine; *Vitis rotundifolia*. Large, sweet, black fruit. Excellent quality compares to Fry. Disease resistant. U.S. Plant Patent No. 5824. *Source History: 2 in 1992; 1 in 2000.* **Sources: Iso.**

Fry, Early - Muscadine; *Vitis rotundifolia*. Bronze female. Uniform ripening clusters. Ripens two weeks before Fry. High yields. 19-21% sugar. U.S. Plant Patent No. 9224. *Source History: 1 in 2000.* **Sources: Iso.**

Fry, Late - Muscadine; *Vitis rotundifolia*. Bronze self-fertile grape. Large clusters of good quality berries. 18-20% sugar. Ripens late. High yields. U.S. Plant Patent No. 9225. *Source History: 1 in 2000.* **Sources: Iso.**

Furmint - *Source History: 1 in 1992; 1 in 2000.* **Sources: Fo8.**

Gamay (Gamay Beaujolais) - European; *Vitis vinifera*. Used in France for Beaujolais. Vine is more productive than others. Ripens late-midseason. *Source History: 2 in 1988; 3 in 1992; 2 in 2000.* **Sources: Fo8, So6.**

Gewurztraminer - European; *Vitis vinifera*. Small, spicy, pinkish red grape from Germany. Produces a unique, aromatic, distinctive, spicy, white, Alsatian wine of excellent quality. May be blended with Riesling type. Also makes wonderful fresh or canned juice. Vine appears significantly less hardy than Chardonnay or White Riesling. Produces moderate crops. Needs 2,000-2,500 growing degree days. Earliest of high quality white wine grapes. *Source History: 11 in 1988; 10 in 1992; 8 in 2000.* **Sources: Do7, FAI, Fo8, ME3, Rom, So6, Wi21, WI4.**

Glenora (NY 35814) - American; *Vitis Labrusca*. Ontario x Russian Seedless. Medium to large, loose, heavy, well-filled clusters. Small to medium, seedless, bluish black grape. Thin, smooth skin. Sweet, spicy, fine textured, highly flavored flesh. Superior quality. Keeps well on the vine. Mildew resistant. High vigor; medium productivity. Ripens 10-20 days before Concord in late August or early September. Buds are hardy to -10 degrees F. Grows well in Zones 5-8. Has the odd trait of being foxy and very American in character some years, then very firm, and meaty like the European *vinifera* in other years. First black seedless variety. Developed at the Geneva Station. Introduced in 1976. *Source History: 17 in 1988; 19 in 1992; 15 in 2000.* **Sources: Do7, Fo3, Gur, KR3, ME3, Mel, Mi1, On3, Or2, Pe3, Rai, Rom, Sc6, St4, We4.**

Goff - American; *Vitis Labrusca.* Dull reddish purple berries have peculiar flattened appearance. Fine quality; rich vinous flavor. Will keep in excellent condition in cold storage into the middle of the winter. Ripens about with Concord. One of the seedlings produced during the first period of grape breeding by Professor E. S. Goff at the New York State Agricultural Experiment Station during the late 19th century. *Source History: 1 in 1988; 1 in 1992; 1 in 2000.* **Sources: Rom.**

Gold - European; *Vitis vinifera.* Handsome muscat table grape with white-yellow skin. Ripens late. *Source History: 2 in 1992; 3 in 2000.* **Sources: Fo8, Rom, So6.**

Golden Muscat - American; *Vitis Labrusca.* Muscat Hamburg x Diamond. Large, dense, well filled, compact clusters; some clusters can weigh 7 lbs. Large, slipskin, egg-shaped green berries maturing to pale golden yellow. Tantalizing muscat aroma. European muscat flavor. Excellent quality when well ripened for both market and home use. Vigorous, productive vines. Prone to powdery mildew and bunch rot, which can be reduced by training the vine to allow good air circulation through it. Ripens 14 days after Concord, from late September to mid-October. Medium hardy; to 0 degrees F. Developed at the New York State Agricultural Experiment Station. Introduced in 1927. *Source History: 15 in 1988; 14 in 1992; 15 in 2000.* **Sources: Bay, Bos, Bu1, CO5, Do7, Fo3, Fo4, HI10, Mel, Mi1, Pa2, Rom, So5, Wbn, We4.**

Grand Noir - *Source History: 1 in 1992; 1 in 2000.* **Sources: Fo8.**

Granny Val - Bronze muscadine; *Vitis rotundifolia.* High yields. Excellent quality. Self-fertile. Ripens mid to late season. U.S. Plant Patent No. 5823. *Source History: 2 in 1992; 1 in 2000.* **Sources: Iso.**

Greek Perfume - American; *Vitis Labrusca.* Blue skin. Table use, juice, jam and jelly. Ripens midseason. *Source History: 1 in 2000.* **Sources: Rom.**

Green Hungarian - White fruited variety. *Source History: 1 in 1992; 2 in 2000.* **Sources: Fo8, So6.**

Green Veltliner - European; *Vitis vinifera.* Green wine grape. Ripens midseason. *Source History: 1 in 1992; 2 in 2000.* **Sources: Fo8, Rom.**

Grenache - European; *Vitis vinifera.* Red fruited variety. Often blended with other varieties to give strong but fruity taste. By itself, produces a pale, very good rose'. *Source History: 3 in 1988; 1 in 1992; 2 in 2000.* **Sources: Fo8, So6.**

Grey Riesling (Trousseau) - European; *Vitis vinifera.* White variety. *Source History: 1 in 1988; 2 in 1992; 2 in 2000.* **Sources: Fo8, So6.**

Gros Colman - European; *Vitis vinifera.* Largest known grape. Black skin. Classic late season European grape requires a long, hot growing season to ripen. Zones 6-9. *Source History: 1 in 2000.* **Sources: Son.**

Heavenly Blue - Seedless, large, deep blue berry. Excellent table grape. *Source History: 1 in 2000.* **Sources: On3.**

Herbemont - Small brown-red fruit grows in medium size, compact clusters.

Resistant to Pierce's disease. Tolerates extreme heat and cold temperatures. *Source History: 1 in 2000.* **Sources: Wom.**

Higgins - *Vitis rotundifolia.* Largest bronze muscadine. Medium to large clusters. Very large, whitish pink to reddish bronze fruit. Thick but edible skin; melting pulp, low acid. Good quality when fully ripe. Very good for commercial or roadside sales. Poor winemaking ability. Female vine; cold hardy; requires pollination. Heavy to overproductive. Fairly disease resistant except for black rot. Ripens from midseason to late. Hardy in Zones 7-9. Developed by the Georgia Experiment Station. Introduced in 1955. *Source History: 9 in 1988; 17 in 1992; 8 in 2000.* **Sources: Bu1, Fo4, Iso, Ju2, Tex, Ty2, WA8, Wel.**

Himrod (Himrod Seedless) - American; *Vitis Labrusca.* Ontario x Thompson Seedless. Large, long, loose clusters. Medium size, oval, seedless golden yellow fruit. Crisp but tender skin. Sweet, delicious, juicy flesh. Fine quality table variety. Pure, sweet juice of delicate flavor. Makes excellent raisins. Self-fruitful. Moderate disease resistance. Ripens 28 days before Concord, but keeps until Christmas if picked at full maturity and then refrigerated. Hardiest white seedless. Requires 100 hours of chilling. Hardy to -15 degrees F. and in Zones 5-8. Developed by the New York State Agricultural Experiment Station. Introduced in 1952. *Source History: 35 in 1988; 47 in 1992; 45 in 2000.* **Sources: Ba8, Ba8, Bay, BO4, Bo5, Bos, Bu7, BU12, Co12, CO3, CO5, Do7, FAI, Fi1, Fo3, Fo8, GR26, Gur, HI10, In5, Jo3, Led, Leu, ME3, Mi1, MO10, On3, Pe2, Pe3, RAM, Rid, Rom, Sc6, SH8, Shu, So5, So6, Tex, VIR, We4, Wh4, WI4, Wom, Wor, ZEL.**

Horizon (GW 7) - American; *Vitis Labrusca.* White fruit. Wine is neutral, fruity, clean, tart; has good body and good balance. Lacks any of the flavors associated with native grape varieties; excellent, neutral blending wine. Ranks above Aurore, below Cayuga White. Vine is vigorous, very productive and hardy. Responds favorably to grafting. Ripens midseason. Introduced in 1983. Patented. *Source History: 1 in 1988; 2 in 1992; 1 in 2000.* **Sources: Rom.**

Hunt - Muscadine; *Vitis rotundifolia.* Grows in large clusters that cling well to the stems. Bunches are clipped from the vine, which makes it possible to keep the fruit several days after picking. Medium to large, black fruit. Dark, juicy flesh. Very sweet flavor. All-purpose; excellent for wine, unfermented juice, jelly and hull preserves. Female vine, requires pollination. Good production. Ripens uniformly on the bunches. Highly recommended for both home and commercial use. Ripens early to midseason. Hardy in Zones 7-9. Developed by the Georgia Agricultural Experiment Station. Introduced in 1919. *Source History: 7 in 1988; 17 in 1992; 9 in 2000.* **Sources: Bu1, Fo4, Iso, Lee, Sav, Tex, Ty2, WA8, Wel.**

Interlaken Seedless (Interlaken) - American; *Vitis Labrusca.* Ontario x Thompson Seedless. Medium size, fairly tight, varying clusters. Small to medium, golden berries. Crisp, solid, meaty, sweet flesh. Pleasant, tangy flavor. Fine for eating fresh; excellent for raisins. Vigorous, disease resistant vines. Self-fruitful. Ripens 30 days before Concord, about August 15-25. Requires 100 hours of chilling. Less vigorous than its sister Himrod, but more productive for its size; smaller, more compact bunches without Himrod's tendency to shell. Good for Eastern states. Medium hardy if not allowed to overcrop; hardy to -15 degrees F. Introduced by the Geneva Station in 1947. *Source History: 36 in 1988; 32 in 1992; 27 in 2000.* **Sources: Bay, Bu1, Bu7, Clo, Co12, Do7, Ed5, Fa1, FAI, Fi1, Fo3, Fo4, GR26, HI10, Leu, ME3, Mi1, Pe2, Rai, RAM, Rom, SH8, So5, Son, Wa16, We4, WI4.**

Iona - American; *Vitis Labrusca.* Light or dark wine red berries are translucent, tender, consistently melting to the center, non-pulpy, juicy and thin skinned. Pure, delicate flavor. Few seeds. Weak grower and tends to overbear. Must be vigorously thinned and pruned closely. Berries ripen unevenly, but superb fruit is worth any effort. Raised from seed of Catawba or Diana by Dr. C. W. Grant of Litchfield, Connecticut, an enthusiastic amateur. Ripens late. Introduced in 1864. *Source History: 1 in 1988; 1 in 1992; 1 in 2000.* **Sources: Rom.**

Isabella - American; *Vitis Labrusca.* Bluish black fruit. Used for wine. Hardy to -10 degrees F. Ripens late-midseason. *Source History: 1 in 1988; 2 in 1992; 2 in 2000.* **Sources: Fo3, Fo8.**

Ison - Muscadine; *Vitis rotundifolia.* Large clusters of black fruit. Dry scar. Self-fertile. Disease resistant. Ripens uniformly, early to midseason. Zones 7-9. U.S. Plant Patent No. 5822. *Source History: 2 in 1992; 3 in 2000.* **Sources: Ed2, Iso, Par.**

Italia - European; *Vitis vinifera.* Golden, Italian muscat. Table grape. Ripens in August. *Source History: 3 in 1988; 3 in 1992; 2 in 2000.* **Sources: Fo8, So6.**

Ivan - American; *Vitis Labrusca.* Resembles Cascade. Blue skin color. Used for wine, juice, jelly and jam. Ripens very early. Highly productive. Chance seedling found in Oregon. *Source History: 1 in 2000.* **Sources: Rom.**

Ives - American; *Vitis Labrusca.* Attractive bunches. Jet-black fruit. Spicy flavor. Heavy bearing. Makes delicious jelly. Originated around Cincinnati. Introduced in 1850. *Source History: 1 in 1988; 2 in 1992; 1 in 2000.* **Sources: Do7.**

Janebell - Bronze muscadine; *Vitis rotundifolia.* Large clusters of good quality fruit. Dry scar. Self-fruitful. Disease resistant. Ripens mid to late season. U.S. Plant Patent No. 7268. *Source History: 2 in 1992; 1 in 2000.* **Sources: Iso.**

Janet - Bronze muscadine; *Vitis rotundifolia.* Large clusters of very large, excellent quality fruit. Wet scar. Vigorous and productive. Self-fertile. Disease resistant. Midseason. Cold hardy. Patent applied for. *Source History: 1 in 1992; 1 in 2000.* **Sources: Iso.**

John Viola - American; *Vitis Labrusca.* Blue skin color. Jam, jelly, juice and table use. Productive. Hardy. Ripens early. *Source History: 1 in 2000.* **Sources: Rom.**

JS 12-428 - French; *Vitis vinifera.* White wine grape. Late midseason ripening. *Source History: 1 in 2000.* **Sources: Rom.**

July Muscat - European; *Vitis vinifera.* Table grape variety. Early white muscat with pungent muscat flavor. Ripens early. Good for cool climates. Zones 6-10. Developed at the University of California at Davis. *Source History: 2 in 1992; 3 in 2000.* **Sources: Fo8, So6, Son.**

Jumbo - *Vitis rotundifolia.* Largest black muscadine. Large clusters. Purplish black fruit up to 1.25" in diameter. Good quality when allowed to fully ripen. Good keeping ability. Vigorous, productive, female vines. Plant with Magnolia for pollination. Good disease resistance. Ripens irregularly over several weeks, making it an excellent variety for home use. Hardy in Zones 7-9. *Source History: 6 in 1988; 18 in 1992; 8 in 2000.* **Sources: Cla, Iso, Ju2, La3, SIM, Tex, Ty2, Wel.**

Jupiter - Large blue berries on medium size clusters. Distinct muscat flavor. Matures early. Developed at the University of Arkansas Breeding Program. *Source History: 1 in 2000.* **Sources: Do7.**

Kandiyohi - Half sister of Swenson Red. Formerly E. S. 414. Very large, blue berries in large clusters. Hardy table grape for the North. Hardy to -20 degrees F. Developed by Elmer Swenson. *Source History: 1 in 1992; 1 in 2000.* **Sources: La5.**

Katta Kourgane - European; *Vitis vinifera*. White variety. Large berries. Jam, juice, jelly and table use. Leaves used for cooking. Female flowers. *Source History: 1 in 2000.* **Sources: Rom.**

Kay Gray - American; *Vitis Labrusca*. Open-pollinated seedling of E. S. 217. Small, short, cylindrical, very uniform clusters. High quality, medium to large, very firm, white grapes. Suited for table use or wine. Mild foxy flavor. Sugar content about 20 B; acid about .70-.90. Very productive vines. High disease resistance. Hangs well on the vine after ripening in early September. White slipskin variety developed by Elmer Swenson. Zone 4. Introduced in 1981. U.S. Plant Patent No. 4943. *Source History: 6 in 1988; 7 in 1992; 6 in 2000.* **Sources: Do7, Ed5, Fed, Rom, SH8, Stl.**

Kee Wah Din - American; *Vitis Labrusca*. Wine grape. Blue skin. Ripens early. Extremely vigorous. Hardy to -35 degrees F. *Source History: 1 in 2000.* **Sources: Rom.**

King of the North, Jung's - American; *Vitis Labrusca*. Medium size, juicy, tart, blue fruits. Good for jelly, juice and wine. Resistant to common grape diseases and insects. Begins growth earlier than other varieties. Ripens about 21 days before Concord. One of the most productive, vigorous grapes Jung's has ever seen. Zones 4-8. *Source History: 1 in 1988; 3 in 1992; 3 in 2000.* **Sources: Jun, KR3, Stl.**

Kiowa - Thorny canes produce extremely large berries. Excellent quality. Very firm. Produces heavily over a six-week harvest season. Released by the University of Arkansas, 1996. *Source History: 1 in 2000.* **Sources: Iso.**

Kishmishi - Table and raisin variety. *Source History: 1 in 1992; 1 in 2000.* **Sources: So6.**

Kishwaukee - American; *Vitis Labrusca*. Blue skin. Table use, jam, jelly and juice. Ripens early midseason. Originated in Illinois. *Source History: 1 in 2000.* **Sources: Rom.**

Kuhlmann (Lucy Kuhlman) - French; *Vitis vinifera*. Blue skin. Wine grape. Ripens early midseason. *Source History: 1 in 1988; 1 in 1992; 2 in 2000.* **Sources: Rom, So5.**

Kyoho - American; *Vitis Labrusca*. Large, dark purple, slip-skinned berry. Light colored flesh is sweet with unique, full bodied flavor like Concord. Grows in large, loose clusters. Ripens late June, early July. Self-fruitful. Requires 100 hours of chilling. *Source History: 2 in 2000.* **Sources: Bay, ORA.**

La Crosse - American; *Vitis Labrusca*. Medium size clusters that are loose to well filled. Medium size, white grapes. Sugar content usually 18-19 B; acid .90-1.10. Prolific bearing vines. Character much like Seyval, one of its ancestors. Very productive in the Pacific Northwest. Has withstood winters of -32 degrees F. without covering. Introduced by Elmer Swenson. U.S. Plant Patent No. 5588. *Source History: 2 in 1988; 3 in 1992; 2 in 2000.* **Sources: Do7, Rom.**

Lady Finger - European; *Vitis vinifera*. Large, elongated, pea-green to yellow fruit is tender and thin skinned. Sweet, mild flavor. Very vigorous, productive vines. Self-fruitful. Ripens during September. Requires 100 hours of chilling. Not cold hardy. Originally known as Olivette Jaune; later changed to Olivette Blanche. Introduced to the U.S. by Felix Gillet. *Source History: 6 in 1988; 4 in 1992; 2 in 2000.* **Sources: CO5, ORA.**

Lagrein - Red fruited variety. *Source History: 1 in 1992; 1 in 2000.* **Sources: So6.**

Lake Emerald - American; *Vitis Labrusca*. Huge clusters of emerald green fruits.

Excellent for fresh eating. Vines will set four clusters of grapes each. Highly disease resistant. Ripens in mid-July. Hardy in Zones 7-9. *Source History: 1 in 1988; 3 in 1992; 3 in 2000.* **Sources: SIM, Wga, Wom.**

Lakemont - American; *Vitis Labrusca*. Developed from California Thompson Seedless. Sister seedling to Himrod and Interlaken, falling between them in vigor; most productive of the three. Largest, tightest clusters of any seedless grape. Crisp, juicy, sweet, yellowish green fruit. Excellent flavor and quality. High in acid. Superior table grape; makes excellent raisins. Vigorous, heavily productive vines; tends to overbear. Ripens 10-20 days before Concord. Buds are hardy to -10 degrees F. and in Zones 5-8. Excellent white seedless grape for the East. Introduced by the Geneva Station in 1972. *Source History: 20 in 1988; 25 in 1992; 19 in 2000.* **Sources: Bo5, Bu1, Bu2, BU12, Clo, Do7, Fa1, Fo3, In5, ME3, Mel, Mi1, Roh, Rom, SH8, So5, St4, VA3, We4.**

Lambrusco - Red fruited variety. *Source History: 1 in 1992; 2 in 2000.* **Sources: Fo8, So6.**

Lamento - *Source History: 1 in 2000.* **Sources: Pa2.**

Last Rose - Munson hybrid. Large red fruit with thin, tough skin. Excellent quality. Requires a pollinator. *Source History: 1 in 1992; 1 in 2000.* **Sources: Hid.**

Lemberger - European; *Vitis vinifera*. Red fruited variety. Makes excellent wine. Originated in the German-Czechoslovak region. *Source History: 1 in 1988; 4 in 1992; 3 in 2000.* **Sources: FAI, Fo8, So6.**

Leon Millot (Kuhlmann 194-2, Millot) - French red hybrid; *Vitis vinifera*. Small, round, juicy bluish black berries. Makes an outstanding red wine in areas with a short growing season. Develops a Burgundy-like bouquet with bottle age. Vigorous growing vinesCane pruning. Very disease resistant and winter hardy. Does well even in the climate of Minnesota. Relative of Foch. Equally healthy; a bit earlier. Ripens in early October. Hardy to -10 degrees F. *Source History: 4 in 2000.* **Sources: Do7.**

Liberty - American; *Vitis Labrusca*. Medium size clusters and medium small blue berries; red in the warmer areas. Best as juice and wine grape. Good vigor vine. High resistance to Pierce's disease; medium resistance to most other diseases. Low resistance to Isariopis blight. Ripens early-midseason. Originated in Leesburg, Florida. *Source History: 1 in 1988; 1 in 2000.* **Sources: Rom.**

Lindley - American; *Vitis Labrusca*. Large, dark brick-red fruit with bluish bloom. Tender without pulpiness. Fine, aromatic flavor. One of the best of the Rogers Hybrids (No. 19). *Source History: 1 in 1988; 1 in 1992; 1 in 2000.* **Sources: Rom.**

Lomanto - American; *Vitis Labrusca*. Medium to large, black fruit. Table, wine, juice and jelly. Vigorous vines. Ripens in mid-June. *Source History: 2 in 1988; 4 in 1992; 2 in 2000.* **Sources: CO5, Wom.**

Long John - American; *Vitis Labrusca*. Blue skin color. Table use. Ripens late midseason. *Source History: 1 in 2000.* **Sources: Rom.**

Loomis - Burgundy fruit with excellent taste and quality. Best for fresh use. Vigorous vine has superior disease resistance. Winter hardy. *Source History: 3 in 1992; 1 in 2000.* **Sources: Ty2.**

Luttie - American; *Vitis Labrusca*. Large clusters of sweet, juicy fruit. Hardy. *Source History: 2 in 1988; 2 in 1992; 1 in 2000.* **Sources: TU5.**

Lynden Blue - American; itis Labrusca. Medium to large bunches. Very large, dark bluish black berries. Sweet, mild flavor with seeds. Good fresh; excellent for juice. Very compact vine. Ripens in early October. Developed in Mission, British Columbia 15-20 years ago. *Source History: 1 in 1988; 1 in 1992; 1 in 2000.* **Sources: Clo.**

Madeleine Angevine - European; *Vitis vinifera.* Heavy crops of greenish white berries ripening to golden yellow. Yields large quantities of juice for wine or fresh eating. Makes an outstanding white Riesling type wine. Vine is a heavy producer. One of the earliest maturing white wine grapes; should be planted where the season is short. Ripens early October. *Source History: 3 in 1988; 2 in 1992; 2 in 2000.* **Sources: Clo, Rai.**

Madeline Sylvaner - European; *Vitis vinifera.* Green variety used for wine. Ripens early. *Source History: 1 in 2000.* **Sources: Rom.**

Magnolia - Bronze muscadine; *Vitis rotundifolia.* Fairly large clusters. Medium to large size, smooth skinned, bronze fruit. Medium skin. Sweet flavor. Excellent quality. Good for commercial plantings. Makes excellent white wine. Vine is perfect flowered, cold hardy, vigorous, prolific, grows well. Self-fertile. Ripens over a long period from September to early October. Picks with wet stem scar. Easily yields a bushel of grapes per plant. Grows well in the Deep South. Introduced in 1961. *Source History: 5 in 1988; 9 in 1992; 3 in 2000.* **Sources: Iso, Jo3, Ju2.**

Magoon - Dark muscadine; *Vitis rotundifolia.* Medium size clusters. Small to medium, reddish black fruit. Excellent quality. Fine for fresh eating. Heavily productive vines. Self-fertile. Grows well in all areas. An old favorite. Ripens in mid-September. Hardy in Zones 7-9. *Source History: 2 in 1988; 1 in 2000.* **Sources: WA8.**

Malaga, Red - *Source History: 1 in 1988; 1 in 1992; 1 in 2000.* **Sources: Fo8.**

Malbec - *Source History: 1 in 1988; 2 in 1992; 2 in 2000.* **Sources: Fo8, So6.**

Malvasia Bianca - White fruited variety. *Source History: 1 in 1992; 2 in 2000.* **Sources: Fo8, So6.**

Marquis - White seedless grape. Large clusters of large berries with rich fruity flavor. Twice the yield of Himrod. Excellent as a table grape. Also produces a delicate white wine. Zones 5-8. Developed at Cornell University. Patent pending. *Source History: 3 in 2000.* **Sources: BU12, Do7, St4.**

Mars (Mars Seedless) - American; *Vitis Labrusca.* Island Belle x Arkansas 1339. Medium to large, compact clusters. Medium to large, sweet, juicy, seedless, slip-skin crimson fruit turn deep blue at maturity. Mildly foxy flavor similar to Concord. Fine for eating fresh, jam, jelly, wine and juice. Ships well; long shelf life. Very productive; dependable. Relatively resistant to the major foliar diseases; slightly resistant to black rot. Mildew resistant. Ripens mid-September; 16-20 days before Concord. Among the most cold hardy of the seedless grapes. Good bud hardiness to -5 degrees F. in Zones 5-8. Developed at the University of Arkansas by Dr. James Moore. Introduced in 1984. U.S. Plant Patent No. 5680. *Source History: 13 in 1988; 25 in 1992; 21 in 2000.* **Sources: Bos, Bu1, BU12, Cla, Do7, Ed2, Ed5, Fa1, Fed, Fo3, Iso, Jun, Pe3, Rid, Rom, Sc6, SH8, Wel, Wh4, Wom, Wor.**

Marsanne - White variety. *Source History: 1 in 1992; 1 in 2000.* **Sources: So6.**

Mataro - *Source History: 1 in 1992; 1 in 2000.* **Sources: Fo8.**

McCampbell - American; *Vitis Labrusca.* Bud sport of Fredonia; similar in all respects except for having larger clusters two to three times normal size. Bluish black grape needs good fertility for consistent quality and cluster size. Often has faint mottled or variegated patches on the leaves, but this is inherited, not a disease.

Ripens midseason. Submitted for trial by Sara McCampbell of Holmdel, New Jersey. Introduced in 1961. *Source History: 3 in 1988; 2 in 1992; 4 in 2000.* **Sources: Bea, ME3, Rom, We4.**

Melody (NY 65.444.4) - American; *Vitis Labrusca*. Seyval x (Pinot Blanc x Ontario). Neutral fruity wine, slightly floral, good body and balance, excellent quality. Vine apparently resistant to powdery mildew and botrytis; productive, vigorous. Moderately hardy to -10 degrees F. Ripens midseason. Named and released by the New York State Agricultural Experiment Station at Geneva. Introduced in 1985. U.S. Plant Patent No. 6159. *Source History: 3 in 1988; 2 in 1992; 3 in 2000.* **Sources: Do7, Fo3, Mi1.**

Melon - *Source History: 1 in 1988; 1 in 1992; 2 in 2000.* **Sources: Fo8, So6.**

Merlot - European; *Vitis vinifera*. Medium size, round, deep black fruit. Produces large yields of high quality, rich, red wine; often blended with Cabernet. Self-fertile. Ripens from August to September. Requires 100 hours of chilling. Gillet introduction. *Source History: 4 in 1988; 7 in 1992; 11 in 2000.* **Sources: Bay, Bos, Do7, FAI, Fo3, Fo8, ME3, On3, ORA, So6, Wi21, WI4.**

Meunier (Pinot Meunier) - European; *Vitis vinifera*. Blue skinned wine grape. Midseason ripening. *Source History: 1 in 1988; 2 in 1992; 3 in 2000.* **Sources: Fo8, Rom, So6.**

Midgely's Purple - American; *Vitis Labrusca*. Medium size, reddish purple fruit. Good for table use and raisins. Ripens during September. *Source History: 1 in 1988; 1 in 1992; 1 in 2000.* **Sources: CO5.**

Millot (Kuhlmann 194.2, Leon Millot) - *Vitis Labrusca* x *V. vinifera*. Sister variety of Marechal Foch. Similar in bunch and berry, but earlier and slightly more productive. Bluish black fruit. Very vigorous vines. May require bunch thinning to prevent overbearing. Does not have much problem with mildew or botrytis. Ripens early. Promising wine grape for Burgundy-type wines. Will ripen dependably west of the Cascades. *Source History: 7 in 1988; 6 in 1992.* **Sources: Do7, Fo3, Mi1, Rom.**

Mission - Red fruited variety. *Source History: 1 in 1992; 2 in 2000.* **Sources: Fo8, So6.**

Mitchell - American; *Vitis Labrusca*. Blue skin. Table grape. Midseason ripening. *Source History: 1 in 2000.* **Sources: Rom.**

Monitor - Wild *Vitis riparia* x Concord. Lesser known sister seedling of Beta and Suelter. Nice large clusters. Hardy. Zone 3b. *Source History: 1 in 2000.* **Sources: La5.**

Monte Senario - European; *Vitis vinifera*. White variety. Shows good vigor and productivity. Ripens close to Concord. When Christ entered Jerusalem, the only place for him to stay was at a poor farmer's. The farmer indicated that the fruit of a grapevine in the corner of the yard was all the food he had, but that Christ was welcome to it. Before leaving, Christ blessed the vine. Cuttings of the vine were taken back to Italy by the Crusaders. In 1933 a start was taken to the Sanctuary of Our Sorrowful Mother in Portland, Oregon. We are offering vines started from the old vine in Portland to our customers in return for a donation to the Sanctuary. *Source History: 1 in 1988; 1 in 2000.* **Sources: Rom.**

Moored - American; *Vitis Labrusca*. Large, seeded, dark red fruit. Foxy flavor. Good for juice and fresh eating. Productive vine. Hardy to -5 degrees F. Introduced in 1973. *Source History: 4 in 1988; 2 in 1992; 1 in 2000.* **Sources: We4.**

Mourvedre (Mataro) - Red fruited variety. *Source History: 1 in 1992; 1 in*

2000. **Sources: So6.**

Mrs. Munson
- Munson hybrid. Large, conical cluster of small to medium, purple fruit. Small seeds. Thin, tough skin. Juicy, melting flesh. Good quality. Disease-free vines. *Source History: 1 in 1992; 1 in 2000.* **Sources: Hid.**

Muller Thurgau
- European; *Vitis vinifera.* Distinctively spicy white grapes in medium compact clusters. Good wine grape. Heavy producer. Ripens in early October. *Source History: 2 in 1988; 4 in 1992; 3 in 2000.* **Sources: Clo, ME3, Rai.**

Munson
- American; *Vitis Labrusca.* Blue skin. Table grape. Female flowers. Midseason ripening. *Source History: 1 in 2000.* **Sources: Rom.**

Muscadine
- Muscadine; *Vitis rotundifolia.* Huge blue grapes. Delicious flavor; just the right amount of tartness. Excellent for eating, canning, wine and desserts. Self-fertile; good pollinator. Hardy in Zones 4-8. *Source History: 1 in 1988; 2 in 1992; 4 in 2000.* **Sources: Bar, Hud, TU5, VIR.**

Muscat
- European; *Vitis vinifera.* Large, green-amber, round fruit hangs in loose clusters. Strongly aromatic, seeded variety. Good for table use, wine or raisins. Ripens in late July. Requires 100 hours of chilling. *Source History: 2 in 1988; 2 in 1992; 2 in 2000.* **Sources: ORA, Pe2.**

Muscat Blanc
(Muscat a Petits Grains) - European; *Vitis vinifera.* Green-white skin color. Wine and table grape. Ripens midseason. *Source History: 1 in 1988; 3 in 1992; 4 in 2000.* **Sources: FAI, Fo8, Rom, So6.**

Muscat Flame
- Table and raisin variety. Small berry with muscat flavor. Ripens early midseason. Zones 7-9. Developed at UC-Davis. *Source History: 1 in 1992; 2 in 2000.* **Sources: So6, Son.**

Muscat Hamburg
- European; *Vitis vinifera.* Outstanding table and raisin variety. Blue skin. Mid-late ripening. *Source History: 1 in 1988; 2 in 1992; 3 in 2000.* **Sources: Fo8, Rom, So6.**

Muscat of Alexandria
- European; *Vitis vinifera.* Large, egg-shaped, dull green grapes. Juicy, distinctive flavor and aroma. Used for fresh, juice, wine and raisins. Vine has medium vigor, productive. Self-fruitful. Ripens during September. Requires 100 hours of chilling. Not suited to hot desert climates. Zones 7-9. Gillet introduction. *Source History: 4 in 1988; 4 in 1992; 5 in 2000.* **Sources: Bay, CO5, So6, Son, WI4.**

Muscat Ottonel
- European; *Vitis vinifera.* Medium size clusters of firm, yellow grapes. Muscat flavor is so rich that it makes a good eating grape; intended for wine. Ripe with or before Flame. Should be picked as soon as ripe for wine or the acid drops rapidly. *Source History: 1 in 1988; 3 in 1992; 4 in 2000.* **Sources: Bu7, Fo8, ME3, So6.**

Muscat Saint-Vallier
- European; *Vitis vinifera.* White fruited variety. *Source History: 1 in 1992; 2 in 2000.* **Sources: Fo8, So6.**

Muscat, Early
- European; *Vitis vinifera.* Excellent yellow muscat grape. Big clusters with meaty berries; highly productive. Makes good raisins, the seeds merely adding crunchiness. Also used to make varietal muscat wine. Ripens 14-21 days before Concord. *Source History: 2 in 1988; 3 in 1992; 4 in 2000.* **Sources: Fo8, ME3, Rom, So6.**

Muscat, Morio
- European; *Vitis vinifera.* Green skin. Wine grape. Leaves used for cooking. Ripens early midseason. *Source History: 1 in 2000.* **Sources: Rom.**

Muscat, Orange
- European; *Vitis vinifera.* White fruited variety with very intense flavor. Midseason ripening. *Source History: 1 in 1988; 3 in 1992; 3 in 2000.*

Sources: Fo8, Rom, So6.

Muscat, Summer - European; *Vitis vinifera. Source History: 1 in 2000.* **Sources: Fo8.**

Muscato di Terracina - European; *Vitis vinifera.* Muscat with orange-yellow skin. Excellent flavor. Ripens midseason. Zones 6-9. Originated in a small coastal area near Rome, Italy. *Source History: 1 in 2000.* **Sources: Son.**

Napa Gamay (Valdiguie) - Red fruited variety. *Source History: 1 in 1992; 2 in 2000.* **Sources: Fo8, So6.**

Nebbiolo - Red fruited variety. *Source History: 2 in 1992; 2 in 2000.* **Sources: Fo8, So6.**

Nebbiolo Lampia - Red fruited variety. *Source History: 1 in 1992; 2 in 2000.* **Sources: Fo8, So6.**

Neptune - Conic-shaped clusters of medium size white berries with high sugar solids. Resists cracking. Ripens midseason. Developed at the University of Arkansas Breeding Program. *Source History: 1 in 2000.* **Sources: Do7.**

Nesbitt - Muscadine; *Vitis rotundifolia.* Very large black fruit. Sweet flavor. Excellent fresh table grape. Vine is perfect flowered, has good vigor, good cold hardiness, good disease resistance. High yields. Good stem scar. Excellent for home garden. Self-fertile. Ripens mid to late September. Hardy in Zones 7-9. Developed at the North Carolina Agricultural Experiment Station. Introduced in 1984. *Source History: 1 in 1988; 8 in 1992; 4 in 2000.* **Sources: Iso, Ju2, Sh3, Ty2.**

New York 62.0122.01 - Courderc 299-35 x Muscat Ottonel. Excellent muscat type wine. Moderately hardy vine. Developed at the Geneva Breeding Program. *Source History: 1 in 1992; 1 in 2000.* **Sources: Do7.**

New York 70.0809.10 - SV 18-307 x Steuben. Produces a vinous, *vinifera* type wine with bell pepper aroma. Vigorous, productive vine. Powdery mildew resistant. Developed at the Geneva Breeding Program. *Source History: 1 in 2000.* **Sources: Do7.**

New York 73.0136.17 - NY 33277 x Chancellor x Steuben. Produces a full bodied red wine with black pepper character and moderate tannin content. Vigorous. Moderately resistant to powdery mildew. Developed at the Geneva Breeding Program. *Source History: 1 in 2000.* **Sources: Do7.**

New York 76.0848.03 - Melody x 65.533.13. Productive and vigorous. Good quality. Developed at the Geneva Breeding Program. *Source History: 1 in 2000.* **Sources: Do7.**

New York Muscat - American; *Vitis Labrusca.* Muscat Hamburg x Ontario. Clusters sometimes tend to be loose. Reddish black to black fruit. Fine muscat flavor is blended with rich sweetness producing delicate and pure flavor. High quality. Excellent for table, juice and wine. Not too vigorous a vine; not highly productive. Responds well to increased fertility. The variety's minor limitations are offset by the pleasure of savoring its fine fruit. Ripens midseason, about 21 days before Concord. Hardy to 0 degrees F. Developed at the New York State Agricultural Experiment Station in Geneva. Introduced in 1961. *Source History: 4 in 1988; 2 in 1992; 4 in 2000.* **Sources: Do7, Fo8, Rai, Rom, So6.**

Niabell - American; *Vitis Labrusca.* Large, round, bluish black fruit. Used fresh or for juice. Vigorous and productive. Excellent for arbors. Succeeds in hot areas where Concord fails. Ripens during August. *Source History: 2 in 1988; 2 in 1992; 4 in 2000.* **Sources: CO5, Fo8, Pa2, So6.**

Niagara (White Concord) - American; *Vitis Labrusca*. White grape that began as a chance seedling of Concord. Has the hardiness and productivity of its parent, but ripens a few days earlier. Heavy producer of large, tight, compact clusters. Huge, thick skinned, light green to white, slipskin fruit. Normally resists cracking. Tangy but delicate flavor; somewhat foxy. Top eating variety; makes a distinctive white wine. Very attractive, vigorous vine; makes an excellent arbor. Self-fruitful. Ripens in late September. Does well in cold Northern states. Hardy to -15 degrees F and in Zones 4-8. Most popular white *Labrusca* hybrid. Introduced in 1882. *Source History: 51 in 1988; 60 in 1992; 53 in 2000.* **Sources: Bar, BO4, Bo5, Bos, Bu1, BU12, Cla, Co12, CO3, CO5, Do7, FAI, FO10, Fo3, Fo4, Fo8, GI3, GR26, HI10, In5, Iso, Jo3, KR3, Led, Lee, Mc3, ME3, Mel, Mi1, MI10, MI5, MO10, Pe3, Pi2, Po2, RAM, Rid, Rom, Sav, SH8, SIM, So5, So6, Son, Tex, TU5, Ty2, WA8, We4, Wel, Wh4, WI4, Wor.**

Noble - Muscadine; *Vitis rotundifolia*. Large clusters of 20-22 small to medium, bluish black fruits that do not shatter easily. Medium skin. Very good quality. Excellent for making red table wine; 15% solids (sugar), pH 3.46, 0.765% acid. Good eating quality; makes fine juice and jelly. Vine is moderately vigorous and very productive. Self-fruitful; good persistence. Good disease resistance, except for powdery mildew. Ripens midseason. Hardy in Zones 7-9. Developed at the North Carolina Agricultural Experiment Station. Introduced in 1971. *Source History: 8 in 1988; 13 in 1992; 7 in 2000.* **Sources: Bu1, Fo4, Iso, Ju2, Tex, Ty2, Wel.**

Odem - *Source History: 1 in 2000.* **Sources: Fo8.**

Okanogan Riesling - American; *Vitis Labrusca*. White Riesling type. Medium size, compact bunches. Medium size golden green grapes. Has pure muscat flavor; as maturity advances, develops foxiness in the flavor, so picking time is important. High quality. Widely grown for wine in British Columbia; also a fine table grape. Vigorous vine; good fruit set in the Northwest. Productive; may overbear. Quite resistant to mildew. Especially good on light soils. Ripens about 14 days before Concord. Zones 4-9. *Source History: 3 in 1988; 1 in 1992; 2 in 2000.* **Sources: Bu7, Rom.**

Ontario - American; *Vitis Labrusca*. Winchell x Diamond. Large, loosely formed clusters. Very sweet small eating grape with white to light yellow fruits. Sweet, rich, distinctive flavor; a pleasantly diluted version of Niagara's type of foxiness. Vine is vigorous and productive; only medium hardy. Disease free; requires no spraying. Ripens 28 days before Concord, usually in late August. Best seeded, white grape. Developed at the New York State Agricultural Experiment Station. Introduced in 1908. *Source History: 4 in 1988; 4 in 1992; 7 in 2000.* **Sources: Fo8, ME3, Mi1, Rom, Sc6, So5, We4.**

Oppenheim - *Source History: 1 in 2000.* **Sources: Fo8.**

Oraniensteiner - White fruited variety from Germany. *Source History: 2 in 2000.* **Sources: Fo8, So6.**

Orlando Seedless - Light green fruit grows in large clusters. Good for home use and Pick Your Own. Resistant to Pierce's disease. Self-fertile. Early ripening. Widely adaptable for the South; Zones 7-9. *Source History: 12 in 1992; 6 in 2000.* **Sources: Iso, Ju2, SIM, Tex, Ty2, Wga.**

Osbu - American; *Vitis Labrusca*. Female flowered variety. Medium size clusters of medium size red berries. Quite sweet, good quality. Ripens early. Old, hardy variety from Professor Nels Hansen of South Dakota. *Source History: 1 in 1988; 1 in 2000.* **Sources: Rom.**

Palomino - White fruited variety. *Source History: 1 in 1992; 2 in 2000.* **Sources: Fo8, So6.**

Pam - Bronze muscadine; *Vitis rotundifolia.* Extra long clusters of large, round fruit. Dry scar. Ripens uniformly midseason. U.S. Plant Patent No. 7707. *Source History: 1 in 1992; 1 in 2000.* **Sources: Iso.**

Perle de Csaba - European; *Vitis vinifera.* White to golden yellow fruit. Crisp, sweet, meaty flesh and thin adherent skin with only a single small seed. Distinct, delicious muscat aroma and flavor. Medium vigor. Shy bearer. Ripens 28 days before Concord. *Source History: 2 in 1988; 1 in 1992; 1 in 2000.* **Sources: Rom.**

Perle Noir - Bluish red berry. *Source History: 1 in 1992; 1 in 2000.* **Sources: Bo5.**

Perlette - European; *Vitis vinifera.* Small to medium, thin skinned, seedless, light green to amber green fruit. Crisp, juicy, table grape. Self-fruitful. Slightly larger than Thompson, ripens 14-21 days earlier, usually in late July. Requires 100 hours of chilling. *Source History: 6 in 1988; 10 in 1992; 7 in 2000.* **Sources: Bay, CO5, ORA, Pe2, So6, STR, WI4.**

Perlette, Loose - Table and raisin variety. *Source History: 1 in 2000.* **Sources: So6.**

Petit Bouschet - *Source History: 1 in 1992; 1 in 2000.* **Sources: Fo8.**

Petite Jewel - Formerly listed as E. S. 3-20-36. The first seedless selection developed by Elmer Swenson. Somewhat small berrry and bunch size. Very attractive red color. Excellent, fruity-spicy flavor. Extra early ripening. May be somewhat tender in Minnesota, especially when young. Hardy to about -30 degrees F. *Source History: 1 in 1992; 1 in 2000.* **Sources: La5.**

Petite Sirah - *Source History: 1 in 1988; 2 in 1992; 2 in 2000.* **Sources: Fo8, So6.**

Petite Verdot - *Source History: 1 in 1988; 2 in 1992; 2 in 2000.* **Sources: Fo8, So6.**

Peverella - White fruited variety. *Source History: 1 in 1992; 2 in 2000.* **Sources: Fo8, So6.**

Pierce - *Source History: 1 in 2000.* **Sources: Fo8.**

Pineapple - Bronze muscadine; *Vitis rotundifolia.* Large clusters of large fruit with taste similar to pineapple. Vigorous, productive, disease resistant vines. Self-fertile. U.S. Plant Patent No. 7266. *Source History: 1 in 1992; 1 in 2000.* **Sources: Iso.**

Pinot Blanc - White fruit. *Source History: 3 in 1992; 3 in 2000.* **Sources: Fo8, ME3, So6.**

Pinot Chardonnay - European; *Vitis vinifera.* Small to medium, round, white fruits. Best quality. Used to make white Burgundy wines. Vine is one of the more hardy *viniferas*; vigorous. Self-fruitful. Ripens in late August. Gillet introduction. *Source History: 4 in 1988; 3 in 1992; 2 in 2000.* **Sources: CO5, Fi1.**

Pinot Gris - European; *Vitis vinifera.* Honey colored, richly flavored wine. Known as "the salmon wine" because of the unforgettable taste created when combined with salmon. Does best in areas with a long cool growing season. *Source History: 1 in 1988; 5 in 1992; 8 in 2000.* **Sources: Clo, Do7, FAI, Fo8, ME3, Rom, So6, Wi21.**

Pinot Noir - European; *Vitis vinifera.* Small, dark blue grape. Very distinctive scent. Takes some special care but produces an award winning, dry, delicate, pinkish red wine. Requires 100 hours of chilling. Self-fruitful. Grows well in central

Washington, but does not have the body and color that the grape produces in its homeland.   Moderately hardy.   Survives most winters without severe pruning. Needs 2,000-2,500 growing degree days. Hardy to 10 degrees F. Introduced from Burgundy, France. Does best in cooler areas. Oregon's pride. *Source History: 12 in 1988; 11 in 1992; 12 in 2000.* **Sources: Bay, Clo, Do7, FAI, Fo3, Fo8, ME3, On3, ORA, So6, Wi21, WI4.**

Pinot St. George (Negrette) - Red fruited variety. *Source History: 1 in 1992; 2 in 2000.* **Sources: Fo8, So6.**

Pinotage - Red fruited variety. *Source History: 1 in 1992; 2 in 2000.* **Sources: Fo8, So6.**

Plavina - Italian; *Vitis vinifera. Source History: 1 in 2000.* **Sources: Fo8.**

Portuguese Blue - European; *Vitis vinifera.* Blue skin. Wine grape. Ripens early. *Source History: 1 in 2000.* **Sources: Rom.**

Price - American; *Vitis Labrusca.* Relatively small, compact clusters; many clusters to the vine. Medium size, bluish black fruit. Flavor is sweet and pure, lacking any of the American foxiness. Good quality. Very good as a table and juice grape; should be tried for wine. One of the best varieties for extra cool areas of the Pacific Northwest, because of its ability to ripen early even in cool weather. Ripens 21 days before Concord. Hardy to -10 degrees F.   Developed in Virginia by Dr. Oberle, who developed the Presidential series of peaches. Introduced in 1973. *Source History: 4 in 1988; 3 in 1992; 4 in 2000.* **Sources: Ed5, Rai, Rom, We4.**

Primitivo - Red fruited variety. *Source History: 1 in 1992; 2 in 2000.* **Sources: Fo8, So6.**

PRK 13-32 - Kay Gray x Veeblanc. Healthy, productive white selection. Ripens midseason. Zone 4a. *Source History: 1 in 2000.* **Sources: La5.**

Queen - Table and raisin variety. *Source History: 1 in 1992; 2 in 2000.* **Sources: Fo8, So6.**

Queen of the Vineyard - European; *Vitis vinifera.* White grapes are seeded, but crisp and delicious. Careful pruning and cluster thinning can produce some magnificent clusters. Even without pruning, the flavor is flowery, delicate and muscat-like.   Called "Scolokertek Kiralynoje" in Hungary, where it originated. *Source History: 1 in 1988; 1 in 2000.* **Sources: Rom.**

Ravat 34 - French; *Vitis vinifera.* Wine recalls Burgundian Aligote. Sturdy vine. Winter hardy and healthy.   Ripens early. *Source History: 1 in 1988; 2 in 1992; 1 in 2000.* **Sources: Do7.**

Ravat 262 - French; *Vitis vinifera.* Black skin color. Wine, jam, juice and jelly. Ripens early. *Source History: 1 in 2000.* **Sources: Rom.**

Rayon d'Or (Seibel 4986) - French; *Vitis vinifera.* Greyish pink fruit at maturity in beautiful winged branches. Should be picked promptly when ripe. Produces a high quality wine. Trim, handsome, healthy, hardy vines. Spur or short cane pruning, depending on vigor. Very regular producer. *Source History: 1 in 1988; 2 in 1992; 1 in 2000.* **Sources: Rom.**

Red Flame - Light red table grape with a crisp flavor. Grows in elongated loose, medium size clusters. Ripens early. Prefers warm temperatures during ripening period. *Source History: 2 in 2000.* **Sources: Iso, Wel.**

Redglobe - Extremely large, red fruit. Keeps well. Good production. Ripens in September. U.S. Plant Patent No. 4787. *Source History: 1 in 1988; 3 in 1992; 2 in 2000.* **Sources: ORA, So6.**

Refosco (Mondeuse Noire) - Red fruited variety. *Source History: 1 in 1992; 2 in*

2000. **Sources: Fo8, So6.**

Regale - Dark muscadine; *Vitis rotundifolia.* Large, dark, wine grapes. Exceptionally heavy yields. Excellent for northernmost muscadine growing region because of its winter hardiness. Ripens early. Hardy in Zones 7-8. *Source History: 1 in 1988; 5 in 1992; 1 in 2000.* **Sources: Ty2.**

Reliance (Arkansas 1163, Reliance Seedless) - American; *Vitis Labrusca.* Ontario x Suffolk Red. Large, well filled clusters. Round, medium size, firm, seedless, pinkish red grapes. Tender skin and flesh; melting texture. Outstanding, mild, fruity flavor. High sugar content. Perhaps the finest quality of any seedless grape; good for jellies and juices. Stores for three months. Vigorous, productive, dependable, adaptable vine. Resists anthracnose, powdery and downy mildews. Black rot susceptible. Ripens 18 days before Concord, during late July or August. Hardy to -34 degrees F. Developed by Dr. Moore at the University of Arkansas in 1965. U.S. Plant Patent No. 5174. *Source History: 19 in 1988; 29 in 1992; 31 in 2000.* **Sources: Bo5, Bos, Bu1, Bu2, Clo, Do7, Ed5, Fa1, Fed, Fi1, Fo3, Gur, In5, Iso, Jo3, Jun, Mi1, On3, Or2, Pe3, Rid, Rom, Sc6, So5, St4, Ty2, VIR, Wa16, Wel, Wom, Wor.**

Remaily (Remaily Seedless) - American; *Vitis Labrusca.* Lady Patricia x (Ontario x Russian Seedless). Large, seedless, white table grape. Oval, white to whitish yellow fruit. Good textured flesh; adherent skin. Vine appears to be only moderately hardy. Good vigor; bears large crops. So productive it often requires thinning of its extra large clusters. Ripens from mid-August to early September. Hardy to 0 degrees F and in Zones 5-8. Developed at the New York State Agricultural Experiment Station in Geneva. Introduced in 1980. *Source History: 7 in 1988; 12 in 1992; 9 in 2000.* **Sources: Bo5, Cla, Fo3, ME3, Or2, Rom, St4, Wbn, We4.**

Ribier (Alphonse Lavallee) - European; *Vitis vinifera.* Very large, round, seeded, jet-black table grape. Mild flavor. Productive vines. Self-fruitful. Ripens early-midseason. Requires 100 hours of chilling. *Source History: 4 in 1988; 5 in 1992; 3 in 2000.* **Sources: Bay, Fo8, WI4.**

Riesling - White fruited variety. *Source History: 3 in 2000.* **Sources: Fo8, So6, Wi21.**

Riparia Gloire - *Source History: 1 in 2000.* **Sources: Fo8.**

Rish Baba - Table variety. *Source History: 1 in 1992; 1 in 2000.* **Sources: So6.**

River Bank - Hardy strain. *Source History: 1 in 2000.* **Sources: Va5.**

Rkatsiteli - White fruited variety from Leningrad. *Source History: 2 in 2000.* **Sources: Fo8, So6.**

Romulus (Romulus Seedless) - American; *Vitis Labrusca.* Ontario x Thompson Seedless. Medium size, compact clusters. Small to medium, high quality, seedless, green to yellowish white, dessert grape. Pleasantly flavored. Good quality where season is long enough to ripen well. Vine is moderately hardy; moderate cropping. Ripens with Concord. Hardy to 0 degrees F. Developed at the New York State Agricultural Experiment Station. Introduced in 1952. *Source History: 8 in 1988; 9 in 1992; 4 in 2000.* **Sources: Fo3, Fo8, ME3, So5.**

Rosa - Muscadine; *Vitis rotundifolia.* Large, sweet, pinkish red fruit. Excellent flavor. Wet scar. Good for home use and Pick Your Own. Ripens mid to late season. Patent applied for. *Source History: 1 in 1992; 1 in 2000.* **Sources: Iso.**

Rose Belle - American; *Vitis Labrusca.* Red skin color. Table grape. Vigorous. Midseason ripening. *Source History: 1 in 2000.* **Sources: Rom.**

Rosette (Seibel 1000) - French; *Vitis vinifera.* Bluish black fruits. Good for blending. Vigorous. Ripens mid-late. Hardy to -15 degrees F. *Source History: 2 in 1988; 2 in 1992; 1 in 2000.* **Sources: Fo3.**

Rougeon (Seibel 5898) - French; *Vitis vinifera.* Bluish black fruit. Good red wine for blending. Vine is a good producer. Ripens late-midseason. Hardy to -10 degrees F. *Source History: 2 in 1988; 1 in 1992; 3 in 2000.* **Sources: Do7, Fo3, Rom.**

Roussanne - White fruited variety. *Source History: 1 in 2000.* **Sources: So6.**

Royal Blue - American; *Vitis Labrusca.* Blue seedless table grape. Midseason ripening. *Source History: 1 in 2000.* **Sources: Rom.**

Royalty - Red fruited variety. *Source History: 1 in 1992; 2 in 2000.* **Sources: Fo8, So6.**

Rubired - Red fruited variety. *Source History: 2 in 1992; 2 in 2000.* **Sources: Fo8, So6.**

Ruby - American; *Vitis Labrusca.* Keuka x Ontario. Large clusters. Sweet and edible while the berries are still greenish tinged with red. Left to hang until completely red and fully ripe, develops a pure sweet flavor that is unapproachable by any other grape. Requires severe pruning and cluster thinning for best results. Developed at the New York State Agricultural Experiment Station in Geneva. *Source History: 1 in 1988; 1 in 1992; 2 in 2000.* **Sources: Rom, So5.**

Ruby Seedless (King's Ruby) - European; *Vitis vinifera.* Large, rather loose clusters of medium to large, red berries. Firm, crisp flesh. Good for table and raisins. Vigorous, productive vines. Ripens about 14 days after Concord, sooner in protected planting sites where they get more heat. Hardy in Zones 7-9. Developed by Dr. Olmo at the University of California at Davis in 1939. *Source History: 5 in 1988; 10 in 1992; 12 in 2000.* **Sources: Bay, CO5, Fo8, ME3, MO10, ORA, Pa2, Rom, So6, STR, Wel, WI4.**

S. V. 5-247 - French; *Vitis vinifera.* Blue skin. Wine grape. Ripens early midseason. *Source History: 1 in 2000.* **Sources: Rom.**

S. V. 23-512 - French; *Vitis vinifera.* Purple skin. Wine and table use. Midseason ripening. *Source History: 1 in 2000.* **Sources: Rom.**

Salvador - Red fruited variety. *Source History: 1 in 1992; 2 in 2000.* **Sources: Fo8, So6.**

Sangiovese - Red fruited variety. *Source History: 2 in 1992; 2 in 2000.* **Sources: Fo8, So6.**

Saturn - American; *Vitis Labrusca.* Dunstan 210 x NY 45791. Red seedless berries. Great table grape; also makes a good wine. Vines occasionally require cluster thinning. Ripens midseason. Hardy to -50 degrees F. Introduced in 1987. U.S. Plant Patent No. 6703. *Source History: 8 in 1992; 6 in 2000.* **Sources: Do7, Fo3, In5, Mi1, Rom, Wel.**

Sauvignon Blanc - Well formed compact clusters. Medium size, greenish grape. Vines are vigorous growers. *Source History: 2 in 1988; 4 in 1992; 4 in 2000.* **Sources: FAI, Fo8, So6, Wi21.**

Sauvignon Gris - White fruited variety. *Source History: 1 in 1992; 2 in 2000.* **Sources: Fo8, So6.**

Sauvignon Musque - White fruited variety. *Source History: 1 in 2000.* **Sources: So6.**

Sauvignon Vert - *Source History: 1 in 1992; 1 in 2000.* **Sources: Fo8.**

Scarlet - Large red fruit with excellent flavor. Disease resistant, vigorous, productive vines. Midseason ripening. *Source History: 1 in 1992; 3 in 2000.* **Sources: Fo8, Jo3, So6.**

Schuyler - American; *Vitis Labrusca.* Zinfandel x Ontario. European type, without slipskin character. Large bunches of medium size, juicy, very sweet, bluish black grapes. Flavor is very sweet with vinous tang. High quality. Good for fresh eating, juice and rose' type wines. Vine is medium hardy, productive and vigorous. Must be pruned very severely to avoid overbearing. Disease resistant, but may get powdery mildew in bad years. Ripens 21-28 days before Concord and is more dependable. Introduced in 1947. *Source History: 7 in 1988; 3 in 1992; 4 in 2000.* **Sources: Fo8, Mi1, Rom, We4.**

Schwarzmann - *Source History: 1 in 2000.* **Sources: Fo8.**

Scuppernong - Oldest, best known and most widely grown variety of muscadine. Large, thick skinned, reddish bronze berries with russet dots. Ripe berries vary from greenish bronze to reddish bronze, depending upon amount of sun the vines receive. Pale flesh; juicy, sweet to agreeably tart, foxy flavor. Excellent quality. Vigorous, productive, female vine; pollinate with Cowart. Bears heavily and consistently. Bred to resist pests and diseases common in hot humid climates. Doesn't fruit in the Northwest. Ripens in early September. Hardy in Zones 7-9. *Source History: 12 in 1988; 12 in 1992; 8 in 2000.* **Sources: Cla, Iso, Jo3, La3, SIM, Tex, Ty2, Wel.**

Seibel 5898 (Rougeon) - Heavy producer of deep red wine. Good blender. *Source History: 1 in 1988; 1 in 1992; 1 in 2000.* **Sources: Mi1.**

Seibel 9110 (Verdelette) - Whitish yellow berries in large clusters. Makes a fragrant, delicate, clear white wine. Ripens mid-July. Winter hardy. *Source History: 4 in 1992; 3 in 2000.* **Sources: Bos, Tex, Wel.**

Seibel 13053 - *Source History: 1 in 1992; 1 in 2000.* **Sources: Fo8.**

Seibel 13666 - French; *Vitis vinifera.* White wine grape. Midseason ripening. *Source History: 1 in 2000.* **Sources: Rom.**

Semillon - European; *Vitis vinifera.* Produces a naturally sweet wine. Ripens midseason. *Source History: 3 in 1988; 5 in 1992; 4 in 2000.* **Sources: FAI, Fo8, Rom, So6.**

Seneca - American; *Vitis Labrusca.* Ontario x Lignan Blanc. Firm, oval, greenish yellow berries turn translucent gold at maturity. Skin may be eaten. Aromatic, sweet, spicy, vinous flavor; unexcelled in quality. Bears heavily on vigorous, healthy vines. Berries hang on the vine in excellent condition almost to the end of the season. Needs heavy pruning to be productive. Training for good air circulation helps reduce tendency to powdery mildew. Good maturity of the canes ensures maximum hardiness of the wood. Predominantly European in fruit characters. Ripens early. Medium winter hardy. Introduced by the Geneva Station in 1930. *Source History: 4 in 1988; 4 in 1992; 3 in 2000.* **Sources: Fo8, Mi1, Rom.**

Seyve-Villard 5-276 (Seyval, Seyval Blanc) - French; *Vitis vinifera.* White fruit. Superior, clean, brisk, white wine; finest quality. Vine has medium vigor; highly productive, compact grower. Requires short pruning and spur pruning to reduce the risk of overcropping. No serious cultural defects. Good disease resistance. Ripens midseason. Hardy to -5 degrees F. Possibly the finest combination of superior wine quality, excellent cultural characteristics and broad adaptability. *Source History: 5 in 1988; 6 in 1992; 5 in 2000.* **Sources: Bos, Do7, Fed, Fo3, Leu, Mi1, Pe3.**

Shakoka - American; *Vitis Labrusca.* White grape. Ripens early. Very hardy. Developed by Professor Hansen. *Source History: 1 in 1988; 1 in 2000.* **Sources:**

Rom.

Sheridan - American; *Vitis Labrusca*. Herbert x Worden. Very large, compact clusters. Very large, firm, sweet, delicately flavored, dark bluish black fruits. Excellent quality. Keeps well until after Christmas. Vine is vigorous, healthy, hardy and heavy bearing; so productive that it requires close pruning to prevent overbearing. Excellent variety in locations where it ripens properly. Ripens in late September or early October. Hardy to -15 degrees F. Developed by the New York State Agricultural Experiment Station in Geneva. Introduced in 1921. *Source History: 4 in 1988; 4 in 1992; 4 in 2000.* **Sources: Do7, Fo3, Mi1, So5.**

Shiraz (Syrah) - Red fruited variety. Produces a wine rich in body, tannin and color. Needs to be aged to develop its full character. *Source History: 2 in 1992; 4 in 2000.* **Sources: Do7, FAI, Fo8, So6.**

Siegerrebe - Cross from Germany. Pink wine grape has muscat bouquet. Low in acid at maturity. Makes good quality white wine. Also tasty for fresh eating. Good choice for the cooler sites in northwest Washington. Ripens in early September. *Source History: 1 in 1988; 2 in 1992; 2 in 2000.* **Sources: Clo, Rai.**

Sonoma - American; *Vitis Labrusca*. White grape. Table use, jam, jelly and juice. Female flowers. Hardy. Ripens early. *Source History: 1 in 2000.* **Sources: Rom.**

Sousao - Red fruits. *Source History: 2 in 1992; 2 in 2000.* **Sources: Fo8, So6.**

Southland - Dark muscadine; *Vitis rotundifolia*. Medium to large, non-glossy, purplish black fruit. Excellent, very sweet flavor. Fine quality. Good for fresh eating, jams and jellies. Vigorous, disease resistant vine; good persistence. Self-fertile. Bred to resist pests and diseases common in hot, humid climates. Recommended for home use and commercial plantings. Ripens midseason. *Source History: 6 in 1988; 9 in 1992; 3 in 2000.* **Sources: Iso, Jo3, SIM.**

St. Croix - American; *Vitis Labrusca*. Medium to large bunches. Medium to large, red fruit. Pure, non-foxy flavor. Suitable for both winemaking and dessert. In high demand for red wine production in Minnesota. Sugar content of 18-20 B; acid .80-.90. Very productive vines. Ripens about 40 days before Concord in late August. Hardy to about -40 degrees F. without protection, a bit less in windy areas. Developed by Elmer Swenson and introduced by Swenson-Smith Vines Inc. U.S. Plant Patent No. 4928. *Source History: 5 in 1988; 7 in 1992; 8 in 2000.* **Sources: BA14, Do7, Ed5, Fed, La5, Rom, SH8, Stl.**

St. Emilion (Ugni Blanc) - White fruited variety. *Source History: 1 in 1992; 2 in 2000.* **Sources: Fo8, So6.**

St. Macaire (Bouton Blanc) - Red fruited variety. *Source History: 1 in 1992; 2 in 2000.* **Sources: Fo8, So6.**

St. Pepin - American; *Vitis Labrusca*. Medium large, rather loose clusters of medium size, somewhat oval, white berries. Quite fruity with sugar and acid much like La Crosse. Wine is very much like Riesling in character. Excellent table grape. Female flowered variety requires pollination. La Crosse makes a good pollinator and blends well with it. About as hardy as La Crosse. Does not need winter covering in Minnesota. Elmer Swenson introduction. U.S. Plant Patent No. 5771. *Source History: 2 in 1988; 3 in 1992; 4 in 2000.* **Sources: Do7, Fed, La5, Rom.**

St. Vincent - Makes very good wine. Culturally reliable. Ripens late midseason. Hardy to -15 degrees F. Grown commercially in the Augusta, Missouri area. *Source History: 1 in 1992; 2 in 2000.* **Sources: Do7, Fo3.**

Steuben - American; *Vitis Labrusca*. Wayne x Sheridan. New York table grape

with Herbert ancestry in its blood. Very large, perfectly formed, long, slender, compact clusters. Handsome lavender blue to purplish black grapes. Delicious, melting, tender, sweet flesh. Delicate, grape-perfume, distinctive, spicy flavor. High quality. Very enjoyable table grape; makes excellent red wine; used for pale pink juice. Keeps until Christmas. Hardy, vigorous, exceedingly productive vines. Resistant to mildew and rot. Ripens a few days before Concord, usually in mid-September. Full crops even after -20 degree F winters. Introduced by the Geneva Station in 1947. *Source History: 12 in 1988; 10 in 1992; 12 in 2000.* **Sources: Do7, Fo3, Leu, Lin, ME3, Mel, Mi1, Rom, Sc6, So5, We4, Wh4.**

Stover - American; *Vitis Labrusca*. Translucent light green to golden fruit; mild flavor. Good for fresh eating and home winemaking. Vigorous and disease resistant. Southern bunch grape bred in a Florida vineyard. Ripens in late June. Hardy in Zones 7-9. *Source History: 3 in 1988; 8 in 1992; 4 in 2000.* **Sources: Iso, SIM, Ty2, Wga.**

Suavis (IP 365) - *Source History: 1 in 1992; 1 in 2000.* **Sources: Fo8.**

Suelter - Sister seedling of Beta with lower acid and less *Labrusca* in flavor. Better for fresh eating and wine. Same hardiness as Beta. Pistillate. Zone 3b. Bred by Louis Suelter in Minnesota, mid 1800s. *Source History: 1 in 1992; 1 in 2000.* **Sources: La5.**

Suffolk Red - American; *Vitis Labrusca*. Fredonia x Black Monukka. Long, loose, medium to large clusters. Round, firm, meaty, seedless berries vary from bright red to grayish pink. Tender skin; crisp, juicy flesh. Pleasing, spicy-sweet flavor. Excellent quality. Fine table grape. Needs direct sun to develop maximum red color; some foliage pruning may be needed. Grows vigorously with constant moisture and fertility; mulch often works. Self-fruitful. Almost disease free; moderately susceptible to mildews. Ripens 14-21 days before Concord, during September. Hardy to -10 degrees F. Introduced by the Geneva Station in 1972. *Source History: 26 in 1988; 25 in 1992; 22 in 2000.* **Sources: Bay, Bea, Bo5, Co12, Do7, FAI, Fi1, Fo3, In5, Leu, ME3, RAM, Roh, Rom, SH8, Shu, So5, St6, VA3, Wbn, We4, WI4.**

Sugargate - Muscadine; *Vitis rotundifolia*. Large clusters of very large, dark fruit. Excellent flavor. Female vine is very vigorous. Production very good. Not recommended for Gulf Coast. Ripens early. U.S. Plant Patent No. 4056. *Source History: 1 in 1988; 1 in 1992; 1 in 2000.* **Sources: Iso.**

Summer Royal - *Source History: 1 in 2000.* **Sources: Fo8.**

Summersweet - E. S. 2-4-13 x E. S. 2-5-5. Formerly E. S. 5-4-35. Smaller berry and cluster size than E. S. 414. One of the first to ripen. Hardy to -30 degrees F. Developed by Elmer Swenson. *Source History: 1 in 1992; 1 in 2000.* **Sources: La5.**

Summit - Bronze muscadine; *Vitis rotundifolia*. Medium size clusters. Large, sweet red fruits with medium thick skin; thinnest of any large fruited variety. Excellent quality. Hardy, vigorous vine; very productive. Female; requires pollination. One of the best bronze varieties for home and commercial plantings. Ripens in mid-September. Hardy in Zones 7-9. *Source History: 3 in 1988; 7 in 1992; 1 in 2000.* **Sources: Iso.**

Sunbelt - Blue juice grape similar to Concord with more heat tolerance and disease resistance. Excellent quality and flavor. Does well in the South where intense heat causes uneven ripening and low vigor. Zones 5-8. Developed at the University of Arkansas. Patented. *Source History: 4 in 2000.* **Sources: Cla, Do7, Ed2, Pe3.**

Sunrise - Bronze Muscadine; *Vitis rotundifolia*. Large grape with crisp sweet texture. Ripens late August. *Source History: 1 in 2000.* **Sources: Ju2.**

Supreme - Muscadine; *Vitis rotundifolia.* Large clusters of large black fruit with edible skin. Dry scar. Ripens mid to late season. U.S. Plant Patent No. 7267. *Source History: 1 in 1992; 1 in 2000.* **Sources: Iso.**

Suwannee - White bunch grape from Florida. Light green berries in large, compact clusters. Excellent flavor similar to Thompson Seedless but with a light muscat flavor. Makes a dry white wine. Vigorous, disease tolerant vines. Ripens late June to early July. *Source History: 1 in 1988; 5 in 1992; 4 in 2000.* **Sources: Ju2, SIM, Ty2, Wga.**

Sweet Jenny - Bronze female. Huge fruit to 1.5" in diameter. Disease resistant. Ripens early to midseason. U.S. Plant Patent No. 7265. *Source History: 2 in 1992; 2 in 2000.* **Sources: Iso, Sh3.**

Sweet Seduction - Seedless grape with delicious muscat flavor. Good producer. Ripens with Interlaken. *Source History: 1 in 2000.* **Sources: Rai.**

Swenson Red (Swenson No. 439) - American; *Vitis Labrusca.* Minnesota 78 x Seibel 11803. Long, compact, distinctive, dumbbell-shaped clusters. Medium to large, non-slipskin, firm, meaty grapes; red to quite blue, depending on conditions. High sugar content; even sweet while green. High quality dessert variety; makes an acceptable white wine. Keeps well in cold storage. Some susceptibility to downy mildew. Ripens 21-30 days before Concord, usually in early September. Hardy to -30 degrees F. Needs winter protection in the far North. Berries are small initially, but vigor, crop and size improve once established. Developed by Elmer Swenson and introduced by the University of Minnesota in 1980. *Source History: 10 in 1988; 15 in 1992; 16 in 2000.* **Sources: BA14, Bu7, CR6, Ed2, Ed5, Fa1, Fed, Fo3, Jun, La5, Rai, Rom, Sc6, SH8, Stl, Wa16.**

Swenson White - American; *Vitis Labrusca.* White grape with excellent fruity flavor. Tender pulp. Very vigorous. Ripens early. Hardy to Zone 5, possibly colder. *Source History: 1 in 2000.* **Sources: Rom.**

Sylvaner (Sylvaner B8) - European; *Vitis vinifera.* White wine grape. Popular commercial variety grown in France and Germany since medieval times. Ripens very early. Shows susceptibility to powdery mildew in hotter climates. Extensive rainy weather during ripening can cause splitting. *Source History: 1 in 1992; 3 in 2000.* **Sources: Bu7, Fo8, So6.**

Symphony - U.S. Plant Patent No. 5013. *Source History: 1 in 1988; 2 in 1992; 2 in 2000.* **Sources: Fo8, So6.**

Tannat - Red fruited variety. *Source History: 1 in 1992; 2 in 2000.* **Sources: Fo8, So6.**

Tara - High yields of good size bronze fruit. Very vigorous. 17% sugar. Cold hardy. Dry scar. Self-fertile. Ripens early to midseason. *Source History: 3 in 2000.* **Sources: Iso, Par, Ty2.**

Teleki - *Source History: 1 in 2000.* **Sources: Fo8.**

Thompson Seedless - European; *Vitis vinifera.* Famous white seedless variety. Large clusters. Medium size, very sweet, pale green to golden fruit. Delicious, high quality table grape. Good for all uses, especially raisins. Strong, vigorous vines. Self-fruitful. Thin the clusters for larger berries. Needs plenty of heat. Does best in low humidity areas. Ripens in August or September depending on location. Requires 100 hours of chilling. Also good in long season areas of the Northwest. Grows best in Zones 7-9. Developed in Yuba City, California. *Source History: 11 in 1988; 20 in 1992; 18 in 2000.* **Sources: Bay, CO5, Fo8, GR26, Gur, HI10,**

Iso, ME3, MI5, MO10, ORA, Pe2, SIM, So6, STR, Ty2, WI4, Wom.

Thompson, Super - *Source History: 1 in 1988; 1 in 1992; 1 in 2000.* **Sources: STR.**

Thomuscat - Table grape. *Source History: 2 in 1992; 2 in 2000.* **Sources: Fo8, So6.**

Thornton - American; *Vitis Labrusca.* Seedless white grape. Table and raisin variety. Ripens very early. *Source History: 1 in 2000.* **Sources: Rom.**

Tinta Amarela - Red fruited variety. *Source History: 1 in 1992; 2 in 2000.* **Sources: Fo8, So6.**

Tinta Cao - Red fruited variety. *Source History: 1 in 1992; 2 in 2000.* **Sources: Fo8, So6.**

Tinto Madeira - Red fruited variety. *Source History: 1 in 1992; 2 in 2000.* **Sources: Fo8, So6.**

Tocai Friulano - *Source History: 1 in 1992; 1 in 2000.* **Sources: Fo8.**

Tokay (Flame Tokay) - European; *Vitis vinifera.* Large, oval, pale red to dark red fruit. Crackling, crisp flesh. Suitable for table use and for wine. Best quality where nights are cool and summer daytime temperatures are moderately hot (90-95 degrees F.). Self-fertile. Ripens in August or September depending on location. Requires 100 hours of chilling. Gillet introduction. *Source History: 6 in 1988; 5 in 1992; 2 in 2000.* **Sources: Fo8, So6.**

Tokay Seedless - Table variety. *Source History: 1 in 1992; 2 in 2000.* **Sources: Fo8, So6.**

Topsail - Muscadine; *Vitis rotundifolia.* Medium to small clusters. Large, greenish bronze fruit. Medium to thick skin. Excellent quality, but low in acid. Vigorous vine; good persistence. Female; requires pollination. Good variety for home vineyards. Ripens midseason. *Source History: 1 in 1988; 1 in 2000.* **Sources: WA8.**

Totmur (Baco 2-16) - French; *Vitis vinifera.* White wine grape. Very early ripening. *Source History: 1 in 2000.* **Sources: Rom.**

Touriga - Red fruited variety. *Source History: 1 in 1992; 2 in 2000.* **Sources: Fo8, So6.**

Traminer - White fruited variety. *Source History: 1 in 1992; 2 in 2000.* **Sources: Fo8, So6.**

Traminette (GF 151) - French; *Vitis vinifera.* Parentage includes Gewurztraminer. Medium size amber berries. Low acidity, smooth and lingering aftertaste. White fruit used for wine. Moderate resistance to powdery mildew. Hardy to -15 degrees F. Ripens late-midseason with Concord. *Source History: 3 in 2000.* **Sources: Do7, Fo3, Mi1.**

Trebiano Toscano - White fruited variety. *Source History: 1 in 1992; 2 in 2000.* **Sources: Fo8, So6.**

Triumph - Bronze muscadine; *Vitis rotundifolia.* Large clusters; dry scar. Large, greenish bronze grapes with thin skin. Good quality. Excels in plant growth and fruit set. Medium production. Self-fertile. Excellent pollinator. Recommended for home or commercial use. Ripens mid-late September. Developed by the Georgia Agricultural Experiment Station. *Source History: 5 in 1988; 9 in 1992; 3 in 2000.* **Sources: Iso, Ju2, La3.**

Trollhaugen - MN 78 x Venus. Formerly E .S. 3-22-18. Blue-black berry with slightly larger fruit and bunch size. Seedless. Nice flavor. Elmer Swenson introduction named for Elmer's Norwegian heritage and hilly Wisconsin location. Zone 4a. *Source History: 1 in 1992; 1 in 2000.* **Sources: La5.**

Troubadour - E. S. 283 x (*Vitis riparia* x Merlot) x (*V. riparia* x Chambourcin). Medium loose clusters of small berries. Makes an excellent red wine in spite of high acid content and late maturity. Extremely vigorous, hardy and healthy vine. Zone 3b. *Source History: 1 in 2000.* **Sources: La5.**

Trousseau - Red fruited variety. *Source History: 2 in 2000.* **Sources: Fo8, So6.**

Utah Giant - European; *Vitis vinifera.* Red table grape. Early ripening. *Source History: 1 in 2000.* **Sources: Rom.**

Valdepenas (Tempranillo) - Red fruited variety. *Source History: 1 in 1992; 2 in 2000.* **Sources: Fo8, So6, So6.**

Valiant - American; *Vitis Labrusca.* Super-hardy grape bred by Dr. Ron Peterson at the University of South Dakota. Cross between Fredonia and a wild grape from Montana. Small, blue, slipskin fruit similar to Beta; matures earlier, has improved quality, not quite as hardy. Borne in compact 4" clusters. Sweet flavor is mildly Concord type; rich and tangy without a trace of tartness. Quality is quite good. Blue juice grape; also good for table use or wine. Ripens at least 30 days before Concord, usually in late August or early September. Has withstood -50 degrees F in Manitoba, Canada without damage. Introduced in 1982. Patented. *Source History: 8 in 1988; 15 in 1992; 12 in 2000.* **Sources: BA14, CR6, Do7, Ed5, Fed, Fi1, Fo3, Pe3, Rom, SH8, Stl, Wa16.**

Van Buren (President Van Buren) - American; *Vitis Labrusca.* Fredonia x Worden. Concord type. Large, compact, uniform size, well formed clusters. Medium size, deep purplish black berries. Sweet, fine flavor. Mainly a table grape; acid is too low for best processing. Vine has outstanding vigor and productivity. Grows well even on poor soil. Growth starts late in the spring, so it is seldom injured by spring frosts. Must be protected against mildew. Ripens 21-28 days before Concord. Hardy to -20 degrees F. Introduced in 1935. *Source History: 11 in 1988; 4 in 1992; 7 in 2000.* **Sources: Bea, Do7, ME3, Mi1, Rom, Sc6, We4.**

Vanessa (GF 136) - American; *Vitis Labrusca.* Seneca x NY 45910. Bunches are medium size, loose to well filled. Firm, oval, medium size, seedless, deep red fruit. Crisp, firm flesh; adherent skin. Flavor is similar to Seneca, one of the parents. Vine is vigorous, moderately hardy, moderately productive. Ripens early; mid-September. Hardy to -5 degrees F. Developed at Niveland, Ontario. Introduced in 1984. *Source History: 3 in 1988; 6 in 1992; 18 in 2000.* **Sources: Ba8, Ba8, Bos, Bu7, Cla, Do7, Ed5, Fo3, HA12, Mi1, Or2, Pe3, Rai, Rom, Sc6, Sh2, So5, We4.**

Ventura - American; *Vitis Labrusca.* Fruit is much like Elvira, but more resistant to cracking and spoilage. Pleasant, fruity, white wine, similar to Elvira. Ripens late-midseason. Introduced in 1974. *Source History: 1 in 1988; 1 in 2000.* **Sources: Rom.**

Venus (Venus Seedless) - American; *Vitis Labrusca.* Medium to large, well filled clusters. Large, seedless, bluish black fruit is larger than Concord. Sweet, crispy flesh. Flavor from slight muscat to just foxy. Good for preserves, jellies, wine and fresh eating. Main flaw is that in some conditions it has reportedly developed partly hardened seeds instead of being totally seedless. Very vigorous; good productivity. Disease resistant; holds well on the vine. Resistant to cracking. Ripens early-mid July to mid-August depending on location. Hardy in Zones 5-8. Developed by the Arkansas Agricultural Experiment Station. Patented. *Source History: 14 in 1988; 23 in 1992; 17 in 2000.* **Sources: Ba8, Ba8, Bay, Bu7, Co12, Do7, Fo3, Jo3, ME3, Or2, Pe3, Po2, Rai, Rom, Tex, Wel, Wom.**

Verdelet (Seibel 9110) - French; *Vitis vinifera*. Very large, loose, well formed bunches. Exceptionally beautiful, large, egg-shaped, whitish or grey-yellow to yellow-gold, dessert-type grape. Crisp, meaty texture with tender, adherent skin. Flavor is good, neutral and pleasingly sweet. Used to make a fragrant, delicate, clear white wine. Vine may not be fully hardy under extreme conditions. Needs some protection from severe winters. Short cane pruning. Should not be allowed to overproduce. Grapes hang on vines from 2-4 weeks after ripening. Ripens midseason. Hardy to -5 degrees F. *Source History: 8 in 1988; 5 in 1992; 3 in 2000.* **Sources: Fo3, Rom, Wom.**

Verdelho - White fruited variety. *Source History: 1 in 1992; 2 in 2000.* **Sources: Fo8, So6.**

Vernaccia - White fruited variety. *Source History: 1 in 1992; 2 in 2000.* **Sources: Fo8, So6.**

Vidal Blanc (Vidal 256) - Hybrid of Trebbiano, the Italian white Chianti grape, which it resembles in both wine and vine. Medium to very large, compact clusters. Small, white grapes. Its wine has a good aroma. Vine is a vigorous, moderately hardy, heavy producer. Mildew resistant. Foliage sometimes shows spots of mite damage which, however, are self healing. Ripens late. Hardy to -5 degrees F. Originated in the French Cognac district. *Source History: 4 in 1988; 4 in 1992; 6 in 2000.* **Sources: Bos, Do7, Fo3, In5, Pe3, Rom.**

Vignoles (Ravat 51) - French; *Vitis vinifera*. Cluster is very tight, quite susceptible to botrytis. White fruit. Fine, white, high acid wine; German style. Vine is medium productive. Appears to have good winter hardiness; has withstood temperatures to -5 degrees F. *Source History: 2 in 1988; 2 in 1992; 3 in 2000.* **Sources: Do7, Fo3, Pe3.**

Villard Blanc (Seyve-Villard 12-375) - French; *Vitis vinifera*. Large, loose, compound clusters up to 5 pounds. White to golden fruits. Fine flavor of *vinifera*, like Thompson Seedless, with disease resistance of American grapes. Outstanding table grape; good for wine. Remarkably vigorous vines; regular producer. Requires spur pruning. Resistant to Pierce's disease. Does best in areas and seasons of low humidity. Not for short season areas, but otherwise widely adapted. Highly recommended for all Eastern states. Best of the French types for the lower South. Hardy in Zones 6-9. *Source History: 7 in 1988; 7 in 1992; 5 in 2000.* **Sources: Ed2, Fo3, Leu, Rom, Wom.**

Villard Noir (Seyve-Villard 18-315) - French; *Vitis vinifera*. Bluish black fruits. Heavy bodied, sound, neutral, very good red wine. Vine has low vigor, but is a heavy producer. Spur pruning. Disease resistant. Most widely grown red wine hybrid in southern France. Well adapted in America in all but short season areas. Ripens late. Quite hardy. *Source History: 3 in 1988; 3 in 1992; 1 in 2000.* **Sources: Fo3.**

Vincent - American; *Vitis Labrusca*. Medium size, dark blue fruit. Wine has a heavy red color; excellent quality. Ripens late-midseason. Released by the Horticultural Research Institute of Ontario at Vineland, Canada. Introduced in 1967. *Source History: 1 in 1988; 1 in 2000.* **Sources: Do7.**

Vineland (71121) - American; *Vitis Labrusca*. Table grape with unusual orange color. Neutral flavor. *Source History: 1 in 2000.* **Sources: Rom.**

Viognier - White fruited variety. *Source History: 2 in 1992; 3 in 2000.* **Sources: Fo8, So6, Wi21.**

Volga Dawn (Muscadelle) - European; *Vitis vinifera*. Supposededly a Russian hybrid. Very large white berries. Ripens late. *Source History: 1 in 2000.*

Sources: Rom.

Welder - Muscadine; *Vitis rotundifolia*. Medium size, very sweet, bronze fruit. Excellent quality. Good for fresh eating; one of the best for wine. Vigorous vine; good production. Recommended for home and commercial plantings and fresh fruit sales. Proven to be the best variety for partial shade. Ripens early. Hardy in Zones 8-9. *Source History: 2 in 1988; 3 in 1992; 1 in 2000.* **Sources: Ju2.**

White Riesling (J. Riesling, Riesling) - European; *Vitis vinifera*. International favorite from Germany. Small to medium, round greenish yellow speckled fruits. Aromatic, lively flavor. Makes a classic, flowery, semisweet to sweet white wine. Self-fruitful. Ripens late. Requires 100 hours of chilling. Needs 2,000-2,500 growing degree days. One of the hardiest white wine grapes for cool regions. Does best in cooler areas. Most consistent of the white wine varieties tested for the central Washington area. Gillet introduction. *Source History: 16 in 1988; 13 in 1992; 7 in 2000.* **Sources: Do7, FAI, Fo3, Fo8, ME3, So6, WI4.**

Wild Grape (Riverbank Grape, Frost Grape) - *Vitis riparia*. Wild grape of North Central North America. Small, very high acid, dark blue berries. Hardy in Zone 4. *Source History: 1 in 1988; 3 in 1992; 2 in 2000.* **Sources: Fo2, No2.**

Wild Grape, Western (California Wild Grape) - *Vitis californica*. Clusters of purple fruit which is delicious raw and used for jelly and wine. Stout vines to 30'. Hardy in Zone 7. *Source History: 3 in 1992; 4 in 2000.* **Sources: Co24, Fo2, Lar, Las.**

Wilder - American; *Vitis Labrusca*. Blue skinned table grape. Female flowers. Midseason ripening. *Source History: 1 in 2000.* **Sources: Rom.**

Worden - American; *Vitis Labrusca*. Open-pollinated seedling of Concord. Slip-skin fruit is larger and blacker than Concord. Excellent for juice, fresh eating and jelly making. Grapes hang onto the stem better than Fredonia but are not quite as sweet. Practically immune to insects and diseases. Equals Concord's yields; hardier and more vigorous grower. Almost never needs winter protection. Ripens early to mid-September. Hardy to -50 degrees F. with occasional winter injury. *Source History: 4 in 1988; 9 in 1992; 11 in 2000.* **Sources: BA14, Do7, Ed5, Fed, Fo3, Mi1, Pe3, Rom, Sc6, SH8, Stl.**

Yates - American; *Vitis Labrusca*. Mills x Ontario. Large, conical, medium compact clusters. Medium to large, attractive, medium red fruit. Juicy, melting, pure, sweet, pleasing flavor. Mainly used as a table grape. Vigorous, productive vines. Ripens late. Hardy to -10 degrees F. Developed at the New York State Agricultural Experiment Station in Geneva. Introduced in 1937. *Source History: 3 in 1988; 2 in 1992; 1 in 2000.* **Sources: Jo3.**

Zinfandel - European; *Vitis vinifera*. Medium size, round, juicy, reddish black fruit. Used to make fruity red wines. Moderately vigorous; very productive. Self-fruitful. Heavy bearing. Prefers mild winters and cool summers. Ripens during August. Requires 100 hours of chilling. *Source History: 7 in 1988; 8 in 1992; 9 in 2000.* **Sources: Bay, CO5, FAI, Fo8, ME3, Pa2, So6, STR, WI4.**

Grape Rootstock

Vitis spp.

039-16 - Patented. *Source History: 2 in 1992; 2 in 2000.* **Sources: Fo8, So6.**

043-43 - Patented. *Source History: 1 in 1992; 1 in 2000.* **Sources: Fo8.**

Cosmo 2 - *Source History: 1 in 1992; 1 in 2000.* **Sources: Fo8.**

Cosmo 10 - *Source History: 1 in 1992; 1 in 2000.* **Sources: Fo8.**

Couderc 161-49 - *Source History: 2 in 2000.* **Sources: Fo8, So6.**

Couderc 1202 - *Source History: 1 in 1992; 1 in 2000.* **Sources: Fo8.**

Couderc 1613 - *Source History: 1 in 1988; 2 in 1992; 1 in 2000.* **Sources: Fo8.**

Couderc 1616 - *Source History: 1 in 1992; 2 in 2000.* **Sources: Fo8, So6.**

Couderc 3306 - *Source History: 2 in 1992; 1 in 2000.* **Sources: Fo8.**

Couderc 3309 (C-3309, 3309) - *Source History: 3 in 1988; 4 in 1992; 3 in 2000.* **Sources: Fo8, So6, Wi21.**

Dog Ridge - Resistant to nematodes and root rot. Offered as rootstock only; fruit is undesirable. *Source History: 1 in 1988; 3 in 1992; 4 in 2000.* **Sources: Fo8, So6, Wga, Wom.**

Foex 333 EM - *Source History: 1 in 1992; 1 in 2000.* **Sources: Fo8.**

Freedom - *Source History: 1 in 1988; 2 in 1992; 2 in 2000.* **Sources: Fo8, So6.**

Gloire - *Vitis riparia. Source History: 1 in 2000.* **Sources: Wi21.**

Harmony - *Source History: 1 in 1988; 2 in 1992; 2 in 2000.* **Sources: Fo8, So6.**

Kober 5BB - *Source History: 2 in 1992; 2 in 2000.* **Sources: Fo8, So6.**

Kober 125AA - *Source History: 1 in 1992; 1 in 2000.* **Sources: Fo8.**

LN 33 - *Source History: 1 in 1992; 1 in 2000.* **Sources: Fo8.**

M.G. 101-14 - *Source History: 1 in 1992; 1 in 2000.* **Sources: So6.**

M.G. 420A - *Source History: 1 in 1992; 1 in 2000.* **Sources: So6.**

Maleque 44-53 - *Source History: 2 in 1992; 2 in 2000.* **Sources: Fo8, So6.**

Millardet et de Grasset 41B - *Source History: 1 in 1992; 1 in 2000.* **Sources: Fo8.**

Millardet et de Grasset 101-14 - *Source History: 1 in 1992; 1 in 2000.* **Sources: Fo8.**

Millardet et de Grasset 125-1 - *Source History: 1 in 2000.* **Sources: Fo8.**

Millardet et de Grasset 219A - *Source History: 1 in 2000.* **Sources: Fo8.**

Millardet et de Grasset 420A - *Source History: 1 in 1992; 1 in 2000.* **Sources: Fo8.**

Paulsen 779 - *Source History: 2 in 1992; 1 in 2000.* **Sources: Fo8.**

Paulsen 1045 - *Source History: 2 in 1992; 1 in 2000.* **Sources: Fo8.**

Paulsen 1103 - *Source History: 2 in 1992; 2 in 2000.* **Sources: Fo8, So6.**

Prosperi Super - *Source History: 1 in 2000.* **Sources: So6.**

Richter 99 - *Source History: 1 in 1992; 2 in 2000.* **Sources: Fo8, So6.**

Richter 110R - *Source History: 2 in 1992; 3 in 2000.* **Sources: Fo8, So6, Wi21.**

Riperia Gloire - *Source History: 1 in 2000.* **Sources: So6.**

Ruggeri 140 - *Source History: 2 in 1992; 2 in 2000.* **Sources: Fo8, So6.**

Ruggeri 225 - *Source History: 2 in 1992; 1 in 2000.* **Sources: Fo8.**

Salt Creek (Ramsey) - *Source History: 1 in 1992; 2 in 2000.* **Sources: Fo8, So6.**

Schwarzmann - *Source History: 1 in 2000.* **Sources: So6.**

SO4 (Oppenheim No. 4) - *Source History: 2 in 1988; 2 in 1992; 2 in 2000.* **Sources: So6, Wi21.**

St. George 15 - *Source History: 1 in 1988; 2 in 1992; 1 in 2000.* **Sources: So6.**
Tampa - *Source History: 2 in 1992; 1 in 2000.* **Sources: Wga.**
Teleki 5C - *Source History: 1 in 1988; 2 in 1992; 3 in 2000.* **Sources: Fo8, So6, Wi21.**

Huckleberry

Vaccinium spp.

Bear Lake No. 4 - *Vaccinium ovalifolium.* Erect shrub to 3'. Small to medium size fruit; black when ripe. Excellent flavor. Ripens in August. Seed from Bear Lake in Rocky Mountain National Park, Colorado. *Source History: 1 in 2000.* **Sources: HA12.**

Dwarf Huckleberry - *Vaccinium caespitosum.* Low, deciduous thicket bears large luscious berries. Native of the Northwest mountains. *Source History: 1 in 2000.* **Sources: Co24.**

Evergreen (California Huckleberry, Box Blueberry) - *Vaccinium ovatum.* Delicious, dark bluish black berries. Tart and flavorful. Can be eaten and prepared like the cultivated blueberry. Compact, shrub grows 6-8' in the shade; only 2-3' in the sun. New growth in spring is coppery red; slow growing when young. Small, glossy, dark green leaves. Drooping, bell-like, pink flowers. Does better in shady areas; can take full sun in cool summer regions. Seems to favor an edge-of-the-woods type environment. Native from British Columbia to northern California and slightly south. Hardy in Zone 6-8. *Source History: 7 in 1988; 9 in 1992; 20 in 2000.* **Sources: Abu, BA9, BO10, BR2, Bu7, Ca12, Clo, Co24, Fo2, Fro, Gr16, Lar, Las, No2, On3, Or2, Rai, VIR, Wbn, We4.**

Jenny Lake No. 1 - *Vaccinium ovalifolium.* Erect shrub grows 3' tall. Fruits are black when ripe; size ranges from 65-120 berries per cup. Excellent flavor is distinctly wild. Ripens in August. Seed from Jenny Lake in the Grand Teton National Park, Wyoming. *Source History: 1 in 2000.* **Sources: HA12.**

Low Growing Mountain Huckleberry - *Vaccinium deliciosum.* Dark blue fruit. Productive bush grows less that 1' tall with fiery red fall color. Ripens late summer. Native to the sub-alpine meadows of the Cascade and Olympic mountains. *Source History: 1 in 2000.* **Sources: Rai.**

Red Huckleberry - *Vaccinium parvifolium.* Small, attractive, .4" diameter, bright red berries. Tangy flavor. Good for making pie or jelly. Deciduous bush is attractive throughout the year; grows 3-5' tall. Produces large crops. Pinkish white flowers. Native from Alaska to California. Hardy in Zone 6. *Source History: 5 in 1988; 6 in 1992; 7 in 2000.* **Sources: Abu, Bu7, Co24, Fo2, Fro, No2, Rai.**

Tall Mountain - *Vaccinium ovalifolium.* Grows into a 3-6' bush with oval leaves. Purple-black tasty fruit. Ripens in August. Zones 4-8. Pacific NW coastal to sub-alpine native. *Source History: 1 in 2000.* **Sources: Rai.**

Thin-Leaf Huckleberry (Blue Huckleberry, Mountain Huckleberry) - *Vaccinium membranaceum.* Small, sweet, aromatic, black berries. Deciduous shrub grows 4' tall. Beautiful scarlet fall color. Native from Ontario and Michigan, westward to British Columbia and southward to northern California. *Source History: 4 in 1988; 3 in 1992; 4 in 2000.* **Sources: Fo2, NA5, No2, Pl5.**

Thunderbird Evergreen - Grows 5-6' tall. New spring foliage is red-bronze. Pink flowers followed by edible purple fruit. Patented clone. *Source History: 1 in 2000.* **Sources: Bu7.**

Kiwi

Actinidia spp.

Actinidia arguta (Arctic Kiwi, Bower Actinidia, Hardy Kiwi, Siberian Gooseberry, Tara Vine, Yang-Tao) - Female and male plants available. Smooth, thin skinned, 1" lime-green fruit on the female; no peeling needed; very sweet; several times more vitamin C than citrus. Keeps 2-3 months when picked firm-ripe and refrigerated. Grape-like, deciduous vine grows vigorously 30-50' long. Fruit hangs below dark green foliage and falls when ripe. Fragrant, inconspicuous, white flowers; susceptible to late frosts. Long-lived; produces for 60 years. Bears in 3-4 years. One male pollinates 6-8 females within 50'. No disease or insect problems. Ripens in late summer. Hardy to -25 degrees F. Native to temperate eastern Asia. *Source History: 25 in 1988; 20 in 1992; 28 in 2000.* **Sources: BO10, Bu7, Clo, Co12, Fi1, Gr16, Gur, Hid, Ju2, Kiw, Me2, Mel, Mi1, On3, Or2, Pa2, Par, Pu2, Sc2, Sh14, Shu, Son, Tri, Wa3, We4, We8, Wh3, Wh4.**

A. arguta: 74-08 - Female. Firm, eliptical fruit; above average in size. Excellent flavor. Productive and adaptable. Requires pollinator. Ripens in the fall. One of the best of the 74 series. *Source History: 3 in 1988; 2 in 1992; 2 in 2000.* **Sources: Kiw, Tri.**

A. arguta: 74-32 - Used as a pollinator. Zone 5. *Source History: 1 in 2000.* **Sources: Ed5, HA12.**

A. arguta: 74-46 - Male. Used as one of the pollinators in the 74 series. Hardy to Zone 4. *Source History: 2 in 1988; 2 in 1992; 2 in 2000.* **Sources: Ha12, Kiw.**

A. arguta: 74-49 - Female. Large, smooth, round fruit. Aromatic, distinctive, sweet flavor. Ripens in the fall. Zones 5b-7b. Several of these numbered varieties were brought to Virginia from a closed experiment station at Chico, California. They were selected for their productivity and fruit quality and have proven to be vigorous and reliable producers in Virginia. Zones 5-8. *Source History: 4 in 1988; 4 in 1992; 7 in 2000.* **Sources: Ed2, Gr16, HA12, Kiw, Me2, On3, Tri.**

A. arguta: 74-55 - Female. Sweet, medium-large, round fruit. Vigorous, fast growing vine; can be grown like grapes. Abundant producer. Requires pollinator. Ripens in the fall. Tested in New Hampshire and upper New York State where they survived -25 degree F. *Source History: 4 in 1988; 2 in 1992; 3 in 2000.* **Sources: Ha12, Kiw, Tri.**

A. arguta: 119-40 - Self-fertile. Will pollinate other females. *Source History: 2 in 2000.* **Sources: Kiw, Pu2.**

A. arguta: 119-40-B - Self-fertile (monoecious) *arguta* from the Arnold Arboretum. Vigorous grower with large, waxy leaves. Will pollinate other *argutas*. Hardy to Zone 5a-7b. *Source History: 2 in 1988; 4 in 1992; 4 in 2000.* **Sources: Ed5, HA12, Me2, Tri.**

A. arguta: 124-40 - Female selected by the USDA in the 1950s for fruit. Large growing vine. 127-40 can be used for pollination. Hardy to Zone 4. *Source History: 1 in 1988; 2 in 1992; 1 in 2000.* **Sources: Me2.**

A. arguta: 125-40 - Female. Large fruit. Vigorous grower. USDA selection. Hardy to Zone 4. *Source History: 2 in 1988; 3 in 1992; 1 in 2000.* **Sources: Me2.**

A. arguta: 127-40 - Male. Used as a pollinator for both 124-40 and 125-40 females. Hardy to Zone 4. *Source History: 1 in 1988; 2 in 1992; 2 in 2000.* **Sources: Kiw, Me2.**

A. arguta: 753-C - Plant obtained from the National Arboretum, but received from the U.S. Plant Inspection Station in Maryland. *Source History: 1 in 1988; 2 in 1992; 1 in 2000.* **Sources: Me2.**

A. arguta: 40537-C - Another plant from the National Arboretum. *Source History: 1 in 1988; 2 in 1992; 1 in 2000.* **Sources: Me2.**

A. arguta: Akin 3 - Female; hardy seedling. Round fruit; larger than Anna. *Source History: 1 in 1988; 2 in 1992; 1 in 2000.* **Sources: Sh3.**

A. arguta: Alabama No. 1 - Male selection from Alabama. *Source History: 1 in 2000.* **Sources: Me2.**

A. arguta: Alabama No. 2 - Male selection from Alabama. *Source History: 1 in 2000.* **Sources: Me2.**

A. arguta: Ananasnaja (Ana, Anna, Anna Kiwi, Annasnaja, Manchurian Pineapple, Ananasnaya) - Female and male plants. Lime-shaped .75-1.5" fruit. Smooth, fuzzless skin; no peeling required. Very sweet, spicy, light green flesh. High in vitamins, phosphorous, calcium and iron; low in sodium, cholesterol and calories. Keeps 5-6 weeks in refrigerator. Vigorous, fast growing, twining vines must be trellised. Glossy, heart-shaped, bright green leaves. One male plant pollinates five females. Insect and disease resistant. Prefers a sunny spot protected from drying winds. Ripens in late September. Requires 800 hours of chilling. Survived -30 degrees F in Pontiac, Michigan. Brought from Belgium. Russian name means "pineapple-like." Introduced in 1972. *Source History: 22 in 1988; 20 in 1992; 23 in 2000.* **Sources: Bea, Bu1, Bu7, Clo, Ed2, Fa1, Fo4, Gr16, HA12, Hid, In5, Int, Kiw, Me2, On3, Or2, Pa2, Pu2, Rai, Sh2, Tri, We4, Wh3, Wh4.**

A. arguta: Cordifolia - Female. Sweet, round fruits. Low chill. Zones 5-9. *Source History: 1 in 1988; 2 in 1992; 5 in 2000.* **Sources: Ed5, HA12, Kiw, Me2, Pu2.**

A. arguta: Cordifolia, Meyer's - Round-shouldered fruit with non-bitter skin. Productive, rapidly growing vine. Proving to be one of the best flavored hardy kiwis. Zones 5-9. *Source History: 1 in 1992; 2 in 2000.* **Sources: Ed2, On3.**

A. arguta: Cornell - Male pollinator for other *A. arguta* cultivars. Can also be used to pollinate *A. callosa* and *A. purpurea*. *Source History: 1 in 1988; 3 in 2000.* **Sources: Kiw, Pu2, Tri.**

A. arguta: Dumbarton Oaks - Female and male plants are available. Excellent flavor. Zones 5a-7b. Old planting found in a garden in Georgetown, Washington, D.C. *Source History: 1 in 1988; 2 in 1992; 5 in 2000.* **Sources: Ed2, Ed5, HA12, Kiw, Tri.**

A. arguta: Geneva - Vigorous, productive vines produce medium to large fruit with excellent flavor. Zones 4-9. *Source History: 1 in 2000.* **Sources: Gr16.**

A. arguta: Geneva 1 - Female. Bears relatively small fruit about 1" long; comparable to Meader. Ripens rather late. Obtained from the New York State Agricultural Experiment Station in Geneva. Hardy to Zone 4. *Source History: 2 in 1988; 3 in 1992; 2 in 2000.* **Sources: Kiw, Me2.**

A. arguta: Geneva 2 - Female. Relatively small fruit about 1" long; good flavor; comparable to Meader. Large leaves. Ripens rather late. Good cold tolerance. Geneva 1 and Geneva 2 were both planted by George Slate in Geneva, New York. Hardy in Zone 4. *Source History: 3 in 1988; 4 in 1992; 4 in 2000.* **Sources: Kiw, Me2, Pu2, Tri.**

A. arguta: Geneva 3 - Female. Bears relatively small fruit about 1" long; comparable to Meader. Ripens rather late. *Source History: 1 in 1988; 1 in 1992; 1 in 2000.* **Sources: Tri.**

A. arguta: Geneva HH I - Female. Fast growing vine. Abundant bearer. Can be grown like grape vines. Survived -25 degrees F. in New Hampshire and upper New York State. *Source History: 1 in 1988; 1 in 1992; 2 in 2000.* **Sources: Ha12, On3.**

A. arguta: Geneva HH II - Female. Very similar in all respects to Geneva HH I. Should be pollinated with male Meader kiwi. Zones 5a-7b. *Source History: 1 in 1988; 1 in 2000.* **Sources: HA12.**

A. arguta: Hardy C-1 - Hardy to -25 degrees F. Prefers partial shade. Obtained from a large fruiting vine growing in China. *Source History: 1 in 2000.* **Sources: Pu2.**

A. arguta: Hardy C-2 - Hardy to -25 degrees F. Partial shade. Originated in China. *Source History: 1 in 2000.* **Sources: Pu2.**

A. arguta: Hardy C-3 - Hardy to -25 degrees F. Partial shade. Originated in China. *Source History: 1 in 2000.* **Sources: Pu2.**

A. arguta: Hardy C-4 - Hardy to -25 degrees F. Partial shade. Originated in China. *Source History: 1 in 2000.* **Sources: Pu2.**

A. arguta: Hardy C-5 - Hardy to -25 degrees F. Partial shade. Originated in China. *Source History: 1 in 2000.* **Sources: Pu2.**

A. arguta: Hardy Red - Vigorous vines bear large, cranberry-red fruit with a sweet-tart flavor. Ripens in October. Requires a pollinator. Zones 4-9. *Source History: 1 in 2000.* **Sources: Gr16.**

A. arguta: Issai - Self-fertile plant; monoecious. Oblong fruit up to 1.75" long; smooth, fuzzless, thin skin. Sweet flesh; high in vitamins and fiber. Keeps many weeks when refrigerated. Grape-like vines need support. Self-fertile; fruit set is increased when planted with an *A. arguta* male; fruit is seedless if not pollinated. Issai is often used as a fruit-producing pollinator. Produces second year. Less vigorous than Ananasnaja, so may escape spring frosts. Pest free; no spraying required. Thrives almost anywhere except in very wet soil. Lives up to 50 years; produces 100 lbs. per year at maturity. Dislikes full sun. Ripens late August. Requires 800 hours of chilling. Hardy in Zones 5-9. Japan. *Source History: 16 in 1988; 29 in 1992; 27 in 2000.* **Sources: Ban, Bay, Bu2, Bu7, BU12, Clo, Ed2, Fi1, Fo2, Ga6, Gr16, GR26, Gur, HA12, Kiw, Me2, Mel, MO10, On3, Or2, Pa2, Pu2, Son, St4, Tri, We4, Wh3, WI4.**

A. arguta: Jumbo - Italian variety with large elongated fruit averaging 1 oz. each. Sweet and tasty. Flavor is milder than that of Anna. Hardy in Zones 4-9. Requires a pollinator. *Source History: 5 in 2000.* **Sources: Clo, Gr16, On3, Or2, Rai.**

A. arguta: Kiev Male - Male pollinator from Ukraine. Necessary for fruit production for all varieties except Issai. Blooms at a young age. Trademarked. *Source History: 1 in 2000.* **Sources: On3.**

A. arguta: Meader - Female and male plants are available. Sweet, tasty, medium size fruit. Good pollinator for Ananasnaja. Apparently somewhat earlier ripening than the other selections; late August. Withstood -28 degrees F. in New Hampshire. Professor Elwyn Meader's name graces many fine plants. This is a tribute to his skill as a horticulturist and plant breeder. After nearly 20 years, this fine seedling variety was selected by him for its productivity and fine, medium size, sweet fruit. *Source History: 5 in 1988; 5 in 1992; 4 in 2000.* **Sources: HA12, Kiw, Me2, Tri.**

A. arguta: Michigan State (MSU) - Female. Good size fruit; excellent taste.

Plant was being grown at Michigan State University. Zones 5a-7b. *Source History:*
2 in 1988; 1 in 1992; 6 in 2000. **Sources: Ed2, HA12, Kiw, Me2, Sh3, Tri.**

A. arguta: National Arboretum 7 - One of a number of different *argutas*
found at the National Arboretum in Washington, D.C. Hardy to Zone 5. *Source
History: 1 in 1988; 2 in 1992; 1 in 2000.* **Sources: Ed2.**

A. arguta: No. 5 - Female. New selection from Virginia. Green fruit; color may
turn purplish in colder areas. Fruits midseason. Zones 5b-7b. *Source History: 1
in 2000.* **Sources: HA12.**

A. arguta: Opitz - Female. Fruit is borne in clusters. *Source History: 1 in 2000.*
Sources: Me2.

A. arguta: Rossana - Italian variety. Medium to large, light green fruit with red
blush. Sweet flavor with a hint of mint. Ripens early to mid-October. *Source History: 1 in 2000.* **Sources: On3.**

A. arguta: Rosy - Italian variety. Large fruit weighs up to 20 grams. Red-green
skin and flesh. Sweet and flavorful. Ripens mid to late September. *Source History: 1 in 2000.* **Sources: On3.**

A. arguta: West - Original name has been lost. Near-bush plant bears many
fruit. *Source History: 1 in 2000.* **Sources: Me2.**

Actinidia callosa - Female. Egg-shaped, white fruit with brown spots. Narrow
leaves like *A. melanandra*. White flowers. *Source History: 1 in 1988; 2 in 1992; 3
in 2000.* **Sources: Me2, Pu2, Tri.**

Actinidia chinensis - Male. Heavy spring bloomer. Flowers earlier than the
Matua male. Hardy to 5 degrees F. Tolerates full sun. *Source History: 3 in 2000.*
Sources: BO10, Me2, Pu2, Sh14.

A. chinensis: Canton Red - Female; male vines unknown. Tolerates full sun.
Hardy to 5 degrees F. *Source History: 1 in 2000.* **Sources: Pu2.**

A. chinensis: First Emperor - Female; male vines unknown. Tolerates full sun.
Hardy to 5 degrees F. *Source History: 1 in 2000.* **Sources: Pu2.**

A. chinensis: Orange - Female. Fruit is more round than the yellow variety.
Flesh is more yellow than orange. Very prolific. Sweetest of the three colored *A.
chinensis*. *Source History: 1 in 2000.* **Sources: Me2, Pu2.**

A. chinensis: Red - Female. Fruit is shaped like Hayward. Flesh is yellow
throughout with occasional streaks of red color. *Source History: 1 in 2000.*
Sources: Me2.

A. chinensis: Yellow - Female. Large fruit with bright yellow flesh with no
green. Claimed to be more tart of the three colored *A. chinensis*. *Source History:
1 in 2000.* **Sources: Me2.**

Actinidia chrysantha - Tetraploid with yellow or golden flowers. Hairless,
spotted fruit. *Source History: 2 in 2000.* **Sources: Me2, Pu2.**

Actinidia deliciosa (Chinese Gooseberry, Kiwi Berry, Yang-Tao) - Female and
male plants are available. Fuzzy, brown skinned fruit. Beautiful emerald-green
flesh. Mild, gooseberry-like flavor. Excellent eating quality. Keeps in the refrigerator for up to four months; keeps at room temperature for two weeks. Large vine.
Plants of both sexes must be grown to secure fruit. Prefers well drained, moist soil
and full to partial sun. Ripens in late October. Hardy in Zones 7-9. Native to the
Yellow Mountains of China. *Source History: 10 in 1988; 9 in 1992; 6 in 2000.*
Sources: Ban, Gr16, Mel, On3, Rai, WI4.

A. deliciosa: Abbott - Female. Medium size, oblong fruit with dense hair.
Good flavor. Vigorous vine. Early flowering variety that sets heavy yields. *Source*

History: 2 in 1988; 2 in 1992; 2 in 2000. **Sources: Me2, Pu2.**

A. *deliciosa*: All-Purpose Male - Vigorous vine does not bear fruit. Can pollinate up to eight Hayward females. *Source History: 1 in 2000.* **Sources: Bay.**

A. *deliciosa*: Allison - Almost identical to Abbott. Prolific producer of small to medium size fruit in low chill areas. *Source History: 2 in 1992; 1 in 2000.* **Sources: Me2.**

A. *deliciosa*: Blake - Self-fertile plant; monoecious. Small to medium size fruit that ends in a point. Very large leaves. Ripens six weeks before Hayward. Requires 500-800 hours of chilling. *Source History: 2 in 1988; 8 in 1992; 2 in 2000.* **Sources: Me2, Pu2.**

A. *deliciosa*: Bruno - Female. Long, brown, cylindrical fruit. Favored by the Japanese for its excellent taste. Best for processing. Early flowering variety. *Source History: 1 in 1988; 3 in 1992; 2 in 2000.* **Sources: Me2, MIS.**

A. *deliciosa*: California - Male; produces no fruit. Sturdy, deciduous vines take up little space; require sturdy support. Almost no disease or pest problems. Plant in well drained, rich soil. Begins bearing in 3-5 years and will continue for up to 40 years. Widely used in California to pollinate the Hayward female. One male vine can pollinate up to eight females. Requires 800 hours of chilling. Hardy to 10 degrees F. Introduced from East Asia by Burbank. First planted in Chico, California. *Source History: 7 in 1988; 5 in 1992; 2 in 2000.* **Sources: Clo, Pu2.**

A. *deliciosa*: Cambridge - Claimed to be self-fruitful; not yet proven in southern California. Originated in England. *Source History: 1 in 1992; 1 in 2000.* **Sources: Me2.**

A. *deliciosa*: CC Early - Early male. Begins blooming in early February in southern California. If early growth is frozen, it recovers and reblooms throughout April and May. *Source History: 1 in 1992; 1 in 2000.* **Sources: Me2.**

A. *deliciosa*: Chico - Female and male plants are available. Requires 500-800 hours of chilling. *Source History: 3 in 1988; 5 in 1992; 2 in 2000.* **Sources: Pa2, Pu2.**

A. deliciosa: Dexter - Very early maturing, low chilling cultivar from the frost-free zone of coastal Australia near the Queensland-NSW border. *Source History: 2 in 1992; 1 in 2000.* **Sources: Me2.**

A. *deliciosa*: Elmwood - Female. Sweetly scented, silver dollar size blossoms. Best low chill variety consistently produces fruit up to 10 ounces each. *Source History: 1 in 1988; 2 in 1992; 2 in 2000.* **Sources: Me2, On3, Pu2.**

A. *deliciosa*: Gracie - Female. Fruit is elongated and distinctly tapers toward the stem end; more width and substance than Bruno. Low to medium chill requirement. Ripens 2-4 weeks ahead of Hayward. *Source History: 1 in 1988; 2 in 1992; 2 in 2000.* **Sources: Me2, Pu2.**

A. *deliciosa*: Hayward - Female. Standard commercial variety in grocery stores. Large, 3" fuzzy, brown fruit. Lime-green flesh with strawberry-like texture, tart taste, pungent aroma. Vine prefers well drained, rich soil; needs sturdy support. Blooms quite late. Pollinate with California male. Yields 70-120 pounds at maturity. Productive in warmer areas of maritime Northwest. Needs warm summers, winters above 5 degrees F., no late spring frosts or much fluctuation. Ripens late November. Requires 500-800 hours of chilling. Zones 8-9. Native to Tangtse River Valley in China; formerly called Chinese Gooseberry or Monkey Peach. Grown in New Zealand since 1906. *Source History: 19 in 1988; 17 in 1992; 9 in 2000.* **Sources: Bay, Bu7, Ju2, Me2, On3, Par, Pu2, We4, WI4.**

A. deliciosa: Koryoku - The sweetest true kiwifruit. First year fruit produced brix levels of 23-24% in ripened fruit. Winter chill requirements not yet determined. _Source History: 1 in 1992; 1 in 2000._ **Sources: Me2.**

A. deliciosa: Kramer - Superior cultivar best thought of as an improved Hayward. Seems to have low chill requirements. Originated in New Zealand. _Source History: 2 in 1992; 1 in 2000._ **Sources: Me2.**

A. deliciosa: M-56 - _Source History: 1 in 1992; 1 in 2000._ **Sources: Me2.**

A. deliciosa: Matsu - Male. Blooms over a longer period; overlaps different varieties. Very vigorous male vine that requires pruning. _Source History: 1 in 1988; 1 in 2000._ **Sources: Pu2.**

A. deliciosa: Matua - Midseason male from New Zealand. Requires 100 hours of chilling. _Source History: 2 in 1988; 4 in 1992; 3 in 2000._ **Sources: Me2, Pa2, Pu2.**

A. deliciosa: Monty - Female. Fruit size is similar to Abbott, but tapering to the stem. Vigorous vine. Late bloomer like Hayward, but has a tendency to overcrop. Low chill requirement. _Source History: 2 in 1988; 2 in 1992; 2 in 2000._ **Sources: Me2, Pu2.**

A. deliciosa: New Zealand Special - Prolific bloomer. _Source History: 1 in 2000._ **Sources: Me2.**

A. deliciosa: RM Special Early - Blooms about two weeks before Matua and Chico. _Source History: 1 in 1992; 1 in 2000._ **Sources: Me2.**

A. deliciosa: Saanichton - Female. Large fruit with fuzzy skin. Sweet, lime-green flesh. Long keeping variety. Vigorous plant; fuzz is vibrant red. Hardy to 10 degrees F.; when frozen out, the plant is usually damaged to ground level only. _Source History: 1 in 1988; 3 in 1992; 4 in 2000._ **Sources: Clo, Or2, Rai, Wh3.**

A. deliciosa: Saanichton 12 - Female. Large, fuzzy fruit. Sweet flesh. Well suited for the backyard grower and small orchardist. Plant has not been injured by winter temperatures that have damaged other varieties. Grown on Vancouver Island, British Columbia for over 30 years. _Source History: 1 in 1988; 4 in 1992; 4 in 2000._ **Sources: Bu7, Me2, On3, Pu2.**

A. deliciosa: Taiwan - Species uncertain. Seedling male from Taiwan. _Source History: 1 in 2000._ **Sources: Me2.**

A. deliciosa: Tewi - Female. Seedling of Hayward. Like Vincent, Tewi needs a shorter chilling time (100 hours or less). Selected in the Canary Islands. _Source History: 3 in 1988; 4 in 1992; 2 in 2000._ **Sources: Me2, Pa2.**

A. deliciosa: Tomuri - Male. Late flowering type; good pollinator for the Vincent and Hayward female. Requires 100 hours of chilling. Originated in New Zealand. _Source History: 6 in 1988; 5 in 1992; 7 in 2000._ **Sources: Bay, Me2, MO10, Pa2, Pu2, Son, WI4.**

A. deliciosa: Tropical - Emerald green, fuzzy fruit. Productive vines bear heavy crops. Disease and pest resistant. High vitamin C content. Plant one male to pollinate up to eight females. Hardy in Zones 7-10. _Source History: 1 in 1988; 1 in 1992; 1 in 2000._ **Sources: St4.**

A. deliciosa: Vincent - Female. Medium size, fuzzy fruit. Better fruit size if thinned at bloom. Mainly grown in southern California because the plant only needs 100 hours of chilling to produce fruit, compared to most varieties that need 600 hours. Hardy to Zone 7. Found in Orange County, California. _Source History: 4 in 1988; 8 in 1992; 7 in 2000._ **Sources: Bay, Gr16, Me2, MO10, Pa2, Son, WI4.**

Actinidia eriantha: Velvet Vine - Female. Leaves and stems have a velvety feel. Diploid. Originated in British Columbia, Canada from plant material originally obtained in Shanghai, China. *Source History: 1 in 1992; 2 in 2000.* **Sources: Me2, Pu2.**

Actinidia hemsleyana - Female. Less cold tolerant than *A. deliciosa*. Ornamental vine has crimson colored fuzz. Can be pollinated by *A. deliciosa* males. Fruit looks like a very fuzzy miniature *A. deliciosa* with green flesh. *Source History: 1 in 2000.* **Sources: Pu2.**

Actinidia kolomikta - Female and male plants are available. Small, smooth skinned fruits. Vine is not as vigorous as *A. arguta*; usually grows only 10-12' tall. Variegated foliage; tips of green leaves turn white and pink. Likes shade. Hardy to -40 degrees F. Should be considered for planting in the coldest parts of the U.S. Originated in Leningrad. Hardy in Zones 4-7. *Source History: 4 in 1988; 11 in 1992; 16 in 2000.* **Sources: Ca7, Clo, Ed2, Ed5, Fo2, Fra, Gos, Gr16, Hud, Kiw, Me2, On3, Sc2, Sh14, Tri, We4.**

A. kolomikta: Arctic Beauty - Female and male plants are available. High quality, .75" diameter, smooth skinned, emerald-green fruits the size of an extra large grape. Delicious, very sweet flavor; very high in Vitamin C. Often eaten fresh right off the vine. Attractive vine is not very vigorous; ideal for more confined locations. Very shade tolerant. Richly variegated leaves. Male plants are particularly striking with pink, white and green foliage. Ripens about September 1. Extremely hardy; known to survive -40 degrees F. in Siberia. *Source History: 5 in 1988; 17 in 1992; 16 in 2000.* **Sources: BO10, Bu7, BU12, Clo, Fi1, Gur, HA12, Int, Jun, Lin, Mel, Or2, Pa2, Rai, Sha, WI4.**

A. kolomikta: Aromatnaya - Female. Medium size fruit. Smooth skin. Green flesh. Ripe fruit has 20% sugar; medium vitamin C content. Productive vine. Diploid. Ripens from early to mid-August. Hardy to -40 degrees F. *Source History: 1 in 1988; 2 in 1992; 3 in 2000.* **Sources: On3, Pu2, Tri.**

A. kolomikta: Broadmoor - Male. Prefers well sheltered location with 50% shade. Hardy to -40 degrees F. *Source History: 1 in 2000.* **Sources: Pu2.**

A. kolomikta: Gil - Male. Prefers well sheltered location with 50% shade. Hardy to -40 degrees F. *Source History: 1 in 2000.* **Sources: Pu2.**

A. kolomikta: Krupnopladnaya - Female. Pineapple-kiwi flavored, smooth skinned fruit has 14% sugar when ripe; high in vitamin C. Very productive vines. Ripens in mid-August. Name means "large fruit" in Russian. Diploid. Zones 3-8. *Source History: 1 in 1988; 3 in 1992; 6 in 2000.* **Sources: Ed5, Kiw, On3, Pu2, Sha, Tri.**

A. kolomikta: Matovaya - Small to medium size fruit; 16% sugar. High vitamin C content. Ripens early to mid-August. *Source History: 2 in 1992; 1 in 2000.* **Sources: On3.**

A. kolomikta: Nahodka - Medium to large fruit; 15% sugar. Ripens mid-August. *Source History: 2 in 1992; 1 in 2000.* **Sources: On3.**

A. kolomikta: Northwoods - Male. Does best in 50% shade. Hardy to -40 degrees F. *Source History: 1 in 2000.* **Sources: Pu2.**

A. kolomikta: Oluyhckos - Female. Selected for its fruit; new from Russia. *Source History: 1 in 1988; 1 in 1992; 1 in 2000.* **Sources: Tri.**

A. kolomikta: Pautske - Large, high quality fruit. Selected in Lithuania by plant breeder, V. Pautske. *Source History: 2 in 1992; 2 in 2000.* **Sources: Kiw, Tri.**

A. kolomikta: Pavlovskaya - Female. Large fruit. Medium high in vitamin C; very productive vines. Ripens from early to mid-August. *Source History: 1 in 1988; 2 in 1992; 1 in 2000.* **Sources: Kiw.**

A. kolomikta: Pozdnjaja (Leningradskayd Pozdnjaja) - Female. Selected for fruit size and taste. Name translates "St. Petersburg Late." New from Russia. *Source History: 1 in 1988; 2 in 1992; 1 in 2000.* **Sources: Kiw.**

A. kolomikta: Red Beauty - Female. Tasty fruit the size of a raisin. Foliage shows a reddish cast in summer and becomes more attractive in autumn. Pollinate with Arctic Beauty. Hardy to -40 degrees F. Zones 3a-7b. *Source History: 1 in 2000.* **Sources: HA12.**

A. kolomikta: Sentyabraskaya (September) - Female. Medium to large, smooth fruit with green flesh. Medium vitamin C content; 18% sugar content when ripe. Productive vines. Diploid. Ripens in mid-August. Hardy to -40 degrees F. *Source History: 1 in 1988; 2 in 1992; 3 in 2000.* **Sources: On3, Pu2, Tri.**

A. kolomikta: Urazainaja - Female. Selected for fruit size. Just arrived from Russia. *Source History: 1 in 1988; 2 in 1992; 1 in 2000.* **Sources: Kiw.**

Actinidia latifolia - Diploid. *Source History: 1 in 2000.* **Sources: Me2.**

Actinidia macrosperma - Male used for pollinating females of this and other species. Vigorous and hardy. Originated in China. *Source History: 1 in 1988; 1 in 1992; 1 in 2000.* **Sources: Pu2.**

Actinidia melanandra - Female. Oval, 1.25" fruit. Tetraploid. Native to China. *Source History: 1 in 1988; 2 in 1992; 3 in 2000.* **Sources: Ban, Me2, Pu2.**

Actinidia polygama (Silver Vine) - Female and male plants. Exotic, plumb bob shaped, 1-1.5" yellowish orange fruit; cylindrical with point at base. Orange flesh with tiny brown seeds. Flavor is a cross between kiwi and ripe persimmon. Tasty when ripe, but not really the best eating fruit. Vigorous, ornamental vine. Sweet scented, creamy white flowers. Heart-shaped, variegated, fuzzy leaves are silvery white and sometimes yellowish. Leaves chemically similar to catnip. Bristly, hairy leafstalks. Partially self-fertile; best when cross-pollinated. Prefers full sun, but can grow in partial shade. Hardy to -20 degrees F. Native to temperate eastern Asia. *Source History: 4 in 1988; 3 in 1992; 4 in 2000.* **Sources: Kiw, Me2, Pu2, Sh14.**

A. polygama: Alabama Seedling - Non-climbing, bush-shaped plant. Developed at Alabama A and M. *Source History: 1 in 1992; 1 in 2000.* **Sources: Me2.**

Actinidia purpurea (Purple Fruited Kiwi) - Female. Like *A. arguta* but with purple fruit. Delicious sweet-tart flavor. Ripens in October. *Source History: 3 in 1992; 7 in 2000.* **Sources: Kiw, Me2, Oik, On3, Pu2, Sh14, Tri.**

A. purpurea: Hardy Red - Cranberry-red fruit with a delicious sweet-tart flavor. Ripens in October. Hardy to -25 degrees F. Pollinized by *arguta* male. *Source History: 1 in 2000.* **Sources: Clo.**

Hybrid: *A. arguta* x Matua - *Source History: 1 in 2000.* **Sources: Pu2.**

Hybrid: Ken's Red - *A. cordifolia* x *A. melanandra*. Female. Fruits turn red when ripe. Red flesh is very sweet. Needs a male to set fruit. Hardy in Zones 5-9. Low chill variety good for the deep South as well as the North. *Source History: 2 in 1992; 11 in 2000.* **Sources: Bu7, Ed2, HA12, Kiw, Me2, On3, Or2, Pu2, Rai, Sh3, Son.**

Hybrid: Red Princess - Skin color is brick red on the outside and bright red on the inside. Orange flesh with flecks of red. Delicious, sweet flavor. Requires a pollinator. Tolerates hot weather. Low chilling requirement. Hardy in Zones 6-9. *Source History: 1 in 1992; 2 in 2000.* **Sources: Kiw, Me2.**

Mulberry

Morus spp.

Bachuus Noir - Distinctly flavored fruit; best eaten fresh or made into pies. No spraying or pruning required. *Source History: 1 in 1992; 1 in 2000.* **Sources: Ty2.**

Beautiful Day - Medium to large, pure white fruit; sweet flavor. Very good for eating fresh; excellent for drying. Medium size, spreading, very productive tree. Requires little care; no spraying. Original tree was from Maryland. Imported white mulberries that are dried like raisins sell in many food stores and are one of the better dried fruits. Hardy in Zones 6-8. *Source History: 1 in 1988; 1 in 1992; 1 in 2000.* **Sources: Ed2.**

Black Beauty - Large, black fruit with blackberry-like flavor. Very attractive to birds. Zone 4. U.S. Plant Patent No. 4913. *Source History: 1 in 2000.* **Sources: CO5.**

Black Mulberry - *Morus nigra.* Large, 1" juicy, red to purplish black fruit similar to blackberries; can be quite delicious. Small, wide spreading, deciduous tree grows 20-30' tall. Very long-lived, becoming gnarled and picturesque. Similar to Russian Mulberry in that it can be used to make a fine hedge; very attractive to birds. Ripens in late spring. Hardy at least to -10 degrees F. Grows well in Zones 5-6. Native to western Asia. *Source History: 6 in 1988; 8 in 1992; 6 in 2000.* **Sources: Fo2, Ga11, JO4, Rai, Sc2, Sh14.**

Boysenberry Black - Seedless black fruit with distinct boysenberry flavor. Excellent for jams. Ripens early to late May. *Source History: 1 in 1992; 1 in 2000.* **Sources: Ju2.**

Coast - Huge 2" fruit. Yields of 40 gallons per tree. Cold Hardy. Zones 8-10. *Source History: 1 in 2000.* **Sources: Ty2.**

Collier - *Morus alba x M. rubra.* Reddish black fruit. Good flavor. Long bearing season. Similar to Illinois Everbearing, but ripens two weeks earlier. Zones 5-8. *Source History: 2 in 1988; 2 in 1992; 3 in 2000.* **Sources: Ed2, Gor, Tri.**

Contorted - *Morus alba.* Tasty small fruit. Small tree has gnarled and twisted branches. Similar to Contorted Filbert, but faster growing. Self-fertile. Can be grown in a container. Hardy to -20 degrees F. Extremely rare and unique. *Source History: 1 in 1992; 5 in 2000.* **Sources: Gr16, On3, Or2, Rai, Wh3.**

David Smith - Everbearing. *Source History: 1 in 1992; 1 in 2000.* **Sources: Ch9.**

Downing - Heavy bearer of large, sweet, pink berries with no tartness. Makes excellent pies and jams. Medium size, graceful, wide spreading tree; grows 15' tall in sun or shade. Hardy and productive; long-lived and trouble free. Requires very little maintenance. *Source History: 2 in 1988; 1 in 1992; 1 in 2000.* **Sources: Co12.**

Eakins - Black fruit. Good flavor. *Source History: 1 in 1988; 1 in 1992; 1 in 2000.* **Sources: Tri.**

Everbearing - Large, flavorful fruits in early summer; second, smaller crop in late summer. Hardy in Zone 4. *Source History: 1 in 1992; 2 in 2000.* **Sources: Fo2, Neb.**

Florida Giant - Long, slender fruit. Reported to be hardy in Zones 5-6. *Source History: 2 in 1992; 1 in 2000.* **Sources: Tri.**

Illinois Everbearing - *Morus alba x M. rubra*. Large, 1-2.5" glossy, virtually seedless fruit; black when ripe. Pleasant mixture of acid and sweet, similar to blackberry but without the large seeds; considered by many to be the best flavored mulberry. Used for dessert, jam, winemaking, fresh eating or in cereals. Handsome tree is slender and fast growing; smaller than other mulberries. Self-fertile. Bears over about an eight week period from early spring into mid-July. Fruits hold well on the tree. Hardy to -25 degrees F. Grows well in Zones 5-8. *Source History: 8 in 1988; 11 in 1992; 12 in 2000.* **Sources: Bea, Bu7, Ed2, Fo2, Gor, Hid, Or2, Rai, Sh3, Tri, Wh3, Wom.**

Kaester - *Morus nigra. Source History: 1 in 2000.* **Sources: Pa2.**

Lavender - *Morus alba*. Medium size, lavender-white fruit. Good fresh, but especially good dried. Begins bearing at two years of age. Ripens midsummer. *Source History: 1 in 1988; 2 in 1992; 1 in 2000.* **Sources: Bu7.**

Middleton - *Morus alba. Source History: 1 in 2000.* **Sources: Pa2.**

Mulberry - About ten species of deciduous trees belonging to the genus *Morus*. Edible fruits somewhat resemble blackberries. Fruit quality varies; some selections are delicious and can be eaten fresh, dried or made into jam, pie or jelly. Generally bears heavy, reliable crops, often beginning at an early age. Eagerly eaten by many species of birds, so useful for distracting birds from other crops. Very easy to grow; usually does well without any care. No serious diseases or insect pests. Foliage and unripe fruit may be poisonous. Succeeds best on good soil; bears profusely for several weeks until midsummer. Hardy in Zones 4-8. *Source History: 6 in 1988; 7 in 1992; 4 in 2000.* **Sources: Fi1, Gur, PL2, So12.**

Mulberry of Cathay - Glossy, sharply pointed foliage. Sweet white, red or black, 1" fruits. Zone 6. Originated in China. *Source History: 1 in 2000.* **Sources: Fo2.**

Noire of Spain - Black fruit. Does well in warm climates. Zones 7-10. *Source History: 1 in 2000.* **Sources: Hid.**

Northrop - *Morus alba*. Young plants may take some winter dieback due to extremely rapid growth in the first few seasons. Propagated by tissue culture rather than by grafting, thus genetically identical to the "parent" from root to tip. Extremely hardy; has suvived -50 degrees F. Parent tree was planted on the Northrop farm in the 1850s just outside of Potsdam. *Source History: 1 in 2000.* **Sources: Stl.**

Oscar's - Fruits are black when fully ripe; edible in the red stage with raspberry flavor. Ripens in the spring. Very drought tolerant and productive even under the worst conditions. Zones 5-9. *Source History: 1 in 1992; 4 in 2000.* **Sources: Bu7, Clo, Or2, Rai.**

Pakistan - *Morus alba*. Red to black fruits are 2.5-3.5" long, firm and sweet. Juice does not stain. Ripens over a six week period. Does well in dry climates. Hardy in Zones 6-9. Originated in Islamabad, Pakistan. *Source History: 2 in 1992; 7 in 2000.* **Sources: Bu7, CO5, Ed2, Or2, Pa2, Po7, Ty2.**

Paradise - Medium size, grey-white fruit; very, very sweet. Good fresh and out of hand. Dwarf tree with heart-shaped leaves; 7' high and 6' wide at maturity in Pennsylvania. Perfect mulberry for limited space. Zones 5-8. *Source History: 1 in 1988; 1 in 2000.* **Sources: Ed2.**

Persian - *Morus nigra*. Large, dark red to black fruit. Juicy flesh; sweet flavor. Tree grows 30' tall. Fairly drought tolerant once established. Often planted to attract birds away from cherries. *Source History: 2 in 1988; 5 in 1992; 4 in 2000.* **Sources: CO5, ORA, Po7, WI4.**

Persian Dwarf - Tender black fruits with good sugar-acid ratio. Tastes like a sweet Cabernet Sauvignon. Dwarf tree grows 8' tall. Hardy to 0 degrees F. *Source History: 1 in 1992; 1 in 2000.* **Sources: Or2.**

Red Mulberry (American Mulberry) - *Morus rubra.* Large, 1" red to dark purple fruit. Tree can grow 60' tall. Native to rich bottomland soils in eastern North America. *Source History: 1 in 1988; 3 in 1992; 4 in 2000.* **Sources: BO10, LO6, LOV, Sc2.**

Russian Mulberry (Common White Mulberry) - *Morus alba tartarica.* Black-berry-shaped, sweet, mild, white fruit, sometimes pink or purple. Dried like raisins; staple food in parts of Asia. Also delicious fresh or in pie and jam. Large, spread-ing, bushy tree grows rapidly to 45-50'; bears in three years. Practically disease free. Tolerates poor conditions. Yellow wood is very durable in soil or water. Of-ten used as an early maturing trap crop for fruit-eating birds, which are strongly drawn to it. Excellent for the edges of poultry and hog yards. Hardy to at least -25 degrees F. Native to China, but naturalized around the world; used to feed silk-worms. *Source History: 13 in 1988; 21 in 1992; 19 in 2000.* **Sources: Bar, Bea, Ca7, Co15, FO10, LA4, Lee, Mc3, Mel, Mi1, MIS, Po2, Sav, Sc2, SH8, TU5, Wa16, WA8, Wom.**

Scott's Jumbo - Good size, black fruit. Fair to good flavor. *Source History: 1 in 1988; 1 in 1992; 1 in 2000.* **Sources: Tri.**

Shangri La - Large, black fruit. Tree has very large, heart-shaped leaves. Good mulberry for the Deep South; may be cultivated in other areas. Has fruited well in Maryland for six out of eight years. Original tree was from Naples, Florida. Hardy in Zones 7-9. *Source History: 1 in 1988; 1 in 1992; 2 in 2000.* **Sources: Ed2, Or2.**

Silk Hope - Large, sweet, 1.25" black fruit. Zones 7-9. Originated in North Carolina. *Source History: 1 in 1992; 1 in 2000.* **Sources: Ed2.**

Stearns - Dark fruit with good flavor. Original tree in central New York state bears fruit from early July until hard frost around the end of September. *Source History: 1 in 2000.* **Sources: Tri.**

Sugar Drop - White fruit with lavender tinge. Tastes like a drop of sugar. Often dried and used as a sweetener. Fairly vigorous tree. Hardy to -10 degrees F. Trademarked. *Source History: 1 in 1992; 1 in 2000.* **Sources: Or2.**

Sugarbaby - Beautiful cut-leaf foliage. Pure white fruit ripens all at one for an easy harvest. Hardy to -20 degrees F. Trademarked. *Source History: 1 in 2000.* **Sources: Or2.**

Sullivan - Attractive, small to medium size tree bears very large, almost black fruit. Zones 5-9. *Source History: 1 in 2000.* **Sources: On3.**

Superberry - Tree grows up to 20' in one year; bears bushels of berries in mid-May. Originated in Florida. *Source History: 1 in 1992; 1 in 2000.* **Sources: Ty2.**

Tehama - Large, pure white fruit up to 3.5" long with very sweet flavor. Hardy in Zones 7-9. *Source History: 2 in 1992; 1 in 2000.* **Sources: Or2.**

Tiger Red - Large, long fruit with raspberry flavor. Ripens late May to mid-June. *Source History: 1 in 1992; 1 in 2000.* **Sources: Ju2.**

Weeping Mulberry (Texas Weeping) - *Morus alba* cv. *pendula.* Grown mainly as an ornamental. Pink to purple fruit. Vigorous growing, dense, weeping tree; slender branches cascade down to the ground. Forms an interesting twisted branching pattern. Glossy, dark green foliage. Tolerant to drought and polluted areas. Suitable for silkworm production. Hardy in Zone 4-8. *Source History: 6 in 1988; 13 in 1992; 14 in 2000.* **Sources: BA14, Bu7, CO5, Ed2, Fo2, GR26, Ju2, MI5, On3, ORA, Rai, SH8, WA8, Wh3.**

Wellington - Medium to large, long, slender, cylindrical, black fruit. Soft flesh; poor to average flavor. Tree is a heavy cropper; ripens over a period of several weeks. Hardy in Zone 5. Possibly the old variety New American, which was sold many years ago as Downing. *Source History: 4 in 1988; 6 in 1992; 6 in 2000.* **Sources: Clo, Fo2, Or2, Rai, Tri, Wh3.**

White Mulberry - *Morus alba.* Medium size, sweet, white fruit shaped like blackberries. Loved by birds. Large, handsome tree grows moderately to 20-60', depending on soil depth and quality. Drought tolerant once established, but produces much faster, denser growth with irrigation; heavy surface feeder roots. Brought to the U.S. by Felix Gillet to start silkworm culture with the Chinese in Nevada City. *Source History: 7 in 1988; 7 in 1992; 13 in 2000.* **Sources: Arb, Bu7, CO5, Fo2, Ju2, LO6, LOV, No2, ORA, Sc2, Sh14, Tri, Wh3.**

Raspberry

Rubus idaeus (and *Rubus spp.)*

Algonquin - Haida x Canby. Bright, non-darkening red fruit. Plant has upright, compact habit; relatively few thorns. Some resistance to spur blight, root rot and to pollen transmission of raspberry bushy dwarf virus. Hardy. Originated in British Columbia. Released in 1984. *Source History: 1 in 1992; 2 in 2000.* **Sources: HA12, In5.**

Allen - Bristol x Cumberland. Large, firm, juicy, very sweet, glossy black berries. Highest quality. Vigorous plant is consistently productive. Disease free. Widely adapted, especially in the Northeast. Ripens in early July. Hardy. Introduced in 1957. *Source History: 7 in 1988; 9 in 1992; 2 in 2000.* **Sources: Mi1, Shu.**

Amber - Large, slightly conical, slightly soft, yellowish amber berries. Extremely sweet and highly flavored. Exceptional quality. Vigorous, productive plant. Heavy bearer; single crop. Ripens very late. Fairly hardy. *Source History: 5 in 1988; 4 in 1992; 2 in 2000.* **Sources: Bu1, Mo8.**

Amity (Amity Everbearing) (Fallred x OR-US 1347) x (PI 338908 x Heritage). Everbearing. Medium-large, very firm, dark red berries. Classic raspberry flavor. Superior quality. Excellent for fresh market; good for shipping, freezing and canning. Strong, self-supporting canes are 5-5.5' tall. Old wood is almost smooth and easily pruned. Often bears one year after planting. Production somewhat higher than Heritage; more resistant to root rot; can take heavier soils. Aphid resistant. Ripens one week earlier than Heritage. Small crop in June and large crop in September and October. Hardy in Zone 3-8. Developed at the Oregon Agricultural Experiment Station in Corvallis. Introduced in 1984. *Source History: 6 in 1988; 9 in 1992; 8 in 2000.* **Sources: Bea, Ced, CO5, Mo8, SH8, Son, Wbn, We4.**

August Red - Everbearing. Large, red berries. Excellent flavor. All-purpose; good for eating fresh, canning or freezing. Erect, compact plants grow 3' tall. Bears in early summer and again from mid-September until frost. Winter hardy; ideal for the North. Developed in New Hampshire. *Source History: 4 in 1988; 5 in 1992; 4 in 2000.* **Sources: Co12, Fed, Fi1, Mo8.**

Autumn Bliss - Everbearing. Parentage includes *Rubus strigosis, R arcticus, R. occidentalis* and six red raspberry varieties. Attractive, red berries. Size, firmness, flavor and yields are superior to Heritage. Ripens two weeks ahead of Heritage.

Very disease resistant. Zones 3-8. Released from England. U.S. Plant Patent No. 6597. Introduced in 1984. *Source History: 10 in 1992; 21 in 2000.* **Sources: Ag4, BA14, Bo5, Bos, Bu7, Clo, DAI, Ed2, Ed5, HA12, HI10, In5, Jun, Lin, On3, Pe3, Sh2, SH8, Stl, Wbn, We4.**

Autumn Britten - Sibling of Autumn Bliss. Large, firm fruit. Harvests with Autumn Bliss. Sparse spines. Promising new cultivar. *Source History: 1 in 2000.* **Sources: Ag4, Nou.**

Bababerry - Everbearing. Extra large, red berries up to 1" long. Fine flavor. Excellent for all uses. Suitable for growing in the warmest climates of the U.S. Does well in hot valley and mild winter areas, yet has a short chilling requirement. Bears a large crop in June and a smaller crop in the fall. Hardy to 0 degrees F. Discovered in the wild in southern California. U.S. Plant Patent No. 4732. Introduced in 1983. *Source History: 4 in 1988; 18 in 1992; 8 in 2000.* **Sources: CO5, Fi1, Gur, HI10, Ju2, Or2, Ty2, Wel.**

BC 86-6-15 - Trial variety. Produces high yields of early dark fruit. Maintains good fruit size. High content of soluble solids makes it suitable for processing; machine harvests well. Highly susceptible to root rot; plant only on well drained soil that is free of rot. *Source History: 1 in 2000.* **Sources: SPO.**

BC 89-2-89 - Comox x Scottish selection. Large, light colored fruit with large drupelets. Vigorous, strong canes with long upright laterals. Good fresh market variety. Ripens late. *Source History: 1 in 2000.* **Sources: SPO.**

BC 89-33-84 - Trial variety from British Columbia. Produces an attractive dark red berry with some fruit rot resistance. Ripens midseason. Used for processing and fresh market. Should machine harvest well. *Source History: 1 in 2000.* **Sources: SPO.**

BC 90-4-48 - High yielding trial variety from British Columbia. Showed greater susceptibility to raspberry bushy dwarf virus. *Source History: 1 in 2000.* **Sources: SPO.**

Black - Delicious, high quality berries. Vigorous plants produce big crops. Best commercial variety in Ohio. Ripens early. Very hardy. *Source History: 1 in 1988; 2 in 1992; 3 in 2000.* **Sources: Lee, Sav, WA8.**

Black Hawk - Quillen x Black Pearl. Large to very large, nearly round, .75" glossy, black berries. Sweet, rich flavor. Exceptional quality. Excellent for eating fresh, jam, jelly, preserves, freezing and canning. Does not crumble, even when a little overripe. Extremely vigorous, high yielding plant; bears large crops despite hot, dry weather. Some resistance to anthracnose. Easy to pick. Good firmness; excellent for shipping and commercial handling. Ripens late-midseason. Picking season lasts from 10-14 days. Hardy in Zones 4-9. Developed at Iowa Agricultural Experiment Station and tested for over 20 years at Iowa State University. Introduced in 1955. *Source History: 20 in 1988; 23 in 1992; 17 in 2000.* **Sources: Bar, Bo5, Bu1, Co12, Fi1, Fo4, Gur, HA12, In5, Iso, KR3, Rid, SH8, Spr, St4, Wel, Wor.**

Blackcap - *Rubus leucodermis.* Blackcap-type raspberry. Excellent for preserving. Shrub to 6'. Northwest and Midwest native. Zone 6. *Source History: 3 in 1988; 4 in 1992; 5 in 2000.* **Sources: Abu, Co24, Fro, No2, So12.**

Boulder - Thimble-like purplish berries hang on slender, thornless, arching branches in late summer. *Source History: 1 in 2000.* **Sources: LI7.**

Boulder Raspberry - *Rubus deliciosus.* Shrub grows 2-5' tall with arching branches. White flowers followed by raspberry-like fruits. Hardy to Zone 5. Rocky Mountain native. *Source History: 1 in 2000.* **Sources: Fo2.**

Boyne - Chief x Indian Summer. Medium size, tender, juicy, dark red berries; aromatic, medium sweet and very good quality. Similar in size to Latham, but with better flavor and cohesion. Not especially firm, but excellent processing quality. Excellent for jam, jelly and freezing. Very productive, heavy, strong, sturdy, summerbearing canes are 5-5.5' tall. Excellent plant maker. Easy to pick. Adapted for the home garden, Pick Your Own and local markets. Ripens in early-midseason. One crop berry developed in Morden, Manitoba for northern areas where extreme hardiness is most needed. Introduced in 1960. *Source History: 11 in 1988; 28 in 1992; 24 in 2000.* **Sources: Ag4, Bos, Co12, CO3, CR6, Cu4, Ed5, Fa1, Fi1, HA12, HI10, In5, Jun, Lin, Mc3, Mo8, Nou, Pe3, SH8, Stl, VIR, Wbn, We4, ZEL.**

Brandywine (Brandywine Purple) - NY 631 x Hilton; cross between black fruited and red fruited varieties. Large to very large, conic, firm, non-crumbling, glossy, round, reddish purple berries. Tart, pleasantly tangy flavor; highly aromatic. Good for eating fresh; excellent for jam and jelly because of its tartness. Large, 8-10', vigorous, strong, erect canes are quite thorny. Productive; bears two years after planting. Does not sucker like red raspberries; best propagated by tipping or tissue culture. Very winter hardy; grows well in Zones 4-9. Developed by the New York Fruit Testing Cooperative Association in Geneva. Introduced in 1976. *Source History: 17 in 1988; 15 in 1992; 7 in 2000.* **Sources: Bar, Co12, In5, KR3, RAM, Wa16, Wbn.**

Bristol - Watson No. 1 x Honeysweet. Large to very large, firm, glossy, jet-black berries. Rich but mild, sweet flavor. Excellent quality. Good for fresh eating, desserts, freezing, canning and jelly. Vigorous, productive, upright plant with compact, sturdy canes that do not need staking. Shows some tolerance to powdery mildew. Good market berry for local sales. Ripens midseason, a few days before Cumberland; continues ripening over a couple of weeks. Hardy in Zones 4-8. Introduced in 1934. *Source History: 17 in 1988; 16 in 1992; 17 in 2000.* **Sources: Bo5, Bos, BU12, Co12, CO3, HA12, In5, Jun, KR3, Mi1, Nou, Roh, SH8, Shu, VA3, Wa16, Wor.**

Canby (Canby Thornless) - Viking x Lloyd George. The only red thornless raspberry. Large to very large, fine flavored, firm, juicy, fine quality, high capped, bright red berries. Delicious flavor. Good for fresh use, cooking, canning and freezing. Vigorous plant with few or no thorns on the canes. Heavy bearer. Shows a high level of virus resistance; aphid immune. Sensitive to root rot. Good soil drainage required. Grows best in regions with cooler summers. Close second to Latham in popularity as a red springbearer. Ripens 14 days earlier than Latham. Excellent winter hardiness in Zones 4-8; marginally hardy in St. Paul. Developed in Oregon. Introduced in 1953. *Source History: 12 in 1988; 15 in 1992; 17 in 2000.* **Sources: Bu1, Co12, CO5, Cu4, Fa1, Fo4, GR26, Gur, HA12, HI10, In5, LI7, Mel, MO10, Mo8, Nou, Pe3.**

Caroline - Everbearing. Large, firm and cohesive fruit. Unique flavor with a special tangy twist. Warmer temperatures and adequate moisture will result in earlier fruiting. Long fruiting period. Shows good tolerance to root rot and yellow rust. Recommended for southern Wisconsin and areas south. Zones 5-8. U.S. Plant Patent No. 10,412. *Source History: 3 in 2000.* **Sources: Jun, Nou, We4.**

Caroline Red (Autumn Bliss x Glen Moy) x Heritage. Everbearing. Considered superior to Autumn Bliss. Large, firm, cohesive flavorful fruit. Vigorous, high suckering canes. More tolerant of root rot and yellow rust than Heritage. Fruits earlier in warmer weather. Hardy to Zone 5. Developed by the University of Maryland, Rutgers, VPI and University of Wisconsin at River Falls collaborative breeding program, 1999. *Source History: 1 in 2000.* **Sources: Fed.**

Centennial - Large, red fruit. Ripens in July. *Source History: 2 in 1992; 1 in 2000.* **Sources: Ced.**

Chilcotin (Chilcoten) - Firm berry. Lacks flavor and sugar content for fresh market. Excellent shipping quality. Long fruiting season; ripens from late July to early August. Tolerates cold weather. *Source History: 3 in 1988; 3 in 1992; 4 in 2000.* **Sources: Mo8, RAM, Wbn, We4.**

Chilliwack - Skeena x (Summer x Carnival). Large, very sweet, firm, bright red berries. Very productive plant; thrives where others will not. Some resistance to spur blight and root rot; slow to become infected by pollen transmission of bushy dwarf virus. Excellent choice for wetter sites. Ripens over a short season in late July or early August. Zones 6-9. Developed in British Columbia. Introduced in 1986. *Source History: 3 in 1988; 12 in 1992; 5 in 2000.* **Sources: Ced, HA12, Rai, RAM, SPO.**

Citadel - Firm fruit. Excellent choice for the commercial trade. Ripens midseason. Tolerates hot summer temperatures. *Source History: 1 in 1992; 1 in 2000.* **Sources: Bos.**

Comox - Improved Latham. Medium size, red fruit. Ripens in July. *Source History: 1 in 1988; 3 in 1992; 1 in 2000.* **Sources: HI10.**

Cumberland (Cumberland Blackcap) - Unknown parentage. The standard for black raspberries; largest blackcap type. Large to very large, round, firm, juicy, glossy, black berries; never seedy. Excellent, sweet, rich, delicious flavor. Fine quality. Excellent for freezing, canning, jam, jelly, sauce, syrup, preserves, cobblers and pie. Healthy, vigorous, strong, upright, heavily rooted plants. Produces immense crops reliably; bears all through the late season. Choice of both commercial and home growers in central and northern regions. Highly recommended for the upper South. Good yields in any soil; grows well in shade. Ripens in late September. Zones 4-9. Introduced before 1900. *Source History: 22 in 1988; 34 in 1992; 20 in 2000.* **Sources: Bar, Bay, Bos, Bu1, Bu2, Co12, CO5, Fi1, Fo4, Gur, HI10, Iso, Mel, MI5, Rid, SH8, SIM, STR, Ty2, Wor.**

Cutleaf Black Raspberry - *Rubus laciniatus.* Vigorous sprawling black raspberry is native everywhere. Bears fruits about .75" long. Attractive dissected foliage. Very disease resistant. Hardy to -25 degrees F. *Source History: 1 in 2000.* **Sources: Oik.**

Dinkum - Firm, dark red fruit. Recommended for trial where fresh market growers are looking for a longer shelf life in a fall bearing variety. Bears a crop in June and again in early September. Can be machine harvested when firm ripe. Developed in Australia where 'Dinkum' is the slang word for 'Great'. PVP. *Source History: 5 in 2000.* **Sources: Clo, Ga6, In5, Wbn, We4.**

Dorman Red - Good red raspberry for the South. Large, firm, juicy, shiny, deep red fruit. Mild flavor like a black raspberry. Fine quality. Excellent fresh or frozen; withstands the worst heat and drought conditions. Requires trellising. Very productive and disease resistant. Excellent commercial variety. Ripens in mid-June. Grows well in Zones 7-10, and as far south as northern Florida. *Source History: 8 in 1988; 17 in 1992; 11 in 2000.* **Sources: Bos, Cla, Iso, Jo3, La3, Pe3, SIM, St4, Ty2, Wel, Wom.**

Dundee - Large, glossy, moderately firm, black berries. Genuine blackcap flavor. Vigorous, productive, quite tall plant. Heavy bearing. Resistant to raspberry mosaic. Susceptible to powdery mildew. Widely adapted, popular, older black raspberry variety. Ripens later than Bristol; somewhat less glossy but is considered larger, more productive and better flavored. Does not ripen all at one time. *Source History: 6 in 1988; 3 in 1992; 1 in 2000.* **Sources: Mc3.**

Durham (Durham Everbearing) - Everbearing. Medium to large, firm, red berries. Good flavor. Excellent for table use and cooking. Healthy, vigorous, sturdy, 3-3.5' canes protect the berries very well. Two full crops; a heavy yield in early summer on the old canes, then again a few weeks later on the new canes. Extremely hardy. *Source History: 3 in 1988; 3 in 1992; 2 in 2000.* **Sources: Bu1, Mo8.**

Emerald Carpet - *Rubus pentalobus,* formerly *R. calcinoides.* Evergreen groundcover produces small orange berries similar to raspberries. Does best in shade. *Source History: 1 in 2000.* **Sources: Bu7.**

Encore (NY 7) - Everbearing. Large, dry berries with good flavor. Sturdy, nearly spineless canes. Average vigor and suckering. Excellent choice for farm stands and wholesale markets. Released from the Geneva, New York Experiment Station. Patent pending. *Source History: 2 in 2000.* **Sources: CO3, Nou.**

Eskimo - *Rubus x stellarcticus.* Bush plant bears pink and lavender blooms in spring and red and orange berries in the fall. *Source History: 1 in 2000.* **Sources: Ga6.**

Estate - Large round berry is sweeter than Brandywine. Color is more red with less purple. More attractive to the retail market than Royalty and Brandywine with similar winter hardiness. Upright canes sucker very little. *Source History: 1 in 2000.* **Sources: In5.**

European Raspberry (Framboise, Red Raspberry) - *Rubus idaeus.* Oblong, conical, dark red berries. Erect, 3-5' plant with thorny canes. Hardy in Zone 4. Native to Eurasia. *Source History: 1 in 1988; 1 in 1992; 1 in 2000.* **Sources: No2.**

Fall Gold (Fall Gold Everbearing) - Taylor crossed with an exotic wild berry from mountains of Korea; resulting seedling was crossed with a sister of Fall Red. Everbearing. Large to very large, conical, non-crumbling, extremely sweet, rather soft, golden berries. Excellent for fresh eating and processing. Vigorous, productive canes. Adaptable to a wide variety of soils. Highly recommended for upper South and mountain areas. Not recommended for extreme northern areas. First crop ripens in July; second crop from late August until the first hard frost. Hardy to -25 degrees F.; Zones 4-8. Bred by Professor Elwyn Meader at the University of New Hampshire. *Source History: 20 in 1988; 35 in 1992; 31 in 2000.* **Sources: BA14, Bea, Bo5, BU12, Clo, Co12, CO3, Ed2, Ed5, Fa1, Fi1, GR26, Gur, HI10, In5, Jo3, KR3, Leu, Lin, Mel, Mi1, Mo8, Par, Pe2, Pe3, RAM, SH8, Ty2, Wa16, Wbn, We4.**

Fall Red (Fall Red Everbearing) - Everbearer developed for the North. Large to very large, firm, bright red berries. Excellent flavor and aroma. Does not crumble when picked. Sturdy, vigorous, disease free plants. Ripens a small crop in early July on overwintered canes; then a larger crop is produced on the current season's canes, ripening from mid-August until frost. Hardy to -25 degrees F. and in Zones 4-8. Developed at the University of New Hampshire. Introduced in 1964. *Source History: 12 in 1988; 12 in 1992; 10 in 2000.* **Sources: Co12, Fa1, Fi1, Gur, Jun, Leu, Mi1, Mo8, Rid, Shu.**

Formosa Carpet - *Rubus calcynoides.* Evergreen groundcover. Spreads fast. Bears amber colored fruit. Low maintenance. Zones 4-8. *Source History: 1 in 2000.* **Sources: VIR.**

Gatineau - Fine flavored, early ripening, Canadian variety. *Source History: 1 in 1992; 1 in 2000.* **Sources: Mo8.**

Golden Harvest   Everbearing. Bright yellow fruit of good quality. Sturdy canes sucker readily. Size, flavor and season compares to Heritage. Good disease resistance. Originated in New York. Plant patent applied for. *Source History: 2 in 1992; 2 in 2000.* **Sources: HA12, In5.**

Golden Himalayan - *Rubus elipticus.* Productive, vigorous, evergreen plant. Bears good quality golden yellow fruit that is used fresh or processed. Collected in the Indian and Nepalese Himalaya. *Source History: 1 in 2000.* **Sources: Or2.**

Golden Queen - Medium size, golden berries with sugary, unique flavor. Good fresh, canned or frozen. Berries have a tendency to turn brown when overripe. Hardy, longer-lived plants. *Source History: 1 in 1988; 2 in 1992; 1 in 2000.* **Sources: Co12.**

Goldie (Graton Gold Cultivar, Goldie Yellow) - Everbearing sport of Heritage. Heavy crop of medium size, deep golden berries turn orange when fully ripe; not soft or crumbly. Better flavor and higher yield than Fall Gold.   Heavily laden canes may need support. Bears from July through October. Zones 4-8. Originated in Sonoma County, California, 1987. Trademarked. U.S. Plant Patent No. 7625. *Source History: 5 in 2000.* **Sources: Bu2, Fed, Jun, Nou, St4, VIR.**

Ground Cover Raspberry - *Rubus x stellarcticus.* Plants grow to 5" tall and spread by rhizomes, forming a thick mat of bright green, trifoliate-leaved ground cover. Pink-lavender flowers are followed by red fruit in midsummer. Foliage changes to shades of red and burgundy in the fall. Hardy to Zone 1. *Source History: 1 in 2000.* **Sources: HA12.**

Heritage (Heritage Everbearing) (Milton x Cuthbert) x Durham. Everbearing. Large, sweet, dark red berries.   Mild flavor; a bit dry. Superior quality. Good fresh, canned, frozen, jam, jelly. Strong, vigorous, very productive, 5-6' upright, self-supporting canes; suckers prolifically, spreads rapidly. Fairly tolerant of heavier soils; develops root rot in poorly drained areas. Widely adapted. Moderate summer crop in early July; heavier, superior fall crop from early September until frost. Holds in good condition on plant and after picking. Heavy fall yields when mowed to ground level in early spring while still dormant. Hardy in Zones 4-9. Developed at Geneva Station in 1969. *Source History: 57 in 1988; 75 in 1992; 66 in 2000.* **Sources: Ag4, Al2, BA14, Bar, Bay, Bo5, Bos, Bu1, Bu2, BU12, Ced, Cla, Co12, CO3, CO5, CR6, Cu4, DAI, Ed2, Fa1, Fi1, Fo4, Ga6, GR26, Gur, HA12, HI10, Hid, In5, Iso, Jo3, Jun, KR3, La3, Led, Leu, LI7, Lin, Mc3, Mel, Mi1, MO10, Mo8, Nou, On3, Par, Pe2, Pe3, Pin, RAM, Rid, SH8, Shu, SPO, Spr, St4, STR, Ty2, VIR, Wa16, Wa3, Wbn, We4, Wh4, Wor, ZEL.**

Hilton - Newburgh x St. Walfried. Large, long, conic, coherent, slightly dull, medium red berries, becoming dark red when overripe; thick, firm, juicy, good quality flesh.   Vigorous, very productive, erect plant seldom needs support when well grown. Good yields. Easy to grow. Maintains quality and berry size throughout the season. Ripens midseason. Usually winter hardy. Introduced in 1965. *Source History: 4 in 1988; 6 in 1992; 3 in 2000.* **Sources: Co12, Fi1, Mo8.**

Honey Queen - Large, golden berries. Sweet flavor. Excellent for jam and eating fresh. Hardy. Originated in Alberta, Canada. *Source History: 1 in 1992; 1 in 2000.* **Sources: Va5.**

Honeygold - Yellow berry. *Source History: 1 in 1992; 1 in 2000.* **Sources: Va5.**

Indian Summer - Everbearing. Large clusters of large, conic, glossy, high quality, aromatic, unusually sweet, bright red berries. Good for fresh eating, quick freezing and canning; makes a tasty jam. One of the earliest everbearers to ripen;

spring crop in mid-June. Produces an excellent fall crop in Missouri and similar climates, but also does well into Canada. *Source History: 6 in 1988; 10 in 1992; 5 in 2000.* **Sources: Bay, Co12, CO5, MO10, ZEL.**

Jewel (Bristol x Dundee) x Dundee. Considered an improvement over Bristol, having much larger fruits.   Compact clusters of large to very large, firm, juicy, slightly woolly, glossy, black berries. Rich raspberry flavor. Very high quality. Good for pies and preserves. Extremely vigorous, reliable plants produce heavily. Most disease resistant of all black raspberries; only slightly susceptible to mildew. Ripens a few days after Bristol. Hardy in Zones 4-8. Developed in New York. Introduced in 1973. *Source History: 9 in 1988; 16 in 1992; 22 in 2000.* **Sources: Al2, Bo5, Bos, Ced, Co12, CO3, Cu4, DAI, HA12, In5, Jo3, Jun, Mel, Mi1, Nou, Pe3, Rai, St4, VIR, Wa16, Wh4, ZEL.**

John Robertson - Large, plump, juicy, black fruit with medium firm flesh. Long-lived plant. For best results, separate from red raspberries by at least 300'. Will grow anywhere in the North; reliable into Canada. *Source History: 1 in 1988; 2 in 1992; 3 in 2000.* **Sources: Co12, Fi1, Gur.**

K-81-6 - Summer bearing. Vigorous, tall plants produce a very large, firm berry. Resistant to powdery mildew and late yellow rust. Tolerant to crown gall. Susceptible to fruit rots, fire blight and Phytophthora root rot. Cold hardy to -34 degrees F. Introduced in Canada. *Source History: 2 in 2000.* **Sources: Ag4, In5.**

Keriberry - *Rubus moluccanus.* Black raspberry from New Zealand. Evergreen; produces year-round there.   Huge, rugous, emerald-green foliage. Needs semi-shade and water. *Source History: 1 in 1988; 3 in 1992; 3 in 2000.* **Sources: Or2, Po7, Sh3.**

Killarney - Early Chief x Indian Summer. Deep red fruit with firm flesh. Highest quality. Very sturdy, medium size canes. Excellent for fresh market, Pick Your Own, freezing and processing. Ripens about one week after Boyne. Zone 3. Developed in Morden, Manitoba, Canada. Introduced in 1961. *Source History: 2 in 1988; 5 in 1992; 10 in 2000.* **Sources: Ag4, DAI, Fed, In5, Mi1, Mo8, Nou, Pe3, St1, VIR.**

Kitsilano (BC 85-18-16) - Medium size, glossy, firm fruit. Retains color. Fresh market type. Ripens late. Low susceptibility to fruit rot; relatively susceptible to root rot in greenhouse trials. Originated in British Columbia. *Source History: 1 in 2000.* **Sources: SPO.**

Kiwigold - Sport of Heritage. Everbearing. Medium to large berries are pale yellow blushed with red. Good size, quality and flavor. More productive with higher fruit quality than Fallgold. Hardy to Zone 5. Discovered in New Zealand. Patent pending. *Source History: 4 in 2000.* **Sources: Bos, Fed, Nou, Sh2.**

Kusa-ichigo Raspberry - *Rubus hirsutus.* Rare species raspberry that is native to eastern Asia. Used for jam, jelly and juice. Suckering shrub grows to 3'. Hardy to -30 degrees F. *Source History: 1 in 2000.* **Sources: Oik.**

Latham - The standard for springbearing red raspberries; extremely popular and widely grown. Large to very large, round, often 1", deep red fruits. Wonderful texture; somewhat noncohesive. Full flavored and aromatic. Good for fresh eating, canning, freezing, jam, juice and pie. Strong, vigorous, heavily productive, upright, 4-5' plants; widely adapted. Disease resistant; mosaic free. Extremely profitable for home or market gardens; extra firm, so good for commercial purposes and Pick Your Own. Ripens evenly for three weeks in late June and early July. Exceptionally hardy; Zones 3-8. Developed by the University of Minnesota. *Source History: 32 in 1988; 53 in 1992; 39 in 2000.* **Sources: Al2, Bo5, Bos, Bu1, BU12, Cla,**

Co12, CO3, CO5, Fa1, Fi1, Fo4, GR26, Gur, HI10, In5, Jun, KR3, Led, Leu, Mc3, Mel, Mi1, MI5, Mo8, Nou, Pe3, RAM, Rid, Roh, SH8, SIM, St4, VA3, VIR, Wa16, Wbn, We4, Wor.

Lauren (CDH-1) - Firm, large berries. Long fruiting season. Produces 20% higher yields than Titan. Excellent for fresh eating, jams and jellies. Root rot resistant. Zones 5-7. U.S. Plant Patent No. 10,610. *Source History: 3 in 2000.* **Sources: Nou, Pe3, St4.**

Logan - Medium to large, flavorful, tart but sweet, glossy, black berries. Vigorous, upright plants. Extra heavy yields. Concentrated harvest requires only 3-4 pickings. Holds its firmness well. Highly resistant to mosaic and other raspberry diseases. Succeeds on all kinds of soil. Ripens early, one week before Cumberland. Good winter hardiness. *Source History: 6 in 1988; 5 in 1992; 3 in 2000.* **Sources: Co12, Fa1, RAM.**

Lowden - Cross of a purple raspberry and a black raspberry; inherited improved vigor from the purple and full flavor from the black. Medium to large berries. Excellent flavor. Good disease resistance; not susceptible to anthracnose. Ripens in midseason, later than other black raspberries. Hardy. *Source History: 5 in 1988; 2 in 1992; 1 in 2000.* **Sources: RAM.**

Mac Black - Medium to large, small seeded, firm, very sweet, black berries. Very disease resistant plants. Occasionally produces fruit on the tips of the new canes in September and October. Ripens late. Hardy. *Source History: 1 in 1988; 1 in 2000.* **Sources: In5.**

Madawaska Red - Sweet, red fruit; larger than any other early bearing variety. Widely adapted. Ripens very early; about two weeks before Latham. *Source History: 2 in 1988; 3 in 1992; 3 in 2000.* **Sources: Bu1, Fo4, Mo8.**

Malahat - Large, firm, conic red berry. Vigorous canes with a fairly upright habit. High yields. Winter hardiness compares to Meeker. Resistant to cane botrytis; fairly susceptible to root rot. Patented. *Source History: 1 in 2000.* **Sources: SPO.**

Mammoth Red Thornless - Very large, conic, sweet, highly flavored, red fruit up to 1" in diameter. Excellent for fresh use, frozen or canned; makes good pie, jelly or jam. Vigorous plants grow 8' tall. High yields. Plant in cool weather; space 3-4' apart. Ripens 5-7 days earlier than Latham. Hardy in Zones 4-8. *Source History: 3 in 1988; 3 in 1992; 4 in 2000.* **Sources: Co12, Fi1, Gur, Leu.**

Meeker - Large, thimble-shaped, firm, deep, rich red fruit; high sugar content and superior flavor. Outstanding quality. Excellent home garden variety for fresh eating and freezing; also good for canning and processing. Long-lived, vigorous plant with long, willowy growth. Very productive; long harvest season. Some resistance to botrytis fruit rot. Ripens midseason. Zones 5-8. Developed at Washington State University. Introduced in 1967. *Source History: 10 in 1988; 9 in 1992; 6 in 2000.* **Sources: Ced, Clo, Pe2, Rai, SPO, We4.**

Munger (Munger Blackcap) - *Rubus occidentalis.* Large, plump, firm, shiny, black berries; not crumbly or seedy. Delicious, sweet flavor. Excellent for preserving; satisfactory for freezing. Plant has stout canes. Appears to be more resistant to fungal diseases than other raspberry varieties. Superb blackcap type. Leading variety in the Pacific Northwest. Ripens midseason. Very hardy; Zone 4. *Source History: 5 in 1988; 5 in 1992; 5 in 2000.* **Sources: Bea, Ced, Pe2, Wbn, We4.**

Mysore - *Rubus albescens.* Small, fast growing bush with thorns. Fruits in the summer months. *Source History: 1 in 1992; 1 in 2000.* **Sources: Ga11.**

Newburgh (Giant Newburgh, Newburgh Red) - Newman x Herbert. Large to extremely large, firm, very sweet, medium acid, light red berries with shallow caps. Mild flavor; fairly good quality. Retains its shape well; does not crumble when picked or shipped. Especially good for jelly and freezing. Vigorous, long-lived, heavy annual producer. Resistant to root rot and mosaic virus. Easy to grow. Wide adaptability; takes heavy, wet soils fairly well. Favorite in New York State; good for market use. Ripens 3-4 days before Latham. Very cold hardy. Developed by the New York State Agricultural Experiment Station. Introduced in 1929. *Source History: 16 in 1988; 15 in 1992; 8 in 2000.* **Sources: Bea, Co12, CO5, HI10, Mo8, RAM, Wbn, We4.**

Nordic (MN 603) - Boyne x Fall Red. Similar to Boyne in size and quality. Superior to Boyne as frozen pack; appears to have more resistance to fungal diseases and aphid feeding. Very productive. Extremely hardy. Ripens in June. Developed at the University of Minnesota. Introduced in 1987. *Source History: 2 in 1988; 7 in 1992; 1 in 2000.* **Sources: BA14.**

Nova - Southland x Boyne. Medium size, dark red fruit. Mild flavor. Medium height canes. Suitable for fresh market, Pick Your Own and freezing. Resistant to most cane diseases. Bears early in the season. Developed by the Canadian Department of Agriculture. Introduced in 1981. *Source History: 2 in 1992; 6 in 2000.* **Sources: Ag4, Bos, Bu2, HA12, In5, Nou.**

Oregon 1030 - Everbearing. Upright plant to 3'. Adapted to warm climates. *Source History: 1 in 1988; 2 in 1992; 2 in 2000.* **Sources: Pa2, Po7.**

ORUS 534-10 - Everbearing. Larger size berry than Summit. Good for freezing; acceptable for fresh market with proper handling. Ripens with Summit. *Source History: 1 in 2000.* **Sources: SPO.**

Pathfinder - *Source History: 1 in 1992; 1 in 2000.* **Sources: Va5.**

Pink Flowering Raspberry - *Rubus coreanus.* Prickly shrub to 6'. Attractive pink flowers later followed by small bland red fruits that turn black. Hardy to -20 degrees F. *Source History: 1 in 2000.* **Sources: Oik.**

Polana - Everbearing. Large, high quality fruit. Each axillary bud produces two fruiting laterals, thus increasing yields. Productive. Ripens 2-3 weeks before Heritage. Developed in Poland. Patent pending. *Source History: 3 in 2000.* **Sources: Bos, Nou, Pe3.**

Prelude (NY 1009) - Everbearer that matures the largest portion of its crop in late June and early July. Very large fruit; firm flesh. Very good processing quality. Suckers freely. Well adapted to the Coastal Plain and Piedmont. Ripens early. Patent pending. *Source History: 2 in 1988; 1 in 1992; 2 in 2000.* **Sources: CO3, Nou.**

Purple Flowering Raspberry (Flowering Raspberry) - *Rubus odoratus.* Fruit somewhat resembles a small, light red raspberry. Edible, but not produced in significant quantities. Attractive but seldom cultivated upright, deciduous shrub grows vigorously 3-6' tall. Large, maple-like leaves. Faintly fragrant, 1.5", rose-purple flowers. Spreads slowly and can eventually form a sizable patch. Grows well in either sun or shade. Hardy in Zones 4-9. Native to eastern North America. *Source History: 2 in 1988; 2 in 1992; 2 in 2000.* **Sources: Ga8, Tri.**

Qualicum - Large, medium red firm fruit. Pleasant flavor. Good shelf life. Vigorous, upright growth habit with numerous primocanes. Powdery mildew resistant; susceptible to root rot. Ripens midseason. Patented. *Source History: 1 in 2000.* **Sources: SPO.**

Red Everbearing - Everbearing. Unusually large berries. Delicious flavor. Produces a large crop in June and another crop in September. Fall crop is considerably earlier than other everbearing raspberries. *Source History: 1 in 1988; 2 in 1992; 2 in 2000.* **Sources: Lee, Sav.**

Redwing (MN 629) - Heritage x Fall Red. Everbearing. Dark red fruit; good, sweet flavor. Superior to Fall Red in firmness; better yields. Good fresh fruit quality; acceptable frozen quality. Stout, green primocanes grow vigorously to 6-7'; moderately dense, short, purple spines. Susceptible to anthracnose; spur blight observed, but not serious. Performs well on heavy soil. Adapted to upper Midwest. Responds well to complete cane removal in spring then bears only the fall crop. Ripens 2-3 weeks before Heritage; not as productive. May be more cold hardy than Heritage, if not mulched. Developed at University of Minnesota. Introduced in 1987. Patented. *Source History: 7 in 1988; 20 in 1992; 6 in 2000.* **Sources: BA14, Fa1, Fi1, HA12, SH8, Stl.**

Reveille (Indian Summer x Sunrise) x September. Large to very large, bright red fruit; will not crumble when handled. Superb flavor. Good for fresh eating, canning and freezing. Productive, vigorous, upright plant with strong canes; suckers freely. Tolerates fluctuating winter and spring temperatures. Excellent for Pick Your Own and local market. Ripens early. Very winter hardy. Developed at the Maryland Agricultural Experiment Station in College Park. Introduced in 1966. *Source History: 5 in 1988; 2 in 1992; 3 in 2000.* **Sources: Bos, Nou, Pe3.**

Royalty (Cumberland x Newburgh) x (Newburgh x Indian Summer). Large to very large, firm, round, very sweet, medium purple fruit. Tastes like a tangy, red raspberry when picked at full red stage; develops stronger, sweeter flavor when fully ripe at royal purple stage. High quality. Good for fresh eating; tartness is ideal for jam, jelly, canning and freezing. Vigorous, productive canes; usually grows from a single crown with only an occasional strong sucker. Immune to raspberry aphids which transmit mosaic virus; resistant to raspberry fruit worms. Ripens late. Hardy in Zones 4-8. Developed at the Geneva Station. Introduced in 1982. U.S. Plant Patent No. 5405. *Source History: 24 in 1988; 21 in 1992; 16 in 2000.* **Sources: Ag4, BA14, Co12, CO3, DAI, Fed, Fi1, HA12, In5, Jun, Mel, Mi1, Nou, Pe3, Rai, VIR.**

Rubus arcticus - Pink flowers followed by red fruit. Great for jam, jelly and wine. North American native. Zone 2. *Source History: 1 in 2000.* **Sources: Fo2.**

Rubus ichangensis - Large, prickly branches. Bright red berries grow in 12" long clusters. Hardy to Zone 6. Native to China. *Source History: 1 in 2000.* **Sources: Fo2.**

Rubus parvus - White flowers are followed by bright red, raspberry-like fruits. Purple and bronze foliage color in winter. Native to New Zealand. Hardy to Zone 8. *Source History: 1 in 2000.* **Sources: Fo2.**

Rubus setchuenensis - Clusters of small pink to purple flowers. Leaves and flowers do not look like a bramble but the black fruit proves it. Hardy to Zone 5. Native to China. *Source History: 1 in 2000.* **Sources: Fo2.**

Rubus trifidus - Upright stems grow 3-6' tall. White flowers in spring. Edible red berries in the fall. Hardy to Zone 7. Originated in Japan. *Source History: 1 in 2000.* **Sources: Fo2.**

Ruby (Watson, NY 114) - Heritage x Titan. Everbearing. Bright red, conical shape fruit with mild, sweet flavor. Extremely large fruit size reduces picking time and cost. Susceptible to pre- and postharvest fruit rot and mosaic virus; resistant to yellow rust and powdery mildew in California. Ripens one week ahead of Heritage. Requires excellent drainage. Hardy in Zones 5-8. Developed in New York. Introduced in 1988. U.S. Plant Patent No. 7067. *Source History: 8 in 1992; 3 in*

2000. **Sources: In5, Nou, St4.**

September - Everbearing. Medium to large, sweet, juicy, firm, rose-red fruit with small seeds. Good, tart flavor. High quality. Excellent fresh or frozen and in desserts, preserves, jam, jelly and pie. Vigorous, productive plants grow to medium height. Bears fruit out in the open where it is easy to see and easy to pick. Mosaic resistant. Among the hardiest of the everbearers. *Source History: 7 in 1988; 15 in 1992; 8 in 2000.* **Sources: Bay, Co12, CO5, Gur, KR3, Mo8, RAM, SH8.**

Sodus - Purple raspberry; cross between red and black varieties. Large, firm, sweet, wine-red to purple fruit often 1" across; does not crumble. Black raspberry taste. Fine quality. Especially good for freezing. Sturdy, strong, upright growth habit; very few thorns. Train canes to trellis or fence for support. Heavy yields. Easy to grow; quick to bear. Good for the Midwest. Produces well into August. *Source History: 4 in 1988; 2 in 1992; 1 in 2000.* **Sources: Fa1.**

Southland - Everbearing. Large, sweet, firm, flavorful, bright red fruit; does not darken as it ripens. Vigorous, disease resistant, dependable, heavily productive plant produces many suckers. Very heat and drought resistant. Best adapted from Indianapolis southward. Heaviest crop ripens in late June or early July; another light crop in September. Hardy in Zones 5-8. *Source History: 6 in 1988; 6 in 1992; 4 in 2000.* **Sources: CO3, Iso, STR, Wel.**

Summit - Everbearing. Large crops of firm, red berries. High yields; will produce a crop the first season. Suitable for machine harvest. Primocane fruiting two weeks earlier than Heritage. Mow off a few inches above the ground each winter and it will produce only a large fall crop the next season. Zones 4-9. Developed in Oregon. Introduced in 1989. *Source History: 3 in 1988; 10 in 1992; 6 in 2000.* **Sources: Ced, HI10, Rai, SPO, Wbn, We4.**

Summit, Golden - Mutation of Summit. Beautiful golden colored berries. *Source History: 1 in 2000.* **Sources: Rai, SPO, We4.**

Sunrise - Large, firm, fine textured, bright red fruit. Excellent flavor and quality. Good for jelly, jam and preserves. High yields. Ripens 10 days earlier than Latham. Hardy in Zones 4-9. Developed by the USDA. *Source History: 2 in 1988; 1 in 1992; 1 in 2000.* **Sources: Bar.**

Tahoma - *Source History: 1 in 1992; 1 in 2000.* **Sources: Va5.**

Taylor - Newman x Lloyd George. Large, long-conic, very firm, light to medium red fruit, often over 1" long. Excellent flavor. Good quality. Tall, vigorous, hardy, very productive plant with sturdy canes that need no support. Excellent for home gardens and commercial use. Ripens over a period of three weeks in midseason. Hardy to Zone 4. Released by the New York Station. Introduced in 1935. *Source History: 4 in 1988; 6 in 1992; 8 in 2000.* **Sources: Bu2, BU12, Cu4, Fed, Mi1, Mo8, Nou, Shu.**

Titan (NY 883) - Hilton x (Newburgh x September). Large to very large, moderately long-conic, sweet, juicy, bright red fruit with large cavity. Outstanding texture; very mild flavor. Fresh and processing quality is average to good. Canes are large, tall, stout, smooth, nearly spineless; generally require trellising due to weight of the crop. Suckers sparsely. High yield potential; over 6.5 tons per acre. High resistance to raspberry aphids which transmit mosaic viruses. Very susceptible to crown gall and root rot. Ripens early; prolonged harvest. Winter hardy to -15 degrees F. Developed at Cornell University. Introduced in 1985. U.S. Plant Patent No. 5404. *Source History: 10 in 1988; 8 in 1992; 4 in 2000.* **Sources: Fi1, In5, Nou, St4.**

Trail Blazer - *Source History: 1 in 1992; 1 in 2000.* **Sources: Va5.**

Tulameen - Nootka parentage. Very large, red fruit make it the largest of all reds. Extremely desirable for the fresh market. Highest yields. Longest harvest season (50 days). Ripens in July. Resists powdery mildew; immune to mosaic virus; moderately susceptible to root rot. Hardy to Zone 4-9. Originated in British Columbia. Introduced in 1989. *Source History: 5 in 1992; 10 in 2000.* **Sources: Ced, Clo, HA12, On3, Rai, Sh2, SPO, Wbn, We4, Wh4.**

Whitebark - *Rubus leucodermis*. Thorny plant bears red or black edible berries. Prefers dry open sites. Native Americans used the berries for fresh or dried food and for stains. *Source History: 1 in 2000.* **Sources: Pl5.**

Willamette - Newburgh x Lloyd George. Large to very large, long-conic, very firm, deep red fruit. Lower sugar content; rich, slightly tart flavor. Outstanding quality for table use, canning or freezing. Tall, vigorous canes bear heavily. Disease resistant. Holds color and shape well. Good for local markets. Requires well drained soil and mild winters. Favorite on the West Coast. Ripens in June. Zones 5-9. Introduced in 1943. *Source History: 11 in 1988; 12 in 1992; 8 in 2000.* **Sources: Bay, CO5, HI10, MO10, Son, SPO, Wbn, We4.**

Serviceberry
Amelanchier spp.

Allegheny Shadbush (Allegheny Serviceberry) - *Amelanchier laevis*. Small, showy, edible, purplish black fruits. Small deciduous tree with irregular stems that grows 20-25' tall. Smooth, gray bark; graceful, narrow, upright form. New spring foliage varies from delicate pink to bronze-purple; turns brilliant copper-orange in autumn. Masses of large, white flowers early in the spring. Prefers moist, well drained, acid soil in partial shade. Tolerates full sun, but excellent in a shaded woodland setting. Ripens during June. Hardy in Zones 4-7. Native to the East. Favorite of the American Indians. *Source History: 4 in 1988; 9 in 1992; 14 in 2000.* **Sources: Arb, BO10, Car, Fed, Fo2, GR26, IM2, IN7, KEE, LA4, LOV, MEA, SH8, We18.**

Amelanchier alnifolia (Serviceberry, Juneberry) - Large, edible, dark purple fruit. Multistemmed, wide, upright tree. Large, thick textured, rounded foliage. Clusters of small white flowers. Hardy. Native to northwestern Montana and other areas in the Northwest. Zone 3. *Source History: 8 in 1988; 8 in 1992; 9 in 2000.* **Sources: Arb, CLI, Co24, Fro, LA4, NA5, No2, Sc2, Sh14.**

Amelanchier canadensis (Juneberry, Shadblow) - Highly ornamental berries turn from red to blue. Delicious, juicy flavor similar to blueberries. Native, small, multistemmed, shrub-like tree grows 10-15' tall; smooth, gray bark. Orangish red foliage in the fall. Fleecy, pure white flowers in early spring. Plant two to ensure pollination. Ripens during June. Hardy in Zones 2-7. *Source History: 11 in 1988; 12 in 1992; 11 in 2000.* **Sources: Arb, Big, BU12, Car, CO3, Fa1, IM2, KEE, LOV, MEA, Sc2.**

Amelanchier canadensis lamarckii - Holland strain. Red-purple, edible fruit. Tree grows 15-25'. Hardy in Zone 4. *Source History: 1 in 1992; 1 in 2000.* **Sources: SH8.**

Amelanchier ovalis - Formerly *A. rotundifolia*. Sweet, red fruit becomes black. Multistemmed, upright plant grows 8' tall. Large flowers in short groups. Ripens during July. Hardy to Zone 3. *Source History: 6 in 1988; 2 in 1992; 1 in 2000.* **Sources: Sh14.**

Autumn Brilliance - *Amelanchier* x *grandiflora* cv. Autumn Brilliance. Abundance of fruit is soon consumed by birds. Excellent grower to an early height of 20-25' due to hybrid vigor. Persistent, dark green leaves turn brilliant red in the fall. Impressive and reliable bloom pattern of soft, white blossoms in spring. Disease resistant. Hardy in Zone 2. U.S. Plant Patent No. 5717. *Source History: 2 in 1988; 12 in 1992; 18 in 2000.* **Sources: BA14, Bea, Big, BO10, BR2, Car, FE7, GR26, IN7, KAN, KI3, LI7, ME3, Rai, SH8, Stl, We8, ZEL.**

Ballerina - *Amelanchier alnifolia*. Tasty, red fruits. Tree grows to 15'. Hardy to Zone 4. Originated in England. *Source History: 4 in 1992; 1 in 2000.* **Sources: SH8.**

Cole's Select - *Amelanchier x grandiflora*. Large shrub or small tree with bright red or orange fall color. Zones 5-9. *Source History: 1 in 2000.* **Sources: Wo2.**

Downy Serviceberry - *Amelanchier arborea*. Edible purple fruit on large shrub or small, multi-stemmed tree with yellow-orange fall color. Hardy in Zone 5. *Source History: 2 in 1992; 2 in 2000.* **Sources: BO10, Sh10.**

Downy Shadblow - *Amelanchier canadensis*. Edible fruit. Small tree with multiple stems. Gray, young foliage contrasts with clusters of pure white flowers in May. Golden to red fall foliage. Tolerates moist soil conditions. Ripens in June or July. *Source History: 1 in 1988; 1 in 1992; 1 in 2000.* **Sources: We8.**

Forest Prince - *Amelanchier x grandiflora*. Flowers grow along the stems. Leathery, dark green foliage all summer; gold or red fall color. Zone 5. *Source History: 1 in 2000.* **Sources: Fo2.**

Forestburg - *Amelanchier alnifolia*. Sweet, juicy berries with mild flavor. Heavy producer. Drought tolerant. Ripens later than Smoky. Originated in Alberta, Canada. Introduced in 1963. *Source History: 1 in 2000.* **Sources: Stl.**

Honeywood - *Amelanchier alnifolia*. Large berries with mild flavor. Flowers later than others and has a longer ripening period. Productive. Hardy in Zone 3. Originated in Saskatchewan, Canada. *Source History: 1 in 1992; 1 in 2000.* **Sources: Stl.**

Juneberry, Dwarf - Large, green berries turn red, then deep blue when ripe. Sweet and juicy. Good for fresh eating, pies, jams and jellies. Extra hardy, dwarf shrub grows only 3' tall. White blossoms in the spring. Bears fruit the second year. Will grow on poor soil. *Source History: 2 in 1988; 1 in 1992; 1 in 2000.* **Sources: Int.**

Juneberry, Grandiflora - Natural hybrid between Woodland Saskatoon (*Amelanchier arborea*) and Allegheny Juneberry (*A. laevis*) with more flowers and larger fruits than either parent. Not a bush but has a trunk instead of many stolons. Widely adaptable from New York to Georgia on the East Coast. Zones 4-8. *Source History: 1 in 1992; 4 in 2000.* **Sources: Ed2, Mc3, Or2, We8.**

Lamarcki - *Amelanchier lamarckii*. Sweet, juicy fruit. Native to eastern Canada. *Source History: 1 in 1992; 4 in 2000.* **Sources: Car, LA4, MEA, Sh14.**

Nantucket - *Amelanchier nantucketensis*. Thicket forming deciduous shrub grows 3' tall. White flowers are followed by edible berries. Rare. *Source History: 1 in 2000.* **Sources: Wo2.**

Northline - Edible berries that look and taste similar to blueberries. Small tree to 10'. Pretty white flowers in early spring. Adaptable to moist or dry soils. Hardy in Zone 2. Canadian introduction from the 1980s. *Source History: 1 in 1988; 2 in 1992; 1 in 2000.* **Sources: Or2.**

Prince William - *Amelanchier canadensis*. Purplish blue, .4-.5" fruit. Multistemmed, large shrub grows 10' tall and 6' wide. Small, green foliage turns orange to red in the fall. Small, white flowers in clusters. Heavy bearer. Hardy in Zone 3. U.S. Plant Patent No. 6040. *Source History: 1 in 1988; 1 in 1992; 2 in 2000.* **Sources: Stl, We8.**

Princess Diana - *Amelanchier grandiflora.* Purplish blue, .4" fruit. Gracefully spreading, small tree grows 20' tall and 15' wide. Small, green leaves turn brilliant red in the fall. White flowers in clusters. Hardy in Zone 3-8. U.S. Plant Patent No. 6041. *Source History: 1 in 1988; 3 in 1992; 4 in 2000.* **Sources: Ed2, Stl, We8, Wo2.**

Regent - *Amelanchier alnifolia.* Abundant crop of extra sweet, high quality, purplish black fruit. Excellent for fresh eating, pies, muffins, desserts and preserves. Showy, native shrub grows 4-6' tall. Spreads by runners; not invasive. White flowers bloom from early to mid-May; both flowers and fruit are very ornamental. Plant two to ensure pollination. Completely resistant to disease. Normally bears the second year after transplanting. Excellent forage plant for birds. Ripens in early summer. Hardy in Zone 2. *Source History: 8 in 1988; 17 in 1992; 14 in 2000.* **Sources: BA14, Car, CR6, Ed2, Ed5, Fa1, Fed, Fo2, GR26, Hid, Mc3, Oik, SH8, Stl.**

Robin Hill (Robin Hill Pink) - *Amelanchier canadensis.* Pink flowering selection of the native shadblow. Tree grows 20-30' tall. Most intense blossom color is developed in cool weather with sufficient moisture. Zone 4. *Source History: 2 in 1988; 1 in 1992; 3 in 2000.* **Sources: Arb, Fo2, GR26.**

Roundleaf (Dwarf Serviceberry) - *Amelanchier sanguinea.* Grows to 4'. *Source History: 1 in 1988; 1 in 1992; 1 in 2000.* **Sources: LOV.**

Running Serviceberry - *Amelanchier stolonifera.* Sweet, juicy fruit. Shrub grows to 4' with slowly spreading habit. Hardy in Zone 5. *Source History: 1 in 1992; 1 in 2000.* **Sources: Fo2.**

Saskatoon (Juneberry, Serviceberry, Shadblow) - *Amelanchier alnifolia.* Sweet, .25-.6", round berries, usually bluish purple, but ranging from cream to red and black. Good flavor; used fresh, for pies, dried, canned or frozen. Multistemmed, deciduous, upright, 6-10' thicket of shrubs or an individual, 20' tree. Lives 25-40 years. Fluffy masses of white flowers. Often dries into raisins on the plant in dry climates. Indians pounded the dried fruits into pemmican; high in vitamin C. Good bird and bee forage. Native to Canadian prairies. Called Shadblow or Serviceberry in the East; Juneberry in the Midwest. Ripens in early July. Hardy in Zones 2-3. *Source History: 6 in 1988; 15 in 1992; 16 in 2000.* **Sources: Abu, Bea, Fi1, GR26, Gur, HA12, In5, KI3, Lin, Mc3, MEA, MI5, Oik, SH8, So12, So5.**

Serviceberry (Juneberry) - *Amelanchier alnifolia.* Fruit resembles tiny, bluish purple crab apples about .5" in diameter when ripe. Blueberry-like flavor. Eaten fresh, cooked in pie or canned. Very rich in Vitamin C. Very showy, white flowers in the spring and colorful foliage in the fall. Native on the Canadian plains. *Source History: 3 in 1988; 10 in 1992; 14 in 2000.* **Sources: BA9, BO4, Bo5, Bu7, Ca8, Co15, GR26, LI7, Lit, MIS, Pl5, Pla, TU5, Va5.**

Shadblow (Juneberry) - *Amelanchier canadensis.* Plump, blue, blueberry-size fruit. Sweet, mild, low acid flavor. Shrub grows 6' tall. Yellow to red autumn color. Hardy to Zone 3. *Source History: 1 in 1988; 14 in 1992; 15 in 2000.* **Sources: BO10, CR6, GR26, KAN, KI3, LA4, LI7, Mc3, MI5, Mu2, SH8, Stl, TR19, WA8, We18.**

Smokey - *Amelanchier alnifolia.* Large fruited selection of Western Serviceberry. Sweet, .5-.75" blueberry-like fruit. Used for fresh eating, pies, muffins or canning. Small, deciduous tree grows 9' tall. Clusters of pretty, white flowers in early spring.

Yellow fall foliage. Bears 2-3 years after planting. Does well in neutral or acid soils. Self-fertile and long-lived. Adaptable to moist or dry soils. Hardy and drought resistant. Developed in northern Alberta. Widely planted commercially in Canada. Single bushes have yielded 88 pounds in government trials; 7 tons per acre in commercial plots. Ripens during July. Hardy in Zone 3. Originated in Alberta, Canada. Selected in 1928; introduced in 1952. *Source History: 3 in 1988; 6 in 1992; 5 in 2000.* **Sources: Bu7, Fo2, Or2, Rai, Stl.**

Thiessen - *Amelanchier alnifolia.* Very large fruit grows in clusters of 10-15. Sweet flavor. Large bush produces few suckers. Height about 10'. The larger size and sweetness of the fruit make it popular for Pick Your Own. Hardy in Zone 2. Originated in Saskatchewan, Canada. Introduced in 1976. *Source History: 2 in 1992; 3 in 2000.* **Sources: Or2, Rai, Stl.**

Tree Serviceberry - *Amelanchier laevis.* Showy, red fruit with high vitamin C content. Deciduous tree grows 25-50' tall. Alternate, oval or oblong leaves. Snowy white flowers in early spring. Hardy to -35 degrees F. *Source History: 2 in 1988; 1 in 1992; 5 in 2000.* **Sources: Fo2, Ga8, Oik, Sc2, Sh14.**

Western Serviceberry - *Amelanchier alnifolia.* Small, purple fruits. Medium-large, deciduous shrub. Yellow to red fall foliage. Covered with white flowers in the spring. Good for birds, bees and wildlife. Hardy in Zones 3-4. Native to the West. *Source History: 2 in 1988; 2 in 1992; 1 in 2000.* **Sources: Fo2.**

Strawberry

Fragaria x Ananassa (and Fragaria spp.)

2310 - Late season trial variety. Vigorous plants bear large sweet fruit with firm flesh. Good color; caps well. Used for fresh or processing, but may be too late for some processors. Patented. *Source History: 1 in 2000.* **Sources: SPO.**

89-31-69 - Trial variety. Large, bright red fruit with firm flesh. Less susceptible to post-harvest rot. Quite tolerant to virus diseases. Fresh market use. Ripens 4-5 days later than Totem. *Source History: 1 in 2000.* **Sources: SPO.**

Allstar (MdUS 2905 x MdUS 2650) x MdUS 3184 (NC 1968 x Surecrop). June-bearer. Very large, symmetrical, light red fruit with tough, glossy skin. Firm, mild, sweet flesh. Excellent internal color. Good quality. Well suited for shipping and freezing. Medium to large, vigorous plants produce runners freely. Resistant to verticillium wilt, leaf scorch, powdery mildew and five eastern races of red stele. Fruit is tolerant to botrytis rot; succumbs to high inoculum levels in some seasons. Outstanding productivity under diverse soil, climate and cultural conditions. Ripens midseason. Developed by the University of Maryland Introduced in 1981. *Source History: 25 in 1988; 29 in 1992; 32 in 2000.* **Sources: Al2, Be4, Bo5, Bos, Bu1, BU12, Co12, Co6, Cu4, DAI, Fa1, In5, Int, Je2, Jo3, Ko2, Kro, Le2, Mey, Mi1, Mo8, NO3, Nou, Pe3, RAM, Roh, Sh2, Sm6, St4, VA3, WA7, Wh4.**

Alpine Strawberry (Fraises des Bois) - *Fragaria vesca.* Small, elongated, pointed, conical, sweet, bright red fruits. Intense strawberry flavor similar to the French Fraise des Bois. Compact, runnerless plants form clumps about 10" tall. Great as edging. Very hardy perennial. Bears continuously from June through October. Hardy in Zone 4. Native to the Alps. *Source History: 6 in 1988; 5 in 1992; 7 in 2000.* **Sources: Dab, Ed2, Fo2, Hud, Pin, Red, Th3.**

Alpine: Alexandria - Everbearing. Improved Alpine Strawberry. Aromatic, very sweet, juicy fruits, .5-.75" long x .5" thick. Wild strawberry taste. Forms a small, neat, 8" bush plant which does not produce runners. Grows well from seed;

75-110 days. Plant in spring in a permanent location along rock walls or borders. Native to the Alps, the Alpine Strawberry was first cultivated in the middle 1700s in France. *Source History: 5 in 1988; 1 in 1992; 1 in 2000.* **Sources: Jo1.**

Alpine: Baron Solemacher - *Fragaria vesca.* Alpine strawberry. Conical, deep red berries about twice the size of wild berries but much smaller than standard strawberries; the size of the tip of a little finger. Sweet and fragrant. 120 days to first year's crop. June to fall production in succeeding years. Plant does very well in partial shade; prefers moist soil. Reproduces itself exactly from seed. Called "Wild Strawberries" in Bavaria. *Source History: 4 in 1988; 2 in 1992; 1 in 2000.* **Sources: Bou.**

Alpine: Charles V (Fraises des Bois, French Woodland Strawberry) - *Fragaria vesca.* Runnerless plants produce small, pointed, deep red berries. Intense flavor. Hardy in Zones 4-7. *Source History: 1 in 1988; 2 in 1992; 2 in 2000.* **Sources: HA12, Pa2.**

Alpine: Lipstick - Rose-red flowers on vigorously spreading plants with long runners. Delicious small red fruits. Zones 5-9. Originated in the Netherlands. *Source History: 3 in 2000.* **Sources: Rai, Sis, WA7.**

Alpine: Rugen (Reugen, Rugen Improved) - *Fragaria vesca.* Somewhat larger fruited and more productive than regular Alpine strawberries, but smaller than Alexandria. Delicious, tangy, deep crimson fruit produced from late June until the end of October. Beautiful, low edging plant. Produces no runners. Heavy bearer from midsummer through fall. Strong grower; cold tolerant. Hardy in Zones 3-9. *Source History: 4 in 1988; 9 in 1992; 8 in 2000.* **Sources: Bu2, Fed, Ni1, Rai, Sh2, Tri, Wa3, WA7.**

Alpine: White (White-Fruited Woodland Strawberry) - *Fragaria vesca.* Tiny, white fruits. White color makes them unattractive to birds. Given moist soil, the creeping stolons can cover a large area with permanent, evergreen foliage. Hardy to -30 degrees F; Zone 4. *Source History: 1 in 1988; 1 in 1992; 3 in 2000.* **Sources: Sh2, Sis, Tri.**

Alpine: Yellow (Wood Strawberry) - *Fragaria vesca.* Fragrant berries that range from a pale cream color to a golden yellow; .75-1" long. Intense concentration of flavor. Bush plant produces no runners. Birds are not attracted to the creamy white fruits. *Source History: 2 in 1988; 2 in 1992; 1 in 2000.* **Sources: Rai.**

Alpine: Yellow Wonder - Runnerless plants. Yellow fruit with tiny seeds; up to 1" long. Delicious aroma and taste. Zones 3-7. *Source History: 1 in 1992; 2 in 2000.* **Sources: Ed2, Pa2.**

Anaheim - University of California. Patented. *Source History: 1 in 2000.* **Sources: Fo8.**

Annapolis (K74-5) (Micmac x Raritan x Early Glo x Kent). Very large, light red fruit with extra firm texture. Size holds throughout the growing season. Plants are very hardy but are susceptible to powdery mildew and some root diseases on poorly drained soils. Developed at Agriculture Canada, Kentville, Nova Scotia, 1984. *Source History: 5 in 1992; 9 in 2000.* **Sources: Ag4, Co6, DAI, In5, Jun, Mi1, Mo8, NO3, Nou.**

Aromas - Everbearing. Developed at the University of California. Patented. *Source History: 2 in 2000.* **Sources: Fo8, NO3.**

Beach Strawberry (Sand Strawberry) - *Fragaria chiloensis.* Hardy in Zone 7. *Source History: 1 in 1988; 1 in 1992; 1 in 2000.* **Sources: Las.**

Benton - Extra hardy Junebearing variety from Oregon State University. Great flavor. For maximum sweetness, allow color to deepen. High yields. Virus resistant. Tolerance to red stele. Ripens late. *Source History: 6 in 1988; 4 in 1992; 6 in 2000.* **Sources: NO3, Rai, SPO, St6, Wbn, We4.**

Berri Basket - Everbearing. Compact, bushy plants do well in hanging baskets. Produces large, flavorful, deep red berries. Seeds. Trademarked. *Source History: 2 in 2000.* **Sources: BAL, Bos.**

Berries Galore - Everbearing. Produces runners. Produces large, tasty fruit. Seeds. Trademarked. *Source History: 1 in 2000.* **Sources: BAL.**

Big Boy - Junebearing. Large, wedge-shaped, dark red berries. Sugary sweet. Hardy and vigorous. Forms an overabundance of runners. Good pollinator for Gurney's Giant. *Source History: 1 in 1988; 1 in 1992; 1 in 2000.* **Sources: Gur.**

Blakemore - Missionary x Howard 17. Small to medium, very firm, bright, light red berries; flesh somewhat lighter. Good flavor. Fair dessert qualities; excellent for preserving. Vigorous growing variety. Foliage is healthy; stands up well during drought. Does well even in poor growing conditions. Resistant to leaf scorch, spot and verticillium wilt. Will stand two or three days without overripening. Ripens early. Introduced in 1920. *Source History: 7 in 1988; 9 in 1992; 6 in 2000.* **Sources: Bar, Lee, Po2, Sav, WA8, Wel.**

Blomidon (K 76-3) - K 72-4 x Holiday. Large, glossy, bright red fruit. Good to excellent flavor. Large, vigorous plants; high yields. Best suited for northern climates. Good for fresh market or shipping. Canadian introduction in 1987. *Source History: 2 in 1988; 9 in 1992; 2 in 2000.* **Sources: DAI, Mo8.**

Bounty - Jerseybelle x Senga Sengana. Medium to large, medium red fruit. Very good flavor. Berries are large but decrease in size with the season. Plants runner freely with vigorous growth. Yield well. Appear to have little or no resistance to soil diseases. Ripens late to very late. Winter hardy. Developed at the Nova Scotia Research Station at Kentville. Introduced in 1977. *Source History: 4 in 1988; 1 in 1992; 1 in 2000.* **Sources: Ag4.**

Cabot - ArKing x K79-5. Large, bright red fruit with firm flesh. Resists several races of red stele. Susceptible to gray mold. Mid to late season. Winter hardiness for the Midwest unknown. Developed at Agriculture Canada, Kentville, Nova Scotia, 1998. *Source History: 1 in 2000.* **Sources: Ag4.**

Californian - *Source History: 1 in 1988; 1 in 1992; 1 in 2000.* **Sources: Red.**

Camarosa - California variety. Patented. *Source History: 4 in 2000.* **Sources: Fo8, NO3, Wbn, We4.**

Capitola - Everbearer. Developed at the University of California. U.S. Plant Patent No. 7615. *Source History: 1 in 1992; 1 in 2000.* **Sources: Fo8.**

Capron - Musk strawberry from Italy. Fruit size is about two-thirds that of an average strawberry. Sweet, soft flesh. Delicious flavor. Aroma resembles raspberry and pineapple. Produces many runners. Zones 5-10. *Source History: 1 in 2000.* **Sources: Rai.**

Cardinal - Earlibelle x Arkansas 5063. Junebearing. Large to very large, firm fruit; vivid red throughout. Fine flavor and texture. Excellent quality fresh or processed. Stays firm when sliced. Vigorous, upright plants produce runners freely. Resistant to leaf spot, leaf scorch, powdery mildew and anthracnose. Susceptible to verticillium and red stele. Good for shipping, Pick Your Own and home gardens. Especially suited to Arkansas, Oklahoma and Missouri, then east to North Carolina and Maryland. Ripens midseason. Hardy in Zones 5-8. Developed by J. N. Moore,

H. L. Bowden and W. A. Sistrunk at the Arkansas Agricultural Experiment Station in 1974. Patent pending. *Source History: 23 in 1988; 29 in 1992; 22 in 2000.* **Sources: Bar, Be4, Bos, Cla, Co12, Co6, DAI, Fi1, In5, Iso, Kro, Le2, Mi1, MI5, NO3, Pe3, Po2, Rid, Sm6, St4, Ty2, Wel.**

Carlsbad - University of California variety. Patented. *Source History: 2 in 2000.* **Sources: Fo8, NO3.**

Catskill - Marshall x Howard 17. Unusually large, long-conic, glossy, bright red fruit. Light red flesh; soft, especially in warmer areas. Soft skin. Not firm enough for shipping. Mild, nearly non-acid flavor. High dessert quality. All-purpose; especially good for freezing. Vigorous plants; average runner production. Resistant to verticillium wilt and leaf scorch. Susceptible to red stele. Fine productivity; widely adapted. Good for home gardens or Pick Your Own. Grown principally in the Northeast, as far west as Minnesota and in higher altitudes to the Carolinas. Midseason. Very hardy. Introduced by the New York Station in 1933. *Source History: 17 in 1988; 13 in 1992; 2 in 2000.* **Sources: Mo8, Sm6.**

Cavendish - Glooscap x Annapolis. Junebearer. Very large, firm fruit with good flavor. Excellent runner production. Good choice for Pick Your Own, roadside markets and home gardens. Resistant to red stele. Ripens midseason. Adaptable to many climates. Originated in Canada, 1990. Plant patent applied for. *Source History: 3 in 1992; 11 in 2000.* **Sources: Ag4, Bo5, Co6, DAI, Gur, In5, Jun, Le2, Mi1, NO3, Nou.**

Chambly - Sparkle x Honeoye. Medium size, conic-shaped fruit with white raised neck. Average firmness. Deep red skin with red flesh. Easily capped. Good flavor. Fresh market or processing. Resists leaf scorch and powdery mildew. Leaf blight tolerant. Medium size plants with low vigor. Good winter hardiness. *Source History: 1 in 2000.* **Sources: Ag4.**

Chandler - Douglas x C55. Large fruit is long-conic to long-flat-wedgy; glossy skin. Very firm flesh; very firm skin. Good dessert and freezing quality. Plants are semierect in growth habit. Runner production is excellent. Self-pollinating. Susceptible to red stele, leaf spot and leaf scorch. One of the main commercial varieties used in California. Also recommended for Florida and along the Gulf Coast. A good fresh market berry. Ripens early. U.S. Plant Patent No. 5262. *Source History: 6 in 1988; 9 in 1992; 13 in 2000.* **Sources: CO5, Co6, Fo8, In5, Iso, Je2, Ju2, NO3, Pe2, Sm6, VIR, Wbn, We4.**

Chief Bemidji - Hardiest everbearer. Large, sweet fruit, solid red throughout. Giant, bushy plants hold fruit well above the ground. Runners as well as original plants bear the same season. Heavy yields. Survives the coldest climates. Hardy in Zones 3-8. Developed in Minnesota. U.S. Plant Patent No. 2147. *Source History: 2 in 1988; 1 in 1992; 1 in 2000.* **Sources: Co12.**

Colossal, Gurney's - Everbearing. Extremely vigorous, disease resistant plants with deep root set. Produces large, deep red berries. Uniform size. Sweet flavor. Great for fresh use, canning and freezing. Self-pollinating. *Source History: 1 in 2000.* **Sources: Gur.**

Crimson King (Hagking Cultivar, Stark Crimson King) - Junebearing. Fruit is very large although marginal in quality. Tends to be soft, limiting the variety to Pick Your Own and home use. Very vigorous plants are not generally affected by leaf disorders. Very winter hardy in native state of Minnesota as well as all other northerly states. Best adapted to the northern Midwest. Ripens early. Hardy in Zones 4-7. Trademarked. U.S. Plant Patent No. 4413. *Source History: 4 in 1988; 2 in 1992; 1 in 2000.* **Sources: St4.**

Cuesta - Developed at the University of California variety. Patented. *Source History: 1 in 2000.* **Sources: Fo8.**

Cyclone - Junebearing. Large, sweet, well shaped, bright red berry developed for homeowners. Solid, red flesh. Outstanding, full bodied flavor. Outstanding dessert and freezing qualities. Early, consistent bearer, very productive, good plant maker. Tolerates virus, resists leaf spot. Does extremely well in Iowa, Minnesota and Dakota regions. Good choice for high-altitude gardens. Ripens early. Hardy to Zone 3. Developed at Iowa State University. *Source History: 5 in 1988; 2 in 1992; 2 in 2000.* **Sources: Rid, SH8.**

Delite - Albritton x MdUS 2650. Medium to large, conical fruit. Glossy, bright red skin. Moderately firm, pink flesh. Slightly acidic flavor; good aroma. Fair dessert and freezing quality. Vigorous plants produce runners freely. Holds size well during harvest. Resistant to verticillium wilt, leaf spot, leaf blight, leaf scorch and at least five races of red stele root rot. Recommended where red stele and verticillium wilt are problems. Highly productive in the Midwest from the Great Lakes south to Missouri and Tennessee, east to Virginia and New York. Ripens late. Developed by Southern Illinois University. Introduced in 1974. *Source History: 13 in 1988; 11 in 1992; 1 in 2000.* **Sources: Co12.**

Delmarvel (MdUS 4923) - Earliglow x Atlas. Symmetrical fruit with good color, good flavor and outstanding aroma. Excellent for fresh eating. Produces well in either light or heavy soil. Resists red stele and most leaf and stem diseases and fruit rots. Early to midseason ripening. Recommended for the mid-Atlantic region and adjacent areas. *Source History: 10 in 2000.* **Sources: Al2, Be4, Bo5, BU12, DAI, In5, Le2, Mey, NO3, Nou.**

Diamante - Day neutral everbearer. Patented. *Source History: 2 in 2000.* **Sources: Fo8, NO3.**

Douglas - Tioga x (Tuffs x Sequoia). Large to very large, somewhat conical fruit; solid bright red throughout. Firm flesh and skin; very sweet. Fair dessert and freezing quality. Holds size well throughout picking season. Plants are vigorous, heavy bearers with extra large, light green leaves. Fair runner production. Susceptible to red stele, leaf spot and leaf scorch. Much better quality and yield than other early ripening, Junebearing varieties. Hardy in Zones 4-8. Developed at the University of California. Introduced in 1974. U.S. Plant Patent expired. *Source History: 7 in 1988; 3 in 1992; 1 in 2000.* **Sources: Fo8.**

Dunlap (Senator Dunlap) - Junebearing. Medium-large, dark crimson fruit; somewhat irregular shape. Extra sweet, rich flavor. Good dessert quality. Best eaten fresh; not firm enough for freezing or preserving. Extremely vigorous plant produces many runners. Set plants 24" apart and thin the runners. Self-pollinating. Very resistant to most foliar diseases. Mild resistance to drought. Susceptible to red stele. Well suited for Pick Your Own. Adapted to a wide range of soils. Produces well over a large area of central U.S. and under adverse conditions. Ripens midseason. Hardy in Zones 4-8. Developed at the University of Missouri. Introduced in 1930. *Source History: 12 in 1988; 10 in 1992; 9 in 2000.* **Sources: Fil, Gur, Jun, Po2, Rid, SH8, Shu, Sm6, Ver.**

Earlibelle - Albritton x MdUS 2101. Medium to large, uniform, long-conic, firm, very glossy, bright red fruit. Good, tart flavor. Excellent for freezing; very good for dessert and processing. Plants are comparatively small; excellent runner production. Susceptible to red stele. Resistant to leaf spot and leaf scorch. Ripens early. Developed by the North Carolina Agricultural Research Service. Introduced in 1963. *Source History: 5 in 1988; 6 in 1992; 3 in 2000.* **Sources: Bar, Sm6,**

Ty2.

Earliglow (Fairland x Midland) x (Redglow x Surecrop). Junebearing. Medium to large, symmetrical, conic fruit. Tough, glossy, deep red skin. Firm, uniformly deep red flesh. Exceptional flavor. Vigorous, productive plants; many runners. Resistant to botrytis rot, five races of red stele root rot, verticillium wilt, leaf scorch and leaf blight. Some resistance to powdery mildew. Withstands adverse weather and handles well due to tough, glossy skin and firm flesh. Excellent for Pick Your Own. Ripens early. Well adapted in the mid-Atlantic, Northeast and North Central states. Zones 4-8. Introduced by the Maryland Station in 1975. *Source History: 34 in 1988; 34 in 1992; 35 in 2000.* **Sources: Al2, Be4, Bo5, Bos, Bu2, BU12, Co12, Co6, Cu4, DAI, Fed, Fi1, Ga6, Gur, In5, Je2, Jun, Kro, Le2, Led, Mey, Mi1, Mo8, NO3, Nou, Pe3, Pin, Rid, Roh, Shu, Sm6, VA3, Ver, Wh4, Wor.**

Ever Red - Everbearing. Large fruit, beautifully colored throughout. Delicious, tangy-sweet flavor. Vigorous plants bear lots of berries all summer long. *Source History: 1 in 1988; 1 in 1992; 1 in 2000.* **Sources: Par.**

Everbearing - *Fragaria chiloensis.* Perennial ground cover grows 6-8" tall. Tasty red fruit. *Source History: 2 in 2000.* **Sources: HI10, Sm6.**

Eversweet - Everbearer. Long, cone-shaped fruit. Produces a nice crop of berries all summer, through the heat and into the fall. Zones 5-8. Trademarked. *Source History: 2 in 2000.* **Sources: St4, Wom.**

Fern - Tufts x CA 69.62-103. Day-neutral, everbearing variety that has shown dramatically high yields under Maryland latitudes with trickle irrigation. Always has fruit in different stages of development. Large, very firm, sweet berries. Leaf spot tolerant. Susceptible to red stele, leaf scorch and verticillium wilt. Should do very well all over the Midwest. Developed at the University of California at Davis in 1983. U.S. Plant Patent No. 5267. *Source History: 5 in 1988; 7 in 1992; 7 in 2000.* **Sources: Ag4, Fo8, In5, NO3, VA3, Wbn, We4.**

Florida 90 - Medium to large, long-conic, pointed, irregular-shaped, deep red berries. Medium-soft to medium-firm, light pink flesh. Delicious flavor. Good to very good dessert quality; ships and freezes well. Prolific fruit and runner production. Susceptible to red stele, leaf spot and leaf scorch. Does well in sandy soil. Recommended for Florida and along the Gulf Coast. An important commercial variety in Florida and other parts of the Deep South. Ripens midseason. Developed by Dr. A. N. Brooks in Florida for commercial and home gardens. Introduced in 1947. *Source History: 7 in 1988; 4 in 1992; 3 in 2000.* **Sources: Bar, Ty2, Wel.**

Floridabelle - Large, dark red, sweet berries. More anthracnose resistance than Florida 90. *Source History: 1 in 1992; 1 in 2000.* **Sources: Ju2.**

Fort Laramie - Everbearing; produces runners, blooms and fruit simultaneously. Resulted from a cross between Chief Bemidji x Earlidawn x Geneva. Large to very large, bright scarlet fruit; dark pink to scarlet interior. Firm, sweet flesh; exceptionally aromatic. Good for eating fresh, freezing and preserving. Vigorous plants produce lots of runners. Self-fertile; pollinates well in cool or warm temperatures. Produces very heavy crop. Somewhat susceptible to mildew. Developed primarily for the North, but widely adaptable. Survives -30 degrees F. with no root or crown injury. Developed at the Cheyenne Experimental Station in Wyoming. *Source History: 15 in 1988; 22 in 1992; 24 in 2000.* **Sources: Bu1, Co12, Fa1, Fi1, Fo4, GR26, Gur, In5, Int, Jun, Ko2, Le2, Lin, NO3, Pe2, Rid, SH8, Sm6, VA3, Wa16, WA7, Wbn, We4.**

Fresca - Everbearing. Produces 1" berries all summer. Starts bearing fruit six weeks before Sweetheart, another variety that is started from seed. Sow in January

or February. Bears fruit 30 days after transplant. *Source History: 1 in 2000.*
Sources: Par.

G-19 - Chandler x Holiday. Large fruit. Size and flavor compares to Kent. Vigorous plant with pale leaves. Unknown winter hardiness. Developed at the University of Guelph, HRIO, Simcoe, Ontario, 1998. *Source History: 1 in 2000.*
Sources: Ag4.

Gaviota - California variety. Patented. *Source History: 2 in 2000.* **Sources: Fo8, NO3.**

Gem Everbearing - So much like Superfection that it is considered to be the same variety. Good for preserving, freezing and canning. Dependable everbearer in the Northeast. *Source History: 3 in 1988; 6 in 1992; 4 in 2000.* **Sources: Bar, Lee, Sav, Wel.**

Glooscap - MicMac X Bounty. Medium size, glossy red fruit. Good for freezing or fresh market. Good yields. Vigorous plant maker. Does best in cool climates. Ripens late midseason. Developed by Agriculture Canada, Kentville, Nova Scotia, 1983. *Source History: 1 in 1988; 6 in 1992; 6 in 2000.* **Sources: Ag4, DAI, In5, NO3, Wbn, We4.**

Goliath - Everbearing. Large sweet, juicy fruit. Plant grows 3-4 in. tall. Does well in strawberry jars or hanging baskets. *Source History: 1 in 2000.* **Sources: Spr.**

Guardian - NC 1768 x Surecrop. Junebearing. More disease resistance than Surecrop. Large, conic, glossy, light red fruit. Flesh is lighter than skin. Excellent flavor; good for desserts, preserving and canning; only fair when frozen, because of light color. Medium size plants produce runners moderately but make a heavy bed. Resistant to verticillium, five races of red stele, leaf scorch and mildew. Moderately susceptible to leaf spot. Good for commercial plantings, shipping, Pick Your Own, home gardens. Adapted from Maryland to Massachusetts and westward throughout the Midwest. Midseason. Zones 4-8. Introduced by the USDA and Maryland Station in 1959. *Source History: 34 in 1988; 35 in 1992; 17 in 2000.* **Sources: Al2, Bar, Be4, Co12, Co6, DAI, Fi1, Gur, In5, Kro, RAM, Rid, SH8, Shu, Sm6, VA3, Wor.**

Gurney's Giant - Junebearer. Fruit measures up to 3" across. Excellent flavor. Used for fresh eating, freezing and canning. Huge yields. Pollinate with Big Boy. *Source History: 1 in 2000.* **Sources: Gur.**

Hecker - Everbearing. Large fruit; good flavor. Excellent marketability. University of California introduction similar to Brighton, but more cold hardy. PVP. *Source History: 3 in 1988; 4 in 1992; 4 in 2000.* **Sources: Fo8, NO3, Wbn, We4.**

Honeoye (NY 1409) - Vibrant x Holiday. Large, conic, symmetrical, bright red fruit. Average firmness; above average quality. Tart flavor. Excellent freezer. Large, very vigorous, dark green plants; good early runner production. Heavy, consistent yields. No resistance to soil-borne diseases. Susceptible to verticillium and red stele. Tolerant of leaf spot, leaf scorch and fruit rot. Long fruiting season. Widely used for Pick Your Own or home garden; good shipper. Best from New England to Pennsylvania and west to Minnesota. May develop off-flavor on heavy clay soil. Midseason. Excellent crown hardiness. Hardy to Zone 3. Introduced by the Geneva Station in 1979. *Source History: 26 in 1988; 34 in 1992; 41 in 2000.*
Sources: Ag4, Al2, Be4, Bo5, Bos, Bu1, BU12, Co12, Co6, Cu4, DAI, Fa1, Fed, Fi1, Gur, In5, Int, Je2, Jun, Ko2, Kro, Le2, Mel, Mi1, Mo8, NO3, Nou, Pin, RAM, Rid, Roh, SH8, Shu, Sm6, VA3, Ver, Wa16, WA7, We4, Wh4.

Hood - Large to very large, bright glossy red fruit turning dark when fully ripe.

Fine, sweet flavor. Excellent fruit quality. Excellent for preserves and jams; good for all other uses. Vigorous, very productive, erect plants make picking easy. Resistant to root rot, mildew and red stele. Bears entire crop over a short period. Popular home garden variety. Ripens in early June. Not particularly winter hardy. *Source History: 8 in 1988; 6 in 1992; 5 in 2000.* **Sources: Clo, NO3, SPO, Wbn, We4.**

Idea (84-86-3) - Sel. 79-12-13 x Etna. Junebearer. Vigorous plants produce moderately firm, large fruit. Red stele resistant; anthracnose tolerant. Late season maturity extends the picking season. Developed at the Italian University Breeding Program in Cesena, Italy. Plant patent pending. *Source History: 1 in 2000.* **Sources: Nou.**

Irvine - Everbearer. Day neutral. University of California release. Patented. *Source History: 2 in 2000.* **Sources: Fo8, NO3.**

Jewel (NY 1221) (Senga Sengana x NY F58) x Holiday. Large to very large, wedge-conic, glossy, bright red fruit. Abrasion resistant skin. Firmer than average flesh. Excellent, slightly aromatic flavor. Good dessert and freezing quality. Relatively compact, dark green plants with a moderate number of runners. Resistant to leaf spot and leaf scorch. Susceptible to verticillium wilt and red stele. Low incidence of fruit rots. Recommended for the Northeast and the Midwest. Outstanding size, appearance and taste. Excellent for all commercial and home uses. Ripens midseason. Good winter hardiness. Introduced by the Geneva Station in 1983. U.S. Plant Patent No. 5897. *Source History: 11 in 1988; 11 in 1992; 15 in 2000.* **Sources: Ag4, Al2, Be4, Bo5, Co12, DAI, HA12, In5, Je2, Jun, Kro, NO3, Nou, Sm6, Wh4.**

Jumbo, Field's - Everbearer. Large yields of sweet, large berries with rich red color. Vigorous, disease resistant plants bear from June to September. Thrives in any soil, even in sand. *Source History: 1 in 2000.* **Sources: Fi1.**

Kent (K68-58) (Redgauntlet x Tioga) x Raritan. Large to very large, firm, uniform, conic berries with long stems; dark red throughout. Mild, subacid flavor. Very good quality. Excellent for fresh eating, freezing and processing. Heavy yielding, vigorous plants; excellent runner production. May require heavy mulch, since fruit tends to rest on the ground. Resistant to leaf spot and verticillium wilt. Slightly susceptible to powdery mildew. Prime market variety that produces heavily in northern areas of the Northeast and Midwest. Ripens midseason. Extremely winter hardy. Developed at the Kentville Research Station in Nova Scotia, 1982. *Source History: 14 in 1988; 14 in 1992; 12 in 2000.* **Sources: Ag4, Be4, Co12, DAI, HA12, In5, Kro, Lin, Mo8, NO3, Nou, Wbn.**

Laguna - California variety. Patented. *Source History: 1 in 2000.* **Sources: Fo8.**

Lateglow (MdUS 4839) - Tamella x MdUS 3184. Junebearing. Large to very large, uniform, symmetrical berries. Firm, glossy, deep scarlet skin. Solid, juicy, sweet, aromatic, medium red flesh. Fancy quality. Medium size plants runner freely. High yields. Very resistant to root rot, red stele and verticillium wilt; varies in reaction to the leaf diseases. Tolerant to powdery mildew, leaf spot, leaf scorch, gray mold and leather rot. Susceptible to anthracnose and leaf blight. Ripens late; often used to extend production. Zones 6-8a. Developed by Dr. Gene Galetta of the USDA, Beltsville, Maryland. Introduced in 1976. *Source History: 6 in 1988; 18 in 1992; 9 in 2000.* **Sources: Al2, Be4, Bo5, Co12, DAI, In5, Mo8, Pe3, Wor.**

Latestar (MdUS 5084) - Lateglow x Allstar. Large attractive, firm, glossy red berries with pleasant, slightly acid flavor. Principal sugar is glucose. Disease resistant but susceptible to leaf blight.   Ripens late.   Best suited to the mid-Atlantic region. *Source History: 7 in 2000.* **Sources: Al2, BU12, Co12, DAI, Mey, Mo8, Nou.**

Lester (MdUS 4359) - Raritan x MdUS 3413.   Medium to large, uniform, symmetrical, deep red fruit.   Firm flesh; superior mild flavor.   Good for home use; fair for processing and freezing.   Vigorous, medium size plants with hardy crowns. Consistently productive.   Highly resistant to five strains of red stele.   Some resistance to powdery mildew, leaf scorch, leaf blight, botrytis and leather rot.   Susceptible to verticillium wilt.   Fine commercial variety for packing and shipping. Adapted to mid-Atlantic and lower New England areas.   Ripens from early to early-midseason depending on location.   Developed at the University of Maryland. *Source History: 14 in 1988; 11 in 1992; 7 in 2000.* **Sources: Be4, Bo5, DAI, Kro, Le2, Mo8, Nou.**

Mara des Bois - Perennial strawberry.   U.S. Plant Patent No. 8517. *Source History: 1 in 2000.* **Sources: HI10.**

Marmolada - Gorella x Selezione No. 15.   Plants perform best in a raised bed situation with drip irrigation.   U.S.   Plant Patent No.   8535. *Source History: 1 in 2000.* **Sources: Nou.**

Mesabi (MnUS 248) - Glooscap x MnUS 99.   Large firm berries with red throughout.   Excellent flavor.   Ripens midseason.   Winter hardy.   Shows excellent disease and root rot resistance.   Developed at the University of Minnesota and USDA-Maryland.   Patent pending. *Source History: 5 in 2000.* **Sources: Ag4, DAI, In5, Kro, Nou.**

Mic Mac - Tioga x Guardsman S1.   Medium to large, glossy, dark red fruits.   Firm flesh and skin.   True strawberry flavor and aroma.   Excellent for freezing; good for dessert and processing.   Extremely vigorous, heavily productive plants.   Good runner production.   Susceptible to red stele, leaf spot and leaf scorch.   Adapted for upper Northwest, upper Midwest and Canada.   Recommended for areas which are subject to winter damage.   Ripens midseason.   Developed in Canada for northern climates. *Source History: 8 in 1988; 2 in 1992; 1 in 2000.* **Sources: Mo8.**

Midway - Dixieland x Temple.   Junebearing.   Medium to large, uniform, long conic, dark red berries with yellow seeds.   Smooth textured, juicy, firm flesh; tough skin.   Fine low acid flavor.   Ideal for dessert, freezing or preserves.   Maintains well during picking and processing.   Good long distance shipper, but lacks flavor. Healthy, vigorous, very productive plants; plenty of runners.   Long bearing season. Resistant to one race of red stele and verticillium.   Susceptible to leaf spot, leaf scorch, extreme heat and drought.   Poor on sandy soils; best on heavier clay or loam.   Ideal for Northeast and North Central states.   Midseason.   Zones 4-8. *Source History: 26 in 1988; 22 in 1992; 9 in 2000.* **Sources: Bar, Be4, Co12, DAI, Fa1, Jun, Kro, Mel, Nou.**

Mira - Scott x Honeoye.   Junebearer.   Glossy, medium red fruit with pleasant flavor.   Moderately vigorous plants.   Consistent producer over a longer time.   Ripens midseason.   Developed by Agriculture Canada, Kentville, Nova Scotia, 1996.   Plant patent pending. *Source History: 2 in 2000.* **Sources: Ag4, Nou.**

Mohawk - MdUS 4587 x Earliglow.   Same size fruit as its parent, Earliglow, with less tough skin.   Ripens 2-3 days earlier.   Shows more tolerance to powdery mildew.   Plant shows high vigor and runnering ability.   Good for fresh shipping or local market.   Recommended for southeastern Canada and northeastern U.S.   Developed by the USDA-MD and Ontario Ministry of Agriculture, 1994. *Source History: 6 in 2000.* **Sources: Ag4, Al2, Bo5, In5, Mo8, NO3.**

Nanaimo - Pacific northwest variety. Patented. *Source History: 2 in 2000.*
Sources: NO3, Wbn.

Nisqually - Everbearing. Large berries, measuring up to 5" around. Firm, rich red fruit from the heart out, without green tips. Produces throughout the entire season right up to snow flurries. *Source History: 1 in 1988; 1 in 1992; 1 in 2000.* **Sources: St6.**

Northeaster (MdUS 4787) - MdUS 4380 x Holiday. Large, firm fruit with strong flavor and aroma. Excellent fresh market or frozen berry for growers with either clay or silt loam soils. Resists red stele root rot; susceptible to powdery mildew. Early maturity. Hardy to Zone 4. Best adapted to the northeastern U.S. Developed by the USDA-Maryland, 1994. *Source History: 12 in 2000.* **Sources: Ag4, Al2, DAI, Fed, In5, Je2, Kro, Mi1, Mo8, NO3, Nou, VIR.**

Ogallala - *Fragaria vesca* (wild Rocky Mountain strawberry) x *F. ananassa.* Combines wild strawberry flavor with large size, heavy fruiting and everbearing habit. Large, plump fruit. Firm flesh, solid red throughout. Excellent for preserves. Plants are vigorous, drought resistant, productive and hardy; limit new runners to 4-5 per plant. Excellent disease resistance. Especially good from the Mississippi and west through the Mountain States. Also ideal for home gardeners in northern or mountainous areas who have less than ideal soil. Hardy in Zones 3-8. Developed by the USDA and the University of Nebraska. *Source History: 12 in 1988; 16 in 1992; 10 in 2000.* **Sources: Co12, Fa1, Fi1, GR26, Gur, Jun, Le2, Pe2, SH8, Wel.**

Oso Grande - Parker x (Tioga x Pjaro Hybrid). Everbearing. Exceptionally large fruit with good quality. Originated in California. U.S. Plant Patent No. 6578. *Source History: 3 in 1992; 3 in 2000.* **Sources: Fo8, NO3, Sm6.**

Ozark Beauty - Everbearing. Large, firm, wedge-shaped, long-necked berries, some 4" across. Bright red, inside and out. High sugar content; won first in Iowa State taste tests. Excellent for eating fresh, canning, freezing and preserves. Unusually vigorous plants; thick foliage and deep roots. Self-pollinating. Thrives in any soil, even sand. Produced over 12,000 quarts per acre at Iowa State; 116 quarts per 100' row. Resistant to leaf spot and leaf scorch. Susceptible to red stele and verticillium wilt. Recommended for home gardens in the North and for southern mountain areas. Hardy in Zones 4-8. Developed in the Ozarks of Arkansas. *Source History: 42 in 1988; 46 in 1992; 38 in 2000.* **Sources: Bar, Bos, Bu1, Bu2, BU12, Co12, Fa1, Fi1, Fo4, Gur, Int, Iso, Jo3, Jun, Ko2, Kro, Le2, Led, Lee, Mel, Mey, Mi1, MI5, Pe2, RAM, Rid, Sav, SH8, Shu, Sm6, Spr, St4, VA3, Ver, Wa16, WA7, Wel, Wor.**

Pacific - Everbearing, day neutral variety. Developed in California. Patented. *Source History: 2 in 2000.* **Sources: Fo8, NO3.**

Pajaro (C-45) - Medium to large, long-conic fruit with slight neck and smooth, glossy, firm skin. Firm flesh; good long distance shipper. Good dessert and freezing quality. Good runner production. Does not have as high a resistance to leaf diseases as its parent, Sequoia. Susceptible to red stele, leaf spot and leaf scorch. Does not do well during extremely dry, hot summers. Recommended for Florida, along the Gulf Coast and in similar areas. Developed at the University of California. Introduced in 1973. U.S. Plant Patent expired. *Source History: 5 in 1988; 3 in 1992; 3 in 2000.* **Sources: Fo8, NO3, Pe2.**

Parker - Large, attractive fruit. Inside color is uniformly red throughout. Very firm flesh; should be a good keeper. Self-pollinating throughout the season. Named for the late Robert Parker. Introduced in 1979. U.S. Plant Patent No. 5263.

Source History: 3 in 1988; 1 in 1992; 2 in 2000. **Sources: Fo8, NO3.**

Pelican - Junebearer. *Source History: 1 in 2000.* **Sources: Le2.**

Pink Panda - Small, edible fruit. Beautiful, pink blooms from late spring until fall. Hardy, vigorous plant grows 6-8" tall with a spreading habit. Makes a good ground cover; works well in window boxes, containers and hanging baskets. Hardy in Zones 3-9. Developed by Adrian Bloom, famed English perennial authority. U.S. Plant Patent No. 7598. *Source History: 2 in 1992; 3 in 2000.* **Sources: Ed2, HI10, Rai.**

Pocahontas - Tennessee Shipper x Midland. Medium to large, blunt conic, bright red fruit; bright green cap and sunken seeds. Firm flesh; tough skin. Tart flavor. Excellent for eating fresh, freezing, jams and jellies. Retains large size, sweetness and fine appearance throughout the season. Exceptionally vigorous plants. Average yield. Resistant to leaf scorch; partially resistant to leaf spot. Susceptible to red stele. Good for shipping, commercial plantings and processing. Grows best from southern Pennsylvania to Upper South and southwest to Missouri. Ripens midseason. Introduced by the Virginia Truck Experiment Station in 1953. *Source History: 12 in 1988; 6 in 1992; 1 in 2000.* **Sources: Wel.**

Premier (Howard 17) - Junebearer. Medium to large, conical, deep red fruit with yellow seeds. Tart flavor. Healthy foliage. Premier's blossoms are so protected by its stem and calyx that they are nearly frostproof. Good yielder. One of the oldest springbearers grown. *Source History: 2 in 1988; 3 in 1992; 1 in 2000.* **Sources: Mo8.**

Primetime (MdUS 5069) - Junebearer. Large, attractive, bright scarlet berries with pink flesh. Pleasant aroma and flavor. Produces well on both light and heavy soils. Disease resistant. Ripens midseason. Recommended for mid-Atlantic region. Introduced in 1996. *Source History: 10 in 2000.* **Sources: Al2, BU12, DAI, In5, Kro, Le2, Mey, Mo8, NO3, Nou.**

Profumata di Tortona (Musk Strawberry) - *Fragaria moschata*. Highly aromatic, small fruit with a hint of both raspberry and pineapple. Plant spreads rapidly, forming a decorative groundcover. Known as the "hautbois strawberry" in France. Once raised commercially in the region of Tortona, Italy. *Source History: 1 in 1992; 1 in 2000.* **Sources: Rai.**

Puget Reliance - June bearer. Large, good quality fruit. Plants are vigorous and virus tolerant. Adapts to a wide range of sites. Pacific Northwest variety. Introduced in 1988. Patented. *Source History: 4 in 2000.* **Sources: Clo, NO3, SPO, We4.**

Quinault - Everbearing. One of the largest strawberries, often as big as teacups. Firm and deep red; tasty. Good for desserts, preserves and eating fresh. Not for freezing. Vigorous plants produce many runners. Actually produces berries on unrooted runners. High yielding. Resistant to leaf spot, leaf scorch and root rot. Mildew susceptible. Fruit too soft for roadside marketing; excellent for Pick Your Own. Very popular for home gardens. Surpassed all other everbearing strawberry varieties in yield and berry size in California during 1977. Good in cold areas. Developed at Washington State University. *Source History: 20 in 1988; 23 in 1992; 18 in 2000.* **Sources: Bu1, CO5, Fa1, Fi1, Fo4, In5, Int, Ko2, Le2, NO3, Pe2, SH8, Sm6, VA3, WA7, Wbn, We4.**

Rainier - High quality, large bright red fruit throughout the season. Wedge-conic shape. Fine flavor. Good for freezing, fresh market or processing. Virus tolerant. Ripens in late spring. *Source History: 6 in 1988; 5 in 1992; 5 in 2000.* **Sources: Bu7, NO3, SPO, Wbn, We4.**

Raritan - Jerseybelle x Redglow. Medium-large to large, glossy, bright red fruit with partially embedded yellow seeds and attractive green cap. Solid flesh; firm skin. Exceptionally good taste. Good for table use and fresh market. Too light colored for freezing. Plants run freely. Very high producer; ships well. Susceptible to red stele and verticillium wilt, powdery mildew, leaf spot and leaf scorch. Well adapted throughout the Northeast and as far south as Norfolk, Virginia; good reports also from the Midwest as far west as Iowa. Ripens midseason. Developed at Rutgers University in New Jersey. Introduced in 1967. *Source History: 16 in 1988; 10 in 1992; 6 in 2000.* **Sources: Be4, Bo5, Mo8, Nou, Roh, Wh4.**

Red Chief - NC 1768 x Surecrop. Medium to large, conic, firm, glossy, medium red fruit; slight necks on secondary berries. Sweet, rich flavor persists when frozen. Good dessert quality; very good for freezing. Moderately vigorous plant produces runners freely. Resistant to five races of red stele, leaf scorch and mildew. Intermediate resistance to verticillium wilt. Somewhat susceptible to leaf spot. Grows well from New England to North Carolina, across to Illinois. Best on medium soils. Maintains size throughout the season. Good for Pick Your Own, home use and processing. Ripens midseason. Developed in Maryland. Introduced in 1968. *Source History: 27 in 1988; 23 in 1992; 20 in 2000.* **Sources: Al2, Be4, Bo5, BU12, Co12, Co6, DAI, GR26, In5, Kro, Led, Mel, Mo8, NO3, Nou, Rid, SH8, Shu, Sm6, Wa16.**

Red Coat - Sparkle x Valentine. Medium to large, glossy, medium red berries. Very sweet, firm flesh and medium tough skin; good shipper. Excellent quality. Good for fresh use, canning or freezing. Husky, vigorous plants hold the fruits well above the ground. Moderate runner production. Susceptible to red stele and verticillium wilt. Resistant to leaf spot and leaf scorch. Very resistant to winter injury; has shown some frost tolerance. Best adapted to eastern Canada, northern New England to New York, and westward through upper Michigan, northern Wisconsin and Minnesota. Ripens early-mid to midseason. Hardy to Zone 3. Developed in Canada. *Source History: 11 in 1988; 6 in 1992; 3 in 2000.* **Sources: Ag4, Le2, SH8.**

Redcrest - *Source History: 3 in 1992; 1 in 2000.* **Sources: NO3.**

Robinson (Giant Robinson, Kardinal King, Scarlet Beauty) - Premier x Washington. Large, conical, blunt-ended berries; bright red outside, lighter red inside. Mild flavor; fair dessert quality. Fair to good for canning and freezing. Large plant produces runners very vigorously. Good results in poorer soils where others fail; grows best in light soil. Produces well where extremely dry. Resistant to verticillium wilt and leaf spot. Susceptible to red stele. Excellent production over a long fruiting season. Soft berries limit its uses to mostly Pick Your Own. Good home garden variety. Does best in the Midwest and the Northeast. Ripens midseason. Developed in Michigan. Introduced in 1930. *Source History: 14 in 1988; 17 in 1992; 10 in 2000.* **Sources: Bu1, Fa1, Fo4, Int, Mel, Mi1, Mo8, Rid, SH8, Sm6.**

Sable - Veestar x Cavendish. Resistant to several races of red stele. Winter hardiness unknown for the Midwest. Good for Pick Your Own but not suited for prepicked. Developed by Agriculture Canada, Kentville, Nova Scotia in 1998. *Source History: 1 in 2000.* **Sources: Ag4.**

Scott (MdUS 4376) - Sunrise x Tioga. Large, uniform, symmetrical, short conic fruit. Bright red skin; firm, light red flesh resists bruising. Rich aroma; mild, sweet flavor. Excellent for fresh eating; holds color during freezing and processing. Very productive when excess runners are removed. Grows even on heavy clay. Resistant to five races of red stele. Some resistance to leaf scorch, powdery mildew and verticillium wilt. Excellent for Pick Your Own, home gardens and roadside markets. Best in Eastern and Central U.S. Midseason. Named after Donald Scott, USDA breeder of disease resistant strawberries. Introduced by Maryland Station in 1979. *Source History: 17 in 1988; 7 in 1992; 2 in 2000.* **Sources: DAI, Sm6.**

Seascape - Everbearer. Extra large, firm berry. Scarlet red color inside and out. Flavorful. Developed in California. U.S. Plant Patent No. 7614. *Source History: 1 in 1992; 7 in 2000.* **Sources: CO5, Fo8, Ga6, In5, NO3, Rai, We4.**

Selva - Everbearer. Large fruit. Firm flesh; excellent flavor. Plants are vigorous and prolific runnermakers. Consistently heavy producer. Berries hold up well under wet conditions. With a minimum of conditioning, will flower and fruit effectively independent of daylength through summer and early fall. Hardy in Zones 5-9. U.S. Plant Patent No. 5266. *Source History: 6 in 1988; 11 in 1992; 10 in 2000.* **Sources: Clo, Ed2, Fi1, Fo8, Gur, In5, NO3, Sm6, Wbn, We4.**

Seneca (NY 1529) - NY 1261 x Holiday. Junebearer. Large, firm fruit of good quality. High yields. Does best on well drained soil because of its susceptibility to red stele and verticillium wilt. Adapted widely in the Great Lakes Region of the U.S. Developed at Geneva, New York. U.S. Plant Patent No. 8991. *Source History: 4 in 1992; 3 in 2000.* **Sources: DAI, Le2, Nou.**

Sequoia - Very large, dark red berries; outstanding flavor. Fair dessert and freezing quality. Productive Junebearing plant; bears over a 2-3 month period. Good runner production. Susceptible to red stele, leaf spot and leaf scorch. At times will produce a fall crop, but not consistent in this regard. Too soft for shipping; excellent for home use in warm climate. Recommended for Florida, along the Gulf Coast and similar areas in the lower South. Sometimes used for roadside market and Pick Your Own. Ripens early. Hardy in Zones 5-9. Developed by the University of California. U.S. Plant Patent No. 3178. *Source History: 11 in 1988; 15 in 1992; 10 in 2000.* **Sources: CO5, Ed2, Ju2, Ko2, Le2, NO3, Pe2, Wbn, We4, Wel.**

Shortcake - Everbearing. Glossy, long red fruit. Larger than most everbearers. Burpee exclusive. *Source History: 1 in 1992; 1 in 2000.* **Sources: Bu2.**

Shuksan - Junebearer. Large, glossy, bright red fruit with slightly indented yellowish red seeds. Medium firm flesh; good flavor. Good for fresh eating; excellent freezer. Plant is large, very vigorous, produces runners freely. Virus tolerant and red stele resistant. Especially suited to the Northwest; widely grown in western Washington. Does not demand perfect drainage. Extremely cold hardy. *Source History: 7 in 1988; 6 in 1992; 6 in 2000.* **Sources: Clo, NO3, On3, Rai, SPO, We4.**

Simonet - *Source History: 1 in 2000.* **Sources: Va5.**

Sparkle - Fairfax x Aberdeen. Medium to large, short, blunt-conic, dark red berries; yellow seeds, large caps. Mildly subacid flavor. Excellent quality. Used for fresh, freezing and preserves. Dependable, productive plants if thinned ruthlessly. Blooms late; rarely affected by frosts. Resistant to leaf spot and red stele. Susceptible to verticillium. Lacks size to be a fancy market berry; fine for home gardens and Pick Your Own. Does well on most soils, extremely well on clay. Adapted to the Northeast, south to Maryland, westward through northern portions of Ohio, Indiana and Illinois. Ripens late. Very hardy; to Zone 3. Developed in New Jersey. Introduced in 1931. *Source History: 30 in 1988; 35 in 1992; 34 in 2000.* **Sources: Al2, Be4, Bo5, BU12, Co12, Co6, Cu4, DAI, Fa1, Fed, Fi1, Gur, In5, Je2, Jun, Kro, Le2, Led, Mel, Mey, Mi1, Mo8, NO3, Nou, Pin, Rid, Roh, SH8, Shu, Sm6, VA3, Ver, Wbn, We4.**

Spring Giant - Junebearing. Huge, dark red berries up to 2.5" across. Firm flesh; extraordinary flavor which is often lacking in the larger varieties. Leaves measure up to 9" across. Not self-fruitful. Plant another variety for pollination and best yields. U.S. Plant Patent No. 3716. *Source History: 1 in 1988; 1 in 1992; 1 in 2000.* **Sources: Fi1.**

Stoplight - Junebearer. Similar to Dunlap. Bright red fruit. Uniform red interior with no noticeable core or stringiness. Excellent flavor. Freezes well. Hardy in Zone 3. *Source History: 1 in 1988; 3 in 1992; 2 in 2000.* **Sources: Rid, SH8.**

Streamliner - Everbearing. Large to very large, high quality, rich red fruit. Firm flesh that stands up to handling. Exceptional flavor. Vigorous and hardy; very high yields. Productive from July until frost. Hardy in Zones 4-8. *Source History: 3 in 1988; 4 in 1992; 2 in 2000.* **Sources: WA8, Wel.**

Sumas - Large, bright red fruit does not darken. Slightly aromatic. High yields. Suitable for fresh use and processing. Winter hardy. Susceptible to leaf spot. Originated in British Columbia, Canada. *Source History: 2 in 1988; 3 in 1992; 3 in 2000.* **Sources: NO3, SPO, Wbn.**

Sunrise - US 4152 x Stelemaster. Medium to large, symmetrical, conic fruit, with slight neck. Glossy, light red skin. Extra firm, subacid flesh. Good flavor; excellent aroma. Dessert quality, but somewhat pale flesh causes poor appearance in frozen pack. Excellent keeper. Holds appearance on or off the vine longer than any other red stele resistant variety. Extremely vigorous plants will runner quite freely. Above average yields. Resistant to three races of red stele fungus and to verticillium wilt. Leaves are resistant to leaf scorch and mildew; susceptible to leaf spot. Drought resistant. Developed in Maryland. Introduced in 1965. *Source History: 12 in 1988; 11 in 1992; 7 in 2000.* **Sources: Bar, Lee, Mel, Mo8, Sav, Ty2, Wel.**

Sunset - Developed at the University of California. Patented. *Source History: 1 in 2000.* **Sources: Fo8.**

Surecrop - Fairland x MdUS 1972. Junebearer. Medium to large fruit; firm flesh. Medium tough, glossy skin; yellow seeds. Irregular, wedge-shaped, primary berries; uniform, short, round-conic secondary berries. Deep rich red throughout. Excellent, slightly tart flavor. Ideal for dessert and freezing. Unusually vigorous. Runners freely under adverse conditions. Above average yields. Good on poor or dry soil. Resistant to red stele, verticillium wilt, leaf spot, leaf scorch and drought. Good size all season; holds well during shipping. Adapted north of North Carolina and throughout Central U.S. One huge crop in June. Zones 3-8. Originated in Maryland. Introduced in 1951. *Source History: 38 in 1988; 36 in 1992; 31 in 2000.* **Sources: Al2, Bar, Be4, Bo5, Bu1, Bu2, BU12, Co12, Co6, DAI, Fa1, Fi1, GR26, Gur, In5, Je2, Kro, Le2, Mel, Mey, Mi1, Mo8, NO3, RAM, Rid, Roh, SH8, Sm6, St4, WA7, Wor.**

Sweet Charlie - Junebearer. Withstands heat and humidity; good for Southern growers. Bears sweet fruit. Self-pollinating. Zones 7-9. Developed by Florida University. Patented. *Source History: 5 in 2000.* **Sources: Ed2, Gur, Je2, Le2, NO3.**

Sweet Delight - Everbearing. Very sweet, bright crimson fruits. Sends out lots of runners which begin bearing fruit almost immediately. *Source History: 1 in 2000.* **Sources: Fi1.**

Temptation - Largest fruit of any other seed strain. Tangy, juicy, sweet flavor. Produces continuously throughout the summer. Plant produces few runners. U.S. Plant Patent No. 3798. *Source History: 1 in 1992; 2 in 2000.* **Sources: Sto, Tho.**

Tennessee Beauty - Medium to large, long-conic, smooth, bright, medium to deep red fruit with large green cap which is easily removed. Firm flesh with slightly tart flavor. Green tipped until fully ripe. Good for fresh eating; excellent for freezing and processing. Healthy, productive plants are vigorous, heavy yielders. Produces lots of runners. Resistant to leaf spot and leaf scorch. Susceptible to red stele. Grows well in all soils. Firm shipper; holds color well. Fine late season variety for the Southeast and South Central states, especially from Maryland to Missouri. Hardy in Zones 5-8. Introduced in 1930. *Source History: 15 in 1988; 16 in 1992; 6 in 2000.* **Sources: Bar, Iso, Lee, Sav, Sm6, Ty2.**

Tioga - Medium to large, long, wedge-shaped fruit; caps easily. Tough, glossy, smooth, light to medium red skin with yellow seeds. Exceptionally firm flesh. Very good flavor. Good dessert quality; excellent shipper. Good appearance even when overripe. One of the best for freezing and commercial use. Vigorous, self-pollinating, heavily productive plants. Moderate resistance to leaf spot and leaf blight. Not resistant to red stele. Primarily grown in warmer or hot climates, such as areas similar to Florida and along the Gulf Coast. Hardy in Zones 7-9. Developed at the University of California. *Source History: 8 in 1988; 6 in 1992; 1 in 2000.* **Sources: Wel.**

Totem - Firm, uniform, conic, bright red berry. Excellent quality. Well suited to processing and fresh market. High yielding; moderate runner. Ripens early. Extra hardy, but can be damaged by late frost. Shows considerable resistance to red stele and virus diseases. Introduced in 1971. *Source History: 3 in 1988; 2 in 1992; 3 in 2000.* **Sources: NO3, SPO, We4.**

Tribute (EB 60) - EB 18 x MdUS 4258. Everbearing. Medium-large berries; short, conic wedge varies from irregular to symmetrical. Bright red skin; firm, light to medium red flesh. Acidic, but pleasant flavor. Starts its heavy spring crop midseason. Best for fresh eating out of season. Good processing quality. Medium size plant; quite vigorous. Resistant to red stele, powdery mildew, leaf blight and leaf scorch. Well adapted to upland areas of the South, mild areas in the East and Pacific Northwest. Favorite among commercial growers and home gardeners. Developed by Dr. Scott and R. Darper at the University of Maryland. Introduced in 1982. *Source History: 18 in 1988; 22 in 1992; 21 in 2000.* **Sources: Ag4, Bos, Clo, Co12, Co6, Coo, DAI, Gur, HA12, In5, Kro, Mi1, NO3, Nou, SH8, Shu, Sm6, Ver, Wbn, We4, Wor.**

Tristar (EB 62) - EB 18 x MdUS 4258. Everbearing. Similar to Tribute, but noticeably sweeter and more aromatic. Medium size, symmetrical, short-conic fruit. Firm, glossy, deep red skin. Solid, medium red flesh. Excellent for fresh eating and freezing. Medium size plants; moderate number of runners which bloom and bear fruit before rooted; good for hanging baskets. Resistant to red stele and verticillium wilt. Tolerant to leaf scorch and leaf blight. Fall crop is heaviest. Cool fall weather brings larger, more elongated fruit. Hardy in Zones 4-8. Developed by Dr. Scott and Dr. Draper at the University of Maryland. Introduced in 1982. *Source History: 23 in 1988; 28 in 1992; 37 in 2000.* **Sources: Ag4, Be4, Bo5, Bu2, Bu7, BU12, Clo, Co12, Cu4, DAI, Ed2, Fed, Ga6, Gur, HA12, In5, Jun, Kro, Lin, Mel, Mey, Mi1, NO3, Nou, On3, Pe2, Po2, Rai, Rid, Sh2, SH8, Sm6, St4, VA3, Wbn, We4, Wor.**

Trumpeter - Medium to large, well-formed, short-conic, intense red fruit. Soft, glossy skin. Excellent flavor. Very good quality for freezing, canning and fresh use. Berry size holds up well through entire picking season. Vigorous plants produce runners freely. Extremely heavy yielder. Susceptible to leaf spot and red stele. Resistance to verticillium wilt is unknown. Recommended for Minnesota, the upper Mississippi Valley and the plains states of the upper Midwest. Hardy to

Zone 3. Developed in Minnesota. Introduced in 1960. *Source History: 8 in 1988; 5 in 1992; 2 in 2000.* **Sources: Rid, SH8.**

Vesper - Utah Shipper x Jerseybelle. Large to very large, deep dark red berries with shiny skins and beautiful caps. Rather soft flesh; firm enough for commercial purposes, but a little too soft for distant shipments. Fair flavor. Small to medium size plants are vigorous, producing many runners. Average yields; requires well drained soil to be productive. Susceptible to red stele, leaf spot and leaf scorch. Good for lengthening the picking season, but lacks disease resistance and flavor. Ripens late. Developed at the New Jersey Agricultural Experiment Station. *Source History: 12 in 1988; 4 in 1992; 1 in 2000.* **Sources: Fa1.**

Wild Strawberry - *Fragaria virginiana.* Small, exceptionally sweet berries in June. Quality of fruit improved by transplanting. Abundant white flowers from April to June. Succeeds in rather dry location. Spreads by runners; makes a good ground cover. Zones 6-9. *Source History: 2 in 1988; 1 in 1992; 7 in 2000.* **Sources: ALD, Ed2, Ga8, Oik, Pl5, Rai, Tri.**

Wild White (Christina White) - *Fragaria virginiana.* Fruits are larger than regular native red strawberry. Plants runner freely. Zones 5-8. *Source History: 1 in 1992; 1 in 2000.* **Sources: Ed2.**

Wildfire - Spreading plant produces numerous runners which root and grow quickly. Dark pink to red flowers appear in May and June and continue less heavily throughout the summer. Edible red fruit. Does best in full sun. *Source History: 1 in 2000.* **Sources: We8.**

Winona (MnUS 210) - Earliglow x MnUS 52. Good trial variety where winter hardiness or diseases have been a problem. Good runner producer in matted row systems. Ripens late with Lateglow. Shows resistance to five eastern races of red stele root rot. Tolerant of powdery mildew, leaf scorch and leaf spot. Developed by the University of Minnesota breeding program, 1995. U.S. Plant Patent No. 10,191. *Source History: 8 in 2000.* **Sources: Ag4, Bo5, Co12, DAI, In5, Jun, Kro, Nou.**

Wood Strawberry - *Fragaria californica.* Tiny but sweet fruit. Spreads by runners to form a fast growing ground cover. Native to the West. Hardy in Zones 5-7. *Source History: 2 in 1988; 2 in 1992; 2 in 2000.* **Sources: Fo2, Las.**

WSU 23-10 - Junebearer. Vigorous plants bear large firm fruit with rich color and sweet, full strawberry flavor. Good yields. Late season ripening. *Source History: 1 in 2000.* **Sources: Rai.**

Almond

Prunus dulcis var. *dulcis*

Aldrich - Well sealed shell; 62% crack out. Blooms with Nonpareil; excellent pollinator for Nonpariel. Upright tree resembles Mission in growth habit. U.S. Plant Patent No. 5320. *Source History: 2 in 2000.* **Sources: Si3, WI4.**

All-In-One - Sweet almond. Soft shelled, sweet, Nonpareil-type nuts. Tree grows 15-20' tall. Late bloomer, 2-3 days before Mission. Heavy bearer. Self-fertile and a good pollinator for other almonds. Requires 500 hours of chilling. Hardy in Zones 6-9. Number one almond for home orchards. Developed by Floyd Zaiger. U.S. Plant Patent No. 4304. *Source History: 6 in 1988; 11 in 1992; 12 in 2000.* **Sources: Bay, Bu7, CO5, MI5, ORA, Pa2, Pe2, Rai, Son, St4, STR, WI4.**

Butte - Texas Mission x Nonpareil. Small to medium size, plump kernel similar to Mission. Semihard shell is well sealed. High yields. Particularly productive when used as pollinator for Nonpareil; good pollinator for Titan. Harvest 2 weeks after Nonpareil. 500 chilling hours. *Source History: 1 in 1988; 4 in 1992; 3 in 2000.* **Sources: Bay, Si3, WI4.**

Carmel - High quality kernels. Well sealed nuts keep well. Young tree sets heavy crops. Requires a pollinator. Excellent pollinator for Nonpareil. Harvest 2-3 weeks after Nonpareil. Requires 400 hours of chilling. *Source History: 3 in 1988; 5 in 1992; 3 in 2000.* **Sources: Si3, STR, WI4.**

Degn - Hard shell with a large, plump, brown kernel. Vigorous, relatively cold hardy tree. Heavy bearer. Requires a pollinator. *Source History: 1 in 1988; 1 in 1992; 1 in 2000.* **Sources: Va2.**

Fritz - Medium to small ovate-shaped nut with soft shell. Upright, somewhat spreading tree. Good pollinator for Nonpareil. Harvest 40 or more days after Nonpareil. U.S. Plant Patent No. 3005. *Source History: 1 in 1988; 2 in 1992; 2 in 2000.* **Sources: Si3, WI4.**

Garden Prince - Attractive, genetic dwarf tree grows 8-12' tall. Requires minimal pruning. Showy, light pink blossoms and dense foliage. Self-fruitful. Begins bearing in 2-3 years. Bears 10-15 lbs. of nuts each season. Large clusters of medium size, soft shelled nuts. Excellent quality. Ripens from late August to late September depending on location. Requires 150-500 hours of chilling. Hardy in Zone 9, except in central Florida and Southern Texas. Best production in climates without heavy February rains. Performance outdoors in the Pacific Northwest is still experimental. Developed by Floyd Zaiger. U.S. Plant Patent No. 5146. *Source History: 9 in 1988; 8 in 1992; 6 in 2000.* **Sources: Bay, CO5, ORA, Pa2, Son, WI4.**

Hall's Hardy - Ornamental tree with dark green foliage grows rapidly to 15-20'. Profusion of pale pink flowers in spring. Blooms late for an almond, but is still subject to late spring frosts. Self-fruitful. Heavy bearer. Produces nuts 2-3 years after planting. Large nuts with hard shells and bittersweet kernels. Hardier than commercial varieties and thicker shelled. Susceptible to brown rot, shot hole fungus and navel orange worm. Requires 600-800 hours of chilling. Hardy in Zones 5-9. Ripens from early September into October depending on location. Only almond suitable for the Pacific Northwest. *Source History: 17 in 1988; 22 in 1992; 14 in 2000.* **Sources: Bo5, CO5, Ed2, Fi1, Gur, JOY, ME3, Mel, MI5, Na4, Rai, Ty2, Wel, WI4.**

Hardy - Large, fine quality nuts. Thin, papery shells are easy to crack. Tree grows 15-25' tall. Pink blossoms in spring. Should bear two years after planting. Will grow anywhere peaches can be grown. *Source History: 2 in 1988; 2 in 1992; 2 in 2000.* **Sources: Bu1, Fo4.**

Ingrid - Possibly a peach x almond hybrid. Self-fertile. Resists peach leaf curl. From Sweden. *Source History: 1 in 2000.* **Sources: Hid.**

IXL - Large nuts with smooth soft shell. *Source History: 2 in 1992; 1 in 2000.* **Sources: Nrs.**

Livingston - Medium size kernel. Well sealed papershell. Very productive, upright, medium to large size tree. Harvest 8 days after Nonpareil. Very productive, upright, medium to large size tree. *Source History: 1 in 2000.* **Sources: WI4.**

Mission (Texas Mission, Texas Prolific Mission) - Round, hard shelled, well sealed nut with a short, plump, sweet kernel. Very productive tree that blooms and ripens late. Requires a pollinator. Inter-fruitful with All-In-One, Nonpareil, Price and Carmel. Resistant to navel orange worm. Susceptible to brown rot and shot hole fungus. Requires 500 hours of chilling. *Source History: 5 in 1988; 6 in 1992; 4 in 2000.* **Sources: Bay, Si3, STR, WI4.**

Monterey - Elongated kernel with high percentage of doubles. Soft, well sealed shell. Small to medium size tree is somewhat spreading. Blooms 2 days after Nonpareil; harvests one month after Nonpareil. *Source History: 1 in 1988; 2 in 1992; 3 in 2000.* **Sources: Si3, STR, WI4.**

Ne Plus Ultra - Smooth, long, broad, flat nut with a soft shell. Significant number of doubles. Spreading tree with a bushy growth habit. Requires a pollinator; satisfactory pollinator for Nonpareil in northern California. Ripens midseason. Requires 250 hours of chilling. *Source History: 7 in 1988; 12 in 1992; 9 in 2000.* **Sources: Bay, CO5, MI5, Nrs, ORA, Si3, STR, Va2, WI4.**

Nonpareil - The leading commercial variety and the standard for quality. Smooth, broad, flat, light brown kernel with a soft, thin shell. Excellent flavor. Tree requires a pollinator. Interfruitful with Price, Mission, All-In-One and Carmel, but only with Ne Plus Ultra in northern California. Early bloomer. Heavy bearer. Susceptible to brown rot, shot hole fungus and navel orange worm. Ripens from August to September depending on location. Requires 400 hours of chilling. About as cold hardy as a peach. Zone 6. *Source History: 10 in 1988; 18 in 1992; 12 in 2000.* **Sources: Bay, CO5, JOY, ME3, MI5, Nrs, ORA, Si3, STR, Va2, Wel, WI4.**

Northland - Hardy to Zone 5, possibly Zone 4. *Source History: 1 in 2000.* **Sources: Ed5.**

Padre - Medium to small kernel. Hard shell. Medium size, upright tree. High yields. Blooms 5 days after Nonpareil; harvests about 1 month after Nonpareil. *Source History: 1 in 1988; 4 in 1992; 2 in 2000.* **Sources: Si3, WI4.**

Peerless - Medium size kernel. Very hard, attractive shell. Used for in-shell market nuts. Medium size tree with moderate, upright growth habit. May be susceptible to frost because of early bloom time. Blooms 4 days before Nonpareil; harvests about 3 weeks after Nonpareil. *Source History: 1 in 1988; 3 in 1992; 2 in 2000.* **Sources: Si3, WI4.**

Price - Small, heavy bearing tree. Requires a pollinator. Blooms and ripens at the same time as Nonpareil and is its best pollinator. Very similar nut. Requires 400 hours of chilling. *Source History: 2 in 1988; 6 in 1992; 3 in 2000.* **Sources: Bay, Si3, WI4.**

Rosetta - *Source History: 1 in 2000.* **Sources: Si3.**

Ruby - Medium to small, plump kernel. Semihard, well sealed shell. Moderately vigorous, productive tree with upright growth habit. Harvest 30 days after Nonpareil. *Source History: 1 in 1992; 1 in 2000.* **Sources: WI4.**

Sonora - Paper thin shells are poorly sealed. Medium, slightly spreading tree. High yields. May have tendency to alternate bearing. Ripens seven days after Nonpareil. Released by the University of California. *Source History: 3 in 1992; 2 in 2000.* **Sources: Si3, WI4.**

Star - Fairly productive tree. Thin shelled, good quality nuts. *Source History: 1 in 1988; 1 in 1992; 1 in 2000.* **Sources: Wom.**

Texas (Mission) - Small, hard shelled nuts with sweet flavor. Self-fertile but yields increased if planted with Hall's. Hardy in Zones 5-8. *Source History: 2 in 1988; 7 in 1992; 5 in 2000.* **Sources: CO5, MI5, Nrs, ORA, Wel.**

Thompson - Small to medium size kernel with "paper" shell. Medium size, upright tree produces consistent heavy yields. Tree is sometimes difficult to shake. Blooms 5 days after Nonpareil; harvests about 2 weeks after Nonpareil. *Source History: 1 in 1988; 3 in 1992; 1 in 2000.* **Sources: WI4.**

Titan - Well sealed, thin shelled nuts. Good flavor. Large, well branched tree. Pollinate with Butte or most peach varieties. Hardiest known true almond variety. Blooms late thus escaping early spring frosts. Hardy to Zone 5. *Source History: 1 in 1988; 4 in 1992; 1 in 2000.* **Sources: Rai.**

Wood Colony - Medium size, elongated kernel. Well sealed soft shell. Spreading growth habit. Harvest 10 days after Nonpareil. U.S. Plant Patent No. 5538. *Source History: 2 in 2000.* **Sources: Si3, WI4.**

Butternut

Juglans cinerea

American - Egg-shaped, thin shelled nut, sometimes 3.5" long. Kernels are white meated. Rich, spicy, buttery flavor. Highly prized for use in baking, confections and for eating fresh. Tree quickly grows 30-60' tall; spreading top and attractive foliage. Heavy, annual production; bears 2-3 years after planting. Best production when cross-pollinated. Tolerates moist soils. Hardy. *Source History: 5 in 1988; 4 in 1992; 2 in 2000.* **Sources: Bu1, Mi1.**

Ayers - Medium size nut. Better meat to nut percentage than most. Upright tree; clean foliage. Late bloomer. Originated in Michigan. *Source History: 2 in 1988; 2 in 1992; 2 in 2000.* **Sources: Nol, Pa6.**

Beckwith - Medium size nut; 35 per pound; 21% kernel. Good cracking qualities. Originated in Ohio, 1985. *Source History: 1 in 2000.* **Sources: Nol.**

Booth - Good nuts. Nice tree. Originated in Ohio. *Source History: 2 in 1988; 1 in 1992; 1 in 2000.* **Sources: Nol.**

Buckley - Large nut. Vigorous grower; clean foliage. Originated in Iowa. *Source History: 1 in 1988; 2 in 1992; 2 in 2000.* **Sources: Nol, Pa6.**

Butternut (White Walnut) - Drooping clusters of large, egg-shaped nuts. Rough, thick shells terminate in a sharp point. Plump, tender kernel; distinctive, rich, oily, buttery flavor. Used in baking. Wide crowned tree reaches 40-70' tall and 40' wide. Ridged, furrowed bark. Short trunk, usually forked; coarsely branched. Large, hairy, compound, 10-20" leaves; yellow in fall. Bears in 2-3 years; life span of 30-80. Self-fertile. Prefers rich, moist, well drained soil. Satiny, light golden wood prized by cabinetmakers and carvers. Ripens late October. Hardier than Black

Walnut; Zones 3-7. Native from New Brunswick to Ontario southward to Arkansas. *Source History: 35 in 1988; 37 in 1992; 31 in 2000.* **Sources: Bar, Bea, Bu7, CA14, Ca8, Fed, Fi1, Fo4, Gur, Ins, Int, La3, LA4, Lee, LOV, Mc3, Mel, Na4, Or2, Pi2, Po2, Rai, Sav, Sc2, St12, Stl, Ty2, Va5, Wa16, WA8, Win.**

Chamberlain - Unknown parentage. Large nut; good cracking quality. Rich flavor. Nut production begins in the second year. Very hardy. Originated in New York, 1967. *Source History: 1 in 1988; 1 in 1992; 2 in 2000.* **Sources: Bea, Nol.**

Cobble No. 1 - *Source History: 1 in 1988; 1 in 1992; 1 in 2000.* **Sources: Nol.**

Craxezy - Medium size nut cracks easily. Good producer. Originated in Michigan. Introduced in 1934. *Source History: 3 in 1988; 2 in 1992; 2 in 2000.* **Sources: Nol, Pa6.**

Creighton - Medium size nut; good cracking quality. Vigorous tree; clean foliage. Well known variety. Ripens late. Originated in Pennsylvania. Introduced in 1944. *Source History: 2 in 1988; 1 in 1992; 1 in 2000.* **Sources: Nol.**

Doud - Good Dooley selection. Originated in Indiana. *Source History: 1 in 1988; 1 in 1992; 1 in 2000.* **Sources: Pa6.**

Morehead No. 1 - *Source History: 1 in 2000.* **Sources: Nol.**

My Joy - John Hershey selection. Originated in Pennsylvania in the 1930s. *Source History: 2 in 1988; 1 in 1992; 1 in 2000.* **Sources: Nol.**

New Discovery - *Source History: 1 in 1988; 1 in 2000.* **Sources: Nol.**

Van Syckle - Very large nut. Cracks out in halves. Heavy bearer. Introduced in 1950. *Source History: 1 in 1988; 1 in 1992; 1 in 2000.* **Sources: Nol.**

Weschcke - Medium to large nut; cracks well. Light kernels. Very productive tree. Extremely hardy. Originated in Wisconsin. Introduced in 1934. *Source History: 1 in 1988; 1 in 1992; 2 in 2000.* **Sources: Nol, Pa6.**

Chestnut

Castanea spp.

American Chestnut - *Castanea dentata.* Produces the best quality chestnuts; flavorful and delicious. Strong, stately, upright, spreading tree grows 50-70' tall and 40-60' wide. Dark green foliage turns yellow in the fall. Medium growth rate; 30-80 year life span. Prefers well drained to moist soil. Exceptionally hardy. Once covered large areas of the eastern U.S. Nearly exterminated by chestnut blight, *Endothia parasitica*, which was introduced in the late 1800s from Asia. Must be planted in isolated locations. *Source History: 12 in 1988; 12 in 1992; 14 in 2000.* **Sources: Bea, Bu7, Ca12, Ca8, Co15, Ed2, Fo2, Ins, Ju2, LA4, Mu2, Or2, Rai, Wa16.**

American: Sweet - While most chestnuts require cooking before consumption, this strain may be eaten raw. Membrane is light; peels easily. Elongated nut is smaller than others. Tall stately tree. *Source History: 2 in 1988; 1 in 1992; 1 in 2000.* **Sources: Gr4.**

AU-Homestead - Medium size nuts. Ripens late. Hardy to -20 degrees F. Reportedly some gall wasp resistance. Selected at Auburn, Alabama. *Source History: 1 in 2000.* **Sources: Emp.**

Carr - Old cultivar with upright growth habit. Medium to large size nuts. *Source History: 1 in 2000.* **Sources: Emp.**

Chandler - Originated in South Carolina. *Source History: 1 in 2000.* **Sources: Emp.**

Chinese Chestnut - *Castanea mollissima*. Highly resistant to chestnut blight. Bristly, apple-size burrs contain 3-7, medium to large, meaty, crisp nuts. Delicious roasted; slightly larger but not quite as sweet as American chestnuts. Low branched, round 40' tree. Dense, glossy green foliage turns from yellow to bronze in fall; white catkins in spring. Moderately productive. Bears in 3-5 years; life span of 30-80. Self-pollinating, but better yields if cross-pollinated. Prefers acid, well drained, loamy soil. Ripens mid to late September. Hardy in Zones 5-9. Widely planted in the East to replace the native American Chestnut. Introduced in 1900. *Source History: 46 in 1988; 49 in 1992; 41 in 2000.* **Sources: Bar, BO4, Bo5, Bu1, Bu7, CA14, Cla, Ed2, Emp, Fi1, FO10, Fo4, Gur, HI7, Hid, Int, Iso, JOY, LA4, Lee, LO6, LOV, MEA, Mel, Mu2, Na4, On3, Or2, Po2, Rai, Sav, Sc2, SIM, To7, TU5, Ty2, Wa16, WA8, Wh3, Wor.**

Chinese: Amy - Medium to large size nuts. Ripens a few days before Eaton. *Source History: 1 in 2000.* **Sources: Emp.**

Chinese: Bear Creek - Seedling from the select cross of the American x Chinese chestnuts grown by Bear Creek Nursery. Produces high quality, excellent nuts with the Chinese flavor and the American sweetness. Heavy producer. Hardy to Zone 5. *Source History: 1 in 2000.* **Sources: Bea.**

Chinese: Eaton - Possibly a seedling of Sleeping Giant. Medium to large size nuts. Ripens early. Selected in Connecticut. *Source History: 1 in 2000.* **Sources: Emp.**

Chinese: Gideon - Medium to large size nuts. Ripens midseason. *Source History: 1 in 2000.* **Sources: Emp.**

Chinese: Mendes - Hardy, productive, medium size nut. Short season. From New York, 1996. *Source History: 1 in 2000.* **Sources: Nol.**

Chinese: Miller's Manchurian - Vigorous, blight resistant tree. Hardy to -28 degrees F. *Source History: 1 in 1988; 1 in 1992; 1 in 2000.* **Sources: Mi1.**

Chinese: Oriental-American - Larger and better quality than native varieties. Spreading, rapid growing, blight resistant tree. Produces in about 3-4 years. Two or more trees are required to produce nuts. Hardy. Introduced by the USDA from China. *Source History: 1 in 1988; 1 in 1992; 1 in 2000.* **Sources: Mi1.**

Chinese: Orrin - Nuts are similar to Henry VIII in size, color and taste. Good cracking quality. Excellent flavor. Small, upright, pear-like tree is a slow grower. Ornamental foliage is shiny and dark green. Blight resistant. Cold hardy to -26 degrees F. Valuable tree for breeding; maternal dominancy transmits many of its fine characteristics to seedling trees. Developed by Orrin Good in Pennsylvania. Introduced in 1963. *Source History: 3 in 1988; 2 in 1992; 1 in 2000.* **Sources: Nol.**

Chinese: Peach - Medium-large size nuts. Ripens midseason. *Source History: 1 in 2000.* **Sources: Emp.**

Chinquapin - *Castanea pumila*. Small, sweet chestnuts on ornamental bush that reaches 6-12'. Long, green leaves turn bright yellow in the fall; spring catkins are also very ornamental. Ripens August-September. Adapted from Maine to Georgia. Zones 5-8. *Source History: 4 in 1992; 4 in 2000.* **Sources: BO10, Ed2, Sh10, Wo2.**

Chinquapin, Allegheny - *Castanea pumila*. Large quantities of tiny nuts; 400-500 per lb. Bush grows to 25'. Hardy in Zones 7-9. *Source History: 1 in 1992; 3 in 2000.* **Sources: Emp, Sh3, Ty2.**

Chinquapin, Florida - *Castanea alnifolia floridana*. Large shrub or small tree bears small edible chestnuts. Zones 6-9. *Source History: 1 in 2000.* **Sources: Wo2.**

Chinquapin, Running - *Castanea alnifolia.* Low growing, deciduous shrub grows in colonies. Shiny leaves. Edible nuts. Found primarily in frequently burned sandy pinelands. Native to southeastern U.S. Zones 7-9. *Source History: 1 in 2000.* **Sources: Wo2.**

Chinquapin, Super - *Castanea alnifolia floridana.* Possibly a hybrid with chestnut. Seedlings from a tree in Madison County, Florida selected for the exceptionally large nuts. *Source History: 1 in 2000.* **Sources: Wo2.**

Crane - Medium size nuts. Upright growth habit. Ripens late. *Source History: 1 in 2000.* **Sources: Emp.**

European: Seedlings (Italian Chestnut) - The seeds selected for growing these seedlings are from trees that produce large, high quality nuts. The seedlings grown from these nuts are quite likely to be hybrids with other species. While there is no certainty of the genetic makeup of these trees, the appearance of the nut, leaf and tree form indicates a predominance of the European species type. *Source History: 3 in 1988; 1 in 1992; 1 in 2000.* **Sources: Gr4.**

European: Spanish (Sweet Spanish Chestnut) - *C. sativa.* Medium to large, good quality nuts. Large, fast growing tree. Susceptible to blight. Hardy in Zone 7. *Source History: 1 in 1988; 1 in 1992; 2 in 2000.* **Sources: Bu7, Fo2.**

Hybrid: Alachua - Sweet, dark brown nuts; 25-35 per pound. Dunstan hybrid. Spreading, upright tree is a good producer and pollinator. Blight resistant. Pollinate with Carpenter, Willamette and Carolina. *Source History: 1 in 1992; 1 in 2000.* **Sources: Pi4.**

Hybrid: Armstrong - Possibly a Chinese x American hybrid; may show timber-type growth. Large nut; very sweet. Originated in Kentucky. Introduced in 1980. *Source History: 1 in 1988; 1 in 1992; 1 in 2000.* **Sources: Nol.**

Hybrid: Bisalta No. 3 - Japanese x European cross. Heavy producer of very large nuts. Good pollinator. Early. Zones 5-8. *Source History: 1 in 2000.* **Sources: Bu7.**

Hybrid: Campbell No. 1 - Layeroka seedling selected by Doug Campbell in Ontario. Large, sweet nut falls free from the burr. Fine spines but not as prickly as others. Earliest producer of the Gellatly strains. Hardy in Zone 5. *Source History: 1 in 1992; 1 in 2000.* **Sources: Bea.**

Hybrid: Carolina - American x Chinese hybrid. Large, glossy, chocolate brown nut; 24-28 per lb. Very sweet. Large tree with spreading branches and dark foliage. Produces heavily; bears in 2-4 years. Pollinator for Revival. Excellent for orcharding, backyard nut production and landscaping. Widely adapted. Bred by Dr. Robert Dunstan. U.S. Plant Patent No. 7041. *Source History: 2 in 1988; 3 in 1992; 1 in 2000.* **Sources: Pi4.**

Hybrid: Carpenter - Large, sweet, red-brown nuts; 20-25 per pound. Dunstan hybrid. Large, upright, productive tree. Pollinates with Willamette, Alachua and Carolina. *Source History: 1 in 1992; 1 in 2000.* **Sources: Pi4.**

Hybrid: Chinese x European - Good size nut; sweeter than typical European chestnuts. Membrane peels off easily. Large yields. *Source History: 1 in 1988; 3 in 1992; 1 in 2000.* **Sources: Gr4.**

Hybrid: Colossal - *Castanea crenata* x *C. mollissima* x *C. sativa*; hybrid of Japanese, Chinese and European chestnuts. Large to very large, sweet nuts; easy to peel. Good quality. Beautiful, large tree; produces up to 400 lbs. of nuts annually.

Two trees are required for pollination. May be blight susceptible, so not suitable for east of the Rocky Mountains. Ripens in October. Requires 400 hours of chilling. Hardy to -20 degrees F. Bred by C. E. Parsons of the Felix Gillet Nursery of Nevada City, California. Introduced in 1925. *Source History: 5 in 1988; 9 in 1992; 11 in 2000.* **Sources: Arb, Bay, Bea, Bu7, Oik, On3, Pa2, Pi4, Rai, Wh3, WI4.**

Hybrid: Colossal Pollinator - Medium size nut. Ripens several weeks after Colossal. Planted as a pollinator to insure that Colossal size nuts are produced on Colossal. *Source History: 3 in 1992; 1 in 2000.* **Sources: Bu7.**

Hybrid: Colossal Seedlings - Each seedling is unique, so crops and quality vary. Bearing often begins in the second year. Large, distinctive shade tree. Plant at least two seedlings for cross-pollination. Requires 400-500 hours of chilling. *Source History: 3 in 1988; 4 in 1992; 2 in 2000.* **Sources: Pa2, Pe2.**

Hybrid: Crane - Chinese hybrid. Medium to large nut; good cracking quality. Fine flavor; good quality. Excellent keeper. Rounded tree grows 40-50' tall. Precocious; bears in 2-3 years. Blight resistant. Originated in Georgia. Introduced in 1963. *Source History: 4 in 1988; 2 in 1992; 1 in 2000.* **Sources: Nol.**

Hybrid: Douglass - Cross between Manchurian Chinese and blight resistant American chestnuts. Smaller size, late flowering and blight resistance of Chinese chestnuts and the shape, sweet flavor, hardiness and upright growth of American chestnuts. Hardy to -28 degrees F. and into Zone 4. *Source History: 2 in 1988; 2 in 1992; 5 in 2000.* **Sources: Bea, Ed5, Fi1, Gor, Wa16.**

Hybrid: Douglass No. 1 - *Source History: 1 in 1988; 2 in 1992; 1 in 2000.* **Sources: Oik.**

Hybrid: Dunstan - American x Chinese hybrid. Easy to peel nuts are far superior in size and taste to Chinese and European chestnuts. High in protein and carbohydrates; low in oil and fat. Grafted tree is fast growing and highly resistant to blight; produces in 3-4 years. Requires pollination; any Chinese chestnut will pollinate any of the Dunstan hybrids. Hardy in Zones 4-9. U.S. Plant Patent No. 5537. *Source History: 2 in 1988; 3 in 1992; 2 in 2000.* **Sources: Sh3, St4.**

Hybrid: Eaton - Chinese hybrid. Large, very sweet nut. Ornamental tree. Thought to be a Chinese x (Japanese x American) cross. Ripens early. Originated in Connecticut. Introduced in 1970. *Source History: 1 in 1988; 1 in 1992; 1 in 2000.* **Sources: Nol.**

Hybrid: Ford's Sweet - American x (Japanese x Chinese). Small, sweet kernel that resembles American chestnut. Heavy bearer. Timber-type growth. Good wildlife food. Originated in Indiana. Introduced in 1980. *Source History: 1 in 1988; 1 in 1992; 1 in 2000.* **Sources: Nol.**

Hybrid: Ford's Tall - Resembles Ford's Sweet with medium size nut. Timber type Chinese. Grows to 70' tall. Originated in Indiana. Introduced in 1980. *Source History: 1 in 1988; 1 in 1992; 1 in 2000.* **Sources: Nol.**

Hybrid: Gellatly Large European - Seedlings of Jack Gellatly's best producing European Chestnut. Large, dark colored nuts with good flavor for a European. Timber type tree grew 10' in two years. Not quite as hardy as the selected Gellatly strains. Hardy in Zone 5-6. *Source History: 1 in 1988; 1 in 1992; 1 in 2000.* **Sources: Bea.**

Hybrid: Hemming - *Source History: 1 in 2000.* **Sources: Gor.**

Hybrid: Japanese x European - Large nuts. Membrane somewhat convoluted. Excellent quality. *Source History: 1 in 1988; 1 in 1992; 1 in 2000.* **Sources: Gr4.**

Hybrid: Layeroka - Earliest ripening Chinese x European hybrid. Combines the blight resistance of the Chinese parent with the timber quality, nut size and productivity of the European. Large to very large, sweet, brown nut falls early and free of the burr when ripe. Precocious, vigorous, pyramidal tree; erect timber-type shape. Early, very productive bearer. Pollen-sterile. Blight resistant. One of the few varieties commercially planted in Canada. Ripens in early October. Substantially hardier than other varieties imported from south central China; Zone 5. (**Bea** is offering "Seedlings from Gellatly's original trees in British Columbia.") *Source History: 8 in 1988; 9 in 1992; 4 in 2000.* **Sources: Bea, Bu7, Gor, Wh3.**

Hybrid: Little Giant - A Seguin hybrid selected in Connecticut. *Source History: 1 in 2000.* **Sources: Emp.**

Hybrid: Manoka - Seedlings grown from one of the best selections that Jack Gellatly developed. Large nuts are easy to peel. Excellent flavor. The parent tree is approaching 60' tall and still growing. Good producer. Hardy in Zone 5. *Source History: 1 in 1992; 1 in 2000.* **Sources: Bea.**

Hybrid: Maraval - Very large nuts. Ripens late. Resists blight and phytopthora. Good pollinator. Zones 5-8. *Source History: 1 in 2000.* **Sources: Bu7.**

Hybrid: Marigoule - Large sweet nuts. Blight and root rot resistant. Good pollinator. Zones 5-8. *Source History: 1 in 2000.* **Sources: Bu7.**

Hybrid: Marissard - European x Japanese cross. Good quality, large to very large nuts. Resists chestnut blight and phytopthora root rot. zones 5-8. *Source History: 1 in 2000.* **Sources: Bu7.**

Hybrid: Marron du Var - Large nut. Peels easily. Ripens late. Pollen sterile. France. *Source History: 1 in 2000.* **Sources: Bu7.**

Hybrid: Meiling - Chinese hybrid. Large, good flavored nut. Good keeping quality. Heavy bearer. Ripens early. Originated in Georgia. Introduced in 1949. *Source History: 1 in 1988; 1 in 1992; 1 in 2000.* **Sources: Nol.**

Hybrid: Mossbarger - Chinese hybrid. Large, sweet nut. Excellent keeper. Very productive. Originated in Kentucky. Introduced in 1983. *Source History: 1 in 1988; 1 in 1992; 1 in 2000.* **Sources: Nol.**

Hybrid: Myoka - Large, sweet, flavorful nut that peels easily. Large, spreading tree can grow 50' tall. Good long season pollinator; best pollinator for Layeroka. Resistant to chestnut blight. Similar in tree form and overall nut quality to Layeroka; nuts ripen a bit later with some remaining in the husk. Originated in the Gellatly orchard in British Columbia. *Source History: 3 in 1988; 1 in 2000.* **Sources: Wh3.**

Hybrid: Nanking - Chinese hybrid. Medium to large nut. Spreading tree; bears well. Second only to Crane in precociousness. Originated in Georgia. Introduced in 1949. *Source History: 2 in 1988; 1 in 1992; 1 in 2000.* **Sources: Emp.**

Hybrid: Nevada - Medium size, very sweet nut with dark brown shell. Light producer. Ripens during October. Requires 400-500 hours of chilling. Selected for pollinating the Colossal variety. Does not tolerate alkaline soil. Dunstan hybrid. *Source History: 2 in 1992; 4 in 2000.* **Sources: Bay, Pe2, Pi4, WI4.**

Hybrid: Paragon - Possibly Sober Paragon, an American-European hybrid widely planted in the early 1900s. Tree has a vigorous, upright growth habit. Consistently bears medium-size nuts. Ripens midseason. Very blight susceptible. Has produced many outstanding offspring, both in terms of nut production and timber-type growth. *Source History: 1 in 2000.* **Sources: Emp.**

Hybrid: Precoce Migoule - Medium to large size nuts. High yields. Ripens early. Anthracnose resistant. Good pollen producer. Zones 5-8. *Source History: 1 in 2000.* **Sources: Bu7.**

Hybrid: Rush Chinknut - Chinquapin (*Castanea pumila*) x American Chestnut (*C. dentata*). *Source History: 1 in 1988; 1 in 1992; 1 in 2000.* **Sources: Sh3.**

Hybrid: Schrader - European. Large sweet nut. Large spreading tree to 40' tall. *Source History: 2 in 1992; 2 in 2000.* **Sources: Rai, Wh3.**

Hybrid: Silverleaf Pollenizer - Heavy crops of large, high quality nuts. Easy to peel and hull. Plant with Silverleaf. Requires 400-500 hours of chilling. Formerly called Eurobella Pollenizer. *Source History: 1 in 1992; 1 in 2000.* **Sources: WI4.**

Hybrid: Simpson - European complex hybrid. Large fruited selection with excellent productivity. Originated in New York. *Source History: 2 in 1988; 2 in 1992; 1 in 2000.* **Sources: Gor.**

Hybrid: Skioka - Chinese hybrid. Large nut with high quality, white kernels. Late blooming timber type; matures later than Layeroka and not as free of the burr. Can pollinate up to 8 trees. Hardy in Zone 5. One of the first selections by Jack Gellatly from Chinese seed. *Source History: 1 in 1988; 3 in 1992; 3 in 2000.* **Sources: Bea, Bu7, Rai.**

Hybrid: Skookum - Chinese hybrid; superior selection from a population of Gellatly seedlings. Large, shiny, well colored, attractive, sweet, tasty nut falls free from the burr. Fast growing, remarkably vigorous timber-type tree; sheds leaves early in the winter. Very heavy, annual bearer; begins producing quite early. Hardy in Zone 5. Selected in the breeding program of Bill Schildgen of Loomis, Washington. *Source History: 4 in 1988; 4 in 1992; 3 in 2000.* **Sources: Bea, Bu7, Wh3.**

Hybrid: Sleeping Giant - Complex cross of Chinese, Japanese and American chestnuts. Medium to large, high quality, easily peeled nut. Timber-type growth. Hardy to Zone 5. Developed in Connecticut. Introduced in 1958. *Source History: 2 in 1988; 2 in 1992; 3 in 2000.* **Sources: Bea, Emp, Nol.**

Hybrid: Willamette - American x Chinese. Extremely large, sweet, easy to peel, reddish brown nut; 18-22 per lb. Medium size, upright, spreading tree. Heavily productive; bears in 2-4 years. Proven to be blight resistant. Widely adapted. One of the best varieties for commercial orchards. Pollinate with Carpenter, Alachua and Carolina. Bred by Dr. Robert Dunstan. U.S. Plant Patent No. 7195. *Source History: 1 in 1988; 2 in 1992; 1 in 2000.* **Sources: Pi4.**

Kohr - Selected in Pennsylvania. *Source History: 1 in 2000.* **Sources: Emp.**

Lockwood - Medium size nuts. Reportedly shows resistance to chestnut weevils. *Source History: 1 in 2000.* **Sources: Emp.**

Orrin - Medium to large size nuts. Resembles Nanking. Ripens midseason. Tends to over-produce, resulting in smaller nut size. *Source History: 1 in 2000.* **Sources: Emp.**

Quing - Vigorous grower and consistent productive bearer of large size nuts with excellent flavor. Excellent keeping quality. Appears to be pure Chinese. Has not yet been tested in trials or orchards. *Source History: 1 in 2000.* **Sources: Emp.**

Smith - Origin in South Carolina. *Source History: 1 in 2000.* **Sources: Emp.**

Sweet Hart (Sweetheart) - West Virginia Sweet Chestnut x Chinese Chestnut. Very sweet nut. Tree grows to 40'. Blight resistant. Plant two trees for better pollination. Hardy in Zones 4-8. *Source History: 4 in 1992; 3 in 2000.* **Sources: Gur, Mel, Ty2.**

Filbert (Hazelnut)

Corylus spp.

American Hazelnut - *Corylus americana*. Clusters of 2-6 round, small nuts with smooth, thick shells; easy to crack. Sweet, round kernels shell out whole. Distinctive taste. Shapely shrub grows slowly 6-10' tall; can be pruned into a small tree if basal suckers are removed. Rough, dark green leaves turn brilliant bronze in the fall. Abundant, annual crops. Bears in 2-3 years; life span of 30-80. Plant two or more for proper cross-pollination. Subject to, but does not carry, Eastern filbert blight. Thrives in full sun or partial shade on fertile, well drained soil. Ripens in September or early October. Hardy in Zones 4-9. Native to eastern U.S. *Source History: 29 in 1988; 32 in 1992; 31 in 2000.* **Sources: Bea, BO10, BO4, Bu1, Bu7, Ca8, CR6, Ed2, FO10, Fo4, Gur, HI7, Int, KEE, KI3, LA4, Lee, Lit, LOV, Mc3, Mel, Na4, Po2, Sav, Sc2, SH8, TU5, Ty2, Wa16, WA8, We18.**

American: Winkler - *C. americana*. Large, thin shelled nut. Good productivity. Hardy to -35 degrees F. *Source History: 1 in 1988; 1 in 1992; 1 in 2000.* **Sources: Oik.**

Beaked Hazelnut (Wild Hazelnut) - *Corylus cornuta*. Tasty nuts up to .7" in diameter. Multistemmed shrub grows 10-15' tall. Often quite productive. Resistant to Eastern filbert blight. Drought tolerant. Hardy in Zone 4. Native from British Columbia to California. *Source History: 3 in 1988; 5 in 1992; 3 in 2000.* **Sources: Bu7, Fo2, Wo2.**

European (European Filbert) - *Corylus avellana*. Clusters of 1-8 small, round nuts that are easy to crack. Crisp, crunchy, sweet kernels shell out whole. Bushy shrub grows 15-25' tall and forms a dense thicket of erect stems; ideal for hedgerows or windbreaks. Dependable bearer of heavy crops. Thick, spreading foliage. More cold and drought tolerant because of taproot growth habit rather than lateral shallow rooting. Ripens early. Hardy anywhere peaches grow; Zones 5-9. *Source History: 11 in 1988; 8 in 1992; 9 in 2000.* **Sources: Bar, Bea, KEE, La3, LA4, Lee, LOV, Sav, Sc2.**

European: Barcelona - Large to very large, round, .75" smooth shelled nut. Readily self-husking; easy to crack. Rough, light brown kernel. Fine, rich flavor; high quality. Strong, vigorous shrub grows 15-18' tall and wide. Leaves and bark susceptible to sunburn; needs afternoon shade in hot climates. Heavy bearer, but tends to produce biennially; up to 40 lbs. of nuts per bush. Pollinate with Duchilly. Possibly the most widely planted commercial type in the Northwest. Ripens during September. Requires 800 hours of chilling. Winter blossoms are hardy to 15 degrees F.; grows well in Zones 5-8. Hardy wherever peaches can be grown. *Source History: 14 in 1988; 16 in 1992; 10 in 2000.* **Sources: Bay, Bea, Bu7, Mi1, Pi4, Rai, St4, Va2, Wh3, WI4.**

European: Butler - Medium-large to large, oval nut; larger than Barcelona or Daviana. Smooth kernel; low blank percentage. Good flavor and quality. Vigorous shrub grows 15' tall and wide. Leaves and bark susceptible to sunburn. Good productivity; better producer than Barcelona or Daviana. Commonly used pollinator for Barcelona and Ennis; one Butler will pollinate eight Ennis trees. Ripens in September or October. Requires 800 hours of chilling. Developed at Oregon State University. *Source History: 9 in 1988; 10 in 1992; 8 in 2000.* **Sources: Bay, Bea, Clo, Mi1, Pi4, Va2, Wh3, WI4.**

European: Casina - Smaller and earlier than Barcelona; perhaps sweeter.

Heavy producer of small, round, thin shelled nuts which are 55% kernel by weight. Excellent flavor. Trees tend toward alternate yields. Ripens during September. Requires 800 chilling hours. Zones 5-8. *Source History: 1 in 1988; 1 in 1992; 5 in 2000.* **Sources: Bay, On3, Pi4, St4, WI4.**

European: Contorted (Contorted European Filbert, Devil's Walking Stick, Harry Lauder's Walking Stick) - *Corylus avellana* var. *contorta.* Striking, ornamental tree or bush grows slowly 8-10'; never grows straight for more than an inch, always twisting off into miraculous curves and contortions. Looks a thousand years old. Catkins are also twisted; leaves become somewhat crinkled in midsummer. Produces small, oval nut if pollinated by another filbert. Prefers good, moist soil in a sunny location. Hardy in Zone 5. Resembles the famed, twisted, corkscrew-like, gnarled walking stick of old-time Scots comedian, Harry Lauder. Discovered in England. *Source History: 7 in 1988; 15 in 1992; 24 in 2000.* **Sources: Arb, Bay, BO10, Bu7, Car, Ed2, Fa1, Fed, Fo2, Fo4, Gir, GR26, IM2, Mel, On3, Or2, Pi4, Rai, SH8, Spr, Wa3, We18, We8, WI4.**

European: Daviana - Medium size, oblong, thin shelled nut. Smooth, medium brown kernels. Delicious, rich, sweet flavor; some growers think it's the best tasting filbert. Very good quality. Bush grows 15' tall and wide. Leaves and bark susceptible to sunburn. Light yields; primarily used as an excellent pollinator for Barcelona. Requires pollination. Ripens with Barcelona in September. Requires 800 hours of chilling. Moderately hardy. *Source History: 9 in 1988; 8 in 1992; 1 in 2000.* **Sources: Wh3.**

European: Duchilly - Large, long nut; some adhere to husks. Oval shaped, rough kernels. Distinctive flavor. Excellent quality. Tree grows slowly 15' tall and wide. Pollinate with Barcelona or Daviana; widely used to pollinate Barcelona. Moderately hardy. *Source History: 8 in 1988; 6 in 1992; 1 in 2000.* **Sources: Va2.**

European: Ennis - First new filbert in 40 years. Produces 40% more nuts with less blanks than Barcelona or Ennis. Large to very large, round nuts; greater percentage in largest size grades. Roundish, smooth kernel. Excellent flavor and quality. Smaller, slow growing tree, 15' tall and wide. Leaves and bark susceptible to sunburn; benefits from afternoon shade in hot climates. Pollinate with Daviana or Butler; good pollinator for Butler. Ripens in September or early October; drops nuts a week after Barcelona. 800 hours of chilling. Hardy to 15 degrees F. Commercial variety for the Northwest developed at Oregon State University. *Source History: 10 in 1988; 12 in 1992; 5 in 2000.* **Sources: Clo, On3, Pi4, Wh3, WI4.**

European: Hall's Giant - Large, round nut. Good quality. Average yields; same blank ratio as Barcelona. Good pollinator, especially for Ennis and Butler. Less susceptible than most to eastern filbert blight. Requires 800 chilling hours. *Source History: 3 in 1988; 3 in 1992; 6 in 2000.* **Sources: Bay, Bea, Bu7, Pi4, Rai, WI4.**

European: Lewis - Flavorful nuts ripen early. Productive. The most blight resistant cultivar known that is of commercial quality. Pollinater for all varieties except Barcelona. Zones 5-8. *Source History: 1 in 2000.* **Sources: Bu7.**

European: Montebello - Large clusters of small to medium, round nuts. Yields better than Tonda Gentile Della Langhe. Good pollinator for Casina and Tonda Gentile Della Langhe. Ripens in September, one week before Ennis. Originated in Italy. *Source History: 2 in 1988; 1 in 1992; 1 in 2000.* **Sources: ME3.**

European: Royal - Very large, smooth, soft shelled, easy to crack nuts; even larger than Barcelona. Better green than dried. Shrub grows 15' tall. Heavily pro-

ductive; bears when young. Pollinator for Barcelona. Ripens in early September. Hardy in Zones 4-8 or wherever peaches can be grown. *Source History: 7 in 1988; 6 in 1992; 2 in 2000.* **Sources: Mi1, Pi4.**

European: Willamette - Medium size, evenly sized nuts. Pollinate with Casina and Hall's Giant. *Source History: 2 in 2000.* **Sources: On3, Pi4.**

Filazel (Hazelbert) - American hazelnut (*Corylus americana*) x European filbert (*C. avellana*). Large nut up to 1" in diameter. Grows 10' tall; can train as a shrub or a tree. Requires two for pollination. Ripens during September. Hardy in Zones 4-8. *Source History: 1 in 1988; 3 in 1992; 3 in 2000.* **Sources: Fed, Mel, Rai.**

Filazel: Big Red - *C. cornuta* x *C. avellana*. Large nut with moderately thick shell. Well filled kernel. Early maturity. Hardy in Zone 4. *Source History: 2 in 1992; 2 in 2000.* **Sources: Bea, Wa16.**

Filazel: Gellatly - This selection represents the best quality early filazels, including a mix of Myoka, Petoka and the Manoka seedlings. Ripens during September. Hardy in Zone 4. *Source History: 1 in 1988; 2 in 1992; 2 in 2000.* **Sources: Bea, Bu7.**

Filazel: Peace River Cross - Seedlings of the original Gellatly Peace River hazel hybrid; likely backcrossed to filbert. Of interest to breeders and short season growers; extremely early. Ripens during September. Hardy in Zone 4. *Source History: 1 in 1988; 2 in 1992; 1 in 2000.* **Sources: Bea.**

Filbert, 88-BS - Medium size, almost round nut. Lightly colored, clean kernel falls easily from the short, open husks. Ripens in September. *Source History: 1 in 1992; 1 in 2000.* **Sources: GR18.**

Filbert, 89-Lisa - Light colored, medium size kernels easily fall from the open husk. Slightly elongated shape. Paper-thin shells. Ripen by mid-September. *Source History: 1 in 2000.* **Sources: GR18.**

Filbert, Blade - *Source History: 1 in 1988; 1 in 1992; 1 in 2000.* **Sources: Gor.**

Filbert, Dwarf - *C. heterophylla*. May provide some dwarfing habit when used as a rootstock. Nuts are equal to or better than *C. avellana*. Zone 5. *Source History: 1 in 2000.* **Sources: LA4.**

Filbert, Fortin - Resembles Rote Zeller with its red-purple leaves. Bears good tasting nuts. *Source History: 1 in 2000.* **Sources: Or2.**

Filbert, G-14 - Large, slightly elongated nuts with thin shells. Clean, well developed kernels. Husks are flared and open and cover about 2/3 of the nut. Resistant to bud mite. Has not been infected by hazel blight after 8 years of exposure. Ripens in late September. *Source History: 1 in 2000.* **Sources: GR18.**

Filbert, G-17 - Medium size, light colored, almost round kernels are well developed. High quality. Kernels fall easily from the husk. Resists bud mite; relatively resistant to hazel blight. Ripens in mid-September. *Source History: 1 in 2000.* **Sources: GR18.**

Filbert, G-22 - Medium size round nuts with a thin shell. Plump, light colored kernel is free of adhering tissue. Mature nuts can be easily shaken from the tree by mid-September. *Source History: 1 in 2000.* **Sources: GR18.**

Filbert, Gellatly's - *Source History: 1 in 1988; 1 in 1992; 1 in 2000.* **Sources: Gor.**

Filbert, Giant - *C. maxima*. Large nuts with closed husks. Tree grows to 30'. Hardy to Zone 4. Rare native hazel from southeastern Europe. *Source History: 2 in 2000.* **Sources: Bea, Oik.**

Filbert, Graham - Winkler patented. *Source History: 1 in 1988; 2 in 1992; 1 in*

2000. **Sources: Gor.**

Filbert, Grand Traverse (81-C) - Controlled cross of Faroka x Royal. Thin shelled, dull brown nut; 51% meat. Excellent flavor. Originated in Michigan. *Source History: 1 in 1992; 1 in 2000.* **Sources: GR18.**

Filbert, Hybrid - *Source History: 1 in 1988; 2 in 1992; 1 in 2000.* **Sources: Va5.**

Filbert, Purple Haze - Upright shrub with vivid burgundy new growth which turns bronze in mid-summer. McKay introduction. *Source History: 1 in 2000.* **Sources: Mc3.**

Filbert, Purple Leaf - Leaves retain rich burgundy color well into the summer. Plant bears clusters of nuts. Cross-pollinate with American Filbert or Tree Hazel. Zones 4-8. *Source History: 1 in 2000.* **Sources: Ed2.**

Filbert, Ro - *Source History: 1 in 2000.* **Sources: Gor.**

Filbert: Rote Zeller (Red-Leaved Filbert) - *C. avellana.* Edible, pink-tinted nuts on 12-20' shrub/tree. Red-purple leaves in spring; bronze-green summer color. "Rot" means red in German. Hardy in Zone 5-8. Originated in Germany. *Source History: 1 in 1992; 3 in 2000.* **Sources: Bu7, Fo2, Or2.**

Filbert, Slate's - *Source History: 1 in 1988; 1 in 1992; 1 in 2000.* **Sources: Gor.**

Filbert, Smeck - *Source History: 1 in 2000.* **Sources: Gor.**

Hazelbert - Hybrids of Eastern hazelnut *Corylus americana* x filbert *C. avellana.* Seedlings of an F2 population growing in Minnesota. Similar to filazels. Nuts have a thinner shell than wild hazels. Tend to bear more heavily with regular crops. Should be particularly interesting to short season growers. Hardy in Zone 4, maybe 3. *Source History: 1 in 1988; 2 in 1992; 2 in 2000.* **Sources: Mel, Stl.**

Hazelbert, Geneva Strain - *Corylus americana x C. avellana.* Produces extra large size nuts. Hardy to -30 degrees F. *Source History: 1 in 2000.* **Sources: Oik.**

Hazelbert, Land of Ozmun Strain - Excellent quality, huge nuts. Extremely productive. Hardy to -30 degrees F. *Source History: 1 in 2000.* **Sources: Oik.**

Hazelbert, Rutter - Hybrid of Eastern hazelnut (*Corylus americana)* x *Corylus avellana* which are filbert seedlings from named varieties growing as an F2 population in Minnesota. Thin shelled nuts the size of wild hazels. Heavy regular cropper. Valuable to short season growers. Hardy to Zone 4, possibly to Zone 3. *Source History: 1 in 2000.* **Sources: Bea.**

Hazelbert, Skinner - Hybrid of the Eastern hazelnut s European filbert. Nut size and tree form resembles the filbert; 30 lbs. of nuts per tree. Consistent producer. Hardy to Zone 4, possibly to Zone 3. *Source History: 1 in 2000.* **Sources: Bea.**

Hazelnut - Large crops of easy to crack nuts with golden nutmeats. Shrub grows just 6' tall. Small, shapely leaves turn crimson and gold in the fall. Plant two or more trees to ensure proper cross-pollination. Cold hardy. *Source History: 3 in 1988; 8 in 1992; 7 in 2000.* **Sources: BA14, Bu7, Co15, Fi1, Fro, To7, Va5.**

Hazelnut, Precocious - *Corylus* x hybrid. Unique seed selection by Oikos Tree Crops created by using plants that flowered 2-3 years from seed. Size is more dwarf than filazels. Shows good disease and insect resistance. Produces a medium size nut with variable shell thickness; easily cracked with a hand cracker. Begins fruiting in 3-4 years. Plant several for adequate pollination. Hardy to -35 degrees F. *Source History: 1 in 2000.* **Sources: Oik.**

Tonda di Giffoni - Leading Italian variety with outstanding flavor. Medium size nuts blanch perfectly. Productive. Shows good blight and mite resistance. Zones

5-8. Pollinate with all varieties except Barcelona. *Source History: 1 in 2000.* **Sources: Bu7.**

Trazel - European filbert (*Corylus avellana*) x Turkish Tree Hazel (*C. colurna*). Oval nut. Rich, hazelnut flavor. Seedling filberts from Turkey that are as winter hardy as Turkish Tree Hazel but grow only 30' tall. Ornamental tree has a beautiful, furrowed bark. Blooms from January to March with yellow catkins. Select two seedlings for pollination or Trazel and Turkish Tree Hazel will cross-pollinate. Winter hardy to -25 degrees F. *Source History: 1 in 1988; 2 in 1992; 1 in 2000.* **Sources: Rai.**

Trazel: Bill's Hybrid - Selected from Turkish Trazels that have been back crossed to filbert making them 3/4 filbert and 1/4 Turkish Tree Hazel. Large, clean kernel. Hardy in Zone 4. *Source History: 2 in 1992; 1 in 2000.* **Sources: Bea.**

Trazel: Chinese - *C. avellana x C. colurna chinensis.* Hybrids of the Turkish Tree Hazel and the European Filbert. Sweet nuts. More hardy than normal filberts. Larger nut size with a slightly thinner shell. Begins bearing in 2-3 years. Mixed seedlings from British Columbia and Oregon. Zones 4-8. *Source History: 1 in 1988; 1 in 1992; 2 in 2000.* **Sources: Bea, Mel.**

Trazel: Faroka - *Source History: 1 in 1992; 1 in 2000.* **Sources: Gor.**

Trazel: Fingerlakes Filbert - Large nut; excellent quality. Combines the productiveness and early bearing capability of the filbert with the vigor, disease resistance and hardiness of the hazel. Needs a pollinator. Resists aphids and bud mites without spraying. *Source History: 1 in 1988; 1 in 1992; 1 in 2000.* **Sources: Mil.**

Trazel: Gellatly Mixed Strains - Mixture of Chinoka, Estoka, Karloka, Laroka, Morrisoka and the 700 series, all developed by Jack Gellatly. Trazels are hybrids of the Asian Tree Hazel, usually Turkish, and the European filbert. Sweeter, cleaner nutmeat than normal filbert. Some combine the non-suckering, hardy, vigorous growth of the Tree Hazel with the larger nut size and early bearing, free falling characteristics of the filbert. *Source History: 1 in 1988; 1 in 2000.* **Sources: Bea.**

Trazel: Gellatly Seedlings - High percentage of usable seedlings. Jack Gellatly was responsible for crossing Peace River, Alberta native hazels with Asiatic filberts, combining large nut size with hardiness. *Source History: 1 in 1988; 1 in 1992; 2 in 2000.* **Sources: Oik, Wa16.**

Trazel: Laroka - Laroka was selected for large nut size; thick shelled. Large, spreading tree can grow 80' tall. Corky, white bark on young limbs. *Source History: 2 in 1988; 2 in 1992; 2 in 2000.* **Sources: Gor, Oik.**

Trazel: Lars - *Source History: 1 in 2000.* **Sources: Gor.**

Trazel: Morrisoka - *Source History: 1 in 1988; 1 in 1992; 1 in 2000.* **Sources: Gor.**

Trazel: Ora - *Source History: 1 in 2000.* **Sources: Gor.**

Trazel: Red Leaf - Maroon-red foliage in spring turns to green with a tinge of red from mid-summer on. Husk and nut color is a soft pink-maroon. Sweet nuts tend toward the filbert size. Bear Creek introduction. *Source History: 1 in 2000.* **Sources: Bea.**

Trazel: Schubert - *Source History: 1 in 1988; 1 in 1992; 1 in 2000.* **Sources: Gor.**

Trazel: Turkish - Cross between the Turkish hazelnut and the European filbert. Combines hazelnut's colored foliage, symmetrical trunk and branch shape, strong disease resistance and exceptional hardiness, with a filbert's early maturity, large nut size and heavy yields. Rich, buttery flavored nut. Tree grows 20' tall and wide. Pale, cream colored bark. Hardy to -30 degrees F and through Zone 4. *Source History: 2 in 1988; 2 in 1992; 1 in 2000.* **Sources: Gur.**

Turkish Filbert (Tree Hazel, Turkish Tree Hazel) - *Corylus colurna.* Clusters of 8-12 long, pointed nuts per husk; delicious, but small and hard as rocks. Good tasting kernels. Pyramidal, symmetrical, non-suckering tree grows 50-70' tall and 30' wide. Striking, corky corrugations of the bark. Dense foliage. Yellowish brown male catkins early in spring. Requires pollination. Resistant to Eastern filbert blight, except occasionally when young. Amazingly drought resistant once established. Winter hardy to -30 degrees F. and throughout Zone 4. Good where too cold for filberts. Excellent dual purpose windbreak. Native to southeastern Europe and western Asia. *Source History: 10 in 1988; 17 in 1992; 17 in 2000.* **Sources: Arb, Bea, Bu7, Ed2, Fo2, Gr16, GR18, GR26, LA4, LI7, Mc3, Mel, Oik, Or2, Sc2, To7, We8.**

Western Hazelnut - *Corylus cornuta* var. *californica.* Beaked hazelnut variety that is native from British Columbia to California. *Source History: 1 in 1988; 1 in 1992; 1 in 2000.* **Sources: Ca12.**

Heartnut
Juglans ailanthifolia var. *cordiformis*

Campbell CW3 - *Source History: 1 in 1988; 1 in 1992; 2 in 2000.* **Sources: Gor, Pa6.**

Canoka - Large nut averages 50-75 nuts per pound. Annual, heavy bearer. Leafs out 1-2 weeks later than other varieties. Originated in British Columbia. *Source History: 1 in 1988; 1 in 1992; 1 in 2000.* **Sources: Nol.**

Cowlitz - Productive tree leafs out late. Large size nut. *Source History: 1 in 2000.* **Sources: Bu7.**

Ebert - Large nut; very good cracking quality. Excellent flavor. Prolific; produces in 2-3 years. *Source History: 1 in 1988; 1 in 1992; 1 in 2000.* **Sources: Bu7.**

Frank - Medium size nut; cracks well. Later to leaf out than other varieties with exception of Canoka. Originated in Kentucky. Introduced in 1980. *Source History: 1 in 1988; 1 in 1992; 1 in 2000.* **Sources: Nol.**

Heartnut (Japanese Walnut) - Long, hanging strings of 10-20 nuts per cluster. Hard, egg-shaped shell cracks easily. Heart-shaped kernel is unusually easy to extract; comes out whole or in halves. Rich, bitter-free flavor similar to butternuts; the sweetest of the walnuts. High in protein. Long keeping. Large, spreading, highly productive, Japanese-type walnut grows rapidly 50-60' tall with a 30-40' spread; bears in 3-5 years. Abundant, luxurious, almost tropical foliage; long, compound, light green leaves turn yellow in the fall. Adapted to heavy or light soils. Hardy in Zones 5-9. *Source History: 10 in 1988; 14 in 1992; 9 in 2000.* **Sources: Bea, Bu7, Ed2, KEE, Mi1, Oik, Or2, Wa16, Win.**

Imshu - *Source History: 1 in 1988; 1 in 1992; 1 in 2000.* **Sources: Gor.**

Marvel - Fodermaier x Wright. Medium to large nut cracks well. Heavy bearer. Originated in New York. Introduced in 1948. *Source History: 1 in 1988; 1 in 1992; 1 in 2000.* **Sources: Nol.**

Mitchell Hybrid - Butternut x heartnut hybrid with heartnut shape. Very productive. Originated in Ontario. Introduced in 1930. *Source History: 1 in 1988; 1 in 1992; 2 in 2000.* **Sources: Nol, Pa6.**

Pyke - *Source History: 1 in 1988; 1 in 2000.* **Sources: Gor.**

Rhodes - Large nut; very good cracking quality. Excellent flavor. Prolific; produces in 2-3 years. Self-fruitful. Originated in Tennessee. *Source History: 2 in 1988; 2 in 1992; 2 in 2000.* **Sources: Nol, Pa6.**

Sauto - *Source History: 1 in 2000.* **Sources: Gor.**

Schubert - Large nut; very good cracking quality. Excellent flavor. Prolific; produces in 2-3 years. Originated in Illinois. *Source History: 1 in 1988; 2 in 1992; 1 in 2000.* **Sources: Nol.**

Wright - Medium to large nut cracks well. Flavor similar to butternut. Heavy bearer. Originated in Pennsylvania. Introduced in 1930. *Source History: 2 in 1988; 2 in 1992; 2 in 2000.* **Sources: Nol, Pa6.**

Hickory / Shagbark
Carya ovata

Abundance - *Source History: 1 in 1992; 1 in 2000.* **Sources: Nol.**

Bridgewater - Very large shagbark with 46.6% kernel. Requires a pollinator. Scab susceptible in the South. Hardy to Zone 4, possibly Zone 3. Originated in Connecticut. *Source History: 1 in 1988; 1 in 1992; 2 in 2000.* **Sources: Ed5, Nol.**

Campbell - *Source History: 1 in 2000.* **Sources: Bu7.**

Cedar Rapids - *Source History: 1 in 1988; 2 in 1992; 1 in 2000.* **Sources: Nol.**

CES-8 - *Source History: 1 in 1992; 1 in 2000.* **Sources: Gor.**

CES-26 - *Source History: 1 in 1992; 1 in 2000.* **Sources: Gor.**

Davis - *Source History: 1 in 1988; 2 in 1992; 2 in 2000.* **Sources: Gor, Nol.**

Etter - *Source History: 1 in 1988; 1 in 1992; 1 in 2000.* **Sources: Nol.**

Fayette - *Source History: 2 in 2000.* **Sources: Bu7, Pa6.**

Felger - High quality nut. Recommended for Nebraska. Developed by Emmet Yoder in Smithfield, Ohio. *Source History: 1 in 1988; 1 in 1992; 1 in 2000.* **Sources: Nol.**

Fox - Consistent bearer of high quality nuts. Ripens early. Originated in New York, 1935. *Source History: 1 in 1988; 2 in 1992; 2 in 2000.* **Sources: Gor, Nol.**

Grainger - Large nut; cracks easily. Tree bears heavily. Ripens late. Originated in Tennessee. Introduced in 1935. *Source History: 2 in 1988; 2 in 1992; 1 in 2000.* **Sources: Nol.**

Grandview - *Source History: 1 in 2000.* **Sources: Pa6.**

Harold - *Source History: 1 in 1988; 1 in 1992; 1 in 2000.* **Sources: Nol.**

Neilson - *Source History: 2 in 1988; 2 in 1992; 1 in 2000.* **Sources: Gor.**

Porter - Large nut; cracks easily. Tree bears well. Ripens late. *Source History: 3 in 1988; 2 in 1992; 2 in 2000.* **Sources: Gor, Nol.**

Retzer - Medium size nut; very good cracking quality. Good flavor. Good bearer; produces in 5-7 years. *Source History: 1 in 1988; 1 in 1992; 1 in 2000.* **Sources: Nol.**

Roof - *Source History: 1 in 1992; 1 in 2000.* **Sources: Nol.**

Russell - *Source History: 1 in 2000.* **Sources: Nol.**

Sauber - *Source History: 1 in 1988; 1 in 1992; 1 in 2000.* **Sources: Nol.**

Shagbark Hickory - Husk is 1.5" in diameter. Nut is almost white and has four parts; falls free. Relatively thin, hard shell; thinner than Shellbark hickory. Large, sweet nutmeats. Outstanding flavor. Large, upright but spreading tree grows 50-100' tall and 40-60' wide. Large, dark green leaves turn golden brown in fall. Peeling strips of bark at maturity. Self-pollinating. Slow growing in early years, while developing large taproot and deep root system. Life span of 80 years. Prefers drier, upland sites. Very tough wood used for tool handles. Hardiest hickory; grows well in Zone 4. Native from Quebec southward to Florida and Texas. *Source History: 17 in 1988; 18 in 1992; 23 in 2000.* **Sources: Arb, Bea, BO10, BO4, Bu7, CA14, Ca7, Ca8, Fo2, HI7, Jun, KEE, LO6, LOV, Mel, Oik, Or2, Sc2, Sh14, St12, Stl, WA8, Wo2.**

Shagbark Hickory Seedlings - Used for pollinating the Weschcke hickory. Zone 3. *Source History: 1 in 1992; 1 in 2000.* **Sources: Ed5.**

Silvis 303 - Large, round, thin shelled nut with 45% kernel. Good quality. Self-fruitful. Good producer. Developed by Ray Silvis in West Richfield, Ohio. *Source History: 2 in 1988; 2 in 1992; 1 in 2000.* **Sources: Nol.**

Weschcke - Medium size, papershell nuts with 53% kernel. Very good cracking quality. Very good flavor. Produces in 5-7 years; bears annually. Matures early. Zone 3. Developed by Carl Weschcke of Fayette, Iowa. Introduced in 1928. *Source History: 3 in 1988; 3 in 1992; 4 in 2000.* **Sources: Ed5, Gor, Nol, Pa6.**

Wilcox - Medium size nut; cracks out in halves. Very good flavor. Prolific; produces in 5-7 years. Good for the North. Ripens early. Originated in Ohio. Introduced in 1934. *Source History: 5 in 1988; 4 in 1992; 1 in 2000.* **Sources: Nol.**

Wilmoth - Large, light colored, thin shelled nut. Good taste. Developed by Leslie Wilmoth in Glendale, Kentucky. Introduced in 1978. *Source History: 1 in 1988; 1 in 1992; 1 in 2000.* **Sources: Nol.**

Wurth - Large, thin shelled nut. Cracks out in halves. Strong vegetative grower. Very good producer with good scab resistance. Introduced in 1978. *Source History: 1 in 1988; 1 in 1992; 1 in 2000.* **Sources: Nol.**

Yoder No. 1 (J. Yoder No. 1, Yoder) - Nut cracks easily. Excellent flavor. Bears young and heavily. Developed by Emmet Yoder in Smithfield, Ohio. *Source History: 4 in 1988; 4 in 1992; 4 in 2000.* **Sources: Gor, Neb, Nol, Pa6.**

Hickory / Shellbark

Carya laciniosa

Bellevue - *Source History: 1 in 1988; 1 in 2000.* **Sources: Gor.**

Big Cypress - Discovered in southwest Indiana in 1985. *Source History: 1 in 1992; 2 in 2000.* **Sources: Nol.**

Bradley - Large nut with medium shell thickness. Excellent cracking quality. Originated in Pennsylvania, 1932. *Source History: 1 in 1988; 1 in 1992; 1 in 2000.* **Sources: Nol.**

Brouse - *Source History: 1 in 1988; 1 in 1992; 1 in 2000.* **Sources: Nol.**

Campbell 24 - *Source History: 1 in 1988; 1 in 1992; 1 in 2000.* **Sources: Gor.**

Chetopa - Medium-large size nuts crack easily. Prolific, reliable producer. Originated in Missouri, 1990. *Source History: 1 in 1988; 1 in 1992; 1 in 2000.* **Sources: Nol.**

Daulton - Extremely vigorous variety produces very large nuts. From Kentucky, 1987. *Source History: 1 in 1992; 1 in 2000.* **Sources: Nol.**

Dewey Moore - Cox selection. Thin shelled nuts with 33% kernel. Originated in Ohio, 1987. *Source History: 1 in 1988; 1 in 1992; 1 in 2000.* **Sources: Nol.**

Ellison No. 1 - *Source History: 1 in 1992; 1 in 2000.* **Sources: Nol.**

Fat Boy - *Source History: 1 in 1992; 1 in 2000.* **Sources: Nol.**

Fayette - Large, thin shelled nut with 33% kernel. Introduced by Fayette Etter in 1932. Originated in Pennsylvania. *Source History: 1 in 1988; 2 in 1992; 2 in 2000.* **Sources: Gor, Nol.**

Florin Smith - *Source History: 1 in 1992; 1 in 2000.* **Sources: Nol.**

Henry - *Source History: 1 in 2000.* **Sources: Bu7, Gor.**

Hoagland - Possible hybrid with shagbark. Originated in Indiana. *Source History: 1 in 1988; 1 in 1992; 1 in 2000.* **Sources: Nol.**

Indiana Strain - *Source History: 1 in 2000.* **Sources: Oik.**

Iowa Strain - *Source History: 1 in 2000.* **Sources: Oik.**

Keystone - Best cracking shellbark; kernel falls free from the shell. Developed by Fayette Etter, Franklin Co., Pennsylvania. Introduced in 1955. *Source History: 2 in 1992; 2 in 2000.* **Sources: Nol, Pa6.**

Lebanon Junction - *Source History: 1 in 2000.* **Sources: Nol.**

Lindauer - Large nuts crack out whole halves. Healthy foliage. Heavy producer. Weevil resistant. Originated in Illinois. *Source History: 1 in 1988; 1 in 1992; 1 in 2000.* **Sources: Nol.**

Longnecker - *Source History: 1 in 1992; 1 in 2000.* **Sources: Neb.**

Mackinaw - *Source History: 1 in 1988; 1 in 1992; 1 in 2000.* **Sources: Nol.**

Missouri Mammoth (Missouri Giant) - Large nut; easily cracked. Seedlings are from a proven strain of shellbark hickory. Tree grows 60' tall. Plant at least two to ensure pollination and best crop. Ripens in late September. Hardy in Zones 5-8. *Source History: 2 in 1988; 2 in 1992; 2 in 2000.* **Sources: LOV, St4.**

Nieman - Very large nuts with fairly thick shell. Cracks well. Good producer. Originated in Illinois. *Source History: 1 in 1992; 1 in 2000.* **Sources: Nol.**

Nook - *Source History: 1 in 2000.* **Sources: Nol.**

Scholl - Large nut. Good cracking qualities. Originated in Ohio. *Source History: 1 in 1992; 1 in 2000.* **Sources: Nol.**

Shellbark Hickory (King Nut) - Larger, 2-3", light brown nut, but thicker shelled than Shagbark hickory. Sweet, tasty nutmeats; excellent flavor. Sturdy, strong, columnar but spreading, high branching tree grows 80-100' tall with a 40-60' spread. Dark green leaves turn brown in fall. Tiny, greenish spring flowers; self-pollinating. Faster growing than Shagbark. Life span of 80 or more years. Hardy in Zones 5-9. Native to moist bottomlands from New York and Pennsylvania to Oklahoma. *Source History: 17 in 1988; 15 in 1992; 19 in 2000.* **Sources: Bar, Bea, Ca8, Fi1, Gur, HI7, KEE, Lee, LO6, Mel, Na4, Or2, Sav, Sc2, Sh14, TU5, Ty2, WA8, Wo2.**

Stephens - *Source History: 1 in 1988; 2 in 1992; 1 in 2000.* **Sources: Nol.**

Totten - *Source History: 1 in 1992; 1 in 2000.* **Sources: Neb.**

Villa Ridge - *Source History: 1 in 2000.* **Sources: Nol.**

Hickory / Other

Carya spp.

Bitternut (Swamp Hickory) - *Carya cordiformis*. Smooth, round, grey nut; kernels are bitter and almost inedible. Tree can grow 90' tall. Sometimes used for crossing. Hardy in Zone 5. Native from Quebec to Florida and Louisiana. *Source*

History: 3 in 1988; 2 in 1992; 3 in 2000. **Sources: Ca8, HI7, Oik.**

Bitternut, Far Northern Strain - *Carya cordiformis.* Ideal as a rootstock.
Adapts to potting, transplanting, extremes in soil pH and soil types and is extremely hardy. Greatly accelerates the growth of many hickories grafted to it. Zone 3. *Source History: 1 in 2000.* **Sources: Ed5.**

Florida Hickory (Scrub) - *Carya floridana.* Multistemmed bush grows 10-20' tall. Prefers dry sand. *Source History: 1 in 1988; 1 in 1992; 1 in 2000.* **Sources: Wo2.**

Hican - Pecan (*Carya illinoinensis*) x hickory cross; the hickory parent can be either Shellbark (*C. laciniosa*) or Shagbark (*C. ovata*). Combines the high quality and rich flavor of pecan with the larger nut size and greater hardiness of hickory. Looks and grows like a pecan tree; can reach 50' tall. Produces large crops. Thrives in loose, fertile soil. Ripens in late September. Hardy in Zones 5-9. Developed in Missouri. Introduced in 1928. *Source History: 4 in 1988; 6 in 1992; 5 in 2000.* **Sources: Fi1, Gur, LO6, SIM, Ty2.**

Hican: Abbott Seedling - Naturally occuring hybrid between pecan and bitternut that grows throughout the Midwest and Northeast where hickories grow. Produces a non-bitter nut that cracks out easily. Tree grows 80' tall. Hardy to -30 degrees F. *Source History: 2 in 2000.* **Sources: Gor, Oik.**

Hican: Bixby - Pecan x Shellbark. Large nut. Heavy producer. Needs pollination. Developed in Illinois. Major is a good pollinator. *Source History: 1 in 1988; 1 in 1992; 1 in 2000.* **Sources: Nol.**

Hican: Burlington - Pecan x Shagbark. Large nuts; 55 per pound. Self-pollinating. Matures early. Does well in the Ohio Valley. Originated in Iowa. Introduced in 1940. *Source History: 2 in 1988; 1 in 1992; 2 in 2000.* **Sources: Nol, Pa6.**

Hican: Burton - Pecan x Shagbark. Medium size nut; larger, thinner shell than hickory parent. Excellent cracking quality. Excellent flavor. Prolific tree; produces in 5-7 years. Self-pollinating. Best suited for the South and Midwest. Will ripen in the maritime Northwest if given a sunny location. Ripens early. Originated in Kentucky. *Source History: 3 in 1988; 4 in 1992; 4 in 2000.* **Sources: Gor, Neb, Nol, Pa6.**

Hican: Country Club - Pecan x Shagbark. Medium size nut. Very heavy producer. Original tree grows 100' from Hartmann hican. Originated in Indiana. Introduced in 1980. *Source History: 1 in 1988; 1 in 1992; 1 in 2000.* **Sources: Nol.**

Hican: Dooley Burton - Seedling of Burton. Pollen parent appears to be shagbark as nuts have more hickory quality. Originated in Indiana. Introduced in 1980. *Source History: 1 in 1988; 1 in 1992; 1 in 2000.* **Sources: Nol.**

Hican: Hartmann (Adkins) - Pecan x Shagbark. Medium size, thin shelled nut. Good producer. Red tinted buds. Originated in Indiana. Originated near and apparently pollinated by Country Club hican. Introduced in 1980. *Source History: 1 in 1988; 1 in 1992; 1 in 2000.* **Sources: Nol.**

Hican: Henke - Pecan x Shellbark. Small to medium nut with high quality kernels that fill well. Good cracking quality. Good flavor. Very good bearer; produces in 5-7 years. Self-pollinating. Ripens early. Originated in Missouri. Introduced in 1928. *Source History: 2 in 1988; 4 in 1992; 3 in 2000.* **Sources: Gor, Neb, Nol.**

Hican: Hershey - Pecan x Shagbark. Medium size nut borne in clusters of three and four. High quality kernels fill well. Originated in Pennsylvania. Introduced in

1980. *Source History: 1 in 1988; 1 in 1992; 1 in 2000.* **Sources: Nol.**

Hican: Horton - *Source History: 1 in 1988; 1 in 1992; 1 in 2000.* **Sources: Nol.**

Hican: HY-6 - *Source History: 1 in 1992; 1 in 2000.* **Sources: Gor.**

Hican: Jackson - Pecan x Shagbark. Medium size nut; tasty kernels. Sets heavy crops when well pollinated. Originated in Kentucky. Introduced in 1985. *Source History: 1 in 1988; 1 in 1992; 1 in 2000.* **Sources: Nol.**

Hican: James - Huge, flavorful nut cracks as easily as a pecan. Tree can grow 60' tall; bears in 5-6 years. Ripens in late September. Hardy from the warmer areas of Zone 5 through Zone 8. Hardy. U.S. Plant Patent No. 3877. *Source History: 1 in 1988; 2 in 1992; 1 in 2000.* **Sources: Pa6.**

Hican: Johnson - *Source History: 1 in 1988; 1 in 1992; 1 in 2000.* **Sources: Nol.**

Hican: L 3 - *Source History: 1 in 1988; 1 in 1992; 1 in 2000.* **Sources: Nol.**

Hican: Marquardt - *Source History: 1 in 1992; 1 in 2000.* **Sources: Gor.**

Hican: McAllister - Pecan x Shellbark. Very large nut; seldom well filled. Needs early pollen. Originated in Indiana. *Source History: 1 in 1988; 1 in 1992; 1 in 2000.* **Sources: Nol.**

Hican: New Baden - *Source History: 1 in 1988; 1 in 1992; 1 in 2000.* **Sources: Nol.**

Hican: Newlin - Nut characteristics resemble Burton. Good bearing quaities. From Indiana. *Source History: 1 in 1988; 1 in 1992; 1 in 2000.* **Sources: Nol.**

Hican: Palmer - Well filled nuts in clusters of 4-5. Originated in Indiana. Introduced in 1985. *Source History: 1 in 1992; 1 in 2000.* **Sources: Nol.**

Hican: Pee-Wee - Does not bear heavily. *Source History: 2 in 1992; 1 in 2000.* **Sources: Wel.**

Hican: Pleas - Medium size, white nut. *Source History: 2 in 1988; 1 in 1992; 1 in 2000.* **Sources: Nol.**

Hican: T-92 - *Source History: 1 in 1992; 1 in 2000.* **Sources: Neb.**

Hican: Underwood - Pecan x Shellbark. Large, thin shelled nut; plump kernel. Originated in Kansas. Introduced in 1952. *Source History: 1 in 1988; 1 in 1992; 1 in 2000.* **Sources: Nol.**

Hican: Wilson - *Source History: 1 in 2000.* **Sources: Nol.**

Hican: Wright - *Source History: 1 in 2000.* **Sources: Nol.**

Mockernut - *Carya tomentosa.* Round, 1.5", light brown nut; sweet, but hard to extract. Tree can grow 90' tall with a 2-3' diameter trunk. Very heavy, strong wood. May be a useful rootstock. Hardy in Zone 5. Native from Massachusetts to Florida and Texas. *Source History: 3 in 1988; 2 in 1992; 11 in 2000.* **Sources: Arb, Ba3, BO10, Ca8, Fo2, HI7, KEE, LO6, Oik, Sh14, Wo2.**

Nutmeg Hickory - *Carya myristicaeformis.* Tree can grow 80-100' tall. Handsome, bronze foliage. Nuts look like nutmeg. Prefers moist soil. Native to northeastern Mexico. Rare. *Source History: 1 in 1988; 2 in 1992; 3 in 2000.* **Sources: LO6, Oik, Wo2.**

Pignut Hickory - *Carya glabra.* Egg-shaped, ridged, 1" nut. Astringent kernel. Tree can grow 40' tall. Good for wildlife and firewood. Native from Maine to Ontario and southward to Florida. Zone 4. *Source History: 3 in 1988; 2 in 1992; 8 in 2000.* **Sources: Arb, BO10, HI7, LO6, Oik, Sh14, WA8, Wo2.**

Macadamia

Macadamia spp.

Arkin - *Macadamia integrifolia.* Paper shell. *Source History: 1 in 2000.* **Sources: Ga11.**

Cate *(Macadamia integrefolia)* x Rough Shelled Macadamia *(M. tetraphylla).* Plant 24' on centers; 70 trees per acre. *Source History: 3 in 1988; 3 in 1992; 2 in 2000.* **Sources: Pa2.**

Dr. Beaumont (Beaumont) - *Macadamia tetraphylla* x *M. integrifolia.* Crisp, flavorful, white nutmeats. Large, handsome, evergreen tree. Remarkably free from diseases and insect pests. Likes sandy loam soils. Long-lived given favorable conditions. Suitable for orchard planting, home production and landscaping in areas relatively frost free, except desert areas. Plant 20' on centers; 108 trees per acre. Ripens from October to April. *Source History: 3 in 1988; 3 in 1992; 4 in 2000.* **Sources: Me2, Pa2, Tr10.**

Fenton - *Source History: 1 in 2000.* **Sources: Pa2.**

Macadamia (Australian Nut, Queensland Nut) - *Macadamia integrifolia.* Sweet .5-1.25" edible nut kernel is covered by a very hard outer shell. Tree can grow 60' tall and 40' wide. Foliage resembles holly leaf, but is thinner, longer leaved and uniquely contorted. Principal species grown commercially. Native to Queensland, Australia. *Source History: 4 in 1988; 6 in 1992; 6 in 2000.* **Sources: An4, Ban, Ca7, MIS, Pa6, Ro13.**

Pecan

Carya illinoinensis

Apache - Burkett x Schley. Soft shell. Kernels are smooth and bright. Good nut filling. Heavy yielding. Sheds pollen late. *Source History: 2 in 1988; 2 in 1992; 1 in 2000.* **Sources: Wom.**

Best's Early - Northern pecan. *Source History: 1 in 1988; 2 in 1992; 1 in 2000.* **Sources: Nol.**

Bolds - *Source History: 1 in 1992; 1 in 2000.* **Sources: Nol.**

Boltens S-24 - Far northern pecan. Ripens good quality nuts by September 24. Originated in Illinois. *Source History: 1 in 1992; 3 in 2000.* **Sources: Neb, Nol, Pa6.**

Bryce - *Source History: 1 in 1992; 1 in 2000.* **Sources: Neb.**

Burkett - Medium to large, round, soft shelled nut. Fills out well; 55% meat. Good flavor. Good producer; prolific. Sheds pollen late. Originated at Clyde, Texas. *Source History: 4 in 1988; 6 in 1992; 4 in 2000.* **Sources: CO5, Tex, Wel, Wom.**

Busseron - Far northern pecan. Produces many large size nuts with high quality kernels. Protogynous. Originated in Indiana. Introduced in 1930. *Source History: 1 in 1988; 1 in 1992; 1 in 2000.* **Sources: Nol.**

C. L. McElroy, Rock - *Source History: 1 in 1992; 1 in 2000.* **Sources: Neb.**

Caddo - Brooks x Alley. Small, football-shaped nut. Excellent kernel quality. Tree grows vigorously; regular producer. Very disease resistant. Protandrous; sheds pollen before its own female flowers are receptive. Eastern variety. *Source History: 1 in 1988; 2 in 1992; 2 in 2000.* **Sources: SIM, Wom.**

Campbell 4 - Far northern pecan. Good quality nuts. Originated in Ontario. Introduced in 1980. *Source History: 1 in 1992; 1 in 2000.* **Sources: Nol.**

Candy - Medium size, thin shelled nut; highly flavored. Beautiful tree is a consistently heavy bearer. Ripens early. Zones 6-9. *Source History: 2 in 1988; 7 in 1992; 3 in 2000.* **Sources: SIM, Tex, Wel.**

Canton - Northern pecan. *Source History: 1 in 1988; 1 in 1992; 1 in 2000.* **Sources: Neb.**

Cape Fear - Kernels do not break when shell is cracked; 55-60 nuts per lb. Long-lived tree bears heavily at an early age. Pollinate with Schley or Stuart. Scab resistant. Best for the southeastern states. Hardy in Zones 6-9. *Source History: 3 in 1988; 9 in 1992; 9 in 2000.* **Sources: Bas, Iso, MI10, SIM, St4, Tex, Ty2, WA8, Wel.**

Carlson 3 - *Source History: 2 in 1992; 1 in 2000.* **Sources: Gor.**

Carlson Center - Far northern pecan. Good sized nuts. Matures early. Originated in Illinois. Introduced in 1980. *Source History: 1 in 1988; 1 in 1992; 1 in 2000.* **Sources: Nol.**

Carlson Crow - *Source History: 1 in 1992; 1 in 2000.* **Sources: Pa6.**

Casey Jones - *Source History: 1 in 2000.* **Sources: Neb.**

Cheyenne (Cheyenne Paper Shell) - Clark x Odom. Medium size nut with thin, soft shell. Usually contains 57-62% meat; 55-60 per lb. Plump, high quality, richly flavored kernels are relatively loose within the shell, making them easy to shell with commercial machinery. Relatively small tree grows 35-45' tall. Protandrous; sheds pollen before its own female flowers are receptive. Pollinate with Choctaw, Stuart or Wichita. Often used to pollinate Wichita in commercial orchards. Very few pests. Excellent for high density commercial orchard plantings. Ripens in October. Requires 250 hours of chilling. Hardy in Zones 7-9. *Source History: 10 in 1988; 12 in 1992; 7 in 2000.* **Sources: CO5, Iso, Li5, SIM, Tex, Wel, Wom.**

Chickasaw - Smaller Indian type. Bears after only five years. Protogynous; female flowers are receptive before their own pollen matures. Highly disease resistant. Good for medium density commercial plantings. Hardy in Zones 7-9. *Source History: 2 in 1988; 3 in 1992; 1 in 2000.* **Sources: SIM.**

Chillicothe - *Source History: 1 in 1992; 1 in 2000.* **Sources: Neb.**

Choctaw - Mahan x Success. Large nut with very thin, soft hull. Resembles Stuart in shape. 45 nuts per pound. Easy to shell. Richly flavored kernel is very smooth, brightly colored and high in oil content; kernel consists of 60% of the total weight of the whole nut. Tree has upright growth habit and good foliage. Produces after 7-8 years. Responds well to pruning. Protogynous; female flowers are receptive before their own pollen matures. Pollinate with Cheyenne or Schley. Disease resistant. Good for medium density commercial plantings. Needs a long, hot summer. Ripens in mid-October. Requires 250 hours of chilling. Hardy in Zones 7-9. *Source History: 9 in 1988; 10 in 1992; 10 in 2000.* **Sources: Bas, CO5, Ed2, Li5, MI10, MI5, SIM, Tex, Wel, Wom.**

Colby (Colby Hardy) - Medium-large to large, long-oval nut with medium thick shell; 55 nuts per lb.; 48-53% meat. Good flavor. Tree quickly reaches a mature height and width of 40'. Heavily productive; bears young. Protogynous; female flowers are receptive before their own pollen matures. Pollinate with Green River, Hirschi, Major, Peruque or Starking Hardy Giant. Good pollinator for James and Major. Used for medium density commercial plantings; produces after 7-8 years. Best early type for size and productivity. Needs 160 day season; ripens in mid-

September. Zones 6-8. Selected by A. S. Colby and J. C. McDaniel at the Urbana Station in 1957. *Source History: 10 in 1988; 10 in 1992; 10 in 2000.* **Sources: Ed2, Fi1, Gur, KEE, Neb, Nol, Pa6, SIM, St4, Ty2.**

Converse Major - *Source History: 1 in 1992; 1 in 2000.* **Sources: Neb.**

Cornfield - Annual bearer. Larger nuts than Snaps; ripens two weeks later. Pollinate with Snaps. *Source History: 1 in 2000.* **Sources: Bu7.**

Coy - *Source History: 1 in 1992; 1 in 2000.* **Sources: Neb.**

Creek - *Source History: 1 in 2000.* **Sources: SIM.**

Curtis - *Source History: 1 in 1988; 2 in 1992; 1 in 2000.* **Sources: SIM.**

Dawson Creek - Wild type. *Source History: 1 in 2000.* **Sources: Oik.**

Desirable - Developed from Stuart. Large, meaty, thin shelled nut. Larger and better quality than Stuart. Excellent cracker; 55% meat; 40-45 nuts per pound. Sweet flavor. Consistent, heavy bearer; produces after 5-6 years. Protandrous; sheds pollen before its own female flowers are receptive. Pollinate with Stuart. Good pollinator for Hastings. Scab resistant. Used for low density commercial plantings. Ripens early. Hardy in Zones 6-9. *Source History: 8 in 1988; 17 in 1992; 16 in 2000.* **Sources: Bas, CO5, Ed2, Fi1, Gur, Iso, Lee, MI10, MI5, Sav, SIM, Tex, Ty2, WA8, Wel, Wom.**

Devore - Northern pecan. *Source History: 2 in 1988; 2 in 1992; 2 in 2000.* **Sources: Neb, Pa6.**

Doc Smith - *Source History: 1 in 1988; 1 in 1992; 1 in 2000.* **Sources: Nol.**

Don Grotjan, Early - *Source History: 1 in 1992; 1 in 2000.* **Sources: Neb.**

Dumbell Lake, Large - *Source History: 1 in 1992; 1 in 2000.* **Sources: Neb.**

Dumbell Lake, Small - *Source History: 1 in 2000.* **Sources: Neb.**

Elliott - Round, thin shelled nut. Size compares to Stuart; 65 per lb.; 53% meat. One of the best tasting pecans. Highly resistant to scab. Zones 6-9. *Source History: 2 in 1988; 8 in 1992; 5 in 2000.* **Sources: Bas, SIM, Tex, Ty2, Wel.**

Farm Thomas - *Source History: 1 in 2000.* **Sources: Neb.**

Fisher - Northern pecan. Cracks well. Good flavor. Originated in Illinois. Introduced in 1939. *Source History: 1 in 1988; 2 in 1992; 1 in 2000.* **Sources: Nol.**

Football II - *Source History: 1 in 2000.* **Sources: Neb.**

Forkert - Success x Schley. Large slender nut. Average 45 nuts per lb.; 60% meat. Thin shell. Moderate scab resistance. Zones 7-9. *Source History: 1 in 1988; 3 in 1992; 4 in 2000.* **Sources: Bas, SIM, Tex, Ty2.**

Foster - Long, thin nut. Ripens in early October. Originated in northern Missouri. *Source History: 2 in 1988; 2 in 1992; 1 in 2000.* **Sources: Neb.**

Fritz Flat - *Source History: 1 in 2000.* **Sources: Gor.**

Gage - *Source History: 1 in 1988; 1 in 1992; 1 in 2000.* **Sources: Nol.**

George, L-12 - *Source History: 1 in 2000.* **Sources: Neb.**

Gibson - Northern pecan. *Source History: 1 in 1988; 2 in 1992; 3 in 2000.* **Sources: Neb, Nol, Pa6.**

Giles - Medium size, thin shelled, well filled nut; 75 per lb.; 53-58% meat. Very good cracking quality. Good flavor. High quality. Prolific; bears in 3-5 years. Somewhat self-pollinating; Green River, Hirschi, Major and Peruque can also be used as pollinators. Grows well as far north as Illinois. Worthy of trial in the Northwest. Short season; ripens in early October. Parent tree grows in southeast Kansas near Chetopa. Located and introduced by J. F. Wilkinson. *Source History:*

4 in 1988; 4 in 1992; 3 in 2000. **Sources: Neb, Nol, Wom.**

Glen Minor - *Source History: 1 in 1992; 1 in 2000.* **Sources: Nol.**

Gloria Grande - Smaller nut than Stuart but of higher quality; 47 nuts per pound. Possibly the most disease resistant pecan available. Pollinate with Hastings or Jackson. Hardy in Zones 7-9. *Source History: 1 in 1988; 5 in 1992; 3 in 2000.* **Sources: Iso, SIM, Ty2.**

Graking - Large nut; 45 per lb.; 52% kernel. Good producer. Good scab resistance. Introduced by O. S. Gray of Arlington. *Source History: 1 in 1988; 1 in 1992; 1 in 2000.* **Sources: Wom.**

Green Island Beaver - *Source History: 1 in 2000.* **Sources: Neb.**

Green Island Hackberry - *Source History: 1 in 2000.* **Sources: Neb.**

Green River - Southern pecan. Medium to large, thin shelled nut; 80 per lb. Very good cracking quality. Plump kernel of fine flavor. Large tree is a prolific and regular bearer. Medium pollen shed; flowers receptive early. Ripens late. Originated in Henderson County, Kentucky at the mouth of the Green River. Bears well in Kentucky and southern states. *Source History: 3 in 1988; 3 in 1992; 3 in 2000.* **Sources: Bay, Nol, WI4.**

Grotjan - *Source History: 1 in 1992; 1 in 2000.* **Sources: Nol.**

Hadu No. 1 - *Source History: 1 in 2000.* **Sources: Neb.**

Hadu No. 2 - *Source History: 1 in 1988; 1 in 1992; 2 in 2000.* **Sources: Neb, Pa6.**

Hadu No. 3 - *Source History: 1 in 2000.* **Sources: Neb.**

Hardy (Northern) - Thrives in the North, unlike other varieties. Good sized, thin shelled, rich flavored nut of excellent quality. Cracks free of the hulls. Beautiful, hardy, long-lived shade tree grows rapidly 50-70' tall. Does not shed its leaves until late fall. Two trees are required for good pollination. Practically immune to insects. Will thrive anywhere peaches can be grown. Hardy throughout Zone 5 to Zone 10. *Source History: 9 in 1988; 8 in 1992; 8 in 2000.* **Sources: Bu1, Fi1, FO10, Fo4, Gur, HI7, Int, TU5.**

Hardy Giant - Medium to large, thin shelled nut. Good quality. Self-fertile. Hardy to -20 degrees F. *Source History: 1 in 1992; 1 in 2000.* **Sources: Bu7.**

Hardy Giant, Starking (James Cultivar) - Nuts often reach 1.5" in diameter with paper thin shells. Plump, golden kernels. Self-pollinating; bears bigger crops if cross-pollinated with Colby. Hardy to -20 degrees F.; Zones 6-9. Trademarked. *Source History: 1 in 1988; 3 in 1992; 3 in 2000.* **Sources: Neb, SIM, St4.**

Hardy Seedlings - Delicious kernels, but usually smaller than grafted pecans. Beautiful, rapid growing, sturdy trees are produced from the seed of thin shelled, hardy varieties. Hardy in Zones 4-9. *Source History: 2 in 1988; 5 in 1992; 5 in 2000.* **Sources: Bar, Lee, Pa6, Po2, Sav.**

Hardy, Southern - Hardy to Zone 8. *Source History: 1 in 2000.* **Sources: HI7.**

Harmon Bunts - *Source History: 1 in 2000.* **Sources: Neb.**

Hastings - Thin shelled nut. Vigorous growing tree. Produces after 4-5 years. Protandrous, but is one of the few pecans capable of pollinating itself; plant with Desirable for even better pollination. Used in low density commercial plantings. *Source History: 2 in 1988; 2 in 1992; 1 in 2000.* **Sources: SIM.**

Hirschi - Thin shelled nut fills well and yields a high quality kernel with 50-55% cracking percentage; 56 nuts per lb. Heavy bearer. Self-pollinating. Ripens in early October. Very hardy. Discovered about 1940 at Rich Hill, Missouri by J. W.

Tiedke. Selected by A. G. Hirschi of Oklahoma City from whom it received its name. First called Stuke. Introduced by the Inter-State Nursery at Hamburg, Iowa in 1954. *Source History: 2 in 1988; 3 in 1992; 2 in 2000.* **Sources: Neb, Nol.**

Hodge - *Source History: 1 in 1988; 1 in 1992; 2 in 2000.* **Sources: Neb, Nol.**

Houma - Curtis x Desirable. Good size nut. *Source History: 2 in 2000.* **Sources: SIM, Tex.**

Howell - *Source History: 1 in 2000.* **Sources: Nol.**

Indiana - Medium size nut; 77 per lb. Medium pollen shed; flowers are receptive in mid-shed. Ripens midseason. Originated in Indiana. *Source History: 1 in 1988; 1 in 1992; 1 in 2000.* **Sources: Nol.**

Jackson - Fine nuts; 35 per lb.; 52% meat. Bears after 5-6 years. Protandrous, but it is one of the few pecans capable of pollinating itself; excellent pollinator. Highly scab resistant. Used for low density commercial plantings. Hardy in Zones 7-9. Originated in southern Mississippi. *Source History: 2 in 1988; 3 in 1992; 3 in 2000.* **Sources: Bas, SIM, Tex.**

James Hardy - Large, thin shelled nut. Self-fruitful, but bears heavier crops if cross-pollinated by Colby. Earliest ripening of the hardy, northern pecans. Needs only 120 days growing season. Hardy in Zones 4-9. *Source History: 1 in 1988; 1 in 1992; 4 in 2000.* **Sources: Neb, Oik, Pa6, Ty2.**

Jay Ford (J. Ford) - Southern pecan. Does not always fill well in O'Fallon, Illinois. Good eating. Produces within 3-5 years. *Source History: 2 in 1988; 2 in 1992; 1 in 2000.* **Sources: Nol.**

Kanza - Northern pecan. Easy shelling nut; 72 per pound. 55% kernel. Sheds pollen late. Scab resistant. Matures early; mid-September. Excellent for the northern pecan areas as well as the warmer areas. *Source History: 3 in 2000.* **Sources: Nol, WI4, Wom.**

Kentucky - Medium size nut; 83 per lb. Good production. Medium pollen shed; flowers are receptive in mid-shed. Ripens mid-late. Originated in Kentucky. *Source History: 1 in 1988; 1 in 1992; 1 in 2000.* **Sources: Nol.**

Kernodle - Medium size nuts; 55% kernel. Tasty. Ripens late, in November. Zones 7-9. Originated in Alabama. *Source History: 1 in 1988; 1 in 1992; 2 in 2000.* **Sources: SIM, Ty2.**

Kiowa - Mahan x Odom. Early bearing Indian type. Large, oblong, thin shelled, very meaty nut; 45-50 per lb. Excellent quality. Vigorous tree bears heavily; produces after 5-6 years. Beautiful, dark green foliage. Self-fruitful. Disease resistant. Requires a long, hot summer and 250 hours of chilling. Some freeze damage reported in northern and mid-Oklahoma on young trees. Better adapted to the East. Used for either high or medium density commercial planting. Hardy in Zones 7-9. *Source History: 6 in 1988; 9 in 1992; 6 in 2000.* **Sources: Bas, Li5, SIM, Tex, Wel, Wom.**

Lattus - Northern pecan. *Source History: 1 in 2000.* **Sources: Nol.**

Loyd - *Source History: 1 in 1992; 1 in 2000.* **Sources: Nol.**

Lucas - Northern pecan. Nuts crack and fill well. Precocious, heavy producer. Originated in Ohio. Introduced in 1965. *Source History: 1 in 1988; 2 in 1992; 4 in 2000.* **Sources: Bu7, Neb, Nol, Pa6.**

Mahan (Giant Mahan) - Enormous, slender, thin shelled nut about 2.5" long; 31 per lb. Similar to Western Schley, except much larger. Richly flavored kernels. First class quality. Very vigorous growing tree; starts bearing earlier than others. Self-fruitful. Very late maturing; does best in low desert climates. Requires 250 hours of chilling.   An old variety; a parent of most of the newer varieties. *Source History: 9 in 1988; 12 in 1992; 15 in 2000.* **Sources: Bas, Bay, CO5, Fi1, Gur, Lee, Li5, MI10, Sav, SIM, STR, Tex, Ty2, WA8, Wel, WI4.**

Major (Major Hardy) - Sometimes called the Stuart of the North. Medium size, round nut; 60-80 per lb. Thin, easy to crack shell.   Small, plump, sweet, buttery, golden kernels. Excellent flavor. Beautiful, vigorous tree produces heavily; bears in 3-5 years. Protandrous; sheds pollen before its own female flowers are receptive. Plant with Colby or Stark Surecrop to ensure proper pollination and better harvests. Perhaps the best of the northern pecans for growth and disease resistance. Ripens medium-early. Hardy in Zones 6-8. Discovered in Henderson County, Kentucky. *Source History: 6 in 1988; 4 in 1992; 7 in 2000.* **Sources: Bay, Neb, Nol, Pa6, SIM, Ty2, WI4.**

Maramec - Large, high quality nut; 59% kernel. Tree is vigorous, productive, well branched. Seedling tree was discovered near Maramec, Oklahoma. *Source History: 1 in 1988; 2 in 1992; 3 in 2000.* **Sources: MI5, Wel, Wom.**

Melrose - Medium-large nut; 54 nuts per lb.; 55% kernel.   Tree has upright growth habit with strong branching. High degree of resistance to scab and shuck disease. Hardy in Zones 8-9. *Source History: 2 in 1988; 5 in 1992; 4 in 2000.* **Sources: Bas, SIM, Tex, Wel.**

Missouri Hardy - Vigorous, regular bearer. Plant at least two for better crops. Hardy in Zones 5-9. *Source History: 1 in 1988; 1 in 1992; 1 in 2000.* **Sources: St4.**

Mohawk (Mohawk Paper Shell) - Mahan x Success. Large to very large, very thin shelled nut; 35-50 per lb.; 60% meat.   Fills well; cracks easily into fancy halves. Distinctive flavor. Excellent quality. Vigorous, upright tree with diffuse branching and dark green foliage. Very productive; bears at a young age. Blooms late; medium heavy pollen shed. Flowers are receptive late. Plant with Cheyenne. Good choice for home planting. Ripens early, so more widely adapted than others. Requires 250 hours of chilling. Hardy from the southern edge of Zone 6 through Zone 9.   Originated in Texas. *Source History: 9 in 1988; 15 in 1992; 14 in 2000.* **Sources: Bay, CO5, Gur, Li5, MI5, Nol, Pa2, Pa6, Pe2, SIM, Son, Tex, Wel, WI4.**

Moreland - Papershell nut with size and shape of Stuart. Nuts fill well; 45 per lb. Extremely high oil content gives them an extra rich flavor and good keeping quali- ties. Upright, disease resistant tree. Self-fruitful. *Source History: 1 in 1992; 1 in 2000.* **Sources: Ju2.**

Mullahy - *Source History: 2 in 2000.* **Sources: Neb, Pa6.**

Native Seedling - Heavy yield of good quality nuts. Exceedingly hardy seed- lings grown from native, papershell nuts. *Source History: 1 in 1988; 1 in 1992; 1 in 2000.* **Sources: Tex.**

Navaho (Moore x Schley) x Wichita. Productive, fast growing tree. Best for central and western areas since it is susceptible to scab. *Source History: 3 in 2000.* **Sources: CO5, Tex, Wom.**

Normal - *Source History: 1 in 2000.* **Sources: Neb.**

Northern - Smaller nuts than cultivated southern varieties; the same excellent quality. Straight trunked, round, spreading, symmetrical tree grows 70-90' tall with a 30-40' spread. Light green leaves turn yellow in the fall. Tiny, greenish flowers in the spring. Plant two trees for pollination. Life span of 80 or more years. Does not fruit in the Northwest.   Grows well as far north as southeastern Nebraska. Hardy to -10 degrees F. and in Zones 4-9. *Source History: 10 in 1988; 16 in 1992;*

7 in 2000. **Sources: Bea, Ca8, KEE, LOV, Na4, Sc2, Wa16.**

Northern Seedlings - *Source History: 1 in 1988; 2 in 1992; 3 in 2000.* **Sources: Mu2, Nol, Wom.**

Norton - *Source History: 1 in 2000.* **Sources: Neb.**

Oconee - Barton x Schley. Good size nut; 55 per lb.; 55% kernel. Good disease resistance. Protandrous. USDA release. *Source History: 2 in 1992; 6 in 2000.* **Sources: Bas, MI5, SIM, Tex, Ty2, Wom.**

Oily Canton - *Source History: 1 in 2000.* **Sources: Neb.**

Osage - Northern pecan. *Source History: 2 in 2000.* **Sources: Nol, SIM.**

Owens - *Source History: 1 in 1988; 2 in 1992; 1 in 2000.* **Sources: SIM.**

Papershell - Thin shelled nut, not quite as large as Mahan and Stuart. Good quality. Fine shaped, fast growing tree. Excellent pollinator. *Source History: 1 in 1988; 1 in 1992; 1 in 2000.* **Sources: Lee.**

Pawnee - Mohawk x Starking Hardy Giant. Large, soft shelled nut; 57 per lb. Excellent quality. Produces five years after planting. High yields; about 2,700 lbs. per acre when mature. Protandrous; sheds pollen before its own female flowers are receptive. Pollen shed similar to Cheyenne. Disease resistant. Used for high density commercial planting in areas with shorter growing seasons. Ripens early. Requires 250 hours of chilling. Hardy in Zones 7-9. Developed at the Brownwood Station in Texas. Introduced in 1984. *Source History: 5 in 1988; 13 in 1992; 15 in 2000.* **Sources: Bas, Bay, Bu7, CO5, Ed2, Iso, Li5, MI5, Nol, Pe2, SIM, Tex, Wel, WI4, Wom.**

Pecan - Hardy seedlings from Missouri. *Source History: 3 in 1988; 4 in 2000.* **Sources: Arb, Bo5, Fo2, WA8.**

Peruque - Medium size nut that fills well; 75-82 per lb.; 59-64% meat. Thinnest shell of any northern variety; excellent cracking quality. Excellent flavor and quality. Tree grows 70-80' tall. Prolific; bears in 3-5 years. Heavy, annual bearer. Protandrous; sheds pollen before its own female flowers are receptive. Pollinate with Colby, Giles, Green River, Hirschi or Major. Ripens early. Hardy in Zones 5-8. Parent tree stands in St. Charles County, Missouri. Introduced in 1955. *Source History: 4 in 1988; 5 in 1992; 7 in 2000.* **Sources: Bay, Ed2, Fi1, Neb, Nol, Pa6, WI4.**

PK 125 Deer Stand - *Source History: 1 in 1988; 1 in 2000.* **Sources: Gor.**

Podsednik - Largest pecan observed; only 22 nuts per lb. Kernel is well filled and has good color in younger trees. Tree has strong structure and large leaves. Pollen is shed slightly ahead of pistil receptivity. Appears to be scab resistant. Matures with Mahan. *Source History: 1 in 1988; 1 in 1992; 1 in 2000.* **Sources: Wom.**

Posey - Northern pecan. Medium to large nut; 72 per lb. Very good cracking quality. Excellent flavor. Bears very well in 5-7 years. Late pollen shed; flowers are receptive early. Ripens medium early. Originated in Indiana. *Source History: 2 in 1988; 2 in 1992; 2 in 2000.* **Sources: Neb, Nol.**

Posey (Alvey-Cook) - *Source History: 1 in 2000.* **Sources: Neb.**

Prilop of Lavaca - Golden nut; 78 per pound. 57% kernel. Scab resistant. Native to Lavaca County, Texas. *Source History: 1 in 2000.* **Sources: Wom.**

Princeton - *Source History: 1 in 1988; 1 in 1992; 1 in 2000.* **Sources: Nol.**

Ralph Upton - *Source History: 1 in 2000.* **Sources: Neb.**

S-24 - Northern pecan. *Source History: 2 in 1988; 1 in 1992; 1 in 2000.* **Sources:**

Nol.

Schley (Eastern Schley, Schley Papershell) - Large, very thin shelled nut; plump, tasty kernels; 60% meat. Fills and shells out well. Fine flavor. Rapid growing tree with beautiful foliage. Self-pollinating, but produces bigger crops when pollinated with Cape Fear. Hardy in Zones 7-9. *Source History: 3 in 1988; 5 in 1992; 2 in 2000.* **Sources: SIM, Wel.**

Schley, Western - Medium size, long, tapered nut with thin, soft shell; 60% meat. Very good quality. Vigorous tree tolerates late freezes better than most thin shelled pecans. Good, dependable producer when cross-pollinated; good pollinator. Sheds pollen early. Very few pests. Tolerates zinc deficiency and poor soil fertility. Very similar to Eastern Schley, except that it thrives better in drier climate and higher altitudes of the West. Ripens from mid to late October. Requires 250 hours of chilling. *Source History: 9 in 1988; 13 in 1992; 10 in 2000.* **Sources: Bay, CO5, Li5, Pa2, Pe2, STR, Tex, Wel, WI4, Wom.**

Select - Soft shell. Sheds pollen early. *Source History: 1 in 1988; 1 in 1992; 1 in 2000.* **Sources: CO5.**

Shawnee - Schley x Barton. Medium size, soft shell pecan. Very high quality kernels. Tree is a heavy, prolific bearer that comes into production early. Sheds pollen late. Suitable for in-shell or shelling trade. Introduced in 1968. *Source History: 2 in 1988; 2 in 1992; 2 in 2000.* **Sources: Tex, Wel.**

Shepherd - *Source History: 1 in 2000.* **Sources: Neb.**

Shoals West - *Source History: 1 in 2000.* **Sources: Neb.**

Shoshoni - Odom x Evers. Large, soft shelled nut; 40-60 per lb. Excellent grower and exceptionally prolific; begins bearing five years after planting. Protogynous; female flowers are receptive before their own pollen matures. Medium pollen shed. Very disease resistant. Used for high density commercial plantings. Ripens in mid-October. Hardy in Zones 7-9. Originated in Texas. *Source History: 5 in 1988; 8 in 1992; 4 in 2000.* **Sources: Li5, SIM, Tex, Wel.**

Sioux - Schley x Carmichael. Small, extremely thin shelled nut; 60-80 per lb. Smooth, bright kernels with a high oil content; considered one of the very best in eye appeal, shape, taste and ease of shelling. Excellent flavor. Sheds pollen late. *Source History: 3 in 1988; 5 in 1992; 3 in 2000.* **Sources: Tex, Wel, Wom.**

Snaps - Annual bearer. Ripens very early. Pollinate with Cornfield. *Source History: 2 in 2000.* **Sources: Bu7, Pa6.**

Snodgrass - *Source History: 1 in 2000.* **Sources: Neb.**

Stuart (Stuart Paper Shell) - Large nut with thin, medium hard, easy to crack shell; fills well; 45 nuts per lb. Kernels are easy to separate; 48% meat; 45 nuts per lb. Excellent quality. Vigorous, fast growing tree reaches 50' tall and wide. Medium to heavy bearer; produces after 7-8 years. Protogynous; female flowers are receptive before their own pollen matures. Pollinate with Cape Fear or Desirable. Good pollinator for Mahan or Papershell. Scab resistant. Widely adapted all across the country and on most soils. Extremely popular from Oklahoma to Virginia. Used for low density commercial plantings. Ripens during September, very early for a large pecan. Hardy in Zones 4-9. *Source History: 13 in 1988; 23 in 1992; 17 in 2000.* **Sources: Bar, Bas, BO10, BO4, Fi1, Iso, Lee, Mel, MI10, MI5, Sav, SIM, St4, Tex, Ty2, WA8, Wel.**

Stuart x Mahan - *Source History: 1 in 1988; 1 in 1992; 1 in 2000.* **Sources: SIM.**

Success - Medium-soft, thin shelled nut; 52% meat. Cracks well; can be taken out in halves. Strong growing tree, early bearer. Sheds pollen early. Ripens almost 10 days later than Stuart. *Source History: 2 in 1988; 5 in 1992; 4 in 2000.* **Sources: CO5, Li5, Tex, Wel.**

Sumner - Large, high quality nut; 55-60 nuts per lb.; 55% kernel. Good scab resistance. Tree produces early. Suitable for close space planting. *Source History: 2 in 1988; 5 in 1992; 6 in 2000.* **Sources: Bas, Iso, SIM, Tex, Ty2, Wel.**

Surecrop, Stark (Sure Crop, Osterman Cultivar) - Large, rich flavored, easy to crack, papershell pecan. Self-pollinating; yields better if cross-pollinated with Major or Starking Hardy Giant. Hardy to -18 degrees F. and in Zones 6-8. Trademarked. U.S. Plant Patent No. 3158. *Source History: 1 in 1988; 3 in 1992; 2 in 2000.* **Sources: SIM, St4.**

Tejas - Thin shelled nut; 50-75 per lb.; 50-56% meat. Fine flavor. Beautiful tree holds its green foliage late in the season. Bears young and heavily. Self-fruitful. Ripens early. Requires 250 hours of chilling. Recommended for northern California Central Valley and other areas where the growing season is too short for Western Schley or Wichita. Name is Spanish for Texas. *Source History: 3 in 1988; 6 in 1992; 6 in 2000.* **Sources: Bay, Li5, Son, Tex, Wel, WI4.**

Warsaw North - *Source History: 1 in 2000.* **Sources: Neb.**

Wichita - Halbert x Mahan. Medium size, thin shelled, well filled nut is moderately elongated like Schley. Slightly smaller than Stuart; 60 per lb. High quality. Vigorous, moderately upright tree produces consistently; bears early and heavily. Dark green foliage is resistant to factors that cause early defoliation. Sheds pollen late. Pollinate with Cheyenne, Desirable or Western Schley. Demands precise soil and nutrition requirements; may be difficult to grow. Ripens midseason. Requires 250 hours of chilling. *Source History: 9 in 1988; 13 in 1992; 9 in 2000.* **Sources: CO5, Li5, MI5, Pa2, SIM, STR, Tex, Wel, Wom.**

Yates 68 - First propagated as the Yates pecan. Nut resembles Major x Posey but is larger than both. 60% kernel. Cracks easily in halves. High quality. Matures with Posey and Major. Originated as a Major seedling in the pecan grove of Ed Yates of Chrisney, Indiana. *Source History: 1 in 2000.* **Sources: Nol.**

Yates 127 - Major seedling, possibly with a Posey pollen parent. Thin shell. 62% kernel. High quality. The entire kernel can be removed from the shell by clipping the ends off the nut. Matures with Major. *Source History: 1 in 2000.* **Sources: Nol.**

Pine Nuts

Pinus spp.

Big Cone (Pitch Pine) - *Pinus coulteri*. Largest cone of any pine bearing good, edible nuts. Fairly fast growing, wide branching, attractive tree is drought tolerant. Grows 40-80'. Native to California mountains. Hardy to western Washington; Zone 7. *Source History: 1 in 1992; 2 in 2000.* **Sources: Co24, Hud.**

Chir Pine (Emodi Pine) - *Pinus roxburghii*. Beautiful Himalayan pine grows to 150' or more. Drooping 12" light green needles in clusters of three. Oval 7" cones. Seeds are eaten in India. Zone 8. Native to the Himalayas. *Source History: 1 in 1988; 1 in 1992; 3 in 2000.* **Sources: Co24, Fo2, Hud.**

Digger Pine - *Pinus sabiniana*. Open, irregular tree grows quickly 40-80' tall. Lacy 9-12" pale bluish green needles in clusters of three. Oval 6-10" cones contain large, edible nuts. Drought resistant. Staple food for the California Indians. Also used to produce turpentine. Native to dry areas in California. Hardy in Zone 7.

Source History: 10 in 1988; 10 in 1992; 8 in 2000. **Sources: Ca12, Ca7, Co24, Fo2, Las, MIS, Pa2, Sc2.**

Korean Pine (Korean White Pine) - *Pinus koraiensis*. Well formed, pyramidal tree grows 60-90' tall with a 30-40' spread; has been known to reach 150'. Small branches are yellowish brown and fuzzy. Dark green 4" needles in groups of five. Conic-oblong 6" cones contain edible nuts. Needs a well drained to moist soil. Very hardy, even into Zone 3, but slow growing in cold northern areas. Life span of 80 or more years. Native from southeast Siberia to northern Japan and Korea. *Source History: 4 in 1988; 3 in 1992; 4 in 2000.* **Sources: Bu7, Co24, Ed5, Hud.**

Limber Pine - *Pinus flexilis*. Beautiful, gnarled pine often seen on windswept, timberline ridges; very slow growing. Under good conditions, tree can reach 60' tall. Stiff 3" yellowish green needles in clusters of five. Oval 3" glossy, yellowish cones hold edible seeds; smaller nut than pinyon. Tolerant to wind and drought. Hardy to -40 degrees F. Native from Alberta south to Texas and California. *Source History: 7 in 1988; 7 in 1992; 6 in 2000.* **Sources: Ca12, Co24, Fo2, No2, Sc2, We8.**

Nepal Nut Pine - *Pinus gerardiana*. Ornamental tree with gray bark that flakes off to show pink, white and green patches. Produces large, edible nuts. Zone 6. Native to the Himalayas. *Source History: 1 in 2000.* **Sources: Fo2.**

Pinyon (Colorado Pinyon, Nut Pine, Pinyon Pine, Two Leaved Nut Pine, Two Needle Pinyon) - *Pinus edulis*. Small, dense, slow growing, pyramidal tree can grow 40' tall with a 30' spread. When the tree is many years old, its roundish 2.5" cones produce delicious nuts that are .5" long, oily, sweet and highly nutritious. These nuts formed a large part of the diet of some Indian tribes, especially in New Mexico and Arizona. Hardy into Zone 3. Native from Wyoming southwest to Texas, northern Mexico and California; found mainly in semiarid regions of the Southwest. *Source History: 14 in 1988; 12 in 1992; 18 in 2000.* **Sources: Abu, ALD, Bu7, Ca12, Ca7, Co24, Fed, Fo2, Hud, LA4, LI7, Mel, Mel, MIS, No2, Or2, Pa2, So12.**

Pinyon, Big Cone - *Pinus maximartinezii*. Vary rare and only recently named. Large tree grows 50' tall. Differs from other pinyons in having very fine, almost lacy, blue green foliage and much larger 8-12" cones and nuts. Native to Mexico. Hardy in Zone 7. *Source History: 1 in 1988; 1 in 1992; 1 in 2000.* **Sources: Fo2.**

Pinyon, Johann's - *Pinus johannis*. Rare and little known, shrubby, high elevation pinyon. Beautiful bluish weeping needles. Native to Mexico. Hardy in Zones 7-8. *Source History: 3 in 1988; 1 in 1992; 1 in 2000.* **Sources: Ca12.**

Pinyon, Mexican - *Pinus discolor*. *Source History: 1 in 1988; 1 in 1992; 1 in 2000.* **Sources: Pa2.**

Pinyon, Nelson's - *Pinus nelsonii*. Tree grows to 30'. Edible .5" nuts. Good flavor. Hardy to Zone 7. Originated in Mexico. *Source History: 2 in 1988; 1 in 1992; 2 in 2000.* **Sources: Ca12, Fo2.**

Pinyon, Paper Shell - *Pinus remota*. Shrub to small tree. Needles in clusters of three. Unique "paper-shell" on its seeds. Likes sun, lime, well drained soil. Native to Texas and Mexico. Hardy in Zones 7-8. *Source History: 2 in 1988; 1 in 1992; 1 in 2000.* **Sources: Ca12.**

Pinyon, Parry - *Pinus quadrifolia*. Similar to Mexican Stone pine (*P. cembroides*), but has needles in groups of four. Edible pinyon nuts. Hardy in Zone 9. Native to southern California and northern Baja, California. *Source History: 2 in 1988; 3 in 1992; 2 in 2000.* **Sources: Ca12, Pa2.**

Pinyon, Pince's - *Pinus pinceana*. *Source History: 2 in 1988; 1 in 1992; 1 in*

2000. **Sources: Ca12.**

Pinyon, Single Leaf (Nut Pine, Single Leaf Pinyon Pine, Stone Pine) - *Pinus monophylla.* Drought tolerant shrub or small tree with round head and often a crooked trunk. Similar to Mexican Stone pine (*P. cembroides*), but has mostly single needles. Cones contain edible pinyon nuts. Hardy in Zone 5. Native from Idaho southward to California and northern Mexico. *Source History: 8 in 1988; 5 in 1992; 5 in 2000.* **Sources: Ca12, Ca7, Co24, Fo2, Pa2.**

Pinyon, Weeping - *Pinus pinceana.* Rare and especially beautiful pinyon with rounded crown with pendant branches. Bluish green, 2-4" needles. Edible nuts. Hardy in Zone 7. Native to Mexico. *Source History: 1 in 1988; 1 in 2000.* **Sources: Fo2.**

Stone Pine, Dwarf Siberian (Dwarf Japanese Stone Pine, Dwarf Siberian Pine, Dwarf Stone Pine, Japanese Stone Pine) - *Pinus pumila.* Very rare shrub with dense, prostrate branches; grows from 1-9' tall. Groups of five 3" long needles. Oval 2" cones. Hardy in Zone 4. Native to the mountain areas of eastern Siberia and Japan. *Source History: 5 in 1988; 3 in 1992; 3 in 2000.* **Sources: Ca12, Hud, Sc2.**

Stone Pine, Dwarf Swiss - *Pinus cembra v. Glauca Compacta.* Dwarf form of Swiss stone pine. Grows to 4-5' tall. Zones 3-8. *Source History: 1 in 2000.* **Sources: Ed2.**

Stone Pine, Italian (Umbrella Pine) - *Pinus pinea.* Picturesque, slow growing, seaside pine with dense, umbrella-like branches, usually 45-75' tall; broad, flat topped crown at maturity. Long, stiff 6-8" bright green needles in clusters of two. Oval 5" cones contain large, sweet, edible seeds (Pignola nuts). Hardy in Zones 7-8. Native to the northern Mediterranean region. Considered sacred to Neptune by the ancient Greeks. *Source History: 11 in 1988; 14 in 1992; 10 in 2000.* **Sources: Ca12, Ca7, Ed2, Fo2, Hud, MIS, Or2, ORA, Pa2, Sc2.**

Stone Pine, Korean - *Pinus koraiensis.* Slow growing, pyramidal tree; similar to Swiss Stone pine (*P. cembra*), but more open branched. Green 2-4" needles with blue undersides in clusters of five. Should bear pine nuts in 6-10 years. Hardy in Zone 4. Native to eastern Asia. *Source History: 10 in 1988; 5 in 1992; 6 in 2000.* **Sources: Ca12, Fo2, Hid, Oik, Or2, Sc2.**

Stone Pine, Mexican - *Pinus cembroides.* Shrub or small tree grows 25' tall; small branches are dark orange. Stiff, slightly curved 3" dark green needles in groups of 2-5. Roundish 2.5" cones. Hardy in Zone 7. Native to Arizona and Mexico. *Source History: 2 in 1988; 2 in 1992; 3 in 2000.* **Sources: Ca12, Fo2, Or2.**

Stone Pine, Swiss (Arolla Pine, Russian Cedar) - *Pinus cembra.* Narrow, pyramidal tree usually grows 30-40', but has been known to reach 80' tall; one of the most formal appearing trees of the pine family. Small branches are orangish brown and fuzzy. Clusters of five dark green 5" needles with silvery markings on the underside. Oval 3.5" deep blue cones filled with nuts (edible seeds). Long-lived; slow growing in the early years. Hardy in Zone 3-8. Native to the Alps of Europe and northern Asia. Adaptable to the North and Mid-Atlantic states. (*Cembra* means alpine village and *P. cembra* is a truly alpine pine). *Source History: 10 in 1988; 10 in 1992; 11 in 2000.* **Sources: BA14, Ca12, Ca7, Co24, Ed2, Fo2, Gir, Hud, Sc2, Va5, We8.**

Sugar Pine - *Pinus lambertiana.* Beautiful white pine with edible seeds. Zone 6. *Source History: 1 in 1992; 1 in 2000.* **Sources: Co24.**

Torrey Pine (Soledad Pine) - *Pinus torreyana.* Broad, open, irregular, picturesque, 25-60' tree. Stiff 7-13" dark green needles in groups of five. Oval 6" cones contain large, edible seeds. Hardy in Zone 7. Known only from a few thousand trees in southern California. Native to southern California. *Source History: 9 in 1988; 8 in 1992; 5 in 2000.* **Sources: Ca12, Ca7, MIS, Pa2, Sc2.**

White Pine, Siberian - *Pinus sibirica.* Narrow conical tree resembles *P. cembra.* Edible seeds. Zone 3. Native to the bogs of Siberia. *Source History: 1 in 2000.* **Sources: Fo2.**

Walnut / Black
Juglans nigra

Beck - *Source History: 2 in 1992; 2 in 2000.* **Sources: Neb, Nol.**

Bicentennial - Extremely hardy black walnut with cracking quality equal to Thomas. Larger than other northern walnuts. Requires a pollinator. Vigorous tree. Zone 3. *Source History: 1 in 1988; 1 in 2000.* **Sources: Ed5.**

Bicentennial Cross - Bicentennial x Weschcke. Displays many of Bicentennial's desirable qualities: large nut, precocious production and vigor of growth. Cracking quality is equal to Thomas. Extremely fast growing. Exhibits good hardiness. *Source History: 1 in 1988; 1 in 1992; 1 in 2000.* **Sources: Stl.**

Black Walnut - Round nut up to 2"; thick, black shell is rather hard to crack. Rich flavor is retained during cooking; twice the protein of Persian walnuts. Round headed tree grows 50-80' tall and 40-50' wide. Diamond pattern on bark. Compound leaves 12-24"; leaflets 3-3.5". Dark green foliage turns yellowish brown in fall. Self-fruitful. Deep taproot; drought resistant. Used as rootstock for black walnut cultivars, heartnuts and Persian walnuts. Gorgeous, dark brown wood; easily worked, highly valued for furniture. Adaptable, but prefers deep, fertile, well drained soil. Zones 4-9. Native from Ontario to Massachusetts, to Florida and Texas. *Source History: 44 in 1988; 58 in 1992; 49 in 2000.* **Sources: Arb, BA14, Bar, Bea, BO10, Bu7, CA14, Ca7, Ca8, Clo, Co15, Fed, FO10, Fo2, Fo4, GR26, Gur, HI7, Ins, Iso, JO4, KEE, LA4, Lee, LO6, LOV, Mc3, MEA, Mel, Mi1, Mu2, Na4, On3, ORA, Pi2, Po2, Rai, Sav, SH8, So12, St12, St4, TU5, Ty2, Va5, Wa16, WA8, Wh3, Win.**

Black Walnut Improved - Improved strain. Nut is larger and has a softer shell; easily cracked in halves. Kernels are meaty with excellent flavor. Quite rapid grower with larger diameter, straight trunk. High yields; often bears the second year after planting. Self-pollinating. Disease resistant. Widely adapted. Hardy. *Source History: 2 in 1988; 2 in 1992; 1 in 2000.* **Sources: La3.**

Black Walnut Seedlings - Good pollinator for other black walnuts or used as rootstock for butternut and black walnuts in the far north. Mother tree ripens early and has small but well filled nuts. Zone 3. Northern Wisconsin. *Source History: 1 in 2000.* **Sources: Ed5.**

Boellner - Precocious tree bears large, well filled nuts. Pollinate with Sparrow. *Source History: 1 in 2000.* **Sources: Bu7.**

Card - *Source History: 1 in 1992; 1 in 2000.* **Sources: Neb.**

Clermont - Medium size, thin shelled nut; 28% kernel. Excellent flavor. Heavy bearer. Similar to Elmer Myers; bears more regularly. Resistant to anthracnose. Ripens better in the north. Originated in Ohio. Introduced in 1912. *Source History: 1 in 1988; 2 in 1992; 2 in 2000.* **Sources: Neb, Nol.**

Cochrane - *Source History: 1 in 1992; 1 in 2000.* **Sources: Neb.**

Cooksey - Produces large quantities of thin shelled, flavorful nuts. Crack whole.

Grafted tree. Self-fertile. Zones 4-9. *Source History: 1 in 2000.* **Sources: Rai.**

Cranz - *Source History: 1 in 1992; 2 in 2000.* **Sources: Bu7, Neb.**

Cutleaf - *Source History: 1 in 1988; 2 in 1992; 2 in 2000.* **Sources: Neb, Nol.**

Daniels - Thin shelled, medium size nut cracks easily. 40% kernel. High quality. Originated in Missouri, 1978. *Source History: 1 in 2000.* **Sources: Nol.**

Davidson - Selected for bearing and nut quality. Hardy; ripens in the North. Originated in Iowa. *Source History: 1 in 1988; 1 in 1992; 3 in 2000.* **Sources: KEE, Nol, Pa6.**

Davidson No. 629 - *Source History: 1 in 1992; 1 in 2000.* **Sources: Neb.**

Davis No. 2 - *Source History: 1 in 1992; 1 in 2000.* **Sources: Neb.**

Demings Purple - *Source History: 1 in 1992; 2 in 2000.* **Sources: Neb, Pa6.**

Eastern - Thick shelled, sweet nut. A grand tree. *Source History: 2 in 1988; 2 in 1992; 1 in 2000.* **Sources: Sc2.**

Eldora - *Source History: 1 in 1992; 1 in 2000.* **Sources: Neb.**

Elmer Myers - Medium size, thin shelled nut; good cracking qualities. Excellent flavor. Upright tree; late to leaf and ripen. Prolific; produces in 3-5 years. Clermont is possibly identical. Originated in Ohio. *Source History: 5 in 1988; 5 in 1992; 4 in 2000.* **Sources: Gor, Neb, Nol, Pa6.**

Emma Kay (Emma K) - Medium to large, thin shelled nut; excellent cracking quality. Excellent flavor. Prolific; bears in 3-5 years. Heavy producer; precocious. Good black walnut for the Midwest. Hardy to -30 degrees F. Originated in Illinois. *Source History: 4 in 1988; 5 in 1992; 4 in 2000.* **Sources: Gor, KEE, Nol, Oik.**

Farrington - Medium to large nut; thick shelled but cracks well. Good flavor. Prolific; produces in 3-5 years. Bears heavily and regularly. Anthracnose resistant. Ripens early. Originated in Kentucky. Introduced in 1954. *Source History: 2 in 1988; 3 in 1992; 2 in 2000.* **Sources: Neb, Nol.**

Football - *Source History: 1 in 2000.* **Sources: KEE.**

Football No. 2 - Nuts crack out in quarters; 26 nuts per pound. Lateral bearing tree produces heavily. *Source History: 1 in 1992; 2 in 2000.* **Sources: Nol, Pa6.**

Garden Tree - Medium size nuts. Annual cropper. Precocious grower. Pollinated by Weschcke or Well Tree. *Source History: 1 in 2000.* **Sources: Stl.**

Grundy - *Source History: 1 in 1992; 1 in 2000.* **Sources: Neb.**

Hare - Large nut. Good shell structure and good cracking qualities. Heavy bearer. Originated in Illinois. Introduced in 1926. *Source History: 1 in 1988; 1 in 1992; 2 in 2000.* **Sources: Bu7, Neb.**

Harney - *Source History: 1 in 1988; 1 in 1992; 1 in 2000.* **Sources: Nol.**

Hay's (Leander Hay) - *Source History: 1 in 1992; 1 in 2000.* **Sources: Neb.**

Iowa No. 1 - *Source History: 1 in 1992; 1 in 2000.* **Sources: Neb.**

Kentucky Strain Seedlings - *Source History: 1 in 1992; 1 in 2000.* **Sources: Nol.**

Kitty - *Source History: 1 in 1992; 1 in 2000.* **Sources: Neb.**

Krause - Large nut. Annual crops. Hardy. Originated in Iowa. *Source History: 1 in 1988; 2 in 1992; 2 in 2000.* **Sources: Neb, Nol.**

Kwik Crop - Large yields of good quality nuts. Bears early. *Source History: 2 in 2000.* **Sources: KEE, Neb.**

Kwik-Krop, Stark (Boellner Cultivar) - Grafted black walnut that produces bountiful crops of large, mild flavored, light colored, easy to shell nuts. Hardy, vigorous tree reaches 40-60'. Often bears 2-3 years after it is planted. Requires pollination. Hardy in Zones 5-9. Trademarked. *Source History: 1 in 1988; 1 in 1992; 1 in 2000.* **Sources: St4.**

Lamb's Curly - Appears to have hybridized with English Walnut. Curly grained wood. Originated in Michigan. Introduced in 1929. *Source History: 1 in 1988; 3 in 1992; 2 in 2000.* **Sources: Nol, Pa6.**

Leavenworth No. 1 - *Source History: 1 in 1992; 1 in 2000.* **Sources: Neb.**

Ludi - *Source History: 1 in 1992; 1 in 2000.* **Sources: Neb.**

Majestic - Large, plump meat cracks out of shell easily. Tree grows 40' tall. Dependable producer of extra large crops. *Source History: 1 in 1988; 1 in 1992; 1 in 2000.* **Sources: Bu1.**

McGinnis - *Source History: 1 in 2000.* **Sources: Neb.**

Medve - Medium-large size nuts; fairly good crackers. Not quite as hardy as Minnesota Native. *Source History: 1 in 1992; 1 in 2000.* **Sources: Stl.**

Minnesota Native - Small nut. Timber-type tree that is exceedingly precocious. Seedlings are uniformly vigorous and fast growing. Mother tree ripens nuts 2-3 weeks before any other black walnut in the Minnesota area. Hardy. *Source History: 2 in 1988; 1 in 1992; 1 in 2000.* **Sources: Stl.**

Mintle - Small nut; fair cracking quality. Excellent flavor. Prolific; produces in 3-5 years. *Source History: 1 in 1988; 1 in 1992; 1 in 2000.* **Sources: Neb.**

Mystery - *Source History: 1 in 2000.* **Sources: Neb.**

North Carolina Cannon Ball - Seed grown hybrid. Nuts are four times larger than Thomas Black walnut. Largest black walnut ever seen; most nuts weigh one pound each. One tree can bear several tons of nuts. Original tree discovered near Wilson, North Carolina. Hardy in Zones 5-9. *Source History: 1 in 1992; 1 in 2000.* **Sources: Ty2.**

Northwestern - Produces small nuts which are pollinated by Well Tree. Seedlings from these nuts are very hardy and uniform growers. *Source History: 1 in 1988; 1 in 2000.* **Sources: Stl.**

Ogden - Large size nut; good cracking quality. Good flavor. Medium bearer; produces in 3-5 years. *Source History: 1 in 1988; 1 in 1992; 1 in 2000.* **Sources: Neb.**

Ohio - Large nut with thick hull; good cracking quality. Good flavor. Ornamental leaves. Medium productive, annual bearer; produces in 3-5 years. *Source History: 3 in 1988; 2 in 1992; 1 in 2000.* **Sources: Neb.**

Old Fashioned - Rapid growing, long-lived tree can exceed 100'. Bears 15-30 bushels when mature. Dark, lustrous wood prized by furniture craftsmen. Plant well away from garden, as enzymes from roots retard growth of certain vegetables, especially tomatoes. Hardy in Zones 3-8. *Source History: 1 in 1988; 1 in 1992; 1 in 2000.* **Sources: Fi1.**

Patterson - Large nut. Vigorous seedlings with straight, timber-type growth habit. Pollinate with Minnesota Native. Extremely hardy. An old classic. Originated in Iowa. *Source History: 2 in 1988; 3 in 1992; 1 in 2000.* **Sources: Stl.**

Peanut - *Source History: 1 in 2000.* **Sources: Neb.**

Pfiester No. 1 - *Source History: 2 in 2000.* **Sources: Neb, Pa6.**

Pritchett - *Source History: 1 in 2000.* **Sources: Neb.**

Purdue - *Source History: 1 in 2000.* **Sources: KEE.**

Putney - Exceptionally large, well filled nuts. Good cracking quality. *Source History: 1 in 1992; 1 in 2000.* **Sources: Stl.**

Ridgeway (Rabbit Ridge) - Large nut; cracks well. Bears heavily. Anthracnose resistant. Originated in Illinois. Two-time Kentucky State Fair winner. Introduced in 1984. *Source History: 1 in 1988; 1 in 1992; 1 in 2000.* **Sources: Nol.**

Rock - *Source History: 1 in 2000.* **Sources: Neb.**

Rowher - Excellent black walnut. 37% kernel; cracks out easily. *Source History: 1 in 1988; 1 in 1992; 3 in 2000.* **Sources: Bu7, Neb, Nol.**

Sauber No. 1 - Large size, high quality nut; about 39% kernel. Cracks well. Excellent production; 20-25 nuts per pound. *Source History: 1 in 1988; 3 in 1992; 2 in 2000.* **Sources: Gor, Nol.**

Sauber No. 2 - *Source History: 1 in 1988; 1 in 1992; 1 in 2000.* **Sources: Gor.**

Schrieber - *Source History: 1 in 1988; 1 in 1992; 1 in 2000.* **Sources: Nol.**

Scrimger - *Source History: 1 in 2000.* **Sources: Neb.**

Sepic No. 2 - *Source History: 1 in 1988; 1 in 1992; 1 in 2000.* **Sources: Nol.**

Southern Appalachian - *Source History: 1 in 1988; 1 in 1992; 1 in 2000.* **Sources: Sc2.**

Sparks - Good quality nut. Very hardy. Originated in Iowa. *Source History: 1 in 2000.* **Sources: KEE.**

Sparks No. 127 - High meat to shell ratio. Self-fertile. Ripens very early. Originated in Iowa. *Source History: 2 in 2000.* **Sources: Bu7, Neb.**

Sparks No. 147 - Selected for superior nut qualities and productivity. Seedlings show slightly faster rate of growth. *Source History: 1 in 1988; 2 in 2000.* **Sources: Bu7, Neb.**

Sparrow - Medium size nut; good to excellent cracking quality. Good, sweet flavor. Prolific, annual bearer; produces in 3-5 years. Hardy to -30 degrees F. Originated in Illinois. Introduced in 1935. *Source History: 3 in 1988; 3 in 1992; 6 in 2000.* **Sources: Bu7, KEE, Neb, Nol, Oik, Pa6.**

Splichal No. 1 - *Source History: 1 in 2000.* **Sources: Neb.**

Stabler - Good cracking quality. May swear by or at it. Originated in Maryland. *Source History: 2 in 1988; 2 in 1992; 2 in 2000.* **Sources: Neb, Nol.**

Stambaugh - Large nut; very good cracking quality. Good flavor. Medium bearer; produces in 3-5 years. *Source History: 2 in 1988; 1 in 1992; 2 in 2000.* **Sources: Bu7, Neb.**

Surprise - *Source History: 1 in 2000.* **Sources: Neb, Nol.**

Thatcher K-11 - *Source History: 1 in 2000.* **Sources: Neb.**

Thielenhaus 47-47-1 - *Source History: 1 in 2000.* **Sources: Neb.**

Thomas Black (Thomas Cultivar) - The standard grafted black walnut for over a century. Large, round, thin shelled nut; cracks easily. Large, plump, light colored kernels shell out in halves and quarters. Three times more meat than a native tree. Excellent, rich, walnut flavor. Large, upright tree grows rapidly 40-65' tall. Abundant crops; starts bearing in 3-5 years. Requires a pollinator. Long-lived; can produce for 90 years. Good for northern and western regions where anthracnose is not a problem. Drought resistant. Best on rich, moist soil, but grows on any deep soil of average fertility. Hardy in Zones 4-9. Originated in Pennsylvania in 1881. *Source History: 17 in 1988; 20 in 1992; 10 in 2000.* **Sources: CO5, KEE, Mi1, Neb, Nol, Or2, SIM, St4, Tex, Wel.**

Thomas Myers - Popular cross of Thomas x Elmer Myers. Large nut; 20 per lb.

Good cracker but not thin shelled. Heavy bearer. Anthracnose resistant. Ripens early. Originated in Missouri. Introduced in 1980. *Source History: 2 in 1988; 2 in 1992; 2 in 2000.* **Sources: Nol, Pa6.**

Throp - *Source History: 1 in 2000.* **Sources: Neb.**

Todd - *Source History: 1 in 2000.* **Sources: Neb.**

Tom Boy - *Source History: 1 in 2000.* **Sources: KEE.**

Vandersloot - Large nut; good cracking qualities. Good flavor. Prolific; produces in 3-5 years. Anthracnose resistant. Originated in Pennsylvania. Introduced in 1926. *Source History: 2 in 1988; 2 in 1992; 1 in 2000.* **Sources: Nol.**

Well Tree - Large nut.   Precocious grower.   Self-pollinated or pollinate with Weschcke. Seedlings from these nuts are vigorous and hardy. *Source History: 1 in 1988; 1 in 1992; 1 in 2000.* **Sources: Stl.**

Weschcke - Seedlings are slow, but uniform growers.   Some are Bicentennial pollinated; remainder pollinated by Well Tree. Bears a very heavy, annual crop of nuts. Hardy. *Source History: 1 in 1988; 1 in 1992; 2 in 2000.* **Sources: Bu7, Stl.**

Wright's G-4 - *Source History: 1 in 2000.* **Sources: Neb.**

Walnut / Persian

Juglans regia

Allegheny - Medium size, thin shelled nut. Tight seal. Cracks out whole halves. Bears a full crop each year.   Self-pollinating. Originated in Pennsylvania. *Source History: 1 in 2000.* **Sources: Nol.**

Ambassador - Carpathian strain.   High quality, thin shelled, well sealed 1.25" nut.   Plump, light colored, buttery kernels; excellent flavor. Vigorous tree grows 50' tall. Young trees set heavy crops; often a slight crop one year after planting and a significant crop after three years.   Self-fruitful.   Good resistance to blight and codling moth. Not drought resistant. Grows best on fertile, deep soils. Ripens in September. Requires 600 hours of chilling. Cold hardy Carpathian hybrid for severe climates; bears well even after extremely cold temperatures of -40 degrees F. Originated in Idaho. U.S. Plant Patent No. 4132. *Source History: 4 in 1988; 4 in 1992; 3 in 2000.* **Sources: Gr16, Pe2, WI4.**

Bauer 2 - *Source History: 1 in 1988; 1 in 1992; 1 in 2000.* **Sources: Gor.**

Broadview - Carpathian strain. Medium to large, round, thin shelled nut; 47% meat.   Kernels are best for culinary purposes. Heavily productive; lateral bearing. Obtained from the Gellatly planting in British Columbia; one of the first selections from the original Russian walnuts. Introduced in 1930. *Source History: 3 in 1988; 3 in 1992; 1 in 2000.* **Sources: Nol.**

Carmelo - Very large, well filled nut. Late in leafing out and blooming. Self-fruitful. Ripens late September to early October. Requires 700 hours of chilling. Adapted to colder climates than Hartley or other popular English walnuts. *Source History: 2 in 1988; 3 in 1992; 3 in 2000.* **Sources: Bay, CO5, WI4.**

Carpathian Walnut (Carpathian English Walnut) - Plump, thin shelled, English-type walnut; slightly smaller, much hardier. Full flavor; excellent quality. Symmetrical tree quickly grows 30-50' tall and 40' wide; spreading crown, sturdy, grey limbs. Dark green, lacy foliage. Bears in 5-7 years. Self-fertile, but better with another. Pest and disease resistant. Likes sunny, deep, fertile, well drained, 6.5-7.0 pH, loam soils. Nuts fall free of husks when ripe in late fall.   Hardy to -30 degrees F.; Zones 3-9. Originated in the Carpathian Mountains of Poland. In 1939,

Reverend Crath distributed seed nuts to the University of Guelph in Ontario and the Wisconsin Horticulture Society. *Source History: 36 in 1988; 42 in 1992; 29 in 2000.* **Sources: Bu1, Co15, Fi1, Fo4, Ga6, Gr8, Int, Iso, Jun, KEE, LA4, Lee, LOV, Mel, Mi1, MI5, Na4, Oik, Sc2, Sh14, SIM, St4, STR, Tex, Ty2, Va2, Wa16, Wel, Wh4.**

Carpathian Walnut, Russian - Bred to produce larger fruit. Possibly the hardiest of all Carpathians for northern climates. Begins fruiting in 4 years. Zones 4-9. True Russian origin. *Source History: 1 in 2000.* **Sources: Wa16.**

Cascade - Russian x Manregion. Clusters of 6-8 nuts set all over the tree. Large nut; fills well. Excellent flavor. Productive tree bears annually and very heavily. Pollinate with Chambers. Widely planted in the Northwest. Very winter hardy. Originated in Washington. *Source History: 3 in 1988; 3 in 1992; 4 in 2000.* **Sources: Bu7, Clo, Nol, Rai.**

Chambers - Selected from Manregian. Medium to large, good quality, flavorful nut. Extremely vigorous tree bears early and is known for heavy production. Leafs out 10 days before Franquette or Spurgeon. Zones 5-9. Developed in Oregon. *Source History: 2 in 1988; 3 in 1992; 2 in 2000.* **Sources: On3, Rai.**

Champion, Stark (Rodhouse Cultivar) - Flavorful, thin shelled nut. Tree grows 30' tall; bears first crop in 6-7 years. Pollinate with Lake. Hardy in Zones 5-9. Trademarked. U.S. Plant Patent No. 3159. *Source History: 1 in 1988; 1 in 1992; 1 in 2000.* **Sources: St4.**

Chandler - Large nut with light colored kernels. Excellent flavor and quality. Small tree. Late blooming. Heavy bearing; begins 2-3 years after planting. Most of the crop is borne on lateral buds of one year old wood, not just on terminal buds. Will produce larger yields when interplanted with Hart or Franquette. Self-fruitful. Well sealed nuts are resistant to codling moth; also resistant to blight. Well suited to high density commercial plantings. Ripens in September or October. Requires 700 hours of chilling. Introduced from the University of California. U.S. Plant Patent No. 4388. *Source History: 8 in 1988; 10 in 1992; 6 in 2000.* **Sources: Bay, Bu7, CO5, Si3, Son, WI4.**

Chico - Good quality nut with light colored kernels. Pruning enhances the size of the nuts. Heavily productive; bears when young. Plant with Payne and Serr for excellent cross-pollination. Requires 600 hours of chilling. *Source History: 2 in 1988; 3 in 1992; 1 in 2000.* **Sources: WI4.**

Chopaka - Carpathian strain. Parent of Cascade; nearly as good and hardier. Sets up to six nuts per cluster. Bears on lateral spurs as well as at the terminal. Heavily productive; very early to bear. Hardy in Zone 4. *Source History: 2 in 1988; 2 in 1992; 2 in 2000.* **Sources: Bea, Bu7.**

Cisco - Large, well sealed nut of good quality and yield. Good pollinator for Chandler. Late leafing variety. Originated in California. *Source History: 2 in 1992; 2 in 2000.* **Sources: Si3, WI4.**

Cobble No. 2 (Cobles No. 2) - Large nuts fill well. Good quality. Lateral bearing. High yields. Originated in Pennsylvania, 1980. *Source History: 2 in 1992; 2 in 2000.* **Sources: Nol, Pa6.**

Colby - Carpathian strain. Medium size, thin shelled nut; 53% meat. Plump kernel; good flavor. Ripens early. Hardy. Developed at the Illinois Agricultural Experiment Station. Introduced in 1951. *Source History: 2 in 1988; 1 in 1992; 1 in 2000.* **Sources: Nol.**

Combe - *Source History: 1 in 1992; 1 in 2000.* **Sources: Gor.**

Cook's Jumbo - Very large, attractive nut. Ripens early. Originated in the Great Lakes region. Zones 4-8. *Source History: 1 in 2000.* **Sources: Bu7.**

Cooke's Giant Sweet - Large size nuts. Does well in areas with little or no rain. Hardy to Zone 4. *Source History: 1 in 1988; 1 in 1992; 2 in 2000.* **Sources: CO5, Gr16.**

Eureka - Large, well sealed nut. Light brown kernel. Excellent quality. Large tree. Self-fruitful, but yields are improved when pollinated with Hartley. Commercial variety. Ripens late. Requires 600 hours of chilling. *Source History: 4 in 1988; 4 in 1992; 2 in 2000.* **Sources: Si3, WI4.**

Fately - Carpathian strain. Large nut. Good quality. Vigorous tree; bears well. Hardy. Originated in Indiana. Introduced in 1940. *Source History: 3 in 1988; 3 in 1992; 1 in 2000.* **Sources: Nol.**

Franquette (Scharsch Franquette) - Medium to large nut with well sealed, thin shell. High quality. Large tree grows 6' tall with an equal spread. Last Persian walnut to leaf out; less susceptible to spring frost damage. Partially self-pollinating. Pollinate with Hartley or Chandler. Good pollinator for Spurgeon. Fair to good production. Older West Coast commercial variety. Makes an excellent, large shade tree. Ripens in October. Requires 700-800 hours of chilling. Gillet introduction. *Source History: 11 in 1988; 10 in 1992; 6 in 2000.* **Sources: Bay, CO5, Pe2, Si3, STR, WI4.**

Greenhaven - Large nuts crack easily. Good quality kernels. Annual bearer. Originated in Michigan, 1937. *Source History: 1 in 1992; 1 in 2000.* **Sources: Nol.**

Hansen - Carpathian strain. Small to medium, thin shelled, well filled nut; 60% meat. Excellent cracking quality. Sweet, very good flavor. Natural semidwarf; slow growing. Early bearing; produces in 3-5 years. Late to leaf out. Reliably self-pollinating; good choice for limited space. Resistant to anthracnose and husk maggot. Most widely planted Eastern cultivar. Many good selections have come from this variety. Ripens early. Hardy in Zone 4. Originated in Ohio. Introduced in 1934. (**Bea** is offering "Open pollinated seedlings from a pure grove of Hansens.") *Source History: 8 in 1988; 8 in 1992; 4 in 2000.* **Sources: Bea, GR18, Nol, Pa6.**

Harrison - *Source History: 1 in 1992; 1 in 2000.* **Sources: Nol.**

Hartley - Large, thin shelled nut with light colored, high quality, flavorful kernel. Considered the best for eating. Smaller tree than Franquette; better producer. Bears when young. Blooms earlier than others; best for lower elevations. Self-fruitful. Well sealed nut resists codling moth; susceptible to blight. Major commercial variety that is a long-time favorite in California for its quality and dependability. Ripens in September or October. Requires 700 hours of chilling. *Source History: 8 in 1988; 7 in 1992; 5 in 2000.* **Sources: Bay, CO5, Si3, STR, WI4.**

Helmle - Carpathian strain. Medium size nut; excellent cracking quality. Very good flavor. Fine quality. Very productive; bears in 3-5 years. Good pollinator for most other Carpathian cultivars; slightly later to leaf out than most. Originated in Illinois. Introduced in 1953. *Source History: 2 in 1988; 2 in 1992; 1 in 2000.* **Sources: Nol.**

Howard - Large, round, smooth, well-sealed nut with 90% light kernels. Late leaf and bloom time shows potential for less blight and codling moth susceptibility. Small to medium size, semi-upright tree. U.S. Plant Patent No. 4405. *Source History: 1 in 1988; 3 in 1992; 2 in 2000.* **Sources: Si3, WI4.**

Idaho - Carpathian strain. Large to very large nut with sweet, high quality kernel;

excellent for eating. Vigorous tree bears young and heavily. Self-fruitful. Susceptible to blight and root diseases. Ripens in September or October. Requires 700 hours of chilling. Extremely hardy. *Source History: 5 in 1988; 5 in 1992; 4 in 2000.* **Sources: Bay, CO5, STR, WI4.**

Kentucky Giant - Large, thin shelled nuts. Good flavor. Bears heavily when pollinated. Originated in Kentucky. Introduced in 1943. *Source History: 1 in 1988; 2 in 1992; 2 in 2000.* **Sources: Nol, Pa6.**

Lake - Carpathian strain. Medium to large, thin shelled nut cracks easily. Very good flavor and quality. Prolific tree grows 30' tall; bears in 3-5 years. Self-pollinating but produces better crops when pollinated with Stark Champion or a seedling Carpathian variety. Hardy in Zones 5-9. Originated in Illinois. Introduced in 1954. *Source History: 4 in 1988; 4 in 1992; 3 in 2000.* **Sources: Nol, Pa6, St4.**

Liddington's Late Leafing - *Source History: 1 in 2000.* **Sources: Bu7.**

Looking Glass - Large, round nuts with a very thin shell; 20 per pound. Ripens the third week of September. Cold hardy to -34 degrees F. *Source History: 1 in 2000.* **Sources: GR18.**

Manregion - Good size, round, soft shelled nut. Mild flavor. Tends to produce large yields of good quality nuts, although quantity and quality will vary. Quite vigorous growing. Requires pollination; good pollinator for others. Hardy in Zone 4. *Source History: 4 in 1988; 4 in 1992; 5 in 2000.* **Sources: Clo, JOY, ME3, Va2, Wh3.**

McKinster - Carpathian strain. Large, well filled nut cracks easily; 48% meat. Very good flavor; good quality. Heavily productive; bears in 3-5 years. Self-pollinating. Originated in Ohio. Introduced in 1952. *Source History: 4 in 1988; 3 in 1992; 1 in 2000.* **Sources: Nol.**

Mesa - Carpathian strain. Large, well sealed nut. Plump, light colored kernels. Good flavor. Late blooming. Self-fruitful. Resistant to sunburn. Requires 700 hours of chilling. Very winter hardy. Originated in New Mexico. *Source History: 2 in 1988; 2 in 1992; 2 in 2000.* **Sources: CO5, WI4.**

Okanogan - Large nut; 20 per lb. Heavy bearing. *Source History: 1 in 1988; 1 in 1992; 1 in 2000.* **Sources: Bu7.**

Papple - *Source History: 1 in 2000.* **Sources: Pa6.**

Papple Pollinator - Large nut. Very winter hardy. *Source History: 1 in 1988; 1 in 1992; 1 in 2000.* **Sources: Gor.**

Payne - Medium size nut with plump kernels. Early blooming, small headed tree. Heavily productive; bears when young. Pollinate with Chico or Hartley. Early harvest. Requires 500 hours of chilling. *Source History: 3 in 1988; 4 in 1992; 3 in 2000.* **Sources: CO5, Si3, WI4.**

Pedro - Well sealed nut similar to Payne. Winner of consumer taste tests; perhaps the finest flavored. Very small tree; about 60% of an average size variety. Self-fruitful. Widely adapted. Excellent choice for home planting. Requires 400 hours of chilling. *Source History: 1 in 1988; 3 in 1992; 5 in 2000.* **Sources: Bay, Pa2, Pe2, Son, WI4.**

Perry - Large clusters of light colored kernels; 56% kernel. Thin shells. Lateral bearing. Bears three years after planting. Good disease resistance. Ripens the third week of September. Hardy to 34 degrees F. *Source History: 1 in 2000.* **Sources: GR18.**

Persian Walnut (English Walnut) - Husk splits open when ripe; walnuts drop to the ground. Large, thin shelled, easy to crack nut is well filled with full meated kernels. Very delicious, fine flavor. Fast growing, productive tree grows 40-50' tall and wide; broad headed, round to oval. Light green foliage turns yellow in the fall. Dependably productive; bears when young. Life span of 30-80 years. Prefers a well drained soil. Ripens early. Hardy in Zones 5-9. *Source History: 9 in 1988; 4 in 1992; 6 in 2000.* **Sources: Bar, Ca7, Pa2, Sav, Sh14, Wor.**

Persian Walnut Improved - *Source History: 2 in 1988; 1 in 1992; 1 in 2000.* **Sources: Sc2.**

Placentia - Medium size nuts with fairly well sealed, thin shells. Mildly flavored, plump kernel. Self-fruitful. Ripens late September to early October. Chilling requirement is less than 300 hours. Adapted to mild winter coastal climates of southern California. *Source History: 2 in 1988; 2 in 1992; 4 in 2000.* **Sources: Bay, CO5, Pa2, WI4.**

Reda - Carpathian strain. Medium size, thin shelled nut. Lateral bearing. Blight and anthracnose resistant. May be a good southern variety. Originated in southern Europe. *Source History: 2 in 1988; 2 in 1992; 1 in 2000.* **Sources: Nol.**

Russian - Carpathian strain. Bear Creek's seedlings are crosses of the Russian parent and large fruited varieties from a nut breeder's orchard. Trees fruit at four years of age. Good for hardy food trees or rootstock. Hardy in Zone 4. Originally brought to British Columbia by Russian Dukubor immigrants. *Source History: 1 in 1988; 1 in 1992; 1 in 2000.* **Sources: Bea.**

Russian No. 3 - Selection from parent material originating in Russia. Good quality nuts. Hardy and productive. Zones 4-8. Originated in North Central Washington. *Source History: 1 in 2000.* **Sources: Bu7.**

S-1 - Medium-large nuts with light sweet kernels. Thin shells with a good seal. Kernels fall clean from husks. Three year-old trees produced 16 lbs. of nuts per tree. Ripens late September. *Source History: 1 in 2000.* **Sources: GR18.**

Sauber Giant - Carpathian strain. Very large nut. Ripens early. Originated in Ohio. Introduced in 1978. *Source History: 1 in 1988; 1 in 1992; 1 in 2000.* **Sources: Nol.**

Schults - Best nut production in areas of good air drainage and sandy loam soil. Compact tree to 30-40' tall with lateral bearing tendency. Originated in Idaho. *Source History: 1 in 1992; 1 in 2000.* **Sources: Oik.**

Sejveno - *Source History: 1 in 2000.* **Sources: Bu7.**

Serr - Large nut with plump, light colored kernels. Fast growing tree bears young and heavily. Self-fruitful, but cross-pollinate with Chico for biggest crops. Highly resistant to sunburn. Excellent for marginal soil and hot climates. Ripens early. Requires 600 hours of chilling. *Source History: 3 in 1988; 4 in 1992; 3 in 2000.* **Sources: CO5, Si3, WI4.**

Shiawassee - Large clusters of light colored kernels in well sealed shells; 58% kernel. Lateral bearing. Disease resistant. Bore two years from seed. Ripens mid-September. Hardy to 34 degrees F. *Source History: 1 in 2000.* **Sources: GR18.**

Shreve S3 - *Source History: 1 in 2000.* **Sources: Gor.**

Sigler - Medium-large size nut fills well. Does well in Great Lakes area. Originated in Indiana. *Source History: 1 in 2000.* **Sources: Nol.**

Somers - Open-pollinated seedling of an early Carpathian strain. Medium size nut cracks easily; 55% meat. Mild pecan-like flavor. Consistent, annual bearer. One of the earliest ripening varieties. Resists the husk maggot. Very hardy; Zone 4. Good choice for low maintenance grower. The most widely recognized of Lee So-

mers' Carpathians; originated in Michigan. Introduced in 1954. *Source History: 3 in 1988; 4 in 1992; 6 in 2000.* **Sources: Bea, Bu7, Ed5, GR18, Nol, Pa6.**

Spurgeon - Average size nut is favored for its fine flavor. Reliable producer; average yields. Partially self-fertile, but yields are improved when pollinated with Franquette. Leafs out even later than Chambers, which enables the flowers to escape late frosts; the best choice for pockets where late spring frosts are a problem. Very winter hardy for a Persian. Zones 7-9. *Source History: 2 in 1988; 3 in 1992; 3 in 2000.* **Sources: Bu7, On3, Rai.**

Tulare - Large, nearly round, well-sealed nut with 75-85% light kernels. Midseason leafing. Moderately vigorous, upright tree. U.S. Plant Patent No. 8268. *Source History: 2 in 2000.* **Sources: Si3, WI4.**

Utah Giant - Carpathian strain. Very large nut; sweet kernels. Leafs out early. Deserves further test planting. Originated in Utah. Introduced in 1986. *Source History: 1 in 1988; 1 in 1992; 1 in 2000.* **Sources: Nol.**

Vina - Medium size, pointed nut with 60% light kernels. Midseason bloom. Shows moderate susceptibility to blight and codling moth. Moderately vigorous, highly productive tree. *Source History: 2 in 1988; 2 in 1992; 2 in 2000.* **Sources: Si3, WI4.**

Young's B-2 - *Source History: 1 in 1988; 1 in 1992; 2 in 2000.* **Sources: Gor, Pa6.**

Young's Broadview - *Source History: 1 in 1988; 1 in 1992; 1 in 2000.* **Sources: Gor.**

Walnut / Other

Juglans spp.

Andean Walnut - *Juglans neotropica.* Fast growing timber tree from the cool mountain regions throughout the Andes. Valued for its fine tasting rich nuts. *Source History: 1 in 2000.* **Sources: Or2.**

Arizona Walnut - *Juglans major.* Nearly round, deeply grooved, thick shelled nut. Tree grows 60' tall. Native to western Texas, New Mexico, Arizona and northern Mexico. Hardy in Zone 7. *Source History: 1 in 1988; 2 in 1992; 2 in 2000.* **Sources: Ca12, So12.**

Buartnut - Butternut (*Juglans cinerea*) x Heartnut (*J. ailantifolia*) . Combines the adaptability, cold tolerance and sweet flavor of butternut with the high yields, easy to crack shells, shapely branches and handsome foliage of heartnut. Vigorous tree grows 80' tall and wide. First bred in British Columbia in the early 1900s. Hardy through Zone 4. *Source History: 2 in 1988; 13 in 1992; 11 in 2000.* **Sources: Bea, Bu7, Fil, LA4, Mel, Mi1, Oik, Or2, Sh14, Stl, Wa16.**

Buartnut: Baker - *Source History: 1 in 1992; 1 in 2000.* **Sources: Gor.**

Buartnut: Filsinger - *Source History: 1 in 1992; 1 in 2000.* **Sources: Gor.**

Calif. Black Walnut, Northern (California Black Walnut, Hinds Black Walnut, Claro Walnut) - *Juglans hindsii.* Seedlings of a large black walnut strain that is native to northern California. Excellent, fast growing, single trunked tree with delicious, high quality, large walnuts. Valuable as hardwood and as rootstock for English walnuts because it is resistant to oak root fungus. Drought tolerant once established. Sensitive to poor water drainage. Does best on lighter soils. Often found at sites of California Indian villages, where they grew 50' tall. Ripens in September or October. *Source History: 9 in 1988; 5 in 1992; 6 in 2000.* **Sources: CO5, LA4,**

Las, Oik, Si3, STR.

Calif. Black Walnut, Oregon (Hinds Walnut Oregon Strain) - *Juglans hindsii.*
Oregon strain. *Source History: 1 in 1988; 1 in 1992; 1 in 2000.* **Sources: Ca12.**

Calif. Black Walnut, Southern (California Black Walnut, California Walnut)
- *Juglans californica.* Smaller 30' multitrunked black walnut that is native to southern California. *Source History: 1 in 1988; 1 in 1992; 2 in 2000.* **Sources: Ca12, Las.**

Chinese Walnut - *Juglans cathayensis.* Vigorous tree to 75' tall. Large leaves.
Nuts have thick spiny shells and small edible meats. *Source History: 1 in 2000.* **Sources: LA4.**

Japanese Walnut - *Juglans ailantifolia.* Similar to heartnut, but with round
nuts. Excellent eating nuts that hang in clusters. Erect, medium size tree with silvery gray bark and large, compound 1-3" leaves that do not drop early with anthracnose like those of black walnuts. Highly valued as food in Japan, where it is native. *Source History: 6 in 1988; 2 in 1992; 1 in 2000.* **Sources: Sc2.**

Juglans neotropica - *Source History: 1 in 2000.* **Sources: Pa2.**

Little Walnut (River Walnut, Texas Black Walnut) - *Juglans microcarpa.*
Round .75" thick shelled nut. Small shrub or tree less than 50' tall. Native to western Oklahoma, Texas, New Mexico and northern Mexico. Hardy in Zone 6. *Source History: 4 in 1988; 1 in 1992; 6 in 2000.* **Sources: Arb, Ca12, GR26, LA4, Oik, Sh14.**

Manchurian Walnut (Mountain Walnut) - *Juglans mandshurica.* Oval 2"
multiridged nut. Attractive tree can grow 60' tall. Native to Manchuria. Hardy in Zone 5. *Source History: 5 in 1988; 3 in 1992; 7 in 2000.* **Sources: Arb, Gor, LA4, Sc2, Sh14, Va5, Wa16.**

Paradox - Persian Walnut (*Juglans regia*) x Northern California Black Walnut (*J.
hindsii*). Sometimes used as a rootstock for walnuts. Vigorous. Tolerates nematode and phytopthora. Originally described by Luther Burbank in 1893. *Source History: 2 in 1988; 3 in 1992; 5 in 2000.* **Sources: Bay, CO5, LA4, Si3, STR.**

Royal Walnut - *Juglans hindsii x J. nigra.* Large tree is a vigorous grower. Recommended for its rich dark wood. Seedlings show resistance to anthracnose. Hardy to -10 degrees F. Created by Luther Burbank in the late 1800s. Found in the Northwest U.S. where the early settlers brought Eastern Black Walnut with them and then it naturally hybridized with the California Walnut. *Source History: 1 in 2000.* **Sources: Oik.**

Miscellaneous Nuts

Almond, Desert (Wild Almond, Wild Peach) - *Prunus fasciculata.* Oval .5"
fruit with smooth stone. Densely branched bush grows 3-8' tall. Native to desert regions of Arizona, Utah and California. Hardy in Zone 7. *Source History: 2 in 1988; 2 in 1992; 2 in 2000.* **Sources: Ca12, No2.**

Almond, Dwarf Flowering - *Prunus glandulosa.* Oval .4" dark red fruits.
Only grows 3-5' tall. Native to Japan and China. Hardy in Zone 4. *Source History: 1 in 1988; 5 in 1992; 1 in 2000.* **Sources: MO10.**

Almond, Dwarf Russian - *Prunus tenella.* Fruits are .75" long. Hardy, ornamental bush grows 5' tall. Rose colored flowers. Hardy in Zone 2. *Source History: 1 in 1988; 5 in 1992; 2 in 2000.* **Sources: CLI, LA4.**

Beech, European - *Fagus sylvatica.* Thin shelled, small, triangular-shaped nuts
with good flavor. Widely adapted, picturesque tree grows to 80'. Purple-green

leaves; golden copper autumn color. Hardy in Zones 5-9. *Source History: 2 in 1992; 5 in 2000.* **Sources: Bea, Bu7, Fo2, MEA, Rai.**

Beech, Oriental - *Fagus orientalis.* Large tree to 100' with yellow fall foliage. Zone 6. *Source History: 1 in 2000.* **Sources: Fo2.**

Beechnut, American - *Fagus grandifolia.* Edible, triangular, brown nut covered with a burr. Tree grows 60-80' tall; rounded crown of many long, spreading and horizontal branches. Hardy in Zones 4-9. Native to eastern North America. *Source History: 2 in 1988; 8 in 1992; 7 in 2000.* **Sources: Bar, Cam, Lee, Po2, Sav, TU5, WA8.**

Betel Nut Palm - *Areca catechu.* Cultivated for the astringent nut (seed) which is chewed with lime. Slender palm with 6" diameter trunk can reach 100' tall. Grows best in the wet tropics. Hardy in Zone 10. *Source History: 1 in 1988; 1 in 2000.* **Sources: PL2.**

Cashew - *Anacardium occidentale.* Large, kidney-shaped seed contains the edible nut; usually roasted. Inner shell contains a toxic substance in its oily resin which can cause a serious skin rash with prolonged contact. Use caution when roasting, as it will travel in the smoke. Handsome tree can grow 40' tall in the tropics; small, handsome tub plant in the greenhouse. Unshelled nuts are planted in moist, warm, humid conditions with bright light and a rich but well-drained soil. Requires 25-40 days above 75 degrees F. to germinate. Hardy in Zone 10. Native to tropical America; grown commercially in India. *Source History: 4 in 1988; 5 in 1992; 6 in 2000.* **Sources: Ban, Ca7, Ga11, Na13, Our, Ro13.**

Golden Chinquapin (Giant Chinquapin) - *Castanopsis chrysophylla.* Rare, evergreen broadleaf nut tree. Spiny, chestnut-like burrs hold several nuts similar to small filberts. Golden, soft, extremely thin shell like a sunflower seed; so thin shelled that they can be safely cracked between the teeth. Exceptionally fine flavor and sweetness. Growth habit ranges from compact shrubs to trees 100' tall. Willow-shaped, leathery, semishiny, green leaves with golden undersides stay on all winter. Tolerant of poor, dry sites. Beautiful, rot resistant wood. Native to mountainous maritime regions on the West Coast from the Olympic Peninsula to northern California. *Source History: 4 in 1988; 1 in 2000.* **Sources: Bu7.**

Maya Breadnut (Breadnut) - *Brosimum alicastrum.* Round 1" diameter yellow fruit with a large, edible seed. Tree can grow 100' tall; grey bark. Grown in lowland areas of the Caribbean. *Source History: 1 in 1988; 1 in 1992; 1 in 2000.* **Sources: Ga11.**

Monkey Puzzle - *Araucaria araucana.* Ornamental, upright, pyramidal, evergreen tree can grow 100' tall; dozens of large cones contain 200-300 nuts that are .5" long with a thin, leathery, easily peeled shell. May be eaten raw; much more flavorful when roasted or steamed. Taste and keeping quality is much like chestnuts. Grows on a variety of well drained soils. Does well in the Northwest; seem to prefer humid climate. Hardy to -10 degrees F. once established. Native to Chile and Argentina. Long, stiff, sharp, overlapping leaves that caused one Englishman to remark, "It would puzzle a monkey to climb such a tree." *Source History: 2 in 1988; 2 in 1992; 9 in 2000.* **Sources: BO10, Bu7, Ca12, Co24, Fo2, On3, Or2, Pa2, Po7.**

Oak, Bur - *Quercus macrocarpa.* Large, edible acorns are low in tannic acid. Largest leaves and acorns of any oak. Widely adapted. *Source History: 4 in 1992; 25 in 2000.* **Sources: Bea, Bo5, Bu7, CLI, Co15, Co24, FE7, GR26, HI7, KAN, KEE, KI3, LI7, LOV, Mc3, MI5, Mu2, Na4, Pa6, Sc2, Sh10, SH8, St12, Wa16, Win.**

Oak, Cork - *Quercus suber*. Evergreen tree with edible acorns. Outer bark is the commercial source of cork. Drought tolerant once established. *Source History: 1 in 1992; 2 in 2000.* **Sources: Bu7, MIS.**

Oak, Swamp Chestnut - *Quercus michauxii*. Hardy to Zone 7. *Source History: 1 in 2000.* **Sources: Fo2.**

Oak, Tan Bark - *Lithocarpus densiflorus*. Evergreen oak relative. Produces edible acorns that were an important Indian staple. Zones 6-9. Native to Oregon and California. *Source History: 1 in 2000.* **Sources: Bu7.**

Oak, White - *Quercus alba*. The nut can be eaten with a little leaching to reduce the tannin content. Zone 4. *Source History: 2 in 1992; 14 in 2000.* **Sources: Bea, Ca8, Co15, FO10, IN7, LO6, Pa6, Pi2, Sc2, Sh14, SH8, Ty2, Wa16, Win.**

Pili Nut - *Canarium ovata*. Called the best tasting nut there is by those who have eaten it. Large tree requires tropical conditions. Uncommonly found. *Source History: 1 in 1988; 1 in 1992; 1 in 2000.* **Sources: Ban.**

Pistachio - *Pistacia vera*. Small, delicious nut surrounded by a bony shell that splits partially. Deciduous tree slowly grows 25-30' tall and wide. Tends to bear biennially. Dioecious; separate male and female plants. Likes long, hot summers and low humidity. Requires a moderately cold winter for chilling. About as hardy as almonds. Native from Iran to Central Asia. Grown commercially in the Mediterranean and the western U.S. *Source History: 4 in 1988; 3 in 1992; 4 in 2000.* **Sources: Ca7, Fo2, Our, Sh14.**

Pistachio, Chinese - *Pistacia chinensis*. Used as grafting stock to produce the edible nuts. No insect or disease problems. Zone 6. *Source History: 2 in 1992; 17 in 2000.* **Sources: Ba3, Ban, Ca7, Co24, Fo2, HI10, LO6, MI5, MI5, MO10, Ne4, ORA, Sc2, Sh14, SIM, Wo2, Wom.**

Pistachio, Far North Hardy - Ripens in the far north. Hardy to -5 degrees F. Trademarked. *Source History: 1 in 2000.* **Sources: Or2.**

Pistachio, Kerman (Female) - *Pistacia vera*. Female plant produces heavy clusters of highly desired nuts. Beautiful, broad, deciduous tree with one or several trunks grows moderately quickly to 30' tall. Yields of up to 50 lbs. per tree. Pollinate with Peters. Established trees are very drought and heat tolerant. Needs full sun and good drainage. Requires 800 hours of chilling. Cold hardy to 15 degrees F. *Source History: 5 in 1988; 4 in 1992; 3 in 2000.* **Sources: Or2, Pa2, WI4.**

Pistachio, Mountain Blue Hardy - Tree grows up to 60' tall. The small oily nutlets are eaten raw or made into a fine salad or cooking oil in North Africa, where this tree originates. Yields a fine lumber. Said to withstand temperatures to -20 degrees F. Trademarked. *Source History: 1 in 2000.* **Sources: Or2.**

Pistachio, Peters (Male) - *Pistacia vera*. Pollinator for Kerman; does not bear fruit. One male tree will pollinate 10-12 females. Wind-pollinated, so space throughout the orchard. Requires 800 hours of chilling. *Source History: 5 in 1988; 4 in 1992; 3 in 2000.* **Sources: Or2, Pa2, WI4.**

Pistachio, UCB No. 1 - *Pistacia atlantica x P. integerrima*. Produces hybrid seedlings with a minimum of variability. Selected by Dr. Lee Ashworth of the UC Berkeley Dept. of Plant Pathology for its resistance to verticillium wilt. *Source History: 1 in 2000.* **Sources: Fo8.**

Pistacia atlantica - Used for rootstock. *Source History: 1 in 1992; 1 in 2000.* **Sources: Ca7.**

Pistacia terebinthus (Cyprus Turpentine Tree) - Shrubby tree to 15'. Often used as rootstock for commercial pistachio nut. *Source History: 1 in 1992; 1 in 2000.*

Sources: Ban.

<u>Singhara Ling</u> - Ancient nut from China that is grown in water, either lakes, streams, ponds or mud holes. Can develop over 30' of underwater vine-like growth in two months. Flowers are pollinated and close within the same day. The base of the flower swells and bends into the water where it forms the nut which is full of sugars and floats at first. These nuts are picked in the first 15-20 days. Tougher, more starchy nuts sink lower in the water and are harvested a month later. When lightly roasted or steamed in the shell, the nuts are eaten like a roasted chestnut. When boiled they are eaten like a fresh vegetable. Yields range from 9,000-20,000 lbs. per acre. A staple food for centuries from China, northern Japan, across the Himalaya and west as far as to the tip of Africa. Trademarked. *Source History: 1 in 2000.* **Sources: Or2.**

<u>Yellowhorn</u> (Goldenhorn) - *Xanthoceras sorbifolia.* Many pea size, sweet nuts produced in 2" seed capsules. White, 1" flowers in spring. Ornamental, small tree with 1' long compound leaves. Leaves, flowers and nuts are edible. Nuts are usu-ally roasted; flavor similar to a macadamia nut. Tolerant of moist sites and partial shade. Hardy to -30 degrees F. Unusual tree native to northern China. *Source History: 4 in 1992; 4 in 2000.* **Sources: Bu7, Co24, Or2, Rai.**

Annona

Annona spp.

Atemoya, African Pride - *Annona cherimola x A. squamosa*. Australian commercial variety. *Source History: 2 in 1988; 1 in 1992; 1 in 2000.* **Sources: Po7.**

Atemoya, Bradley - *Annona cherimola x A. squamosa. Source History: 1 in 1988; 2 in 1992; 2 in 2000.* **Sources: Ga11, Pa2.**

Atemoya, Gefner - *Annona cherimola x A. squamosa*. Originated in Israel. *Source History: 1 in 1988; 1 in 1992; 2 in 2000.* **Sources: Ga11, On4.**

Atemoya, Page - *Source History: 1 in 2000.* **Sources: On4.**

Cherimoya (Cherimalla, Chirimoya, Custard Apple) - *Annona cherimola*. Round to conical, smooth, light green to greenish brown fruit to 5" long. Sweet, juicy, custard-like, creamy white flesh with fine fruity flavor. Evergreen shrub or small tree with large tropical-looking leaves; grows 25' tall. Hardy to 25 degrees F. Drought resistant; will grow in California. Native to the Andes of Peru and Ecuador. Widely cultivated in tropical highlands and in the subtropics. Hardy in Zone 10. *Source History: 3 in 1988; 5 in 1992; 8 in 2000.* **Sources: Al8, An4, De5, Ga11, Me2, Or2, Po7, Sh14, Tr10.**

Cherimoya, Booth - *Annona cherimola*. Medium to large fruit; occasional darkening on the outside. Good flavor. Good for inland growing. Needs hand pollination for commercial purposes. *Source History: 3 in 1988; 2 in 1992; 1 in 2000.* **Sources: Pa2.**

Cherimoya, Chaffey - *Annona cherimola*. Medium to large fruit with excellent flavor. Some production without hand-pollination. Does well in inland coastal areas. *Source History: 2 in 1988; 1 in 1992; 1 in 2000.* **Sources: Pa2.**

Cherimoya, Dr. White - *Source History: 1 in 2000.* **Sources: On4.**

Cherimoya, El Bumpo - *Annona cherimola. Source History: 1 in 1988; 1 in 1992; 1 in 2000.* **Sources: Pa2.**

Cherimoya, Honeyhart - *Annona cherimola. Source History: 1 in 1988; 1 in 1992; 1 in 2000.* **Sources: Pa2.**

Cherimoya, Libby - *Annona cherimola. Source History: 1 in 1988; 1 in 1992; 1 in 2000.* **Sources: Pa2.**

Cherimoya, Mariella - *Annona cherimola. Source History: 1 in 1988; 1 in 1992; 1 in 2000.* **Sources: Pa2.**

Cherimoya, Pierce - *Annona cherimola*. Medium size, flavorful fruit. Some production without hand-pollination. Does well in coastal areas with long fruiting season. *Source History: 3 in 1988; 2 in 1992; 1 in 2000.* **Sources: Pa2.**

Cherimoya, Sabor - *Annona cherimola. Source History: 2 in 1988; 1 in 1992; 1 in 2000.* **Sources: Pa2.**

Cherimoya, Selma - Pink fruit. Seedlings. *Source History: 1 in 2000.* **Sources: Po7.**

Cherimoya, Spain - *Annona cherimola*. Small to medium size fruit with excellent flavor. Hardy tree. *Source History: 2 in 1988; 3 in 1992; 1 in 2000.* **Sources: Pa2.**

Cherimoya, Villa Park - *Annona cherimola. Source History: 1 in 1988; 1 in 1992; 1 in 2000.* **Sources: Pa2.**

Cherimoya, White - *Annona cherimola*. Flavorful fruit with few seeds. Poor production without hand-pollination. *Source History: 2 in 1988; 2 in 1992; 1 in 2000.* **Sources: Pa2.**

Custard Apple (Bullock's Heart, Prickly Custard Apple, True Custard Apple) - *Annona reticulata.* Oval or heart-shaped, nearly smooth, reddish yellow or brown fruit to 5" across. Fruits not as tasty as other *Annona* varieties. Attractive tree grows 18-40' tall. Should be grown in rich, loamy soil with bright sunlight and warmth. Widely cultivated in lowland tropics. Hardy in Zone 10. *Source History: 3 in 1988; 2 in 1992; 6 in 2000.* **Sources: Ban, Ga11, Pa2, PI3, Po7, Ro13.**

Ilama (Mexican Red Cherimoya) - *Annona diversifolia.* *Source History: 1 in 1992; 1 in 2000.* **Sources: Po7.**

Montana - *Source History: 1 in 2000.* **Sources: Tr10.**

Pond Apple - *Annona glabra.* Grown as grafting stock. Tree grows to 40'. Handsome foliage. Fragrant yellow flowers. *Source History: 2 in 1992; 3 in 2000.* **Sources: Ban, Ga11, Tr10.**

Raimondia ginduensis - Rare, edible *Annona.* *Source History: 1 in 2000.* **Sources: Po7.**

Rollinia deliciosa (South American Custard Apple) - Tropical *Annona.* Sweet creamy fruits. Rare. *Source History: 1 in 1992; 1 in 2000.* **Sources: Our.**

San Pablo - Grafted. *Source History: 1 in 2000.* **Sources: Ga11.**

Sancoya - *Annona purpurea.* Sweet juicy fruit with orange pulp. Spreading tree to 30'. Requires warm tropical climate; south Florida is too cool. *Source History: 1 in 2000.* **Sources: Ban.**

Soncoya - *Source History: 1 in 2000.* **Sources: Po7.**

Soursop (Guanabana, Prickly Custard Apple) - *Annona muricata.* Largest of the *Annonas.* Oval, dark green fruit covered with short fleshy spines is 8" long and up to 6 lbs. Very tender, white flesh. Evergreen tree grows 20' tall with shiny green, leathery leaves. Used for sherbert and refreshing drinks. Can be grown in the warmest parts of Zone 10 in Florida. *Source History: 3 in 1988; 8 in 1992; 11 in 2000.* **Sources: An4, Ban, Ga11, Hud, Me2, On4, Pa2, PI3, PL2, Po7, Ro13.**

Sugar Apple (Custard Apple, Sweetsop) - *Annona squamosa.* Round to conical, yellowish green fruit to 3.5" across. Dessert quality, custard flavored fruit. Evergreen tree grows 10-20' tall. Unusual pale leaves turn dark green with maturity. Widely cultivated in the lowland tropics and subtropical Florida. Hardy in Zone 10. Best of the tropical *Annonas.* *Source History: 2 in 1988; 5 in 1992; 8 in 2000.* **Sources: Ban, Ga11, Me2, Na13, Pa2, PI3, Po7, Tr10.**

Sugar Apple, Asian - *Annona squamosa.* White flesh. *Source History: 1 in 2000.* **Sources: On4.**

Sugar Apple, Borneo Mauve - *Annona squamosa.* Purple skin. *Source History: 1 in 2000.* **Sources: On4.**

Sugar Apple, Kampong Mauve - *Annona squamosa.* *Source History: 1 in 2000.* **Sources: Ga11.**

Sugar Apple, Purple - *Annona squamosa.* Purple fruited variety. *Source History: 1 in 2000.* **Sources: Po7.**

Avocado

Persea americana

Avocado - *Source History: 2 in 1992; 3 in 2000.* **Sources: An4, Na13, PI3.**

Bacon - *Persea americana* var. *drymifolia.* Medium size, green fruit. Evergreen tree. Ripens in winter. *Source History: 1 in 1988; 5 in 1992; 1 in 2000.* **Sources: Pa2.**

Brogdon - *Source History: 1 in 2000.* **Sources: Ga11.**

Cado, Little - *Source History: 1 in 1992; 2 in 2000.* **Sources: Me2, Or2.**

Carrizo Norte - Seedling. Delicious fruit. Mother tree withstood 8 degrees F. Trademarked. *Source History: 1 in 2000.* **Sources: Or2.**

Fuerte - *Persea americana* var. *drymifolia*. High quality, medium size green fruit with smooth, thin skin. Large evergreen tree. Ripens from November through June. *Source History: 1 in 1988; 6 in 1992; 3 in 2000.* **Sources: Or2, Pa2, PL2.**

Fujikawa - Spring bearer. *Source History: 1 in 2000.* **Sources: PL2.**

Green Gold - Bears in winter to spring. *Source History: 1 in 1992; 1 in 2000.* **Sources: PL2.**

Gwen - Medium to large, flavorful fruit. Dwarf tree grows to 14'. Heavy bearer. Frost sensitive; Zone 9. U.S. Plant Patent No. 5298. *Source History: 1 in 1988; 5 in 1992; 1 in 2000.* **Sources: Pa2.**

Hass - Black, pebbly skinned, supermarket avocado. Excellent flavor. Heavy producer. Frost sensitive. Spring and summer season. *Source History: 1 in 1988; 5 in 1992; 1 in 2000.* **Sources: Pa2.**

Jim - Good flavor. Very frost hardy. *Source History: 1 in 1992; 1 in 2000.* **Sources: Or2.**

Kahaluu - Fall bearer. *Source History: 1 in 1992; 1 in 2000.* **Sources: PL2.**

Linda - Spring bearer. *Source History: 1 in 1992; 1 in 2000.* **Sources: PL2.**

Marcus - *Source History: 1 in 2000.* **Sources: Ga11.**

Mexicola - Small fruit with black skin. Good flavor. Fall crop. Self-fruitful. Hardy to frost. *Source History: 3 in 1992; 4 in 2000.* **Sources: Ju2, Ne4, Or2, Pa2.**

Nabal - *Source History: 1 in 1988; 2 in 1992; 1 in 2000.* **Sources: Pa2.**

Pinkerton - *Persea americana* var. *drymifolia*. Small seeded fruit has thick, green skin. Excellent flavor. Bears heavily. Frost sensitive. Season is November-March. U.S. Plant Patent No. 3712. *Source History: 1 in 1988; 3 in 1992; 1 in 2000.* **Sources: Pa2.**

Reed - *Source History: 1 in 1988; 3 in 1992; 1 in 2000.* **Sources: Pa2.**

Russell - *Source History: 1 in 2000.* **Sources: Ga11.**

Sharwil - Winter bearer. *Source History: 1 in 1992; 1 in 2000.* **Sources: PL2.**

Whitsell - Dwarf. U.S. Plant Patent No. 5299. *Source History: 1 in 1988; 2 in 1992; 1 in 2000.* **Sources: Pa2.**

Yamagata - Summer bearer. *Source History: 1 in 1992; 1 in 2000.* **Sources: PL2.**

Zutano - *Persea americana* var. *drymifolia*. Hardy to 28 degrees F. *Source History: 2 in 1988; 4 in 1992; 1 in 2000.* **Sources: Pa2.**

Banana

Musa spp.

Abyssinian - Produces tasty yellow fruit about every other year, around Thanksgiving. Found growing at an old plantation house 50 years ago. *Source History: 1 in 2000.* **Sources: Ty2.**

Ae Ae (Koae, Ae Aae) - Beautiful Hawaiian variety. Fruit has excellent flavor; primarily used as a cooking banana, although it may be eaten fresh. Trunk, leaves and fruit are variegated white, gray and green. Mature height about 16'. Prefers a protected location in partial sun. Suckers sparsely. Extremely rare. *Source History: 2 in 1992; 3 in 2000.* **Sources: An4, Go7, Pa2.**

Ae Ae, Green - Wide leaved plant resembles Popoulo. Grows up to 20'. *Source History: 1 in 2000.* **Sources: An4.**

African Rhino Horn (Golden Rhino Horn) - *Musa acuminata.* Unusual fruit up to 24" long and three pounds; cooked green or eaten ripe. Very decorative plant with a lot of wine-red color in leaf and pseudostem; quickly grows 10-12' tall. Poor wind resistance due to its slender form. Originated in Africa. *Source History: 4 in 1988; 6 in 1992; 5 in 2000.* **Sources: Go7, Na13, Our, Pa2, Ty2.**

Apple (Dwarf Apple, Santa Katrina, Monzano) - *Musa acuminata.* Small, tart 3" fruits; sweet, apple-like taste. Must be allowed to ripen fully or will taste chalky. Plant grows 10-15' tall; yellowish green trunk with a tinge of red at the junction of the leaf and pseudostem. Originated in the Caribbean. *Source History: 5 in 1988; 5 in 1992; 4 in 2000.* **Sources: Go7, Ju2, Pa2, PL2.**

Basjoo - Seeded variety grows 12' tall. Frequently sends out rhizomes 2-3' from the pseudostem. Cool tolerant. *Source History: 1 in 2000.* **Sources: Go7.**

Blood Banana - Perennial with blue-green leaves striped with red. Can bear small sweet bananas. Full sun. Zones 10-11. *Source History: 1 in 2000.* **Sources: MO10, Ty2.**

Brazilian - Very good quality fruit to 5" long; may be allowed to ripen on the plant without splitting. Requires 25 months growing time. Large, broad leaved tree; one of the tallest bananas, reaching 18-20'. Solid green with no red color; good landscaping plant due to the majesty of its size. Excellent wind tolerance, in spite of its height, since it is a stout plant with a strong root system and massive trunk. Originated in Brazil. *Source History: 3 in 1988; 4 in 1992; 5 in 2000.* **Sources: Al8, An4, Go7, Our, Pa2, Ty2.**

Brazilian, Dwarf - Dwarf form of Brazilian grows up to 12' tall; produces 25-50 pounds of fruit per plant. *Source History: 1 in 2000.* **Sources: Al8, An4.**

Burro (Bluggo) - Plant grows 16-18'. Bears large bunches of tasty cooking bananas. *Source History: 1 in 2000.* **Sources: Al8.**

Cardaba (Caradaba) - Philippine cooking variety. Grows 10-16' tall. Stubby fruit has an irregular shape. Very white pulp. Hardy and vigorous. *Source History: 2 in 2000.* **Sources: Al8, An4, Go7.**

Carolina King - Dwarf banana showing great promise in extending the range of growing bananas in the Coastal areas and parts of the Upper South. Hardy in Zones 8-10. *Source History: 1 in 1992; 1 in 2000.* **Sources: Ty2.**

Cavendish, Dwarf (Chinese Dwarf Banana) - *Musa acuminata.* Tasty, sweet, 5", yellow fruit. Short, compact plant grows 5-7' tall with large, broad, shapely, leathery leaves. Good wind resistance. Usually bears within 2-3 years. Can be grown indoors or on patios in pots, due to its small size. One of the oldest and most popular bananas grown in this country. Originated in the Canary Islands. *Source History: 8 in 1988; 10 in 1992; 8 in 2000.* **Sources: An4, Ban, Ga11, Go7, Ju2, Me2, Our, Pa2.**

Cavendish, Giant - *Musa acuminata.* Very large heads of excellent quality fruit. Plant grows 18-20' tall. Not very wind resistant, due to its height and large heads. Central American commercial variety. *Source History: 3 in 1988; 4 in 1992; 1 in*

2000. **Sources: Go7.**

Chiapas - *Source History: 1 in 2000.* **Sources: Pa2.**

Cocos (Highgate) - Dwarf form of Bluefields with similar bunch size and fruit quality, but with shorter individual bananas. Mature height of 14-16' makes it more windproof. *Source History: 1 in 1992; 1 in 2000.* **Sources: An4.**

Colorado Blanco - Resembles Jamaican Red and Green Red in plant growth and fruit character. Mature plant height 20-25'. *Source History: 1 in 1992; 1 in 2000.* **Sources: Al8, An4.**

Colorado Blanco, Dwarf - Grows up to 10'. *Source History: 1 in 2000.* **Sources: An4.**

Cuban Red (Jamaican Red) - *Musa acuminata.* Dwarf. *Source History: 1 in 1988; 2 in 1992; 4 in 2000.* **Sources: An4, Na13, Pa2, PL2.**

Double (Mahoi) - Unusual 4-7' dwarf that can produce 2-4 stalks of fruit at the same time. Very tasty fruit, similar in sweetness and size to Cavendish. Fairly wind resistant; should be planted in a protected place. First generation will be normal with one head; subsequent generations will have multiple heads of fruit that usually emerge opposite each other and balance the weight. Rare. *Source History: 3 in 1988; 3 in 1992; 2 in 2000.* **Sources: An4, Go7.**

Dwarf (Dwarf Chinese) - *Musa acuminata.* Sweet 5" edible, yellow fruits. Compact 5-9' tree. Grows outdoors year-round in Zone 10 only; elsewhere, bring it inside. Originated in South China. *Source History: 2 in 1988; 7 in 1992; 5 in 2000.* **Sources: Ban, Bu1, Fi1, Gur, Int.**

Ebon Musak - Grows 10-12' tall. Fruit ripens with only a slight color change instead of turning yellow. Pleasant sub-acid flavor. *Source History: 1 in 2000.* **Sources: Go7.**

Ele Ele (Hawaiian Black) - Very firm fruits with orange pulp. Broad leaved, dark trunk. Grows up to 25'. Cooking type from Hawaii. *Source History: 2 in 1992; 2 in 2000.* **Sources: An4, Go7.**

Enano Gigante - *Musa acuminata.* Delicious fruit. 6-8' tall plant has large green leaves with red marbling. Fast growing. Widely planted as a commercial banana in Mexico and Central America; seemingly well adapted in California. Zones 10-11. *Source History: 1 in 1988; 4 in 1992; 3 in 2000.* **Sources: Al8, An4, MO10, Pa2.**

Fehi (Fe'I) - *Musa fehi.* Most unusual. Head of fruit shoots vertically straight up into the air; does not hang over like most bananas. Blunt, very fat, bronze-orange fruit. Also known for causing urine to be of chartreuse color. Best when cooked. Plant reaches 8-12'; solid green with fairly narrow leaves. Violet sap in the trunk. Unfortunately it rarely fruits in this country, since it is very cold sensitive. Rare. Originated in New Guinea. *Source History: 3 in 1988; 3 in 1992; 1 in 2000.* **Sources: Go7.**

French Horn - Large, curved fruits about 12" long. May be eaten raw when very ripe; usually eaten fried or boiled when green, fried or baked when ripe. Rather slender plant grows about 8-12' tall; mostly green with red margins on the leaf. Fair wind resistance. Originated in the West Indies. *Source History: 3 in 1988; 3 in 1992; 2 in 2000.* **Sources: An4, Go7.**

Giant Pisang (Abaca, Textiles) - Largest tree of all; maximum height of 80'. Fruit contains numerous large seeds throughout the edible pulp. Impressive in sheer size. Rare. Originated in Borneo. *Source History: 2 in 1988; 1 in 1992; 1 in 2000.* **Sources: Go7.**

Giant Plantain - Large fruit; usually cooked rather than eaten fresh. Plant is rather slender and very beautiful; grows 12-14' tall. Not very wind tolerant, but will grow well in protected areas. The cooking plantain of commerce. Originated in India. *Source History: 3 in 1988; 3 in 1992; 1 in 2000.* **Sources: Go7.**

Golden Aromatic - Very sweet, aromatic fruit. Plant grows 10-14'. Originated in China, where it is known as Go San Heong which translates, "you can smell it from over the next mountain." *Source History: 2 in 1992; 2 in 2000.* **Sources: An4, Go7.**

Golden Pillow - Short, fat fruit looks like a plump little pillow; thin skin. Very sweet. Plant reaches 10-12' tall; mostly green with some red at the junction of the leaf and pseudostem. Moderate wind tolerance. Lady Finger type from Southeast Asia, where it is a favorite. *Source History: 3 in 1988; 3 in 1992; 2 in 2000.* **Sources: Al8, An4, Go7.**

Goldfinger (FHIA-1) - Fruit grows 6-8" long. Tasty, slightly sub-acid flesh. Shows only a slight color change at maturity. Disease resistant plant grows 10-12'. *Source History: 4 in 2000.* **Sources: An4, Go7, Our, Pa2.**

Gran Nain (Chiquita Banana) - *Musa acuminata*. Newest commercial variety developed in Central America. Delicious fruit. Grows to 7' tall. Prolific bearer of very large heads weighing as much as 150 lbs. Wind resistant; attractive for landscaping. *Source History: 4 in 1988; 6 in 1992; 4 in 2000.* **Sources: Al8, An4, Go7, Our, Pa2.**

Green Red - Medium bunches of beautiful, brilliant red bananas ripening to gold. Aromatic, cream colored flesh. Mature height 24-28'. Time to bear 20-30 months; one year cycle thereafter. *Source History: 1 in 1992; 1 in 2000.* **Sources: An4.**

Gros Michel - Once the standard commercial variety of Central America now replaced by Grand Nain. Large, superior tasting, excellent quality fruit. Slender plant grows 9-14' tall. Very cold sensitive; easily toppled by the wind. Rarely produces in this country; still grown in collections for nostalgia's sake. *Source History: 3 in 1988; 2 in 1992; 1 in 2000.* **Sources: Go7.**

Haa Haa (Ha'a) - Medium size heads. Firm, yellow fruit. Delicious, pinkish orange flesh with low moisture content. Good cooked. Dwarf, stocky, 6-8' plant. Bright green leaves, except for the new leaves which have burgundy overtones. Rare. Originated in the South Pacific. *Source History: 4 in 1988; 5 in 1992; 2 in 2000.* **Sources: Al8, An4, Go7.**

Hua Moa - Name means chicken egg. Medium size heads of unusual, round, 4" fruits. Best of all bananas when sliced green and fried in hot oil like French fries; also excellent when ripe, either eaten fresh or baked. Plant grows 8-12' tall; solid green color with medium wide leaves. Can stand up to wind with a little protection. Originated in the South Pacific. *Source History: 3 in 1988; 3 in 1992; 4 in 2000.* **Sources: Al8, An4, Go7, Na13, Pa2.**

Ice Cream - *Musa acuminata*. Tight, closely packed, bluish green heads. Medium length fruit with silver blue outer skin. Snow white, excellent quality flesh. Silver-green plant grows 14-18' tall. Stands up to wind quite well because of a stout pseudostem and strong root system. Hardy; shows good cold tolerance. Originated in South America. *Source History: 5 in 1988; 6 in 1992; 4 in 2000.* **Sources: Al8, An4, Go7, Ju2, Pa2.**

Igcpoca - Plump, delicious light green fruit with a pointed end. Grows 10-12'. *Source History: 1 in 2000.* **Sources: Go7.**

Iholene Red (Iholena Red) - *Musa acuminata*. Fairly small heads of very sweet, yellow, horn-shaped fruits borne on a brilliant red stem. Fruit turns yellow about two weeks after emergence into the air, but takes about three months to develop and ripen. Beautiful plant grows 8-12' tall; deep pink trunk. Leaves are green on the upper surface; pink on the bottom. Moderate wind tolerance. Mostly used as an ornamental plant, but fruit is very good. Originated in Hawaii. *Source History: 4 in 1988; 5 in 1992; 5 in 2000.* **Sources: Al8, An4, Go7, Na13, Our, Pa2.**

Iholene White (Iho Lena) - Similar to Red Iholene, but with less color. Heads are not large; good, quite sweet fruit. Vigorous, hardy, 10-13' mostly green plant; slight pink hue on the undersides of the new leaves. Moderate wind resistance. Originated in Hawaii. *Source History: 3 in 1988; 5 in 1992; 2 in 2000.* **Sources: An4, Go7.**

Jamaican Red (Cuban) - Reddish maroon fruit with excellent flavored orange flesh. Excellent eaten fresh or cooked. Beautiful, stout, dull red plant grows 14-18' tall. Green leaves with a thin red border. Takes wind fairly well. Requires up to 18 months to produce fruit. Originated in Jamaica. *Source History: 3 in 1988; 4 in 1992; 2 in 2000.* **Sources: An4, Go7.**

Jamaican Red Dwarf - Recent development from the standard Jamaican Red. Maroon fruit with excellent flavored orange flesh; smaller but much richer in flavor than commercial bananas. Excellent quality. Fruit is produced in about 13 months. Plant has wide leaves and grows 6-8' tall; trunk and bottom of leaves are dull red. Excellent wind resistance. Very rare. Originated in Jamaica. *Source History: 6 in 1988; 9 in 1992; 5 in 2000.* **Sources: Al8, An4, Gl3, Go7, Our, Pa2.**

Kaualau - Thick trunk to 10'. Grows up to 16'. Mild flavored cooking t ,e. Pronounced kahoo-a-Iowa; means "rain on the leaf." *Source History: 2 in 1992; 1 in 2000.* **Sources: Al8, An4.**

KM-5 (Yangambi KM-5) - Small dessert banana with excellent flavor. Very disease resistant. Grows to 12'. Originated in West Central Africa. *Source History: 1 in 2000.* **Sources: Go7.**

Kru - *Musa acuminata.* Resembles Jamaican Red in appearance and fruit; produces more quickly and is more delicious. Red fruits with orange flesh. Highly esteemed flavor. Beautiful 10-12' tree with red trunk. Moderate wind tolerance. Very rare plant. Recently imported from New Guinea. *Source History: 4 in 1988; 4 in 1992; 4 in 2000.* **Sources: Al8, An4, Go7, Our, Pa2.**

Lacatan - Chiquita brand banana. Fruits are of excellent quality. Hardy plant grows 8-14' tall. Quite wind resistant. Central American commercial variety. Originated in the Philippines. *Source History: 3 in 1988; 4 in 1992; 1 in 2000.* **Sources: Go7.**

Lady Finger (Ney Poovan) - *Musa acuminata.* Slender plant grows 20-25' tall. Plump, cigar-shaped fruit is thin skinned. Crunchy and creamy when ripe. Most cold hardy of the banana family. *Source History: 1 in 1988; 3 in 1992; 2 in 2000.* **Sources: Ju2, Pa2.**

Lady Finger Dwarf - *Musa acuminata.* Sweet, small fruit. Plant grows to 5'. Rare. *Source History: 1 in 1988; 2 in 1992; 1 in 2000.* **Sources: Pa2.**

Maia Maoli - Favorite cooking banana in the local Hawaiian markets. Mature plant height is 18-22'. *Source History: 1 in 1992; 2 in 2000.* **Sources: An4, Go7.**

Manzano - Fruit is 3-6" long. Thoroughly ripened fruit is sweet with a distinct apple flavor; unripe fruit is quite astringent. Flesh is drier than other bananas. Eaten fresh or cooked. Vigorous plant is one of the most rapid producers; time from planting until harvest is about 15 months. Height is 18-20'. A favorite in the tropics. *Source History: 2 in 1992; 1 in 2000.* **Sources: Al8, An4.**

Mauritius - Short Cavendish type plant grows 4' tall. Produces a small bunch of full size, sweet, creamy fruit. Good for container culture or small areas. *Source History: 1 in 2000.* **Sources: Go7.**

Misi Luki - Popular Lady Finger banana with a long shelf life. Grows 12-14'. Originated in India. *Source History: 1 in 2000.* **Sources: Go7.**

Monkey Finger - Large bunches of long thin, slightly curved fruit, resembling the elongated fingers of a large monkey hand. Firm flesh with a sweet, sub-acid flavor. The racemes can reach 6' long and weigh 70-90 lbs. Grows 10-12' tall. *Source History: 2 in 2000.* **Sources: An4, Go7.**

Monthan - Cooking banana from South India. Grows 10-16' tall. Produces long, heavy bunches of sweet fruit. *Source History: 2 in 2000.* **Sources: Al8, An4, Go7.**

Musa acuminata - Primitive seeded variety which is one of the presumed predecessors of many of the dessert bananas of today. Susceptible to fusarium wilt. Grows to 10'. Rare. *Source History: 1 in 2000.* **Sources: Go7.**

Musa balbisiana - Grows 12-15'. Suckers are borne with maturity. Primitive seeded variety thought to be an ancestor of many modern day bananas and plantains. Originated in India. *Source History: 1 in 1988; 1 in 1992; 1 in 2000.* **Sources: Go7.**

Musa banksii - Primitive seeded variety. Grows 8-10'. *Source History: 1 in 2000.* **Sources: Go7.**

Musa basjoo - Grows at substantially cooler temperatures than any other *Musa* species. Plants double or triple in size in six months. After the third season a fat red spike of flower clusters grows from the center of the plant and forms a "bunch" of fruits which look like apple bananas with small black seeds. Grown in north central China. *Source History: 1 in 2000.* **Sources: Or2.**

Musa cavendishii - Tasty, 5" bananas. Plant grows 5-6' tall. Usually bears within 2-3 years. *Source History: 3 in 1992; 3 in 2000.* **Sources: Fa1, Fo4, Mel.**

Musa coccinea - Grows 8' tall. Grown mainly as an ornamental. Originated in Java. Tropical. *Source History: 1 in 1988; 3 in 1992; 3 in 2000.* **Sources: Ban, Ga6, Go7.**

Musa malaccensis - Primitive variety produces small, 4" long, thin seeded fruit on an 8-10' tall plant. Resistant to Panama disease and sigatoka. *Source History: 1 in 2000.* **Sources: Go7.**

Musa sumatrana x Grand Nain - Hybridized. Long, red fruit is edible but not very sweet. Plant grows 6-7 ft. tall. Gets its beautiful color from the *M. sumatrana* parent; growth habit from Gran Nain parent. Good landscaping plant. *Source History: 1 in 1992; 2 in 2000.* **Sources: An4, Go7.**

Mysore - Medium size, closely packed heads of fruit. Lady Finger type; probably the smallest of all bananas. Thin skinned and very sweet. Vigorous, productive plant grows 15-18' tall; red trunk. Fairly wind tolerant. Originated in southern India. *Source History: 3 in 1988; 5 in 1992; 4 in 2000.* **Sources: Al8, An4, Go7, Ju2, Pa2.**

Nehumbahoka - Rare dessert banana with "chocolate" color in the pseudostem. Grows 10-12' tall. Plump fruit is 6" long with a refreshing, slightly sub-acid flavor. *Source History: 1 in 2000.* **Sources: Go7.**

Ney Poovan (Orito) - Very sweet fruit similar to Nino with larger fruit size. Height is 20-25'. *Source History: 2 in 1992; 1 in 2000.* **Sources: An4.**

Nino (Honey Banana, Sucrier) - Medium size heads of thin skinned, 3-4" long, very sweet fruit. Excellent quality. Fairly slender, 8-12' plant heavily marked with tan and brown. Fair wind tolerance. Originated in South America. *Source History: 3 in 1988; 4 in 1992; 2 in 2000.* **Sources: An4, Go7.**

Oriana - Discovered growing in the very dense jungle under low light conditions. Red 5" fruit with very sweet, seeded, white flesh. Grows only 2.5-5' tall. Ideal for indoor culture. Introduced from South America. *Source History: 1 in 1988; 1 in 1992; 1 in 2000.* **Sources: Pa2.**

Orinoco - Fast growing plantain; reaches 11' tall. Perhaps the easiest to grow. Fruit is quite palatable fresh but is primarily an excellent cooking variety. First grown in Cuba in 1516. *Source History: 1 in 1988; 2 in 1992; 2 in 2000.* **Sources: An4, Go7.**

Orinoco Dwarf (Horse Banana) - Large heads weighing 40-50 lbs. Thick three-cornered fruit with thick skin. Fair to good quality; best when cooked. Solid green plant like regular Orinoco with no red color at all. Mature height is only 7'. Rather uncommon. Hardy. Originated in South America. *Source History: 3 in 1988; 5 in 1992; 3 in 2000.* **Sources: An4, Gl3, Go7.**

Orito - Fruit resembles Nino but the plant is larger. Grows up to 20'. *Source History: 1 in 2000.* **Sources: An4.**

Pelipita - Cooking banana. Hardy, disease resistant plant grows 10-12' tall. Used as a progenitor for many other hybrids. *Source History: 1 in 2000.* **Sources: Go7.**

Pisang Awak (Namwa) - Dwarf and tall varieties. Lady Finger banana that produces sweet fruit that is prized in Indonesia. Dwarf grows to 8'; tall to 12'. Shows some sensitivity to Panama disease. *Source History: 1 in 2000.* **Sources: Go7.**

Pisang Jari Buaya - Dessert variety produces long, slender fruit with slightly sub-acid, sweet flavor. Grows 8-10' tall on a thin pseudostem. Rare and unique. *Source History: 1 in 2000.* **Sources: Go7.**

Pitogo - Fruit looks more like a fig than a banana. Delicious. Grows 10-12' tall. *Source History: 1 in 2000.* **Sources: Go7.**

Popoulu - Well liked Hawaiian variety. Salmon-pink flesh with pleasing, subacid, apple-like flavor. Slender plant grows to 14'. Prefers a protected location in filtered light with ample moisture. Name translates, "ball shaped like a bread-fruit." *Source History: 1 in 1992; 2 in 2000.* **Sources: Al8, An4, Go7.**

Praying Hands - Fruit is fused together, resembling a baseball mit or hands in the praying position. Unusual, delicious flavor. Plant grows 12-16'. One of the more cold tolerant varieties. *Source History: 2 in 1992; 3 in 2000.* **Sources: An4, Go7, Ju2.**

Puerto Rican Dwarf Plantain - Fruits are just like Giant Plantain, except the heads of the fruit are larger and the pseudostem is stouter. Large, attractive, horn-shaped fruits are cooked rather than eaten fresh. Short, fast growing, 7-9' plant. More wind resistant. Cold sensitive. *Source History: 4 in 1988; 6 in 1992; 1 in 2000.* **Sources: Go7.**

Pysang Raja (Pisang Raja) - "Royal Banana" of Malaysia. Thin skinned, horn-type fruit is 10" long and blunt on the end. Firm, very sweet, orange flesh. One of the most delicious bananas. Solid green, 8-10' plant with bluish overtones. Thick pseudostem is very tightly packed. Wind resistant; quite cold tolerant. Originated in the Far East where it is highly esteemed. *Source History: 3 in 1988; 4 in 1992; 2 in 2000.* **Sources: Al8, An4, Go7.**

Raja Puri - *Musa acuminata.* Medium size heads of very sweet, medium size fruit. Plant grows 6-8' tall; trace of red stain in the leaves. Very wind resistant.

Probably the toughest and cold hardiest of all varieties next to Orinoco Victoria. One of the favorite bananas of India. *Source History: 4 in 1988; 6 in 1992; 4 in 2000.* **Sources: Al8, An4, Go7, Ju2, Na13.**

Red - Produces clusters of red bananas in August in South Georgia. Unusually hardy; Zones 8-10. *Source History: 1 in 1992; 1 in 2000.* **Sources: Ty2.**

Rose - Plant grows 6-8' tall with a slender pseudostem. Small, delicate, sweet fruit. Resists fusarium wilt. *Source History: 1 in 2000.* **Sources: Go7.**

Sabah (Saba) - Compact heads of short, tasty fruits. Plant grows 16-20' tall. Cold tolerant. Similar to Orinoco. Originated in the Philippines. *Source History: 1 in 1988; 2 in 1992; 1 in 2000.* **Sources: Go7.**

San Jose - *Source History: 1 in 2000.* **Sources: Pa2.**

Seeded - *Musa acuminata.* Bears small hands of seeded fruit with pink or yellow flesh. *Source History: 1 in 1988; 1 in 1992; 1 in 2000.* **Sources: Na13.**

SH 3640 - Dessert type, sweet, full size fruit produced on an 8-9' plant. Fast grower. Rare. Honduras Research Station introduction. *Source History: 1 in 2000.* **Sources: Go7.**

Super Dwarf - Plant grows 3-6' tall in containers. Can produce tasty fruit if grown outside in warm months. *Source History: 2 in 2000.* **Sources: Ed2, Go7.**

Texas Star - Possibly the most hardy of all bananas; survived 16 degree F. temperatures in Texas. *Source History: 1 in 2000.* **Sources: Ty2.**

Thousand Finger - Hundreds of tiny 1.5" round sweet bananas on 12-14' plant. Can produce a bunch up to 8' long. *Source History: 2 in 1992; 4 in 2000.* **Sources: Al8, An4, Go7, Ju2, Na13.**

Tuu Gia - Long, yellow, curly fruits. Grows 10-16'. Originated in Viet Nam. *Source History: 1 in 1992; 2 in 2000.* **Sources: An4, Go7.**

Valery - *Musa acuminata.* Very large heads of high quality fruit. Light, sweet, delicate flavor. Plant grows 6-7' tall. Wind resistant. Very hardy and productive. Central American commercial variety; often found in U.S. supermarkets. *Source History: 4 in 1988; 4 in 1992; 4 in 2000.* **Sources: An4, Go7, Pa2, PL2.**

Viente Cohol - Dessert variety from the Philippines area. Produces small, plump, 3-4" long fruit with soft, sweet flesh. Grows to 10'. *Source History: 1 in 2000.* **Sources: Go7.**

Williams Hybrid (Williams) - *Musa acuminata.* Very large heads weighing up to 150 lbs. Delicious, very sweet fruit. Plant grows 8-10' tall. Wind resistant; cold hardy. One of the main commercial varieties of Central America. *Source History: 4 in 1988; 4 in 1992; 4 in 2000.* **Sources: An4, Go7, Our, PL2.**

Zanmoreno - Excellent fruit quality. Similar to Dwarf Chinese except it has a smaller bunch and the plant is slower to flower, slower growing and reaches a maximum height of only 5-6'. Excellent choice for container growing or where space is limited. *Source History: 1 in 1992; 2 in 2000.* **Sources: An4, Go7.**

Zebrina (Zebrina Blood Banana, Sumatrana, Blood) - Uncultivated banana grown for its red and green foliage and red flowers. Velvet coated, seeded, inedible fruit. Rather slender, 4-5' plant. Trunk and pseudostems are completely red. Narrow leaves have green upper surfaces that are splotched with red; bottom surfaces are solid wine red. Not very wind tolerant. Ideal for container culture. Beautiful ornamental banana from Java; rare in the Western Hemisphere. *Source History: 3 in 1988; 4 in 1992; 2 in 2000.* **Sources: Ca7, Go7.**

Citrus Rootstock

<u>Amblicarpa</u> - *Source History: 1 in 1988; 1 in 1992; 1 in 2000.* **Sources: Wi6.**

<u>Citrange: C-32</u> - *Citroncirus (Citrus sinensis x Poncirus trifoliata).* Fruit is intermediate between the parents. Vigorous trees are equal to Troyer in volume but less dense. Major advantage over Troyer is tolerance of citrus nematode, biotypes 1, 2 and 3. *Source History: 1 in 1988; 1 in 1992; 2 in 2000.* **Sources: BZN, Wi6.**

<u>Citrange: C-35</u> - Same parentage as C-32 Citrange; smaller tree but otherwise similar. *Source History: 1 in 1988; 1 in 1992; 1 in 2000.* **Sources: Wi6.**

<u>Citrange: Carrizo</u> - Possibly identical to Troyer. Adapts to a wide range of soils except calcareous. Tree is comparable to Troyer in size, yield and quality. Tolerant to burrowing nematode and citrus nematode. *Source History: 2 in 1988; 1 in 1992; 1 in 2000.* **Sources: Wi6.**

<u>Citrange: Morton</u> - Hardy to 5 degrees F. *Source History: 1 in 2000.* **Sources: Sh3.**

<u>Citrange: Troyer</u> - *Citrus sinensis x Poncirus trifoliate.* Standard size trees produce large fruit of good quality. High yields. Major drawbacks include rind creasing, high acid in cooler areas and lime induced chlorosis. Standard rootstock by which new rootstock performance in California is judged. *Source History: 1 in 1988; 1 in 1992; 1 in 2000.* **Sources: Wi6.**

<u>Citremon: 1449</u> - Citron (*Citrus medica*) x Lemon (*Citrus limon*). *Source History: 1 in 1988; 1 in 1992; 1 in 2000.* **Sources: Wi6.**

<u>Citrumelo: 4475</u> (Swingle Citrumelo) - *Citrus paradisi x Poncirus trifoliata.* Not adapted to heavy clay soils but moderately tolerant of drought, cold and salt. Equal to Troyer in fruit yield and quality. Has a tendency to fruit creasing and scion overgrowth with oranges and grapefruits. *Source History: 1 in 1988; 1 in 1992; 1 in 2000.* **Sources: Wi6.**

<u>Citrus macrophylla</u> (Alemow) - Adapted to a wide range of soils; cold sensitive. Fruit has low internal quality. Large, vigorous trees. High yields. Mainly used with lemon scions. *Source History: 1 in 1988; 1 in 1992; 1 in 2000.* **Sources: Wi6.**

<u>Citrus moi</u> - *Citrus pennivesciulats.* *Source History: 1 in 1988; 1 in 2000.* **Sources: Wi6.**

<u>Citrus taiwanica</u> (Nansho daidai of Japan) - Possibly a sour orange hybrid. Cold, salt and high water table tolerant. Needs loam to clay-loam soil. Performance is quite variable; usually intermediate yield and quality. *Source History: 1 in 1988; 1 in 1992; 1 in 2000.* **Sources: Wi6.**

<u>Citrus volkameriana</u> - Produces a large, vigorous tree with high yields of low quality fruit. Adapts to many soil types but does best on deep sandy soils. Drought tolerant. *Source History: 1 in 1988; 1 in 1992; 2 in 2000.* **Sources: BZN, Wi6.**

<u>Cleopatra Mandarin</u> - *Citrus reticulata blanco.* Large trees with high quality, small fruit (especially with Valencia scions). Adapted to wide range of soils. Susceptible to chlorosis except on sandy soil. Cold and chloride tolerant; not drought tolerant. Slow to reach full production. *Source History: 1 in 1988; 1 in 1992; 1 in 2000.* **Sources: Wi6.**

<u>CRC 343 Grapefruit</u> - *Source History: 1 in 1988; 1 in 1992; 1 in 2000.* **Sources: Wi6.**

<u>Cuban Shaddock</u> - *Source History: 1 in 1988; 1 in 2000.* **Sources: Wi6.**

India Lemon - Characteristics and production similar to rough lemon. Experimental rootstock with little promise as performance has been poor with lemons. *Source History: 1 in 1992; 1 in 2000.* **Sources: Wi6.**

Keothan - *Source History: 1 in 1988; 1 in 1992; 1 in 2000.* **Sources: Wi6.**

Lime, Mexican - *Source History: 1 in 1988; 1 in 1992; 1 in 2000.* **Sources: Wi6.**

Lime, Palestine Sweet - *Source History: 1 in 1988; 1 in 1992; 2 in 2000.* **Sources: BZN, Wi6.**

Madam Vinus - *Source History: 1 in 1988; 1 in 1992; 1 in 2000.* **Sources: Wi6.**

Milam - *Source History: 1 in 1988; 1 in 1992; 1 in 2000.* **Sources: Wi6.**

Rangpur Lime - *Citrus reticulata* var. *Austera* hybrid. Not a true lime. Produces large, vigorous trees. Good yields of medium quality fruit. Adapts to wide range of soils. Exocortis and phytophora sensitive. *Source History: 1 in 1988; 2 in 1992; 4 in 2000.* **Sources: Ju2, Pa2, PL2, Wi6.**

Rough Lemon - *Citrus jambhiri.* Large trees produce high yields of low quality fruit. Does best on deep sandy soil. Drought tolerant. Poor cold tolerance. *Source History: 1 in 1988; 1 in 1992; 2 in 2000.* **Sources: BZN, Wi6.**

Rough Lemon, Estes - *Source History: 1 in 1988; 1 in 1992; 1 in 2000.* **Sources: Wi6.**

Rough Lemon, Schaub - *Source History: 1 in 1988; 1 in 1992; 1 in 2000.* **Sources: Wi6.**

Rough Lemon, Soh Jahlia - *Source History: 1 in 1988; 1 in 2000.* **Sources: Wi6.**

Rough Lemon, Stowe Red - *Source History: 1 in 1988; 1 in 2000.* **Sources: Wi6.**

Rough Lemon, UCLA - *Source History: 1 in 1988; 1 in 1992; 1 in 2000.* **Sources: Wi6.**

Rough, W-N Red - *Source History: 1 in 1988; 1 in 1992; 1 in 2000.* **Sources: Wi6.**

Sacaton and Yuma - *Source History: 1 in 1988; 1 in 2000.* **Sources: Wi6.**

Sanguine Grosse Ronde - *Source History: 1 in 2000.* **Sources: Wi6.**

Sour Orange - *Citrus aurantium.* Produces standard size tree with excellent quality, medium size fruit. Does best on moderately heavy soils. Can be grown where tristeza is present with a lemon scion. *Source History: 2 in 1988; 1 in 1992; 1 in 2000.* **Sources: Wi6.**

Sour Orange, Brazilian - *Source History: 1 in 1988; 1 in 1992; 1 in 2000.* **Sources: Wi6.**

Sour Orange, Keen - *Source History: 1 in 1988; 1 in 1992; 1 in 2000.* **Sources: Wi6.**

Sour Orange, Sicilian - *Source History: 1 in 1988; 1 in 1992; 1 in 2000.* **Sources: Wi6.**

Sweet Orange - *Citrus sinensis.* Produces good quality fruit. Does best on sandy to heavy soils. Poor drought tolerance. Susceptible to phytophthora. *Source History: 1 in 1988; 1 in 1992; 1 in 2000.* **Sources: Wi6.**

Swingle (4475) - *Source History: 1 in 1988; 1 in 2000.* **Sources: Wi6.**

Trifoliate Orange - *Poncirus trifoliata.* Produces trees smaller than Troyer.

High quality fruit although rinds have tendency to crease and split. Poor salt toler-ance. Does best on heavy clay, non-calcareous soils. Good cold hardiness when planted in cool areas; same cold tolerance as more tender rootstocks when planted in warm areas.   Zones 6-9. *Source History: 2 in 1988; 8 in 1992; 14 in 2000.* **Sources: Ba3, Ban, Car, Co24, Ed2, Fo2, Ga11, Hid, LO6, Sc2, Sh3, Tri, Wi6, Wo2.**

Trifoliate: Barnes - *Poncirus trifoliata* (formerly *Citrus trifoliata*). *Source His-tory: 1 in 1988; 1 in 1992; 1 in 2000.* **Sources: Wi6.**

Trifoliate: Beneke - *Poncirus trifoliata. Source History: 1 in 1988; 1 in 1992; 1 in 2000.* **Sources: Wi6.**

Trifoliate: Flying Dragon - *Poncirus trifoliata monstrosa.* Wildly mutated form of the Trifoliate Orange. Yellow 2" fruits yield a small amount of juice that is used as a spicy lemon seasoning; higher juice yield after two weeks of refrigeration. Trees are twisted and extremely thorny. Hardy to -20 degrees F. The trees have been used in many crosses with common oranges, resulting in hybrids known as "citranges." *Source History: 1 in 1988; 3 in 1992; 9 in 2000.* **Sources: BZN, Car, Ed2, Fo2, Or2, Po7, Sh3, Tri, Wi6.**

Trifoliate: Marks Mississippi - *Source History: 1 in 1988; 1 in 1992; 1 in 2000.* **Sources: Wi6.**

Trifoliate: Pomeroy - *Source History: 1 in 1988; 1 in 1992; 1 in 2000.* **Sources: Wi6.**

Trifoliate: Rich 16-6 - *Source History: 1 in 2000.* **Sources: Wi6.**

Trifoliate: Rubidoux - *Poncirus trifoliata. Source History: 1 in 1988; 1 in 1992; 2 in 2000.* **Sources: Pa2, Wi6.**

Yuma Ponderosa Lemon - Experimental rootstock has produced high yields with Olinda Valencias, Minneola tangelos and Washington navels. However, qual-ity is low. *Source History: 1 in 1992; 1 in 2000.* **Sources: Wi6.**

Yuzu x Trifoliata - *Source History: 1 in 2000.* **Sources: Sh3.**

Citrus / Miscellaneous

Australian Finger Lime - *Microcitrus australasica.* Greenish yellow fruit; 4" long and 1" in diameter. Tree grows 30-40' tall. Cold hardy. Native to eastern Australia. *Source History: 1 in 1988; 2 in 1992; 2 in 2000.* **Sources: Or2, Pa2.**

Calamondin (Panama Orange, Miniature Orange, Chinese Dwarf Orange) - *Citrofortunella.* Sour Mandarin (*Citrus reticulata*) x Kumquat (*Fortunella spp.*). Sometimes incorrectly identified as *Citrus madurensis.* Fruit is larger than kum-quat, similar to a small, acid tangerine. Sweet rind with tart, juicy center when fully ripe. Makes excellent preserves; juice is a great lemon juice substitute. Everbear-ing; stores well on the tree. Highly decorative, columnar tree is almost thornless with fine branches and small, oval leaves. Highly productive. Easily grown from seed.   Good for hedges or container culture.   Excellent ornamental.   Very cold hardy. Zones 9-10. *Source History: 5 in 1988; 15 in 1992; 15 in 2000.* **Sources: Ban, Fou, Ga11, HA12, Hid, Ju2, Lo5, MO10, On4, Pa2, PI3, PL2, Rai, Tr10, Wi6.**

Calamondin, Variegated - *Source History: 1 in 1988; 3 in 1992; 2 in 2000.* **Sources: Lo5, Pa2.**

Chinese Box Orange - *Severina buxifolia.   Source History: 1 in 2000.* **Sources: Po7.**

Choa Chou Tien Chich Kat - Small tangerine type fruit. *Source History: 1 in*

2000. **Sources: Sh3.**

Citrangadin: Glen - Four-way cross of a kumquat, orange, tangerine and a cold hardy *Poncirus.* Shy bearer of 1" fiery orange fruits that look like a tangelo. Extremely flavorful. The concentrated juice is mixed with water. Ripens in the fall. Hardy to 10 degreees F. Very rare. *Source History: 1 in 2000.* **Sources: Or2.**

Citrange - Hybrid of *Poncirus* x sweet orange. Mandarin size fruits with acid pulp like lemons or grapefruits. Tree grows 4-6' tall. Hardy to 0 degrees F. *Source History: 1 in 1992; 1 in 2000.* **Sources: Or2.**

Citrange: Benton - *Source History: 1 in 2000.* **Sources: Wi6.**

Citrange: Morton - Most closely resembles the common navel orange in size, color and flavor. Juicy, often seedless, 3-3.5" fruits are about as sweet as tangelos. Good for fresh eating, juice or marmalade. Hardy to 25 degrees F. *Source History: 2 in 1988; 4 in 1992; 2 in 2000.* **Sources: Or2, Wi6.**

Citrange: Rusk - Small, dark orange, thin skinned fruit with red blush. Very juicy flesh with grapefruit-like bitterness. Low acid. Ornamental tree is a fast grower. Has borne fruit after lows of 0 degrees F. *Source History: 1 in 1988; 2 in 1992; 1 in 2000.* **Sources: Wi6.**

Citrange: Savage - Yellow 2.5-3" fruits with more fragrance and acid than Morton. Spiny, productive tree tends to be semideciduous, which suggests a more cold tolerant tree than the Morton. *Source History: 1 in 1988; 1 in 1992; 2 in 2000.* **Sources: Or2, Wi6.**

Citrange: Snow Sweet - Orange x grapefruit x *Poncirus.* Fragrant large white flowers followed by fruits the size of Valencia oranges. May be picked when the flesh is green. Ripen in late October. Hardy to 10 degrees F. Trademarked. *Source History: 1 in 2000.* **Sources: Or2.**

Citrange: Uvalde - *Source History: 1 in 1988; 1 in 2000.* **Sources: Wi6.**

Citrangequat: Maccioroli - Sweet Orange (*Citrus sinensis*) x Trifoliate Orange (*Poncirus trifoliata*) x Kumquat (*Fortunella spp.*) *Source History: 1 in 1988; 1 in 1992; 1 in 2000.* **Sources: Pa2.**

Citrangequat: Sinton - Kumquat hybrid. Juicy, nearly seedless fruit turns red as it ripens in late summer. Small compact tree bears heavy crops. Hardy to 6 degrees F. *Source History: 1 in 1992; 1 in 2000.* **Sources: Or2.**

Citrangequat: Thomasville - Kumquat x Citrange hybrid. For gardeners in areas too cold for growing lemons or limes. Orange 2" fruit with mildly pungent peel. Makes pleasantly flavored, acid juice. May be eaten out of hand when fully mature. Ornamental evergreen trees. Hardy to 0 degrees F. *Source History: 1 in 1988; 2 in 1992; 2 in 2000.* **Sources: Or2, Sh3.**

Citremello - Grapefruit x *Trifoliata.* Flavor and smell similar to grapefruit but more bitter. Very hardy; has withstood 0 degree temperatures. *Source History: 1 in 1992; 1 in 2000.* **Sources: Or2.**

Citremon - *Poncirus trifoliata* x lemon hybrid. Upright growth habit. Fragrant flowers. Fruit is possibly only semi-edible. *Source History: 1 in 1992; 1 in 2000.* **Sources: Fo2.**

Citremon: Ponderosa (American Wonder) - Very large, grapefruit size fruits to 3-5 pounds each. Lots of juice. Tangy, lemon flavor. Miniature tree grows 2' tall. Fragrant, waxy, white flowers. Branches require support. Zone 9. *Source History: 6 in 1988; 9 in 1992; 3 in 2000.* **Sources: Fou, Lo5, Pa2.**

Citron: Etrog - *Source History: 1 in 2000.* **Sources: Ga11, Pa2.**

Citron: Fingered (Buddha's Hand) - *Citrus hystrix*. So named because of the unusual finger-like appendages. Thick yellow rind is used as a substitute for orange rind and is candied. Cold sensitive. *Source History: 1 in 1988; 5 in 1992; 8 in 2000.* **Sources: BZN, Ju2, On4, Or2, Pa2, PL2, Po7, Tr10.**

Citrum - *Source History: 1 in 1992; 1 in 2000.* **Sources: Sh3.**

Citrus oboboidea - *Source History: 1 in 2000.* **Sources: Or2.**

Citrus sulcata - Sour yellow, nippled, grapefruit-like fruits. Medium size evergreen tree with fragrant white flowers. Native to Japan. Zones 8-10. *Source History: 1 in 2000.* **Sources: Wo2.**

Cocktail Grapefruit - Pummelo x grapefruit. Large fruit with white flesh and sweet-tart flavor. Good for container growing. *Source History: 2 in 1992; 1 in 2000.* **Sources: Pa2.**

Cocktail Pummelo - *Citrus* x Cocktail. Pummelo-Mandarin hybrid produces sweet, juicy fruit with a distinctive flavor. Ripens to green-orange with a light orange flesh. Evergreen tree is vigorous; grows 15-20' tall and wide. Full sun. Grafted on Troyer Citrange rootstock. Zones 9-10. *Source History: 1 in 2000.* **Sources: MO10.**

Erimo Citrus Glauca - *Source History: 1 in 2000.* **Sources: Sh3.**

Finger Lime - Ancient form of citrus. Banana-shaped fruit contains hundreds of lime juice filled bubbles that are sprinkled in salads, pies or cocktails. *Source History: 1 in 2000.* **Sources: Ju2.**

Glycosmis pentaphylla - Unusual citrus from Australia. Produces sweet, juicy fruit similar to the Wampi. *Source History: 1 in 2000.* **Sources: Po7.**

Ichandarin: Shangjuan - Giant Pummello parentage. Fruit up to 6"; one of the largest of all hardy citrus fruits. Round, bumpy, bright yellow skin. Extremely juicy, seedy flesh. Twenty-five fruits may yield a gallon of pure juice. Great substitute for lemons. More hardy than Satsuma mandarin. *Source History: 1 in 1992; 1 in 2000.* **Sources: Or2.**

Ichandarin: Sudachi - Natural hybrid long cultivated in China and Japan. Light orange, seedy flesh with good, tart, mandarin-lime flavor. Faster growing tree than Yuzu; less cold tolerant. *Source History: 1 in 1992; 1 in 2000.* **Sources: Or2.**

Ichandarin: Yuzu - *Citrus junos*. Medium size, 2.5-3" fruit with loose, deep yellow skin. Easy to peel. Pleasant lemon-lime flavor when eaten fresh; valued in Japan for culinary uses. Supposedly hardy to 0 degrees F. *Source History: 1 in 1988; 2 in 1992; 2 in 2000.* **Sources: Or2, Wi6.**

Kaffir – *Citrus hystrix*. Fruit rind is candied or dried and used in curry pastes in Thai and Cambodian cooking. Fruits are eaten with fish or made into drinks. *Source History: 1 in 1988; 4 in 2000.* **Sources: Ed2, Or2, PL2, Tr10.**

Kumquat - *Source History: 1 in 1988; 1 in 1992; 1 in 2000.* **Sources: BZN.**

Kumquat x Trifoliata - *Source History: 1 in 1992; 1 in 2000.* **Sources: Sh3.**

Kumquat: Australian Razzlequat - *Eremocitrus x C. limona meyer*. Round, smooth fruits are 1-1.5". The edible yellow peels are speckled and blushed with attractive red oil cells. Sweet peel and sweet-tart lemon-lime flavored flesh. Drought tolerant trees are well suited to the western deserts of the U.S. Does equally well in humid or dry air conditions. Delayed dormancy gives it the ability to escape late freezes. Hardy to -10 degrees F. Trademarked. *Source History: 2 in 2000.* **Sources: Or2, Sh3.**

Kumquat: Changshou (Fukushu Kumquat) - *Fortunella obovata. Source History: 1 in 2000.* **Sources: Pa2.**

Kumquat: Lee's Sharp - Hardy to 10 degrees F. *Source History: 1 in 2000.* **Sources: Sh3.**

Kumquat: Longevity - *Fortunella obavata.* Slow grower; slow to bear. Tender, soft and extremely flavorful fruit. Hardy to 10 degrees F. Originated in China. Trademarked. *Source History: 1 in 2000.* **Sources: Or2.**

Kumquat: Meiwa - *Fortunella spp.* Round or oval 1-1.25" orange fruit with sweet rind. Ideal citrus for container growing. Hardy to 18 degrees F; Zones 8-10. *Source History: 4 in 1988; 13 in 1992; 7 in 2000.* **Sources: Ed2, Ga11, Ju2, On4, Pa2, PL2, Ty2.**

Kumquat: Mr. John's Longevity - Longevity kumquat (*Fortunella obovata)* x citrange (*Poncirus* x sweet orange). Slightly larger fruits than the *F. obovata* parent but retains the kumquat flavor. Trademarked. *Source History: 1 in 2000.* **Sources: Or2.**

Kumquat: Nagami (Oval Kumquat) - Small, oval, bright orange fruit. Thick, tender, sweet rind. Moderately sour flesh. Used in marmalade or jelly; candied or preserved whole. Also eaten fresh, rind and all. Holds well on the tree. Ornamental, dwarf plant grows densely 4' tall. Rich, orange blossom perfume from the flowers. Fruit ripens year-round. Fruits best in warmer areas. Hardy to 18 degrees F. *Source History: 6 in 1988; 16 in 1992; 9 in 2000.* **Sources: Fou, Ju2, MO10, On4, Pa2, PI3, PL2, Rai, Ty2.**

Lemon x Trifoliata - *Source History: 1 in 1992; 1 in 2000.* **Sources: Sh3.**

Limequat - Lime (*Citrus aurantiifolia*) x kumquat (*Fortunella spp.*) Thin skinned lime with flavor similar to Florida Key lime and edible skin. Small tree bears fruit year round. Requires less heat to produce fruit. Fine container plant. *Source History: 1 in 1988; 2 in 1992; 3 in 2000.* **Sources: Ed2, HA12, Ju2.**

Limequat: Eustis - Mexican lime (*Citrus aurantiifolia*) x round kumquat (*Fortunella japonica*). Light yellow fruit; olive shape and size. Flavor and aroma of lime. Erratic branching. Bears prolifically. Ripens from late fall to winter. Hardy to 18 degrees F. *Source History: 3 in 1988; 5 in 1992; 3 in 2000.* **Sources: Fou, Or2, Pa2.**

Limequat: Lakeland - Better than Mexican lime. Not hardy. *Source History: 1 in 2000.* **Sources: Sh3.**

Long Hwang Kat - Small tangerine-type fruit. *Source History: 1 in 2000.* **Sources: Sh3.**

Melogold - Pummelo x grapefruit. Pummelo-like fruit shape; larger size than Marsh and Oro Blanco regardless of crop size. Juice content equal to Marsh, but with better flavor. December to February harvest. Zones 9-10. Developed in California. U.S. Plant Patent No. 6001. *Source History: 3 in 1992; 4 in 2000.* **Sources: BZN, MO10, Pa2, Wi6.**

Mineola x Trifoliata - *Source History: 1 in 2000.* **Sources: Sh3.**

Nansho Daidai - *Citrus taiwanica.* Sour orange species used in Japan like a grapefruit. Hardy evergreen bears large 4" fruits. Tangy, seedy, orange flesh. Resembles orange trees in leaf, flower and fruit. Self-fertile. Has survived temperatures of 6 degrees F. *Source History: 1 in 1992; 2 in 2000.* **Sources: Or2, Wo2.**

Orangequat: Nippon - *Citrus unshiu* x *Fortunella crassifolia.* Larger and sweeter than a kumquat. Small tree is extremely cold hardy; makes a good hedge or container plant. Zones 8-10. *Source History: 1 in 1988; 3 in 1992; 2 in 2000.*

Sources: Ju2, Ty2.

Papeda, Ichang - *Citrus ichangensis*. Pale yellow, 3-4" fruits with rough peel. Closely related to the Khasi Papeda but bears distinctively different fruit. Hardy parent of the Ichandarins. Hardy to 6 degrees F. in the U.S. Evergreen tree found growing wild in the hills of the upper Yangtze Valley. Cultivated by the inhabitants of the Ichang region. *Source History: 1 in 1988; 3 in 1992; 2 in 2000.* **Sources: Or2, Wi6.**

Papeda, Khasi - Large 3-4" fruit resembles grapefruit in size, shape and color. Juicy, seedy, white flesh with tough segment membranes. Spicy flavor with peppery tang. Eaten like grapefruit. Hardy to 0 degrees F. or lower. Originated in the Khasi Hills of Northeast India at 5000-6000' elevation. *Source History: 1 in 1992; 1 in 2000.* **Sources: Or2.**

Pummelo: Ben Hu - *Source History: 1 in 2000.* **Sources: PL2.**

Pummelo: Chandler - *Citrus maxima* (formerly *C. grandis*). Very large, round to pear-shaped, yellowish orange fruit with very thick skin. Fruits are borne singly and can weigh up to 20 lb. Round-shaped tree grows 15-30' tall. Hardy in Zone 10. *Source History: 3 in 1988; 6 in 1992; 7 in 2000.* **Sources: An4, BZN, Me2, MO10, On4, Pa2, PL2.**

Pummelo: Cuban Shaddock - *Source History: 1 in 1992; 1 in 2000.* **Sources: Wi6.**

Pummelo: Hirado Bunan - Pink fleshed fruit with sweet grapefruit flavor. *Source History: 2 in 1992; 1 in 2000.* **Sources: Ju2.**

Pummelo: Red Shaddock - *Source History: 1 in 1988; 2 in 1992; 1 in 2000.* **Sources: Pa2.**

Pummelo: Reinking - *Source History: 2 in 1988; 2 in 1992; 2 in 2000.* **Sources: Me2, Pa2.**

Siamelo - *Source History: 1 in 1988; 1 in 2000.* **Sources: Wi6.**

Snow Picked Mini-Mandarin - New *Citrus* hybrid. Orange 2" round fruit with delicious aroma. Flavor is that of traditional mandarin oranges with an appealing sweet-tartness. Trademarked. *Source History: 1 in 2000.* **Sources: Or2.**

Sour Orange: Bergamot - *Source History: 1 in 2000.* **Sources: Pa2.**

Sour Orange: Bouquet de Fleurs - *Citrus aurantium*. Round, somewhat flattened, 3", bright reddish orange fruit. Ornamental, spiny tree grows 20-30' tall; lush, dark foliage. *Source History: 1 in 1988; 1 in 1992; 1 in 2000.* **Sources: Pa2.**

Sour Orange: Chinotto - *Source History: 1 in 1988; 2 in 1992; 1 in 2000.* **Sources: Pa2.**

Sour Orange: Myrtifolia - *Citrus myrtifolia*. Round orange fruit. Fragrant flowers and myrtle-like leaves. Zone 9. *Source History: 1 in 1992; 1 in 2000.* **Sources: Lo5.**

Sour Orange: Seville - *Source History: 1 in 1988; 1 in 1992; 1 in 2000.* **Sources: Pa2.**

Sucaton - *Source History: 1 in 2000.* **Sources: Sh3.**

Suenkat (Sunki) - *Source History: 1 in 1988; 1 in 2000.* **Sources: Wi6.**

Sweet Lime, Gloria Gold - *Citrus limettioides*. *Source History: 1 in 2000.* **Sources: Pa2.**

Tangelo - Tangerine (*Citrus reticulata*) x Grapefruit (*C. maxima x C. sinensis*). Thin skinned, orangish red fruit. Tastes like a tangerine. Ripens in the winter.

Source History: 2 in 1988; 1 in 2000. **Sources: Mel.**

Tangelo: Allspice - Hardy to 20 degrees F. *Source History: 1 in 1988; 1 in 1992; 1 in 2000.* **Sources: Pa2.**

Tangelo: Minneola - Dancy tangerine x Duncan grapefruit. Large, smooth, reddish orange fruit. Juicy flesh with few seeds. Rich, tart flavor. Vigorous tree has an open, rounded shape; very productive. Grows to 12' tall and wide. Large, long, pointed leaves. Blooms in the spring. Ripens in the winter; leave fruit on the tree for rich tangerine flavor in late spring and summer. Hardy in Zones 9-10. Developed in Florida. *Source History: 5 in 1988; 11 in 1992; 8 in 2000.* **Sources: BZN, Fou, Ga11, MO10, Pa2, PI3, PL2, Wi6.**

Tangelo: Orlando - Duncan grapefruit x Dancy mandarin. Medium to large, easy to peel, juicy, sweet fruit. For best results, pollinate with Algerian tangerine. Ripens in December and January. *Source History: 3 in 1988; 6 in 1992; 4 in 2000.* **Sources: Ga11, Ju2, Pa2, Wi6.**

Tangelo: Sampson - Yellow fruit. Very attractive tree. Good along the West Coast. Ripens in late spring. *Source History: 2 in 1988; 1 in 1992; 1 in 2000.* **Sources: Fou.**

Tangelo: Wekiwa (Lavender Gem) - *Citrus reticulata x C. paradisi. Source History: 1 in 1992; 1 in 2000.* **Sources: Pa2.**

Tangelo: Williams - *Source History: 1 in 1988; 1 in 2000.* **Sources: Wi6.**

Tangor: Mency - Tangerine (*Citrus reticulata*) x Sweet Orange (*C. sinensis*). Hardy to 20 degrees F. *Source History: 1 in 1988; 1 in 2000.* **Sources: Wi6.**

Tangor: Murcott - *Source History: 1 in 1988; 2 in 1992; 1 in 2000.* **Sources: Pa2.**

Tangor: Ortanique - *Source History: 1 in 1988; 2 in 1992; 1 in 2000.* **Sources: Pa2.**

Tangor: Temple (Temple Orange) - Red-orange fruit with pebbly skin. Rich, spicy flavor when grown in hot areas; without heat it becomes very tart. Self-fertile. January-February harvest. *Source History: 1 in 1988; 5 in 1992; 3 in 2000.* **Sources: Pa2, PI3, PL2.**

Tanquat: Kirby's - *Source History: 1 in 2000.* **Sources: Sh3.**

Thomasville x Clementine - *Source History: 1 in 1992; 1 in 2000.* **Sources: Sh3.**

U.S. No. 119 - Hybrid trifoliate; 0-17% soluble solids. *Source History: 1 in 1992; 1 in 2000.* **Sources: Sh3.**

Grapefruit

Citrus paradisi

Bloomsweet - *Source History: 1 in 2000.* **Sources: Sh3.**

Duncan - Old Florida grapefruit which has been replaced by seedless varieties. Excellent flavor but is only used for juice. Work is being done to eliminate the seediness. Future research is pending. *Source History: 3 in 1992; 1 in 2000.* **Sources: Ju2.**

Dunstan - *Source History: 1 in 1992; 1 in 2000.* **Sources: Sh3.**

Flame Red - Medium size fruit with red blush on skin. Deep red flesh is very juicy with few seeds. *Source History: 1 in 1992; 2 in 2000.* **Sources: BZN, Ju2.**

Marsh Seedless - Large, light yellow fruit. Buff colored flesh is tender, juicy and seedless. Requires prolonged summer heat for quality. Especially beautiful tree; globular shape; vigorous, spreading, dense foliage. Grows 12' tall; good espalier type. Spring bloom; overlaps previous year's fruit. Season is 18 months after bloom. November to June harvest. Originated in Florida. *Source History: 3 in 1988; 8 in 1992; 4 in 2000.* **Sources: BZN, Fou, Ga11, PI3.**

Oro Blanco – Grapefruit (*Citrus paradisi*) x Pummelo *(C. grandis).* Large, white fruit is the sweetest fresh eating grapefruit. Seedless. Easy to peel. Hardy to 26 degrees F. Ripens in the winter. Originated in California. U.S. Plant Patent No. 4645. *Source History: 1 in 1988; 10 in 1992; 7 in 2000.* **Sources: BZN, Fou, MO10, On4, Or2, Pa2, Wi6.**

Red - Miniature trees thrive indoors; outdoors in Zones 9-10. *Source History: 1 in 1988; 1 in 1992; 1 in 2000.* **Sources: Mel.**

Redblush - Large, crimson blushed fruit. Tender, juicy, seedless, pigmented flesh. Needs a hot location to achieve edibility and pigmentation. Large tree is globular shaped; vigorous, spreading and productive. Dense foliage; large leaves. Spring bloom; overlaps previous year's fruit. Season is 18 months after bloom. Zones 9-10. Originated in Texas. *Source History: 2 in 1988; 2 in 1992; 2 in 2000.* **Sources: BZN, MO10.**

Rio Red - Darker than Ray Ruby. Delicious. Harvest from November to May. *Source History: 1 in 1988; 5 in 1992; 2 in 2000.* **Sources: BZN, Pa2.**

Ruby Blush - *Source History: 2 in 1988; 1 in 1992; 1 in 2000.* **Sources: Pa2.**

Ruby Pink - Pink fleshed sport of Marsh Seedless. *Source History: 2 in 1988; 2 in 1992; 1 in 2000.* **Sources: Fou.**

Ruby Red (Red Blush, Red Marsh) - Standard pink variety. Very sweet and juicy. Similar to Marsh except for red blush and pinkish flesh. Does not color well except in desert areas. Harvest from November to May. *Source History: 2 in 1988; 7 in 1992; 3 in 2000.* **Sources: Ga11, Ju2, PI3.**

Star Ruby - Large, attractive, faintly blushed fruit. Extremely dark red flesh. Compact tree. Leaves are extremely sensitive to herbicide damage and low temperatures. Ripens mid-December to February. Originated in Texas. U.S. Plant Patent No. 3222. *Source History: 3 in 1988; 7 in 1992; 6 in 2000.* **Sources: BZN, Ga11, MO10, Or2, Pa2, PL2.**

Guava

Psidium spp.

Arabian - *Source History: 1 in 2000.* **Sources: An4.**

Beaumont - *Psidium guajava. Source History: 3 in 1992; 1 in 2000.* **Sources: Or2.**

Cas (Costa Rican Guava) - *Psidium friedrichsthalianum.* Sulphur yellow fruit to 2.5" long; smaller than the common guava. White flesh. Tart, agreeable flavor. Sometimes used for jellies. Shrub or small tree grows 25' tall. *Source History: 1 in 1988; 2 in 1992; 4 in 2000.* **Sources: Ban, Ga11, Me2, Po7.**

Common Guava (Apple Guava, Yellow Guava) - *Psidium guajava.* Oval to pear-shaped fruit, 1-4" long. Yellow or dark pink flesh with musky flavor. Somewhat tasteless when raw. Good canned, preserved or spiced, for jams, relish, chutney or juice. Shrub or small tree 30' tall with scaly, greenish brown bark. Hardy in Zone 10. *Source History: 1 in 1988; 3 in 1992; 5 in 2000.* **Sources: Al8, Ban, Ga11, Our, Po7, Sh14.**

Detwiler - *Psidium guajava*. *Source History: 1 in 1988; 1 in 1992; 1 in 2000.* **Sources: Pa2.**

Giant Bangkok - *Psidium guajava*. *Source History: 1 in 1992; 1 in 2000.* **Sources: Or2.**

Guayaba Agria - *Psidium acutangulum*. Flavor is a combination of lemon and banana. Very juicy flesh. Guava relative. *Source History: 1 in 2000.* **Sources: Po7.**

Guyana - *Psidium guineense*. Large, red fruit. Slightly acid taste. Evergreen tree to 15'. *Source History: 1 in 1992; 1 in 2000.* **Sources: Ban.**

Hawaiian White - *Source History: 1 in 2000.* **Sources: Pa2.**

Kattuakula - *Source History: 1 in 2000.* **Sources: PL2.**

Lemon Guava - *Psidium littorale* var. *lucidium*. Yellow fruits with mild, sweet, lemon flavor. Withstands temperatures near 20 degrees F. *Source History: 1 in 1988; 1 in 1992; 1 in 2000.* **Sources: Or2.**

Malaysia Magenta - *Psidium guajava*. Purple flesh. *Source History: 1 in 2000.* **Sources: On4.**

Mardi Red Seedling - *Source History: 1 in 2000.* **Sources: Pa2.**

Mexican Cream - *Psidium guajava*. *Source History: 2 in 1992; 2 in 2000.* **Sources: An4, Or2.**

Mexican Yellow - *Source History: 1 in 2000.* **Sources: Me2.**

Ong - *Psidium guajava*. White flesh. *Source History: 1 in 2000.* **Sources: On4.**

Pear Guava - *Psidium guajava* var. *pyriferum*. Pear-shaped fruits. Australian seed. *Source History: 1 in 1988; 3 in 1992; 2 in 2000.* **Sources: Or2, Ro13.**

Pink - *Psidium guajava*. *Source History: 1 in 1992; 1 in 2000.* **Sources: Or2.**

Psidium involucrata - Foliage resembles a giant Cattley guava; 2.5" fruit. Creamy texture. Flavor is between Cattley and subtropical guava. *Source History: 1 in 2000.* **Sources: Po7.**

Purple Strawberry Guava (Cattley Guava, Purple Guava, Red Strawberry Guava) - *Psidium littorale*. Purplish red fruits are 1-1.5" in diameter. Sweet, white flesh. Used for fresh eating, juice or jellies. High in vitamin C. Dense, fast growing, evergreen shrub or tree grows 25' tall. Green, hairless, 3" leaves turn reddish after a few fall frosts. White flowers about 1" across in early summer. Bears in two years. Usually not bothered seriously by pests or diseases in North America. Ripens during summer. Hardy to about 20 degrees F; perhaps lower with trunk protection. Hardy in Zones 9-10. Grows well wherever oranges are grown. Native to Brazil. (**Hud** is offering seed). *Source History: 9 in 1988; 11 in 1992; 10 in 2000.* **Sources: Ca7, Ga11, Hud, Mel, MIS, Or2, Our, Pa2, Ro13, Tr10.**

Red Indian - *Psidium guajava*. *Source History: 1 in 1988; 3 in 1992; 2 in 2000.* **Sources: Or2, Pa2.**

Ruby X Guava - *Psidium guajava*. Yellow skin. Dark pink flesh. Excellent for juice. *Source History: 1 in 1992; 1 in 2000.* **Sources: Ro13.**

Strawberry Guava - *Psidium cattleianum*. Deep claret colored fruits have the flavor and consistency of strawberries. Makes a fine foliage plant for the greenhouse. Native to Brazil. *Source History: 1 in 1992; 5 in 2000.* **Sources: An4, Fi1, Fra, Gur, Tr10.**

Thai - *Psidium guajava*. *Source History: 1 in 2000.* **Sources: Or2.**

Thai Purple - *Psidium guajava*. Purple foliage. Deep purple skin. Light to medium purple flesh. *Source History: 1 in 2000.* **Sources: Ro13.**

Tropical - *Source History: 1 in 2000.* **Sources: Me2.**

Uma - *Psidium guajava. Source History: 1 in 1988; 1 in 1992; 1 in 2000.* **Sources: Pa2.**

Waikea Pink - Commercial acid type. *Source History: 1 in 1992; 1 in 2000.* **Sources: PL2.**

Weber Supreme - *Source History: 1 in 2000.* **Sources: Pa2.**

White - *Psidium guajava.* Low evergreen shrub. Large yellow fruit with creamy white flesh. *Source History: 1 in 1992; 1 in 2000.* **Sources: Ro13.**

White Indian - *Psidium guajava. Source History: 1 in 1988; 2 in 1992; 1 in 2000.* **Sources: Pa2.**

White Indonesian - Sweet white flesh. *Source History: 1 in 1992; 2 in 2000.* **Sources: Pa2, PL2.**

Yellow Strawberry Guava (Yellow Cattley Guava) - *Psidium littorale.* Firm, yellow, sweet flavored fruit; 1-3" in diameter. Superb for fresh eating or jelly making. Large bush or small tree, if uncontrolled. Withstands temperatures of about 25 degrees F. *Source History: 5 in 1988; 7 in 1992; 4 in 2000.* **Sources: Ca7, Ga11, MIS, Pa2.**

Lemon

Citrus limon

Allen Eureka - Medium-small, oblong fruit with short neck and protruding nipple end. Few seeds. High acid flavor. Large, vigorous tree with open spreading growth habit. Cold sensitive. Four to five harvest periods throughout the year. Known more as a coastal lemon. Developed in California. *Source History: 2 in 1992; 1 in 2000.* **Sources: BZN.**

Eureka - Medium size, yellow fruit. Tender, juicy, highly acid flesh is greenish yellow; few seeds. Densely foliated tree is upright, spreading and thornless; open growth habit. Grows to 20' tall and wide. Year round bloom; purple tinted flowers. Highly productive. Zones 9-10. Developed in California. *Source History: 7 in 1988; 8 in 1992; 7 in 2000.* **Sources: Fou, Ga11, HI10, MO10, Pa2, PL2, Tr10.**

Eureka Variegated - Evergreen tree with creamy white and green variegated leaves with a pink tinge to new growth. Produces an abundance of juicy bright yellow market quality lemons year-round. Zones 9-10. *Source History: 2 in 2000.* **Sources: BZN, MO10.**

Frost Lisbon - Typical Lisbon lemon. Consistent producer. Should be avoided in Ventura County due to seive tube necrosis. *Source History: 1 in 1988; 2 in 1992; 1 in 2000.* **Sources: BZN.**

Galgal - Hardy. Originated in India. *Source History: 1 in 1992; 1 in 2000.* **Sources: Sh3.**

Lailuani Sweet - Foliage is splashed with white and green. Fruit looks like small green and white striped watermelons. Good for making pink lemonade. *Source History: 1 in 2000.* **Sources: Ju2.**

Lemon - Grows up to 2'. Evergreen foliage, fragrant white blooms, golden fruit. *Source History: 2 in 1988; 3 in 1992; 3 in 2000.* **Sources: Fi1, Gur, Mel.**

Limco 8-A - *Source History: 1 in 1988; 1 in 1992; 1 in 2000.* **Sources: BZN.**

Limoneira 8A Lisbon - Medium size, round to oblong fruit with smoother texture than Eureka lemons. Very acidic flavor. Few seeds. Trees are more hardy and vigorous than Eureka. Harvest in winter and spring. Originated in Portugal.

Source History: 1 in 1992; 1 in 2000. **Sources: Wi6.**

Lisbon - Fruit practically identical to Eureka. Highly decorative tree; vigorous growth, thorny branches. Spring bloom. More resistant to cold than Eureka. Most hardy, productive and tolerant of the true lemons. Originated in Portugal. *Source History: 4 in 1988; 3 in 1992; 4 in 2000.* **Sources: Fou, MO10, Ty2, Wi6.**

Lisbon Dwarf - Evergreen tree produces fruit year-round in most areas. Grows 8-12' tall and wide. Productive commercial variety. More tolerant of heat, cold and wind. *Source History: 1 in 2000.* **Sources: MO10.**

Lisbon Seedless - Evergreen tree, 30' tall and wide. Produces seedless fruit year-round in most areas. Zones 9-10. *Source History: 1 in 2000.* **Sources: MO10.**

Meyer - Medium size fruit is quite different from other lemons; rounder, thin skinned and more orange colored. Tangy, very juicy, but less acid than others. Slightly sweet when fully ripe. Dwarf tree; stays 6' in a five gallon pot. Glossy green leaves are good for tea; beautiful, fragrant, waxy white flowers. Makes a nice house plant over winter, going outside in summer. Hardiest variety of lemon; can withstand 17 degrees F. *Source History: 7 in 1988; 14 in 1992; 9 in 2000.* **Sources: Ed2, Ga11, Ju2, Lo5, Or2, Our, Sh3, Tr10, Ty2.**

Meyer Improved - Derived from Four Winds Virus Free S3E5 clone. Medium size, juicy lemons almost year-round. Not as tart as Eureka. Grows 8-10 ft. tall and 12 ft. wide outdoors. Prolific, regular bearer. Very winter hardy for citrus; can withstand 18 degrees F. Originated in China. *Source History: 3 in 1988; 7 in 1992; 9 in 2000.* **Sources: BZN, Fou, HI10, Hid, MO10, Pa2, PL2, Rai, Spr.**

Monroe Lisbon - Fruit quality may be slightly less desirable than Frost. Heavy producer. Does well in coastal areas. *Source History: 1 in 1992; 1 in 2000.* **Sources: Wi6.**

Pink Lemonade - *Source History: 1 in 2000.* **Sources: Pa2.**

Pink Variegated - Everbearing tree with variegated green and white foliage. New growth and blooms are tipped in purple. Fruit is green and yellow striped with pink flesh. The only true lemon for pink lemonade. Zones 9-10. *Source History: 1 in 1992; 1 in 2000.* **Sources: Ed2.**

Ponderosa (Nine Pound Lemon) - Huge grapefruit size fruit. Juicy and acidic. Bears fruit year-round; excellent for container culture. Makes great lemonade. *Source History: 3 in 2000.* **Sources: Ed2, Ju2, Ty2.**

Ponderosa Bough - *Source History: 1 in 2000.* **Sources: Ga11.**

Spanish Pink - Green and yellow striped fruit with pink flesh. Beautiful tree with variegated green and white foliage; new growth and blooms tipped in purple. Ever-bearing; good for container growing. The only source for pink lemonade. *Source History: 1 in 1992; 1 in 2000.* **Sources: Our.**

Sungold - Evergreen tree produces green striped fruit. Leaves are yellow and green. Full to partial sun. Zones 9-10. U.S. Plant Patent No. 4828. *Source History: 1 in 1992; 1 in 2000.* **Sources: MO10.**

Sungold Variegated - Patented. *Source History: 1 in 1988; 2 in 1992; 1 in 2000.* **Sources: Pa2.**

Sweet - *Source History: 2 in 1988; 3 in 1992; 1 in 2000.* **Sources: Pa2.**

Tiawanica - *Source History: 1 in 1988; 1 in 2000.* **Sources: Sh3.**

Villa Franca - Fruit characteristics similar to Eureka, but harvested in the winter like the Lisbons. Tree characteristics similar to Lisbon but more open and less up-right. *Source History: 1 in 1992; 1 in 2000.* **Sources: Wi6.**

Lime

Citrus aurantiifolia

<u>Bearss</u> (Bearss Seedless, Tahitian Lime, Persian Lime) - Tahitian type; larger than Mexican lime. Fruit is almost seedless and about the size of a small lemon. Tender, juicy, very acid flesh is greenish yellow. Broad, spreading, drooping, 8-10' tree is nearly thornless. Dense, dark green foliage. Blooms mainly in the spring; some year-round. Highly productive. Good in cool areas; does not require much heat to ripen. Hardy to 28 degrees F. *Source History: 9 in 1988; 19 in 1992; 17 in 2000.* **Sources: BZN, Ed2, Fi1, Fou, Ga11, HI10, Hid, Lo5, MO10, On4, Our, Pa2, PI3, PL2, Rai, Tr10, Ty2.**

<u>Ci Clem No. 9</u> - Golden lime. Very hardy. *Source History: 1 in 2000.* **Sources: Sh3.**

<u>Indonesian</u> (Kieffer) - *Source History: 1 in 1988; 1 in 1992; 1 in 2000.* **Sources: Pa2.**

<u>Lime</u> (Sweet Lime) - Miniature trees thrive indoors in containers; outdoors in Zones 9-10. *Source History: 2 in 1988; 3 in 1992; 2 in 2000.* **Sources: Gur, Mel.**

<u>Mexican</u> (Key Lime, Mexican Everbearing, Mexicanii, Bartender's Lime) - Small to medium-small, green to yellowish green fruit. Tender, very juicy, very acid, seedless, greenish yellow flesh. Spreading, bushy, 8' tree with willowy, small branches. Small, pale green leaves. Spring bloom, but produces some blossoms year-round. Everbearing; ripens year-round. Frost sensitive. Originated in India. *Source History: 5 in 1988; 14 in 1992; 6 in 2000.* **Sources: Ed2, Fou, Lo5, Pa2, PI3, Tr10.**

<u>Mexican, Thornless</u> (Thornless Key Lime, Thornless) - Improved Mexican lime with a more upright branching habit, thornless branches and larger fruit. Evergreen tree grows to 15' tall. Full sun. Grafted on Carrizo Citrange rootstock by **MO10**. Zones 9-11. *Source History: 4 in 2000.* **Sources: Ga11, MO10, Our, Pa2.**

<u>West Indian Key</u> - Persian. *Source History: 1 in 2000.* **Sources: Ga11.**

Loquat

Eriobotrya spp.

<u>Advance</u> - Medium-large, round to pear-shaped fruit. Good flavor. Small tree is a good pollinator. *Source History: 2 in 1988; 3 in 1992; 2 in 2000.* **Sources: Or2, Pa2.**

<u>Big Jim</u> - Large orange fruit. Excellent sweet flavor. Ripens late. *Source History: 2 in 1988; 2 in 2000.* **Sources: On4, Pa2.**

<u>Champagne</u> - Light yellow fruits. White flesh is juicy with a sweet-tart flavor. *Source History: 2 in 1988; 3 in 1992; 2 in 2000.* **Sources: Or2, Pa2.**

<u>Gold Nugget</u> - Grafted *Eriobotrya japonica*. Round fruit with yellow-orange flesh. Good flavor. Vigorous upright growth. Late ripening. *Source History: 2 in 1988; 3 in 1992; 4 in 2000.* **Sources: Ga11, Or2, Pa2, PL2.**

<u>Himalayan Loquat</u> (Juri Kaphal) - Broad leaved evergreen tree to 15' bears apple-like flowers all winter and spring with jasmine-like fragrance. Clusters of 1" red-yellow fruits are borne at the end of the branches. Taste is that of apple, citrus and spice. Native to the mid-Himalaya where light snow and frost may occur. Little written botanical information is noted. Trademarked. *Source History: 1 in*

2000. **Sources: Or2.**

<u>Loquat</u> (Green Loquat, Japanese Medlar, Japanese Plum, Naspoli) - *Eriobotrya japonica.* Loose clusters of fruit that look like round 1-2" yellowish orange apricots. Tastes like an orange-flavored pear; very sweet, mild and aromatic. Tropical-looking evergreen grows 15-25' tall. Large, dark green leaves are leathery on top and fuzzy underneath. Fragrant flowers; blooms very early in the spring. Self-fertile. Easy to keep small; can be container grown. Ripens in early summer. Hardy to 12 degrees F and in Zone 7. Can be grown outside in a sheltered spot as far north as Seattle. *Source History: 11 in 1988; 18 in 1992; 15 in 2000.* **Sources: An4, Ban, BO10, Bu7, Ca7, Co24, Ed2, Fo2, Ju2, MIS, Na13, ORA, Ro13, Ty2, Wo2.**

<u>Loquat, Bronze</u> - *Eriobotrya deflexa.* Small tree with bright coppery colored leaves. Shy bearer of bronze colored fruit with a flavor that is a bit different than the other species. Bears fruit in coastal northern California. Native to Taiwan. *Source History: 2 in 1988; 2 in 1992; 4 in 2000.* **Sources: Ca7, MIS, Ne4, Or2.**

<u>Mammoth</u> - Large sweet fruit. *Source History: 1 in 1992; 1 in 2000.* **Sources: PL2.**

<u>McBeth</u> - *Source History: 1 in 2000.* **Sources: Pa2.**

<u>Strawberry</u> - *Source History: 1 in 1988; 1 in 2000.* **Sources: Po7.**

<u>X-mas</u> - Bears clusters of sweet, bright yellow fruit with pale yellow flesh. Excellent flavor. Ripens around Christmas. *Source History: 1 in 1992; 2 in 2000.* **Sources: Ga11, Ju2.**

Mango

Mangifera indica

<u>Bailey's Marvel</u> - *Source History: 2 in 2000.* **Sources: On4, Pa2.**

<u>Bombay</u> - *Source History: 1 in 2000.* **Sources: Pa2.**

<u>Brooks Late</u> - Ripens September-October. *Source History: 1 in 1992; 1 in 2000.* **Sources: PL2.**

<u>Carrie</u> - *Source History: 3 in 2000.* **Sources: Ga11, On4, Pa2.**

<u>Chuchua</u> - *Source History: 1 in 2000.* **Sources: Pa2.**

<u>Dam Tong</u> - *Source History: 1 in 2000.* **Sources: On4.**

<u>Edgehill</u> - *Source History: 1 in 1988; 2 in 1992; 1 in 2000.* **Sources: Pa2.**

<u>Edwards</u> - *Source History: 1 in 1988; 1 in 1992; 2 in 2000.* **Sources: On4, Pa2.**

<u>Glenn</u> - *Source History: 1 in 1988; 2 in 1992; 1 in 2000.* **Sources: Pa2.**

<u>Golden Nugget</u> - *Source History: 1 in 2000.* **Sources: On4.**

<u>Govea</u> - *Source History: 1 in 2000.* **Sources: PL2.**

<u>Haden</u> - Hawaiian standard. Ripens in June. *Source History: 2 in 1992; 3 in 2000.* **Sources: On4, Pa2, PL2.**

<u>Jakarta</u> - *Source History: 2 in 2000.* **Sources: On4, Pa2.**

<u>Julie</u> - Dwarf. *Source History: 1 in 1988; 3 in 1992; 2 in 2000.* **Sources: Ga11, Pa2.**

<u>Keitt</u> - Anthracnose resistant. Ripens in July. *Source History: 2 in 1988; 5 in 1992; 3 in 2000.* **Sources: On4, Pa2, PL2.**

<u>Kent</u> - *Source History: 1 in 1988; 4 in 1992; 2 in 2000.* **Sources: On4, Pa2.**

<u>Mango</u> - Heart-shaped, 3-5" fruit with tough, thin, smooth skin, juicy pulp and a

large, fibrous seed. Tree can grow 90' tall. Commercially important tropical fruit. Hardy in Zone 10. *Source History: 1 in 1988; 4 in 1992; 5 in 2000.* **Sources: An4, Ca7, Me2, Pl3, Tr10.**

Manilla - *Source History: 2 in 1992; 2 in 2000.* **Sources: On4, Pa2.**

Manzanillo - Similar to Haden with fewer problems. *Source History: 1 in 1992; 1 in 2000.* **Sources: PL2.**

Mapalehu - *Source History: 1 in 2000.* **Sources: PL2.**

Marty - *Source History: 1 in 2000.* **Sources: On4.**

Nam Doc Mi - *Source History: 1 in 2000.* **Sources: On4.**

Okrung - *Source History: 1 in 2000.* **Sources: Ga11.**

Oro - *Source History: 1 in 2000.* **Sources: Pa2.**

Philippine - *Source History: 1 in 2000.* **Sources: Pa2.**

Pin Sen Mann - *Source History: 1 in 2000.* **Sources: On4.**

Pirie - Smooth flavor. Ripens in June. *Source History: 3 in 1992; 1 in 2000.* **Sources: PL2.**

Pope - Smooth flavor. Ripens in July-August. *Source History: 1 in 1992; 1 in 2000.* **Sources: PL2.**

Raposa - Ripens in July. Developed at the University of Hawaii. *Source History: 1 in 1992; 1 in 2000.* **Sources: PL2.**

Tommy Atkins - *Source History: 1 in 1988; 3 in 1992; 1 in 2000.* **Sources: Pl3.**

Valencia Pride - *Source History: 2 in 2000.* **Sources: On4, Pa2.**

Zill Late - Large, colorful fruit. Ripens September-October. *Source History: 1 in 1992; 1 in 2000.* **Sources: PL2.**

Orange

Citrus sinensis

Ambersweet - Rich, sweet flavor makes the best fresh squeezed orange juice. Few seeds. *Source History: 2 in 1992; 1 in 2000.* **Sources: Ju2.**

Atwood Navel - Bud sport of Parent Washington with slightly earlier color. Medium thick, smooth rind. Excellent overall quality. Ripens from November to February. Originated in California. *Source History: 1 in 1988; 2 in 1992; 2 in 2000.* **Sources: BZN, Wi6.**

Autumngold Late Navel - Patented. *Source History: 2 in 2000.* **Sources: BZN, Wi6.**

Beck Earli Navel - U.S. Plant Patent No. 7700. *Source History: 1 in 1988; 1 in 1992; 1 in 2000.* **Sources: BZN.**

Blood Orange - Deep blood-red flesh and juice with raspberry overtones. Originated in the Mediterranean. *Source History: 1 in 1988; 2 in 1992; 1 in 2000.* **Sources: Ju2.**

Blood Orange: Moro - Name comes from the red blotches on its skin and deep blood-red flesh; almost purplish red even in cool areas of northern California. Medium size fruit. Very sweet, highly exotic flavor, with a hint of strawberry or raspberry aftertaste. Vigorous tree produces handsome fruit on clusters on the outside of the tree. Very productive. Early maturing; ripens before Sanguinella in late winter and early spring. Hardy to about 25 degrees F. *Source History: 7 in 1988; 12 in 1992; 7 in 2000.* **Sources: Ed2, Fou, MO10, Or2, Pa2, PL2, Rai.**

Blood Orange: Sanguinella - Oval fruit with beautiful red blush. Flesh and juice are deep blood-red; few seeds. Rich, tart, spicy flavor. Excellent quality. Good keeping quality; holds well on the tree. Ornamental tree has an open growth habit and is almost thornless with dense, long, narrow, light green foliage. Good producer. Hardy to 25 degrees F. Originated in Spain. *Source History: 6 in 1988; 6 in 1992; 3 in 2000.* **Sources: Fou, Or2, Pa2.**

Cara Cara Navel - Very large fruits look like grapefruit on the tree. Deep orange skin; red-pink seedless flesh. Good navel flavor; mild and sweet. Easy to peel. Grows 12-15'. Zone 10. *Source History: 1 in 1992; 4 in 2000.* **Sources: BZN, MO10, Pa2, Wi6.**

Chinotto - Dense dwarf tree with small pointed leaves. Sweetly scented blossoms are followed by tight clusters of medium size tangerines. Juicy and tangy; make great juice. Self-fertile. *Source History: 1 in 2000.* **Sources: Ju2.**

Chislett Late Navel - U.S. Plant Patent No. 8212. *Source History: 2 in 2000.* **Sources: BZN, Wi6.**

Dwarf - Sweet, juicy fruit. Virus free plant. Hardy in Zone 9. *Source History: 1 in 1992; 1 in 2000.* **Sources: Mel.**

Fisher Navel - Parent Washington bud sport. Fruit reaches early juice maturity; very sweet flavor; good quality. Large, vigorous, spreading tree. Ripens from November to February. Hardy to 25 degrees F. Originated in California. *Source History: 3 in 1988; 4 in 1992; 3 in 2000.* **Sources: BZN, Pa2, PL2.**

Fukumoto Navel - *Source History: 2 in 2000.* **Sources: BZN, Wi6.**

Hamlin - Small, thin skinned, easy to peel fruit. Tender, juicy flesh; usually seedless. Used for juice and eating. October to February harvest. Originated in Florida. *Source History: 1 in 1988; 4 in 1992; 2 in 2000.* **Sources: Ga11, PI3.**

Lane Late Navel - Medium to medium-large fruit is not deep orange but is very acceptable. Holds well on the tree into May in cooler areas; flavor may become somewhat insipid if held too long. Medium size tree. Ripens very late season. Zones 9-10. *Source History: 1 in 1988; 3 in 1992; 5 in 2000.* **Sources: BZN, MO10, Pa2, PL2, Wi6.**

Navel (F56-12) - Evergreen foliage. Fragrant white flowers. Produces seedless 3" fruit. *Source History: 1 in 1992; 1 in 2000.* **Sources: Spr.**

Newhall Navel - Large, elongated, deep red-orange fruit. Slightly earlier than Parent Washington. Originated in California. *Source History: 1 in 1992; 1 in 2000.* **Sources: Wi6.**

Otaheite - Four to six bright, full size fruits on a two-year-old tree; more when older. Dwarf tree with glossy, green leaves. Fragrant, orange blossoms. Often used as a tropical container plant in houses. *Source History: 2 in 1988; 4 in 1992; 1 in 2000.* **Sources: Gur.**

Parson Brown - Heavy crops of large sweet juice oranges. Strong trees show good cold tolerance. *Source History: 1 in 2000.* **Sources: Ju2.**

Pineapple - High quality fruit with fine texture and rich, sweet flavor. Good for processing but fruit does not hold well on the tree. Ripens from December to February. From Florida. *Source History: 1 in 1988; 4 in 1992; 2 in 2000.* **Sources: On4, Wi6.**

Powell Late Navel - U.S. Plant Patent No. 6733. *Source History: 2 in 2000.* **Sources: BZN, Wi6.**

Republic of Texas - *Source History: 1 in 2000.* **Sources: Sh3.**

Robertson Navel - Selected from Washington Navel. Fruit is identical, but 2-3 weeks earlier. Fruit grows in tight clusters causing it to become somewhat distorted. Tree grows 8' tall; amazingly productive for a dwarf. Ripens in the winter. Hardy to 25 degrees F. *Source History: 5 in 1988; 6 in 1992; 3 in 2000.* **Sources: Fou, Or2, Pa2.**

Shamouti (Jaffa) - Flavorful fruit with few seeds. Attractive tree. Ripens in the spring. Hardy to 25 degrees F. Originated in Palestine. *Source History: 3 in 1988; 4 in 1992; 2 in 2000.* **Sources: Fou, Pa2.**

Spring Navel - Fruit has good orange color; firm, smooth rind. Holds into June with a sweet flavor and good sugar-acid ratio. Harvests earlier than Lane Late, from December to June. Originated in California. *Source History: 1 in 1992; 1 in 2000.* **Sources: Pa2.**

Summer Navel - Large, flavorful, seedless eating orange; easy to peel and section. Large leaves; ideal for espaliering. Ripens from November to January. Hardy to 25 degrees F. *Source History: 4 in 1988; 2 in 1992; 1 in 2000.* **Sources: Pa2.**

Summergold Late Navel - Patented. *Source History: 2 in 2000.* **Sources: BZN, Wi6.**

Tahitian - Dwarf tree grows 2-3' tall. Will fruit in 2-3 years if given proper care. Grown indoors. *Source History: 1 in 1992; 1 in 2000.* **Sources: Fi1.**

Thomson Navel - *Source History: 1 in 1992; 1 in 2000.* **Sources: BZN.**

Trovita - Believed to be a chance seedling from Parent Washington. Excellent flavor. Heavy producer. Good for cool areas. Ripens in spring. Hardy to 25 degrees F. Introduced by Dr. Frost at the Citrus Experiment Station. *Source History: 3 in 1988; 5 in 1992; 4 in 2000.* **Sources: Fou, MO10, Or2, Pa2.**

Valencia - Standard juice orange for the industry; medium to large, very sweet, yellowish orange fruit. Very juicy flesh, slightly acid; few or no seeds. Fruit stores exceptionally well on the tree; will hang for months, improving in sweetness to acid ratio. Vigorous, 10' tree has dense, upright growth habit; large leaves. Prolific producer. Takes 15 months to mature; ripens from February to May. World's most popular and most widely planted juice orange. Zones 9-10. Origin is unknown. *Source History: 6 in 1988; 11 in 1992; 9 in 2000.* **Sources: Fou, Ga11, HI10, Lo5, MO10, Pa2, PI3, PL2, Ty2.**

Valencia, Campbell - Nucellar budline dating back to 1871. Medium-large, oblong fruit. Excellent juice characteristics. Holds well. Columnar tree is very large, thorny and vigorous. Requires high heat units for best production. Young trees are slow to start producing. Subject to more chimeras than other nucellar budlines. Originated in California. *Source History: 1 in 1988; 2 in 1992; 2 in 2000.* **Sources: BZN, MO10.**

Valencia, Cutter - Overall characteristics are similar to Campbell. Medium-large, oblong, juicy fruit holds well on the tree. Few chimeras. Originated in California. *Source History: 2 in 1992; 1 in 2000.* **Sources: BZN.**

Valencia, Delta - *Source History: 1 in 2000.* **Sources: BZN.**

Valencia, Midknight - Nearly seedless variety with improved flavor, higher juice content and earlier maturity than the standard Valencia. Zones 9-10. *Source History: 1 in 1992; 3 in 2000.* **Sources: BZN, MO10, Pa2.**

Valencia, Olinda - Medium size, round, somewhat flattened fruit. Excellent for packing and shipping. Similar tree characteristics as Campbell and Cutter. Currently the industry favorite. Originated in California. *Source History: 2 in 1988; 2 in 1992; 1 in 2000.* **Sources: BZN.**

<u>Valencia, Rhode Red</u> - *Source History: 1 in 2000.* **Sources: Ga11.**

<u>Valencia, Seedless</u> - Seedless strain of Valencia. Fruit size, quality and season are the same as Valencia; not as productive. Excellent foliage. Ripens from early to mid-summer. *Source History: 2 in 1988; 2 in 1992; 3 in 2000.* **Sources: Fou, Pa2, Wi6.**

<u>Valencia, Variegated</u> - *Source History: 1 in 2000.* **Sources: Pa2.**

<u>Washington Navel</u> - Standard eating orange for the industry. Medium to large fruit. Very sweet, juicy, seedless flesh. Attractive, heavy bearing tree grows 8' tall. Best in warmer zones. Fruit matures in 10 months; ripens from December to February. Hardy to 24 degrees F. Volume seller that originated in California. *Source History: 6 in 1988; 11 in 1992; 8 in 2000.* **Sources: Fou, Ga11, HI10, MO10, On4, Pa2, PL2, Rai.**

<u>Washington Navel, Parent</u> (Old Line) - Deep orange fruit. Juicy, seedless flesh; easy to peel and segment. Rich flavor. Tree has rounded shape, slightly drooping; as wide as it is tall. Dense foliage. Winter and spring bloom. Ripens in the winter. Originated in Brazil. *Source History: 2 in 1988; 2 in 1992; 2 in 2000.* **Sources: BZN, Wi6.**

Papaya
Carica spp.

<u>Babaco</u> (Mountain Papaya) - *Carica pentandra.* Hardiest of the papayas. Fruit is seedless; quite aromatic but does not have the rich flavor of the tropical varieties. Similar to Toronchi but with smaller fruit. Tree grows 6-7' tall; begins bearing in 4-9 months. Self-fertile. Best for container culture. More adapted to cooler subtropical climates. Needs protection in temperatures below 28 degrees F.; shade during hot summers. Originated in the highlands of Ecuador and Columbia. *Source History: 3 in 1988; 5 in 1992; 6 in 2000.* **Sources: Ka3, Me2, On4, Or2, Pa2, Rai.**

<u>Cariflora</u> - *Source History: 1 in 2000.* **Sources: Ga11.**

<u>Chamburros Mountain Papaya</u> - *Carica pubescens.* Similar to Toronchi with smaller, more round fruit with ridges. Seed cavity of the fruit is filled with creamy white pulp which is best eaten fresh. Flavor is peach-lime and papaya with a very appealing aroma. Flesh has a firm chewy texture and is baked, juiced and used in ice cream, pies, jam or preserves. Used as a rootstock to graft Babaco. Hardy to 25 degrees F. Cultivated from Venezuela to Argentina. *Source History: 3 in 1992; 3 in 2000.* **Sources: Ban, Or2, Pa2.**

<u>Dwarf</u> - *Source History: 1 in 1988; 1 in 1992; 1 in 2000.* **Sources: Red.**

<u>Dwarf Zaire</u> - *Source History: 1 in 2000.* **Sources: Ga11.**

<u>Lady Red</u> - Large, sweet, red fleshed fruits. Makes an attractive tropical plant. *Source History: 1 in 2000.* **Sources: Our.**

<u>Mexican</u> - Fruit weighs 2-4 lbs. Yellow-orange pulp is not quite as sweet as Solo, but more hardy and very rich tasting. Needs both male and female to produce. *Source History: 1 in 1988; 2 in 2000.* **Sources: Ban, On4.**

<u>Papaya</u> - *Carica papaya.* Sometimes called Tropical Melon Tree. Fruits attached in clusters just under the canopy of foliage. Short-lived. *Source History: 1 in 1988; 4 in 1992; 2 in 2000.* **Sources: Ban, Na13.**

<u>Red Mountain</u> - Fruit weighs up to 10 lbs. *Source History: 1 in 2000.* **Sources: Ro13.**

<u>Solo</u> - Small, grapefruit size, melon-like fruits. Extremely sweet. Fruits contain

the enzyme papair, which aids digestion. Small, dwarf tree grows 6' or more; slender trunk. Very attractive foliage. Best variety for growing in tubs indoors or in the greenhouse. Everbearing. Tends to be hermaphroditic, bearing male and female flowers on the same plant; does not require separate male plant for cross-pollination. Called "tree melon" because its fruit resembles a good, sweet melon. Sensitive to frost; needs warm temperatures. *Source History: 5 in 1988; 5 in 1992; 3 in 2000.* **Sources: Al8, Ban, On4, Pa2.**

Solo: Hawaiian - Fruit is high in vitamins. *Source History: 1 in 1992; 2 in 2000.* **Sources: Ech, Ro13.**

Solo: Sunrise - Medium size fruit with red-orange, sweet flesh. *Source History: 5 in 1992; 2 in 2000.* **Sources: Ro13, Uni.**

Solo: Sunset - Small fruits weigh about 1 lb. Very sweet, yellow-orange flesh shows more pink than Sunrise. *Source History: 4 in 1992; 2 in 2000.* **Sources: Ban, Uni.**

Solo: Waimanolo - Orange-yellow flesh with sweet flavor. Can produce fruit when only 4-5' tall. *Source History: 4 in 1992; 2 in 2000.* **Sources: Ban, Uni.**

Thai - *Source History: 2 in 2000.* **Sources: On4, Tr10.**

Passionflower

Passiflora spp.

Banana - *Passiflora antioquensis.* Bright cerise-pink flowers. Elongated, yellow fruit for fresh eating or juices. Hardy to 28 degrees F. *Source History: 1 in 1992; 1 in 2000.* **Sources: Al8, Tho.**

Blue Passionflower - *Passiflora caerulea.* Oval, 1.5-2.5" long, yellow to orange fruit; used to flavor beverages. Vigorous, rampant, perennial vine. Five-lobed leaves. Lightly fragrant, 4" flowers with white or pinkish petals; blue corona shading through white to purplish at the center. Tolerant of most soils; easy to grow. Hardy to Zone 8; root hardy to Zones 6 or 7. Temperatures below 20 degrees F. will kill the top of the plant, but it will regrow, flower and fruit the next year. Hardier than *Passiflora edulis.* Native to southern Brazil. *Source History: 4 in 1988; 10 in 1992; 16 in 2000.* **Sources: Co24, Fo2, Fra, Gl3, Gr16, HI10, Hud, Ka3, Lee, Or2, Par, Rai, Sc2, Sh14, Tho, Wo2.**

Bountiful Beauty - *Passiflora edulis.* Stong healthy vines produce many large fruits the size of tangerines. Pleasant citrus flavor. Needs winter protection in northern regions. *Source History: 1 in 2000.* **Sources: HA12.**

Corona de Cristo - *Passiflora foetida* var. *gossypifolia.* White to lavender flowers. Red fruit. Native to Texas and Mexico. *Source History: 1 in 1992; 1 in 2000.* **Sources: Wo2.**

Frederick - *Passiflora edulis. Source History: 2 in 2000.* **Sources: Ka3, On4.**

Giant Granadilla - *Passiflora quadrangularis.* Oval, 8-12" fruit, often three-grooved; thick rind. Pulp and rind are edible. Perennial vine with fragrant flowers. Hardy to 30 degrees F. Widely cultivated in tropical America. *Source History: 3 in 1988; 5 in 1992; 6 in 2000.* **Sources: Ban, Ga11, HI10, Or2, Ro13, Tho.**

Hua-Shan-Guo - *Passiflora sp.* var. *kuangxii.* Translates as Flower Mountain Melon. Small plum size fruits are partially covered by a lacy calyx. Flavor is a sweet mix of banana and apricot. *Source History: 1 in 2000.* **Sources: Or2.**

Maypop (Apricot Vine, Wild Passionflower, Mollypop) - *Passiflora incarnata.* Egg-shaped, 2" yellow fruit; edible when ripe. Orange-yellow pulp with many seeds. Pleasing, tropical, apricot-like flavor. Good for fresh eating, jelly and as a flavorful fruit juice. Hardy, vigorous, perennial, 10-15' vine with three-lobed leaves; spreads by runners. Cream or yellowish, 2" flowers with a purple or pink corona; intricate structure, very showy. Plant two for pollination. Likes average, slightly acid, sandy loam and a sunny location. Hardy to -10 degrees F; survives into Zone 4 under heavy mulch. Native to the eastern and southeastern U.S. Used by the Indians for food and medicine. *Source History: 7 in 1988; 8 in 1992; 14 in 2000.* **Sources: BO10, Ed2, Gl3, Hud, Jun, Ka3, Lo5, Na13, On3, Or2, Tho, Tr10, Tri, Wo2.**

Morita - *Passiflora suberosa.* Tropical vine bears 1" flowers followed by red or black, .5-1" edible fruit. *Source History: 1 in 2000.* **Sources: Hud.**

Passiflora decaisnea - Large flowers are carmine-red with purple and a white banded crown. Produces huge edible fruit. Hardy to 32 degrees F. *Source History: 1 in 2000.* **Sources: Ka3.**

Passiflora Herbertiana - Vines grow to 16'. Produce edible green, 2.75" fruit with fragrant white pulp. Eaten by the aborigines of North Australia. *Source History: 1 in 2000.* **Sources: Hud.**

Passiflora lutea - Very rare, cold hardy native *Passiflora* with the smallest leaves, flowers and fruits. Small, .25" purple berries. *Source History: 1 in 1992; 1 in 2000.* **Sources: Or2.**

Passiflora platyloba - Fragrant purple and white flowers. Fruit has grape-like flavor. Hardy to 32 degrees F. *Source History: 1 in 2000.* **Sources: Ka3.**

Passiflora serratifolia - Fragrant red-purple flowers. Large sweet fruit. Requires a pollinator to produce fruit. *Source History: 1 in 2000.* **Sources: Ka3.**

Passiflora x Decaisneana - *Passiflora alata x P. quadrangularis.* Vigorous, heavy vine produces huge edible fruit when hand pollinated. Bears fragrant 4" flowers from summer into fall. Hardy to Zone 10. *Source History: 1 in 2000.* **Sources: Lo5.**

Pink Banana (Banana Passion Flower) - *Passiflora mollissima.* Edible, 3-4" long, yellow fruit. Extremely fast growing, rampant, evergreen climbing vine. Soft green, three-lobed foliage. Pendant, long-tubed, pink or rose flowers up to 5" long and 3" wide. Prefers light, loamy soil and cool temperatures of about 48 degrees F. Native to the Andes. Hardy in Zone 8. *Source History: 2 in 1988; 6 in 1992; 7 in 2000.* **Sources: Ban, HI10, Hud, Ka3, Or2, Sc2, Tho.**

Purple Granadilla (Passion Fruit) - *Passiflora edulis.* Deep purple, 3" fruits. Orange flesh. Delicious, sweet, aromatic, subacid flavor. Good in beverages and sherbet. Tender, vigorous climber. Glossy, toothed leaves with three deep lobes. White, 2" flowers with a curly, white banded, purple corona. Root hardy to 25 degrees F; needs a greenhouse for best results except in very warm climates. Can be grown in Florida and California. Native to Brazil. *Source History: 8 in 1988; 17 in 1992; 16 in 2000.* **Sources: Al8, Ban, Ca7, Ga11, Gl3, HA12, Hud, Ka3, Lo5, Me2, MIS, Na13, Or2, PL2, Ro13, Sc2, Tr10.**

Purple Granadilla, Black Knight - *Passiflora edulis.* Flowering vines bear tasty, egg-shaped, purple fruit. Purple varieties have the best flavored fruit. Hardy to 30 degrees F. *Source History: 2 in 1988; 1 in 1992; 1 in 2000.* **Sources: Rai.**

Purple Granadilla, Possum Purple - *Passiflora 'edulis.* White and purple frilled flowers. Large, round, red-purple fruit. Self-fertile. *Source History: 1 in 2000.* **Sources: Ka3.**

Red Passionflower - *Passiflora coccinea.* Large red flowers followed by edible fruit. Hardy in Zones 9-10. *Source History: 2 in 1992; 2 in 2000.* **Sources: Lo5, Tr10.**

Red Sunset - *Passiflora edulis.* White and purple frilled flowers. Large, deep red fruit. *Source History: 1 in 2000.* **Sources: Ka3.**

Ruby Glow (Showy Granadilla) - *Passiflora alata.* Delicious 5" yellow fruits borne on a free blooming plant with tropical looking 6" oval glossy green leaves. Not bothered by pests. Requires pollination. Hardy to 25 degrees F. Native to eastern Brazil and northeastern Peru. *Source History: 1 in 1992; 2 in 2000.* **Sources: Ho8, Ka3.**

Scarlet Flame - *Passiflora vitifolia.* Egg shaped fruit with green and white stripes with the flavor of strawberries. Brilliant scarlet passionflowers are produced all year. Requires pollination. Grows well in southern California. Hardy to 32 degrees F. Native from Nicaragua to Venezuela and Peru. *Source History: 1 in 1992; 1 in 2000.* **Sources: Ka3.**

Shannon - *Passiflora alata.* Showy large scarlet flowers. Produces large edible fruit. Hardy to 32 degrees F. *Source History: 1 in 2000.* **Sources: Ka3.**

Sweet Granadilla - *Passiflora ligularis.* Sweet, yellow to purplish fruits. Excellent flavor. Vining plant to 14' with broadly ovate leaves to 6". Prefers moderate summer temperatures. Hardy to 32 degrees F. *Source History: 1 in 1992; 4 in 2000.* **Sources: Ban, Ka3, Ro13, Tho.**

Tiger - *Passiflora pfordtii.* Vigorous vine with beautiful flowers. Can produce sweet fruit. *Source History: 1 in 2000.* **Sources: Al8.**

White Passionflower - *Passiflora incarnata alba.* Rare, white form. Herbaceous. Hardy in Zone 6. *Source History: 2 in 1988; 2 in 1992; 1 in 2000.* **Sources: Wo2.**

Winged Stem - *Passiflora alata.* Attractive 4" flowers with sweet fragrance from spring to autumn. Produces edible fruit. Popular in Brazilian markets. *Source History: 1 in 2000.* **Sources: Tho.**

Yellow Passionfruit - *Passiflora edulis flavicarpa.* Edible yellow fruit. Most often used as an understock. Tolerates coolness better than most. *Source History: 1 in 2000.* **Sources: Ban.**

Yellow Passionfruit, Lilikoi - *Passiflora edulis flavircarpa.* Large yellow fruit. Tart flavor. Vigorous vine to 30'. Valued for its high vitamin C content. Hawaiian commercial variety. *Source History: 3 in 1992; 4 in 2000.* **Sources: Hud, Pa2, Ro13, Tr10.**

Yellow Passionfruit, McCain - *Passiflora flavicarpa.* Yellow fruit is more tart than *P. edulis* and has larger fruit. Self-fertile. *Source History: 1 in 2000.* **Sources: Ka3.**

Yellow Seedlings - *Passiflora spp.* Flowering vines which also bear tasty, egg-shaped fruit. Yellow variety is used for juice. Hardy to 30 degrees F. *Source History: 1 in 1988; 1 in 1992; 1 in 2000.* **Sources: Ech.**

Pepino
Solanum muricatum

Pepino dulce - Ornamental, shrubby plant with small oval leaves bears smooth, egg-shaped fruit with cream-yellow skin striped with purple. Sweet, mild taste. Originated in the Andes. *Source History: 1 in 1992; 2 in 2000.* **Sources: Al8, Me2.**

Rio Bamba - Purple stemmed plant with 3" dark green leaves. Purple striped oval, 4-6" fruits ripen from light green to yellow. Nearly seedless flesh. Tastes like a blend of melon, banana, peach and pear. Hand-pollination recommended for maximum fruit production. Hardy to 25 degrees F. Named for the area of Ecuador from which it originated. *Source History: 1 in 1988; 3 in 1992; 2 in 2000.* **Sources: Ka3, Or2.**

Temptation - *Source History: 2 in 1988; 2 in 1992; 1 in 2000.* **Sources: Or2.**

Toma - *Source History: 2 in 1988; 2 in 1992; 1 in 2000.* **Sources: Or2.**

Vista - Nearly seedless, juicy flesh with flavor tasting like a blend of melons, bananas, peaches and pears. Green stemmed plant. Hardy to 25 degrees F. *Source History: 1 in 1988; 1 in 1992; 1 in 2000.* **Sources: Ka3.**

Pineapple Guava
Feijoa sellowiana

Beechwood - Minimum temperature tolerance of 15 degrees F. *Source History: 1 in 1988; 1 in 1992; 1 in 2000.* **Sources: Pa2.**

Coolidge - Produces silvery green, 1-4" fruits in the fall. Resembles guava in appearance, but has a sweet pineapple-like flavor when soft ripe. Beautiful evergreen shrub grows 15-20' tall and 15' wide, or prune to any shape. Leaves are dark bluish green with silvery cast underneath. Flowers are striking crimson red with pink petals; sweet cinnamon taste is a wonderful addition to salads. Usually blooms the first season. Moderate annual yields. Self-fruitful. Grows well in all soils. No chilling requirement. Hardy to 12-18 degrees F. Developed in California. *Source History: 5 in 1988; 6 in 1992; 4 in 2000.* **Sources: On3, Or2, Pa2, Rai.**

Nazemetz - Produces 1-4" fruits in the fall. Pineapple-like flavor. Evergreen shrub grows 15' tall by 15' wide. Bluish green leaves. Self-fruitful; bears best if planted with a pollinator. No chilling requirement. Hardy to 18 degrees F. *Source History: 4 in 1988; 6 in 1992; 3 in 2000.* **Sources: Ju2, Or2, Pa2.**

Pineapple Guava - Soft, 2-4" long, dull green fruits; pear-like texture. Flavor blends pineapple, strawberry and banana. Good for fresh eating, cooking, jams and jelly. Best after drop to ground. Dense, fast growing, 10-18' evergreen shrub or tree. Oval leaves; glossy dark green on top, silver and fuzzy on bottom. June flowers have thick, edible, aromatic, flavorful petals; purplish inside, white outside. Dark red stamens protrude like fuchsias. Bears young. Plant two for pollination. Prefers light soil. Tolerates salt spray. Easy culture; good greenhouse specimen. Ripens in late summer. Hardy to 7 degrees F. *Source History: 13 in 1988; 16 in 1992; 16 in 2000.* **Sources: Ca7, Co24, Fo2, Ga11, Gr16, Gur, HI10, Hud, Mel, MIS, MO10, On3, Or2, ORA, Sc2, Wo2.**

Premier - *Source History: 1 in 2000.* **Sources: Pa2.**

Trask - Large round fruit with very good flavor. Requires pollination. *Source History: 2 in 1988; 5 in 1992; 3 in 2000.* **Sources: Ju2, Or2, Pa2.**

Pomegranate
Punica granatum

Balegal - Sweet fruited cultivar is creamy white with pink blush. Light pink seeds. Mild and sweet. Hardy in Zones 7-10. Originated in California. *Source History: 3 in 1992; 1 in 2000.* **Sources: Ju2.**

California Sunset (Madame Legrelle) - Medium size shrub with double coral-red flowers variegated with white. Native to Europe and Asia. Zones 8-9. *Source History: 1 in 2000.* **Sources: Wo2.**

Dwarf - *Punica granatum cv. Nana.* Small, rounded, reddish orange fruit. Deciduous shrub grows 3-4' tall and 2' wide; narrow leaves. Produces many 2" funnel-shaped, orangish scarlet flowers in late summer. Very attractive garden or container plant; also good for bonsai. Hardy to 12 degrees F. Grows well in Zones 7-10. *Source History: 6 in 1988; 13 in 1992; 19 in 2000.* **Sources: Ca7, Ed2, Fo2, Fra, Gl3, Gr16, Gur, HI10, Hud, Lo5, Mel, MIS, MO10, Par, Rai, Sh14, Sh3, Ty2, Wo2.**

Eve - *Source History: 1 in 2000.* **Sources: Sh3.**

Fleishmann - Sweet fruited cultivar. Self-fruitful. Hardy to 15 degrees F. Bred by horticulturist, Paul Thomson. *Source History: 1 in 1988; 4 in 1992; 2 in 2000:* **Sources: Ju2, On4.**

Grenada - Bud sport of Wonderful, which it resembles in tree form. Fruit is a darker color and less tart. Can be shaped to a bush or tree form. Ripens 30 days before Wonderful. Requires 150-200 hours of chilling. Hardy in Zones 7-10. U.S. Plant Patent No. 2618. *Source History: 2 in 1988; 4 in 1992; 4 in 2000.* **Sources: Bay, CO5, Or2, Sh3.**

Indian Apple - *Punica granatum.* Delicious fruit. Deciduous tree or shrub to 5'. Lustrous, narrow leaves. Showy orange flowers. Blossoms sometimes when 12" tall. Likes sun, warmth and semi-dry conditions; will take great heat. Young plants freeze to the ground at 15 degrees F unless against a south wall. *Source History: 4 in 1988; 2 in 1992; 2 in 2000.* **Sources: Ban, Ga11.**

King - Medium size light red fruit with rich sweet flesh. Strong grower. *Source History: 2 in 1992; 1 in 2000.* **Sources: Ju2.**

Malcolm's Extra Sweet - Hardy to Zone 8. *Source History: 1 in 1992; 1 in 2000.* **Sources: Hid.**

Nochi Shibari - Double dark red-orange flowers. Native to Europe and Asia. Zones 8-10. *Source History: 1 in 2000.* **Sources: Wo2.**

North Carolina Seedling - *Source History: 1 in 2000.* **Sources: Sh3.**

Plantation Sweet - Original tree was found growing on a Georgia plantation. Believed to be over 100 years old, measures more than one foot in diameter and is more than 15' tall. Hardy in Zones 7-10. *Source History: 1 in 1992; 1 in 2000.* **Sources: Ty2.**

Purple - Medium size, red fruit. Deep purple-crimson flesh. Tart flavor. Can be sweetened and diluted with water for a drink. *Source History: 1 in 1992; 1 in 2000.* **Sources: Hud.**

Russian Dwarf - Has survived 12 degrees F. No fruit yet. *Source History: 1 in 2000.* **Sources: Hid.**

Sweet - Fruit remains slightly greenish with red blush in sunny exposure even when ripe; much sweeter than other varieties. Highly ornamental plant. Bears heavily, even when young. Self-fruitful. Adapted to all well drained, warm sites. Requires 100-200 hours of chilling. Hardy in Zones 7-10. *Source History: 3 in 1988; 7 in 1992; 11 in 2000.* **Sources: Bay, CO5, Ed2, On4, Or2, ORA, Pa2, Pe2, Son, STR, WI4.**

Toyosho - Grows to 12'. Double peach or apricot flowers. Hardy in Zones 8-10. *Source History: 1 in 2000.* **Sources: Wo2.**

Utah Sweet - Hardy to 15 degrees F. *Source History: 1 in 1988; 1 in 1992; 1 in 2000.* **Sources: Pa2.**

White - Large pink fruit. Non-staining, white transparent flesh. Sweet and juicy when ripe. Bush grows to 12'. Orange-red flowers. Self-fruitful. Ripens in early September. Requires 150-200 hours of chilling. *Source History: 2 in 2000.* **Sources: Bay, CO5.**

Wonderful - Best, largest, most highly colored cultivar. Glossy, greenish red to reddish orange fruit the size of a large orange. Rich, crimson heart. Delicious, tangy flavor. Finest quality. Main ingredient of grenadine syrup. Deciduous, very ornamental, somewhat spiny plant quickly grows 12 x 12'; prune to tree or bush. Small, glossy leaves. Gaudy 3" orangish red, double flowers; up to three sets yearly. Self-fertile, fruit set is increased by planting two or more. No pests or diseases; adapts to most soils. Lives up to 200 years. Ripens during October. Killed to ground level below 10 degrees F. 150 hours of chilling. Zones 7-10. *Source History: 17 in 1988; 26 in 1992; 22 in 2000.* **Sources: Bay, Co24, CO5, Fo2, HI10, Iso, MI5, MO10, On3, Or2, ORA, Pa2, Par, Rai, Sh3, SIM, Son, STR, Tri, Ty2, WI4, Wom.**

Wonderful, Early - Distinct variety. Large, red fruit with thin skin. Delicious flavor. Medium size tree. Late blooming with large, fertile, orangish red flowers. Ripens about 14 days before Wonderful. U.S. Plant Patent No. 3520. *Source History: 1 in 1988; 1 in 1992; 1 in 2000.* **Sources: ORA.**

Yellow Flowered - Grows 12' tall. Hardy in Zones 7-10. *Source History: 1 in 1988; 1 in 1992; 1 in 2000.* **Sources: Wo2.**

Sapote / White

Casimiroa edulis

Bravo - *Source History: 1 in 1988; 1 in 1992; 1 in 2000.* **Sources: Pa2.**

Densler - *Source History: 1 in 2000.* **Sources: PL2.**

Lemon Gold - *Source History: 1 in 1988; 1 in 1992; 2 in 2000.* **Sources: Or2, Pa2.**

Louise - *Source History: 1 in 1988; 1 in 1992; 1 in 2000.* **Sources: Pa2.**

Malibu - *Source History: 1 in 1988; 1 in 2000.* **Sources: PL2.**

McDill - Round, flavorful fruit. Early ripening. Hardy to 25 degrees F. *Source History: 3 in 1988; 2 in 1992; 2 in 2000.* **Sources: Or2, Pa2.**

Suebelle - Yellow, 3" fruits with rich, sweet, creamy flesh. Considered by many to be the finest flavored White Sapote. Not a good keeper. Bears over a long season. Ideal for backyard growing. *Source History: 3 in 1988; 3 in 1992; 3 in 2000.* **Sources: Or2, Pa2, PL2.**

White Sapote (Mexican Apple, Zapote Blanco) - Yellowish green fruit, 3-4" across; somewhat resembles a yellow apple. Soft, very sweet, cream colored pulp. Fast growing tropical fruit tree grows 50' tall; shiny, green leaves. Grows in Mexico and Central America above 3,000' and in subtropical areas of Florida and California; Zone 9. *Source History: 2 in 1988; 3 in 1992; 6 in 2000.* **Sources: An4, Ga11, Me2, Na13, Po7, Tr10.**

Wooly Leaf - *Source History: 1 in 2000.* **Sources: Ga11.**

Sapote / Other

Abiu - *Pouteria caimito.* Best true sapote. *Source History: 1 in 1992; 2 in 2000.* **Sources: Na13, PL2.**

Black Sapote (Black Persimmon, Chocolate Pudding Fruit) - *Diospyros digyna.* Oblong, 4" fruit ripens from olive green to nearly black. Very soft, chocolate-brown flesh, when eaten with sugar and spices is said to resemble a chocolate dessert. Tree grows to 60' tall. Attractive foliage. Related to the persimmon. Popular in Mexico. Tender to frost; hardy in Zone 10. *Source History: 4 in 1988; 6 in 1992; 8 in 2000.* **Sources: An4, Ga11, Me2, Na13, Pa2, PL2, Po7, Tr10.**

Canistel (Yellow Sapote, Eggfruit) - *Pouteria campechiana.* Large, yellow fruit with a dry texture like that of a hard boiled egg yolk. Can be eaten fresh or used in cooking. Large, fast growing tree with pointed leaves bears fruit in late summer, early fall. Hardy to 28 degrees F. *Source History: 2 in 1992; 5 in 2000.* **Sources: An4, Me2, Our, Po7, Ro13.**

Chico Sapote (Sapodilla) - *Archras sapota.* Hard skinned, round fruit. Flesh has refreshing flavor. Tree can reach a height of over 30' under proper conditions. Slow grower; sensitive to frost. Good ornamental qualities. This is the plant from which chicle is extracted for use in chewing gum. *Source History: 1 in 1988; 1 in 1992; 1 in 2000.* **Sources: Me2.**

Cinnamon Apple - *Pouteria hypoglauca. Source History: 1 in 1992; 1 in 2000.* **Sources: Ga11.**

Egg Fruit (Canistel) - *Pouteria campechiana.* Pear-shaped 4" yellow fruit. Very sweet, musky flavor. Grows 50' tall. Grown as a garden tree in Cuba, Mexico and other Caribbean countries as well as southern Florida. Hardy in Zone 10b. *Source History: 1 in 1988; 1 in 1992; 2 in 2000.* **Sources: Ga11, Na13.**

Green Sapote - *Pouteria viride. Source History: 2 in 1988; 1 in 1992; 2 in 2000.* **Sources: Ga11, Tr10.**

Lucuma (Ecuadorian Mountain Sapote) - *Pouteria obovata.* Small tree bears sweet yellow fruit. Translucent flesh with butterscotch/caramel flavor. *Source History: 1 in 1992; 1 in 2000.* **Sources: Ro13.**

Mamey Sapote (Mamey Colorado, Mammee Sapote, Marmalade Fruit, Marmalade Plum, Sapota) - *Pouteria sapota.* Oval fruit grows 8" long with roughened, russet brown skin. Very sweet, reddish flesh; one large, brown seed. Eaten fresh or made into thick preserves. Tree grows 90' tall. Hardy to 28 degrees F. Native to lowland areas of the Caribbean. *Source History: 2 in 1988; 5 in 1992; 7 in 2000.* **Sources: Ca7, Ga11, Me2, On4, Pa2, PI3, Tr10.**

Tangerine
Citrus reticulata

Algerian - *Source History: 1 in 2000.* **Sources: On4.**

Batanges - *Source History: 1 in 1988; 1 in 2000.* **Sources: Wi6.**

Caffin - *Source History: 1 in 2000.* **Sources: BZN.**

Calamondrin - Fruit is vertically striped with pale yellow and green and matures to a pale yellow. Holds well on the tree. Evergreen. Full sun. Grows 10-15'.

Zones 9-11. *Source History: 1 in 1992; 2 in 2000.* **Sources: MO10, Wo2.**

Changsha - Sweet, juicy fruit resembles Satsuma except it has more seeds and a lower acid content. Self-fertile. Very early ripening. Probably the most cold hardy mandarin known; has withstood 4 degrees F. Excellent for container growing. *Source History: 1 in 1988; 4 in 1992; 3 in 2000.* **Sources: Ju2, Or2, Sh3.**

Clem Yuzu-2-2 - Hardy to 10 degrees F. *Source History: 1 in 2000.* **Sources: Sh3.**

Clem Yuzu-3-3 - Hardy to 10 degrees F. *Source History: 1 in 2000.* **Sources: Sh3.**

Clementine (Algerian Tangerine, Clementine Algerian) - Medium size, easy to peel, sweet, delicious fruit with few seeds. Excellent quality. Hangs on the tree for months. Tree grows 8' tall. Needs a pollinator such as Marrs, Orlando Tangelo or Valencia for best production. Increasing in popularity. Ripens about one month after Satsuma from October to December. Zones 9-10. *Source History: 6 in 1988; 8 in 1992; 9 in 2000.* **Sources: BZN, Fou, Ju2, MO10, Pa2, PL2, Rai, Tr10, Wi6.**

Clemenules Mandarin - *Source History: 1 in 2000.* **Sources: Wi6.**

Daisy - *Source History: 1 in 1988; 1 in 1992; 1 in 2000.* **Sources: Pa2.**

Dancy - Best known Mandarin type. Small, deep orangish red fruit with thin, loose skin. Juicy, tender, deep orange flesh with some seeds. Extremely flavorful; rich and sprightly. Dwarf, upright, erect, branching tree with moderately dense, narrow, bright green leaves. Grows to 12' tall and wide. Productive. Spring bloom. Makes an excellent container specimen. Ripens in late winter. Zones 9-10. Originated in Morocco. *Source History: 9 in 1988; 19 in 1992; 11 in 2000.* **Sources: Fa1, Fi1, Fou, Gur, Mel, MO10, Or2, Pa2, PI3, PL2, Wi6.**

Encore - *Source History: 2 in 1988; 1 in 1992; 1 in 2000.* **Sources: Pa2.**

Fairchild - Clementine x Orlando. Deep-orange, medium-thin skin. Peels somewhat poorly. Good for juice. Matures early like Clementine. Pollinate with Dancy, Clementine, Kinnow and Temple. *Source History: 2 in 1992; 1 in 2000.* **Sources: BZN.**

Fina Sodea - *Source History: 1 in 2000.* **Sources: BZN.**

Fremont - Clementine x Ponkan. Bright, reddish orange fruit. Tender, juicy flesh. Somewhat seedy. Rich, sprightly flavor. Heavy bearing. Ripens in the winter. *Source History: 2 in 1988; 4 in 1992; 2 in 2000.* **Sources: Fou, PL2.**

Honey - King x Willowleaf. Very small fruit with very sweet flavor. *Source History: 1 in 1988; 4 in 1992; 3 in 2000.* **Sources: On4, Pa2, PL2.**

Kara - King x Owari Satsuma. Medium large fruit. Good flavor when fully mature. Fruit will become pithy and puffy if left on the tree. Tree more open than Kinnow. Grows to 12' tall and wide. Good for backyard plantings. Ripens from March to June. Zones 9-10. Another Dr. Frost hybrid. *Source History: 4 in 1988; 7 in 1992; 5 in 2000.* **Sources: Fou, Mel, MO10, Pa2, Wi6.**

Keraji - Mandarin. *Source History: 2 in 2000.* **Sources: Or2, Sh3.**

Kinnow - King x Willowleaf. Medium size fruit. Rich, aromatic flavor. Very seedy. Tendency to alternate bearing. Keeps for months on the tree. Densely foliated. Ripens from January to May. Developed by Dr. Frost. *Source History: 3 in 1988; 5 in 1992; 3 in 2000.* **Sources: Fou, Or2, Pa2.**

Lee - *Source History: 1 in 1988; 3 in 1992; 2 in 2000.* **Sources: On4, Pa2.**

Marisol Mandarin - *Source History: 1 in 2000.* **Sources: Wi6.**

Murcott (Honey) - Tender, orange, juicy flesh with rich tangerine flavor. Ripens in spring. Good for backyard. *Source History: 2 in 1992; 1 in 2000.* **Sources: Fou.**

Nova - Clementine x Orlando. Very similar to Orlando tangelo. Yellow-orange fruit with thin skin. Peels easily. Good flavor. Pollinate with Dancy, Clementine, Kinnow and Temple. *Source History: 1 in 1992; 1 in 2000.* **Sources: BZN.**

Page - Rich, sweet fruit; too small and soft for shipping. Pollinate with Orlando Tangelo. *Source History: 1 in 1988; 3 in 1992; 4 in 2000.* **Sources: BZN, Ju2, On4, Pa2.**

Pixie - King x Dancy. Good for backyard use. *Source History: 1 in 1988; 3 in 1992; 2 in 2000.* **Sources: On4, Pa2.**

Ponkan - Asian variety. Sweet flavor. Ripens early; holds well on the tree. Does best in tropical areas. *Source History: 1 in 1988; 3 in 1992; 4 in 2000.* **Sources: Ju2, Sh3, Tr10, Wi6.**

Rangpur - Small, loose skinned, deep orange fruit. Bushy, strongly branched tree. Fragrant, purple-tinged, winter blossoms; some year-round. Fruit ripens year-round with peak crop in winter. Hardy to 20 degrees F. Originated in India. *Source History: 4 in 1988; 2 in 1992; 1 in 2000.* **Sources: Fou.**

Satsuma Orange - Orange rind is loose and bumpy; peels easily. Flesh is melting, tender and seedless. Rich flavor. Small, slow growing tree has wide, spreading habit and large, dark green leaves. Fragrant, white flowers. Blooms in the spring. Ripens in the winter. Hardy. Originated in Ikiriki, Japan. *Source History: 2 in 1988; 10 in 1992; 9 in 2000.* **Sources: BZN, Ed2, Ga11, Ju2, On4, PL2, Sh3, Ty2, Wi6.**

Satsuma, Owari - Medium to large fruit with loose, easy to peel skin; almost seedless. Mild, juicy flesh. Does not keep on the tree, but stores well in the refrigerator. Tree grows 6-12' tall. Fruit ripens in the winter. Among the hardiest citrus; hardy to 20 degrees F. *Source History: 2 in 1988; 5 in 1992; 3 in 2000.* **Sources: MO10, Or2, Pa2.**

Satsuma, Owari (Strain A) (Dr. Frost's Nucellar Strain A, Nucellar Strain A) - Seedless. Ripens extremely early from November to December. *Source History: 1 in 1988; 2 in 1992; 1 in 2000.* **Sources: Fou.**

Shekwasha - Small, flattened fruit. Originated in Taiwan. *Source History: 1 in 1988; 1 in 1992; 1 in 2000.* **Sources: Wi6.**

Summertime - *Source History: 1 in 1988; 1 in 1992; 1 in 2000.* **Sources: Pa2.**

Sunburst - *Source History: 3 in 1992; 1 in 2000.* **Sources: Ga11.**

W. Murcott - *Source History: 1 in 2000.* **Sources: BZN.**

Willowleaf - Mediterranean mandarin. For backyard use only. *Source History: 1 in 1988; 1 in 1992; 1 in 2000.* **Sources: Wi6.**

Hops

Humulus spp.

Bianca - Golden yellow vine grows to 18'. *Source History: 1 in 2000.* **Sources: Sha.**

Bullion - English bittering hop; 7-8% bitterness. Good yielding. *Source History: 1 in 1992; 1 in 2000.* **Sources: Fr4.**

Cascade - Fuggles x Serebrianka. Ornamental type with variegated leaves. Excellent taste. Adds flavor and aroma to light lagers; 4-6% bitterness. Hardy in Zone 3-8. Bred at Oregon State University. *Source History: 4 in 1992; 3 in 2000.* **Sources: Ed2, Fr4, Mi1.**

Fuggle - Mild, spicy aroma. Ancestor of many modern varieties. 4-5% bitterness. Found in England in the mid-1800s in the backyard of Richard Suggles. *Source History: 2 in 2000.* **Sources: Fr4, Ni1.**

Hops - Twining vine grows up to 20-30' and dies back to the ground in the fall. Hops are papery aromatic cone-like strobiles that are used extensively in the brewing industry. Tolerates shade. Adapts to most well drained soils. No serious pests or diseases. Hardy to Zone 3. Native to Eurasia. *Source History: 6 in 1992; 7 in 2000.* **Sources: Fed, Fi1, GR26, Gur, LI7, Mel, We4.**

Kent Golding - English aroma type. Moderate yields. 4-6% bitterness. *Source History: 1 in 2000.* **Sources: Fr4.**

Liberty - Hallertauer triploid cross. German lager type with pleasant aroma; 4-5% bitterness. More vigorous and disease resistant. Developed in Corvallis, Oregon at the OSU Hop Research Station. *Source History: 2 in 2000.* **Sources: Fr4, Ni1.**

Mt. Hood - Hallertauer hybrid; 4-6% bitterness. Good yielding. More vigorous and disease resistant. *Source History: 1 in 1992; 1 in 2000.* **Sources: Fr4.**

Nugget - Most popular high alpha variety in the U.S. Vigorous producer of large hop cones that ripen late summer. High bittering: 12-15%. Shows moderate resistance to downy mildew. *Source History: 2 in 1992; 4 in 2000.* **Sources: Fed, Fr4, Ni1, Sha.**

Perle - All-purpose German type; 7-8% bitterness. *Source History: 1 in 1992; 1 in 2000.* **Sources: Fr4.**

Saaz - Czech aroma type; 3-4% bitterness. Difficult to grow. Low yields. *Source History: 1 in 2000.* **Sources: Fr4.**

Santiam - Spicy German Tettnanger hybrid with 5-7% bitterness. Moderate yields. *Source History: 1 in 2000.* **Sources: Fr4.**

Sunbeam Golden - Brilliant yellow foliage. Aromatic cones are suitable for Northern European type pilsners. Released by USDA and Northwest Agricultural Experiment Stations in 1995. *Source History: 1 in 2000.* **Sources: Ni1.**

Willamette - Improved Fuggle type with higher yields; 4-6% bitterness. Good finishing hop for brewing English ales and stout; disease resistant. Ripens late summer. Introduced in 1976. *Source History: 2 in 1992; 3 in 2000.* **Sources: Fed, Fr4, Ni1.**

Rhubarb

Rheum rhabarbarum

Canada Red (Canadian Red) - Large, sweet, juicy stalks are cherry-red throughout. Keeps its color when cooked. Tender; no need to peel. High in sugar. Produces into summer. Hardy to Zone 3. *Source History: 8 in 1988; 24 in 1992; 16 in 2000.* **Sources: BA14, Bea, Bo5, BU12, Co12, CR6, DAI, Fa1, Ga6, In5, Jun, Led, Mc3, RAM, SH8, Stl.**

Canada Red, Chipman's - Perennial. Large stalks and leaf ribs cherry-red from top to bottom. Does not lose color when cooked. Hardy, vigorous grower. Very sweet and productive. Usually does not seed. *Source History: 5 in 1988; 6 in 1992; 5 in 2000.* **Sources: Be4, Fi1, Gur, Mo8, Rid.**

Cherry Red - Large, juicy, tender, sweet stalks are red inside and out. Heavy producer. Holds quality all season. Developed by Mr. Simonet, Alberta plant breeder. *Source History: 1 in 1988; 5 in 1992; 1 in 2000.* **Sources: Gur.**

Crimson Red (Crimson Cherry Red) - Perennial. Fleshy but not tough or stringy; sweet yet agreeably tart. Plump stalks to 24". Heavy yields. Very winter hardy and drought resistant. Produces for years. Hardy to Zone 3. *Source History: 4 in 1988; 7 in 1992; 6 in 2000.* **Sources: Coo, Fi1, Gur, Pe2, SH8, Wbn.**

Glaskin's Perpetual - Delicious stalks can be cut first year of sowing. Low in oxalic acid. Grow in rich well-drained loamy soil. *Source History: 1 in 1988; 1 in 1992; 1 in 2000.* **Sources: Bou.**

Green Victoria - The standard for rhubarb. The upright growing stalks are thick and tender with good old fashioned zingy flavor. Reliable production after three years. *Source History: 1 in 2000.* **Sources: In5.**

MacDonald Strain - Large, tender stalks. Leaves not edible. Excellent production for commercial growers and home gardeners. Shows resistance to root rot problems. Developed at MacDonald College, Quebec, Canada. Native to Russia. *Source History: 2 in 1988; 5 in 1992; 6 in 2000.* **Sources: Bu2, Fed, Nou, Pin, Stl, Wh4.**

Queen Victoria - Hardy perennial. Tasty, tart red stalks. Good for jelly, jam and pies. *Source History: 1 in 1988; 1 in 2000.* **Sources: Roh.**

Red Rhubarb - Full shapely leaves. Tall, thick stalks up to 2' long. Blush-red throughout. Tender, juicy flesh. Rich in natural sugars. Drought resistant. Extremely winter hardy. Heavy yields. *Source History: 2 in 1992; 4 in 2000.* **Sources: Bu1, Fo4, Gr16, Int.**

Starkrimson (K-1 Cultivar) - Sweeter flavor and less acidity than others. Zones 4-9. U.S. Plant Patent No. 4575. Stark Brothers Nursery exclusive. *Source History: 1 in 1992; 1 in 2000.* **Sources: St4.**

Tilden Strain - Selected for fine red color and thick stalks. Heavy feeder; requires annual or biennial feeding and well-drained soil. Leaves not edible. Hardy to Zone 3. Native to northern Asia. *Source History: 2 in 1992; 2 in 2000.* **Sources: Fed, Nou.**

Valentine (Valentine Red) - Perennial. Deep red flesh; 18-20" stalks are 1-1.5 x 1" thick. Very sweet; high quality. Free of seed stalks. Used for pies or stewed. Best of 25 varieties in Canadian tests. *Source History: 6 in 1988; 19 in 1992; 13 in 2000.* **Sources: Bo5, Bu2, Co12, DAI, Fi1, Gur, HA12, Jun, Mel, Mi1, RAM, Stl, Wor.**

<u>Victoria</u> (Giant Victoria, Large Victoria, Victoria Strawberry, Victoria Cherry) - Perennial. Standard main crop variety with broad crimson stalks that shade slightly to crimson inside. Thick and tender. Tart flavor. Average quality. Vigorous upright grower; reliably hardy. Heavy commercial producer. Used mainly for pie filling. *Source History: 30 in 1988; 32 in 1992; 14 in 2000.* **Sources: Bay, BU12, Clo, CO5, Ed2, Fi1, La3, Led, Mel, MI5, Pin, Sc2, Shu, WA8.**

Miscellaneous

Acerola Cherry - *Malpighia glabra*. Shrub grows 10' tall. Dark green leaves. Small, red flowers. Hardy to 28 degrees F. Native from Texas to northern South America and the West Indies. *Source History: 1 in 1988; 2 in 1992; 2 in 2000.* **Sources: Ga11, Ka3.**

Acerola Cherry, Manoa Sweet - *Malpighia glabra*. Prefers a warm climate with either light or no frost. Vitamin C plant. Hardy to 26 degrees F. *Source History: 2 in 1988; 2 in 1992; 2 in 2000.* **Sources: Pa2, PL2.**

Acerola Cherry, Florida Sweet - *Malpighia punicifolia*. *Source History: 1 in 2000.* **Sources: On4.**

Akebia (Fiveleaf Akebia, Chocolate Vine) - *Akebia quinata*. Fruit looks like something from a foreign planet; 5" long outer shell opens in late summer to reveal sweet, sausage-shaped fruit filled with white pulp that looks like tapioca pudding and tastes like watermelon, but with many small, black seeds. Vigorous, pliable, strong, fast growing, evergreen vine can reach 20' long; durable stems are prized for basket making. Prune severely each year to control its rapid growth. Five petaled, compound leaves. Hardy to -25 degrees F. Native to northern Japan. (Raintree Nursery offers both purple and white flowered varieties.) *Source History: 3 in 1988; 10 in 1992; 13 in 2000.* **Sources: Ban, Car, Ed2, Fra, Gr16, Or2, Rai, Sh14, Sha, Tri, Wa13, We8, ZEL.**

Akebia, Bouquet - *Akebia quinata*. Compact vine with dark green, lacy foliage and dark purple, fragrant flowers. Two varieties needed for fruit production. Hardy to -30 degrees F; Zone 3. Trademarked. *Source History: 1 in 2000.* **Sources: On3.**

Akebia, Deep Purple - *Akebia trifoliata*. Semi-compact vine with large deep green foliage. Fragrant, almost black flowers. Rare. Trademarked. *Source History: 1 in 2000.* **Sources: On3.**

Akebia, Rosea - *Akebia quinata*. Vigorous vine with red-purple flowers and medium green foliage. Plant two varieties for proper pollination. *Source History: 1 in 2000.* **Sources: On3.**

Akebia, Silver Bells - *Akebia quinata*. Vigorous vine with light pink and red-purple flowers. Light green foliage. Akebia can produce an edible sausage-shaped fruit if two varieties are planted for cross-pollination. Hardy to -30 degrees F; Zone 3. Trademarked. *Source History: 1 in 2000.* **Sources: On3.**

Akebia, Trifoliate - White fleshed, deep purple fruit. Eaten fresh or made into refreshments. Zones 6-9. *Source History: 1 in 2000.* **Sources: Ed2.**

Akee - *Blighia sapida*. Oblong, 3", red and orange fruit; triangular in cross-section. Leathery, red shell which opens when ripe, exposing white pulp. Seed coat is poisonous as well as immature or overripe fruit. Extremely ornamental, tropical fruit tree from West Africa. Hardy in Zone 10. *Source History: 2 in 1988; 3 in 1992; 4 in 2000.* **Sources: Ga11, Me2, Pl3, Tr10.**

Algerita - *Mahonia trifoliata*. Red berries make excellent jelly. Evergreen shrub to 8' with blue-green holly-like foliage. Good wildlife habitat. Very drought tolerant. Native range is southern New Mexico, Arizona and east through Texas. *Source History: 1 in 1992; 1 in 2000.* **Sources: Pla.**

Allspice - *Pimenta dioica*. Dark brown, .25" fruit. Tree grows 40' tall. White flowers. Fruit is dried when unripe to make Allspice. *Source History: 2 in 1988; 3 in 1992; 1 in 2000.* **Sources: PL2.**

Amazonian Tree Grape - *Pouruma*. Fruits look like small bunches of deep purple olives. Extremely rich, sweet, grape jam-like flavor. Suitable for greenhouse culture. Grows wild in the Colombian rainforest. *Source History: 1 in 2000.* **Sources: Or2.**

Ambarella - *Spondias cytherea*. Oval, 1-3" fruit. Tough, orange-yellow skin. Juicy, pale yellow flesh. Eaten fresh or used for preserves and pickles. Erect tree grows 60' tall with smooth, gray bark. Ripens in spring. Hardy in Zone 10. Native to Society Island. *Source History: 1 in 1988; 2 in 1992; 4 in 2000.* **Sources: Ga11, Na13, On4, Pl3.**

Aronia, Dabrowice - *Aronia melanocarpa*. Polish variety. Hardy to Zone 3. *Source History: 1 in 2000.* **Sources: On3.**

Aronia, Egerta - *Aronia melanocarpa*. Polish variety. Hardy to -40 degrees F. *Source History: 1 in 2000.* **Sources: On3.**

Aronia, Nero - *Aronia melanocarpa*. Reaches a height of 3-4'. Fruit and ornamental qualities are similar to Viking but somewhat less vigorous. *Source History: 2 in 2000.* **Sources: Hid, On3.**

Aronia, Viking - *Aronia melanocarpa*. Produces many tasty, almost black berries the size of large blueberries. Vigorous, productive plant grows to 6' tall. Used fresh, for juice and as a stable natural food coloring. Hardy to Zones 3-8. Bred in Sweden. *Source History: 4 in 2000.* **Sources: Hid, Mel, On3, Rai.**

Australian Bush Cherry - *Syzygium paniculatum*. Fragrant, oval .75" rose-purple berries. Sometimes used in jelly. Tree grows 40' tall. Native to Australia. *Source History: 1 in 1988; 1 in 1992; 1 in 2000.* **Sources: MIS.**

Autumn Olive - *Elaeagnus umbellata*. Small, orange fruit. Used for eating fresh or making jam and jelly. Spreading shrub grows 10-15' tall and 8' wide. Attractive, tan-colored bark. Narrow, willow-like, silvery grey leaves. Small, fragrant, yellowish white flowers in May. Bears in about six years. Very tough and drought resistant. Grows well in ordinary soil, normal moisture and full or half day sun. Fixes nitrogen; sometimes used as an understory in orchards. Excellent honey plant and wildlife food. Dense cover provides shelter and food for small animals and birds. Hardy in Zones 3-7. Native to China and the Himalayas. *Source History: 10 in 1988; 22 in 1992; 23 in 2000.* **Sources: Abu, BO10, BU12, CA14, Co15, GR26, HI7, JO4, LA4, LO6, Mc3, MEA, Mel, Mu2, No2, On3, Pi2, Pl5, SH8, TR19, TU5, Wa16, WA8.**

Autumn Olive, Brilliant Rose - *Elaeagnus umbellata*. Large fruit with good flavor. *Source History: 1 in 2000.* **Sources: Hid.**

Autumn Olive, Cardinal - *Elaeagnus umbellata*. Edible .25" silvery brown berries turn bright red in fall; tiny, chewy seeds. Fruit is sold fresh in Japan where it is used for sauce, preserves and pie. Excellent wildlife food. Those that escape the birds shrivel into delicious, sweet raisins. Nitrogen fixing, shade tolerant, spiny, spreading shrub grows 15' tall; silvery foliage. Highly fragrant flowers in early summer. Produces profusely. Frost and drought resistant. Hardy in Zones 4-5. Originated in the Himalayas. *Source History: 6 in 1988; 12 in 1992; 9 in 2000.* **Sources: Bea, Fo2, Fo4, HI7, Jun, KEE, LOV, Or2, So5.**

Autumn Olive, Charlie's Golden - *Elaeagnus umbellata*. Medium size, yellow fruits with excellent flavor. *Source History: 1 in 2000.* **Sources: Hid.**

Autumn Olive, Delightful - *Elaeagnus umbellata*. Large, mild flavored fruit. *Source History: 1 in 2000.* **Sources: Hid.**

Autumn Olive, Jewel - *Elaeagnus umbellata*. Smaller size berry with excellent flavor. *Source History: 1 in 2000.* **Sources: Hid.**

Autumn Olive, Oleaster (Autumn Oleaster) - Small, sweet, scarlet to silvery fruit. Shrub grows 5-18' tall. Silvery leaf undersides. Bears in about six years. Hardy to Zone 3. Native to Japan, Korea and China. (Note: *Hortus Third* classifies this as Russian Olive, *Elaeagnus angustifolia.*) *Source History: 1 in 1988; 1 in 1992; 1 in 2000.* **Sources: Hud.**

Autumn Olive, Sweet n' Tart - *Elaeagnus umbellata.* Sweet flavor with nice tart undertones. *Source History: 1 in 2000.* **Sources: Hid.**

Bael Fruit (Bael Tree, Indian Bael) - *Aegle marmelos.* Oval, hard shelled, 4-6" greenish white fruit with pungent tasting pulp. Thorny, deciduous tree grows 10' tall. Hardy in Zone 10. *Source History: 2 in 1988; 2 in 1992; 2 in 2000.* **Sources: Ban, Ga11.**

Ban'Suanla - *Tetrastigma.* Grape-like clusters of tart, juicy, 1" fruits. *Source History: 1 in 2000.* **Sources: Or2.**

Ban-Tangla - *Cissus.* Golden fruits look and taste almost the same as the Loquat of commerce. *Source History: 1 in 2000.* **Sources: Or2.**

Baobab Tree (Lemonade Tree, Monkeybread Tree) - *Adansonia digitata.* Gourd-like, 12" long fruit filled with lemon flavored, white pulp and edible seeds. Used for a lemonade-type drink. Famous African tree with a huge swollen trunk up to 30' in diameter; not more than 60' tall. Trunk stores considerable water and is used as a reservoir. Leaves are eaten like spinach. Large, white, hibiscus-like, 6" flowers. Pollinated by bats. Worshiped as a fertility tree. *Source History: 2 in 1988; 2 in 1992; 2 in 2000.* **Sources: Ga11, Pa2.**

Barbados Cherry - *Malpighia glabra.* Produces tart, red berries with high vitamin C content. One of the best and most nutritious edibles for container culture. *Source History: 5 in 1992; 3 in 2000.* **Sources: Ban, Ka3, Na13.**

Bearberry - *Arctostaphylos Uva-ursi.* Evergreen groundcover. Glossy green foliage changes to bronze fall color. Berries harvested in the fall are used like cranberries, fresh or dried. Grows 6-12" tall. Zones 2-8. Native from coast to coast. *Source History: 4 in 2000.* **Sources: HA12, Ho8, MIS, VIR.**

Berchemia racemosa - Mounding shrub or vine grows to 30'. Bears 6" pyramidal clusters of small red fruits which turn black when ripe. Striking and attractive. Originated in Japan. Hardy to Zone 6. *Source History: 1 in 2000.* **Sources: Fo2.**

Biew Kiew - *Euphoria longan.* *Source History: 1 in 2000.* **Sources: On4.**

Bignay - *Antidesma bunius.* *Source History: 1 in 1992; 2 in 2000.* **Sources: Ga11, Po7.**

Black Haw - *Viburnum prunifolium.* Pink, .5" fruits turn bluish black in the fall. Sweet flavor improves after a frost. Used to make preserves. Round headed, small tree or multistemmed shrub grows 12-15' tall; growth habit similar to Hawthorn. Creamy white, 4" flat clusters of flowers in April and May. Beautiful, rich red fall foliage. Adaptable to wide range of soils; succeeds in either sun or shade. Remembered by many old-timers as a wilding, which was often much sought after in earlier farm days by small boys and girls. Hardy in Zones 3-9. Native to the eastern U.S. *Source History: 13 in 1988; 25 in 1992; 18 in 2000.* **Sources: BA14, BO10, Co15, Fo2, KEE, LA4, LI7, LOV, Mc3, Or2, Sc2, Sh10, SH8, So5, Tri, Wa3, WA8, We8.**

Black Haw, Native Missouri - *Viburnum prunifolium.* Strong grower. Comes true and uniform. *Source History: 1 in 1988; 1 in 1992; 1 in 2000.* **Sources: LOV.**

Blackberry Jam - *Randia formosa*. Berry is 2" long with many seeds. Tastes like blackberry jam. Spineless plant. Bears fruit when container grown. Gardenia relative is native to tropical South America. *Source History: 1 in 1988; 3 in 2000.* **Sources: Ga11, Na13, Po7.**

Blue Banana Bean - *Decaisnea Fargesii*. Deciduous shrub bears an odd metallic blue pod full of white juicy pulp with a sweet fig-grape-banana flavor. Collected in the cold Qinling mountain range in central China. Hardy to Zone 5. Trademarked. *Source History: 1 in 2000.* **Sources: Or2.**

Blue Grape - *Myrciaria vexator*. *Source History: 1 in 1988; 1 in 1992; 1 in 2000.* **Sources: Ga11.**

Brazilian Plum (Brazil Cherry) - *Eugenia dombeyi*. Sweet purple berry used fresh or in jams and juices. Small evergreen tree with dark green, waxy leaves. Ripens in April-May. *Source History: 2 in 1992; 2 in 2000.* **Sources: Ban, Ro13.**

Breadfruit, Tahitian - Small, seedless fruit. *Source History: 1 in 1992; 1 in 2000.* **Sources: PL2.**

Buffalo Berry (Silver Buffalo Berry) - *Shepherdia argentea*. Oval, .25" red or yellow berries hang in clusters like currants. Superb for jam, jelly and sauce. Also make fine relish and keep their flavor when dried. Extremely attractive, relatively slow growing, 6-12', thorny shrub with silvery grey foliage similar to Russian Olive. Good yields. Both male and female plants are needed to produce fruit. Tolerates drought and high pH. Attracts birds from early fall and throughout the winter. Native to the Canadian plains and the Midwest. Indians traditionally dried the berries and served them with buffalo meat. Hardy to Zone 2. *Source History: 18 in 1988; 30 in 1992; 28 in 2000.* **Sources: Bea, Ca12, CLI, Co15, CR6, Fa1, Fo2, Fro, GR26, Hid, LA4, Las, LI7, Mc3, Mel, NA5, No2, Oik, Or2, Pl5, Pla, Red, Sc2, SH8, So5, Stl, Va5, We8.**

Buffalo Berry, Russet (Soapberry) - *Shepherdia canadensis*. Orangish red berries; bitter and sour. Thornless, nitrogen-fixing, native shrub grows 8' high and 4-6' wide. Leaves, twigs and buds are coated with a coppery scurf. Adapted to shady, dry or rocky soils, where few other shrubs can thrive. Used by Indians for "Indian ice cream" made by whipping the berries into a frothy mixture and sweetening with saskatoons. Hardy in Zone 3. *Source History: 4 in 1988; 8 in 1992; 6 in 2000.* **Sources: Fo2, GR26, NA5, No2, Pl5, Va5.**

Bunchberry - *Cornus canadensis*. Beautiful ground cover produces bright red, edible berries. Grows to 6" high. Good for forest openings. Dies back each winter. Hardy to 0 degrees F. *Source History: 2 in 2000.* **Sources: Abu, Rai.**

Bunchosia - Unusual tropical fruit with bright red flesh. Appealing flavor. Bears at a small size in a container. *Source History: 1 in 2000.* **Sources: Na13.**

Burdekin Plum - *Pleiogynium cerasiferum*. *Source History: 1 in 1992; 2 in 2000.* **Sources: Ga11, Pa2.**

Burmese Strazberry - *Rubus spp*. Evergreen plant bears small clusters of pink fruit with sweet-tart flavor. Trademarked. *Source History: 1 in 2000.* **Sources: Or2.**

Cactus, Airampu - *Opuntia soehrensis*. Andean cactus. Seeds and fruits used for red-purple color in foods, especially chicha, a corn beverage of the Altiplano. *Source History: 1 in 2000.* **Sources: So12.**

Cactus, Blueberry - *Myrtillo*. Plant grows to 8' tall and produces many arms resembling the giant Saguaro cactus. Covered with puffs of white cereus flowers which mature into fruits only a couple weeks later. The blueberry-like fruits have an excellent sweet flavor that can be likened to blueberries. *Source History: 1 in 2000.* **Sources: Or2.**

Cactus, Desert Strawberry - Egg-size fruit in colors of pinks, reds and yellows. Ripe fruit is covered with small thorns that are easily removed. Mexican Indians serve them with cream for a delicious dish suggesting strawberries. Ripens in early summer. Prefers gravel soil. Unharmed by 0 degree temperatures. *Source History: 1 in 1992; 1 in 2000.* **Sources: Or2.**

Cactus, Hardy Rainbow - Strawberry-size fruit with sweet flesh considered a rare delicacy by the native Southwest people. Stems of the plant grow 15" tall with many .25" thorns that form a dense layer over the entire growth. The last spines of each season's growth form bands of color around the plant. Needs well drained, rocky soil. Hardy to 0 degrees F. *Source History: 1 in 1992; 1 in 2000.* **Sources: Or2.**

Cactus, Mexican Fruit Barrel - Oblong, 2-3" long fruit is sweet and delicious. Golden yellow flowers grow on 2-3' stems. Highly prized by Mexican Indians. Plant in a sunny location in sand or gravel loam. Withstands temperatures to 0 degrees F. *Source History: 1 in 2000.* **Sources: Or2.**

Cactus, Pitaya - *Cereus peruvianus.* Upgrowing cactus with edible fruit. Full sun. *Source History: 1 in 2000.* **Sources: Po7.**

Cactus, Reina de Noche - Translates as Queen of the Night. Red fruit is edible as well as the fleshy beet-like root which weighs up to 100 pounds. The root serves as a reservoir of water and food that lasts for more than two years. Flowers grow 7-10" long and 6" across with a delightful spicy fragrance that carries for miles. Plant blossoms only one night each year. Hardy to 8 degrees F. *Source History: 1 in 1992; 1 in 2000.* **Sources: Or2.**

Cactus, San Pedro - *Trichocereus pachanoi.* Cylindrical, blue colored cactus grows up to the size of a large tree; also can be kept small and container grown. Fragrant, 8" blossoms are followed only very rarely by edible fruits with small black seeds. *Source History: 1 in 1992; 1 in 2000.* **Sources: Na13.**

California Fan Palm - *Washingtonia filifera.* Small black, edible fruit. Grows 20-70' tall with 8-10' long flower stalks. Native to deserts of California. *Source History: 1 in 1992; 1 in 2000.* **Sources: Hud.**

Carissa edulis - Spiny shrub bears tasty, round, purple-black fruit. Excellent groundcover. Easy container culture. *Source History: 1 in 2000.* **Sources: Na13.**

Carissa Plum (Amatungulu) - *Carissa grandiflora.* Oval, 2" long, scarlet fruit. Tastes rather like raspberries. Good for jelly and preserves. Dense shrub grows 18-25' tall and wide. Oval, glossy, dark green leaves form tiers of leathery discs on the stems. Fragrant, white flowers. Good indoor grower, but needs warmth, much light and humidity. Relative of the Natal plum. *Source History: 2 in 1988; 2 in 1992; 2 in 2000.* **Sources: Po7, Sc2.**

Carob (Algaroba Bean, Locust Bean, St. John's Bread) - *Ceratonia siliqua.* Thick, fleshy, shiny brown, 4-12" pods are called carob beans. Seed and pods are roasted as coffee substitutes; may be fermented and distilled. Seeds are ground into a flour with 60% protein and no sugar or starch, suitable for diabetics. Pods are good for livestock feed; 200-450 pounds per tree annually. Beautiful, round headed, 40-50' evergreen tree. Slow growing and very long-lived. Blossoms in fall and ripens its crop the following fall. Crop can be damaged by winter temperatures below 26 degrees F and by rain, fog or extended periods of high humidity during ripening. Hardy to 18 degrees F. European origin. *Source History: 9 in 1988; 13 in 1992; 11 in 2000.* **Sources: Ban, Ca7, Fo2, Hud, MIS, MO10, Na13, Pa2,**

Sc2, So12, Tri.

Cedar Bay Cherry - *Eugenia reinwardtiana*. Produces bright red, sweet fruit when only 18" tall. Native to Australia. *Source History: 1 in 2000.* **Sources: Po7.**

Ceriman (Breadfruit Vine, Mexican Breadfruit, Split-Leaf Philodendron, Fruit Salad Plant) - *Monstera deliciosa*. Fruit is formed within a casing that falls away when the fruit ripens. Good aroma; tastes like a combination of banana, pineapple and strawberry. Makes a great house plant; climbs 30' tall in frost-free areas. Native to Mexico and Central America. Strictly tropical. *Source History: 1 in 1988; 3 in 1992; 3 in 2000.* **Sources: An4, Ga11, Na13.**

Ceylon Gooseberry - *Dovyalis hevecarpa* x *D. abyssinica*. Large bush with small, white, powderpuff flowers followed by grape-size, semi-tart fruit. Can be used fresh or in cooking. *Source History: 1 in 1992; 1 in 2000.* **Sources: An4.**

Chali-Chali - *Allophylus edulis*. Rare tree from a comparable latitude in Brazil. Produces clusters of bright red, sweet, edible berries. Attractive foliage. *Source History: 1 in 2000.* **Sources: Po7.**

Charchuala - *Rheedia macrophylla*. Leathery fruit with 1-5 seeds enclosed in edible pulp. *Source History: 1 in 1988; 1 in 2000.* **Sources: Ga11.**

Che Tree (Seedless Che) - *Cudrania tricuspidata*. Cherry size fruit is pink when ripe with watermelon flavor. Fruits in the fall. Birds don't bother the fruit. Hardy in Zone 6. Native to China. *Source History: 1 in 1992; 2 in 2000.* **Sources: Ed2, Hid.**

Cherry of the Rio Grande - *Eugenia aggregata*. Sweet, purplish fruit. Small, evergreen shrub with small pointed, dark green leaves. Fruits in late spring. Native to Brazil. Zone 9. *Source History: 2 in 1988; 3 in 1992; 5 in 2000.* **Sources: An4, Me2, Na13, Pa2, Po7.**

Chestnut Dioon - *Dioon edule*. Edible seeds. Stocky, palm-like plant with 6' trunk. Leaflets look like plastic combs. Nutlets can be boiled, roasted or ground into a starchy arrowroot flour from which tortillas are made. Very ornamental. Hardy to 15 degrees F. Collected in Veracruz, Mexico. *Source History: 2 in 1988; 2 in 1992; 1 in 2000.* **Sources: Or2.**

Chilean Guava - *Ugni molinae*. Small evergreen shrub bears small fragrant white flowers followed by sweet, tasty red berries with a spritely guava-like flavor and fragrance. Fresh eating, jam and jelly. Sun or partial shade. No pest or disease problems. Hardy to 10 degrees F. *Source History: 1 in 2000.* **Sources: On3.**

Chilean Guava, Round Leaf - *Ugni molinae*. Small red berries taste similar to strawberry guava. Compact shrub has round cupped leaves. Prefers some shade in hot climates. Grows well on the west coast. Hardy to about 10 degrees F. *Source History: 1 in 1992; 2 in 2000.* **Sources: Or2, Po7.**

China Blue Vine - *Holboellia coriacea*. Evergreen vine bears cascades of small, very fragrant, creamy white flowers. Can bear small but attractive, edible purple fruit. Hardy to 0 degrees F; Zone 7. Native to Asia. *Source History: 1 in 2000.* **Sources: On3.**

Chinese Chee (Che) - Thorny bush. Sweet red fruit. Needs a male for pollination. Hardy in Zones 5-10. *Source History: 1 in 1988; 2 in 1992; 1 in 2000.* **Sources: Sh3.**

Chinese Magnolia Vine - *Schisandra chinensis*. Fragrant white flowers followed by scarlet berries in 6" long clusters. Fruits are eaten fresh, dried and made into juice. High in trace elements and vitamin C. Hardy to Zone 4-9. *Source His-*

tory: 2 in 2000. **Sources: Bu7, Ed2.**

Chinese Magnolia Vine, Eastern Prince - *Schisandra chinensis.* Self-fertile cloned selection. Crimson berries have a tart flavor. High vitamin C content. Used for juice and preserves. Vigorous and pest resistant. Hardy to -25 degrees F; Zone 5. Native to the forests of Northern China and the Russian Far East. *Source History: 5 in 2000.* **Sources: Bu7, Mel, On3, Rai, Wa3.**

Chinese Quince - *Pseudocydonia sinensis.* Large, yellow fruit can be used in preserves. Fast growing tree reaches 40' tall. Beautiful, mottled bark. Leaves turn red and orange in fall. Plant two trees for proper pollination. Hardy in Zone 5. *Source History: 1 in 1988; 1 in 1992; 1 in 2000.* **Sources: Cam.**

Chinese Strawberry Tree - *Myrica rubra.* Subtropical evergreen with leathery leaves and succulent, deep red-purple edible fruit. Full sun. Grows 15' tall. Zones 7-11. *Source History: 1 in 2000.* **Sources: MO10.**

Chokeberry, Autumn Magic - *Aronia melanocarpa.* Dark glossy green foliage turns brilliant red-purple in the fall. Large edible black-purple berries. *Source History: 4 in 2000.* **Sources: BA14, Gos, Mc3, We4.**

Chokeberry, Black - *Aronia melanocarpa.* Edible black fruit used for jams and jellies; also enjoyed by wildlife. Widely adaptable tree with leaves that turn dark red in the fall. Hardy to Zones 3-9. *Source History: 9 in 1992; 28 in 2000.* **Sources: BA14, Bea, BO10, CLI, Clo, Co15, CR6, Fo2, GR26, HI7, Jun, KAN, KI3, LA4, LI7, Lit, Mc3, MEA, Mu2, Oik, On3, Or2, Sh10, Sh14, SH8, Stl, WA8, Wbn.**

Chokeberry, Viking - *Aronia melanocarpa.* Tasty, almost black berries. Used for juice, wine and a stable natural coloring agent. Vigorous, productive plant. Self-fertile. Zones 3-9. *Source History: 1 in 2000.* **Sources: On3.**

Chokeberry, Viking Black - *Aronia melanocarpa.* Shrub grows to 4' tall. Glossy foliage with bright red fall color. Large fruit. Hardy to -35 degrees F. *Source History: 1 in 2000.* **Sources: Oik.**

Chulta (Chulta, Elephant Apple) - *Dillenia indica.* Round, 4" fruit contains acidic, colorless pulp. Edible when fresh; used in curry and jelly. Tree has oblong, 14" leaves and showy, white, 8" flowers. Grows to 35'. Hardy in Zone 10. Native to India and Southeast Asia. Known in India as Chulta. *Source History: 2 in 1988; 1 in 1992; 2 in 2000.* **Sources: Ban, Ga11.**

Coco Plum - *Chrysobalanus Icaco.* Fruit is 1.5" long; edible but insipid. Evergreen tree grows 30' tall. Native from southern Florida to northern South America. Hardy in Zone 10. *Source History: 1 in 1988; 1 in 2000.* **Sources: Ga11.**

Cocoa - *Theobroma cacao.* Seeds are fermented and roasted to make cocoa and chocolate. Native to Central and South America. Hardy to 32 degrees F. *Source History: 1 in 1988; 4 in 1992; 4 in 2000.* **Sources: Me2, Na13, PL2, Ro13.**

Coconut Palm - *Cocos nucifera. Source History: 1 in 2000.* **Sources: Ga11.**

Coffea canephora - Shorter than *Coffea arabica* with longer leaves. Grows to 3' tall. May be grown indoors in bright light *Source History: 1 in 2000.* **Sources: Ban.**

Coffea catura - Makes excellent flavored coffee. Can be grown in direct sun. Requires no cloud cover or tree shade. Grows to 3.5' tall. *Source History: 1 in 2000.* **Sources: Ban.**

Coffea kona - Popular coffee of Hawaii. Excellent quality. Upright 3-8' shrub bears heavily; can produce one pound of coffee. *Source History: 1 in 2000.* **Sources: Al8, Ban.**

<u>Coffea racemosa</u> - Similar to *Coffea canephora* but with more branching, compact habit. Grows 4' tall. Excellent quality. A favorite of growers. *Source History: 1 in 2000.* **Sources: Ban.**

<u>Coffee</u> - *Coffea arabica*. Small red berry can be eaten fresh or dried and made into coffee. Small tree with attractive leaves. Zones 9-10. *Source History: 1 in 1992; 9 in 2000.* **Sources: Ban, Ca7, Ed2, Ga11, Na13, Our, Pa2, PL2, Sh14.**

<u>Coffeeberry</u> - *Rhamnus californica*. Red berries in the fall turn black when ripe. Evergreen bush grows 10' tall. Great bee fodder; produces delicious honey. Native from Oregon to California and Arizona. Hardy in Zone 7. *Source History: 2 in 1988; 3 in 1992; 4 in 2000.* **Sources: Co24, Fo2, Lar, MIS.**

<u>Cornelian Cherry</u> - *Cornus mas*. Sweet, dark red fruit is like a small plum with cranberry sauce consistency; about .75" long and .5" wide. Makes delicious jam. Large shrub or small tree. Close relative of dogwood; leaves are similar, having red fall color. Tiny, very plentiful, yellow blossoms on naked, grey branches rival witch hazel in beauty and striking effect in the spring, when it is the earliest plant to bloom. Cultivated in Europe for centuries for its fruit and ornamental value. Hardy in Zone 5. (**So5** is offering a "large fruiting variety widely grown in Russia as cultivated fruit.") *Source History: 2 in 1988; 21 in 1992; 28 in 2000.* **Sources: Arb, Bea, Big, BO10, Bu7, Ca12, Car, Co24, CO3, Ed2, Fed, Fo2, Fra, Gr16, GR26, Hid, IM2, KAN, LA4, LI7, LOV, Mel, Oik, Or2, Rai, Sh3, So5, We8.**

<u>Cornelian Cherry, Chanticleer</u> - *Cornus mas*. *Source History: 1 in 2000.* **Sources: On3.**

<u>Cornelian Cherry, Elegant</u> - *Cornus mas*. Bright red, long, pear-shaped fruit is sweet and delicious. Zone 4. Bred by Svetlana Klimenko, a Ukrainian botanist at the Central Botanic Garden in Kiev. Trademarked. *Source History: 2 in 2000.* **Sources: Gr16, On3.**

<u>Cornelian Cherry, Eugene</u> - *Cornus mas*. *Source History: 1 in 2000.* **Sources: On3.**

<u>Cornelian Cherry, Golden</u> - *Cornus mas*. Rounded shrub or small tree. Red, edible fruit in summer. Zone 4. *Source History: 1 in 2000.* **Sources: Wa13.**

<u>Cornelian Cherry, Golden Glory</u> - *Cornus mas*. Large columnar shrub to 15-20'. Bright yellow flowers followed by deep red plum-like fruits and red foliage. Pest resistant. Zone 5. *Source History: 1 in 2000.* **Sources: Fo2.**

<u>Cornelian Cherry, Joy</u> - *Cornus mas*. *Source History: 1 in 2000.* **Sources: On3.**

<u>Cornelian Cherry, Oleg</u> - *Cornus mas*. *Source History: 1 in 2000.* **Sources: On3.**

<u>Cornelian Cherry, Pioneer</u> - *Cornus mas*. Large, dark red, pear-shaped fruit up to 1.5" long. Juicy, sweet and aromatic. Hardy to Zone 4. Bred by Svetlana Klimenko, a Ukrainian botanist at the Central Botanic Garden in Kiev. Trademarked. *Source History: 3 in 2000.* **Sources: Gr16, Mel, On3.**

<u>Cornelian Cherry, Red Star</u> - *Cornus mas*. Large, oval, glossy dark red fruit is 1.25" long. Sweet, juicy and aromatic. Sweet-tart flavor resembles that of a good pie cherry. Bears 2-5 years after planting. Plant two varieties to ensure good crops. Zones 4-8. Bred by Svetlana Klimenko, a Ukrainian botanist at the Central Botanic Garden in Kiev. Trademarked. *Source History: 3 in 2000.* **Sources: Gr16, Mel, On3.**

<u>Cornelian Cherry, Redstone</u> - *Cornus mas*. Produces more fruit than common Cornelian cherry. Developed by the USDA. *Source History: 1 in 1992; 1 in 2000.*

Sources: LOV.

Cornelian Cherry, Siretski - *Cornus mas*. Large, cylindrical fruit with a pleasing sweet-tart flavor. Vigorous. Disease resistant. Zones 4-8. Originated in the Ukraine. *Source History: 1 in 2000.* **Sources: On3.**

Cornelian Cherry, Vavilov - *Cornus mas*. Named in honor of one of Russia's most respected horticulturists who disappeared during Stalin's rule. Produces large, tasty, oblong fruit. Medium size shrub. Vigorous. Disease resistant. Zones 4-8. *Source History: 1 in 2000.* **Sources: On3.**

Cornelian Cherry, Yellow - *Cornus mas*. Unique yellow fruited variety with 1" long fruit. Delicious, sweet-tart taste. Makes tasty jams and compotes. Zones 4-8. Bred by Svetlana Klimenko, a Ukrainian botanist at the Central Botanic Garden in Kiev. Trademarked. *Source History: 2 in 2000.* **Sources: On3, Rai.**

Cornelian Cherry, Yellow Leaved - *Cornus mas*. Large shrub with bright yellow flowers along the bare branches in spring. In summer it bears yellow-green leaves followed by red berries in the fall. Zone 5. *Source History: 1 in 2000.* **Sources: Fo2.**

Cudraina tricuspidata - Spiny tree to 20' or cut back for as a hedge. Leaves are used in the feeding of silkworms. Produces edible 1" globose, bright orange-red fruit. Hardy to Zone 5. *Source History: 1 in 2000.* **Sources: Ban.**

Damarru, Himalayan - *Maclura conchinensis*. Grown as a vine on a trellis or cut back as a shrub. Bears sweet round velvety raspberry size yellow fruits with a flavor that tastes like a mixture of raspberries, peaches and cream. Hardy in Zones 7-9. *Source History: 1 in 2000.* **Sources: Rai.**

Davidson's Plum - *Davidsonia pruriens*. Unique attractive foliage. Produces fruits the size and color of a plum. Used for jam. Australian rainforest native. *Source History: 1 in 2000.* **Sources: Po7.**

Decaisna fargesii - Shrubby tree to 15' with 3' long pinnate leaves. Bears edible sausage-shaped fruits that are 3-4" long; metallic-blue color when ripe. Sweet, juicy, white pulp. Hardy to 20 degrees F. Native to central China. *Source History: 1 in 2000.* **Sources: Ban.**

Dewberry - *Rubus ursinus*. Large, sweet, glossy, 1-1.5" bluish black berries; similar to blackberries except larger, milder and grow on a vine instead of a bush. Ripens 7-10 days earlier. *Source History: 4 in 1988; 6 in 1992; 4 in 2000.* **Sources: Bu1, Fo4, Iso, Pl5.**

Dewberry, Austin - Best dewberry available. Medium to large fruit. Delicious flavor. Very good for making cobblers, pies and jellies. Heavy, annual producer. Widely adapted. Easy to grow. Ripens in late May. Hardy in Zones 4-9. *Source History: 6 in 1988; 11 in 1992; 8 in 2000.* **Sources: Bar, Bos, CO5, MI5, Pe3, Ty2, Wel, Wom.**

Dewberry, Lucretia - Sweet, coreless, blue-black berries up to 1.5" long; milder than a raspberry and much larger. Excellent flavor. Makes delicious preserves. Thornless vines with a trailing growth habit. Require support to hold fruit off the ground. Self-fruitful. Disease resistant. Ripens 10 days earlier than blackberries. Thrives south of central Illinois. Hardy in Zones 5-9. *Source History: 4 in 1988; 8 in 1992; 4 in 2000.* **Sources: Co12, Fi1, RAM, Wel.**

Dioon spinulosa - Grown in the southern Mexican rainforests. Tree grows 50' tall in the wild. Blue-green, comb-like leaves are 4-6' long with spiny teeth. Golden brown, 2.5" nutlets grow on the trunk. Native to Australia. *Source History: 1 in 2000.* **Sources: Or2.**

<u>Dogwood, Big Apple</u> - *Cornus kousa.* Large flowers followed by cascades of very large, edible fruit up to 2". Zones 6-8. *Source History: 2 in 2000.* **Sources: Ed2, Sh3.**

<u>Dogwood, Milky Way</u> - *Cornus kousa.* White bracted flowers followed by red strawberry-like fruit. *Source History: 1 in 1992; 6 in 2000.* **Sources: Arb, Gos, KEE, Oik, Sh14, Sh3.**

<u>Dogwood, Oriental</u> (Chinese Dogwood) - *Cornus kousa.* Large white flower bracts in June last about one month, followed by large, strawberry-red, edible fruit. Scarlet leaves in the fall. Tree grows to 25'. Anthracnose resistant. Does not do well in dry soil. Hardy to -20 degrees F. Originated in China. *Source History: 22 in 1992; 39 in 2000.* **Sources: Bea, Big, BO10, BO4, Bo5, Bu7, Ca7, Co24, Ed2, Fed, FO10, Fo2, Gir, Gir, Gr16, GR26, IM2, IN7, KEE, LO6, MEA, Mel, MI10, MI5, MIS, Mu2, Na4, On3, Or2, Pi2, Rai, Sc2, SH8, TR19, Wa13, Wa3, WA8, We8, Wo2.**

<u>Downy Rosemyrtle</u> - *Rhodomyrtus tomentosa.* Fruit is similar to Feijoa with flavor resembling grape jam and fig. Plant grows 2-6' tall. Makes an excellent container plant. Found in Vietnam and the Philippines. Rare. *Source History: 1 in 2000.* **Sources: Or2.**

<u>Durian</u> - *Source History: 1 in 2000.* **Sources: An4.**

<u>Durian, Gom Pong</u> - Originated in Thailand. *Source History: 1 in 1992; 1 in 2000.* **Sources: PL2.**

<u>Durian, Montong</u> - *Source History: 1 in 2000.* **Sources: PL2.**

<u>*Elaeagnus pungens*</u> (Thorny Elaeagnus) - *Source History: 1 in 1988; 1 in 1992; 2 in 2000.* **Sources: BO10, Ca7.**

<u>Emerald Carpet</u> - *Rubus calcinoides.* Orange berries resemble small raspberries. Thornless, creeping plant grows well in shade or partial sun. Clover-shaped, leathery, green leaves turn an attractive coppery color in the autumn. In colder climates the plant may lose its leaves; otherwise it is evergreen. Ripens during July. Collected from Taiwan and Japan via the University of British Columbia. *Source History: 1 in 1988; 2 in 2000.* **Sources: Or2, Rai.**

<u>*Eugenia cassiodes*</u> - Compact tree bears good tasting fruit. *Source History: 1 in 2000.* **Sources: Na13.**

<u>*Eugenia stipulata*</u> - Little known species currently being tried as a juice. Smooth, red, 2" fruits with acidic taste. High vitamin C content. Shrubby plant to 5'. Seeds; plants are not offered. *Source History: 1 in 1992; 1 in 2000.* **Sources: Ban.**

<u>*Eugenia uvalha*</u> - Large yellow fruits up to 2.5". Very juicy flesh with a nice tart flavor. Large plant. *Source History: 1 in 1992; 1 in 2000.* **Sources: Po7.**

<u>*Eugenia victoriana*</u> - Flavor of the 3" bright orange fruit resembles that of passion fruit. Attractive ornamental tree with a more oval shape than *Eugenia stipulata.* *Source History: 1 in 2000.* **Sources: Ban.**

<u>*Garcinia hombroniana*</u> - Produces a nice tart fruit. Mangosteen relative but more hardy. *Source History: 1 in 2000.* **Sources: Po7.**

<u>Garcinia, Himalayan</u> - *Garcinia xanthochymus.* Round, 2-3" dark yellow fruit. Tree grows 40' tall. Thick, leathery, 18" oblong leaves. Small, white flowers. Native to the western Himalayas. *Source History: 1 in 1988; 1 in 1992; 1 in 2000.* **Sources: Ga11.**

<u>Garcinia, Imbe</u> - *Garcinia Livingstonei.* Round, 1" orangish yellow fruit. Upright tree grows 35' tall. Oblong, 5" leathery leaves. Native to tropical Africa.

Hardy in Zone 10. *Source History: 1 in 1988; 2 in 1992; 2 in 2000.* **Sources: Ga11, Po7.**

Garcinia, Rata - *Garcinia dulcis. Source History: 1 in 2000.* **Sources: Ga11.**

Gaylussacia baccata - Shrub grows 1-3'. Bears small sweet berries in early summer. Brilliant scarlet-red fall color. Zone 4. *Source History: 1 in 2000.* **Sources: Fo2.**

Gooseberry Tree (Emblic, Amla) - *Phyllanthus acidus.* Edible, yellow 1-2" fruits hang in dense clusters from the branches and the trunk. Used in preserves. Ornamental tree to 35'. Native to Southeast Asia. *Source History: 1 in 1992; 1 in 2000.* **Sources: Ban.**

Goumi (Cherry Elaeagnus, Gumi, Silverberry) - *Elaeagnus multiflora.* Scarlet, 1" long, cherry-like fruit in the summer. Tart but quite pallatable. Good for jelly and pie. Also enjoyed by birds. Rounded, 6-10' shrub. Dark green leaves, silvery beneath. Fragrant flowers resemble small, yellow fuchsias. Native to Japan and China. Hardy in Zone 5. *Source History: 5 in 1988; 4 in 1992; 14 in 2000.* **Sources: Ban, Bu7, Clo, Fo2, Gr16, Hid, Mel, Or2, Pa2, Rai, Sh14, Sh3, Tri, Wh3.**

Goumi, Sweet Scarlet - *Elaeagnus multiflora.* Goumi is a relative of Autumn Olive (*Elaeagnus umbellata*) and Russian Olive (*Elaeagnus angustifolia*) which forms a 6' shrub. Creamy white flowers in April. Tasty red berries in late June. Hardy to Zone 4. Selected at the Main Botanic Garden in Kiev, Ukraine. Trademarked. *Source History: 1 in 2000.* **Sources: On3.**

Governor's Plum - *Flacourtia indica.* Deciduous shrub or small tree. Round, .5" rather astringent, blackish red fruit; translucent when ripe. Hardy in Zone 10. *Source History: 1 in 1988; 1 in 1992; 1 in 2000.* **Sources: Ga11.**

Grumichama - *Eugenia brasiliensis.* Cherry-size fruit ripens from dark red to black. Eaten fresh or used for jelly, jam, pie and candied fruit. Tree can grow 50' tall. Native to southern Brazil. Hardy in Zone 10. *Source History: 3 in 1988; 2 in 1992; 3 in 2000.* **Sources: Ga11, Pa2, Po7.**

Guadalupe Palm - *Brahea edulis.* Fruit is 1" in diameter; black when ripe. Tree grows slowly 20' tall or more. Hardy in Zone 9. Native to Guadalupe Island, Mexico. *Source History: 1 in 1988; 1 in 1992; 2 in 2000.* **Sources: MIS, Pa2.**

Guyana Chestnut - *Bombax glabra.* Fast growing tree produces 4" pods filled with nuts that can be eaten fresh or roasted. Good flavor. Good for container culture. Zone 10. *Source History: 1 in 2000.* **Sources: Na13.**

Hackberry (Sugarberry, Northern Hackberry, Nettle Tree) - *Celtis occidentalis.* Fruit varies in color from reddish orange to dark purple; edible out of hand reported to be very sweet. Tree grows 50-120' tall. Deep rooted; withstands heat, wind, much drought and alkaline soil. Hardy in Zone 4. Native from Quebec to North Carolina and Alabama. *Source History: 2 in 1988; 32 in 1992; 39 in 2000.* **Sources: Arb, BA14, Bea, Big, BO10, BO4, Ca7, Ca8, CLI, Co15, CO5, CR6, FE7, Fo2, GR26, KAN, KEE, LA4, LI7, LOV, Mc3, MEA, Mel, MI5, MIS, Mu2, No2, Oik, Or2, ORA, Sc2, Sh14, SH8, Stl, TU5, Va5, Wa16, WA8, Wom.**

Hackberry, European (Honeyberry) - *Celtis australis.* Cherry-size, dark purple fruit; much eaten in Spain, Greece and Iran. Large tree grows 60-80' tall. Fine shade tree for California and the South. Native to the Mediterranean and central Asia. *Source History: 1 in 1988; 1 in 1992; 5 in 2000.* **Sources: Ca7, CO5, MIS, Or2, ORA.**

Hackberry, Netleaf - *Celtis reticulata.* Small orange fruits. Small tree is drought tolerant. Hardy in Zone 4. *Source History: 1 in 1992; 3 in 2000.* **Sources: Ca12, Fo2, No2.**

Hawberry, Chinese - *Crataegus pinnatifida major*. Small tree with rich red autumn color. Few thorns. Glossy, 1" crimson fruits are grown for market in China. Zone 6. *Source History: 1 in 2000.* **Sources: Fo2.**

Hawthorn, Black (Douglas Hawthorn, Pacific Douglas Hawthorn, Western Black Hawthorn) - *Crataegus Douglasii*. Bluish black fruit is used for jelly. Small, thorny, deciduous tree or thicket-forming shrub; useful as a barrier. Reddish orange fall color. Native from Alaska to California and east into the Rockies and Minnesota. *Source History: 5 in 1988; 4 in 1992; 9 in 2000.* **Sources: Abu, BA9, Bu7, Ca12, Fo2, Fro, NA5, No2, Pl5.**

Hawthorn, Cockspur Haw - *Crataegus crus-galli*. Edible, .4" red fruit hangs on the tree into winter. Wide, thorny tree to 35' with red-orange fall foliage. Hardy to Zone 4. *Source History: 5 in 1992; 13 in 2000.* **Sources: Arb, Ca7, FE7, GR26, KAN, KI3, LI7, LO6, LOV, Mc3, ME3, MEA, WA8.**

Hawthorn, Red - *Crataegus columbiana*. Purplish red fruit. Thorny shrub or small tree can grow 15' tall. Native from British Columbia to northern California. Hardy to -25 degrees F. Referred to as "thorn apples" by early settlers and Native Americans. Excellent bird habitat. *Source History: 1 in 1988; 3 in 1992; 4 in 2000.* **Sources: Ca12, NA5, No2, Oik.**

Hawthorn, Red Azarole (Mediterranean Medlar) - *Crataegus azarolus*. Orange fruits with the flavor of tart apple are made into jelly. Tree to 20'. Glossy red-green foliage. Self-fertile. Hardy in Zone 5-9. Grown since the 17th century. Native to Europe. *Source History: 1 in 1992; 2 in 2000.* **Sources: Hid, Rai.**

Hawthorn, Red Haw - *Crataegus mollis*. Small, pear-shaped, red fruit with thick, mealy flesh suitable for jelly. Small tree with stout thorns. Probably the most decorative of the hawthorns with bright green leaves and showy flowers and fruit. Native from Ontario and Minnesota southward to Alabama and Mississippi. Hardy in Zone 5. *Source History: 3 in 1988; 3 in 1992; 1 in 2000.* **Sources: So5.**

Hawthorn, Russian - *Crataegus ambigua*. One of the best hawthorns for fruit production and hardiness. Dwarf tree grows to 10'. Fruits look like a dark cherry. Shows good resistance against black spot. Hardy to -35 degrees F. *Source History: 1 in 2000.* **Sources: Oik.**

Hawthorn, Succulent - *Crataegus succulenta*. Bright scarlet fruit, .5" in diameter. Small tree or large bush has stout, thorny branches which bear white flowers in May. Ripens in September or October. Fully hardy. Indian tribes pressed the berries into cakes and dried them for winter use. Native from New England to Minnesota. *Source History: 1 in 1988; 2 in 1992; 2 in 2000.* **Sources: GR26, So12.**

Hawthorn, Yellow - *Crataegus flava*. Small crooked tree bears yellow to red fruit. Hardy in Zone 5. *Source History: 1 in 1992; 1 in 2000.* **Sources: Wo2.**

Himalayan Bramble - *Rubus tricolor*. Semi-evergreen ground cover for shady places; 12" tall. Dark, glossy green leaves on soft-bristly, red stems. White, 1" flowers are sometimes followed by large, edible, bright red fruits. Hardy in Zone 6. Native to China. *Source History: 1 in 1988; 1 in 1992; 1 in 2000.* **Sources: Fo2.**

Himalayan Honeysuckle (Chocolate Berry) - *Leycesteria formosa*. Semi-evergreen shrub grows to 6' tall. Produces small round green berries that turn dark purple when ripe. Flavor resembles bitter chocolate. Rare. Originated in Tibet. *Source History: 1 in 2000.* **Sources: Rai.**

Himalayan Peach Berry (Himalayan Damarru) - *Maclura conchinensis*. Small Himalayan fruit tree related to North America's osage orange. Vines grow 50' reaching for sunlight in native forests. Translucent yellow fruits have a melting peachy-cream raspberry flavor. Low in acid. Matures in late September and October. Can be kept to bush size for pot culture. Tree remains evergreen in temperatures above 10 degrees F. Drought tolerant. Trademarked. *Source History: 1 in 2000.* **Sources: Or2.**

Holboellia latifolia - Related to the fruiting Japanese Akebia. Sausage-shaped, rosy-purple fruits about 2-4" long. Sweet flesh. Hardy to 0 degrees F. Native to the Himalayas. *Source History: 1 in 1992; 1 in 2000.* **Sources: Or2.**

Honeyberry - *Lonicera kamchatika*. Small shrub produces blueberry-like fruit a month before the earliest blueberries. Two needed for pollination. Hardy to -40 degrees F. Native to Siberia. *Source History: 2 in 2000.* **Sources: Bu7, Mel.**

Honeyberry, Berry Blue (Edible Bush Honeysuckle) - *Lonicera kamchatika*. Unique member of the Honeysuckle family with edible blue berries. Very upright and vigorous growth habit. Not self-fertile; plant at least two varieties to insure pollination. Reaches 8' or more. Zone 3. Native to Eastern Siberia. Trademarked. *Source History: 3 in 2000.* **Sources: Ed2, Gr16, On3.**

Honeyberry, Blue Belle - *Lonicera kamchatika*. Attractive bush with a spreading habit; shows moderate vigor. Should grow to 4-5' tall. Member of the Honeysuckle family with tasty small fruits about the size and flavor of blueberries. Zone 3. Trademarked. *Source History: 4 in 2000.* **Sources: Bu7, Clo, On3, Rai.**

Honeyberry, Blue Bird - *Lonicera kamchatika*. Unique member of the Honeysuckle family with no disease or pest problems. Upright bush shows less vigor; reaches 5-6' height. Small white slightly fragrant flowers appear in March. Fruit ripens two weeks before strawberries. Native to Eastern Siberia. Zone 3. Trademarked. *Source History: 2 in 2000.* **Sources: On3, Rai.**

Honeyberry, Blue Velvet - *Lonicera kamchatika*. Deciduous bush with attractive grey-green, velvet-like foliage. Should reach 3-4' tall. Plant at least two varieties for pollination. Hardy to -40 degrees F. Trademarked. *Source History: 4 in 2000.* **Sources: Bu7, Clo, Gr16, On3.**

Honeysuckle, Edible (Bearberry Honeysuckle) - *Lonicera caerulea* var. *edulis*. Blue teardrop-shaped berries used for jam and jelly. Contain small seeds like a blueberry. Flavor of blueberry but not as sweet. Grows 3' tall; earliest plant in the nursery to leaf out, flower and set fruit. Hardy in Zones 4-8. Developed at Beaverlodge Experiment Station in Alberta, Canada. *Source History: 1 in 1988; 2 in 1992; 3 in 2000.* **Sources: Oik, Stl, Tri.**

Horseradish Tree - *Moringa oleifera*. Seeds are roasted and eaten. Fast growing 30' tree with fern-like foliage and pendulous seedpods. Roots taste like horseradish. Native to India. *Source History: 1 in 1988; 3 in 1992; 3 in 2000.* **Sources: Ban, Ca7, Ga11.**

Huckleberry, Black - *Gaylussacia baccata*. Low maintenance groundcover bears sweet, flavorful berries. Shade tolerant but requires light for fruit production. Requires a sandy, somewhat acidic soil. *Source History: 1 in 2000.* **Sources: Tri.**

Huckleberry, Box - *Gaylussacia brachycera*. Blue, edible fruit. Slow growing, low mound plant wih thick, leathery, bright green leaves that turn bronze-red in winter. Spreads by underground stems. Prefers partial sun and well drained soil. Native to the mountains of Pennsylvania and Tennessee. *Source History: 1 in 1992; 1 in 2000.* **Sources: We8.**

Ice Cream Bean - *Inga paterno*. Pods contain a sweet, edible pulp that resembles cotton candy. Majestic, fast growing tree. Hardy in Zone 10. *Source History: 3 in 1988; 1 in 1992; 2 in 2000.* **Sources: Ga11, Po7.**

Illawarra Plum - *Podocarpus elatus.* Australian native. Produces rich purple-black fruits. The inedible seed grows outside the fruit. A popular plant in the resurgence of Australian "bushfood" down under. *Source History: 1 in 2000.* **Sources: Po7.**

Jaboticaba - *Myrciaria cauliflora.* Round, .75-1.5" purple fruit. Tree can grow 40' tall. Native to southern Brazil. (**Na13** is also offering the species *Myrciaria trunciflora.* Please specify). *Source History: 4 in 1988; 7 in 1992; 10 in 2000.* **Sources: Ban, Ga11, Na13, On4, Pa2, PI3, PL2, Po7, Ro13, Tr10.**

Jaboticaba, Giant - *Myrciaria jaboticaba.* *Source History: 1 in 2000.* **Sources: Po7.**

Jaboticaba, Yellow - *Myrciaria glomirata.* *Source History: 2 in 1988; 1 in 1992; 1 in 2000.* **Sources: Po7.**

Jackfruit - *Artocarpus heterophyllus.* Oblong, 24" fruit covered with hard points. Eaten fresh when ripe or cooked as a vegetable when unripe. Upright tree grows 5' or taller. Native to lowland tropics. *Source History: 2 in 1988; 5 in 1992; 11 in 2000.* **Sources: An4, Ga11, Me2, Na13, On4, Our, Pa2, PI3, PL2, Po7, Tr10.**

Jackfruit, Black Gold - Firm flesh type. *Source History: 1 in 1992; 1 in 2000.* **Sources: PL2.**

Jackfruit, Singapore Dwarf - *Artocarpus heterophyllus.* *Source History: 1 in 2000.* **Sources: On4.**

Jambolan (Java Plum) - *Syzygium cumini.* Oval, .5" long, purplish red berries. Tree grows 50-80' tall. Hardy to 26 degrees F. Native to India, Ceylon and Malaysia. *Source History: 1 in 1988; 1 in 1992; 1 in 2000.* **Sources: Pa2.**

Japanese Raisin Tree - *Hovenia dulcis.* Large, fleshy fruit stem tastes like a raisin or date. Tiny seeds at the end of the stem are not eaten. Medium size, deciduous tree to 30'. Heart-shaped leaves. White flowers. Hardy to -20 degrees F. *Source History: 3 in 1988; 15 in 1992; 17 in 2000.* **Sources: Arb, Ban, Co24, Fo2, Fra, Gr16, Ju2, Me2, Mel, Na13, On3, Or2, Pa2, Pa6, Sc2, Sh14, Tri.**

Java Plum (Jambolan) - *Syzygium cumini.* Clusters of purple grape-like berries with tart-sweet flavor. *Source History: 1 in 1992; 3 in 2000.* **Sources: An4, Pa2, Po7.**

Jelly Palm - *Butia captitata.* Edible, oval, orange fruit; 1" long and 1.5" in diameter. Pineapple-coconut flavor. Slow growing, 20' palm with 18" diameter trunk and bluish gray recurving fronds. Hardy in Zone 8. Native to Brazil. *Source History: 2 in 1988; 5 in 1992; 6 in 2000.* **Sources: Ga11, LO6, Or2, Pa2, Sc2, We15.**

Jojoba (Goat Nut) - *Simmondsia chinensis.* Nut-like, edible fruit .25-.75" long. Mainly pressed for oil that is used by industry as a substitute for sperm whale oil. Seed oil has proven superior to any known cooking oil; odorless and does not turn rancid. Stiff branched, multistemmed desert plant grows 6-12' tall. May take 5-7 years for first fruiting. Currently being planted commercially in Texas and West Africa. Hardy in Zone 10. Native to southern California and desert areas in the Southwest. *Source History: 8 in 1988; 13 in 1992; 7 in 2000.* **Sources: Ban, Ca12, Ca7, Ksa, Or2, Pla, Sc2.**

Jojoba, Pacific - *Simmondsia chinensis.* Male. *Source History: 1 in 2000.* **Sources: Pa2.**

Jojoba, Paul Thomson - *Simmondsia chinensis.* Female. *Source History: 1 in*

2000. **Sources: Pa2.**

Juniper, Oneseed - *Juniperus monosperma.* Evergreen shrub or small tree to 25' tall. Dark blue juicy berries are sweet and resinous. *Source History: 1 in 2000.* **Sources: So12.**

Juniper, Rocky Mountain - *Juniperus scopulorum.* Tree grows to 40'. *Source History: 1 in 2000.* **Sources: Fo2.**

Kaffir Plum - *Harpephyllum caffrum.* Dark red fruit, 1" long and .5" across. Used in jelly. Delicate, attractive, 30', subtropic tree. Irregular branching and numerous 2.5", glossy, leathery leaves produce an unusually appealing asymmetrical shape. White or greenish flowers. Grown in Zone 10 as an ornamental. *Source History: 5 in 1988; 4 in 1992; 3 in 2000.* **Sources: Ban, Ca7, Po7.**

Kaphal - *Myrica nagai.* Tall spreading evergreen bears tasty purple berries. Makes a sparkling wine colored juice. Native to the forests of the mid-Himalaya. Trademarked. *Source History: 1 in 2000.* **Sources: Or2.**

Kei Apple - *Dovyalis caffra.* Smooth, 1-2" yellowish orange fruit is quite tart. Juicy, acidic, yellow pulp. Used for making preserves, jelly and pickles. Contains 83 mg of Vitamin C per 100 grams. Thorny shrub or small tree grows 20' tall. Good hedge plant. Hardiest species, standing some frost and drought. Native to South Africa where it is called Umkokolo by the Xhosa tribe. *Source History: 3 in 1988; 1 in 1992; 3 in 2000.* **Sources: Pa2, Po7, Tr10.**

Kei Apple, Sweet Clone - *Dovyalis caffra. Source History: 1 in 1988; 1 in 1992; 1 in 2000.* **Sources: Ga11.**

King Haw - *Docynia.* Golden fruits are 3 in. across. Evergreen tree. Trademarked. *Source History: 1 in 2000.* **Sources: Or2.**

Kinnikinnick, Massachusetts - *Arctostaphylos Uva-ursi.* Evergreen ground cover with bright red, edible berries which last well into winter. Thrives in poor, dry soil. Scarify and stratify; difficult to germinate. *Source History: 1 in 1992; 6 in 2000.* **Sources: Abu, GR26, HI10, LA4, NA5, Rai.**

Lardizabala biternata - Twining plant to 12'. Chocolate-purple flowers followed by purple "sausage" fruit on female plant. Hardy to Zone 9. Native to Chile. *Source History: 1 in 2000.* **Sources: Fo2.**

Lemonade Berry - *Rhus integrifolia.* Evergreen with shiny round leaves. Red fruit is used for ades. Height to 8'. Zone 8. *Source History: 2 in 2000.* **Sources: Co24, Fo2, So12.**

Lilly-Pilly, Blue - *Syzygium oleossum.* Australian fruit. *Source History: 1 in 2000.* **Sources: Po7.**

Lime Berry - *Triphasia trifolia.* Dull red fruit is .5" in diameter and contains a slimy, mucus-like pulp. Tree grows 15' tall. Native to Malaysia. Hardy in Zone 9. *Source History: 1 in 1988; 1 in 1992; 1 in 2000.* **Sources: Ga11.**

Lingonberry (Foxberry, Lingenberry, Cowberry, Mountain Cranberry) - *Vaccinium vitis-idaea.* Popular ground cover from Europe. Produces large quantities of tiny, tasty, sour, long lasting, cranberry-like, dark red berries. Used for preserves and syrups. Dainty, creeping evergreen only 10-12" tall. Shiny, dark green, leathery leaves. Pinkish white, bell-shaped flowers in nodding clusters. Prefers a cool, fairly sunny spot on rocky, acid, peaty soil. Needs constant moisture and partial shade in hot summer areas. Ripens in late spring. Hardy in Zone 4-7. Native to Arctic regions of Europe and North Asia where it is highly valued. *Source History: 5 in 1988; 8 in 1992; 15 in 2000.* **Sources: BR2, Bu7, Clo, Fo2, HA12, Hud, In5, Jun, Par, Sis, TOW, VIR, Wbn, We4, We8.**

Lingonberry, Dwarf (Mountain Cranberry) - *Vaccinium vitis-idaea* var. *minor*. Miniature version that is native to North America. Small, sour, .4" red berries. Dwarf plant forms a dense mat and spreads by underground runners. Small, shining green summer foliage turns mahogany-red in winter. Pink to reddish pink flowers in May. Prefers full sun and rich, humusy, well-drained soil. Ripens during August. Hardy in Zone 2. *Source History: 3 in 1988; 6 in 1992; 3 in 2000.* **Sources: BR2, Rai, Sis.**

Lingonberry, Erntedank Cultivar - *Vaccinium vitis-idaea*. Medium size red fruit. Produces both a heavy spring and summer crop. Zone 5. Developed in Germany. *Source History: 3 in 2000.* **Sources: BA10, BR2, Fo2.**

Lingonberry, Erntekrone Cultivar - *Vaccinium vitis-idaea*. Leaves are more rounded than the species. Large dark red fruit. Zones 5-7. Developed in Germany. *Source History: 3 in 2000.* **Sources: BA10, BR2, Fo2.**

Lingonberry, Erntestegen Cultivar - *Vaccinium vitis-idaea*. Evergreen shrub to 1'. Dark green, shiny leaves. Produces clusters of red berries. Requires acid soil. Disease resistant. Zones 4-7. *Source History: 4 in 2000.* **Sources: De2, Ed5, HA12, Hid.**

Lingonberry, European Red - *Vaccinium vitis-idaea*. Related to both blueberries and cranberries. Bears two crops, one in July and the second, larger crop in October. Fruit is eaten fresh and made into jams, juices or wine. Hardy to Zone 4. Native to North America but has been an important fruit crop for the Scandinavian countries for many years. *Source History: 1 in 2000.* **Sources: Or2.**

Lingonberry, Koralle Cultivar - *Vaccinium vitis-idaea* var. *major*. Small, round fruit of excellent quality compared to other cultivars. Plant height 12-15" and spreads to 12" at maturity. Zone 4. West German origin. *Source History: 3 in 1992; 12 in 2000.* **Sources: BA10, BR2, Co12, De2, Ed2, FAL, Fo2, Gr16, HA12, On3, Or2, Rai.**

Lingonberry, Masovia Cultivar - *Vaccinium vitis-idaea*. Heavy crops of red fruit. Zone 5. Developed by the Warsaw (Poland) Agricultural University. *Source History: 2 in 2000.* **Sources: BA10, Fo2.**

Lingonberry, Red Pearl - *Vaccinium vitis-idaea*. Large, dark red berries are 7-10 mm in diameter. Excellent quality. Grows upright to 16 in. tall. Not as productive as Koralle but is more adaptable to varying soil types and grows faster. Good pollinator for Koralle. Good disease resistance. Zones 3-8. Originated in West Germany. *Source History: 8 in 2000.* **Sources: Bea, Bu7, De2, Ed5, FAL, HA12, Hid, Rai.**

Lingonberry, Regal - *Vaccinium vitis-idaea*. Plants grow to a height of 8-15". Medium to large berries are firm. Good flavor. Shows resistance to root disease. Developed at the Univ. of Wisconsin. PVP. *Source History: 5 in 2000.* **Sources: Ag4, De2, Ed5, HA12, Stl.**

Lingonberry, Sanna - Moderately spreading bush grows to 8-12 in. tall. Produces a good quality berry. Flavor has distinct acidity and sweetness. No problem with root disease. Yields of 6 tons per acre are reported in Sweden. U.S. Plant Patent No. VF 829.940525. *Source History: 4 in 2000.* **Sources: De2, Ed5, FAL, HA12.**

Lingonberry, Scarlet Cultivar - *Vaccinium vitus-idaea* var. *majus*. Plant height is 12-15" with 15-18" spread at maturity. Used as pollinator for Koralle lingonberry. Originated in Norway. *Source History: 3 in 1992; 2 in 2000.* **Sources: BA10, Co12.**

Lingonberry, Splendor - *Vaccinium vitis-idaea*. Sister selection of Regal.

Vigorous plants grows 8-15". Medium to large size berries of good quality. Shows resistance to Phytophthera root disease. Developed at the University of Wisconsin. PVP. *Source History: 6 in 2000.* **Sources: Ag4, De2, Ed5, HA12, Mel, Stl.**

Lingonberry, Sussi - Spreading, 6-18" tall bush produces high quality, medium to large size berries. Good sweet-acid flavor. Excellent vigor. Moderate production. Uniform ripening. No root disease problem. Patented by the Swedish Agricultural Department. *Source History: 4 in 2000.* **Sources: De2, FAL, HA12, Mel.**

Lo Han Kuo - Chinese edible fruiting *Podocarpus* bears translucent green, red and purple berries with much the same texture and taste of a Thompson Seedless grape, but not as rich. Fruit is borne in clusters at the ends of branches; easily shaken from the tree when ripe. Evergreen trees grow 10-15' tall. *Source History: 1 in 2000.* **Sources: Or2.**

Longan (Lungan) - *Euphoria longan.* Yellowish brown, 1" fruit with white, juicy flesh. Evergreen tree can grow 40' tall. Native to India. Hardy in Zone 10. *Source History: 1 in 1988; 1 in 1992; 4 in 2000.* **Sources: An4, Ga11, Po7, Tr10.**

Longan, Diamond River - *Euphoria longan. Source History: 1 in 2000.* **Sources: On4.**

Longan, Ewai - *Source History: 1 in 2000.* **Sources: PL2.**

Longan, Kohala - *Euphoria longan. Source History: 2 in 1988; 3 in 1992; 5 in 2000.* **Sources: Me2, On4, Pa2, PI3, PL2.**

Longan, New - *Source History: 1 in 2000.* **Sources: Pa2.**

Longan, Sri Champoo - Pink fleshed fruit. Originated in Thailand. *Source History: 1 in 1992; 3 in 2000.* **Sources: On4, Pa2, PL2.**

Longan, Tiger Eye - *Source History: 1 in 2000.* **Sources: Pa2.**

Longan, View Kiew - *Source History: 1 in 2000.* **Sources: PL2.**

Lychee (Leechee, Lichi, Litchi, Litchee) - *Litchi chinensis.* Bright red, 1.5" fruit looks somewhat like a strawberry, but has a brittle shell that covers a firm, juicy, white, grape-like flesh. Excellent fresh, dried or canned. Tree can grow 40' tall. Long, leathery leaves. Very ornamental; difficult to grow. Hardy to 28 degrees F. Native to China. *Source History: 1 in 1988; 3 in 1992; 3 in 2000.* **Sources: An4, Po7, Tr10.**

Lychee: Bosworth - *Litchi chinensis.* Pink skinned fruit. Regular bearing. *Source History: 1 in 1992; 2 in 2000.* **Sources: On4, PL2.**

Lychee: Brewster - *Litchi chinensis. Source History: 3 in 1988; 4 in 1992; 5 in 2000.* **Sources: Ga11, Me2, On4, Pa2, PI3.**

Lychee: Emperor - *Litchi chinensis. Source History: 1 in 2000.* **Sources: On4.**

Lychee: Farwell Ranch - *Source History: 1 in 2000.* **Sources: Pa2.**

Lychee: Groff - Small seed. Late season. *Source History: 1 in 1992; 2 in 2000.* **Sources: Pa2, PL2.**

Lychee: Hak Ip - *Litchi chinensis. Source History: 1 in 2000.* **Sources: On4.**

Lychee: Kaimana - *Litchi chinensis.* Regular bearing. Originated in Hawaii. *Source History: 1 in 1992; 2 in 2000.* **Sources: On4, PL2.**

Lychee: Kwai Mi - *Source History: 1 in 1988; 2 in 1992; 2 in 2000.* **Sources: Pa2, PL2.**

Lychee: Mauritius - *Litchi chinensis. Source History: 1 in 1988; 4 in 1992; 4 in 2000.* **Sources: Ga11, On4, Pa2, PI3.**

Lychee: Sweet Cliff - *Litchi chinensis. Source History: 1 in 1988; 1 in 1992; 2 in 2000.* **Sources: On4, Pa2.**

Madrone - *Arbutus menziesii.* Edible red fruits. Large tree with red, peeling bark and large, glossy leaves. Hardy in Zone 7. *Source History: 1 in 1992; 2 in 2000.* **Sources: Fo2, Las.**

Madrono - *Rheedia madruno.* Leathery fruit contains 1-5 seeds surrounded by edible pulp. Native to Ecuador. *Source History: 1 in 1988; 1 in 1992; 2 in 2000.* **Sources: Ga11, Or2.**

Malay Apple - *Syzygium malaccense.* Pear-shaped, 2" brown fruit that contains large seeds. Eaten raw or cooked; also used for preserves and wine. Beautiful tropical tree grows 15-40' tall. *Source History: 1 in 1988; 2 in 1992; 5 in 2000.* **Sources: Ga11, Me2, On4, Po7, Ro13.**

Mamey Apple (Mammee Apple, Mamey de Cartagena) - *Mammea americana.* Grapefruit size fruits with brown, leathery skin and peach-like flesh with one large, lime size seed. Large tropical tree. *Source History: 2 in 1992; 1 in 2000.* **Sources: Ga11.**

Mandarin Melon Berry (Che) - *Cudrania tricuspidata.* Bright red, 1-1.5" fruits with sweet, papaya-melon flavor. Acidless flesh. Mature trees bear up to 400 pounds of fruit each season. Trees need a warm, sunny area with rich soil and adequate water throughout the growing season. Hardy in Zone 5. Native to China. *Source History: 1 in 1992; 2 in 2000.* **Sources: Or2, Pa6.**

Mangosteen - *Rheedia aristata.* Edible aril. *Source History: 1 in 1992; 3 in 2000.* **Sources: Ga11, On4, PL2.**

May Apple - *Podophyllum peltatum.* Fruit resembles a small lemon and is edible when fully ripe. Unusual but agreeable flavor. Best eaten in small quantities. All other parts of the plant are poisonous. Perennial woodland plant grows 12-18" tall and can form a dense colony. Two large, deeply divided, umbrella-like, light green leaves. Leaves tend to die off in late summer. Single, white, nodding, waxy, 6-9 petaled flower opens in late spring but is mostly hidden by the leaves. Prefers the moist, rich soil and the partial shade of a woodland environment. Native from Quebec southward to Florida and Texas. *Source History: 6 in 1988; 8 in 1992; 6 in 2000.* **Sources: Dab, Fa1, Ga8, Gra, Lit, Sha.**

Mayhaw (Jellymaker) - *Crataegus aestivalis.* Fruit is excellent for jelly and pies. Tree grows 30' tall. Prefers wet soil. Hardy in Zones 7-10. *Source History: 2 in 1988; 3 in 1992; 5 in 2000.* **Sources: Bu7, Fo2, LO6, Rai, Ty2.**

Mayhaw: Big Red (No. 1 Big) - *Crataegus aestivalis.* Deep red fruit about 1" in diameter. Vigorous and ornamental. Ripens in May. Requires 500-600 hours of chilling. Hardy to -26 degrees F. *Source History: 1 in 1988; 2 in 1992; 4 in 2000.* **Sources: Bay, Hid, Ju2, Or2.**

Mayhaw: Blazing Star - Bright red fruit has a six-sided shape, resembling a pumpkin. Snappy flavor. *Source History: 1 in 2000.* **Sources: Ju2.**

Mayhaw: Crimson - Large red fruit up to .75" makes a deep red jelly. *Source History: 1 in 2000.* **Sources: Ju2.**

Mayhaw: Duck Lake - Blooms late. Disease resistant. Zones 6-9. *Source History: 1 in 2000.* **Sources: Hid.**

Mayhaw: Elite - Red fruits ripen at one time for easier harvest. *Source History: 1 in 2000.* **Sources: Or2.**

Mayhaw: Fall - Bushy upright tree bears 1" fruit. Ripens in the fall instead of spring. Zones 6-8. *Source History: 1 in 2000.* **Sources: Ed2.**

Mayhaw: Golden Farris - Golden yellow berries make a nice yellow jelly. Productive. Bears young. *Source History: 2 in 2000.* **Sources: Ju2, Or2.**

Mayhaw: Goldie - Similar to Golden Farris with later bloom time. *Source History: 1 in 2000.* **Sources: Or2.**

Mayhaw: Goliath - Dark red fruits make red juice. Productive. *Source History: 1 in 2000.* **Sources: Or2.**

Mayhaw: Harrison - Pink, 1" fruit. *Source History: 1 in 2000.* **Sources: Sh3.**

Mayhaw: Heavy - *Crataegus aestivalis.* Heaviest bearing mayhaw. Bright red fruit. Hardy in Zone 6. *Source History: 1 in 1992; 1 in 2000.* **Sources: Hid.**

Mayhaw: Ivan - *Source History: 1 in 2000.* **Sources: Sh3.**

Mayhaw: Jerry Means - Matures late. *Source History: 1 in 2000.* **Sources: Sh3.**

Mayhaw: King Haw - *Crataegus scabrifolia.* *Source History: 1 in 2000.* **Sources: Sh3.**

Mayhaw: Radiant Red - Blooms late. Red fruit with dark red flesh. Zones 6-9. *Source History: 1 in 2000.* **Sources: Hid.**

Mayhaw: Reliable - Light orange, large berry. Blooms late. *Source History: 2 in 2000.* **Sources: Ju2, Or2.**

Mayhaw: Royalty - *Crataegus aestivalis.* Red, 1" fruit. Tough skin. Ripens medium late. Zones 6-8. *Source History: 3 in 2000.* **Sources: Ed2, Hid, Sh3.**

Mayhaw: Shan Cha (China's Fall Haw) - *Crataegus pinnatifida.* Fruit is five times larger than American spring ripening haw species. Cultivated for more than 2000 years in China; valuable economic cash crop for modern Chinese arborists. Has a shelf-life of several months without refergeration. Ripens in the fall. *Source History: 1 in 2000.* **Sources: Or2.**

Mayhaw: Super Spur - *Crataegus aestivalis.* Finest mayhaw found yet. Best of all for jelly and syrup. Hardy in Zone 6. *Source History: 2 in 1988; 4 in 1992; 3 in 2000.* **Sources: Ju2, Or2, Sh3.**

Mayhaw: T. O. Warren's Opaca - *Crataegus opaca.* Blooms a few days later than Texas Superberry. Bears both orange and red fruit at the same time. Delicious. *Source History: 1 in 1992; 2 in 2000.* **Sources: Ju2, Or2.**

Mayhaw: T. O. Warren's Super Berry - Blooms early. Large dark red fruits hang well on the plant for a long time. *Source History: 1 in 2000.* **Sources: Or2.**

Mayhaw: Texas Star - Fruit is borne in clusters with seven or more berries up to 1" in size. Blooms late. Good fall leaf color. Zones 6-8. *Source History: 2 in 2000.* **Sources: Ed2, Hid.**

Mayhaw: Texas Superberry (Superberry) - *Crataegus aestivalis.* Large fruit with quite a lot of purple color. Makes good preserves. Self-fruitful. Moderate chilling requirement. Hardy in Zone 6. *Source History: 2 in 1988; 2 in 1992; 1 in 2000.* **Sources: Bay.**

Mayhaw: The Gem - Blooms late. Dark red fleshed fruit. *Source History: 1 in 2000.* **Sources: Hid.**

Mayhaw: Western - *Crataegus opaca.* Small deciduous tree bears white flowers followed by edible fruits that make excellent jelly. Native to the western Gulf Coast. Zones 7-9. *Source History: 1 in 2000.* **Sources: Wo2.**

Mayhaw: Yellow - *Crataegus aestivalis.* Yellow fruited variety with good flavor. Appears somewhat less vigorous in growth. Hardy in Zone 6. *Source History:*

1 in 1992; 1 in 2000. **Sources: Or2.**

Medlar - *Mespilus germanica.* Apple-shaped, 1-2" brown fruit is edible when completely ripe; also used for preserves. Unusual, old-fashioned, picturesque tree grows 12-20' tall. Oblong, 5" hairy leaves; 3" white flowers. Garden favorite for centuries in Europe and England. Hardy in Zone 6. *Source History: 1 in 1988; 1 in 1992; 4 in 2000.* **Sources: Arb, Fo2, Mel, Sc2.**

Medlar: Breda Giant - *Mespilus germanica.* Slow growing tree to 20'. Medium size, apple-like fruit with a spicy, applesauce-like flavor and texture. Ripens in late fall when the trees begin to lose their leaves. Self-fertile. Originated in Holland. *Source History: 1 in 1988; 1 in 1992; 4 in 2000.* **Sources: Clo, Hid, On3, Or2.**

Medlar: Large Russian - Medium fruited variety. Mild flavor is similar to pear. Tough, disease free plant. Hardy to -35 degrees F. *Source History: 1 in 1988; 1 in 1992; 2 in 2000.* **Sources: Hid, Oik.**

Medlar: Macrocarpa - Classic European garden favorite. The 8-10' tree bears large white flowers at the branch tips, followed by 2" brown fruit. Usually eaten after frost when completely ripe and soft. *Source History: 1 in 2000.* **Sources: On3.**

Medlar: Nottingham (Northern Loquat) - Botanically somewhere between pear and hawthorn. Dark russet brown fruit forms without stem at the end of a shoot and becomes the half of a sphere with the sepals arranged around the edge of the flattish top. Picked after hard frost, flesh is still hard, green and austere; must be kept on dry, cool shelf for 1-2 months until pulp softens. Distinctive, pleasantly acid flavor. Small, ornamental tree grows 15-20' tall. White flowers resemble single, white roses. Easy to grow. Hardy. *Source History: 2 in 1988; 4 in 1992; 5 in 2000.* **Sources: Ed2, Hid, On3, Or2, So5.**

Medlar: Royal - *Mespilus germanica.* Fruit is 1" in diameter. Cinnamon-applesauce flavor. May be eaten raw or made into jelly. Fruit is hard at harvest time and must be allowed to ripen for a few weeks in a cool light place where it becomes soft and spicy. This process is called bletting. Moderate sized, spreading tree. Self-fertile. Zones 5-9. *Source History: 1 in 1988; 1 in 1992; 3 in 2000.* **Sources: On3, Or2, Rai.**

Medlar: Russian Giant - *Source History: 1 in 2000.* **Sources: Or2.**

Medlar: Seedless - *Mespilus germanica.* Beautiful ornamental 8-20' tree. Tasty 2" fruit is eaten when completely ripe and soft, usually after frost. Texture and taste resembles applesauce. *Source History: 1 in 2000.* **Sources: On3.**

Medlar: Supermol - Italian variety. *Source History: 1 in 2000.* **Sources: Hid.**

Medlar: Westerveld (Westerfield) - *Mespilus germanica.* Striking tropical looking foliage on a small 8-10' tree. Brown fruit is eaten when completely ripe and soft, usually after frost. Has the texture and taste of applesauce. *Source History: 2 in 2000.* **Sources: On3, Or2.**

Mesquite, Honey - *Prosopis juliflora.* Pods are 3-8" long and are filled with sweet, dry, nutritious pulp. Pounded and eaten by the Indians, added to cornmeal as a sweetener and made into a drink. Shrub or small tree grows 20' tall. Pinnate leaves. Slender, 2-3" spikes of flowers. Native from the U.S. Southwest to Chile. Introduced to India to control desertification. Can survive as a shrub on 3" annual rainfall while enriching the soil. *Source History: 1 in 1988; 2 in 1992; 1 in 2000.* **Sources: So12.**

Mimusops balata - Attractive tree bears tasty, round yellow fruit. Native to

Madagascar. *Source History: 1 in 2000.* **Sources: Na13.**

Mimusops obovata - Produces edible orange-red or yellow fruit. Native to South Africa. *Source History: 1 in 2000.* **Sources: Po7.**

Miracle Fruit (Miraculous Fruit) - *Synsepalum dulcificum.* Succulent, oval, holly-like, red fruit; 8" long and .4" in diameter. Other acid citrus fruits are said to taste sweet for up to two hours after chewing these berries; that is the "miracle" they perform. Shrub grows 12' tall. Native to West Africa. *Source History: 4 in 1988; 4 in 1992; 9 in 2000.* **Sources: Al8, Ban, Ga11, Me2, Na13, On4, Pa6, Pl3, Po7, Ro13.**

Mombin - *Spondias mombin.* Fern leaved trees yield a yellow date-like fruit which looks and tastes like a natural lemon meringue when eaten fresh. Bears heavy crops. Found in China's Jianxi hills to the Nepalese sub-Himalaya. Trademarked. *Source History: 1 in 1992; 2 in 2000.* **Sources: Me2, Or2.**

Mountain Apple, Red - Red edible fruit. *Source History: 2 in 1992; 1 in 2000.* **Sources: PL2.**

Mountain Apple, White - White edible fruit. *Source History: 1 in 1992; 1 in 2000.* **Sources: PL2.**

Mountain Ash, Chequer Tree - *Sorbus torminalis.* Fruits are high in vitamin C. Used in jellies. Tree grows to 80'. Hardy to -25 degrees F. Native to Britain. *Source History: 1 in 2000.* **Sources: Oik.**

Mountain Ash, Ivan's Beauty - *Sorbus aucuparia x aronia.* Mountain Ash x Chokeberry. Grows to 12-15' tall. Produces large clusters of white flowers with a pink tinge, followed by dark purple edible fruit the size of small pie cherries. Eaten fresh and used in preserves, pastry, juice and wine. Hardy to Zone 3. Ivan's Beauty and Ivan's Belle are named in honor of Ivan Michurin, one of Russia's most famous horticulturists and plant breeders. Trademarked. *Source History: 2 in 2000.* **Sources: On3, Or2.**

Mountain Ash, Ivan's Belle - *Sorbus aucuparia x Crataegus.* Attractive cross of Hawthorne and Mountain Ash. Resembles Ivan's Beauty in size, form and foliage. Wine-red fruit with a pleasing sweet-tart flavor. Somewhat self-fertile; plant two varieties to insure pollination. Zone 3. Trademarked. *Source History: 4 in 2000.* **Sources: Mel, On3, Or2, Rai.**

Mountain Ash, Rabina - *Sorbus aucuparia.* Selection of true Mountain Ash from Russia. Upright tree grows to 25' tall. Bears large bright orange fruit which is quite tasty eaten fresh. Zone 3. *Source History: 3 in 2000.* **Sources: On3, Or2, Rai.**

Mountain Ash, Rosina - *Sorbus aucuparia.* Selection of true Mountain Ash with long slender foliage. Bright orange fruit. Zone 3. Developed in the former East Germany. *Source History: 1 in 2000.* **Sources: On3.**

Mountain Ash, Shipova - *Sorbus x Pyrus.* Unique hybrid of Mountain Ash and Pear. Yellow-orange fruit is round and about the size of a large apricot. Seedless. Delicate rose-like aroma. The medium size pyramid shaped tree has dark silver-grey foliage. Requires a pollinator. Zone 3. Developed in Yugoslavia. *Source History: 3 in 2000.* **Sources: Mel, On3, Rai.**

Mountain Ash, Whitebeam - *Sorbus aria.* White flower clusters in May are followed by bright red-orange fruit that has the flavor of orange gummy bears. Excellent heat and drought tolerance. Attractive to birds. Hardy to -25 degrees F. *Source History: 1 in 2000.* **Sources: Oik.**

Mulberry, Paper - *Broussonetia papyrifera.* Sweet, orangish red fruit is .75" across. Quick growing, roundish tree grows 20-50' tall. Lobed, 8" leaves resemble fig leaves. Flowers are in drooping catkins and ball-like heads. Inner bark is used in papermaking and medicine. Juice is used as glue. Naturalized in the eastern U.S.; good street tree. Native to China and Japan. *Source History: 1 in 1988; 1 in 1992; 1 in 2000.* **Sources: Hud.**

Myrica rubra - Large, dark red fruit is eaten in Japan. Evergreen shrub. Hardy in Zones 9-10. *Source History: 1 in 1992; 1 in 2000.* **Sources: Co24.**

Myrobalan (Emblic) - *Phyllanthus emblica.* Sister tree to *P. acidus.* Deciduous, 50' tree with flaking bark. Small oval 1" fruits are eaten as pickles or stewed with sugar. *Source History: 1 in 2000.* **Sources: Ban.**

Nannyberry (Black Haw, Wild Raisin, Sheepberry) - *Viburnum lentago.* Oval, dark bluish black fruit with a bloom. Date-like flavor. Hangs on well into winter. Sought after by birds and hunters alike. Deciduous, upright shrub grows 10-20' tall. Shiny green leaves turn purplish red in the fall. Large clusters of fragrant, white flowers. Grows well in either shade or sun. Hardy in Zone 2. Native from the Hudson Bay to Georgia and Mississippi. *Source History: 13 in 1988; 25 in 1992; 30 in 2000.* **Sources: BA14, BO10, Ca8, Co15, CO3, CR6, Fed, Fo2, Fra, Ga8, GR26, HI7, KAN, KEE, LA4, LI7, Lit, LOV, Mc3, MEA, Mu2, Or2, Pi2, Sc2, Sh10, Sh14, SH8, Stl, Tri, WA8.**

Naranjilla (Lulo) - *Solanum quitoense.* Fruit resembles a small orange in size, color and taste. Greenish flesh has a peculiar fragrance. Excellent for dessert or as a refreshing juice. Robust shrub grows 4-8' tall. Large, 8-20", purple leaves. Bears in 6-12 months and continues for about two years. Grows best on fertile, well-drained slopes of humid, upland valleys with 60" of rainfall. Native to the northern Andes at 3,000-6,000' elevations. Hardy in Zone 10. *Source History: 2 in 1988; 5 in 1992; 3 in 2000.* **Sources: Ban, Ga11, Pa2.**

Natal Plum - *Carissa grandiflora.* Green and red, 1" fruit makes fine jelly. Slow growing, tropical, evergreen plant. Hardy in Zones 8-9 or indoors. *Source History: 2 in 1992; 4 in 2000.* **Sources: Ban, Ga11, Mel, Pa2.**

Needle Palm - Clusters of sweet, edible, 1" brown fruits. Hardy to 10 degrees F. *Source History: 1 in 1992; 1 in 2000.* **Sources: Or2.**

Nitre Bush (Karambi) - *Nitraria schoberi.* Olive-size, purplish red or golden fruit in September. Shrub grows 3-7' tall with whitish branches. White flowers in 1" clusters in June. Fruit is eaten throughout its range from Australia to southern Russia. *Source History: 1 in 1988; 1 in 1992; 1 in 2000.* **Sources: Hud.**

Ogechee Plum - *Nyssa ogeche.* Large red fruit can be used as lime substitute and for making jelly. Native the southern U.S. Hardy in Zones 7-9. *Source History: 1 in 1992; 1 in 2000.* **Sources: Wo2.**

Olive (Common Olive) - *Olea europaea.* Oblong, 1.5" fruit turns glossy black when ripe. Table olives are made by soaking and preserving in salt solution, thereby removing the bitterness. Oil is obtained by pressing; 70% oil. Highly nutritious. Broad crowned tree grows 10-60' tall. Narrow, silvery bottomed leaves. Fragrant, creamy flowers. Normally begins to bear at five years, but may bear during its second year. Yields average 3,000 lbs. per acre. Grown where minimum temperatures are above 15 degrees F. Hardy in Zone 9. Native to the Mediterranean region where it is a valuable economic crop. *Source History: 3 in 1988; 5 in 1992; 10 in 2000.* **Sources: Ban, Ca7, Co24, Fra, Hud, Na13, Ne4, ORA, Sc2, Sh14.**

Olive, Ascolano - *Olea europaea. Source History: 1 in 2000.* **Sources: Pa2.**

Olive, Grapolo - *Olea europaea. Source History: 1 in 2000.* **Sources: Pa2.**

Olive, Little Ollie - *Olea europaea. Source History: 1 in 2000.* **Sources: Pa2.**

Olive, Lucca - *Olea europaea. Source History: 1 in 2000.* **Sources: Pa2.**

Olive, Manzanillo - *Olea europaea.* Slow growing, 20-50' tree. Commercial cultivar grown for production of olives and the oil. *Source History: 1 in 1988; 2 in 1992; 2 in 2000.* **Sources: Ju2, Pa2.**

Olive, Mission - *Olea europaea. Source History: 1 in 2000.* **Sources: Pa2.**

Olive, Sevillano - *Olea europaea. Source History: 1 in 2000.* **Sources: Pa2.**

Opuntia compressa (Prickly Pear Cactus) - Prostrate cactus grows 8-10" tall. Pads are 4-7" long. Attractive, 2-3" yellow flowers are held upright above the plant. Purplish, edible, 2" fruits. Does well in poor, dry soils. Hardy to Zone 4. Collected in Nebraska. *Source History: 3 in 1988; 2 in 1992; 3 in 2000.* **Sources: Hud, Or2, So12.**

Opuntia compressa (Sel. No. 1) (Prickly Pear Cactus) - Low, spreading growth habit. Spineless pads are mostly 3-5" long. Yellow flowers up to 3" across, appearing mainly in June. Bears reasonably palatable fruit, which remains on the plant and in good condition all winter. Fruit tastes best in its second year on the plant. Hardy in Zones 4-10. Native to the U.S.; collected on the Connecticut coast. *Source History: 1 in 1988; 1 in 1992; 1 in 2000.* **Sources: Tri.**

Opuntia compressa (Sel. No. 2) (Prickly Pear Cactus) - Showiest flowers of these three selections. *Source History: 1 in 1988; 1 in 1992; 1 in 2000.* **Sources: Tri.**

Opuntia ficus indica (Burbank Spineless) - Large fruits with watermelon flavor. Spineless cactus grows 8-10' tall. Not hardy below 20 degrees F. Popular in the Southwest. *Source History: 2 in 1992; 3 in 2000.* **Sources: Ju2, Or2, Tri.**

Opuntia fragilis (Prickly Pear Cactus) - Small pads about 2" long. Relatively large, yellow flowers about 3" across appear in June. Said to grow wild as far north as the Arctic Circle. Hardy in Zones 3-10. Native to North America. *Source History: 1 in 1988; 1 in 1992; 1 in 2000.* **Sources: Tri.**

Opuntia humifusa (Prickly Pear Cactus) - Low growing plant with large pads to 8" long. Bears yellow flowers to 3" across in summer. Hardy in Zones 4-10. Native to U.S. *Source History: 1 in 1988; 1 in 1992; 1 in 2000.* **Sources: Tri.**

Opuntia humifusa rafinesquei - Similar to *Opuntia humifusa* but with smaller pads. Grows to 8". Zones 4-10. Native to Arkansas. *Source History: 1 in 1992; 1 in 2000.* **Sources: Tri.**

Opuntia macroriza - Small, narrow pads droop toward the ground. Pink, 2-3" fruits fall when ripe. Fair flavor. Ripens in November. *Source History: 1 in 1992; 1 in 2000.* **Sources: Or2.**

Opuntia phaeacantha (Prickly Pear Cactus) - Prostrate, or sometimes a low shrub to 12". Large pads to 8" long. Bears yellow flowers in June. Quite showy in fall when the large, dark red fruits ripen. Hardy in Zones 5-10. Native to the U.S. Southwest. *Source History: 1 in 1988; 1 in 1992; 1 in 2000.* **Sources: Tri.**

Opuntia: Honeydew - *Opuntia ficus indica tuna.* Pale lime-green, 3-4" fruits with a hint of honeydew flavor. Vigorous large spineless pads. *Source History: 1 in 2000.* **Sources: Or2.**

Opuntia: Kima's Supra Nopalito - *Opuntia sp. Supra noplaes.* Spineless, forest-green, thin, succulent pads. *Source History: 1 in 2000.* **Sources: Or2.**

Opuntia: Papaya - *Opuntia ficus indica tuna.* Large 3-4" oval pink fruits change to deep orange inside and out. Flavor of papaya. Pads also edible. Tall plant to 8'. *Source History: 1 in 2000.* **Sources: Or2.**

Opuntia: White - *Opuntia ficus indica tuna.* Extra large fruit with light colored flesh. Large pads with very small spines. *Source History: 1 in 2000.* **Sources: Or2.**

Orange-Berry - *Glycosmis pentaphylla. Source History: 1 in 2000.* **Sources: Ga11.**

Oregon Grape - *Mahonia aquifolium.* Medium-large shrub can reach 3-6' tall. Holly-like foliage. Bears clusters of blue fruit. Hardy in Zone 5. *Source History: 9 in 1992; 23 in 2000.* **Sources: Abu, BR2, BR6, Bu7, Ca7, Co24, Fo2, Fro, Gr16, GR26, HI10, IM2, LA4, LI7, MEA, MIS, MO10, NA5, No2, Pl5, Sc2, Sh14, Wa3.**

Oregon Grape, Dwarf (Creeping Mahonia, Holly Grape) - *Mahonia repens.* Metallic looking, .4" bluish black fruit ripens in August. Tart and tasty. Makes an interesting flavored jelly or wine. Used by Native Americans for jam or canned fruit. Root yields a tonic and blood purifier containing berberine, which is especially good for chronic liver complaints. Low growing, spreading, evergreen shrub is often used as a ground cover. Glossy leaves resemble English holly; turn a bronze color in winter. Bright yellow, bell-shaped flowers in spring. Very tough and drought resistant. Grows well in either sun or partial shade; requires shade in hot, dry climates. Zone 4. *Source History: 2 in 1988; 16 in 1992; 22 in 2000.* **Sources: Abu, ALD, Bea, BR6, Ca12, Ca7, Fo2, Gr16, GR26, HI10, LA4, Las, LI7, MIS, MO10, NA5, No2, Pl5, Pla, Sc2, Sh14, Wo2.**

Oregon Grape, Longleaf (Cascade Oregon Grape, Shining Oregon Grape, Coastal Oregon Grape) - *Mahonia nervosa.* Handsome shrub grows 2-3' tall. Fern-like growth habit. Tart, blue grape-like fruit. Prefers forest shade, lower elevations and coastal climates. Hardy in Zone 6. *Source History: 3 in 1992; 10 in 2000.* **Sources: Abu, ALD, Bu7, Fo2, Fro, MEA, NA5, No2, Sc2, Sh14.**

Oregon Grape, Red-Fruited - *Mahonia nevinii.* Red fruits used for jelly. Hardy in Zone 9. *Source History: 1 in 1992; 1 in 2000.* **Sources: Las.**

Oso Berry - *Oemlaria cerasiformis.* Small blue fruits grow in clusters. Hardy in Zone 6. *Source History: 1 in 1992; 1 in 2000.* **Sources: Fo2.**

Otaheitt Gooseberry - *Phyllanthus acidus.* Sour and sweet. Air layered. *Source History: 1 in 2000.* **Sources: On4.**

Parry Manzanita - *Arctostaphylos manzanita.* Fruit ripens from white to red. Sometimes used for jelly. Hardy in Zone 7. *Source History: 1 in 1988; 1 in 1992; 2 in 2000.* **Sources: Ca12, Las.**

Partridge Berry (Squawberry, Twinberry) - *Mitchella repens.* Bright red, .4", twin berries persist through the winter. Edible, but flavorless. Delicate, trailing, prostrate, clumpy, woodland plant forms a thick mat beneath either hardwoods or evergreens. Tiny, rounded, lustrous, dark green leaves veined with white on woody stems. Trumpet-shaped, fragrant, pale pink flowers fused in pairs; blooms in spring and early summer. Hardy in Zone 4. Native to eastern and central U.S. Named after Dr. John Mitchell (1680-1768), a physician, author, mapmaker and botanist, who corresponded with famous Swedish botanist Carl Linnaeus about native eastern North American plants. *Source History: 9 in 1988; 11 in 1992; 5 in 2000.* **Sources: Ba3, Fa1, Gra, Sha, Tri.**

Peach Palm - *Bactris gasipaes.* Bright red-orange fruits with high protein content. Grows to 60'. *Source History: 2 in 1992; 1 in 2000.* **Sources: Ga11.**

Peanut Butter Fruit - *Bunchosia argentea. Source History: 1 in 1988; 1 in 2000.* **Sources: Ga11.**

Pear x Mountain Ash Cross - *Sorbopyrus*. Plum size fruit. Coarse flesh with sweet pear flavor. Hardy to Zone 5. *Source History: 1 in 2000.* **Sources: Hid.**

Peruvian Apple Cactus, Pitaya - *Cereus peruvianus*. Red skinned fruits with white, edible flesh of fine quality. Plant grows to 10'. *Source History: 2 in 1992; 1 in 2000.* **Sources: Or2.**

Pigeon Plum - *Coccoloba diversifolia*. *Source History: 1 in 2000.* **Sources: Ga11.**

Pineapple - *Ananas comosus*. Fruit will be produced when the plant matures, after about 24 months. Nice houseplant. *Source History: 1 in 1988; 3 in 1992; 2 in 2000.* **Sources: Ga11, Our.**

Pineapple: Hawaiian King - Grown commercially in Hawaii. Plants grow to 2-3' and are covered with large violet blooms on dense spiked heads from January to March. Harvest from May through September. *Source History: 1 in 1992; 1 in 2000.* **Sources: Ju2.**

Pineapple: Sugar Loaf - *Ananas comosus*. *Source History: 1 in 1988; 2 in 1992; 1 in 2000.* **Sources: Pa2.**

Pineapple: Variegated - White fruit, skin and flesh. Plant leaves are striped with yellow and green. Plant signals approaching maturity by turning a beautiful cherry pink at the base of all its fronds. Fruits are borne on short stalks. *Source History: 1 in 1992; 2 in 2000.* **Sources: Ju2, Me2.**

Pineulas, Huichol - *Bromeliaceae*. Known by the Huichol as a relative to pineapples and bromeliads which are found growing in shaded nooks of canyons in Zacategas, Mexico. Egg-like fruits with a sweet-tart pineapple-like juice. *Source History: 1 in 2000.* **Sources: Or2.**

Pitahaya - *Hylocereus undatus*. Tasty fruit. May be self-fruitful near the coast but does best with cross-pollination. *Source History: 3 in 2000.* **Sources: Me2, On4, Po7.**

Pitomba - *Eugenia luschnathiana*. Soft, juicy, round, 1" orangish yellow fruit. Mildly acid, aromatic flavor. Good for jelly. Shrub. Native to Brazil. *Source History: 1 in 1988; 2 in 1992; 2 in 2000.* **Sources: Ga11, Po7.**

Porcelain Berry, Variegated - *Ampelopsis brevipedunculata*. Bland but edible pea size berries in several colors; blue, pink, white, lime-green and purple. Zones 5-9. *Source History: 1 in 2000.* **Sources: Rai.**

Prinsepia sinensis - Member of the Rose family bearing juicy, red to purple fruits that look like cherries. Pleasantly acid flavor. Plants grow 4-6' tall with slender, arching, spiny branches. Prefers well drained soil in a sunny location. Hardy to Zone 3. Native to Manchuria. *Source History: 1 in 1992; 1 in 2000.* **Sources: Or2.**

Provision Tree - *Pachira aquatica*. Bears brown, football size pods containing 2" seeds which are roasted and eaten. Resembles the Guyana Chestnut. Will grow at water's edge but will also tolerate dry conditions. Zone 9. *Source History: 1 in 2000.* **Sources: Na13.**

Quandong (Australian Peach) - *Santalum acuminata*. Thick skinned, .75" red fruit with pleasantly tart flavor. Used to make jam. Seed is also edible. The seed coat may be burned as a candle. Not commonly found. *Source History: 1 in 2000.* **Sources: Ban.**

Queen Haw - *Docynia*. Evergreen tree bears golden fruit. Trademarked. *Source History: 1 in 2000.* **Sources: Or2.**

Queen Palm - *Arecastrum romanzoffianum*. Edible, 1-1.5" yellowish orange fruit. Tree grows 40' tall; smooth trunk. Graceful, arching fronds. Hardy in Zone 9. Native from southern Brazil to Argentina. *Source History: 1 in 1988; 2 in 1992; 1 in 2000.* **Sources: Pa2.**

Raisin Tree - Known for its chewy, sweet, raisin-flavored flower stems. Tree grows 15-25'. Hardy to about -10 degrees F. Chinese refer to it as Falcon's Claw because of the bizarre shaped fruits. *Source History: 1 in 2000.* **Sources: Or2.**

Rambutan - *Nephelium jappaceum.* Small tree produces red fruit that is covered with soft spines. Resembles the Lychee fruit but is much larger. Seedling can be male or female. *Source History: 1 in 2000.* **Sources: Ro13.**

Red Mombin (Jocote, Purple Mombin, Spanish Plum) - *Spondias purpurea.* Spicy, dark red fruit; large seed. Eaten fresh, cooked or dried. Native to tropical America. Hardy in Zone 10. *Source History: 1 in 1988; 1 in 1992; 1 in 2000.* **Sources: Ga11.**

Rheedia edulis - New World counterpart to the *Garcinia* with leathery foliage and edible fruit. *Source History: 1 in 2000.* **Sources: Po7.**

Rose Apple (Malabar Plum, Poma Rosa) - *Syzygium jambos.* Oval, 1.5" long, creamy yellow fruit. Crisp, dry, fragrant flesh tastes like a rose smells. Used to make jelly. Hardy to 25 degrees F. Native to Southeast Asia. *Source History: 3 in 1988; 6 in 1992; 7 in 2000.* **Sources: An4, Ban, Ga11, Me2, Pa2, Po7, Ro13.**

Rose Hips - *Rosa sericea pteracantha.* Fern leaved foliage. Four-petaled flowers. Bright red, pear-shaped hips. Originated in China. *Source History: 1 in 2000.* **Sources: Fo2.**

Rose Hips, Alba Suaveolens - Considered an old form of *Rosa alba.* White flowers bloom in early summer. Bears large crop of red hips which are unexcelled for flavor. *Source History: 1 in 2000.* **Sources: Fo2.**

Rose Hips, Apple Rose - *Rosa pomifera.* Single pink flowers. Extra large red fruits over 1" in diameter. Shrub grows to 7' high and wide. Yellow fall color. Hardy to Zone 3. Native to Europe. *Source History: 3 in 2000.* **Sources: Ed2, Fo2, Gr4.**

Rose Hips, Applecrisp Roses - Several varieties are offered. Golden yellow, 2" fruits are as crisp and sweet as an apple. Grows 4-8' tall. Red blushed foliage. Recently introduced from Asian. Trademarked. Plant patent applied for. *Source History: 1 in 2000.* **Sources: Or2.**

Rose Hips, Blanc Double - Extremely fragrant. White flowers. Large crimson hips. *Source History: 1 in 2000.* **Sources: Gr4.**

Rose Hips, Brier Rose - *Rosa canina.* White to pink single flowers followed by red or orange edible hips. Hardy to Zone 4. *Source History: 1 in 2000.* **Sources: Hud.**

Rose Hips, Carolina Rose - *Rosa carolina.* Single pink flowers. Red fruits appear in early fall. Hardy to Zone 5. *Source History: 1 in 2000.* **Sources: Fo2.**

Rose Hips, Cherryberry Roses - Rose hybrids that bear tasty red fruit in the fall. Plants reach 10' tall; relatively thorn-free. Trademarked. *Source History: 1 in 2000.* **Sources: Or2.**

Rose Hips, Dart's Dash - Disease resistant compact shrub bears masses of fragrant mauve-red double flowers all summer and fall, and large, delicious orange hips. *Source History: 1 in 2000.* **Sources: Rai.**

Rose Hips, Davids Rose - *Rosa Davidii.* Large shrub to 10'. Dark pink flowers produce an abundance of scarlet, bottle-shaped hips about 1" long. Disease free. Hardy to -25 degrees F. Native to western China. Rare. *Source History: 1 in 2000.*

Sources: Oik.

Rose Hips, Double Fragrance - Recent introduction. Highly fragrant, pale coral flowers. Sets very large hips. *Source History: 1 in 2000.* **Sources: Fo2.**

Rose Hips, Frau Dagmar Hastrup - Danish rose known for its extremely large, crimson hips. Disease resistant, 4-5' tall plant can be grown on a trellis or allowed to spread for a mass planting. Pale pink flowers appear in June through autumn, with flowers and hips on the plant at the same time. *Source History: 2 in 2000.* **Sources: Fo2, Rai.**

Rose Hips, Hansa - Large red-violet flowers. Shrub grows to 6'. Large red hips. Bred in Germany around the turn of the century. Zones 3-9. *Source History: 3 in 2000.* **Sources: CLI, Ed2, Or2.**

Rose Hips, Jubilee - *Rosa rugosa.* Russian variety bears striking red fruit with thick, tasty flesh. High vitamin C content. Can be eaten fresh, dried and powdered or used to make jelly. Vigorous, disease resistant shrub grows 5'. *Source History: 1 in 2000.* **Sources: On3.**

Rose Hips, Laxa - *Rosa laxa.* Nearly thornless form of *Rosa canina.* Single pale flowers followed by a large crop of hips. Often used as understock. *Source History: 1 in 2000.* **Sources: Gr4.**

Rose Hips, Meadow Rose - *Rosa blanda.* Native shrub grows to 3' with few thorns. Single pink flowers are followed by dark red hips. Eventually forms a small colony of plants. Easily pruned and managed in a small space. Hardy to -35 degrees F. *Source History: 1 in 2000.* **Sources: Oik.**

Rose Hips, Moyesii - Canes can reach 10' tall. Bears huge flagon-shaped hips in the fall. Native to China. *Source History: 1 in 2000.* **Sources: Gr4.**

Rose Hips, Nootka Rose (Nutka Rose) - *Rosa nutkana.* Native western species produces bottle-shaped, pink-red hips starting in mid-August. Fragrant, bright pink flowers grow on a compact thorny bush. Attracts butterflies and bumblebees. Hardy to -40 degrees F. *Source History: 9 in 2000.* **Sources: Abu, CLI, Fo2, LA4, MIS, NA5, Oik, Or2, Pl5.**

Rose Hips, Pasture Rose (Walters Strain) - *Rosa carolina.* Thought to be a naturally occuring hybrid of two native roses. Compact shrub to 3'. Pink flowers followed by an abundance of .5" red hips. Hardy to -40 degrees F. *Source History: 1 in 2000.* **Sources: Oik.**

Rose Hips, Peak Experience - *Rugosa x palustris* cross. Large, dark orange to red hips. Large fragrant single pink flowers. Hardy to -30 degrees F. *Source History: 1 in 2000.* **Sources: Oik.**

Rose Hips, Prickly Wild Rose - *Rosa acicularis.* Single pink round flowers appear in early spring. Long, dark red hips. Plant grows to 2' or less; hips are often found on plants only 6" tall. Hardy to -45 degrees F. *Source History: 1 in 2000.* **Sources: Oik.**

Rose Hips, Red Leaf Rose - *Rosa rubrifolia.* Single pink and red flowers. Purple stems. Red tinged foliage. Grows 6-7' tall. Bears .5" red hips. *Source History: 1 in 2000.* **Sources: Or2.**

Rose Hips, Red Rugosa Rose (Turkestan Rose) - *Rosa rugosa.* Hardy bush bears large, attractive red rose hips which ripen in midsummer. Used for making jelly. Contain more vitamin C than orange juice. Hardy in Zones 2-7. *Source History: 9 in 2000.* **Sources: Abu, Bea, Bu7, Fi1, Fo4, Mel, Mu2, So5, Stl.**

Rose Hips, Rosa Canina - Single, apple blossom-pink flowers with a delicate scent. Excellent tasting rose hips in the summer and fall. Zones 5-7. *Source His-*

tory: 1 in 2000. **Sources: Ed2.**

Rose Hips, Rubrifolia - *Rosa rubrifolia.* Deep rose-pink 3.5" blooms all summer followed by orange or red fruits. Purple foliage. Grows 4-6'. *Source History: 1 in 2000.* **Sources: Wa16.**

Rose Hips, Scabrosa - Large, disease resistant plant with 5" pink flowers which bloom for months. Large fleshy hips look like cherry tomatoes. *Source History: 1 in 2000.* **Sources: Rai.**

Rose Hips, Scotch Rose - *Rosa pimpinellifolia.* White, pink or yellow flowers. Sweet fruits yield a beautiful violet dye. Made into jellies. *Source History: 1 in 2000.* **Sources: Hud.**

Rose Hips, Sweet Briar (Elagantine Rose) - *Rosa eglanteria.* Fragrant pink flowers and leaves. Red edible hips. Disease resistant shrub to 6-8' tall. Foliage smells like fresh-cut apples. Hardy to Zone 4. Originated in Europe. *Source History: 5 in 2000.* **Sources: Fo2, Hud, LA4, Or2, Rai.**

Rose Hips, Tomato Rose - *Rosa rugosa.* Large, fragrant white, pink or red flowers followed by large edible hips. Hardy to Zone 3. Originated in Asia. *Source History: 2 in 2000.* **Sources: Fo2, Or2.**

Rose Hips, White Rugosa Rose - *Rosa rugosa alba.* Single white flowers followed by large orange hips, nickel to quarter size. Highest vitamin C content. Disease and insect resistant. Hardy to -45 degrees F; Zones 2-9. *Source History: 8 in 2000.* **Sources: Bea, Bu7, Ed2, Hud, LA4, Oik, Rai, Wh2.**

Rose Hips, Wild Dog - *Rosa canina.* Naturalized selection of a rose collected in southern Michigan by Oikos Tree Crops. Shrub grows to 6'. Covered with single pink flowers in early summer and followed by bright red globular hips which remain on through December. Disease and insect free. Hardy to -30 degrees F. *Source History: 1 in 2000.* **Sources: Oik.**

Rose Hips, Wild Rose - *Rosa rugosa.* Sweet-tart, 1"+ fruit on 10-12' shrubs. *Source History: 1 in 2000.* **Sources: So12.**

Rose Hips, Woods Rose - *Rosa woodsii.* Red hips can be eaten raw, stewed, candied or made into preserves. Edible flower petals can be candied or used in salads. Sun or part shade. *Source History: 1 in 2000.* **Sources: Pl5.**

Russian Olive (Oleaster, Silverberry, Wild Olive) - *Elaeagnus angustifolia.* Edible, .5", silvery yellow fruit; sweet-acid and mealy. Made into a dessert called "zinzeyd" in Persia. Used for distilling in Yarkland. Open, spreading tree grows 12-20' tall and wide. Brown, shedding bark. Long, narrow, silvery gray leaves. Small, fragrant, silvery yellow flowers in June. Nitrogen fixing ornamental; often used as windbreak for orchards and gardens. Makes an attractive, impenetrable hedge; favored by landscapers. Suitable for any soil; highly salt tolerant. Withstands drought, highway and seacoast conditions. Prefers full sun or partial shade. Hardy in Zones 2-6. *Source History: 37 in 1988; 63 in 1992; 53 in 2000.* **Sources: Ban, Bar, Bea, BO10, BO4, Bo5, Ca12, Ca7, CLI, Co15, Co24, CO3, CO5, Fi1, Fo2, Fo4, Fra, Gr16, GR26, HI10, HI7, Hud, Int, Jun, KEE, LA4, Lee, LI7, LO6, LOV, MEA, Mel, MI5, MIS, MO10, Mu2, No2, Pi2, Pl5, Po2, Sav, Sc2, SH8, So5, Stl, STR, TR19, TU5, Ty2, Va5, Wa16, WA8, Wom.**

Russian Olive: King Red (Red King Russian Olive) - *Elaeagnus angustifolia.* Selection of Russian Olive with extra large, bright, rusty red fruit. *Source History: 3 in 1988; 4 in 1992; 2 in 2000.* **Sources: CLI, Fo2.**

Salal - *Gaultheria shallon.* Bluish black berries the size of blueberries. Mild, pleasant taste. Medium size shrub is sometimes used as a ground cover in sunny

locations. If planted in the sun, will grow only about 2' tall; in shade it can reach 5-10'. Large, leathery, dark green leaves on red stalks. Pink, urn-shaped spring flowers resemble Lily of the Valley. One of the fruits most valued by Native Americans before the coming of the white man. Was used widely by all the coastal Indians as a staple in their diet; eaten both dried in cakes and fresh from the bush. Hardy in Zone 6. Native to the West. Often grows with huckleberry. *Source History: 3 in 1988; 8 in 1992; 9 in 2000.* **Sources: Abu, Bu7, Co24, Fo2, Fro, Lar, MIS, Or2, Rai.**

Salmonberry - *Rubus spectabilis.* Edible, salmon colored fruit. Medium size shrub; only slightly prickly. Deep pink flowers. The first *Rubus* species to fruit. Hardy in Zones 4-9. Native from Alaska to Idaho and California. *Source History: 4 in 1988; 4 in 1992; 9 in 2000.* **Sources: Abu, ALD, BA9, Bu7, Co24, Fo2, Fro, No2, Rai.**

Sandberry, Radient - *Arctostaphylos Uva-ursi.* *Source History: 2 in 2000.* **Sources: Las, Pe3.**

Sapodilla - *Manilkara Zapota.* Fruit varies in shape, usually 4" in diameter with thin, rough, brown skin. Sweet, clear, yellowish brown flesh. Tree can grow 100' or taller. Produces chicle which is the latex base used for chewing gum. Hardy to 28 degrees F. Native to Mexico and Central America. *Source History: 2 in 1988; 4 in 1992; 9 in 2000.* **Sources: An4, Ban, Ca7, Ga11, Na13, Pa2, PI3, Po7, Ro13.**

Sapodilla, Alano - *Manilkara Zapota.* *Source History: 1 in 2000.* **Sources: On4.**

Sapodilla, Hasya - *Manilkara Zapota.* *Source History: 1 in 2000.* **Sources: On4.**

Sapodilla, Morena - *Manilkara Zapota.* *Source History: 1 in 2000.* **Sources: On4.**

Sapodilla, Oxkutzcab - *Manilkara Zapota.* *Source History: 1 in 2000.* **Sources: On4.**

Sea Berry (Sallow Thorn, Sea Buckthorn) - *Hippophae rhamnoides.* Acidic, .25", bright orangish yellow berries staying through the winter. Eaten fresh and made into jelly in Europe, Siberia and Asia. High in vitamin C. Medicinal value. All parts yield yellow dye. Thorny shrub grows 15-30' tall; male and female plants. Attractive, lance-shaped, gray foliage. Nitrogen fixing. Hardy to Zone 3. *Source History: 3 in 1988; 4 in 1992; 10 in 2000.* **Sources: Abu, Bea, Fo2, GR26, Hid, LA4, LI7, Mel, On3, Or2, Stl.**

Sea Berry, Byantes - *Hippophae rhamnoides.* German variety. Medium size shrub bears sweet fruit. Zones 3-9. *Source History: 1 in 2000.* **Sources: On3.**

Sea Berry, Dorana - *Hippophae rhamnoides.* Dorana is a great variety for the home garden with a more compact growth habit. The deep orange fruit remains on the bush for most of the winter if not harvested. The Sea Berry is highly valued in Russia, China and Eastern Europe. Previously used only as a wildlife and shelter belt plant in our country. Tasty berries are an excellent source of vitamin C and make a delicious juice. Blooms in April; not injured by late spring frosts. Hardy to -40 degrees F. No sign of pest or disease problems. Ripens from August to October. Male and female plants are required to produce fruit. *Source History: 1 in 2000.* **Sources: On3.**

Sea Berry, Frugana - *Hippophae rhamnoides.* Bright orange berries with a mild pleasant taste. Should be harvested by September as the berry quality decreases. Upright, strong bush with open growth habit. Will reach 12-15' without pruning.

The long fruit stems make this variety easy for hand harvesting. Ripens early to late August.   Zone 3.   Developed by an East German breeding program. *Source History: 4 in 2000.* **Sources: Clo, Ed2, On3, Or2.**

Sea Berry, Hergo - *Hippophae rhamnoides.* Branches are densely covered with large orange fruits. The upright growth habit makes Hergo the most preferred variety for commercial planting. Ripens from mid-August to September.   Zone 3. *Source History: 2 in 2000.* **Sources: On3, Or2.**

Sea Berry, Leikora - *Hippophae rhamnoides.* Valued for both its fruit and ornamental quality. The fruit-laden branches are a nice addition to florist displays. Bears large bright orange berries on a fairly compact spreading plant.   Ripens in September and remains on the plant until heavy frosts. Zone 3. *Source History: 6 in 2000.* **Sources: Bu7, Clo, On3, Or2, Rai, Wa3.**

Sea Berry, Male - *Hippophae rhamnoides.* Attractive ornamental. Necessary for fruit production but does not produce fruit. One male will pollinate up to 8 females. Zones 4-7. *Source History: 7 in 2000.* **Sources: Bu7, Clo, Ed2, On3, Or2, Rai, Wa3.**

Sea Berry, Russian Orange (Otradnaya) - *Hippophae rhamnoides.* Productive bush with large green-gray foliage.   Large, deep orange berries make delicious juice. Early ripening. Zone 3. *Source History: 2 in 2000.* **Sources: Bu7, On3.**

Sea Berry, Seedlings - *Hippophae rhamnoides.* Grown from seed of large fruited varieties. Should bear better than average crops. Some will be males with no fruit. *Source History: 1 in 2000.* **Sources: On3.**

Sea Buckthorn - *Hippophae salicifolia.* Edible, orangish yellow berries. Deciduous shrub grows 10-50' tall. Graceful, drooping branches. Slightly less hardy than *H. rhamnoides.* Native to the Himalayas. *Source History: 1 in 1988; 1 in 1992; 1 in 2000.* **Sources: Va5.**

Sea Grape - *Coccoloba uvifera.* Purple fruit resembles bunches of grapes. Good for jelly. Tree grows 20' tall.   Native along ocean beaches from southern Florida to South America. *Source History: 1 in 1988; 3 in 1992; 5 in 2000.* **Sources: Ban, Ga11, Na13, Po7.**

Siberian Pea Shrub - *Caragana arborescens.* Small, 2" long, edible, pea-like pods in late spring. Shrub or small tree that grows 20' tall. Attractive yellow flowers in May; good for bee forage. Often used in windbreaks and hedges. Native to Siberia and Manchuria. Hardy in Zone 2-3. *Source History: 2 in 1988; 25 in 1992; 16 in 2000.* **Sources: Abu, Ban, Bea, Bo5, CLI, CR6, Fo2, GR26, Hud, LA4, MEA, Mel, No2, Pl5, Stl, WA8.**

Solanum topiro - Juicy, tart fruit is covered with a light down. Looks like an eggplant, to which it is related. Can be eaten stewed, fried, as fresh fruit or as a drink. Grows to 5'. Ideal for a tropical greenhouse. *Source History: 1 in 1988; 1 in 1992; 1 in 2000.* **Sources: Ban.**

Sorbus aucuparia edulis (Edible Mountain Ash) - Large red fruits used for making jelly and wine. Good pest and disease resistance. Hardy in Zone 3. *Source History: 2 in 1992; 2 in 2000.* **Sources: Bu7, Fo2.**

Sorbus pohuashanensis (Chinese Mountain Ash) - Edible, bright red, cherry-like berries. Used fresh after frost. Good for jams, jellies and wines. More mildew resistant than *S. aucuparia.* Hardy in Zone 5. Name means "Mountain of the Flowers." *Source History: 2 in 1992; 1 in 2000.* **Sources: Or2.**

Spanish Lime (Genip, Mamoncillo) - *Melicoccus bijugatus.* Round, 1" green fruit. Juicy, clear, yellow pulp.   Tree grows slowly to 60' tall. Hardy in Zone 10.

Native to tropical America. *Source History: 1 in 1988; 1 in 1992; 4 in 2000.* **Sources: Ga11, Me2, Pl3, Po7.**

Sparkleberry - *Vaccinium arobreum. Source History: 1 in 1988; 1 in 2000.* **Sources: BO10.**

Squaw Apple - *Paraphyllum ramosissimum. Source History: 1 in 1988; 1 in 1992; 1 in 2000.* **Sources: Ca12.**

Star Apple (Caimito) - *Chrysophyllum Cainito.* Smooth, round, 4" purple fruit; cross section is star-shaped. Clear, white flesh. Eaten fresh when fully ripe. Handsome tree grows 50' tall. Oval, 3-5" glossy, green leaves with velvety brown undersides. Requires warmth, bright light, high humidity and a well drained, slightly acid soil. Hardy in Zone 10. Native to tropical America. *Source History: 2 in 1988; 5 in 1992; 10 in 2000.* **Sources: An4, Ban, Ga11, Me2, On4, Pl3, PL2, Po7, Ro13, Tr10.**

Star Fruit (Carambola) - *Averrhoa carambola.* Gorgeous, 5" long, yellow fruit has a star shape with five deep ribs when cut into cross sections. Ornamental tree grows 30' tall. White and purple flowers. Hardy in Zone 10. Native to Malaysia. *Source History: 2 in 1988; 5 in 1992; 9 in 2000.* **Sources: An4, Ban, Ga11, Me2, Na13, Pa2, Pl3, Po7, Ro13.**

Star Fruit, Arkin - *Averrhoa carambola.* Sweet, crisp, elongated fruit with five ribs. Excellent fresh or in salads. Medium size tree with small leaves and pink flowers. Fruits from September to April. *Source History: 1 in 1988; 3 in 1992; 1 in 2000.* **Sources: On4.**

Star Fruit, B-10 - *Averrhoa carambola. Source History: 1 in 2000.* **Sources: On4.**

Star Fruit, Fenton - *Averrhoa carambola. Source History: 1 in 2000.* **Sources: On4.**

Star Fruit, Kajang - Large, sweet, yellow fruit. Originated in Hawaii. *Source History: 1 in 1992; 1 in 2000.* **Sources: PL2.**

Star Fruit, Kari - Sweet, yellow fruit; high brix. Originated in Hawaii. *Source History: 1 in 1992; 1 in 2000.* **Sources: PL2.**

Star Fruit, Sri Kambamga - *Averrhoa carambola.* Sweet, yellow fruit. Hawaiian standard. *Source History: 1 in 1992; 2 in 2000.* **Sources: On4, PL2.**

Stauntonia hexaphylla - Vigorous evergreen vine with large, purple, edible fruits. Hardy to Zone 7 with protection. *Source History: 1 in 1992; 1 in 2000.* **Sources: Or2.**

Strawberry Tree - *Arbutus unedo.* Gets its name from the showy, small, round, red, strawberry-like fruits that ripen in the fall and winter. Fruit varies in quality and size. Sweet, somewhat mealy flesh. Used for preserves and distilling. Large, warm climate shrub grows slowly 15-25' tall. Rich, reddish brown bark. Evergreen, serrated, 4" glossy, dark green leaves tinted amber; similar to laurel. Masses of white flowers in the fall. Grows well in both wet and dry climates. Makes an attractive screen. Hardy in Zones 7-8. Native to Ireland. *Source History: 6 in 1988; 5 in 1992; 13 in 2000.* **Sources: Ban, Ca12, Ca7, Co24, Fo2, HI10, MIS, MO10, Na13, Ne4, Or2, ORA, Pa2.**

Strawberry Tree, Dwarf - *Arbutus unedo cv. compacta.* Large red fruits. Grows only 6-8' tall. Perfect for landscapes that need a beautiful, short, evergreen shrub. Hardy in Zone 7. *Source History: 1 in 1988; 2 in 1992; 3 in 2000.* **Sources: Fo2, MO10, Ty2.**

Strawberry Tree, Hybrid - *Arbutus x andrachnoides.* Small evergreen tree with white flowers followed by pink, strawberry-like fruit. The bark becomes a pretty maroon color on older trees. Zones 8-9. *Source History: 1 in 2000.* **Sources: Wo2.**

Strawberry Tree, Marina - *Arbutus x Marina*. Evergreen tree with larger dark green leaves than the species. Grows 20-30' tall. Rosy pink flowers are followed by red and yellow strawberry-like fruit from previous season flowers. Full sun. Zones 7-9. *Source History: 2 in 2000.* **Sources: MO10, Ty2.**

Strawberry Vine - *Schizandra rubriflora*. Rare vine is a close relative of Magnolia Vine (*Schizandra chinensis*). Bears bright red strawberry-like flowers in May; scarlet berries in the fall. Vigorous and easy to grow. Hardy to Zone 7. *Source History: 1 in 2000.* **Sources: On3.**

Sumac, Laciniata Staghorn - *Rhus typhina*. Cone-shaped clusters of red berries from which a lemonade-like drink is made. Light green, fern-like foliage. Attracts songbirds, butterflies and bees. Hardy to Zone 4. *Source History: 2 in 2000.* **Sources: Hid, Va5.**

Sumac, Sugar - *Rhus ovata*. Evergreen shrub or small tree to 15'. Useful for erosion control. Edible, sweet reddish fruit pulp. *Source History: 1 in 2000.* **Sources: So12.**

Sumac, Tanner's - *Rhus coriaria*. Shrub grows to 15'. Leaves and downy twigs are used in the tanning of Moroccan leather. Tiny white flowers are followed by hairy, purple berries. Zone 8. Originated in southern Europe. *Source History: 1 in 2000.* **Sources: Fo2.**

Surinam Cherry (Barbados Cherry, Brazil Cherry, Pitanga, Pumpkin Cherry) - *Eugenia uniflora*. Round-oval, 1.25" cherry-like, bright red fruit with eight distinctive ribs. Flavor resembles a tangerine; very rich aftertones when fully ripe. Good for jam and jelly. Contains more vitamin C than virtually any other fruit. Beautiful, ornamental shrub or small tree. Not difficult to grow; likes warmth, moisture and light. Often used for hedges. Good plant for containers and even for hanging baskets. Hardy to 28 degrees F. Native to tropical America. *Source History: 4 in 1988; 7 in 1992; 10 in 2000.* **Sources: An4, Ban, Ca7, Ga11, Me2, Our, Pa2, PL2, Po7, Ro13, Tr10.**

Surinam Cherry: Beth - *Eugenia uniflora*. Grafted variety. *Source History: 1 in 2000.* **Sources: Pa2.**

Surinam Cherry: Bountiful Beauty - *Eugenia uniflora*. Grafted variety. *Source History: 1 in 2000.* **Sources: Pa2.**

Surinam Cherry: Chamba - *Eugenia uniflora*. Large, orange-red fruit. *Source History: 1 in 1992; 1 in 2000.* **Sources: Or2.**

Surinam Cherry: Lolita - *Eugenia uniflora*. Small fruits with tangerine-like flavor. Small plant produces heavily throughout the year. California type. *Source History: 3 in 1988; 2 in 1992; 1 in 2000.* **Sources: Pa2.**

Surinam Cherry: Lorver - *Eugenia uniflora*. Fruit the size of a quarter and larger. Delicious nectarine-like flavor. Light producer with fewer crops per year. Florida type. *Source History: 1 in 1988; 1 in 2000.* **Sources: Or2.**

Surinam Cherry: Seth - *Eugenia uniflora*. Grafted variety. *Source History: 1 in 2000.* **Sources: Pa2.**

Surinam Cherry: Tina - *Eugenia uniflora*. Grafted variety. *Source History: 1 in 2000.* **Sources: Pa2.**

Surinam Cherry: Vermillion - *Eugenia uniflora*. Quarter-size fruit. Nectarine-like flavor. Light producer with fewer crops per year. Florida type. *Source*

History: 1 in 1988; 1 in 2000. **Sources: Or2, Pa2.**

Swamp Haw (Wild Raisin, Appalachian Tea, Withe-Rod) - *Viburnum cassinoides.* Sweet, edible, blue-black berries. Rounded shrub grows 8-12'. Ripens in late summer. Tolerant of wet soil and partial shade. Zones 3-8. *Source History: 1 in 1992; 2 in 2000.* **Sources: Fo2, Tri.**

Sweet Olive - *Osmanthus thunbergii fragrans.* Beautiful shrub grows 4-6' tall. Small yellow flowers bloom in spring and fall that smell like ripe apricots. Fruits are rare, but can be pickled like an olive. Native to western China. *Source History: 1 in 2000.* **Sources: Rai.**

Syzygium leuhmanni - Edible fruit. Australian native. *Source History: 1 in 2000.* **Sources: Po7.**

Tamarind (Tamarindo) - *Tamarindus indica.* Brown pods are 2-8" long. Wonderful, tart-sweet flavor. Pods are soaked in water an hour or two, when the husk and seeds can be removed easily. Pulp is then beaten smooth and added to fresh or cooking fruit. Blends with other fruits more subtly than lemon juice. Superb with bland, dried fruit like figs or pears. Handsome tree grows 80' tall. Attractive foliage resembles Acacia or Sensitive Mimosa. Hardy in Zone 10. *Source History: 4 in 1988; 7 in 1992; 7 in 2000.* **Sources: An4, Ban, Ga11, Hud, On4, Or2, Tr10.**

Tamarind, Meakong Dream - Fruit has a rich sweet flavor free of all tartness. Flesh has a raisin-like texture. Edible seeds. Fruit dries naturally on the tree. Hardy to 28 degrees F. Native to the Meakong River on the Laos/Thailand border. Trademarked. *Source History: 1 in 2000.* **Sources: Or2.**

Tapioca - *Manihot esculenta.* Shrub grows 9' tall. Tapioca is made from roots. *Source History: 1 in 1988; 3 in 1992; 3 in 2000.* **Sources: Ga11, Ka3, Ne4.**

Tatelo (Himalayan Sword Fruit) - *Oroxylum indicum.* Sword-like fruit may reach 3' in length. Harvest when young. Tree grows to 30' tall. Requires rich soil and ample water. Hardy to 20 degrees F. Trademarked. *Source History: 1 in 2000.* **Sources: Or2.**

Thimbleberry - *Rubus parviflorus.* Native American raspberry. Small, reddish orange berries. Seedy and sparse, but very tasty. Young shoots were eaten by Native Americans in the spring. Attractive, untemperamental, low suckering, nearly thornless shrub grows 2-5' tall. Soft, fuzzy, maple-shaped leaves up to 8" across turn yellow in the fall. Large, 2" white petaled flowers crinkled like muslin. Prefers damp, well drained, shady sites. Requires minimum annual precipitation of 20". Hardy into Zone 3. Native from Alaska to Michigan, southward to Mexico. *Source History: 6 in 1988; 10 in 1992; 11 in 2000.* **Sources: Abu, Bu7, Co24, Fo2, Fro, Las, Ll7, No2, Oik, Pl5, Rai.**

Tika Berry - *Berberis cristata.* Multicolored bush grows 5-6' tall. Bears clusters of deep purple berries that dry easily and seldom spoil because of the high vitamin C content. Native to the Himalayas. Trademarked. *Source History: 1 in 2000.* **Sources: Or2.**

Tree Tomato (Tamarillo, Tamarillo Tree) - *Cyphomandra betacea.* Juicy, egg-shaped, smooth, orangish red to deep red fruit; 2-3" long. Tart, tomato-like flavor. Eaten raw, cooked, stewed or in jam; can be sweetened with sugar. High in vitamin C. Fast growing, 10' tree looks like a rubber plant with glossy, downy, heart-shaped leaves up to 12" long. Large, fragrant, pink, star-shaped flowers cascade down the sides of the tree in large clusters. Yields up to 30 lbs. per year. Likes sun; needs warmth like an eggplant. Hardy in California and the South; grown in tubs in the North. *Source History: 6 in 1988; 8 in 1992; 6 in 2000.* **Sources: Ban, Ca7, Hud, Me2, Pa2, Ro13.**

Tropical Apricot - *Dovyalis hebecarpa x D. caffra* var. Prodigal.   Spiny shrub or small tree grows 20' tall.   Smooth, edible, 1" juicy berries.   Good for preserves and jelly. *Source History: 1 in 1988; 2 in 1992; 2 in 2000.* **Sources: Ga11, Na13.**

Tulo-Saauji - *Xylosma controversum*.   Rare, 30' tree from central Himalaya. Small red fruit ripens from July to November. *Source History: 1 in 2000.* **Sources: Or2.**

Velvet Apple - Unique, velvet-like fruit with the flavor of cheese. Rare. *Source History: 1 in 2000.* **Sources: Our.**

Viburnum: Arrowwood - *V. dentatum*. Bluish black berries.   Excellent shrub for wet soils; grows 10-12'.   White flowers in June.   Reddish purple foliage in the fall. Hardy in Zone 3-8. *Source History: 1 in 1988; 19 in 1992; 34 in 2000.* **Sources: Ba3, Big, BO10, BO4, CO3, CR6, FO10, Fo2, Gr16, HI7, IM2, IN7, Jun, KEE, LA4, Lee, LI7, LO6, LOV, Mc3, MEA, Mel, MI5, Sc2, Sh10, Sh14, SH8, So5, TU5, Wa16, WA8, We18, We8, ZEL.**

Viburnum: Tea - *V. setigerum*. Red, .5" egg-shaped fruit. Hardy in Zone 6. *Source History: 1 in 1992; 1 in 2000.* **Sources: Sh14.**

Viburnum: Wayfaring Tree (Twistwood) - *V. Lantana*. Red fruit turns black in fall. Shrub grows 10-15' tall.   Upright growing, leathery foliage. Tolerates dry soils. Zones 3-7. *Source History: 1 in 1988; 15 in 1992; 18 in 2000.* **Sources: Co24, CO3, CR6, Fo2, Fra, GR26, KAN, LA4, LI7, LOV, Mc3, MEA, Sc2, Sh14, SH8, So5, WA8, We18.**

Wampi - *Clausena Lansium*. Small, brown, berry-like fruit. Small tree. Hardy to 26 degrees F. Native to China. *Source History: 3 in 1988; 3 in 1992; 3 in 2000.* **Sources: Ga11, On4, Pa2.**

Water Apple - *Eugenia aquea*. Flat, pink-white fruit with a crunchy texture and a hint of cinnamon flavor.   Refreshing. *Source History: 1 in 1992; 1 in 2000.* **Sources: Ro13.**

Wax Jambu - *Syzygium samarangense* (formerly *S. javanicum*).   Pear-shaped, 1.5" fruit; edible, but tasteless. Tree grows 20-30' tall. Native to Malaysia. *Source History: 1 in 1988; 1 in 1992; 4 in 2000.* **Sources: Ga11, On4, Pa2, PI3.**

West Indian Cherry - *Mutingia calabura*. *Source History: 1 in 2000.* **Sources: On4.**

Whortleberry (Bilberry) - *Vaccinium myrtillus*.   Pleasant tasting, .3" bluish black berries.   Good for preserves and wine.   Much eaten in Scotland.   Also used medicinally for cystitis.   Tiny, deciduous shrub rarely over 18" tall and wide. Leathery, myrtle-like leaves. White or pink, .25" flowers in short racemes.   Prefers sun or partial shade. Hardy in Zones 4-9.   Native to the British moorlands. *Source History: 3 in 1988; 1 in 1992; 2 in 2000.* **Sources: Abu, Hud.**

Whortleberry, Grouse - *Vaccinium scoparium*. *Source History: 1 in 1992; 1 in 2000.* **Sources: No2.**

Wild Amlaki - Species of *Emblica* from the sub-Himalaya.   Crisp, juicy fruit looks like a giant green gooseberry. High vitamin C content. Made into pickles and preserves. Trademarked. *Source History: 1 in 2000.* **Sources: Or2.**

Wild Cranberry (European Cranberry, Small Cranberry) - *Vaccinium oxycoccos*. Small, prostrate, spreading, evergreen shrub with tiny leaves on wiry stems. Small flowers followed by berries.   Likes moist, peaty soils.   Native to the East. Hardy in Zone 5. *Source History: 1 in 1988; 1 in 1992; 3 in 2000.* **Sources: Bu7, Fo2, Gr16.**

Wineberry (Japanese Wineberry) - *Rubus phoenicolasius*.   Small, raspberry-shaped, orangish red fruit is enclosed by sepals which form a husk that opens when ripe; husk is orange inside, covered with red hairs outside. Tangy flavor is favored by winemakers. Upright, arching, deciduous shrub grows 6-9'; usually trellised. Showy, red stems are covered with prickles and reddish hairs. Large, trifoliate leaves, felted beneath. Clusters of small, pale pink, summer flowers. Practically immune to disease. Can escape by tip rooting and form dense thickets. Prefers cool, moist soil. Does well in partial shade. Hardy in mild areas of Zone 5. Native to China and Japan. *Source History: 5 in 1988; 8 in 1992; 5 in 2000.* **Sources: Co12, Ed2, Fo2, Tri, We8.**

Wintergreen (Christmas Wintergreen, Teaberry, Checkerberry) - *Gaultheria procumbens*. White, bell-shaped flowers in summer followed by bright red, edible fruits in late fall, lasting until June of the following year.   Original wintergreen flavoring is produced from the fruit. Low growing, attractive ground cover. Grows in full sun or shade. Hardy in Zones 3-8. *Source History: 8 in 1992; 10 in 2000.* **Sources: BO10, BR2, Bu7, Co12, Ed2, Fo2, HA12, Mel, Rai, Tri.**

Yellowhorn - *Xanthoceras sorbifolia*. Leaves, flowers and nuts are edible. Nuts resemble small horse chestnuts. Tasty, mild, chestnut flavor. Small tree grows to 25'. Flowers look like small, white, wisteria clusters.   Hardy in Zone 5. *Source History: 1 in 1992; 1 in 2000.* **Sources: Hid.**

Yucca - Evergreen perennial. Produces large pulpy edible fruits. Drought hardy. *Source History: 1 in 2000.* **Sources: So12.**